INSTRUCTOR'S RESOURCE MANUAL WITH SOLUTIONS MANUAL

Richard N. Aufmann
Palomar College

Vernon C. Barker
Palomar College

Joanne S. Lockwood
Plymouth State College

Christine S. Verity

INTERMEDIATE ALGEBRA WITH APPLICATIONS

SIXTH EDITION

Aufmann/Barker/Lockwood

HOUGHTON MIFFLIN COMPANY   BOSTON NEW YORK

Senior Sponsoring Editor: Lynn Cox
Senior Development Editor: Dawn Nuttall
Editorial Associate: Melissa Parkin
Manufacturing Manager: Florence Cadran
Senior Marketing Manager: Ben Rivera

Printed in the U.S.A.

ISBN: 0-618-30620-X

2 3 4 5 6 7 8 9 – MA – 07 06 05

Table of Contents

PREFACE

The Instructor's Resource Manual with Solutions for Aufmann/Barker/Lockwood's *Intermediate Algebra with Applications* contains suggested Course Sequences, Solutions to the exercises in the text, and AIM for Success Slide Show printouts.

A PowerPoint® Slide Show, which presents a lesson plan for the AIM for Success student preface in the text, is available on the instructor's Class Prep CD as well as the text website. Full printouts of the ten slides (which may be used as transparency masters) as well as a smaller printout of each slide with its accompanying instructor notes are provided in the resource manual.

INSTRUCTOR'S RESOURCE MANUAL WITH SOLUTIONS MANUAL

Basic Course Sequence

Week

1	Section 1.1	Introduction to Real Numbers
	Section 1.2	Operations on Rational Numbers
	Section 1.3	Variable Expressions

2	Section 1.4	Verbal Expressions and Variable Expressions
	Section 2.1	Equations in One Variable
	Section 2.3	Value Mixture and Motion Problems

3	Section 2.4	Applications: Problems Involving Percents
	Section 2.5	Inequalities in One Variable
	Section 2.6	Absolute Value Equations and Inequalities

4 ***Test Chapters 1 and 2***
	Section 3.1	The Rectangular Coordinate System
	Section 3.2	Introduction to Functions

5	Section 3.3	Linear Functions
	Section 3.4	Slope of a Straight Line
	Section 3.5	Finding Equations of Lines

6	Section 3.6	Parallel and Perpendicular Lines
	Section 3.7	Inequalities in Two Variables
	Section 4.1	Solving Systems of Linear Equations by Graphing and by the Substitution Method

7	Section 4.2	Solving Systems of Linear Equations by the Addition Method
	Section 4.3	Application Problems

Test Chapters 3 and 4

8	Section 5.1	Exponential Expressions
	Section 5.2	Introduction to Polynomials
	Section 5.3	Multiplication of Polynomials

9	Section 5.4	Division of Polynomials (Objective 1)
	Section 5.5	Factoring Polynomials
	Section 5.6	Special Factoring (Objective 1)

10	Section 6.1	Introduction to Rational Expressions
	Section 6.2	Operations on Rational Expressions
	Section 6.3	Complex Fractions

11	Section 6.4	Rational Equations
	Section 6.5	Proportions and Variation

Test Chapters 5 and 6

12	Section 7.1	Rational Exponents and Radical Expressions
	Section 7.2	Operations on Radical Expressions
	Section 7.4	Solving Equations Containing Radical Expressions

13	Section 7.5	Complex Numbers
	Section 8.1	Solving Quadratic Equations by Factoring or by Taking Square Roots
	Section 8.2	Solving Quadratic Equations by Completing the Square and by Using the Quadratic Formula (Objective 2)

14	Section 8.4	Applications of Quadratic Functions

Test Chapters 7 and 8
	Section 9.1	Graphs of Functions
	Section 9.3	Algebra of Functions

15	Section 9.4	One-to-one and Inverse Functions
	Section 10.1	Exponential Functions
	Section 10.2	Introduction to Logarithms

2

Week

Average Course Sequence

<u>**Week**</u>

4

Week

14 Section 9.3   Algebra of Functions
    Section 9.4   One-to-one and Inverse Functions
    Section 10.1   Exponential Functions
    Section 10.2   Introduction to Logarithms

15 Section 10.3   Graphs of Logarithmic Functions
    Section 10.4   Exponential and Logarithmic Equations
    Section 10.5   Applications of Exponential and Logarithmic Functions

16 Section 11.1   Introduction to Sequences and Series
    Section 11.4   Binomial Expansions
    Test Chapters 9, 10 and 11

© Houghton Mifflin Company. All rights reserved.

Comprehensive Course Sequence

Week

1	Section 2.1	Equations in One Variable
	Section 2.3	Value Mixture and Motion Problems
	Section 2.4	Applications: Problems Involving Percents
	Section 2.5	Inequalities in One Variable
	Section 2.6	Absolute Value Equations and Inequalities
2	Section 3.1	The Rectangular Coordinate System
	Section 3.2	Introduction to Functions
	Section 3.3	Linear Functions
	Section 3.4	Slope of a Straight Line
3	Section 3.5	Finding Equations of Lines
	Section 3.6	Parallel and Perpendicular Lines
	Section 3.7	Inequalities in Two Variables

Test Chapters 2 and 3

4	Section 4.1	Solving Systems of Linear Equations by Graphing and by the Substitution Method
	Section 4.2	Solving Systems of Linear Equations by the Addition Method
	Section 4.3	Solving Systems of Linear Equations by Using Determinants and by Using Matrices
5	Section 4.4	Application Problems
	Section 4.5	Solving Systems of Linear Inequalities
	Section 5.1	Exponential Expressions
	Section 5.2	Introduction to Polynomials
6	Section 5.3	Multiplication of Polynomials
	Section 5.4	Division of Polynomials
	Section 5.5	Factoring Polynomials
7	Section 5.6	Special Factoring

Test Chapters 4 and 5

	Section 6.1	Introduction to Rational Expressions
	Section 6.2	Operations on Rational Expressions
8	Section 6.3	Complex Fractions
	Section 6.4	Rational Equations
	Section 6.5	Proportions and Variation
9	Section 6.6	Literal Equations
	Section 7.1	Rational Exponents and Radical Expressions
	Section 7.2	Operations on Radical Expressions
10	Section 7.3	Radical Functions
	Section 7.4	Solving Equations Containing Radical Expressions
	Section 7.5	Complex Numbers

Test Chapters 6 and 7

11	Section 8.1	Solving Quadratic Equations by Factoring or by Taking Square Roots
	Section 8.2	Solving Quadratic Equations by Completing the Square and by Using the Quadratic Formula
	Section 8.3	Equations That Are Reducible to Quadratic Equations
12	Section 8.4	Applications of Quadratic Functions
	Section 8.6	Properties of Quadratic Functions
	Section 9.1	Graphs of Functions
13	Section 9.3	Algebra of Functions
	Section 9.4	One-to-one and Inverse Functions

Test Chapters 8 and 9

	Section 10.1	Exponential Functions

<u>**Week**</u>

Solutions Manual

Chapter 1: Review of Real Numbers

Prep Test

1. $\dfrac{5}{12}+\dfrac{7}{30}=\dfrac{25}{60}+\dfrac{14}{60}=\dfrac{39}{60}=\dfrac{13}{20}$

2. $\dfrac{8}{15}-\dfrac{7}{20}=\dfrac{32}{60}-\dfrac{21}{60}=\dfrac{11}{60}$

3. $\dfrac{2}{9}$

4. $\dfrac{4}{15}\div\dfrac{2}{5}=\dfrac{4}{15}\cdot\dfrac{5}{2}=\dfrac{2}{3}$

5. 44.405

6. 73.63

7. 7.446

8. 54.06

9. a, c, d

10a. $\dfrac{1}{2}=0.5$ C

10b. $\dfrac{7}{10}=0.7$ D

10c. $\dfrac{3}{4}=0.75$ A

10d. $\dfrac{89}{100}=0.89$ B

Go Figure

Since the other three smaller rectangles are of different sizes, the possible values for x cannot be the same as any of the three other rectangles. The first possible value of x is 1. The lengths of the sides of the rectangles are shown below.

The second possible value of x is 4.
The first possible value of x is 4. The lengths of the sides of the rectangles are shown below.

The third possible value of x is 9. The lengths of the sides of the rectangles are shown below.

Section 1.1

Concept Review 1.1

1. Sometimes true
   The only exception to this statement is for zero. $|0|=0,$ which is not a positive number.

2. Sometimes true
   The value of x can be 3 or –3.

3. Sometimes true
   If x is a positive integer, then $-x$ is a negative integer.
   If x is a negative integer, then $-x$ is a positive integer.

4. Always true

5. Never true
   $-4<-2$ but $(-4)^2$ is not less than $(-2)^2$.

6. Never true
   $2<4<6$ but $\dfrac{1}{2}$ is not less than $\dfrac{1}{4}$, and $\dfrac{1}{4}$ is not less than $\dfrac{1}{6}$.

7. Always true

Objective 1.1.1 Exercises

1. -14: c, e
   9: a, b, c, d
   0: b, c
   53: a, b, c, d
   7.8: none
   -626: c, e

2. 31: a, b, c, d
   -45: c, e
   -2: c, e
   9.7: none
   8600: a, b, c, d
   $\dfrac{1}{2}$: none

3. $-\dfrac{15}{2}$: b, d
   0: a, b, d
   -3: a, b, d
   π: c, d
   $2.\overline{33}$: b, d
   4.232232223: c, d
   $\dfrac{\sqrt{5}}{4}$: c, d
   $\sqrt{7}$: c, d

4. −17: a, b, d

0.3412: b, d

$\dfrac{3}{\pi}$: c, d

−1.010010001: c, d

$\dfrac{27}{91}$: b, d

$6.1\overline{2}$: b, d

5. A terminating decimal is a decimal number that has only a finite number of decimal places – for example, 0.75.

6. A repeating decimal is a decimal number that has a block of digits that repeats and no other digits between the repeating blocks; an example is $8.454545 \ldots = 8.\overline{45}$.

7. The additive inverse of a number is the number that is the same distance from zero on the number line but on the opposite side of zero.

8. The absolute value of a number is a measure of its distance from zero on the number line.

9. −27

10. 3

11. $-\dfrac{3}{4}$

12. $-\sqrt{17}$

13. 0

14. π

15. $\sqrt{33}$

16. 1.23

17. 91

18. $\dfrac{2}{3}$

19. Replace x with each element in the set and determine whether the inequality is true.

$x < 5$

−3 < 5 True

0 < 5 True

7 < 5 False

The inequality is true for −3 and 0.

20. Replace z with each element in the set and determine whether the inequality is true.

$z > -2$

−4 > −2 False

−1 > −2 True

4 > −2 True

The inequality is true for −1 and 4.

21. Replace y with each element in the set and determine whether the inequality is true.

$y > -4$

−6 > −4 False

−4 > −4 False

7 > −4 True

The inequality is true for 7.

22. Replace x with each element in the set and determine whether the inequality is true.

$x < -3$

−6 < −3 True

−3 < −3 False

3 < −3 False

The inequality is true for −6.

23. Replace w with each element in the set and determine whether the inequality is true.

$w \le -1$

−2 ≤ −1 True

−1 ≤ −1 True

0 ≤ −1 False

1 ≤ −1 False

The inequality is true for −2 and −1.

24. Replace p with each element in the set and determine whether the inequality is true.

$p \ge 0$

−10 ≥ 0 False

−5 ≥ 0 False

0 ≥ 0 True

5 ≥ 0 True

The inequality is true for 0 and 5.

25. Replace b with each element in the set and evaluate the expression.

$-b$

−(−9) = 9

−(0) = 0

−(9) = −9

26. Replace a with each element in the set and evaluate the expression.

$-a$

−(−3) = 3

−(−2) = 2

−(0) = 0

27. Replace c with each element in the set and evaluate the expression.

$|c|$

$|-4| = 4$

$|0| = 0$

$|4| = 4$

28. Replace q with each element in the set and evaluate the expression.

$|q|$

$|-3| = 3$

$|0| = 0$

$|7| = 7$

29. Replace m with each element in the set and evaluate the expression.

$-|m|$

$-|-6| = -6$

$-|-2| = -2$

$-|0| = 0$

$-|1| = -1$

$-|4| = -4$

30. Replace x with each element in the set and evaluate the expression.

$-|x|$

$-|-5| = -5$

$-|-3| = -3$

$-|0| = 0$

$-|2| = -2$

$-|5| = -5$

Objective 1.1.2 Exercises

31. The union of two sets will contain all the elements that are in either set. The intersection of the two sets will contain only the elements that are in both sets.

32. $\{x \mid x < 5\}$ does not include the value 5, but $\{x \mid x \leq 5\}$ does include the value 5.

33. $\{-2, -1, 0, 1, 2, 3, 4\}$

34. $\{-3, -2, -1\}$

35. $\{2, 4, 6, 8, 10, 12\}$

36. $\{1, 3, 5, 7, 9, 11, 13\}$

37. $\{3, 6, 9, 12, 15, 18, 21, 24, 27, 30\}$

38. $\{-20, -16, -12, -8, -4\}$

39. $\{-35, -30, -25, -20, -15, -10, -5\}$

40. $\{6, 12, 18, 24, 30, 36\}$

41. $\{x \mid x > 4, x \text{ is an integer}\}$

42. $\{x \mid x < -2, x \text{ is an integer}\}$

43. $\{x \mid x \geq -2\}$

44. $\{x \mid x \leq 2\}$

45. $\{x \mid 0 < x < 1\}$

46. $\{x \mid -2 < x < 5\}$

47. $\{x \mid 1 \leq x \leq 4\}$

48. $\{x \mid 0 \leq x \leq 2\}$

49. $A \cup B = \{1, 2, 4, 6, 9\}$

50. $A \cup B = \{-1, 0, 1, 2\}$

51. $A \cup B = \{2, 3, 5, 8, 9, 10\}$

52. $A \cup B = \{1, 2, 3, 4, 5, 6, 7, 8\}$

53. $A \cup B = \{-4, -2, 0, 2, 4, 8\}$

54. $A \cup B = \{-3, -2, -1, 0, 1\}$

55. $A \cup B = \{1, 2, 3, 4, 5\}$

56. $A \cup B = \{0, 1, 2, 3, 4, 5\}$

57. $A \cap B = \{6\}$

58. $A \cap B = \{0\}$

59. $A \cap B = \{5, 10, 20\}$

60. $A \cap B = \{1, 9\}$

61. $A \cap B = \varnothing$

62. $A \cap B = \varnothing$

63. $A \cap B = \{4, 6\}$

64. $A \cap B = \{-5, 0, 7\}$

65. $\{x \mid -1 < x < 5\}$

66. $\{x \mid 1 < x < 3\}$

67. $\{x \mid 0 \leq x \leq 3\}$

68. $\{x \mid -1 \leq x \leq 1\}$

69. $\{x \mid x < 2\}$

70. $\{x \mid x < -1\}$

71. $\{x \mid x \geq 1\}$

72. $\{x \mid x \leq -2\}$

73. $\{x \mid x > 1\} \cup \{x \mid x < -1\}$

74. $\{x \mid x \leq 2\} \cup \{x \mid x > 4\}$

75. $\{x \mid x \le 2\} \cap \{x \mid x \ge 0\}$

76. $\{x \mid x > -1\} \cup \{x \mid x \le 4\}$

77. $\{x \mid x > 1\} \cap \{x \mid x \ge -2\}$

78. $\{x \mid x < 4\} \cap \{x \mid x \le 0\}$

79. $\{x \mid x > 2\} \cup \{x \mid x > 1\}$

80. $\{x \mid x < -2\} \cup \{x \mid x < -4\}$

81. $\{x \mid 0 < x < 8\}$

82. $\{x \mid -2 < x < 4\}$

83. $\{x \mid -5 \le x \le 7\}$

84. $\{x \mid 3 \le x \le 4\}$

85. $\{x \mid -3 \le x < 6\}$

86. $\{x \mid 4 < x \le 5\}$

87. $\{x \mid x \le 4\}$

88. $\{x \mid x < -2\}$

89. $\{x \mid x > 5\}$

90. $\{x \mid x \ge -2\}$

91. $(-2, 4)$

92. $(0, 3)$

93. $[-1, 5]$

94. $[0, 3]$

95. $(-\infty, 1)$

96. $(-\infty, 6]$

97. $[-2, 6)$

98. $[3, \infty)$

99. $(-\infty, \infty)$

100. $(-1, \infty)$

101. $(-2, 5)$

102. $(0, 3)$

103. $[-1, 2]$

104. $[-3, 2]$

105. $(-\infty, 3]$

106. $(-\infty, -1)$

107. $[3, \infty)$

108. $[-2, \infty)$

109. $(-\infty, 2] \cup [4, \infty)$

110. $(-3, 4] \cup [-1, 5)$

111. $[-1, 2] \cap [0, 4]$

112. $[-5, 4) \cap (-2, \infty)$

113. $(2, \infty) \cup (-2, 4]$

114. $(-\infty, 2] \cup (4, \infty)$

Applying Concepts 1.1

115. $A \cup B$ is
$\{x \mid -1 \le x \le 1\} \cup \{x \mid 0 \le x \le 1\} = \{x \mid -1 \le x \le 1\} = A$

116. $A \cup A$ is set A.

117. $B \cap B$ is set B.

118. $A \cup C$ is $\{x \mid -1 \le x \le 1\}$, which is set A.

119. $A \cap R$ is $\{x \mid -1 \le x \le 1\}$, which is set A.

120. $C \cap R$ is $\{x \mid -1 \le x \le 0\}$, which is set C.

121. $B \cup R$ is the set of real numbers, R.

122. $A \cup R$ is the set of real numbers, R.

123. $R \cup R$ is the set R.

124. $R \cap \varnothing$ is the empty set $\varnothing$.

125. $B \cap C$ is $\{x | 0 \le x \le 1\} \cap \{x | -1 \le x \le 0\}$, which contains only the number 0.

126. $-3 > x > 5$ means the numbers that are less than -3 and greater than 5. There is no number that is both less than -3 and greater than 5. Therefore, this is incorrect.

127.

$-\frac{1}{2}$ $\frac{3}{2}$

128.

-2.5 1.5

129.

$-\frac{5}{2}$ $\frac{7}{3}$

130.

3.5

131.

132.

133.

134.

135. $A \cup B = \{x | x > 0,\ x \text{ is an integer}\}$

136. $A \cup B = \{x | x < 0,\ x \text{ is an integer}\}$

137. $A \cap B = \{x | x \ge 15,\ x \text{ is an odd integer}\}$

138. $A \cap B = \{x | x \ge -4,\ x \text{ is an integer}\}$

139. The answer is b and c. For example:

a. $\dfrac{5-4}{3-2} \le 0$

$1 \le 0$

False

b. $\dfrac{2-3}{5-4} \le 0$

$-1 \le 0$

True

c. $\dfrac{5-4}{2-3} \le 0$

$-1 \le 0$

True

d. $\dfrac{4-5}{2-3} \le 0$

$1 \le 0$

False

Section 1.2

Concept Review 1.2

1. Sometimes true
$(-2) + 4 = 2$, a positive number
$(-8) + 4 = -4$, a negative number

2. Always true

3. Never true
$\dfrac{1}{2} + \dfrac{2}{3} = \dfrac{7}{6}$
$\dfrac{1+2}{2+3} = \dfrac{3}{5}$

4. Always true

5. Always true

6. Never true
The rule states that the product of two fractions is the product of the numerators over the product of the denominators.

7. Never true
The Order of Operations says to work inside parentheses before doing exponents.

8. Sometimes true
The Order of Operations Agreement says to do multiplication or division as it occurs from left to right.

9. Always true

Objective 1.2.1 Exercises

1a. Students should paraphrase the rule: Add the absolute values of the numbers; then attach the sign of the addends.

1b. Students should paraphrase the rule: Find the absolute value of each number; subtract the smaller of the two numbers from the larger; then attach the sign of the number with the larger absolute value.

2. The word *minus* refers to the operation of subtraction, and the word *negative* indicates a number that is less than zero.

3. To rewrite $8 - (-12)$ as addition of the opposite, change the subtraction to addition and change -12 to the opposite of -12:
$8 - (-12) = 8 + 12$.

4a. To multiply two integers with the same sign, find the product of the absolute values of the two integers.

4b. To multiply two integers with different signs, find the product of the absolute values of the two integers and then write the opposite of that product.

5. $-18 + (-12) = -30$

6. $-18 - 7 = -18 + (-7) = -25$

7. $5 - 22 = 5 + (-22) = -17$

8. $16 \cdot (-60) = -960$

9. $3 \cdot 4(-8) = 12 \cdot (-8) = -96$

10. $18 \cdot 0(-7) = 0 \cdot (-7) = 0$

11. $18 \div (-3) = -6$

12. $25 \div (-5) = -5$

13. $-60 \div (-12) = 5$

14. $(-9)(-2)(-3)(10) = 18(-3)(10) = -54(10) = -540$

15. $-20(35)(-16) = -700(-16) = 11{,}200$

16. $54(19)(-82) = 1026(-82) = -84{,}132$

17. $(-271)(-365) = 98{,}915$

18. $|(-16)(10)| = |-160| = 160$

19. $|12(-8)| = |-96| = 96$

20. $|7 - 18| = |-11| = 11$

21. $|15 - (-8)| = |15 + 8| = |23| = 23$

22. $|-16 - (-20)| = |-16 + 20| = |4| = 4$

23. $|-56 \div 8| = |-7| = 7$

24. $|81 \div (-9)| = |-9| = 9$

25. $|-153 \div (-9)| = |17| = 17$

26. $|-4| - |-2| = 4 - 2 = 2$

27. $-|-8| + |-4| = -8 + 4 = -4$

28. $-|-16| - |24| = -16 - 24 = -40$

29. $-30 + (-16) - 14 - 2 = -30 + (-16) + (-14) + (-2)$
$\qquad = -46 + (-14) + (-2)$
$\qquad = -60 + (-2)$
$\qquad = -62$

30. $3 - (-2) + (-8) - 11 = 3 + 2 + (-8) + (-11)$
$\qquad = 5 + (-8) + (-11)$
$\qquad = -3 + (-11)$
$\qquad = -14$

31. $-2 + (-19) - 16 + 12 = -2 + (-19) + (-16) + 12$
$\qquad = -21 + (-16) + 12$
$\qquad = -37 + 12$
$\qquad = -25$

32. $-6 + (-9) - 18 + 32 = -6 + (-9) + (-18) + 32$
$\qquad = -15 + (-18) + 32$
$\qquad = -33 + 32$
$\qquad = -1$

33. $13 - |6 - 12| = 13 - |6 + (-12)|$
$\qquad = 13 - |-6|$
$\qquad = 13 - 6$
$\qquad = 13 + (-6)$
$\qquad = 7$

34. $-9 - |-7 - (-15)| = -9 - |-7 + 15|$
$\qquad = -9 - |8|$
$\qquad = -9 - 8$
$\qquad = -9 + (-8)$
$\qquad = -17$

35. $738 - 46 + (-105) = 738 + (-46) + (-105)$
$\qquad = 692 + (-105)$
$\qquad = 587$

36. $-871 - (-387) - 132 = -871 + 387 + (-132)$
$\qquad = -484 + (-132)$
$\qquad = -616$

37. $-442 \div (-17) = 26$

38. $621 \div (-23) = -27$

39. $-4897 \div 59 = -83$

40. $-17(-5) = 85$

Objective 1.2.2 Exercises

41a. The least common multiple of two numbers is the smallest number that is a multiple of each of those numbers.

41b. The greatest common factor of two numbers is the largest integer that divides evenly into both numbers.

42. If the two rational numbers are fractions, change the division to multiplication, write the reciprocal of the second fraction, and then multiply the two fractions. If the two rational numbers are decimals, divide by long division.

43. $\dfrac{7}{12} + \dfrac{5}{16} = \dfrac{28}{48} + \dfrac{15}{48} = \dfrac{28 + 15}{48} = \dfrac{43}{48}$

44. $\dfrac{3}{8} - \dfrac{5}{12} = \dfrac{9}{24} - \dfrac{10}{24} = \dfrac{9 - 10}{24} = -\dfrac{1}{24}$

45. $-\dfrac{5}{9} - \dfrac{14}{15} = -\dfrac{25}{45} - \dfrac{42}{45} = \dfrac{-25 - 42}{45} = -\dfrac{67}{45}$

46. $\dfrac{1}{2} + \dfrac{1}{7} - \dfrac{5}{8} = \dfrac{28}{56} + \dfrac{8}{56} - \dfrac{35}{56} = \dfrac{28 + 8 - 35}{56} = \dfrac{1}{56}$

47. $-\dfrac{1}{3} + \dfrac{5}{9} - \dfrac{7}{12} = -\dfrac{12}{36} + \dfrac{20}{36} - \dfrac{21}{36}$
$\qquad = \dfrac{-12 + 20 - 21}{36}$
$\qquad = -\dfrac{13}{36}$

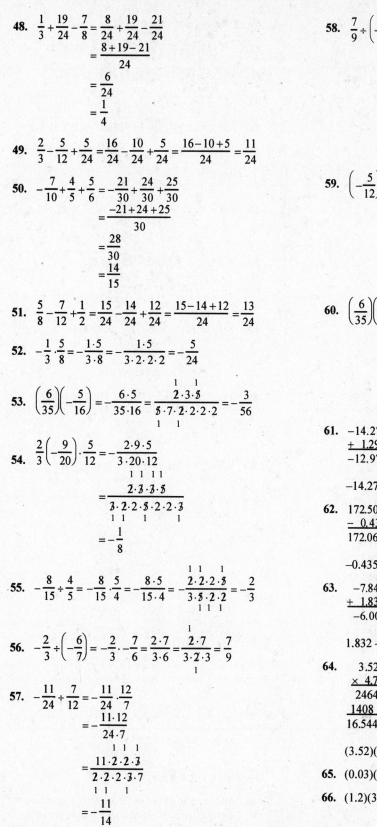

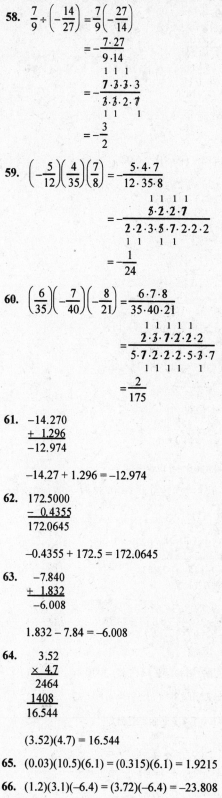

48. $\dfrac{1}{3}+\dfrac{19}{24}-\dfrac{7}{8}=\dfrac{8}{24}+\dfrac{19}{24}-\dfrac{21}{24}$

$\qquad\qquad\quad=\dfrac{8+19-21}{24}$

$\qquad\qquad\quad=\dfrac{6}{24}$

$\qquad\qquad\quad=\dfrac{1}{4}$

49. $\dfrac{2}{3}-\dfrac{5}{12}+\dfrac{5}{24}=\dfrac{16}{24}-\dfrac{10}{24}+\dfrac{5}{24}=\dfrac{16-10+5}{24}=\dfrac{11}{24}$

50. $-\dfrac{7}{10}+\dfrac{4}{5}+\dfrac{5}{6}=-\dfrac{21}{30}+\dfrac{24}{30}+\dfrac{25}{30}$

$\qquad\qquad\qquad=\dfrac{-21+24+25}{30}$

$\qquad\qquad\qquad=\dfrac{28}{30}$

$\qquad\qquad\qquad=\dfrac{14}{15}$

51. $\dfrac{5}{8}-\dfrac{7}{12}+\dfrac{1}{2}=\dfrac{15}{24}-\dfrac{14}{24}+\dfrac{12}{24}=\dfrac{15-14+12}{24}=\dfrac{13}{24}$

52. $-\dfrac{1}{3}\cdot\dfrac{5}{8}=-\dfrac{1\cdot5}{3\cdot8}=-\dfrac{1\cdot5}{3\cdot2\cdot2\cdot2}=-\dfrac{5}{24}$

53. $\left(\dfrac{6}{35}\right)\left(-\dfrac{5}{16}\right)=-\dfrac{6\cdot5}{35\cdot16}=-\dfrac{2\cdot3\cdot\cancel{5}}{\cancel{5}\cdot7\cdot2\cdot2\cdot2\cdot2}=-\dfrac{3}{56}$

54. $\dfrac{2}{3}\left(-\dfrac{9}{20}\right)\cdot\dfrac{5}{12}=-\dfrac{2\cdot9\cdot5}{3\cdot20\cdot12}$

$\qquad\qquad\qquad=\dfrac{2\cdot3\cdot3\cdot5}{3\cdot2\cdot2\cdot5\cdot2\cdot2\cdot3}$

$\qquad\qquad\qquad=-\dfrac{1}{8}$

55. $-\dfrac{8}{15}\div\dfrac{4}{5}=-\dfrac{8}{15}\cdot\dfrac{5}{4}=-\dfrac{8\cdot5}{15\cdot4}=-\dfrac{2\cdot2\cdot2\cdot5}{3\cdot5\cdot2\cdot2}=-\dfrac{2}{3}$

56. $-\dfrac{2}{3}\div\left(-\dfrac{6}{7}\right)=-\dfrac{2}{3}\cdot-\dfrac{7}{6}=\dfrac{2\cdot7}{3\cdot6}=\dfrac{2\cdot7}{3\cdot2\cdot3}=\dfrac{7}{9}$

57. $-\dfrac{11}{24}\div\dfrac{7}{12}=-\dfrac{11}{24}\cdot\dfrac{12}{7}$

$\qquad\qquad\qquad=-\dfrac{11\cdot12}{24\cdot7}$

$\qquad\qquad\qquad=-\dfrac{11\cdot2\cdot2\cdot3}{2\cdot2\cdot2\cdot3\cdot7}$

$\qquad\qquad\qquad=-\dfrac{11}{14}$

58. $\dfrac{7}{9}\div\left(-\dfrac{14}{27}\right)=\dfrac{7}{9}\left(-\dfrac{27}{14}\right)$

$\qquad\qquad\qquad=-\dfrac{7\cdot27}{9\cdot14}$

$\qquad\qquad\qquad=-\dfrac{7\cdot3\cdot3\cdot3}{3\cdot3\cdot2\cdot7}$

$\qquad\qquad\qquad=-\dfrac{3}{2}$

59. $\left(-\dfrac{5}{12}\right)\left(\dfrac{4}{35}\right)\left(\dfrac{7}{8}\right)=-\dfrac{5\cdot4\cdot7}{12\cdot35\cdot8}$

$\qquad\qquad\qquad\qquad=-\dfrac{5\cdot2\cdot2\cdot7}{2\cdot2\cdot3\cdot5\cdot7\cdot2\cdot2\cdot2}$

$\qquad\qquad\qquad\qquad=-\dfrac{1}{24}$

60. $\left(\dfrac{6}{35}\right)\left(-\dfrac{7}{40}\right)\left(-\dfrac{8}{21}\right)=\dfrac{6\cdot7\cdot8}{35\cdot40\cdot21}$

$\qquad\qquad\qquad\qquad=\dfrac{2\cdot3\cdot7\cdot2\cdot2\cdot2}{5\cdot7\cdot2\cdot2\cdot2\cdot5\cdot3\cdot7}$

$\qquad\qquad\qquad\qquad=\dfrac{2}{175}$

61. $\begin{array}{r}-14.270\\ +\ \ 1.296\\ \hline -12.974\end{array}$

$-14.27+1.296=-12.974$

62. $\begin{array}{r}172.5000\\ -\ \ 0.4355\\ \hline 172.0645\end{array}$

$-0.4355+172.5=172.0645$

63. $\begin{array}{r}-7.840\\ +\ 1.832\\ \hline -6.008\end{array}$

$1.832-7.84=-6.008$

64. $\begin{array}{r}3.52\\ \times\ 4.7\\ \hline 2464\\ 1408\ \ \\ \hline 16.544\end{array}$

$(3.52)(4.7)=16.544$

65. $(0.03)(10.5)(6.1)=(0.315)(6.1)=1.9215$

66. $(1.2)(3.1)(-6.4)=(3.72)(-6.4)=-23.808$

67. $0.9 \to 9$

$5.418 \to 54.18$

$$
\begin{array}{r}
6.02 \\
9\overline{)54.18} \\
-54 \\
\hline
0\,1 \\
-0 \\
\hline
18 \\
-18 \\
\hline
0
\end{array}
$$

$5.418 \div (-0.9) = -6.02$

68. $0.023 \to 23$

$0.2645 \to 264.5$

$$
\begin{array}{r}
11.5 \\
23\overline{)264.5} \\
-23 \\
\hline
34 \\
-23 \\
\hline
115 \\
-115 \\
\hline
0
\end{array}
$$

$-0.2645 \div (-0.023) = 11.5$

69. $0.065 \to 65$

$0.4355 \to 435.5$

$$
\begin{array}{r}
6.7 \\
65\overline{)435.5} \\
-390 \\
\hline
455 \\
-455 \\
\hline
0
\end{array}
$$

$-0.4355 \div 0.065 = -6.7$

70. $-6.58 - 3.97 + 0.875 = -6.58 + (-3.97) + 0.875$
$ = -10.55 + 0.875$
$ = -9.675$

71. $38.241 \div [-(-6.027)] - 7.453$
$= 38.241 \div 6.027 + (-7.453)$
$\approx 6.345 + (-7.453)$
≈ -1.11

72. $-9.0508 - (-3.177) + 24.77$
$= -9.0508 + 3.177 + 24.77$
$= -5.8738 + 24.77$
≈ 18.90

73. $-287.3069 \div 0.1415 \approx -2030.44$

74. $6472.3018 \div (-3.59) \approx -1802.87$

Objective 1.2.3 Exercises

75. $5^3 = 5 \cdot 5 \cdot 5 = 125$

76. $3^4 = 3 \cdot 3 \cdot 3 \cdot 3 = 81$

77. $-2^3 = -(2 \cdot 2 \cdot 2) = -8$

78. $-4^3 = -(4 \cdot 4 \cdot 4) = -64$

79. $(-5)^3 = (-5)(-5)(-5) = -125$

80. $(-8)^2 = (-8)(-8) = 64$

81. $2^2 \cdot 3^4 = (2)(2) \cdot (3)(3)(3)(3) = 4 \cdot 81 = 324$

82. $4^2 \cdot 3^3 = (4)(4) \cdot (3)(3)(3) = 16 \cdot 27 = 432$

83. $-2^2 \cdot 3^2 = -(2)(2) \cdot (3)(3) = -4 \cdot 9 = -36$

84. $-3^2 \cdot 5^3 = -(3)(3) \cdot (5)(5)(5) = -9 \cdot 125 = -1125$

85. $(-2)^3 \cdot (-3)^2 = (-2)(-2)(-2) \cdot (-3)(-3)$
$ = -8 \cdot 9$
$ = -72$

86. $(-4)^3 \cdot (-2)^3 = (-4)(-4)(-4) \cdot (-2)(-2)(-2)$
$ = -64 \cdot (-8)$
$ = 512$

87. $4 \cdot 2^3 \cdot 3^3 = 4 \cdot (2)(2)(2) \cdot (3)(3)(3)$
$ = 4 \cdot 8 \cdot 27$
$ = 32 \cdot 27$
$ = 864$

88. $-4(-3)^2(4)^2 = -4(-3)(-3) \cdot (4)(4)$
$ = -4(9)(16)$
$ = -36(16)$
$ = -576$

89. $2^2 \cdot (-10)(-2)^2 = (2)(2) \cdot (-10) \cdot (-2)(-2)$
$ = 4 \cdot (-10)(4)$
$ = -40(4)$
$ = -160$

90. $-3(-2)^2(-5) = -3 \cdot (-2)(-2) \cdot (-5)$
$ = -3 \cdot 4 \cdot (-5)$
$ = -12 \cdot (-5)$
$ = 60$

91. $(-3)^3 \cdot 15 \cdot \left(-\dfrac{1}{3}\right)^4 = \dfrac{(-27) \cdot 15}{-81}$
$\phantom{(-3)^3 \cdot 15 \cdot \left(-\dfrac{1}{3}\right)^4} = -5$

92. $-\dfrac{1}{4} \cdot 2^2 \cdot 5^5 = -\dfrac{1}{4} \cdot 4 \cdot 3125 = -3125$

93. $\left(\dfrac{2}{3}\right)^3 \cdot (-3)^4 \cdot 4^5 = \left(\dfrac{8}{27}\right) \cdot (81) \cdot 1024$
$\phantom{\left(\dfrac{2}{3}\right)^3 \cdot (-3)^4 \cdot 4^5} = 24 \cdot 1024$
$\phantom{\left(\dfrac{2}{3}\right)^3 \cdot (-3)^4 \cdot 4^5} = 24,576$

94. $4^4(-3)^5\left(-\dfrac{3}{2}\right)^2 = 256 \cdot (-243) \cdot \dfrac{9}{4}$
$\phantom{4^4(-3)^5\left(-\dfrac{3}{2}\right)^2} = -64 \cdot 2187$
$\phantom{4^4(-3)^5\left(-\dfrac{3}{2}\right)^2} = -139,968$

Objective 1.2.4 Exercises

95. We need an Order of Operations Agreement to ensure that there is only one way in which an expression can be correctly simplified.

96. Students should describe the steps in the Order of Operations Agreement.
Step 1: Perform operations inside grouping symbols.
Step 2: Simplify exponential expressions.
Step 3: Do multiplication and division as they occur from left to right.
Step 4: Do addition and subtraction as they occur from left to right.

97. $5 - 3(8 \div 4)^2 = 5 - 3(2)^2 = 5 - 3(4) = 5 - 12 = -7$

98. $4^2 - (5-2)^2 \cdot 3 = 4^2 - (3)^2 \cdot 3$
$= 16 - 9 \cdot 3$
$= 16 - 27$
$= -11$

99. $16 - \dfrac{2^2 - 5}{3^2 + 2} = 16 - \dfrac{4-5}{9+2}$
$= 16 - \dfrac{-1}{11}$
$= 16 + \dfrac{1}{11}$
$= \dfrac{177}{11}$

100. $\dfrac{4(5-2)}{4^2 - 2^2} \div 4 = \dfrac{4(3)}{4^2 - 2^2} \div 4$
$= \dfrac{4(3)}{16 - 4} \div 4$
$= \dfrac{12}{12} \div 4$
$= 1 \div 4$
$= \dfrac{1}{4}$

101. $\dfrac{3 + \frac{2}{3}}{\frac{11}{16}} = \dfrac{\frac{11}{3}}{\frac{11}{16}} = \dfrac{11}{3} \cdot \dfrac{16}{11} = \dfrac{16}{3}$

102. $\dfrac{\frac{11}{14}}{4 - \frac{6}{7}} = \dfrac{\frac{11}{14}}{\frac{22}{7}} = \dfrac{11}{14} \cdot \dfrac{7}{22} = \dfrac{1}{4}$

103. $5[(2-4) \cdot 3 - 2] = 5[(-2) \cdot 3 - 2]$
$= 5[-6 - 2]$
$= 5[-8]$
$= -40$

104. $2[(16 \div 8) - (-2)] + 4 = 2[2 - (-2)] + 4$
$= 2[2 + 2] + 4$
$= 2[4] + 4$
$= 8 + 4$
$= 12$

105. $16 - 4\left(\dfrac{8-2}{3-6}\right) \div \dfrac{1}{2} = 16 - 4\left(\dfrac{6}{-3}\right) \div \dfrac{1}{2}$
$= 16 - 4(-2) \div \dfrac{1}{2}$
$= 16 - (-8) \div \dfrac{1}{2}$
$= 16 - (-8) \cdot 2$
$= 16 - (-16)$
$= 16 + 16$
$= 32$

106. $25 \div 5\left(\dfrac{16+8}{-2^2 + 8}\right) - 5 = 25 \div 5\left(\dfrac{16+8}{-4+8}\right) - 5$
$= 25 \div 5\left(\dfrac{24}{4}\right) - 5$
$= 25 \div 5(6) - 5$
$= 5(6) - 5$
$= 30 - 5$
$= 25$

107. $6[3 - (-4 + 2) \div 2] = 6[3 - (-2) \div 2]$
$= 6[3 - (-1)]$
$= 6[3 + 1]$
$= 6[4]$
$= 24$

108. $12 - 4[2 - (-3 + 5) - 8] = 12 - 4[2 - (2) - 8]$
$= 12 - 4[-8]$
$= 12 - (-32)$
$= 12 + 32$
$= 44$

109. $\dfrac{1}{2} - \left(\dfrac{2}{3} \div \dfrac{5}{9}\right) + \dfrac{5}{6} = \dfrac{1}{2} - \left(\dfrac{2}{3} \cdot \dfrac{9}{5}\right) + \dfrac{5}{6}$
$= \dfrac{1}{2} - \dfrac{6}{5} + \dfrac{5}{6}$
$= \dfrac{15}{30} - \dfrac{36}{30} + \dfrac{25}{30}$
$= \dfrac{15 - 36 + 25}{30}$
$= \dfrac{4}{30}$
$= \dfrac{2}{15}$

110. $\left(-\dfrac{3}{5}\right)^2 - \dfrac{3}{5} \cdot \dfrac{5}{9} + \dfrac{7}{10} = \dfrac{9}{25} - \dfrac{3}{5} \cdot \dfrac{5}{9} + \dfrac{7}{10}$
$= \dfrac{9}{25} - \dfrac{1}{3} + \dfrac{7}{10}$
$= \dfrac{54}{150} - \dfrac{50}{150} + \dfrac{105}{150}$
$= \dfrac{54 - 50 + 105}{150}$
$= \dfrac{109}{150}$

111. $\dfrac{1}{2} - \dfrac{\frac{17}{25}}{4 - \frac{3}{5}} + \dfrac{1}{5} = \dfrac{1}{2} - \dfrac{\frac{17}{25}}{\frac{17}{5}} + \dfrac{1}{5}$

$\qquad = \dfrac{1}{2} - \left(\dfrac{17}{25} \cdot \dfrac{5}{17}\right) + \dfrac{1}{5}$

$\qquad = \dfrac{1}{2} - \dfrac{1}{5} + \dfrac{1}{5}$

$\qquad = \dfrac{1}{2}$

112. $\dfrac{3}{4} + \dfrac{3 - \frac{7}{9}}{\frac{5}{6}} \cdot \dfrac{2}{3} = \dfrac{3}{4} + \dfrac{\frac{20}{9}}{\frac{5}{6}} \cdot \dfrac{2}{3}$

$\qquad = \dfrac{3}{4} + \left(\dfrac{20}{9} \cdot \dfrac{6}{5}\right) \cdot \dfrac{2}{3}$

$\qquad = \dfrac{3}{4} + \dfrac{8}{3} \cdot \dfrac{2}{3}$

$\qquad = \dfrac{3}{4} + \dfrac{16}{9}$

$\qquad = \dfrac{27}{36} + \dfrac{64}{36}$

$\qquad = \dfrac{91}{36}$

113. $\dfrac{2}{3} - \left[\dfrac{3}{8} + \dfrac{5}{6}\right] \div \dfrac{3}{5} = \dfrac{2}{3} - \left[\dfrac{9}{24} + \dfrac{20}{24}\right] \div \dfrac{3}{5}$

$\qquad = \dfrac{2}{3} - \dfrac{29}{24} \div \dfrac{3}{5}$

$\qquad = \dfrac{2}{3} - \dfrac{29}{24} \cdot \dfrac{5}{3}$

$\qquad = \dfrac{2}{3} - \dfrac{145}{72}$

$\qquad = \dfrac{48}{72} - \dfrac{145}{72}$

$\qquad = -\dfrac{97}{72}$

114. $\dfrac{3}{4} \div \left[\dfrac{5}{8} - \dfrac{5}{12}\right] + 2 = \dfrac{3}{4} \div \left[\dfrac{15}{24} - \dfrac{10}{24}\right] + 2$

$\qquad = \dfrac{3}{4} \div \dfrac{5}{24} + 2$

$\qquad = \dfrac{3}{4} \cdot \dfrac{24}{5} + 2$

$\qquad = \dfrac{18}{5} + 2$

$\qquad = \dfrac{18}{5} + \dfrac{10}{5}$

$\qquad = \dfrac{28}{5}$

115. $0.4(1.2 - 2.3)^2 + 5.8 = 0.4(-1.1)^2 + 5.8$

$\qquad = 0.4(1.21) + 5.8$

$\qquad = 0.484 + 5.8$

$\qquad = 6.284$

116. $5.4 - (0.3)^2 \div 0.09 = 5.4 - 0.09 \div 0.09$

$\qquad = 5.4 - 1$

$\qquad = 4.4$

117. $1.75 \div 0.25 - (1.25)^2 = 1.75 \div 0.25 - 1.5625$

$\qquad = 7 - 1.5625$

$\qquad = 5.4375$

118. $(3.5 - 4.2)^2 - 3.50 \div 2.5 = (-0.7)^2 - 3.50 \div 2.5$

$\qquad = 0.49 - 3.50 \div 2.5$

$\qquad = 0.49 - 1.4$

$\qquad = -0.91$

119. $25.76 \div (6.54 \div 3.27)^2 = 25.76 \div (2)^2$

$\qquad = 25.76 \div 4$

$\qquad = 6.44$

120. $(3.09 - 4.77)^2 - 4.07 \cdot 3.66 = (-1.68)^2 - 4.07 \cdot 3.66$

$\qquad = 2.8224 - 14.8962$

$\qquad = -12.0738$

Applying Concepts 1.2

121. 0

122. 1 and −1

123. No, the multiplicative inverse of zero is undefined.

124. $11^{22} = 81,402,749,386,839,761,113,321$
The tens digit is 2.

125. $7^{18} = 1,628,413,597,910,449$
The ones digit is 9.

126. $5^{33} = 116,415,321,826,934,814,453,125$
The last two digits are 25.

127. 5^{234} has over 150 digits. The last three are 625.

128. $(2^3)^4 = 8^4 = 4096$
$2^{(3^4)} = 2^{81} = 2,417,851,639,229,258,349,412,352$
They do not equal each other, and the second expression is larger.

129. Find b^c. Then find $a^{(b^c)}$.

Section 1.3

Concept Review 1.3

1. Sometimes true
   The reciprocal of 1 is 1, a whole number. The reciprocal of 2 is $\dfrac{1}{2}$, not a whole number.

2. Always true

3. Sometimes true
   $2xy$ and $3xy$ are like terms with the same variables. $2xy$ and $2x^2y$ are unlike terms with same variables.

4. Never true
   The sum of 2 and its multiplicative inverse $\dfrac{1}{2}$ is $2\dfrac{1}{2}$.

5. Always true

6. Sometimes true
The real number zero does not have a
multiplicative inverse.

Objective 1.3.1 Exercises

1. $3 \cdot 4 = 4 \cdot 3$

2. $7 + 15 = 15 + 7$

3. $(3 + 4) + 5 = 3 + (4 + 5)$

4. $(3 \cdot 4) \cdot 5 = 3 \cdot (4 \cdot 5)$

5. $\dfrac{5}{0}$ is undefined.

6. $4 + 0 = 4$

7. $3(x + 2) = 3x + 6$

8. $5(y + 4) = 5y + 20$

9. $\dfrac{0}{-6} = 0$

10. $(x + y) + [-(x + y)] = 0$

11. $\dfrac{1}{mn}(mn) = 1$

12. $x \cdot 1 = x$

13. $2(3x) = (2 \cdot 3) \cdot x$

14. $ab + bc = bc + ab$

15. A Division Property of Zero

16. The Inverse Property of Addition

17. The Inverse Property of Multiplication

18. The Commutative Property of Multiplication

19. The Addition Property of Zero

20. The Associative Property of Addition

21. A Division Property of Zero

22. The Distributive Property

23. The Distributive Property

24. The Addition Property of Zero

25. The Associative Property of Multiplication

26. The Commutative Property of Addition

Objective 1.3.2 Exercises

27. "Evaluate a variable expression" means replace
the variable expression by a numerical value and
simplify the resulting expression.

28. The value of the variable is a numerical value
that replaces a variable wherever it appears in an
expression. The value of a variable expression is
the number to which the expression simplifies
when the value of a variable is substituted into
the expression and the expression is simplified.

29. $ab + dc$
$(2)(3) + (-4)(-1) = 6 + 4 = 10$

30. $2ab - 3dc$
$$2(2)(3) - 3(-4)(-1) = 4(3) - 3(-4)(-1)$$
$$= 12 - (-12)(-1)$$
$$= 12 - 12$$
$$= 0$$

31. $4cd \div a^2$
$$4(-1)(-4) \div (2)^2 = 4(-1)(-4) \div 4$$
$$= (-4)(-4) \div 4$$
$$= 16 \div 4$$
$$= 4$$

32. $b^2 - (d - c)^2$
$$3^2 - [(-4) - (-1)]^2 = 3^2 - [(-4) + 1]^2$$
$$= 3^2 - [-3]^2$$
$$= 9 - 9$$
$$= 0$$

33. $(b - 2a)^2 + c$
$$[3 - 2(2)]^2 + (-1) = [3 - 4]^2 + (-1)$$
$$= [-1]^2 + (-1)$$
$$= 1 + (-1)$$
$$= 0$$

34. $(b - d)^2 \div (b - d)$
$$[3 - (-4)]^2 \div [3 - (-4)] = (3 + 4)^2 \div (3 + 4)$$
$$= (7)^2 \div 7$$
$$= 49 \div 7$$
$$= 7$$

35. $(bc + a)^2 \div (d - b)$
$$[(3)(-1) + 2]^2 \div (-4 - 3) = [-3 + 2]^2 \div (-7)$$
$$= [-1]^2 \div (-7)$$
$$= -\frac{1}{7}$$

36. $\dfrac{1}{3}b^3 - \dfrac{1}{4}d^3$
$$\frac{1}{3}(3)^3 - \frac{1}{4}(-4)^3 = \frac{1}{3}(27) - \frac{1}{4}(-64)$$
$$= 9 - (-16)$$
$$= 9 + 16$$
$$= 25$$

37. $\frac{1}{4}a^4 - \frac{1}{6}bc$

$$\frac{1}{4}(2)^4 - \frac{1}{6}(3)(-1) = \frac{1}{4}(16) - \frac{1}{6}(3)(-1)$$
$$= 4 - \frac{1}{6}(3)(-1)$$
$$= 4 - \frac{1}{2}(-1)$$
$$= 4 - \left(-\frac{1}{2}\right)$$
$$= 4 + \frac{1}{2}$$
$$= \frac{9}{2}$$

38. $2b^2 \div \frac{ad}{2}$

$$2(3)^2 \div \frac{2(-4)}{2} = 2(3)^2 \div \frac{-8}{2}$$
$$= 2(3)^2 \div (-4)$$
$$= 2(9) \div (-4)$$
$$= 18 \div (-4)$$
$$= -\frac{18}{4}$$
$$= -\frac{9}{2}$$

39. $\frac{3ac}{-4} - c^2$

$$\frac{3(2)(-1)}{-4} - (-1)^2 = \frac{6(-1)}{-4} - (-1)^2$$
$$= \frac{-6}{-4} - (-1)^2$$
$$= \frac{3}{2} - (-1)^2$$
$$= \frac{3}{2} - 1$$
$$= \frac{1}{2}$$

40. $\frac{2d - 2a}{2bc}$

$$\frac{2(-4) - 2(2)}{2(3)(-1)} = \frac{-8 - 4}{6(-1)} = \frac{-12}{-6} = 2$$

41. $\frac{3b - 5c}{3a - c}$

$$\frac{3(3) - 5(-1)}{3(2) - (-1)} = \frac{9 - (-5)}{6 - (-1)} = \frac{9 + 5}{6 + 1} = \frac{14}{7} = 2$$

42. $\frac{2d - a}{b - 2c}$

$$\frac{2(-4) - 2}{3 - 2(-1)} = \frac{-8 - 2}{3 - (-2)}$$
$$= \frac{-10}{3 + 2}$$
$$= \frac{-10}{5}$$
$$= -2$$

43. $\frac{a - d}{b + c}$

$$\frac{2 - (-4)}{3 + (-1)} = \frac{2 + 4}{3 + (-1)} = \frac{6}{2} = 3$$

44. $\left| a^2 + d \right|$

$$\left| 2^2 + (-4) \right| = \left| 4 + (-4) \right| = \left| 0 \right| = 0$$

45. $-a\left| a + 2d \right|$

$$-2\left| 2 + 2(-4) \right| = -2\left| 2 + (-8) \right|$$
$$= -2\left| -6 \right|$$
$$= -2(6)$$
$$= -12$$

46. $d\left| b - 2d \right|$

$$-4\left| 3 - 2(-4) \right| = -4\left| 3 - (-8) \right|$$
$$= -4\left| 3 + 8 \right|$$
$$= -4\left| 11 \right|$$
$$= -4(11)$$
$$= -44$$

47. $\frac{2a - 4d}{3b - c}$

$$\frac{2(2) - 4(-4)}{3(3) - (-1)} = \frac{4 - (-16)}{9 - (-1)}$$
$$= \frac{4 + 16}{9 + 1}$$
$$= \frac{20}{10}$$
$$= 2$$

48. $\frac{3d - b}{b - 2c}$

$$\frac{3(-4) - 3}{3 - 2(-1)} = \frac{-12 - 3}{3 - (-2)}$$
$$= \frac{-15}{3 + 2}$$
$$= \frac{-15}{5}$$
$$= -3$$

49. $-3d \div \left| \frac{ab - 4c}{2b + c} \right|$

$$-3(-4) \div \left| \frac{2(3) - 4(-1)}{2(3) + (-1)} \right| = -3(-4) \div \left| \frac{6 - (-4)}{6 + (-1)} \right|$$
$$= -3(-4) \div \left| \frac{6 + 4}{6 + (-1)} \right|$$
$$= -3(-4) \div \left| \frac{10}{5} \right|$$
$$= -3(-4) \div \left| 2 \right|$$
$$= -3(-4) \div 2$$
$$= 12 \div 2$$
$$= 6$$

50. $-2bc + \left| \dfrac{bc+d}{ab-c} \right|$

$-2(3)(-1) + \left| \dfrac{3(-1)+(-4)}{2(3)-(-1)} \right| = -2(3)(-1) + \left| \dfrac{-3+(-4)}{6-(-1)} \right|$

$\qquad = -2(3)(-1) + \left| \dfrac{-7}{6+1} \right|$

$\qquad = -2(3)(-1) + \left| \dfrac{-7}{7} \right|$

$\qquad = -2(3)(-1) + |-1|$

$\qquad = -2(3)(-1) + 1$

$\qquad = -6(-1) + 1$

$\qquad = 6 + 1$

$\qquad = 7$

51. $2(d-b) \div (3a-c)$

$2(-4-3) \div [3(2)-(-1)] = 2(-7) \div [6-(-1)]$

$\qquad = 2(-7) \div [6+1]$

$\qquad = 2(-7) \div 7$

$\qquad = -14 \div 7$

$\qquad = -2$

52. $(d-4a)^2 \div c^3$

$[-4-4(2)]^2 \div (-1)^3 = [-4-8]^2 \div (-1)^3$

$\qquad = [-12]^2 \div (-1)^3$

$\qquad = 144 \div (-1)$

$\qquad = -144$

53. $-d^2 - c^3 a$

$-(-4)^2 - (-1)^3 (2) = -16 - (-1)(2)$

$\qquad = -16 + 2$

$\qquad = -14$

54. $a^2 c - d^3$

$(2)^2 (-1) - (-4)^3 = 4(-1) - (-64)$

$\qquad = -4 + 64$

$\qquad = 60$

55. $-d^3 + 4ac$

$-(-4)^3 + 4(2)(-1) = -(-64) + 8(-1)$

$\qquad = 64 - 8$

$\qquad = 56$

56. b^a

$3^2 = 9$

57. $4^{(a)^2}$

$4^{(2^2)} = 4^4 = 256$

58. a^b

$2^3 = 8$

59. $V = LWH$

$V = (14)(10)(6)$

$V = 840$

The volume is 840 in^3.

60. $V = \dfrac{1}{3}\pi r^2 h \qquad r = \dfrac{1}{2}d = \dfrac{1}{2}(12) = 6$

$V = \dfrac{1}{3}\pi (6)^2 14$

$V = 168\pi$

$V \approx 527.79$

The volume is 168π ft^3.

The volume is approximately 527.79 ft^3.

61. $V = \dfrac{1}{3}s^2 h$

$V = \dfrac{1}{3}(3^2)5$

$V = 15$

The volume is 15 ft^2.

62. $V = s^3$

$V = 7.5^3$

$V = 421.875$

The volume is 421.875 m^3.

63. $V = \dfrac{4}{3}\pi r^3 \qquad r = \dfrac{1}{2}d = \dfrac{1}{2}(3) = 1.5$

$V = \dfrac{4}{3}\pi (1.5)^3$

$V = 4.5\pi$

$V \approx 14.14$

The volume is 4.5π cm^3.

The volume is approximately 14.14 cm^3.

64. $V = \pi r^2 h \qquad r = \dfrac{1}{2}d = \dfrac{1}{2}(8) = 4$

$V = \pi (4^2)8$

$V = 128\pi$

$V \approx 402.12$

The volume is 128π cm^3.

The volume is approximately 402.12 cm^3

65. $SA = 2LW + 2LH + 2WH$

$SA = 2(5)(4) + 2(5)(3) + 2(4)(3)$

$SA = 40 + 30 + 24$

$SA = 94$

The surface area is 94 m^2.

66. $SA = 6s^2$

$SA = 6(14^2)$

$SA = 1176$

The surface area is 1176 ft^2.

67. $SA = s^2 + 4\left(\dfrac{1}{2}\right)bh$

$SA = 4^2 + 2(4)(5)$

$SA = 16 + 40 = 56$

The surface area is 56 m^2.

68. $SA = 4\pi r^2$ $r = \frac{1}{2}d = \frac{1}{2}(2) = 1$

$SA = 4\pi(1^2)$
$SA = 4\pi$
$SA \approx 12.57$
The surface area is 4π cm^2.
The surface area is approximately 12.57 cm^2.

69. $SA = 2\pi r^2 + 2\pi rh$
$SA = 2\pi(6^2) + 2\pi(6)(2)$
$SA = 72\pi + 24\pi$
$SA = 96\pi$
$SA \approx 301.59$
The surface area is 96π in^2.
The surface area is approximately 301.59 in^2.

70. $SA = \pi r^2 + \pi rl$ $r = \frac{1}{2}d = \frac{1}{2}(3) = 1.5$

$SA = \pi(1.5)^2 + \pi(1.5)(9)$
$SA = 2.25\pi + 13.5\pi$
$SA = 15.75\pi$
$SA \approx 49.48$
The surface area is 15.75π ft^2.
The surface area is approximately 49.48 ft^2.

Objective 1.3.3 Exercises

71. If there are two terms with a common variable factor, the Distributive Property allows us to combine the two terms into one term. Add the coefficients of the variable factor, and write the sum as the coefficient of the common variable factor.

72. $5x + 7x = 12x$

73. $3x + 10x = 13x$

74. $-8ab - 5ab = -13ab$

75. $-2x + 5x - 7x = 3x - 7x = -4x$

76. $3x - 5x + 9x = -2x + 9x = 7x$

77. $-2a + 7b + 9a = 7a + 7b$

78. $5b - 8a - 12b = -8a - 7b$

79. $12\left(\frac{1}{12}\right)x = x$

80. $\frac{1}{3}(3y) = y$

81. $-3(x - 2) = -3x + 6$

82. $-5(x - 9) = -5x + 45$

83. $(x + 2)5 = 5x + 10$

84. $-(x + y) = -x - y$

85. $-(-x - y) = x + y$

86. $3(a - 5) = 3a - 15$

87. $3(x - 2y) - 5 = 3x - 6y - 5$

88. $4x - 3(2y - 5) = 4x - 6y + 15$

89. $-2a - 3(3a - 7) = -2a - 9a + 21 = -11a + 21$

90. $3x - 2(5x - 7) = 3x - 10x + 14 = -7x + 14$

91. $2x - 3(x - 2y) = 2x - 3x + 6y = -x + 6y$

92. $3[a - 5(5 - 3a)] = 3[a - 25 + 15a]$
$\qquad = 3[16a - 25]$
$\qquad = 48a - 75$

93. $5[-2 - 6(a - 5)] = 5[-2 - 6a + 30]$
$\qquad = 5[28 - 6a]$
$\qquad = 140 - 30a$

94. $3[x - 2(x + 2y)] = 3[x - 2x - 4y]$
$\qquad = 3[-x - 4y]$
$\qquad = -3x - 12y$

95. $5[y - 3(y - 2x)] = 5[y - 3y + 6x]$
$\qquad = 5[-2y + 6x]$
$\qquad = -10y + 30x$

96. $-2(x - 3y) + 2(3y - 5x) = -2x + 6y + 6y - 10x$
$\qquad = -12x + 12y$

97. $4(-a - 2b) - 2(3a - 5b) = -4a - 8b - 6a + 10b$
$\qquad = -10a + 2b$

98. $5(3a - 2b) - 3(-6a + 5b) = 15a - 10b + 18a - 15b$
$\qquad = 33a - 25b$

99. $-7(2a - b) + 2(-3b + a) = -14a + 7b - 6b + 2a$
$\qquad = -12a + b$

100. $3x - 2[y - 2(x + 3[2x + 3y])]$
$= 3x - 2[y - 2(x + 6x + 9y)]$
$= 3x - 2[y - 2(7x + 9y)]$
$= 3x - 2[y - 14x - 18y]$
$= 3x - 2[-17y - 14x]$
$= 3x + 34y + 28x$
$= 31x + 34y$

101. $2x - 4[x - 4(y - 2[5y + 3])]$
$= 2x - 4[x - 4(y - 10y - 6)]$
$= 2x - 4[x - 4(-9y - 6)]$
$= 2x - 4[x + 36y + 24]$
$= 2x - 4x - 144y - 96$
$= -2x - 144y - 96$

102. $4 - 2(7x - 2y) - 3(-2x + 3y)$
$= 4 - 14x + 4y + 6x - 9y$
$= 4 - 8x - 5y$

103. $3x + 8(x - 4) - 3(2x - y)$
$= 3x + 8x - 32 - 6x + 3y$
$= 5x - 32 + 3y$

104. $\frac{1}{3}[8x - 2(x - 12) + 3] = \frac{1}{3}[8x - 2x + 24 + 3]$
$\qquad = \frac{1}{3}[6x + 27]$
$\qquad = 2x + 9$

105. $\dfrac{1}{4}[14x - 3(x - 8) - 7x] = \dfrac{1}{4}[14x - 3x + 24 - 7x]$

$\qquad\qquad\qquad\qquad\quad = \dfrac{1}{4}[4x + 24]$

$\qquad\qquad\qquad\qquad\quad = x + 6$

Applying Concepts 1.3

106. $-4(5x - y) = -20x + 4y$
The statement is correct; it uses the Distributive Property.

107. $4(3y + 1) = 12y + 4$
The statement is correct; it uses the Distributive Property.

108. $6 - 6x = 0x = 0$
The statement is not correct; it incorrectly uses the Distributive Property. The correct answer is $6 - 6x$.

109. $2 + 3x = (2 + 3)x = 5x$
The statement is not correct; it mistakenly uses the Distributive Property. It is in an irreducible statement. That is, the answer is $2 + 3x$.

110. $3a - 4b = 4b - 3a$
The statement is not correct; it incorrectly uses the Commutative Property of Addition. The correct answer is $3a - 4b = -4b + 3a$.

111. $2(3y) = (2 \cdot 3)(2y) = 12y$
The statement is not correct; it incorrectly uses the Associative Property of Multiplication. The correct answer is $(2 \cdot 3)y = 6y$.

112. $x^4 \cdot \dfrac{1}{x^4} = 1$
The statement is correct; it uses the Inverse Property of Multiplication.

113. $-x^2 + y^2 = y^2 - x^2$
The statement is correct; it uses the Commutative Property of Addition.

114. $3(x + y) + 2x$

a. $(3x + 3y) + 2x$ Distributive Property

b. $(3y + 3x) + 2x$ Commutative Property of Addition

c. $3y + (3x + 2x)$ Associative Property of Addition

d. $3y + (3 + 2)x$ Distributive Property
$\quad 3y + 5x$

115. $3a + 4(b + a)$

a. $3a + (4b + 4a)$ Distributive Property

b. $3a + (4a + 4b)$ Commutative Property of Addition

c. $(3a + 4a) + 4b$ Associative Property of Addition

d. $(3 + 4)a + 4b$ Distributive Property
$\quad 7a + 4b$

116. $y + (3 + y)$

a. $y + (y + 3)$ Commutative Property of Addition

b. $(y + y) + 3$ Associative Property of Addition

c. $(1y + 1y) + 3$ Multiplication Property of One

d. $(1 + 1)y + 3$ Distributive Property
$\quad 2y + 3$

117. $5(3a + 1)$

a. $5(3a) + 5(1)$ Distributive Property

b. $(5 \cdot 3)a + 5(1)$ Associative Property of
$\quad 15a + 5(1)$ Multiplication

c. $15a + 5$ Multiplication Property of One

Section 1.4

Concept Review 1.4

1. Never true
   The smaller number is represented by $12 - x$.

2. Never true
   The other piece is represented by $L - x$.

3. Never true
   The sum of twice x and 4 is represented by $2x + 4$.

4. Never true
   Four times the difference between x and 3 is represented by $4(x - 3)$.

5. Sometimes true
   The square of $-x$ is represented by $(-x)^2$. The only exception is for the number 0.
   $-0^2 = (-0)^2 = 0$

6. Always true

Objective 1.4.1 Exercises

1. the unknown number: n
   The sum of the number and two: $n + 2$
   $n - (n + 2) = n - n - 2 = -2$

2. the unknown number: n
The difference between five and the number:
$5 - n$
$n - (5 - n) = n - 5 + n = 2n - 5$

3. the unknown number: n
one-third of the number: $\frac{1}{3}n$

four-fifths of the number: $\frac{4}{5}n$

$\frac{1}{3}n + \frac{4}{5}n = \frac{5}{15}n + \frac{12}{15}n = \frac{17}{15}n$

4. the unknown number: n
three-eighths of the number: $\frac{3}{8}n$

one-sixth of the number: $\frac{1}{6}n$

$\frac{3}{8}n - \frac{1}{6}n = \frac{9}{24}n - \frac{4}{24}n = \frac{5}{24}n$

5. the unknown number: n
the product of eight and the number: $8n$
$5(8n) = 40n$

6. the unknown number: n
two-thirds of the number: $\frac{2}{3}n$

$n + \frac{2}{3}n = \frac{5}{3}n$

7. the unknown number: n
the product of seventeen and the number: $17n$
twice the number: $2n$
$17n - 2n = 15n$

8. the unknown number: n
six times the number: $6n$
the total of six times the number and twenty-two:
$6n + 22$
$\frac{1}{2}(6n + 22) = 3n + 11$

9. the unknown number: n
the square of the number: n^2
the total of twelve and the square of the number:
$12 + n^2$
$n^2 - (12 + n^2) = n^2 - 12 - n^2 = -12$

10. the unknown number: n
the square of the number: n^2
the difference between the number and
seventeen: $n - 17$
$n^2 + 11 + (n - 17) = n^2 + 11 + n - 17 = n^2 + n - 6$

11. the unknown number: n
the sum of five times the number and 12: $5n + 12$
the product of the number and fifteen: $15n$
$15n + (5n + 12) = 15n + 5n + 12 = 20n + 12$

12. the unknown number: n
twice the sum of the number and 11: $2(n + 11)$
$2(n + 11) - 4 = 2n + 22 - 4 = 2n + 18$

13. Let the smaller number be x.
The larger number is $15 - x$.
The sum of twice the smaller number and two
more than the larger number
$2x + (15 - x + 2) = 2x + (17 - x) = x + 17$

14. Let the smaller number be x.
The larger number is $20 - x$.
The difference between five times the larger
number and three less than the smaller number
$5(20 - x) - (x - 3) = 100 - 5x - x + 3 = -6x + 103$

15. Let the larger number be x.
Then the smaller number is $34 - x$.
The difference between two more than the
smaller number and twice the larger number
$[(34 - x) + 2] - 2x = 34 - x + 2 - 2x = 36 - 3x$

16. Let the larger number be x.
Then the smaller number is $33 - x$.
The difference between six more than twice the
smaller number and three more than the larger
number
$[2(33 - x) + 6] - (x + 3) = 66 - 2x + 6 - x - 3$
$= 69 - 3x$

Objective 1.4.2 Exercises

17. The population of Milan, Italy: P
The population of San Paolo, Brazil: $4P$

18. Number of deaths each year by accident: d
Number of deaths each year by heart disease: $7d$

19. Distance from Earth to the moon: d
Distance from Earth to sun: $390d$

20. Length of the longest road tunnel: L
Length of the longest rail tunnel: $L + 23.36$

21. Amount of the first account: x
Amount of the second account: $10{,}000 - x$

22. Length of the longer piece: L
Length of the shorter piece: $3 - L$

23. Flying time between San Diego and New York: t
Flying time between New York and San Diego:
$13 - t$

24. Length of the shorter piece: L
Length of the longer piece: $12 - L$

25. The measure of angle B: x
The measure of angle A is twice that of angle B:
$2x$
The measure of angle C is twice that of angle A:
$2(2x) = 4x$

26. The width of the rectangle is W.
The length is three more than twice the width:
$2W + 3$

Applying Concepts 1.4

27. The sum of twice a number and three.

28. Four less than five times a number.

29. Twice the sum of a number and three

30. The product of five and four less than a number.

31. One-half the acceleration due to gravity: $\frac{1}{2}g$

Time squared: t^2

The product: $\frac{1}{2}gt^2$

32. The product of m and a: ma

33. The product of A and v^2: Av^2

34. The quotient of k and m: $\frac{k}{m}$

The square root of the quotient: $\sqrt{\frac{k}{m}}$

Focus on Problem Solving

1. a. *Understand the problem.* We must determine the weight of water in the cup. To do this, we need the volume of the cup and the density (weight per unit volume) of water. The dimensions of the cup are in inches, so the volume will be in cubic inches. Therefore, the density must be found in ounces per cubic inch.

b. *Devise a plan.* Consult a reference book to find the formula for the volume of a cone and the density of water. The formula for the volume of a cone is $V = \frac{1}{3}\pi r^2 h$. The density of water is 62.4 lb/ft^3. The plan is to convert the density to ounces per cubic inch and then use the formula $w = dv$ where w is the weight in ounces, d is the density of water in ounces per cubic inch, and v is the volume in cubic inches.

c. *Carry out the plan.* Find the volume of the cone.

$r = 1.5$, $h = 4$

$V = \frac{1}{3}\pi r^2 h = \frac{1}{3}\pi(1.5)^2(4) \approx 9.425 \text{ in}^3$

Convert 62.4 lb/ft^3 to ounces per cubic inch.

$d = 62.4\dfrac{\text{lb}}{\text{ft}^3}$

$= 62.4\dfrac{\text{lb}}{\text{ft}^3} \cdot \dfrac{1 \text{ ft}^3}{1728 \text{ in}^3} \cdot \dfrac{16 \text{ oz}}{\text{lb}}$

$\approx 0.578\dfrac{\text{oz}}{\text{in}^3}$

Substitute the values in the formula $w = dv$.

$w \approx 0.578\dfrac{\text{oz}}{\text{in}^3} \cdot 9.425 \text{ in}^3 \approx 5.45 \text{ oz}$

The cup will hold 5.45 oz of water.

d. *Review the solution.* A cup 4 in. tall is a fairly large cup, so it seems reasonable that it would hold about one-third of a pound.

2. a. *Understand the problem.* We are to determine the dimensions of a 12-oz soft drink can. We are to use an approximation of the distance that a hand can reach around 75% of the circumference of the can. We need to know the formula for the volume of a right circular cylinder and the volume in cubic inches of 12 fl oz. We also need to make an approximation of the length of a hand.

b. *Devise a plan.* From a resource book, we find that the volume of a right circular cylinder is $V = \pi r^2 h$. Approximate the length of a hand is 7 in. From this approximation, we can use the formula $C = 2\pi r$ to find the radius of the can. After finding the volume of 12 fl oz and the radius of the can, we find the height of the can.

c. *Carry out the plan.* The length of the hand is 75% of the circumference.

$7 = 0.75C$

$9.33 \approx C$

Use the formula $C = 2\pi r$ to find the radius.

$C = 2\pi r$

$9.333 = 2\pi r$

$1.485 \approx r$

Use the fact that 128 fl oz = 1 gal and 1 gal = 231 in^3 to find the volume of 12 fl oz.

$V = 12 \text{ fl oz}$

$= 12 \text{ fl oz} \cdot \dfrac{1 \text{ gal}}{128 \text{ fl oz}} \cdot \dfrac{231 \text{ in}^3}{1 \text{ gal}}$

$\approx 21.656 \text{ in}^3$

Use the formula for the volume of a right circular cylinder to find the height of the can.

$V = \pi r^2 h$

$21.656 = \pi(1.485)^2 h$

$\dfrac{21.656}{\pi(1.495)^2} = h$

$3.13 \approx h$

The radius of the can is approximately 1.5 in., and the height is approximately 3.1 in.

d. *Review the solution.* The diameter of the can is approximately the same as the height of the can. The diameter seems too large and the height seems too small. The approximation of the distance of the hand reaching around the can may be too large.

Projects and Group Activities

Water Displacement

1. Volume of the cylinder is $V = \pi r^2 h$, where $r = 2$ and $h = 10$.

   $V = \pi(2)^2(10)$

   $V = 40\pi$

   The volume of the water displaced is $V = LWH$, where $L = 30$, $W = 20$, and $H = x$.

   $40\pi = (30)(20)x$

   $\dfrac{2}{30}\pi = x$

   $0.21 \approx x$

   The water will rise approximately 0.21 cm.

2. The volume of $\dfrac{2}{3}$ of the sphere is

   $V = \dfrac{2}{3}\left(\dfrac{4}{3}\pi r^3\right)$, where $r = 6$.

   $V = \dfrac{8}{9}\pi(6)^3$

   $V = 192\pi$

   The volume of the water displaced is $V = LWH$, where $L = 20$, $W = 16$ and $H = x$.

   $192\pi = (20)(16)x$

   $\dfrac{3}{5}\pi = x$

   $1.88 \approx x$

   The water will rise approximately 1.88 in.

3. Find the volume of the statue by finding the volume of the water displaced by the statue.

   $V = LWH$, where $L = 12$, $W = 12$ and $H = 0.42$.

   $V = (12)(12)(0.42) = 60.48$

   The volume of the statue is 60.48 cubic inches.

   density = weight ÷ volume

   density = $15 \div 60.48 \approx 0.25$

   The density of the statue is approximately 0.25 lb/in³.

Chapter Review Exercises

1. $\dfrac{3}{4}$: $-\dfrac{3}{4} + \dfrac{3}{4} = 0$

2. Replace x with the elements in the set and determine whether the inequality is true.

   $x > -1$

   $-4 > -1$ False

   $-2 > -1$ False

   $0 > -1$ True

   $2 > -1$ True

   The inequality is true for 0 and 2.

3. $p \in \{-4, 0, 7\}$

   $-|p|$

   $-|-4| = -4$

   $-|0| = 0$

   $-|7| = -7$

4. $\{-2, -1, 0, 1, 2, 3\}$

5. $\{x \mid x < -3\}$

6. $\{x \mid -2 \le x \le 3\}$

7. $A \cup B = \{1, 2, 3, 4, 5, 6, 7, 8\}$

8. $A \cap B = \{2, 3\}$

9. $[-3, \infty)$

10. $\{x \mid x < 1\}$

11. $\{x \mid x \le -3\} \cup \{x \mid x > 0\}$

12. $(-2, 4]$

13. $-10 - (-3) - 8 = -10 + 3 + (-8) = -7 + (-8) = -15$

14. $-204 \div (-17) = 12$

15. $18 - |-12 + 8| = 18 - |-4| = 18 - 4 = 14$

16. $-2 \cdot (4^2) \cdot (-3)^2 = -2 \cdot 16 \cdot 9 = -32 \cdot 9 = -288$

17. $-\dfrac{3}{8} + \dfrac{3}{5} - \dfrac{1}{6} = -\dfrac{45}{120} + \dfrac{72}{120} - \dfrac{20}{120}$

    $= \dfrac{-45 + 72 - 20}{120}$

    $= \dfrac{7}{120}$

18. $\dfrac{3}{5}\left(-\dfrac{10}{21}\right)\left(-\dfrac{7}{15}\right) = \dfrac{3 \cdot 10 \cdot 7}{5 \cdot 21 \cdot 15}$

    $= \dfrac{\overset{1}{3} \cdot 2 \cdot \overset{1}{5} \cdot \overset{1}{7}}{\underset{1}{5} \cdot \underset{1}{3} \cdot \underset{1}{7} \cdot 3 \cdot 5}$

    $= \dfrac{2}{15}$

19. $-\dfrac{3}{8} \div \dfrac{3}{5} = -\dfrac{3}{8} \cdot \dfrac{5}{3}$

    $= \dfrac{\overset{1}{3} \cdot 5}{8 \cdot \underset{1}{3}}$

    $= -\dfrac{5}{8}$

20. $-4.07 + 2.3 - 1.07 = -1.77 - 1.07 = -2.84$

21. $-3.286 \div (-1.06) = 3.1$

22. $20 \div \dfrac{3^2 - 2^2}{3^2 + 2^2} = 20 \div \dfrac{9 - 4}{9 + 4}$

$= 20 \div \dfrac{5}{13}$

$= 20 \cdot \dfrac{13}{5}$

$= 52$

23. $2a^2 - \dfrac{3b}{a} = 2(-3)^2 - \dfrac{3(2)}{-3}$

$= 2(-3)^2 - \dfrac{6}{-3}$

$= 2(-3)^2 - (-2)$

$= 2(9) - (-2)$

$= 18 + 2$

$= 20$

24. $(a - 2b^2) \div ab$

$(4 - 2(-3)^2) \div (4)(-3) = (4 - 2(9)) \div (4)(-3)$

$= (4 - 18) \div (4)(-3)$

$= -14 \div [(4)(-3)]$

$= -14 \div -12$

$= \dfrac{-14}{-12}$

$= \dfrac{7}{6}$

25. 3

26. y

27. (ab)

28. 4

29. The Inverse Property of Addition

30. The Associative Property of Multiplication

31. $-2(x - 3) + 4(2 - x) = -2x + 6 + 8 - 4x = -6x + 14$

32. $4y - 3[x - 2(3 - 2x) - 4y] = 4y - 3[x - 6 + 4x - 4y]$

$= 4y - 3[5x - 6 - 4y]$

$= 4y - 15x + 18 + 12y$

$= 16y - 15x + 18$

33. The unknown number: x

The sum of the number and four: $x + 4$

$4(x + 4) = 4x + 16$

34. The unknown number: x

The difference between the number and two: $x - 2$

Twice the difference between the number and two: $2(x - 2)$

$2(x - 2) + 8 = 2x - 4 + 8 = 2x + 4$

35. Let x be the smaller of the numbers. Then the larger number is $40 - x$

The sum of twice x and five more than $40 - x$.

$2x + (40 - x + 5) = x + 45$

36. Let x be the larger number.

Then the smaller number is $9 - x$.

The difference between three more than twice $(9 - x)$ and one more than x.

$[2(9 - x) + 3] - (x + 1) = 18 - 2x + 3 - x - 1$

$\qquad\qquad\qquad\qquad\qquad = -3x + 20$

37. The width of the rectangle: W

The length is 3 feet less than $3W$.

The length is $3W - 3$.

38. Let the first integer be x.

The second integer is five more than four times x.

$4x + 5$ is the magnitude of the second integer.

Chapter Test

1. 12

2. Replace x with each element in the set and determine whether the inequality is true.

$-1 > x$

$-1 > -5$ True

$-1 > 3$ False

$-1 > 7$ False

The inequality is true for -5.

3. $2 - (-12) + 3 - 5 = 2 + 12 + 3 + (-5)$

$= 14 + 3 + (-5)$

$= 17 + (-5)$

$= 12$

4. $(-2)(-3)(-5) = (6)(-5) = -30$

5. $-180 \div 12 = -15$

6. $|-3 - (-5)| = |-3 + 5| = |2| = 2$

7. $-5^2 \cdot 4 = -25 \cdot 4 = -100$

8. $(-2)^3 (-3)^2 = (-8)(9) = -72$

9. $\dfrac{2}{3} - \dfrac{5}{12} + \dfrac{4}{9} = \dfrac{24}{36} - \dfrac{15}{36} + \dfrac{16}{36}$

$= \dfrac{24 - 15 + 16}{36}$

$= \dfrac{25}{36}$

10. $\left(-\dfrac{2}{3}\right)\left(\dfrac{9}{15}\right)\left(\dfrac{10}{27}\right) = -\dfrac{\overset{1}{\cancel{2}} \cdot \overset{1}{\cancel{3}} \cdot \cancel{3} \cdot 2 \cdot \overset{1}{\cancel{5}}}{\underset{1}{\cancel{3}} \cdot \underset{1}{\cancel{3}} \cdot \underset{1}{\cancel{5}} \cdot 3 \cdot 3 \cdot 3}$

$= -\dfrac{4}{27}$

11. $4.27 - 6.98 + 1.3 = -2.71 + 1.3 = -1.41$

12. $-15.092 \div 3.08 = -4.9$

13. $12 - 4\left(\dfrac{5^2 - 1}{3}\right) \div 16 = 12 - 4\left(\dfrac{25 - 1}{3}\right) \div 16$

$\qquad\qquad\qquad\qquad = 12 - 4\left(\dfrac{24}{3}\right) \div 16$

$\qquad\qquad\qquad\qquad = 12 - 4(8) \div 16$

$\qquad\qquad\qquad\qquad = 12 - 32 \div 16$

$\qquad\qquad\qquad\qquad = 12 - 2$

$\qquad\qquad\qquad\qquad = 10$

14. $8 - 4(2 - 3)^2 \div 2 = 8 - 4(-1)^2 \div 2$

$\qquad\qquad\qquad\quad = 8 - 4(1) \div 2$

$\qquad\qquad\qquad\quad = 8 - 4 \div 2$

$\qquad\qquad\qquad\quad = 8 - 2$

$\qquad\qquad\qquad\quad = 6$

15. $(a - b)^2 \div (2b + 1) = (2 - (-3))^2 \div (2(-3) + 1)$

$\qquad\qquad\qquad\qquad = (5)^2 \div (-6 + 1)$

$\qquad\qquad\qquad\qquad = (5)^2 \div (-5)$

$\qquad\qquad\qquad\qquad = 25 \div (-5)$

$\qquad\qquad\qquad\qquad = -5$

16. $\dfrac{b^2 - c^2}{a - 2c} = \dfrac{(3)^2 - (-1)^2}{2 - 2(-1)}$

$\qquad\qquad = \dfrac{9 - 1}{2 - (-2)}$

$\qquad\qquad = \dfrac{8}{4}$

$\qquad\qquad = 2$

17. 4

18. The Distributive Property

19. $3x - 2(x - y) - 3(y - 4x)$
$= 3x - 2x + 2y - 3y + 12x$
$= 13x - y$

20. $2x - 4[2 - 3(x + 4y) - 2]$
$= 2x - 4[2 - 3x - 12y - 2]$
$= 2x - 4[-3x - 12y]$
$= 2x + 12x + 48y$
$= 14x + 48y$

21. the unknown number: n
three less than the number: $n - 3$
the product of three less than the number and
nine: $(n - 3)(9)$
$13 - (n - 3)(9) = 13 - 9n + 27 = 40 - 9n$

22. The unknown number: n
The total of twelve times the number and twenty-
seven: $12n + 27$
$\dfrac{1}{3}(12n + 27) = 4n + 9$

23. $A \cup B = \{1, 2, 3, 4, 5, 7\}$

24. $A \cup B = \{-2, -1, 0, 1, 2, 3\}$

25. $A \cap B = \{5, 7\}$

26. $A \cap B = \{-1, 0, 1\}$

27. $(\infty, -1]$

28. $(3, \infty)$

29. $\{x | x \le 3\} \cup \{x | x < -2\}$

30. $\{x | x < 3\} \cap \{x | x > -2\}$

Chapter 2: First-Degree Equations and Inequalities

Prep Test

1. -4 [1.2.1]

2. -6 [1.2.1]

3. 3 [1.2.1]

4. 1 [1.2.2]

5. $-\dfrac{1}{2}$ [1.2.2]

6. $10x - 5$ [1.3.3]

7. $6(x-2) + 3 = 6x - 12 + 3$ [1.2.1]
$\qquad\qquad\quad = 6x - 9$

8. $3n + 6$ [1.3.3]

9. $0.08x + 0.05(400 - x)$ [1.3.3]
$\quad = 0.08x + 20 - 0.05x$
$\quad = 0.03x + 20$

10. $20 - n$ [1.4.2]

Go Figure

First, reduce the fraction $\dfrac{95}{100} = \dfrac{19}{20}$. So 20 votes seems to satisfy the question, but is it the least possible number of votes? Next try nineteen total votes $\dfrac{18}{19} \approx 0.947$. Then try eighteen total votes $\dfrac{17}{18} \approx 0.944$. And try seventeen total votes $\dfrac{16}{17} \approx 0.941$. Try sixteen total votes $\dfrac{15}{16} = 0.9375$. Since sixteen votes does not fit the greater than 94% restriction, the answer is seventeen votes.

Section 2.1

Concept Review 2.1

1. Never true
   An equation must have an equals sign.

2. Sometimes true
   The first degree equation $x + 2 = 3$ has a solution, but $x = x + 3$ does not.

3. Sometimes true
   $8 = 4 + 2$ is a false equation. $6 = 6$ is a true equation. Neither equation contains a variable.

4. Never true
   This equation is an identity. Any number will be a solution.

5. Never true
   This equation has no solution. Any replacement value for x will result in a false equation.

6. Always true

7. Always true

8. Sometimes true
   The only exception to this statement is when c is equal to zero. Division by zero is not defined.

Objective 1.1.1 Exercises

1. An equation contains and equals sign; an expression does not.

2. The solution of an equation is a replacement value of the variable that will make the equation true.

3. The Addition Property of Equations states that the same quantity can be added to each side of an equation without changing the solution of the equation. This property is used to remove a term from one side of an equation by adding the opposite of that term to each side of the equation.

4. The Multiplication Property of Equations states that each side of an equation can be multiplied by the same nonzero number without changing the solution of the equation. This property is used to remove a coefficient from a variable term by multiplying each side of the equation by the reciprocal of the coefficient.

5. $\begin{aligned} 7 - 3m &= 4 \\ 7 - 3(1) &= 4 \\ 4 &= 4 \end{aligned}$
   Yes

6. $\begin{aligned} 4y - 5 &= 3y \\ 4(5) - 5 &= 3(5) \\ 20 - 5 &= 15 \\ 15 &= 15 \end{aligned}$
   Yes

7. $\begin{aligned} 6x - 1 &= 7x + 1 \\ 6(-2) - 1 &= 7(-2) + 1 \\ -12 - 1 &= -14 + 1 \\ -13 &= -13 \end{aligned}$
   Yes

8. $\begin{aligned} x^2 &= 4x - 5 \\ (3)^2 &= 4(3) - 5 \\ 9 &= 12 - 5 \\ 9 &\neq 7 \end{aligned}$
   No

9. $\begin{aligned} x - 2 &= 7 \\ x - 2 + 2 &= 7 + 2 \\ x &= 9 \end{aligned}$
   The solution is 9.

10.
$$x - 8 = 4$$
$$x - 8 + 8 = 4 + 8$$
$$x = 12$$
The solution is 12.

11.
$$a + 3 = -7$$
$$a + 3 - 3 = -7 - 3$$
$$a = -10$$
The solution is -10.

12.
$$-12 = x - 3$$
$$-12 + 3 = x - 3 + 3$$
$$-9 = x$$
The solution is -9.

13.
$$3x = 12$$
$$\frac{3x}{3} = \frac{12}{3}$$
$$x = 4$$
The solution is 4.

14.
$$8x = 4$$
$$\frac{8x}{8} = \frac{4}{8}$$
$$x = \frac{1}{2}$$
The solution is $\frac{1}{2}$.

15.
$$\frac{2}{7} + x = \frac{17}{21}$$
$$\frac{2}{7} - \frac{2}{7} + x = \frac{17}{21} - \frac{2}{7}$$
$$x = \frac{17}{21} - \frac{6}{21}$$
$$x = \frac{11}{21}$$
The solution is $\frac{11}{21}$.

16.
$$x + \frac{2}{3} = \frac{5}{6}$$
$$x + \frac{2}{3} - \frac{2}{3} = \frac{5}{6} - \frac{2}{3}$$
$$x = \frac{5}{6} - \frac{4}{6}$$
$$x = \frac{1}{6}$$
The solution is $\frac{1}{6}$.

17.
$$\frac{5}{8} - y = \frac{3}{4}$$
$$\frac{5}{8} - \frac{5}{8} - y = \frac{3}{4} - \frac{5}{8}$$
$$-y = \frac{6}{8} - \frac{5}{8}$$
$$-y = \frac{1}{8}$$
$$(-1)(-y) = \frac{1}{8}(-1)$$
$$y = -\frac{1}{8}$$
The solution is $-\frac{1}{8}$.

18.
$$\frac{2}{3}y = 5$$
$$\frac{3}{2}\left(\frac{2}{3}y\right) = \frac{3}{2}(5)$$
$$y = \frac{15}{2}$$
The solution is $\frac{15}{2}$.

19.
$$\frac{3}{5}y = 12$$
$$\frac{5}{3}\left(\frac{3}{5}y\right) = \frac{5}{3}(12)$$
$$y = 20$$
The solution is 20.

20.
$$\frac{3t}{8} = -15$$
$$\frac{8}{3}\left(\frac{3}{8}t\right) = \frac{8}{3}(-15)$$
$$t = -40$$
The solution is -40.

21.
$$\frac{3a}{7} = -21$$
$$\frac{7}{3}\left(\frac{3}{7}a\right) = \frac{7}{3}(-21)$$
$$a = -49$$
The solution is -49.

22.
$$-\frac{5}{8}x = \frac{4}{5}$$
$$-\frac{8}{5}\left(-\frac{5}{8}x\right) = -\frac{8}{5}\left(\frac{4}{5}\right)$$
$$x = -\frac{32}{25}$$
The solution is $-\frac{32}{25}$.

23.
$$-\frac{5}{12}y = \frac{7}{16}$$
$$-\frac{12}{5}\left(-\frac{5}{12}y\right) = -\frac{12}{5}\left(\frac{7}{16}\right)$$
$$y = -\frac{21}{20}$$
The solution is $-\frac{21}{20}$.

24.
$$-\frac{3}{4}x = -\frac{4}{7}$$
$$-\frac{4}{3}\left(-\frac{3}{4}x\right) = -\frac{4}{3}\left(-\frac{4}{7}\right)$$
$$x = \frac{16}{21}$$
The solution is $\frac{16}{21}$.

25.
$$b - 14.72 = -18.45$$
$$b - 14.72 + 14.72 = -18.45 + 14.72$$
$$b = -3.73$$
The solution is -3.73.

26.
$$b + 3.87 = -2.19$$
$$b + 3.87 - 3.87 = -2.19 - 3.87$$
$$b = -6.06$$
The solution is -6.06.

27.
$$3x + 5x = 12$$
$$8x = 12$$
$$\frac{8x}{8} = \frac{12}{8}$$
$$x = \frac{3}{2}$$
The solution is $\frac{3}{2}$.

28.
$$2x - 7x = 15$$
$$-5x = 15$$
$$\frac{-5x}{-5} = \frac{15}{-5}$$
$$x = -3$$
The solution is -3.

29.
$$2x - 4 = 12$$
$$2x - 4 + 4 = 12 + 4$$
$$2x = 16$$
$$\frac{2x}{2} = \frac{16}{2}$$
$$x = 8$$

30.
$$3x - 12 = 5x$$
$$3x - 3x - 12 = 5x - 3x$$
$$-12 = 2x$$
$$\frac{-12}{2} = \frac{2x}{2}$$
$$-6 = x$$
The solution is -6.

31.
$$4x + 2 = 4x$$
$$4x - 4x + 2 = 4x - 4x$$
$$2 = 0$$
The equation has no solution.

32.
$$3m - 7 = 3m$$
$$3m - 3m - 7 = 3m - 3m$$
$$-7 = 0$$
The equation has no solution.

33.
$$2x + 2 = 3x + 5$$
$$2x - 3x + 2 = 3x - 3x + 5$$
$$-x + 2 = 5$$
$$-x + 2 - 2 = 5 - 2$$
$$-x = 3$$
$$(-1)(-x) = (-1)(3)$$
$$x = -3$$
The solution is -3.

34.
$$7x - 9 = 3 - 4x$$
$$7x + 4x - 9 = 3 - 4x + 4x$$
$$11x - 9 = 3$$
$$11x - 9 + 9 = 3 + 9$$
$$11x = 12$$
$$\frac{11x}{11} = \frac{12}{11}$$
$$x = \frac{12}{11}$$

35.
$$2 - 3t = 3t - 4$$
$$2 - 3t - 3t = 3t - 3t - 4$$
$$2 - 6t = -4$$
$$2 - 2 - 6t = -4 - 2$$
$$-6t = -6$$
$$\frac{-6t}{-6} = \frac{-6}{-6}$$
$$t = 1$$
The solution is 1.

36.
$$7 - 5t = 2t - 9$$
$$7 - 5t - 2t = 2t - 2t - 9$$
$$7 - 7t = -9$$
$$7 - 7 - 7t = -9 - 7$$
$$-7t = -16$$
$$\frac{-7t}{-7} = \frac{-16}{-7}$$
$$t = \frac{16}{7}$$
The solution is $\frac{16}{7}$.

37.
$$2a - 3a = 7 - 5a$$
$$-a = 7 - 5a$$
$$-a + 5a = 7 - 5a + 5a$$
$$4a = 7$$
$$\frac{4a}{4} = \frac{7}{4}$$
$$a = \frac{7}{4}$$
The solution is $\frac{7}{4}$.

38.
$$3a - 5a = 8a + 4$$
$$-2a = 8a + 4$$
$$-2a - 8a = 8a - 8a + 4$$
$$-10a = 4$$
$$\frac{-10a}{-10} = \frac{4}{-10}$$
$$a = -\frac{2}{5}$$
The solution is $-\frac{2}{5}$.

39.
$$\frac{5}{8}b - 3 = 12$$
$$\frac{5}{8}b - 3 + 3 = 12 + 3$$
$$\frac{5}{8}b = 15$$
$$\frac{8}{5}\left(\frac{5}{8}b\right) = \frac{8}{5}(15)$$
$$b = 24$$
The solution is 24.

40.
$$\frac{1}{3} - 2b = 3$$
$$\frac{1}{3} - \frac{1}{3} - 2b = 3 - \frac{1}{3}$$
$$-2b = \frac{9}{3} - \frac{1}{3}$$
$$-2b = \frac{8}{3}$$
$$-\frac{1}{2}(-2b) = -\frac{1}{2}\left(\frac{8}{3}\right)$$
$$b = -\frac{4}{3}$$
The solution is $-\frac{4}{3}$.

41.
$$b + \frac{1}{5}b = 2$$
$$\frac{6}{5}b = 2$$
$$\frac{5}{6}\left(\frac{6}{5}b\right) = \frac{5}{6}(2)$$
$$b = \frac{5}{3}$$
The solution is $\frac{5}{3}$.

42.
$$3x - 2x + 7 = 12 - 4x$$
$$x + 7 = 12 - 4x$$
$$x + 4x + 7 = 12 - 4x + 4x$$
$$5x + 7 = 12$$
$$5x + 7 - 7 = 12 - 7$$
$$5x = 5$$
$$\frac{5x}{5} = \frac{5}{5}$$
$$x = 1$$
The solution is 1.

43.
$$2x - 9x + 3 = 6 - 5x$$
$$-7x + 3 = 6 - 5x$$
$$-7x + 5x + 3 = 6 - 5x + 5x$$
$$-2x + 3 = 6$$
$$-2x + 3 - 3 = 6 - 3$$
$$-2x = 3$$
$$\frac{-2x}{-2} = \frac{3}{-2}$$
$$x = -\frac{3}{2}$$
The solution is $-\frac{3}{2}$.

44.
$$7 + 8y - 12 = 3y - 8 + 5y$$
$$8y - 5 = 8y - 8$$
$$8y - 8y - 5 = 8y - 8y - 8$$
$$-5 = -8$$
The equation has no solution.

45.
$$2y - 4 + 8y = 7y - 8 + 3y$$
$$10y - 4 = 10y - 8$$
$$10y - 10y - 4 = 10y - 10y - 8$$
$$-4 = -8$$
The equation has no solution.

46.
$$2x - 5 + 7x = 11 - 3x + 4x$$
$$9x - 5 = 11 + x$$
$$9x - x - 5 = 11 + x - x$$
$$8x - 5 = 11$$
$$8x - 5 + 5 = 11 + 5$$
$$8x = 16$$
$$\frac{8x}{8} = \frac{16}{8}$$
$$x = 2$$
The solution is 2.

47.
$$9 + 4x - 12 = -3x + 5x + 8$$
$$4x - 3 = 2x + 8$$
$$4x - 2x - 3 = 2x - 2x + 8$$
$$2x - 3 = 8$$
$$2x - 3 + 3 = 8 + 3$$
$$2x = 11$$
$$\frac{2x}{2} = \frac{11}{2}$$
$$x = \frac{11}{2}$$
The solution is $\frac{11}{2}$.

48.
$$3.24a + 7.14 = 5.34a$$
$$3.24a - 3.24a + 7.14 = 5.34a - 3.24a$$
$$7.14 = 2.1a$$
$$\frac{7.14}{2.1} = \frac{2.1a}{2.1}$$
$$3.4 = a$$
The solution is 3.4.

49.
$$5.3y + 0.35 = 5.02y$$
$$5.3y - 5.3y + 0.35 = 5.02y - 5.3y$$
$$0.35 = -0.28y$$
$$\frac{0.35}{-0.28} = \frac{-0.28y}{-0.28}$$
$$-1.25 = y$$
The solution is -1.25.

Objective 2.1.2 Exercises

50.
$$2x + 2(x+1) = 10$$
$$2x + 2x + 2 = 10$$
$$4x + 2 = 10$$
$$4x = 8$$
$$\frac{4x}{4} = \frac{8}{4}$$
$$x = 2$$
The solution is 2.

51.
$$2x + 3(x-5) = 15$$
$$2x + 3x - 15 = 15$$
$$5x - 15 = 15$$
$$5x = 30$$
$$\frac{5x}{5} = \frac{30}{5}$$
$$x = 6$$
The solution is 6.

52.
$$2(a-3) = 2(4-2a)$$
$$2a - 6 = 8 - 4a$$
$$6a - 6 = 8$$
$$6a = 14$$
$$\frac{6a}{6} = \frac{14}{6}$$
$$a = \frac{7}{3}$$
The solution is $\frac{7}{3}$.

53.
$$5(2-b) = -3(b-3)$$
$$10 - 5b = -3b + 9$$
$$10 = 2b + 9$$
$$1 = 2b$$
$$\frac{1}{2} = \frac{2b}{2}$$
$$\frac{1}{2} = b$$
The solution is $\frac{1}{2}$.

54.
$$3 - 2(y-3) = 4y - 7$$
$$3 - 2y + 6 = 4y - 7$$
$$-2y + 9 = 4y - 7$$
$$-6y + 9 = -7$$
$$-6y = -16$$
$$\frac{-6y}{-6} = \frac{-16}{-6}$$
$$y = \frac{8}{3}$$
The solution is $\frac{8}{3}$.

55.
$$3(y-5) - 5y = 2y + 9$$
$$3y - 15 - 5y = 2y + 9$$
$$-2y - 15 = 2y + 9$$
$$-4y - 15 = 9$$
$$-4y = 24$$
$$\frac{-4y}{-4} = \frac{24}{-4}$$
$$y = -6$$
The solution is -6.

56.
$$4(x-2) + 2 = 4x - 2(2-x)$$
$$4x - 8 + 2 = 4x - 4 + 2x$$
$$4x - 6 = 6x - 4$$
$$-2x - 6 = -4$$
$$-2x = 2$$
$$\frac{-2x}{-2} = \frac{2}{-2}$$
$$x = -1$$
The solution is -1.

57.
$$2x - 3(x-4) = 2(3-2x) + 2$$
$$2x - 3x + 12 = 6 - 4x + 2$$
$$-x + 12 = 8 - 4x$$
$$3x + 12 = 8$$
$$3x = -4$$
$$\frac{3x}{3} = \frac{-4}{3}$$
$$x = -\frac{4}{3}$$
The solution is $-\frac{4}{3}$.

58.
$$2(2d+1) - 3d = 5(3d-2) + 4d$$
$$4d + 2 - 3d = 15d - 10 + 4d$$
$$2 + d = 19d - 10$$
$$2 = 18d - 10$$
$$12 = 18d$$
$$\frac{12}{18} = \frac{18d}{18}$$
$$\frac{2}{3} = d$$
The solution is $\frac{2}{3}$.

59.
$$-4(7y-1) + 5y = -2(3y+4) - 3y$$
$$-28y + 4 + 5y = -6y - 8 - 3y$$
$$-23y + 4 = -9y - 8$$
$$-14y + 4 = -8$$
$$-14y = -12$$
$$\frac{-14y}{-14} = \frac{-12}{-14}$$
$$y = \frac{6}{7}$$
The solution is $\frac{6}{7}$.

60.
$$4[3+5(3-x)+2x] = 6-2x$$
$$4[3+15-5x+2x] = 6-2x$$
$$4[18-3x] = 6-2x$$
$$72-12x = 6-2x$$
$$72-10x = 6$$
$$-10x = -66$$
$$\frac{-10x}{-10} = \frac{-66}{-10}$$
$$x = \frac{33}{5}$$

The solution is $\frac{33}{5}$.

61.
$$2[4+2(5-x)-2x] = 4x-7$$
$$2[4+10-2x-2x] = 4x-7$$
$$2[14-4x] = 4x-7$$
$$28-8x = 4x-7$$
$$28-12x = -7$$
$$-12x = -35$$
$$\frac{-12x}{-12} = \frac{-35}{-12}$$
$$x = \frac{35}{12}$$

The solution is $\frac{35}{12}$.

62.
$$2[b-(4b-5)] = 3b+4$$
$$2(b-4b+5) = 3b+4$$
$$2b-8b+10 = 3b+4$$
$$-6b+10 = 3b+4$$
$$-9b+10 = 4$$
$$-9b = -6$$
$$\frac{-9b}{-9} = \frac{-6}{-9}$$
$$b = \frac{2}{3}$$

The solution is $\frac{2}{3}$.

63.
$$-3[x+4(x+1)] = x+4$$
$$-3(x+4x+4) = x+4$$
$$-3(5x+4) = x+4$$
$$-15x-12 = x+4$$
$$-16x-12 = 4$$
$$-16x = 16$$
$$\frac{-16x}{-16} = \frac{16}{-16}$$
$$x = -1$$

The solution is -1.

64.
$$4[a-(3a-5)] = a-7$$
$$4(a-3a+5) = a-7$$
$$4(-2a+5) = a-7$$
$$-8a+20 = a-7$$
$$-9a+20 = -7$$
$$-9a = -27$$
$$\frac{-9a}{-9} = \frac{-27}{-9}$$
$$a = 3$$

The solution is 3.

65.
$$5-6[2t-2(t+3)] = 8-t$$
$$5-6(2t-2t-6) = 8-t$$
$$5-12t+12t+36 = 8-t$$
$$41 = 8-t$$
$$33 = -t$$
$$-33 = t$$

The solution is -33.

66.
$$-3(x-2) = 2[x-4(x-2)+x]$$
$$-3x+6 = 2(x-4x+8+x)$$
$$-3x+6 = 2(-2x+8)$$
$$-3x+6 = -4x+16$$
$$x+6 = 16$$
$$x = 10$$

The solution is 10.

67.
$$3[x-(2-x)-2x] = 3(4-x)$$
$$3[x-2+x-2x] = 12-3x$$
$$3(-2) = 12-3x$$
$$-6 = 12-3x$$
$$-18 = -3x$$
$$\frac{-18}{-3} = \frac{-3x}{-3}$$
$$6 = x$$

The solution is 6.

68.
$$\frac{2}{9}t - \frac{5}{6} = \frac{1}{12}t$$
$$36\left(\frac{2}{9}t - \frac{5}{6}\right) = 36\left(\frac{1}{12}t\right)$$
$$\frac{36 \cdot 2t}{9} - \frac{36 \cdot 5}{6} = \frac{36 \cdot t}{12}$$
$$8t-30 = 3t$$
$$-30 = -5t$$
$$\frac{-30}{-5} = \frac{-5t}{-5}$$
$$6 = t$$

The solution is 6.

69.
$$\frac{3}{4}t - \frac{7}{12}t = 1$$
$$12\left(\frac{3}{4}t - \frac{7}{12}t\right) = 12 \cdot 1$$
$$\frac{12 \cdot 3t}{4} - \frac{12 \cdot 7t}{12} = 12$$
$$9t-7t = 12$$
$$2t = 12$$
$$\frac{2t}{2} = \frac{12}{2}$$
$$t = 6$$

The solution is 6.

70.

$$\frac{2}{3}x - \frac{5}{6}x - 3 = \frac{1}{2}x - 5$$

$$6\left(\frac{2}{3}x - \frac{5}{6}x - 3\right) = 6\left(\frac{1}{2}x - 5\right)$$

$$\frac{6 \cdot 2x}{3} - \frac{6 \cdot 5x}{6} - 6 \cdot 3 = \frac{6 \cdot x}{2} - 6 \cdot 5$$

$$4x - 5x - 18 = 3x - 30$$

$$-x - 18 = 3x - 30$$

$$-4x - 18 = -30$$

$$-4x = -12$$

$$\frac{-4x}{-4} = \frac{-12}{-4}$$

$$x = 3$$

The solution is 3.

71.

$$\frac{1}{2}x - \frac{3}{4}x + \frac{5}{8} = \frac{3}{2}x - \frac{5}{2}$$

$$8\left(\frac{1}{2}x - \frac{3}{4}x + \frac{5}{8}\right) = 8\left(\frac{3}{2}x - \frac{5}{2}\right)$$

$$\frac{8 \cdot x}{2} - \frac{8 \cdot 3x}{4} + \frac{8 \cdot 5}{8} = \frac{8 \cdot 3x}{2} - \frac{8 \cdot 5}{2}$$

$$4x - 6x + 5 = 12x - 20$$

$$-2x + 5 = 12x - 20$$

$$-14x + 5 = -20$$

$$-14x = -25$$

$$\frac{-14x}{-14} = \frac{-25}{-14}$$

$$x = \frac{25}{14}$$

The solution is $\frac{25}{14}$.

72.

$$\frac{3x - 2}{4} - 3x = 12$$

$$4\left(\frac{3x - 2}{4} - 3x\right) = 4(12)$$

$$\frac{4(3x - 2)}{4} - 4 \cdot 3x = 48$$

$$3x - 2 - 12x = 48$$

$$-9x - 2 = 48$$

$$-9x = 50$$

$$\frac{-9x}{-9} = \frac{50}{-9}$$

$$x = -\frac{50}{9}$$

The solution is $-\frac{50}{9}$.

73.

$$\frac{2a - 9}{5} + 3 = 2a$$

$$5\left(\frac{2a - 9}{5} + 3\right) = 5 \cdot 2a$$

$$\frac{5(2a - 9)}{5} + 5 \cdot 3 = 10a$$

$$2a - 9 + 15 = 10a$$

$$2a + 6 = 10a$$

$$6 = 8a$$

$$\frac{6}{8} = \frac{8a}{8}$$

$$\frac{3}{4} = a$$

The solution is $\frac{3}{4}$.

74.

$$\frac{x - 2}{4} - \frac{x + 5}{6} = \frac{5x - 2}{9}$$

$$36\left(\frac{x - 2}{4} - \frac{x + 5}{6}\right) = 36\left(\frac{5x - 2}{9}\right)$$

$$\frac{36(x - 2)}{4} - \frac{36(x + 5)}{6} = \frac{36(5x - 2)}{9}$$

$$9(x - 2) - 6(x + 5) = 4(5x - 2)$$

$$9x - 18 - 6x - 30 = 20x - 8$$

$$3x - 48 = 20x - 8$$

$$-17x - 48 = -8$$

$$-17x = 40$$

$$\frac{-17x}{-17} = \frac{40}{-17}$$

$$x = -\frac{40}{17}$$

The solution is $-\frac{40}{17}$.

75.

$$\frac{2x - 1}{4} + \frac{3x + 4}{8} = \frac{1 - 4x}{12}$$

$$24\left(\frac{2x - 1}{4} + \frac{3x + 4}{8}\right) = 24\left(\frac{1 - 4x}{12}\right)$$

$$\frac{24(2x - 1)}{4} + \frac{24(3x + 4)}{8} = \frac{24(1 - 4x)}{12}$$

$$6(2x - 1) + 3(3x + 4) = 2(1 - 4x)$$

$$12x - 6 + 9x + 12 = 2 - 8x$$

$$21x + 6 = 2 - 8x$$

$$29x + 6 = 2$$

$$29x = -4$$

$$\frac{29x}{29} = \frac{-4}{29}$$

$$x = -\frac{4}{29}$$

The solution is $-\frac{4}{29}$.

76.
$$\frac{2}{3}(15-6a) = \frac{5}{6}(12a+18)$$
$$6\left[\frac{2}{3}(15-6a)\right] = 6\left[\frac{5}{6}(12a+18)\right]$$
$$4(15-6a) = 5(12a+18)$$
$$60-24a = 60a+90$$
$$60 = 84a+90$$
$$-30 = 84a$$
$$\frac{-30}{84} = \frac{84a}{84}$$
$$-\frac{5}{14} = a$$

The solution is $-\dfrac{5}{14}$.

77.
$$\frac{1}{5}(20x+30) = \frac{1}{3}(6x+36)$$
$$15\left[\frac{1}{5}(20x+30)\right] = 15\left[\frac{1}{3}(6x+36)\right]$$
$$3(20x+30) = 5(6x+36)$$
$$60x+90 = 30x+180$$
$$30x+90 = 180$$
$$30x = 90$$
$$\frac{30x}{30} = \frac{90}{30}$$
$$x = 3$$

The solution is 3.

78.
$$\frac{1}{3}(x-7)+5 = 6x+4$$
$$\frac{x}{3}-\frac{7}{3}+5 = 6x+4$$
$$3\left(\frac{x}{3}-\frac{7}{3}+5\right) = 3(6x+4)$$
$$\frac{3x}{3}-\frac{21}{3}+15 = 18x+12$$
$$x-7+15 = 18x+12$$
$$x+8 = 18x+12$$
$$8 = 17x+12$$
$$-4 = 17x$$
$$\frac{-4}{17} = \frac{17x}{17}$$
$$-\frac{4}{17} = x$$

The solution is $-\dfrac{4}{17}$.

79.
$$2(y-4)+8 = \frac{1}{2}(6y+20)$$
$$2y-8+8 = \frac{6y}{2}+\frac{20}{2}$$
$$2y = 3y+10$$
$$-y = 10$$
$$(-1)(-y) = (-1)(10)$$
$$y = -10$$

The solution is −10.

80.
$$\frac{1}{4}(2b+50) = \frac{5}{2}\left(15-\frac{1}{5}b\right)$$
$$4\left[\frac{1}{4}(2b+50)\right] = 4\left[\frac{5}{2}\left(15-\frac{1}{5}b\right)\right]$$
$$1(2b+50) = 10\left(15-\frac{1}{5}b\right)$$
$$2b+50 = 150-2b$$
$$4b+50 = 150$$
$$4b = 100$$
$$\frac{4b}{4} = \frac{100}{4}$$
$$b = 25$$

The solution is 25.

81.
$$\frac{1}{4}(7-x) = \frac{2}{3}(x+2)$$
$$12\left[\frac{1}{4}(7-x)\right] = 12\left[\frac{2}{3}(x+2)\right]$$
$$3(7-x) = 8(x+2)$$
$$21-3x = 8x+16$$
$$21-11x = 16$$
$$-11x = -5$$
$$\frac{-11x}{-11} = \frac{-5}{-11}$$
$$x = \frac{5}{11}$$

The solution is $\dfrac{5}{11}$.

82.
$$-4.2(p+3.4) = 11.13$$
$$-4.2p-14.28 = 11.13$$
$$-4.2p = 25.41$$
$$\frac{-4.2p}{-4.2} = \frac{25.41}{-4.2}$$
$$p = -6.05$$

The solution is −6.05.

83.
$$-1.6(b-2.35) = -11.28$$
$$-1.6b+3.76 = -11.28$$
$$-1.6b = -15.04$$
$$\frac{-1.6b}{-1.6} = \frac{-15.04}{-1.6}$$
$$b = 9.4$$

The solution is 9.4.

Objective 2.1.3 Exercises

84. Strategy

To find the Celsius temperature, write and solve an equation using C to represent the Celsius temperature.

Solution

The Fahrenheit temperature (59°) is 32° more than $\frac{9}{5}$ the Celsius temperature (C).

$$59 = 32 + \frac{9}{5}C$$
$$5(59) = 5\left(32 + \frac{9}{5}C\right)$$
$$295 = 160 + 5\left(\frac{9}{5}C\right)$$
$$295 = 160 + 9C$$
$$135 = 9C$$
$$\frac{135}{9} = \frac{9C}{9}$$
$$15 = C$$

The temperature is 15°C.

85. Strategy

To find the number of bags purchased, write and solve an equation using b to represent the number of bags purchased.

Solution

The first bag purchased cost $10.90. That means that $b - 1$ bags cost $10.50(b - 1)$.
$$84.40 = 10.90 + 10.50(b - 1)$$
$$84.40 = 10.90 + 10.50b - 10.50$$
$$84.40 = 0.40 + 10.50b$$
$$84 = 10.50b$$
$$8 = b$$

The customer purchased 8 bags of feed.

86. Strategy

To find the number of children, write and solve an equation using c to represent the number of children.

Solution

The cost for the children's meals was $7.25c$.
$$79.35 = 7.25c + 11.95(3)$$
$$79.35 = 7.25c + 35.85$$
$$43.50 = 7.25c$$
$$6 = c$$

There were 6 children in the family.

87. Strategy

To find the charge per hour for labor, write and solve an equation using L to represent the charge per hour for labor.

Solution

The total charge for labor was $4L$ dollars.
$$316.55 = 4L + 148.55$$
$$168 = 4L$$
$$42 = L$$

Labor cost $42 per hour.

88. Strategy

To find the teacher's take-home pay, write and solve an equation using P to represent the take-home pay.

Solution

The take-home pay is the total pay minus the deductions (26.8% of the gross biweekly pay).
$$P = 1620 - 0.268(1620)$$
$$P = 1620 - 434.16$$
$$P = 1185.84$$

The teacher's take-home pay is $1185.84.

89. Strategy

To find the employee's regular hourly rate, write and solve an equation using h to represent the hourly rate and $1.5h$ to represent the overtime rate.

Solution

The wages earned for the first forty hours plus the wages earned for overtime are $642.
$$40h + 9(1.5h) = 642$$
$$40h + 13.5h = 642$$
$$53.5h = 642$$
$$h = 12$$

The regular hourly rate is $12.

90. Strategy

To find the number of adult and children's tickets, write and solve an equation using a to represent the number of adult tickets and $6 - a$ to represent the number of children's tickets.

Solution

The cost for the family of six was $34.50.
$$34.50 = 7.75a + 4.75(6 - a)$$
$$34.50 = 7.75a + 28.50 - 4.75a$$
$$34.50 = 3a + 28.50$$
$$6 = 3a$$
$$2 = a$$

The family purchased 2 adult tickets and 4 children's tickets.

91. Strategy
To find the number of each type of ticket, write and solve an equation using g to represent the number of outfield grandstand tickets and $12 - g$ to represent the number of right field box tickets.

Solution
The total price of the tickets was \$335.
$$25g + 32(12 - g) = 335$$
$$25g + 384 - 32g = 335$$
$$-7g + 384 = 335$$
$$-7g = -49$$
$$g = 7$$
The fraternity purchased 7 outfield grandstand tickets and 5 right field box tickets.

92. Strategy
To find the number of people in the family, write and solve an equation using x to represent the number of people in the family.

Solution
The cost for the first person is \$7.50 and the cost for the rest of the family is $\$4.25(x - 1)$.
$$28.75 = 7.50 + 4.25(x - 1)$$
$$28.75 = 7.50 + 4.25x - 4.25$$
$$28.75 = 3.25 + 4.25x$$
$$25.50 = 4.25x$$
$$6 = x$$
There were 6 people in the family.

93. Strategy
To find the number of mezzanine tickets purchased, write and solve an equation using m to represent the number of mezzanine tickets and $7 - m$ to represent the number of balcony tickets.

Solution
The total cost of the tickets was \$275.00.
$$50m + 35(7 - m) = 275$$
$$50m + 245 - 35m = 275$$
$$15m + 245 = 275$$
$$15m = 30$$
$$m = 2$$
Two mezzanine tickets were purchased.

Applying Concepts 2.1

94.
$$8 \div \frac{1}{x} = -3$$
$$8x = -3$$
$$\frac{8x}{8} = \frac{-3}{8}$$
$$x = -\frac{3}{8}$$
The solution is $-\frac{3}{8}$.

95.
$$\frac{1}{\frac{1}{y}} = -9$$
$$y = -9$$
The solution is -9.

96.
$$\frac{6}{\frac{a}{7}} = -18$$
$$6\left(\frac{a}{7}\right) = -18$$
$$\frac{6}{7}a = -18$$
$$\frac{7}{6}\left(\frac{6}{7}a\right) = (-18)\frac{7}{6}$$
$$a = -21$$
The solution is -21.

97.
$$\frac{10}{\frac{x}{3}} - 5 = 4x$$
$$10\left(\frac{x}{3}\right) - 5 = 4x$$
$$\frac{10}{3}x - 5 = 4x$$
$$\frac{10}{3}x - \frac{10}{3}x - 5 = 4x - \frac{10}{3}x$$
$$-5 = \frac{2}{3}x$$
$$\frac{3}{2}(-5) = \frac{3}{2}\left(\frac{2}{3}x\right)$$
$$-\frac{15}{2} = x$$
The solution is $-\frac{15}{2}$.

98.
$$3[4(y + 2) - (y + 5)] = 3(3y + 1)$$
$$3[4y + 8 - y - 5] = 9y + 3$$
$$3(3y + 3) = 9y + 3$$
$$9y + 9 = 9y + 3$$
$$9y - 9y + 9 = 9y - 9y + 3$$
$$9 = 3$$
There is no solution.

99.
$$2[3(x + 4) - 2(x + 1)] = 5x + 3(1 - x)$$
$$2[3x + 12 - 2x - 2] = 5x + 3 - 3x$$
$$2(x + 10) = 2x + 3$$
$$2x + 20 = 2x + 3$$
$$2x - 2x + 20 = 2x - 2x + 3$$
$$20 = 3$$
There is no solution.

100.
$$\frac{4(x - 5) - (x + 1)}{3} = x - 7$$
$$\frac{4x - 20 - x - 1}{3} = x - 7$$
$$\frac{3x - 21}{3} = x - 7$$
$$x - 7 = x - 7$$
$$-7 = -7$$
The solution is all real numbers.

101.
$$\frac{4[(x-3)+2(1-x)]}{5} = x+1$$
$$\frac{4(x-3+2-2x)}{5} = x+1$$
$$\frac{4(-x-1)}{5} = x+1$$
$$\frac{-4x-4}{5} = x+1$$
$$5\left(\frac{-4x-4}{5}\right) = 5(x+1)$$
$$-4x-4 = 5x+5$$
$$-4x+4x-4 = 5x+4x+5$$
$$-4 = 9x+5$$
$$-4-5 = 9x+5-5$$
$$-9 = 9x$$
$$\frac{-9}{9} = \frac{9x}{9}$$
$$-1 = x$$
The solution is -1.

102.
$$2584 \div x = 54\frac{46}{x}$$
$$\frac{2584}{x} = \frac{54x+46}{x}$$
$$x\left(\frac{2584}{x}\right) = x\left(\frac{54x+46}{x}\right)$$
$$2584 = 54x+46$$
$$2584-46 = 54x+46-46$$
$$2538 = 54x$$
$$\frac{2538}{54} = \frac{54x}{54}$$
$$47 = x$$
The solution is 47.

103.
$$3(2x+2)-4(x-3) = 2(x+9)$$
$$6x+6-4x+12 = 2x+18$$
$$2x+18 = 2x+18$$
$$2x-2x+18 = 2x-2x+18$$
$$18 = 18$$
$$0 = 0$$
The solution is all real numbers.

104. a. $C = 5.34Y+52.9$
$C = 5.34(10)+52.9$
$C = 53.4+52.9$
$C = 106.3$
The model predicted $106.3 billion for 2002.

b. $|106.8-106.3| = 0.5$

The difference between the predicted amount and the actual amount is $0.5 billion.

c. $\left(\dfrac{|106.3-106.8|}{106.8}\right)100 \approx 0.5$

The percent error is 0.5%.

105. $4c+1 = 9$
$4c+1-1 = 9-1$
By the Addition Property of Equations, the same number can be added to each side of an equation without changing the solution of the equation.
$4c+0 = 8$
By the Inverse Property of Addition, the sum of a number and its additive inverse is 0.
$4c = 8$
By the Addition Property of Zero, the sum of a number and 0 is the number.
$$\frac{1}{4}\cdot 4c = \frac{1}{4}\cdot 8$$
By the Multiplication Property of Equations, each side of an equation can be multiplied by the same nonzero number without changing the solution of the equation.
$1c = 2$
By the Inverse Property of Equations, the product of a number and its multiplicative inverse is 1.
$c = 1$
By the Multiplication Property of One, the product of 1 and a number is the number.

Section 2.2

Concept Review 2.2

1. Always true

2. Sometimes true
   If n is odd, then n and $n+2$ represent two consecutive odd integers.
   If n is even, then n and $n+2$ represent two consecutive even integers.

3. Always true

4. Never true
   If one of the numbers is x, the other number is $n-x$.

5. Sometimes true
   If n is even, then $n+1$, $n+3$, and $n+5$ represent consecutive odd integers.
   If n is odd, then $n+1$, $n+3$, and $n+5$ represent consecutive even integers.

Objective 2.2.1 Exercises

1. The number of coins is represented by x, and a quarter is worth 25 cents, so the total value of x quarters is $25x$ cents.

2. To find the total value of the coins in the purse, you can find the total value of all the nickels and add it to the total value of all the dimes.

3. Strategy

Number of nickels: x

Number of dimes: $56 - x$

Coin	Number	Value	Total Value
Nickel	x	5	$5x$
Dime	$56 - x$	10	$10(56 - x)$

The sum of the total values of each type of coin equals the total value of all the coins (400 cents).

$5x + 10(56 - x) = 400$

Solution

$$5x + 10(56 - x) = 400$$
$$5x + 560 - 10x = 400$$
$$-5x + 560 = 400$$
$$-5x = -160$$
$$x = 32$$
$$56 - x = 56 - 32 = 24$$

There are 24 dimes in the bank.

4. Strategy

Number of dimes: x

Number of quarters: $22 - x$

Coin	Number	Value	Total Value
Dime	x	10	$10x$
Quarter	$22 - x$	25	$25(22 - x)$

The sum of the total values of each type of coin equals the total value of all the coins (445 cents).

$10x + 25(22 - x) = 445$

Solution

$$10x + 25(22 - x) = 445$$
$$10x + 550 - 25x = 445$$
$$-15x + 550 = 445$$
$$-15x = -105$$
$$x = 7$$
$$22 - x = 22 - 7 = 15$$

There are 15 quarters in the bank.

5. Strategy

Number of twenty-dollar bills: x

Number of five-dollar bills: $68 - x$

Bill	Number	Value	Total Value
20-dollar	x	20	$20x$
5-dollar	$68 - x$	5	$5(68 - x)$

The sum of the total values of each type of bill equals the total value of all the bills (730 dollars).

$20x + 5(68 - x) = 730$

Solution

$$20x + 5(68 - x) = 730$$
$$20x + 340 - 5x = 730$$
$$15x + 340 = 730$$
$$15x = 390$$
$$x = 26$$

The cashier has 26 twenty-dollar bills.

6. Strategy

Number of ten-dollar bills: x

Number of five-dollar bills: $2x$

Bill	Number	Value	Total Value
10-dollar	x	10	$10x$
5-dollar	$2x$	5	$5(2x)$

The sum of the total values of each type of bill equals the total value of all the bills (2500 dollars).

$10x + 5(2x) = 2500$

Solution

$$10x + 5(2x) = 2500$$
$$10x + 10x = 2500$$
$$20x = 2500$$
$$x = 125$$
$$2x = 2(125) = 250$$

The store obtained 250 five-dollar bills.

7. Strategy

Number of 20¢ stamps: x

Number of 15¢ stamps: $3x - 8$

Stamp	Number	Value	Total Value
20¢	x	20	$20x$
15¢	$3x - 8$	15	$15(3x - 8)$

The sum of the total values of each type of stamp equals the total value of all the stamps (400 cents). $20x + 15(3x - 8) = 400$

Solution

$$20x + 15(3x - 8) = 400$$
$$20x + 45x - 120 = 400$$
$$65x - 120 = 400$$
$$65x = 520$$
$$x = 8$$

$3x - 8 = 3(8) - 8 = 24 - 8 = 16$

There are eight 20¢ stamps and sixteen 15¢ stamps.

8. Strategy

Number of 20¢ stamps: x

Number of 28¢ stamps: $140 - x$

Stamp	Number	Value	Total Value
20¢	x	20	$20x$
28¢	$140 - x$	28	$28(140 - x)$

The sum of the total values of each type of stamp equals the total value of all the stamps (3120 cents).

$20x + 28(140 - x) = 3120$

Solution

$$20x + 28(140 - x) = 3120$$
$$20x + 3920 - 28x = 3120$$
$$-8x + 3920 = 3120$$
$$-8x = -800$$
$$x = 100$$

$140 - x = 140 - 100 = 40$

There were one hundred 20¢ stamps and forty 28¢ stamps.

9. Strategy

Number of quarters: x

Number of dimes: $4x$

Number of nickels: $25 - 5x$

Coin	Number	Value	Total Value
Quarter	x	25	$25x$
Dime	$4x$	10	$10(4x)$
Nickel	$25 - 5x$	5	$5(25 - 5x)$

The sum of the total values of each type of coin equals the total value of all the coins (205 cents).

$25x + 10(4x) + 5(25 - 5x) = 205$

Solution

$$25x + 10(4x) + 5(25 - 5x) = 205$$
$$25x + 40x + 125 - 25x = 205$$
$$40x + 125 = 205$$
$$40x = 80$$
$$x = 2$$

$4x = 4 \cdot 2 = 8$

There are 8 dimes in the bank.

10. Strategy

Number of quarters: x

Number of dimes: $2x$

Number of nickels: $2x + 7$

Coin	Number	Value	Total Value
Quarter	x	25	$25x$
Dime	$2x$	10	$10(2x)$
Nickel	$2x + 7$	5	$5(2x + 7)$

The sum of the total values of each type of coin equals the total value of all the coins (310 cents).

$25x + 10(2x) + 5(2x + 7) = 310$

Solution

$$25x + 10(2x) + 5(2x + 7) = 310$$
$$25x + 20x + 10x + 35 = 310$$
$$55x + 35 = 310$$
$$55x = 275$$
$$x = 5$$

There are 5 quarters in the collection.

11. Strategy

Number of 3¢ stamps: x
Number of 8¢ stamps: $2x - 3$
Number of 13¢ stamps: $2(2x - 3)$

Stamp	Number	Value	Total Value
3¢	x	3	$3x$
8¢	$2x - 3$	8	$8(2x - 3)$
13¢	$2(2x - 3)$	13	$13(2)(2x - 3)$

The sum of the total values of each type of stamp equals the total value of all the stamps (253 cents).
$3x + 8(2x - 3) + 26(2x - 3) = 253$

Solution
$$3x + 8(2x - 3) + 26(2x - 3) = 253$$
$$3x + 16x - 24 + 52x - 78 = 253$$
$$71x - 102 = 253$$
$$71x = 355$$
$$x = 5$$

There are five 3¢ stamps in the collection.

12. Strategy

Number of 15¢ stamps: x
Number of 20¢ stamps: $4x$
Number of 40¢ stamps: $300 - 5x$

Stamp	Number	Value	Total Value
15¢	x	15	$15x$
20¢	$4x$	20	$20(4x)$
40¢	$300 - 5x$	40	$40(300 - 5x)$

The sum of the total values of each type of stamp equals the total value of all the stamps (7380 cents).
$15x + 20(4x) + 40(300 - 5x) = 7380$

Solution
$$15x + 20(4x) + 40(300 - 5x) = 7380$$
$$15x + 80x + 12{,}000 - 200x = 7380$$
$$-105x + 12{,}000 = 7380$$
$$-105x = -4620$$
$$x = 44$$

$300 - 5x = 300 - 5(44) = 300 - 220 = 80$
There were eighty 40¢ stamps purchased.

13. Strategy

Number of 18¢ stamps: x
Number of 8¢ stamps: $2x$
Number of 11¢ stamps: $x + 3$

Stamp	Number	Value	Total Value
18¢	x	18	$18x$
8¢	$2x$	8	$8(2x)$
11¢	$x + 3$	11	$11(x + 3)$

The sum of the total values of each type of stamp equals the total value of all the stamps (348 cents).
$18x + 8(2x) + 11(x + 3) = 348$

Solution
$$18x + 8(2x) + 11(x + 3) = 348$$
$$18x + 16x + 11x + 33 = 348$$
$$45x + 33 = 348$$
$$45x = 315$$
$$x = 7$$

There are seven 18¢ stamps in the collection.

14. Strategy

Number of 12¢ stamps: x
Number of 3¢ stamps: $5x$
Number of 15¢ stamps: $x - 4$

Stamp	Number	Value	Total Value
12¢	x	12	$12x$
3¢	$5x$	3	$3(5x)$
15¢	$x - 4$	15	$15(x - 4)$

The sum of the total values of each type of stamp equals the total value of all the stamps (318 cents).
$12x + 3(5x) + 15(x - 4) = 318$

Solution
$$12x + 3(5x) + 15(x - 4) = 318$$
$$12x + 15x + 15x - 60 = 318$$
$$42x - 60 = 318$$
$$42x = 378$$
$$x = 9$$

$x - 4 = 9 - 4 = 5$
There are five 15¢ stamps in the collection.

Objective 2.2.2 Exercises

15. Let x represent the smallest integer. Because consecutive integers differ by 1, the next integer can be represented by $x + 1$. The third integer can be represented by $(x + 1) + 1$, or just $x + 2$.

16. Consecutive odd integers and consecutive even integers always differ by 2. If n is even, then $n + 2$ and $n + 4$ are also even. If n is odd, then $n + 2$ and $n + 4$ are also odd. It all depends on whether n is even or odd.

17. Strategy

The smaller integer: n

The larger integer: $10 - n$

Three times the larger integer is three less than eight times the smaller integer.

$3(10 - n) = 8n - 3$

Solution

$3(10 - n) = 8n - 3$

$30 - 3n = 8n - 3$

$-11n = -33$

$n = 3$

$10 - n = 10 - 3 = 7$

The integers are 3 and 7.

18. Strategy

The smaller integer: n

The larger integer: $30 - n$

Eight times the smaller integer is six more than five times the larger integer.

$8n = 5(30 - n) + 6$

Solution

$8n = 5(30 - n) + 6$

$8n = 150 - 5n + 6$

$13n = 156$

$n = 12$

$30 - n = 30 - 12 = 18$

The integers are 12 and 18.

19. Strategy

The larger integer: n

The smaller integer: $n - 8$

The sum of the two integers is fifty.

$n + (n - 8) = 50$

Solution

$n + (n - 8) = 50$

$2n - 8 = 50$

$2n = 58$

$n = 29$

$n - 8 = 29 - 8 = 21$

The two integers are 21 and 29.

20. Strategy

The first integer: n

The second integer: $n + 4$

The sum of the integers is 26.

$n + (n + 4) = 26$

Solution

$n + (n + 4) = 26$

$2n + 4 = 26$

$2n = 22$

$n = 11$

$n + 4 = 11 + 4 = 15$

The two integers are 11 and 15.

21. Strategy

The first number: n

The second number: $2n + 2$

The third number: $3n - 5$

The sum of the three numbers is 123.

Solution

$n + (2n + 2) + (3n - 5) = 123$

$6n - 3 = 123$

$6n = 126$

$n = 21$

$2n + 2 = 2(21) + 2 = 42 + 2 = 44$

$3n - 5 = 3(21) - 5 = 63 - 5 = 58$

The numbers are 21, 44, and 58.

22. Strategy

The first number: n

The second number: $2n$

The third number: $2n - 3$

the sum of the three numbers is 42.

Solution

$n + 2n + (2n - 3) = 42$

$5n - 3 = 42$

$5n = 45$

$n = 9$

$2n = 2(9) = 18$

$2n - 3 = 2(9) - 3 = 18 - 3 = 15$

The numbers are 9, 18, and 15.

23. Strategy

The first integer: n

The second consecutive integer: $n + 1$

The third consecutive integer: $n + 2$

The sum of the integers is -57.

$n + (n + 1) + (n + 2) = -57$

Solution

$n + (n + 1) + (n + 2) = -57$

$3n + 3 = -57$

$3n = -60$

$n = -20$

$n + 1 = -20 + 1 = -19$

$n + 2 = -20 + 2 = -18$

The integers are -20, -19, and -18.

24. Strategy

The first integer: n

The second integer: $n + 1$

The third integer: $n + 2$

The sum of the integers is 129:

$n + (n + 1) + (n + 2) = 129$

Solution

$n + (n + 1) + (n + 2) = 129$

$3n + 3 = 129$

$3n = 126$

$n = 42$

$n + 1 = 42 + 1 = 43$

$n + 2 = 42 + 2 = 44$

The integers are 42, 43, and 44.

25. Strategy
The first odd integer: n
The second consecutive odd integer: $n + 2$
The third consecutive odd integer: $n + 4$
Five times the smallest of the three integers is ten more than twice the largest.
$5n = 2(n + 4) + 10$

Solution
$$5n = 2(n + 4) + 10$$
$$5n = 2n + 8 + 10$$
$$5n = 2n + 18$$
$$3n = 18$$
$$n = 6$$
Since 6 is not an odd integer, there is no solution.

26. Strategy
The first even integer: n
The second consecutive even integer: $n + 2$
The third consecutive even integer: $n + 4$
Twice the sum of the first and third integers is 21 more than the second integer.
$2[n + (n + 4)] = (n + 2) + 21$

Solution
$$2[n + (n + 4)] = (n + 2) + 21$$
$$2(2n + 4) = n + 23$$
$$4n + 8 = n + 23$$
$$3n + 8 = 23$$
$$3n = 15$$
$$n = 5$$
Since 5 is not an even integer, there is no solution.

27. Strategy
The first odd integer: n
The second consecutive odd integer: $n + 2$
The third consecutive odd integer: $n + 4$
Three times the middle integer is seven more than the sum of the first and third integers.
$3(n + 2) = [n + (n + 4)] + 7$

Solution
$$3(n + 2) = [n + (n + 4)] + 7$$
$$3n + 6 = 2n + 11$$
$$n = 5$$
$$n + 2 = 5 + 2 = 7$$
$$n + 4 = 5 + 4 = 9$$
The odd integers are 5, 7, and 9.

28. Strategy
The first even integer: n
The second consecutive even integer: $n + 2$
The third consecutive even integer: $n + 4$
Four times the sum of the first and third integers is twenty less than six times the middle integer.
$4[n + (n + 4)] = 6(n + 2) - 20$

Solution
$$4[n + (n + 4)] = 6(n + 2) - 20$$
$$4(2n + 4) = 6n + 12 - 20$$
$$8n + 16 = 6n - 8$$
$$2n = -24$$
$$n = -12$$
$$n + 2 = -12 + 2 = -10$$
$$n + 4 = -12 + 4 = -8$$
The even integers are -12, -10, and -8.

Applying Concepts 2.2

29. Strategy
Number of nickels: x
Number of dimes: $2x - 2$
The number of nickels plus the number of dimes is the total number of coins in the bank (52).

Solution
$$x + (2x - 2) = 52$$
$$3x - 2 = 52$$
$$3x = 54$$
$$\frac{3x}{3} = \frac{54}{3}$$
$$x = 18$$
$$2x - 2 = 2(18) - 2 = 36 - 2 = 34$$
There are 18 nickels in the bank and 34 dimes in the bank.
The value of the coins in the bank is equal to the value of the dimes ($.10)(34) plus the value of the nickels ($.05)(18).
$.10(34) + $.05(18) = $3.40 + $.90 = $4.30
The total value of the coins in the bank is $4.30.

30. Strategy
First consecutive odd integer: n
Second consecutive odd integer: $n + 2$
Third consecutive odd integer: $n + 4$
Four times the first of the three consecutive odd integers is five less than the product of three and the third integer.

Solution
$$4n = 3(n + 4) - 5$$
$$4n = 3n + 12 - 5$$
$$4n = 3n + 7$$
$$n = 7$$
$$n + 2 = 7 + 2 = 9$$
$$n + 4 = 7 + 4 = 11$$
The three integers are 7, 9, and 11.

31. Strategy

Number of 5¢ stamps: x

Number of 3¢ stamps: $x + 6$

Number of 7¢ stamps: $(x + 6) + 2 = x + 8$

Stamp	Number	Value	Total Value
5¢	x	5	$5x$
3¢	$x + 6$	3	$3(x + 6)$
7¢	$x + 8$	7	$7(x + 8)$

The sum of the total value of each type of stamp equals the total value of all the stamps (194 cents.)

$5x + 3(x + 6) + 7(x + 8) = 194$

Solution

$$5x + 3(x + 6) + 7(x + 8) = 194$$
$$5x + 3x + 18 + 7x + 56 = 194$$
$$15x + 74 = 194$$
$$15x = 120$$
$$x = 8$$

$x + 6 = 8 + 6 = 14$

There are fourteen 3¢ stamps on the collection.

32. Strategy

First even integer: n

Second consecutive even integer: $n + 2$

Third consecutive even integer: $n + 4$

Fourth consecutive even integer: $n + 6$

The sum of the four integers is 100.

$n + (n + 2) + (n + 4) + (n + 6) = 100$

Solution

$$n + (n + 2) + (n + 4) + (n + 6) = 100$$
$$4n + 12 = 100$$
$$4n = 88$$
$$n = 22$$

$n + 6 = 22 + 6 = 28$

The smallest of the four integers is 22. The largest of the integers is 28. The sum of the smallest and largest integers is $22 + 28$ or 50.

33. Strategy

First odd integer: n

Second consecutive odd integer: $n + 2$

Third consecutive odd integer: $n + 4$

Fourth consecutive odd integer: $n + 6$

The sum of the four integers is -64.

$n + (n + 2) + (n + 4) + (n + 6) = -64$

Solution

$$n + (n + 2) + (n + 4) + (n + 6) = -64$$
$$4n + 12 = -64$$
$$4n = -76$$
$$n = -19$$

$n + 6 = -19 + 6 = -13$

The smallest of the four integers is -19.

The largest of the four integers is -13.

The sum of the smallest and largest integers is $-19 + (-13)$ or -32.

34. Strategy

The first odd integer: n

The second consecutive odd integer: $n + 2$

The third consecutive odd integer: $n + 4$

The product of the second and third minus the product of the first and second is 42.

Solution

$$(n + 2)(n + 4) - n(n + 2) = 42$$
$$n^2 + 6n + 8 - n^2 - 2n = 42$$
$$4n + 8 = 42$$
$$4n = 34$$
$$n = \frac{17}{2}$$

There is no solution, because n is not an integer.

35. Strategy

Units digit: x

Tens digit: $x - 1$

Hundreds digit: $6 - (x + x - 1)$

The value of the number is 12 more than 100 times the hundreds digit.

Solution

$$x + 10(x - 1) + 100[6 - (x + x - 1)] = 100[6 - (x + x - 1)] + 12$$
$$x + 10x - 10 + 100[6 - 2x + 1)] = 100[6 - 2x + 1] + 12$$
$$11x - 10 + 600 - 200x + 100 = 600 - 200x + 100 + 12$$
$$-189x + 690 = -200x + 712$$
$$11x = 22$$
$$x = 2$$

$x - 1 = 2 - 1 = 1$

$6 - (x + x - 1) = 6 - (2 + 2 - 1) = 6 - 3 = 3$

The number is 312.

Section 2.3

Concept Review 2.3

1. Sometimes true
   This is true only when the same amounts of gold at each price are mixed.

2. Always true

3. Never true
   It takes a time of $t - \dfrac{1}{2}$ for the cyclist to overtake the runner.

4. Always true

5. Never true
   The car travels 3 h at a rate of 40 mph and 2 h at a rate of 60 mph for a total travel time of 5 h. The total distance traveled is 240 mi. The average speed is $240 \div 5 = 48$. The average speed is 48 mph.

Objective 2.3.1 Exercises

1. The amount of juice is x quarts, and the unit cost is $1.40 per quart. Let V be the value. Then $V = 1.40x$.

2. The value of the peanuts is $4 time the amount of peanuts, A, or $4A$. The value of the raisins is $2 times the amount of the raisins, B, or $2B$. The value of the mixture is $4A + 2B$.

3. Strategy
   Cost of mixture: x

	Amount	Cost	Value
Snow peas	20	1.99	39.80
Petite onions	14	1.19	16.66
Mixture	34	x	$34x$

   The sum of the values before mixing equals the value after mixing.
   $39.80 + 16.66 = 34x$

   Solution
   $$56.46 = 34x$$
   $$1.66 = x$$
   The cost per pound of the mixture is $1.66.

4. Strategy
   Pounds of $5.50 coffee: x
   Pounds of $3.00 coffee: $40 - x$

	Amount	Cost	Value
$5.50 coffee	x	5.50	$5.50x$
$3.00 coffee	$40 - x$	3.00	$3(40 - x)$
Mixture	40	4.00	$4(40)$

   The sum of the values before mixing equals the value after mixing.
   $5.50x + 3(40 - x) = 4(40)$

   Solution
   $$5.50x + 3(40 - x) = 4(40)$$
   $$5.50x + 120 - 3x = 160$$
   $$2.50x + 120 = 160$$
   $$2.50x = 40$$
   $$x = 16$$
   $$40 - x = 40 - 16 = 24$$
   The blend must contain 24 lb of the $3.00 grade of coffee and 16 lb of the $5.50 grade.

5. Strategy
   Number of adult tickets: x
   Number of child tickets: $460 - x$

	Amount	Cost	Value
Adult tickets	x	5.00	$5x$
Child tickets	$460 - x$	2.00	$2(460 - x)$

   The sum of the values of each type of ticket sold equals the total value of all the tickets sold (1880 dollars).
   $5x + 2(460 - x) = 1880$

   Solution
   $$5x + 2(460 - x) = 1880$$
   $$5x + 920 - 2x = 1880$$
   $$3x + 920 = 1880$$
   $$3x = 960$$
   $$x = 320$$
   There were 320 adult tickets sold.

6. Strategy

Number of adult tickets sold x

Number of other tickets sold $505 - x$

	Amount	Cost	Value
Adults	x	6	$6x$
Children and Senior	$505 - x$	3	$3(505 - x)$

The sum of the values of each kind of ticket equals the value of all the tickets (1997 dollars)

$6x + 3(505 - x) = 1977$

Solution

$6x + 1515 - 3x = 1977$

$3x + 1515 = 1977$

$3x = 462$

$x = 154$

There were 154 adult tickets sold.

7. Strategy

Liters of imitation maple syrup: x

	Amount	Cost	Value
Imitation Syrup	x	4.00	$4x$
Maple Syrup	50	9.50	$9.50(50)$
Mixture	$50 + x$	5.00	$5(50 + x)$

The sum of the values before mixing equals the value after mixing.

$4x + 9.50(50) = 5(50 + x)$

Solution

$4x + 9.50(50) = 5(50 + x)$

$4x + 475 = 250 + 5x$

$-x + 475 = 250$

$-x = -225$

$x = 225$

The mixture must contain 225 L of imitation maple syrup.

8. Strategy

Bushels of soybeans: x

Bushels of wheat: $800 - x$

	Amount	Cost	Value
Soybeans	x	8.50	$8.50x$
Wheat	$800 - x$	4.50	$4.50(800 - x)$
Mixture	800	5.50	$5.50(800)$

The sum of the values before mixing equals the value after mixing.

$8.50x + 4.50(800 - x) = 5.50(800)$

Solution

$8.50x + 4.50(800 - x) = 5.50(800)$

$8.50x + 3600 - 4.50x = 4400$

$4x + 3600 = 4400$

$4x = 800$

$x = 200$

$800 - x = 800 - 200 = 600$

200 bushels of soybeans and 600 bushels of wheat were used.

9. Strategy

Number of pounds of nuts used x

Number of pounds of pretzels used $20 - x$

	Amount	Cost	Value
Nuts	x	3.99	$3.99x$
Pretzels	$20 - x$	1.29	$1.29(20 - x)$
Mixture	20	2.37	47.40

The sum of the values before mixing equals the value after mixing.

$3.99x + 1.29(20 - x) = 47.40$

$3.99x + 25.80 - 1.29x = 47.40$

$2.70x + 25.80 = 47.40$

$2.70x = 21.60$

$x = 8$

The mixture must contain 8 pounds of nuts.

10. Strategy
Ounces of pure silver: x

	Amount	Cost	Value
Pure silver	x	5.20	$5.20x$
Silver alloy	50	2.80	280(50)
Mixture	$50 + x$	4.40	$4.40(50 + x)$

The sum of the values before mixing equals the value after mixing.
$5.20x + 2.80(50) = 4.40(50 + x)$

Solution
$$5.20x + 2.80(50) = 4.40(50 + x)$$
$$5.20x + 140 = 220 + 4.40x$$
$$0.80x = 80$$
$$x = 100$$
100 oz of pure silver must be used.

11. Strategy
Cost per pound of mixture: x

	Amount	Cost	Value
$6.00 tea	30	6.00	6.00(30)
$3.20 tea	70	3.20	3.20(70)
Mixture	100	x	$100x$

The sum of the values before mixing equals the value after mixing.
$6.00(30) + 3.20(70) = 100x$

Solution
$$6.00(30) + 3.20(70) = 100x$$
$$180 + 224 = 100x$$
$$404 = 100x$$
$$4.04 = x$$
The cost of the mixture is $4.04 per pound.

12. Strategy
Cost per ounce of salad dressing x

	Amount	Cost	Value
Olive oil	64		8.29
Vinegar	20		1.99
Salad dressing	84	x	$84x$

The sum of the values before mixing equals the value after mixing.
$8.29 + 1.99 = 84x$

Solution
$$10.28 = 84x$$
$$.12 = x \text{ or } x = .12$$
The cost per ounce of salad dressing is $.12.

13. Strategy
Gallons of cranberry juice: x

	Amount	Cost	Value
Cranberry	x	4.20	$4.20x$
Apple	50	2.10	50(2.10)
Mixture	$50 + x$	3.00	$3(50 + x)$

The sum of the values before mixing equals the value after mixing.
$4.20x + 50(2.10) = 3(50 + x)$

Solution
$$4.20x + 50(2.10) = 3(50 + x)$$
$$4.20x + 105 = 150 + 3x$$
$$1.20x + 105 = 150$$
$$1.20x = 45$$
$$x = 37.5$$
The mixture must contain 37.5 gal of cranberry juice.

14. Strategy
Kilograms of walnuts: x
Kilograms of cashews: $50 - x$

	Amount	Cost	Value
Walnuts	x	4.05	$4.05x$
Cashews	$50 - x$	7.25	$7.25(50 - x)$
Mixture	50	6.25	6.25(50)

The sum of the values before mixing equals the value after mixing.
$4.05x + 7.25(50 - x) = 6.25(50)$

Solution
$$4.05x + 7.25(50 - x) = 6.25(50)$$
$$4.05x + 362.50 - 7.25x = 312.50$$
$$-3.20x + 362.50 = 312.50$$
$$-3.20x = -50$$
$$x = 15.625$$
$$50 - x = 50 - 15.625 = 34.375$$
The mixture must contain 15.6 kg of walnuts and 34.4 kg of cashews.

Objective 2.3.2 Exercises

15. Strategy
To find the rate of speed solve the equation $d = rt$ for r using $d = 20$ mi, and $t = 30$ min $= 0.5$ h.

Solution
$$d = rt$$
$$20 = r0.5$$
$$40 = r$$
The student drives at 40 mph.

16. Strategy
To find the distance solve the equation $d = rt$ for d using $r = 16$ mph, and $t = 45$ min $= 0.75$ h.

Solution
$d = rt$
$d = 16 \cdot 0.75$
$d = 12$
The cyclist rides 12 mi.

17. Strategy
To find the time for the Boeing 737-800, first solve the equation $d = rt$ for r using $d = 1680$ mi, and $t = 3$ h. Then since the Boeing 747-400 is 30 mph faster, subtract 30 mph from the value of r. Finally, solve the equation $d = rt$ for t, using $d = 1680$ mi and r.

Solution
$d = rt$
$1680 = r3$
$560 = r$
$560 - 30 = 530$ mph
$d = rt$
$1680 = 530t$
$3.2 \approx t$
It would take the Boeing 737-800 3.2 h.

18. Strategy
To find the time solve the equation $d = rt$ for t using $d = 195$ ft, and $r = 5 + 7 = 12$ ft/s.

Solution
$d = rt$
$195 = 12t$
$16.25 = t$
It takes the guess 16.25 s.

19. Strategy
Time spent riding: t

	Rate	Time	Distance
1st cyclist	17	t	$17t$
2nd cyclist	19	t	$19t$

The total distance is 54 mi.

Solution
$17t + 19t = 54$
$36t = 54$
$t = 1.5$
The cyclists will meet 1.5 hours after 1 P.M., or at 2:30 P.M.

20. Strategy
$r = $ Carla's jogging rate

	Rate	Time	Distance
Katrina	4	1	4
Carla	r	0.5	$0.5r$

Katrina and Carla travel the same distance.
$4 = 0.5r$
$8 = r$
Carla jogs at 8 mph.

21. Strategy
$t = $ time for bicyclist
$t + 0.5 = $ time for in-line skater

	Rate	Time	Distance
Bicyclist	18	t	$18t$
In-line skater	10	$t + 0.5$	$10(t + 0.5)$

The bicyclist and in-line skater travel the same distance.
$18t = 10(t + 0.5)$
$18t = 10t + 5$
$8t = 5$
$t = 0.625$
$d = 18t = 11.25$
The bicyclist will overtake the in-line skater after 11.25 miles.

22. Strategy
Time for the car: t
Time for the helicopter: $t - \dfrac{1}{2}$

	Rate	Time	Distance
Car	90	t	$90t$
Helicopter	120	$t - \dfrac{1}{2}$	$120\left(t - \dfrac{1}{2}\right)$

The car and the helicopter travel the same distance.
$90t = 120\left(t - \dfrac{1}{2}\right)$

Solution
$90t = 120\left(t - \dfrac{1}{2}\right)$
$90t = 120t - 60$
$-30t = -60$
$t = 2$
$d = rt = 90(2) = 180$
The helicopter will overtake the car 180 mi from the starting point.

23. Strategy

Rate of the first plane: r

Rate of the second plane: $r + 80$

	Rate	Time	Distance
1st plane	r	1.5	$1.5r$
2nd plane	$r + 80$	1.5	$1.5(r + 80)$

The total distance traveled by the two planes is 1380 mi.

$1.5r + 1.5(r + 80) = 1380$

Solution

$1.5r + 1.5(r + 80) = 1380$

$1.5r + 1.5r + 120 = 1380$

$3r + 120 = 1380$

$3r = 1260$

$r = 420$

$r + 80 = 420 + 80 = 500$

The speed of the first plane is 420 mph.

The speed of the second plane is 500 mph.

24. Strategy

rate of slower skier: r

rate of faster skier: $r + 14$

	r	t	d
slower skier	r	0.5	$0.5r$
faster skier	$r + 14$	0.5	$0.5(r + 14)$

The skiers are 48 miles apart.

$0.5r + 0.5(r + 14) = 48$

So

$0.5r + 0.5(r + 14) = 48$

$0.5r + 0.5r + 7 = 48$

$r + 7 = 48$

$r = 41$

The rate of the slower skier is 41 mph.

25. Strategy

Time to the island: t

Time returning from the island: $6 - t$

	Rate	Time	Distance
Going	18	t	$18t$
Returning	12	$6 - t$	$12(6 - t)$

The distance to the island is the same as the distance returning.

$18t = 12(6 - t)$

Solution

$18t = 12(6 - t)$

$18t = 72 - 12t$

$30t = 72$

$t = 2.4$

$d = rt = 18(2.4) = 43.2$

The distance to the island is 43.2 mi.

26. Strategy

Time flying to a city: t

Time returning to the international airport: $4 - t$

	Rate	Time	Distance
Going	210	t	$210t$
Returning	140	$4 - t$	$140(4 - t)$

The distance to the city is the same as the distance returning to the international airport.

$210t = 140(4 - t)$

Solution

$210t = 140(4 - t)$

$210t = 560 - 140t$

$350t = 560$

$t = 1.6$

$d = rt = 210(1.6) = 336$

The distance between the two airports is 336 mi.

27. Strategy

Rate of the second plane: r

Rate of the first plane: $r - 50$

	Rate	Time	Distance
2nd plane	r	2.5	$2.5r$
1st plane	$r - 50$	2.5	$2.5(r - 50)$

The total distance traveled by the two planes is 1400 mi.

$2.5r + 2.5(r - 50) = 1400$

Solution

$2.5r + 2.5(r - 50) = 1400$

$2.5r + 2.5r - 125 = 1400$

$5r - 125 = 1400$

$5r = 1525$

$r = 305$

$r - 50 = 305 - 50 = 255$

The rate of the first plane is 255 mph.

The rate of the second plane is 305 mph.

28. Strategy
Rate of the first hiker: r
Rate of the second hiker: $r + 0.5$

	Rate	Time	Distance
1st hiker	r	2	$2r$
2nd hiker	$r + 0.5$	2	$2(r + 0.5)$

The total distance traveled by the two hikers is 13 mi.
$2r + 2(r + 0.5) = 13$

Solution
$2r + 2(r + 0.5) = 13$
$2r + 2r + 1 = 13$
$4r + 1 = 13$
$4r = 12$
$r = 3$
$r + 0.5 = 3 + 0.5 = 3.5$
The first hiker walks at 3 mph.
The second hiker walks at 3.5 mph.

29. Strategy
Time to the repair shop: t
Time walking home: $1 - t$

	Rate	Time	Distance
To repair shop	14	t	$14t$
Walking home	3.5	$1 - t$	$3.5(1 - t)$

The distance to the repair shop is the same as the distance walking home.
$14t = 3.5(1 - t)$

Solution
$14t = 3.5(1 - t)$
$14t = 3.5 - 3.5t$
$17.5t = 3.5$
$t = 0.2$
$d = rt = 14(0.2) = 2.8$
The distance between the student's home and the bicycle shop is 2.8 mi.

30. Strategy
rate of freight train: r
rate of express train: $r + 15$

	r	t	d
Freight train	r	4	$4r$
Express train	$r + 15$	3	$3(r + 15)$

The trains both travel the same distance.
$4r = 3(r + 15)$

Solution
$4r = 3(r + 15)$
$4r = 3r + 45$
$r = 45$
$r + 15 = 60$
The rate of the freight train is 45 mph. The rate of the express train is 60 mph.

31. Strategy
Time Washington to Pittsburgh train travels: t
Time Pittsburgh to Washington train travels: $t - 1$

	r	t	d
Washington to Pittsburgh	60	t	$60t$
Pittsburgh to Washington	40	$t - 1$	$40(t - 1)$

The trains together cover the distance from Washington to Pittsburgh, 260 miles.
$60t + 40(t - 1) = 260$

Solution
$60t + 40t - 40 = 260$
$100t - 40 = 260$
$100t = 300$
$t = 3$
$t - 1 = 2$
The two trains will pass each other after 2 hours.

32. Strategy
Rate of the first plane: r
Rate of the second plane: $r + 150$

	Rate	Time	Distance
1st plane	r	4	$4r$
2nd plane	$r + 150$	3	$3(r + 150)$

The second plane travels 250 mi more than the first plane.
$4r = 3(r + 150) - 250$

Solution
$4r = 3(r + 150) - 250$
$4r = 3r + 450 - 250$
$r = 200$
$3(r + 150) = 3(200 + 150) = 3(350) = 1050$
The second plane traveled 1050 mi.

Applying Concepts 2.3

33. Strategy
To find the distance solve the equation $d = rt$ for t using $d = 260$ trillion miles $= 260,000,000$ million miles, and $r = 18$ million mph.

Solution
$$d = rt$$
$$260,000,000 = 18t$$
$$t \approx 14,444,444 \text{ h}$$
$$= 14,444,444 \text{ h} \cdot \frac{1 \text{ day}}{24 \text{ h}} \cdot \frac{1 \text{ yr}}{365 \text{ day}}$$
$$\approx 1648 \text{ yr}$$
$$\approx 1600 \text{ yr}$$
It will take about 1600 years.

34. Distance for the parade: d

Distance for the jogger: $d + 2$

	Rate	Distance	Time
Parade	3	d	$\dfrac{d}{3}$
Jogger	6	$d + 2$	$\dfrac{d+2}{6}$

The parade and the jogger reach a certain point at the same time.

$$\frac{d}{3} = \frac{d+2}{6}$$
$$3d + 6 = 6d$$
$$6 = 3d$$
$$d = 2$$
$$t = \frac{d+2}{6}$$
$$t = \frac{4}{6} = \frac{2}{3}$$

The jogger will catch up with the front of the parade in $\dfrac{2}{3}$ hour.

36. Strategy

Distance from 40 ft tower to grass seed: x

Distance from top of 40 ft tower to seed (using Pythagorean theorem): $\sqrt{40^2 + x^2}$

Distance from top of 30 ft tower to seed: $\sqrt{30^2 + (50-x)^2}$

Solution

Let the rate of both birds be r, because they are flying at the same rate.

	Rate	Distance	Time
Bird 1	r	$\sqrt{40^2 + x^2}$	$\dfrac{\sqrt{40^2 + x^2}}{r}$
Bird 2	r	$\sqrt{30^2 + (50-x)^2}$	$\dfrac{\sqrt{30^2 + (50-x)^2}}{r}$

They arrive at the seed at the same time, so $\dfrac{\sqrt{40^2 + x^2}}{r} = \dfrac{\sqrt{30^2 + (50-x)^2}}{r}$

Thus

$$\sqrt{40^2 + x^2} = \sqrt{30^2 + (50-x)^2}$$
$$40^2 + x^2 = 30^2 + (50-x)^2$$
$$1600 + x^2 = 900 + 2500 - 100x + x^2$$
$$-1800 = -100x$$
$$x = 18$$

The grass seed is 18 ft from the 40 ft tower.

35. The distance between them 2 min before impact is equal to the sum of the distances each one can travel during 2 min.

$$2 \text{ minutes} \cdot \frac{1 \text{ hour}}{60 \text{ minutes}} = 0.03\overline{3} \text{ hour}$$

Distance between cars

= rate of first car $\cdot 0.03\overline{3}$ + rate of second car $\cdot 0.03\overline{3}$

Distance between cars = $40 \cdot 0.03\overline{3} + 60 \cdot 0.03\overline{3} = 3.3\overline{3}$

The cars are $3.3\overline{3}$ $\left(\text{or } 3\dfrac{1}{3} \right)$ miles apart 2 min before impact.

37. Rate during the second mile: x

	Rate	Distance	Time
1st mile	30	1	$\frac{1}{30}$
2nd mile	x	1	$\frac{1}{x}$
Both miles	60	2	$\frac{2}{60}=\frac{1}{30}$

The time traveled during the first mile plus the time traveled during the second mile is equal to the total time traveled during both miles.

$$\frac{1}{30}+\frac{1}{x}=\frac{1}{30}$$

Solution
$$\frac{1}{30}+\frac{1}{x}=\frac{1}{30}$$
$$\frac{1}{x}=0$$
$$x\left(\frac{1}{x}\right)=0\cdot x$$
$$1=0$$

There is no solution to the equation. No, it is not possible to increase the speed enough.

38. a. $216 \div 24 = 9$
9 days from December 14 is December 23.
They landed on December 23.

b. 3 min = 0.05 h
44 s ≈ 0.01 h
216 h 3 min 44 s ≈ 216 h + 0.05h + 0.01h
       = 216.06 h
24,986.727 mi ÷ 216.06 h ≈ 116 mph
Their average speed was 116 mph.

c. The circumference of Earth is 24,900 mi.
The diameter of Earth is 7926 mi.
The radius of Earth is 3963 mi.
The flight was 24,986.727 mi.
$$C = \pi d$$
$$24,986.727 \approx \pi d$$
$$7953.522 \approx d$$
$$3976.761 \approx r$$
$$3976.761 - 3963 \approx 14$$
The flight was flown approximately 14 mi above Earth.

39. If a student jogs 1 mi at a rate of 8 mph and jogs back at a rate of 6 mph, then

$$\text{Total time} = \frac{1\text{ mi}}{8\text{ mph}}+\frac{1\text{ mi}}{6\text{ mph}}=\frac{7}{24}\text{h}$$

$$\text{Average rate} = \frac{\text{distance}}{\text{time}}=\frac{2\text{ mi}}{\frac{7}{24}\text{h}}\approx 6.86\text{ mph}.$$

Therefore, the student's average rate is about 6.86 mph, not 7 mph.

Section 2.4

Concept Review 2.4

1. Never true
   The amount invested in the other account is $10,000 - x$.

2. Always true

3. Never true
   A mixture can never have a greater concentration of an ingredient than the concentrations of both substances going into the mixture.

4. Always true

Objective 2.4.1 Exercises

1. In the equation $I = Pr$, r represents the interest rate given as a decimal, P represents the principal, and I represents the amount of interest earned. If you invest $2000 in a bank that pays 4 percent interest, you can find the interest by evaluating 0.4(2000).

2. In the equation $0.06x + 0.07(5000 - x) = 330$, x represents the amount invested at 6%, and $0.06x$ represents the interest earned from this account. The remainder of the money, $5000 - x$, earns 7% interest, and $0.07(5000 - x)$. The total interest is $330.

3. Strategy
   To find the total interest solve the equation $I = Pr$ for I using $P = \$2000$, and $r = 5.5\% = 0.055$, solve the equation $I = Pr$ again for I using $P = \$3000$, and $r = 7.25\% = 0.0725$, and add the interest.

   Solution
   $I = Pr$
   $= 2000(0.055)$
   $= 110$
   $I = Pr$
   $= 3000(0.0725)$
   $= 217.50$
   $110 + 217.50 = 327.50$
   Joseph earns $327.50.

4. Strategy
   To find the interest Kristi earned, solve the equation $I = Pr$ for I using $P = \$1500$, and $r = 7.25\% = 0.0725$.
   To find the interest Kari earned, solve the equation $I = Pr$ for I using $P = \$2000$, and $r = 6.75\% = 0.0675$.

   Solution
   $I = Pr$
   $\quad = 1500(0.0725)$
   $\quad = 108.75$
   $I = Pr$
   $\quad = 2000(0.0675)$
   $\quad = 135$
   $135 - 108.75 = 26.25$
   Kari earned \$26.25 more in interest than Kristi.

5. Strategy
   To find the amount invested in the 8% account, first solve the equation $I = Pr$ for I using $P = \$2000$, and $r = 6.4\% = 0.064$. Then, solve the equation $I = Pr$ for P using I, and $r = 8\% = 0.08$.

   Solution
   $I = Pr$
   $\quad = 2000(0.064)$
   $\quad = 128$
   $I = Pr$
   $128 = P(0.08)$
   $1600 = P$
   Deon must invest \$1600 in the 8% account.

6. Strategy
   To find the amount invested in the 6.5% account, first solve the equation $I = Pr$ for I using $P = \$5000$, and $r = 5.2\% = 0.052$. Then, solve the equation $I = Pr$ for P using I, and $r = 6.5\% = 0.06.5$.

   Solution
   $I = Pr$
   $\quad = 5000(0.052)$
   $\quad = 260$
   $I = Pr$
   $260 = P(0.065)$
   $4000 = P$
   There must be \$4000 invested in the 6.5% account.

7. Strategy
   Amount invested at 6.75%: x
   Amount invested at 7.25%: $40,000 - x$

	Principal	Rate	Interest
Amount at 6.75%	x	0.0675	$0.0675x$
Amount at 7.25%	$40,000 - x$	0.0725	$0.0725(40,000 - x)$

   The sum of the interest earned by the two investments equals the total annual interest earned (\$2825)
   $0.0675x + 0.0725(40,000 - x) = 2825$

   Solution
   $0.0675x + 0.0725(40,000 - x) = 2825$
   $0.0675x + 2900 - 0.0725x = 2825$
   $-0.005x = -75$
   $x = 15,000$
   The amount invested in the certificate of deposit is \$15,000.

8. Strategy
   Amount invested at 8.5%: x
   Amount invested at 10.2%: $8000 - x$

	Principal	Rate	Interest
Amount at 8.5%	x	0.085	$0.085x$
Amount at 10.2%	$8000 - x$	0.102	$0.102(8000 - x)$

   The sum of the interest earned by the two investments equal the total annual interest earned($765).
   $0.085x + 0.102(8000 - x) = 765$

   Solution
   $$0.085x + 0.102(8000 - x) = 765$$
   $$0.085x + 816 - 0.102x = 765$$
   $$-0.017x = -51$$
   $$x = 3000$$
   $8000 - x = 8000 - 3000 = 5000$
   The amount invested at 8.5% is $3000.
   The amount invested at 10.2% is $5000.

9. Strategy
   Amount invested at 10.5%: x

	Principal	Rate	Interest
Amount at 8.4%	5000	0.084	$0.084(5000)$
Amount at 10.5%	x	0.105	$0.105x$
Amount at 9%	$5000 + x$	0.09	$0.09(5000 + x)$

   The sum of the interest earned by the two investments equals the interest earned by the total investment.
   $0.084(5000) + 0.105x = 0.09(5000 + x)$

   Solution
   $$0.084(5000) + 0.105x = 0.09(5000 + x)$$
   $$420 + 0.105x = 450 + 0.09x$$
   $$0.015x = 30$$
   $$x = 2000$$
   $2000 more must be invested at 10.5%.

10. Strategy
    Amount invested at 5.5%: x
    Amount invested at 4.5%: $9600 - x$

	Principal	Rate	Interest
Amount at 5.5%	x	0.055	$0.055x$
Amount at 4.5%	$9600 - x$	0.045	$0.045(9600 - x)$

    The sum of the interest earned by the two investments equals the total annual interest earned ($465).
    $0.055x + 0.045(9600 - x) = 465$

    Solution
    $$0.055x + 432 - 0.045x = 465$$
    $$0.010x = 33$$
    $$x = 3300$$
    $9600 - x = 9600 - 3300 = 6300$
    The amount that should be invested at 5.5% is $3300. The amount that should be invested at 4.5% is $6300.

11. Strategy
    Amount invested at 8.5%: x
    Amount invested at 6.4%: $8000 - x$

	Principal	Rate	Interest
Amount at 8.5%	x	0.085	$0.085x$
Amount at 6.4%	$8000 - x$	0.064	$0.064(8000 - x)$

The sum of the interest earned by the two investments equals the total annual interest earned ($575).
$0.085x + 0.064(8000 - x) = 575$

Solution
$$0.085x + 0.064(8000 - x) = 575$$
$$0.085x + 512 - 0.064x = 575$$
$$0.021x = 63$$
$$x = 3000$$
$8000 - x = 8000 - 3000 = 5000$
The amount invested at 8.5% is $3000.
The amount invested at 6.4% is $5000.

12. Strategy
    Amount invested at 6.5%: x

	Principal	Rate	Interest
Amount at 4%	6000	0.04	$0.04(6000)$
Amount at 6.5%	x	0.065	$0.065x$
Amount at 5%	$6000 + x$	0.05	$0.05(6000 + x)$

The sum of the interest earned by the two investments equals the interest earned by the total investment.
$0.04(6000) + 0.065x = 0.05(6000 + x)$

Solution
$$0.04(6000) + 0.065x = 0.05(6000 + x)$$
$$240 + 0.065x = 300 + 0.05x$$
$$0.015x = 60$$
$$x = 4000$$
$4000 more must be invested at 6.5%.

13. Strategy
    Amount of additional money at 10%: x

	Principal	Rate	Interest
Amount at 5.5%	6000	0.055	330
Amount at 10%	x	0.10	$0.10x$
Combined Investment	$6000 + x$	0.07	$0.07(6000 + x)$

The interest from the combined investment is the sum of the interests from each investment.
$330 + 0.10x = 0.07(6000 + x)$
$$330 + 0.10x = 420 + 0.07x$$
$$0.03x = 90$$
$$x = 3000$$
The additional amount that should be invested at 10% is $3000.

14. Strategy
Amount invested at 3.5%: x
Amount invested at 4.5%: $42,000 - x$

	Principal	Rate	Interest
Amount at 3.5%	x	0.035	0.035x
Amount at 4.5%	42,000 − x	0.045	0.045(42,000 − x)

The interest earned on one investment is equal to interest earned on the other investment.
$0.035x = 0.045(42,000 - x)$

Solution
$0.035x = 0.045(42,000 - x)$
$0.035x = 1890 - 0.045x$
$0.08x = 1890$
$x = 23,625$
$42,000 - x = 42,000 - 23,625 = 18,375$
The amount that should be invested at 3.5% is $23,625.
The amount that should be invested at 4.5% is $18,375.

15. Strategy
Amount invested at 4.2%: x
Amount invested at 6%: $13,600 - x$

	Principal	Rate	Interest
Amount 4.2%	x	0.042	0.042x
Amount at 6%	13,600 − x	0.006	0.006(13,600 − x)

The interest earned on one investment is equal to the interest earned on the other investment.
$0.042x = 0.06(13,600 - x)$

Solution
$0.042x = 0.06(13,600 - x)$
$0.042x = 816 - 0.06x$
$0.102x = 816$
$x = 8000$
$13,600 - x = 13,600 - 8000 = 5600$
The amount that should be invested at 4.2% is $8000.
The amount that should be invested at 6% is $5600.

16. Strategy
Amount to be invested: x
Amount invested at 4%: $0.25x$
Amount invested at 6%: $0.40x$
Amount invested at 9%: $0.35x$

	Principal	Rate	Interest
Amount at 4%	0.25x	0.04	0.04(0.25x)
Amount at 6%	0.4x	0.06	0.06(0.4x)
Amount at 9%	0.35x	0.09	0.09(0.35x)

The total annual interest earned is $6550.
$0.04(0.25x) + 0.06(0.4x) + 0.09(0.35x) = 6550$

Solution
$0.04(0.25x) + 0.06(0.4x) + 0.09(0.35x) = 6550$
$0.01x + 0.024x + 0.0315x = 6550$
$0.0655x = 6550$
$x = 100,000$
The total amount to be invested is $100,000.

Objective 2.4.2 Exercises

17. The substance that is being mixed is acid. The amount of acid in the 6% solution plus the amount of acid in the 12% solution is the same amount of acid in the mixture.

18. The amount of gold in the 75% alloy is 25(0.75). The amount of gold in the 50% alloy is 40(0.50). The term 65x stands for the amount of gold in the mixture, where 65 is the total grams of mixture and x is the percent of that mixture that is gold.

19. Strategy
To find the amount of juice in the 40-ounce bottle, first solve the equation $Q = Ar$ for r using $Q = 8$ oz, and $A = 32$ oz. Then, solve the equation $Q = Ar$ for Q using r, and $A = 40$ oz.

Solution
$Q = Ar$
$8 = 32r$
$0.25 = r$
$Q = Ar$
$\quad = 40(0.25)$
$\quad = 10$
There is 10 oz of juice in the 40-ounce bottle.

20. Strategy
To find the amount of acid in the 6 L solution, first solve the equation $Q = Ar$ for r using $Q = 0.36$ L, and $A = 4$ L. Then, solve the equation $Q = Ar$ for Q using r, and $A = 6$ L.

Solution
$Q = Ar$
$0.36 = 4r$
$0.09 = r$
$Q = Ar$
$\quad = 6(0.09)$
$\quad = 0.54$
There is 0.54 L of acid in the 6 L solution.

21. Strategy
To find how much more hydrogen peroxide, solve the equation $Q = Ar$ for Q using $A = 750$ ml, and $r = 4\% = 0.04$, solve the equation $Q = Ar$ for Q using $A = 850$, and $r = 5\% = 0.05$, and find the difference.

Solution
$Q = Ar$
$\quad = 750(0.04)$
$\quad = 30$
$Q = Ar$
$\quad = 850(0.05)$
$\quad = 42.5$
$42.5 - 30 = 12.5$
There is 12.5 ml of hydrogen peroxide in the 850-milliliter solution.

22. Strategy
To find the total amount of the bars, solve the equation $Q = Ar$ for Q using $A = 8$ oz, and $r = 30\% = 0.30$, solve the equation $Q = Ar$ for Q using $A = 12$, and $r = 35\% = 0.35$, and find the sum.

Solution
$Q = Ar$
$\quad = 8(0.30)$
$\quad = 2.4$
$Q = Ar$
$\quad = 12(0.35)$
$\quad = 4.2$
$2.4 + 4.2 = 6.6$
There is 6.6 oz of silver in the bars.

23. Strategy
Percent concentration of resulting alloy: x

	Amount	Percent	Quantity
60% alloy	15	0.60	9
20% alloy	45	0.20	9
Mixture	60	x	$60x$

The sum of the quantities before mixing is equal to the quantity after mixing.
$9 + 9 = 60x$

Solution
$9 + 9 = 60x$
$18 = 60x$
$0.30 = x$
The resulting alloy is 30% silver.

24. Strategy
Percent concentration of the resulting alloy: x

	Amount	Percent	Quantity
50%	10	0.50	0.50(10)
15%	40	0.15	0.15(40)
Mixture	50	x	$50x$

The sum of the quantities before mixing is equal to the quantity after mixing.
$0.50(10) + 0.15(40) = 50x$

Solution
$0.50(10) + 0.15(40) = 50x$
$5 + 6 = 50x$
$11 = 50x$
$0.22 = x$
The resulting alloy is 22% gold.

25. Strategy

Percent concentration of the resulting alloy: x

	Amount	Percent	Quantity
70%	25	0.70	0.70(25)
15%	50	0.15	0.15(50)
Mixture	75	x	$75x$

The sum of the quantities before mixing is equal to the quantity after mixing.

$0.70(25) + 0.15(50) = 75x$

Solution

$$0.70(25) + 0.15(50) = 75x$$
$$17.5 + 7.5 = 75x$$
$$25 = 75x$$
$$0.3\overline{3} = x$$

the resulting alloy is $33\frac{1}{3}\%$ silver.

26. Strategy

Percent concentration of mixture: x

	Amount	Percent	Quantity
8% solution	100	0.08	0.08(100)
5% solution	60	0.05	0.05(60)
Mixture	160	x	$160x$

The sum of the quantities before mixing is equal to the quantity after mixing.

$$0.08(100) + 0.05(60) = 160x$$
$$8 + 3 = 160x$$
$$11 = 160x$$
$$x = 0.06875$$

The resulting mixture is a 6.875% saline solution.

27. Strategy

Pounds of 12% aluminum alloy: x

	Amount	Percent	Quantity
12%	x	0.12	$0.12x$
30%	400	0.30	0.30(400)
20%	$400 + x$	0.20	$0.20(400 + x)$

The sum of the quantities before mixing is equal to the quantity after mixing.

$0.12x + 0.30(400) = 0.20(400 + x)$

Solution

$$0.12x + 0.30(400) = 0.20(400 + x)$$
$$0.12x + 120 = 80 + 0.20x$$
$$-0.08x + 120 = 80$$
$$-0.08x = -40$$
$$x = 500$$

500 lb of the 12% aluminum alloy must be used.

28. Strategy

Number of pounds of 20% alloy: x

Number of pounds of 27.5% alloy: $600 + x$

	Amount	Percent	Quantity
20% alloy	x	0.20	$0.20x$
30% alloy	600	0.30	0.30(600)
Mixture	$600 + x$	0.275	$0.275(600 + x)$

The sum of the quantities before mixing is equal to the quantity after mixing.

$0.20x + 0.30(600) = 0.275(600 + x)$

Solution

$$0.20x + 0.30(600) = 0.275(600 + x)$$
$$0.20x + 180 = 165 + 0.275x$$
$$-0.075x = -15$$
$$x = 200$$

200 pounds of the 30% alloy must be used.

29. Strategy

Liters of 65% solution: x

Liters of 15% solution: $50 - x$

	Amount	Percent	Quantity
65% solution	x	65%	$0.65x$
15% solution	$50 - x$	15%	$0.15(50 - x)$
Mixture	50	40%	$0.40(50)$

The sum of the quantities before mixing is equal to the quantity after mixing.

$0.65x + 0.15(50 - x) = 0.40(50)$

Solution

$$0.65x + 0.15(50 - x) = 0.40(50)$$
$$0.65x + 7.5 - 0.15x = 20$$
$$0.5x = 12.5$$
$$x = 25$$

25 L of 65% disinfectant solution and 25 L of 15% disinfectant solution were used.

30. Strategy
Number of pounds of 20% fat meat: x
Number of pounds at 12% fat meat: $80 - x$

	Amount	Percent	Quantity
20% fat	x	0.20	$0.20x$
12% fat	$80 - x$	0.12	$0.12(80 - x)$
Mixture	80	0.17	$0.17(80)$

The sum of the quantities before mixing is equal to the quantity after mixing.
$0.20x + 0.12(80 - x) = 0.17(80)$

Solution
$$0.20x + 0.12(80 - x) = 0.17(80)$$
$$0.20x + 9.6 - 0.12x = 13.6$$
$$0.08x = 4$$
$$x = 50$$
50 pounds of 20% hamburger and 30 pounds of 12% hamburger should be mixed.

31. Strategy
Number of quarts of water: x

	Amount	Percent	Quantity
Water	x	0	0
80% antifreeze	5	0.80	4
50% antifreeze	$5 + x$	0.50	$0.50(5 + x)$

The sum of the quantities before mixing is equal to the quantity after mixing.
$0 + 4 = 0.50(5 + x)$

Solution
$$4 = 2.5 + 0.50x$$
$$1.5 = 0.5x$$
$$x = 3$$
3 quarts of water should be added.

32. Strategy
Ounces of 70% alcohol: x
Ounces of water: $3.5 - x$

	Amount	Percent	Quantity
70% alcohol	x	0.70	$0.70x$
Water	$3.5 - x$	0	0
45% alcohol	3.5	0.45	$0.45(3.5)$

The sum of the quantities before mixing is equal to the quantity after mixing.
$0.70x + 0 = 0.45(3.5)$

Solution
$$0.70x + 0 = 0.45(3.5)$$
$$0.70x = 1.575$$
$$x = 2.25$$
2.25 oz of 70% alcohol and 1.25 oz of water should be combined.

33. Strategy
Ounces of water to be added: x
Ounces of 5% solution: $60 + x$

	Amount	Percent	Quantity
Water	x	0	0
7.5% solution	60	0.075	4.5
5% solution	$60 + x$	0.05	$0.05(60 + x)$

The sum of the quantities before mixing is equal to the quantity after mixing.
$0 + 4.5 = 0.05(60 + x)$

Solution
$$0 + 4.5 = 0.05(60 + x)$$
$$4.5 = 3 + 0.05x$$
$$1.5 = 0.05x$$
$$x = 30$$
30 oz of water should be added.

34. Strategy
Gallons of water to be evaporated: x
Gallons in 15% solution: $10 - x$

	Amount	Percent	Quantity
12% solution	10	0.12	$0.12(10)$
Evaporated water	x	0	0
15% solution	$10 - x$	0.15	$0.15(10 - x)$

The difference between the quantities before mixing is equal to the quantity after mixing.
$0.12(10) - 0 = 0.15(10 - x)$

Solution
$$0.12(10) - 0 = 0.15(10 - x)$$
$$1.2 = 1.5 - 0.15x$$
$$-0.3 = -0.15x$$
$$x = 2$$
2 gallons of water should be evaporated.

35. Strategy
Percent concentration of result: x

	Amount	Percent	Quantity
5% fruit juice	12	0.05	$0.05(12)$
Water	2	0	0
Result	10	x	$10x$

The sum of the quantities before mixing is equal to the quantity after mixing.
$0.05(12) + 0 = 10x$

Solution
$$0.05(12) + 0 = 10x$$
$$0.60 = 10x$$
$$x = 0.06$$
The result is 6% fruit juice.

36. Strategy

Percent concentration of resulting mixture: x

	Amount	Percent	Quantity
3% solution	50	0.03	0.03(50)
12% solution	30	0.12	0.12(30)
Mixture	80	x	$80x$

The sum of the quantities before mixing is equal to the quantity after mixing.
$0.03(50) + 0.12(30) = 80x$

Solution
$$0.03(50) + 0.12(30) = 80x$$
$$1.5 + 3.6 = 80x$$
$$5.1 = 80x$$
$$x = 0.06375$$
The mixture is about 6.4% hydrogen peroxide.

37. Strategy

Percent concentration of the resulting alloy: x

	Amount	Percent	Quantity
54%	80	0.54	0.54(80)
22%	200	0.22	0.22(200)
Mixture	280	x	$280x$

The sum of the quantities before mixing is equal to the quantity after mixing.
$0.54(80) + 0.22(200) = 280x$

Solution
$$0.54(80) + 0.22(200) = 280x$$
$$43.2 + 44 = 280x$$
$$87.2 = 280x$$
$$0.3114 \approx x$$
The resulting alloy is about 31.1% copper.

38. Strategy

Percent concentration of the resulting mixture: x

	Amount	Percent	Quantity
15%	100	0.15	0.15(100)
Pure alcohol	50	1.00	1.00(50)
Mixture	150	x	$150x$

The sum of the quantities before mixing is equal to the quantity after mixing.
$0.15(100) + 1.00(50) = 150x$

Solution
$$0.15(100) + 1.00(50) = 150x$$
$$15 + 50 = 150x$$
$$65 = 150x$$
$$0.4\overline{3} = x$$
The resulting mixture is about 43.3% alcohol.

Applying Concepts 2.4

39. Strategy
    Total amount invested: x
    Amount invested at 9%: $0.25x$
    Amount invested at 8%: $0.30x$
    Amount invested at 9.5%: $0.45x$

	Amount	Percent	Quantity
Amount at 9%	$0.25x$	0.09	$0.09(0.25x)$
Amount at 8%	$0.30x$	0.08	$0.08(0.30x)$
Amount at 9.5%	$0.45x$	0.095	$0.095(0.45x)$

The total annual interest earned is $1785.

Solution
$$0.09(0.25x) + 0.08(0.3x) + 0.095(0.45x) = 1785$$
$$0.0225x + 0.024x + 0.04275x = 1785$$
$$0.08925x = 1785$$
$$x = 20,000$$

$0.25x = 0.25(20,000) = 5000$
$0.3x = 0.3(20,000) = 6000$
$0.45x = 0.45(20,000) = 9000$
The amount invested at 9% was $5000.
The amount invested at 8% was $6000.
The amount invested at 9.5% was $9000.

40. Strategy
    Percent concentration of the resulting alloy: x

	Amount	Percent	Quantity
40%	90	0.40	$0.40(90)$
60%	120	0.60	$0.60(120)$
Mixture	210	x	$210x$

The sum of the quantities before mixing is equal to the quantity after mixing.
$$0.40(90) + 0.60(120) = 210x$$

Solution
$$0.40(90) + 0.60(120) = 210x$$
$$36 + 72 = 210x$$
$$108 = 210x$$
$$0.5142857 = x$$

The percent concentration of the resulting alloy is 51.4% silver.

41. Strategy

Cost per pound of mixture: x

	Amount	Cost	Value
$5.50 tea	50	550	550(50)
$4.40 tea	75	440	440(75)
Mixture	125	x	125x

The sum of the quantities before mixing is equal to the quantity after mixing.
$550(50) + 440(75) = 125x$

Solution

$$550(50) + 440(75) = 125x$$
$$27,500 + 33,000 = 125x$$
$$60,500 = 125x$$
$$484 = x$$

The tea mixture would cost $4.84 per pound.

42. Strategy

Kilograms of evaporated water: x

	Amount	Percent	Quantity
Pure water	x	0	0
15%	75	0.15	0.15(75)
20%	$75 - x$	0.20	0.20(75 − x)

The difference between the quantity of the 15% solution and the quantity of evaporated water is equal to the quantity after mixing.
$0.15(75) - 0 = 0.20(75 - x)$

Solution

$$0.15(75) - 0 = 0.20(75 - x)$$
$$11.25 = 15 - 0.20x$$
$$-3.75 = -0.20x$$
$$18.75 = x$$

18.75 kg of water must be evaporated.

43. Strategy

Grams of water: x

	Amount	Percent	Quantity
Pure water	x	0	0
Pure acid	20	1.00	1.00(20)
25% acid	$20 + x$	0.25	0.25(20 + x)

The sum of the quantities before mixing is equal to the quantity after mixing.
$0 + 1.00(20) = 0.25(20 + x)$

Solution

$$0 + 1.00(20) = 0.25(20 + x)$$
$$20 = 5 + 0.25x$$
$$15 = 0.25x$$
$$60 = x$$

60 g of pure water were in the beaker.

44. Strategy
Liters of 25% antifreeze replaced: x
Liters of pure antifreeze added: x

	Amount	Percent	Quantity
25% antifreeze in the radiator	6	0.25	0.25(6)
25% antifreeze replaced by pure antifreeze	x	0.25	0.25x
Pure antifreeze added	x	1.00	x
50% antifreeze	6	0.50	0.50(x)

The quantity in the radiator minus the quantity replaced plus the quantity added equals the quantity in the resulting solution.
$0.25(6) - 0.25x + x = 0.50(6)$

Solution
$$0.25(6) - 0.25x + x = 0.50(6)$$
$$1.5 + 0.75x = 3$$
$$0.75x = 1.5$$
$$x = 2$$
2 L will have to be replaced with pure antifreeze.

45. a. The percent increase for 1990 is higher.

b. Since there was a positive percent increase every year, the costs were highest in 2000.

46. Annual percentage rate (APR) refers to the simple interest rate that is equivalent to an annual compound interest rate. For instance, an annual interest rate of 8% compounded daily gives
$$APR = \left(1 + \frac{0.08}{365}\right)^{365} - 1$$
$$= 0.083277572...$$
or 8.33%. Annual percentage rate is also used in home loans. By federal law, each bank must include certain loan costs in the calculation of APR. These include prepaid interest (points), application fee, document fees, and other costs.

47. Retailers who purchase products from a wholesaler may receive various discounts on the items purchased. The discounts are usually related to the number of items purchased. Two or more discounts given on the same item constitute a series discount. For instance, a series discount of 25/10 means that the retailer receives a 25% discount off the list price and then a 10% discount off the discounted price. For example, if the recommended retail price of an item is $40, then the cost to a retailer receiving a series discount of 25/10 is calculated as follows:
$40 - 40(0.25) = 30$
$30 - 30(0.10) = 27$
The retailer would pay $27 for the item.
There may be more than two discounts available, such as 25/10/5.
To convert a series discount to a single-discount equivalent, subtract the complements of the discount rates from 1 (100%). For the example above,
$1 - (0.75)(0.90) = 1 - 0.675 = 0.325 = 32.5\%$
The cost to the retailer can be calculated directly by using the product of the complements of the percents.

Section 2.5

Concept Review 2.5

1. Always true

2. Never true
The reciprocal of the smaller number is larger than the reciprocal of the larger number.

3. Sometimes true
The rule states that when dividing an inequality by a negative integer, we must reverse the inequality.

4. Never true
The rule states that we can subtract the same number from both sides of an inequality without reversing the inequality.

5. Sometimes true
This is not true for $a = 0$.

6. Always true

Objective 2.5.1 Exercises

1. The Addition Property of Inequalities states that the same number can be added to each side of an inequality without changing the solution set of the inequality. Examples will vary. For instance,
$$8 > 6$$
$$8 + 4 > 6 + 4$$
$$12 > 10$$
and
$$-5 < -1$$
$$-5 + (-7) < -1 + (-7)$$
$$-12 < -8$$

2. Rule 1 of the Multiplication Property of Equations states that when each side of an inequality is multiplied by a positive number, the inequality symbol remains the same. Rule 2 states that when each side of an inequality is multiplied by a negative number, the inequality symbol must be reversed. Examples will vary. For instance,
$$8 > 6$$
$$3 \bullet 8 > 3 \bullet 6$$
$$24 > 18$$
and
$$8 > 6$$
$$-3 \bullet 8 < -3 \bullet 6$$
$$-24 < -18$$

3. $x + 7 \leq -3$
$\quad x \leq -10$
The solution is a, c.

4. $2x - 1 > 5$
$\quad 2x > 6$
$\quad x > 3$
The solution is a, d.

5. $x - 3 < 2$
$\quad x < 5$
$\quad \{x | x < 5\}$

6. $x + 4 \geq 2$
$\quad x \geq -2$
$\quad \{x | x \geq -2\}$

7. $4x \leq 8$
$\quad \dfrac{4x}{4} \leq \dfrac{8}{4}$
$\quad x \leq 2$
$\quad \{x | x \leq 2\}$

8. $6x > 12$
$\quad \dfrac{6x}{6} > \dfrac{12}{6}$
$\quad x > 2$
$\quad \{x | x > 2\}$

9. $-2x > 8$
$\quad \dfrac{-2x}{-2} < \dfrac{8}{-2}$
$\quad x < -4$
$\quad \{x | x < -4\}$

10. $-3x \leq -9$
$\quad \dfrac{-3x}{-3} \geq \dfrac{-9}{-3}$
$\quad x \geq 3$
$\quad \{x | x \geq 3\}$

11. $3x - 1 > 2x + 2$
$\quad x - 1 > 2$
$\quad x > 3$
$\quad \{x | x > 3\}$

12. $5x + 2 \geq 4x - 1$
$\quad x + 2 \geq -1$
$\quad x \geq -3$
$\quad \{x | x \geq -3\}$

13. $2x - 1 > 7$
$\quad 2x > 8$
$\quad \dfrac{2x}{2} > \dfrac{8}{2}$
$\quad x > 4$
$\quad \{x | x > 4\}$

14. $4x + 3 \leq -1$
$\quad 4x \leq -4$
$\quad \dfrac{4x}{4} \leq \dfrac{-4}{4}$
$\quad x \leq -1$
$\quad \{x | x \leq -1\}$

15. $6x + 3 > 4x - 1$
$\quad 2x + 3 > -1$
$\quad 2x > -4$
$\quad \dfrac{2x}{2} > \dfrac{-4}{2}$
$\quad x > -2$
$\quad \{x | x > -2\}$

16. $7x + 4 < 2x - 6$
$\quad 5x + 4 < -6$
$\quad 5x < -10$
$\quad \dfrac{5x}{5} < \dfrac{-10}{5}$
$\quad x < -2$
$\quad \{x | x < -2\}$

17. $8x + 1 \geq 2x + 13$
$6x + 1 \geq 13$
$6x \geq 12$
$\dfrac{6x}{6} \geq \dfrac{12}{6}$
$x \geq 2$
$\{x | x \geq 2\}$

18. $5x - 4 < 2x + 5$
$3x - 4 < 5$
$3x < 9$
$\dfrac{3x}{3} < \dfrac{9}{3}$
$x < 3$
$\{x | x < 3\}$

19. $7 - 2x \geq 1$
$-2x \geq -6$
$\dfrac{-2x}{-2} \leq \dfrac{-6}{-2}$
$x \leq 3$
$\{x | x \leq 3\}$

20. $3 - 5x \leq 18$
$-5x \leq 15$
$\dfrac{-5x}{-5} \geq \dfrac{15}{-5}$
$x \geq -3$
$\{x | x \geq -3\}$

21. $4x - 2 < x - 11$
$3x - 2 < -11$
$3x < -9$
$\dfrac{3x}{3} < \dfrac{-9}{3}$
$x < -3$
$\{x | x < -3\}$

22. $6x + 5 \geq x - 10$
$5x + 5 \geq -10$
$5x \geq -15$
$\dfrac{5x}{5} \geq \dfrac{-15}{5}$
$x \geq -3$
$\{x | x \geq -3\}$

23. $x + 7 \geq 4x - 8$
$-3x + 7 \geq -8$
$-3x \geq -15$
$\dfrac{-3x}{-3} \leq \dfrac{-15}{-3}$
$x \leq 5$
$(-\infty, 5]$

24. $3x + 1 \leq 7x - 15$
$-4x + 1 \leq -15$
$-4x \leq -16$
$\dfrac{-4x}{-4} \geq \dfrac{-16}{-4}$
$x \geq 4$
$[4, \infty)$

25. $6 - 2(x - 4) \leq 2x + 10$
$6 - 2x + 8 \leq 2x + 10$
$14 - 2x \leq 2x + 10$
$14 - 4x \leq 10$
$-4x \leq -4$
$\dfrac{-4x}{-4} \geq \dfrac{-4}{-4}$
$x \geq 1$
$[1, \infty)$

26. $4(2x - 1) > 3x - 2(3x - 5)$
$8x - 4 > 3x - 6x + 10$
$8x - 4 > -3x + 10$
$11x - 4 > 10$
$11x > 14$
$\dfrac{11x}{11} > \dfrac{14}{11}$
$x > \dfrac{14}{11}$
$\left(\dfrac{14}{11}, \infty \right)$

27. $2(1 - 3x) - 4 > 10 + 3(1 - x)$
$2 - 6x - 4 > 10 + 3 - 3x$
$-6x - 2 > 13 - 3x$
$-3x - 2 > 13$
$-3x > 15$
$\dfrac{-3x}{-3} < \dfrac{15}{-3}$
$x < -5$
$(-\infty, -5)$

28. $2 - 5(x + 1) \geq 3(x - 1) - 8$
$2 - 5x - 5 \geq 3x - 3 - 8$
$-5x - 3 \geq 3x - 11$
$-8x - 3 \geq -11$
$-8x \geq -8$
$\dfrac{-8x}{-8} \leq \dfrac{-8}{-8}$
$x \leq 1$
$(-\infty, 1]$

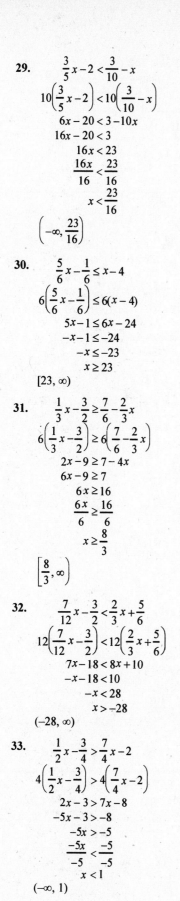

29. $\dfrac{3}{5}x - 2 < \dfrac{3}{10} - x$

$10\left(\dfrac{3}{5}x - 2\right) < 10\left(\dfrac{3}{10} - x\right)$

$6x - 20 < 3 - 10x$

$16x - 20 < 3$

$16x < 23$

$\dfrac{16x}{16} < \dfrac{23}{16}$

$x < \dfrac{23}{16}$

$\left(-\infty, \dfrac{23}{16}\right)$

30. $\dfrac{5}{6}x - \dfrac{1}{6} \le x - 4$

$6\left(\dfrac{5}{6}x - \dfrac{1}{6}\right) \le 6(x - 4)$

$5x - 1 \le 6x - 24$

$-x - 1 \le -24$

$-x \le -23$

$x \ge 23$

$[23, \infty)$

31. $\dfrac{1}{3}x - \dfrac{3}{2} \ge \dfrac{7}{6} - \dfrac{2}{3}x$

$6\left(\dfrac{1}{3}x - \dfrac{3}{2}\right) \ge 6\left(\dfrac{7}{6} - \dfrac{2}{3}x\right)$

$2x - 9 \ge 7 - 4x$

$6x - 9 \ge 7$

$6x \ge 16$

$\dfrac{6x}{6} \ge \dfrac{16}{6}$

$x \ge \dfrac{8}{3}$

$\left[\dfrac{8}{3}, \infty\right)$

32. $\dfrac{7}{12}x - \dfrac{3}{2} < \dfrac{2}{3}x + \dfrac{5}{6}$

$12\left(\dfrac{7}{12}x - \dfrac{3}{2}\right) < 12\left(\dfrac{2}{3}x + \dfrac{5}{6}\right)$

$7x - 18 < 8x + 10$

$-x - 18 < 10$

$-x < 28$

$x > -28$

$(-28, \infty)$

33. $\dfrac{1}{2}x - \dfrac{3}{4} > \dfrac{7}{4}x - 2$

$4\left(\dfrac{1}{2}x - \dfrac{3}{4}\right) > 4\left(\dfrac{7}{4}x - 2\right)$

$2x - 3 > 7x - 8$

$-5x - 3 > -8$

$-5x > -5$

$\dfrac{-5x}{-5} < \dfrac{-5}{-5}$

$x < 1$

$(-\infty, 1)$

34. $\dfrac{2-x}{4} - \dfrac{3}{8} \ge \dfrac{2}{5}x$

$40\left(\dfrac{2-x}{4} - \dfrac{3}{8}\right) \ge 40\left(\dfrac{2}{5}x\right)$

$10(2-x) - 15 \ge 16x$

$20 - 10x - 15 \ge 16x$

$5 - 10x \ge 16x$

$5 - 26x \ge 0$

$-26x \ge -5$

$\dfrac{-26x}{-26} \le \dfrac{-5}{-26}$

$x \le \dfrac{5}{26}$

$\left(-\infty, \dfrac{5}{26}\right]$

35. $2 - 2(7 - 2x) < 3(3 - x)$

$2 - 14 + 4x < 9 - 3x$

$-12 + 4x < 9 - 3x$

$-12 + 7x < 9$

$7x < 21$

$\dfrac{7x}{7} < \dfrac{21}{7}$

$x < 3$

$(-\infty, 3)$

36. $3 + 2(x + 5) \ge x + 5(x + 1) + 1$

$3 + 2x + 10 \ge x + 5x + 5 + 1$

$2x + 13 \ge 6x + 6$

$-4x + 13 \ge 6$

$-4x \ge -7$

$\dfrac{-4x}{-4} \le \dfrac{-7}{-4}$

$x \le \dfrac{7}{4}$

$\left(-\infty, \dfrac{7}{4}\right]$

Objective 2.5.2 Exercises

37a. When a compound inequality is combined with *or*, the set operation union is used.

37b. When a compound inequality is combined with *and*, the set operation intersection is used.

38. Writing $-3 < x > 4$ does not make sense because there is no number that is greater than -3 *and* greater than 4.

39. $3x < 6$ and $x + 2 > 1$

   $x < 2$ $x > -1$

   $\{x | x < 2\}$ $\{x | x > -1\}$

   $\{x | x < 2\} \cap \{x | x > -1\} = (-1, 2)$

40. $x - 3 \le 1$ and $2x \ge -4$

   $x \le 4$ $x \ge -2$

   $\{x | x \le 4\}$ $\{x | x \ge -2\}$

   $\{x | x \le 4\} \cap \{x | x \ge -2\} = [-2, 4]$

41. $x + 2 \geq 5$ or $3x \leq 3$
$\qquad x \geq 3 \qquad x \leq 1$
$\{x | x \geq 3\} \quad \{x | x \leq 1\}$
$\{x | x \geq 3\} \cup \{x | x \leq 1\} = (-\infty, 1] \cup [3, \infty)$

42. $2x < 6$ or $x - 4 > 1$
$\qquad x < 3 \qquad x > 5$
$\{x | x < 3\} \ \{x | x > 5\}$
$\{x | x < 3\} \cup \{x | x > 5\} = (-\infty, 3) \cup (5, \infty)$

43. $-2x > -8$ and $-3x < 6$
$\qquad x < 4 \qquad x > -2$
$\{x | x < 4\} \quad \{x | x > -2\}$
$\{x | x < 4\} \cap \{x | x > -2\} = (-2, 4)$

44. $\frac{1}{2}x > -2$ and $5x < 10$
$\qquad\qquad\qquad x < 2$
$\quad x > -4$
$\{x | x > -4\} \quad \{x | x < 2\}$
$\{x | x > -4\} \cap \{x | x < 2\} = (-4, 2)$

45. $\frac{1}{3}x < -1$ or $2x > 0$
$\qquad x < -3 \qquad x > 0$
$\{x | x < -3\} \ \{x | x > 0\}$
$\{x | x < -3\} \cup \{x | x > 0\} = (-\infty, -3) \cup (0, \infty)$

46. $\frac{2}{3}x > 4$ or $2x < -8$
$\qquad x > 6 \qquad x < -4$
$\{x | x > 6\} \ \{x | x < -4\}$
$\{x | x > 6\} \cup \{x | x < -4\} = (-\infty, -4) \cup (6, \infty)$

47. $x + 4 \geq 5$ and $2x \geq 6$
$\qquad x \geq 1 \qquad x \geq 3$
$\{x | x \geq 1\} \quad \{x | x \geq 3\}$
$\{x | x \geq 1\} \cap \{x | x \geq 3\} = [3, \infty)$

48. $3x < -9$ and $x - 2 < 2$
$\qquad x < -3 \qquad x < 4$
$\{x | x < -3\} \ \{x | x < 4\}$
$\{x | x < -3\} \cap \{x | x < 4\} = (-\infty, -3)$

49. $-5x > 10$ and $x + 1 > 6$
$\qquad x < -2 \qquad x > 5$
$\{x | x < -2\} \quad \{x | x > 5\}$
$\{x | x < -2\} \cap \{x | x > 5\} = \varnothing$

50. $7x < 14$ and $1 - x < 4$
$\qquad x < 2 \qquad -x < 3$
$\qquad\qquad\qquad x > -3$
$\{x | x < 2\} \quad \{x | x > -3\}$
$\{x | x < 2\} \cap \{x | x > -3\} = (-3, 2)$

51. $2x - 3 > 1$ and $3x - 1 < 2$
$\qquad 2x > 4 \qquad 3x < 3$
$\qquad x > 2 \qquad x < 1$
$\{x | x > 2\} \qquad \{x | x < 1\}$
$\{x | x > 2\} \cap \{x | x < 1\} = \varnothing$

52. $4x + 1 < 5$ and $4x + 7 > -1$
$\qquad 4x < 4 \qquad 4x > -8$
$\qquad x < 1 \qquad x > -2$
$\{x | x < 1\} \qquad \{x | x > -2\}$
$\{x | x < 1\} \cap \{x | x > -2\} = (-2, 1)$

53. $3x + 7 < 10$ or $2x - 1 > 5$
$\qquad 3x < 3 \qquad 2x > 6$
$\qquad x < 1 \qquad x > 3$
$\{x | x < 1\} \qquad \{x | x > 3\}$
$\{x | x < 1\} \cup \{x | x > 3\} = (-\infty, 1) \cup (3, \infty)$

54. $6x - 2 < -14$ or $5x + 1 > 11$
$\qquad 6x < -12 \qquad 5x > 10$
$\qquad x < -2 \qquad x > 2$
$\{x | x < -2\} \qquad \{x | x > 2\}$
$\{x | x < -2\} \cup \{x | x > 2\} = (-\infty, -2) \cup (2, \infty)$

55. $\qquad -5 < 3x + 4 < 16$
$-5 - 4 < 3x + 4 - 4 < 16 - 4$
$\qquad -9 < 3x < 12$
$\qquad \dfrac{-9}{3} < \dfrac{3x}{3} < \dfrac{12}{3}$
$\qquad -3 < x < 4$
$\{x | -3 < x < 4\}$

56. $\qquad 5 < 4x - 3 < 21$
$5 + 3 < 4x - 3 + 3 < 21 + 3$
$\qquad 8 < 4x < 24$
$\qquad \dfrac{8}{4} < \dfrac{4x}{4} < \dfrac{24}{4}$
$\qquad 2 < x < 6$
$\{x | 2 < x < 6\}$

57. $\qquad 0 < 2x - 6 < 4$
$0 + 6 < 2x - 6 + 6 < 4 + 6$
$\qquad 6 < 2x < 10$
$\qquad \dfrac{6}{2} < \dfrac{2x}{2} < \dfrac{10}{2}$
$\qquad 3 < x < 5$
$\{x | 3 < x < 5\}$

58. $\qquad -2 < 3x + 7 < 1$
$-2 - 7 < 3x + 7 - 7 < 1 - 7$
$\qquad -9 < 3x < -6$
$\qquad -\dfrac{9}{3} < \dfrac{3x}{3} < -\dfrac{6}{3}$
$\qquad -3 < x < -2$
$\{x | -3 < x < -2\}$

59. $4x - 1 > 11$ or $4x - 1 \le -11$

$\quad 4x > 12 \qquad\quad 4x \le -10$

$\quad x > 3 \qquad\qquad x \le -\dfrac{5}{2}$

$\{x | x > 3\} \qquad \left\{x | x \le -\dfrac{5}{2}\right\}$

$\{x | x > 3\} \cup \left\{x | x \le -\dfrac{5}{2}\right\}$

$= \left\{x | x > 3 \text{ or } x \le -\dfrac{5}{2}\right\}$

60. $3x - 5 > 10$ or $3x - 5 < -10$

$\quad 3x > 15 \qquad\quad 3x < -5$

$\quad x > 5 \qquad\qquad x < -\dfrac{5}{3}$

$\{x | x > 5\} \qquad \left\{x | x < -\dfrac{5}{3}\right\}$

$\{x | x > 5\} \cup \left\{x | x < -\dfrac{5}{3}\right\}$

$= \left\{x | x > 5 \text{ or } x < -\dfrac{5}{3}\right\}$

61. $2x + 3 \ge 5$ and $3x - 1 > 11$

$\quad 2x \ge 2 \qquad\quad 3x > 12$

$\quad x \ge 1 \qquad\qquad x > 4$

$\{x | x \ge 1\} \qquad \{x | x > 4\}$

$\{x | x \ge 1\} \cap \{x | x > 4\} = \{x | x > 4\}$

62. $6x - 2 < 5$ or $7x - 5 < 16$

$\quad 6x < 7 \qquad\quad 7x < 21$

$\quad x < \dfrac{7}{6} \qquad\qquad x < 3$

$\left\{x | x < \dfrac{7}{6}\right\} \qquad \{x | x < 3\}$

$\left\{x | x < \dfrac{7}{6}\right\} \cup \{x | x < 3\} = \{x | x < 3\}$

63. $9x - 2 < 7$ and $3x - 5 > 10$

$\quad 9x < 9 \qquad\quad 3x > 15$

$\quad x < 1 \qquad\qquad x > 5$

$\{x | x < 1\} \qquad \{x | x > 5\}$

$\{x | x < 1\} \cap \{x | x > 5\} = \varnothing$

64. $8x + 2 \le -14$ and $4x - 2 > 10$

$\quad 8x \le -16 \qquad\quad 4x > 12$

$\quad x \le -2 \qquad\qquad x > 3$

$\{x | x \le -2\} \cap \{x | x > 3\} = \varnothing$

65. $3x - 11 < 4$ or $4x + 9 \ge 1$

$\quad 3x < 15 \qquad\quad 4x \ge -8$

$\quad x < 5 \qquad\qquad x \ge -2$

$\{x | x < 5\} \qquad \{x | x \ge -2\}$

$\{x | x < 5\} \cup \{x | x \ge -2\}$

$= \{x | x \text{ is a real number}\}$

66. $5x + 12 \ge 2$ or $7x - 1 \le 13$

$\quad 5x \ge -10 \qquad\quad 7x \le 14$

$\quad x \ge -2 \qquad\qquad x \le 2$

$\{x | x \ge -2\} \qquad \{x | x \le 2\}$

$\{x | x \ge -2\} \cup \{x | x \le 2\}$

$= \{x | x \text{ is a real number}\}$

67. $3 - 2x > 7$ and $5x + 2 > -18$

$\quad -2x > 4 \qquad\quad 5x > -20$

$\quad x < -2 \qquad\qquad x > -4$

$\{x | x < -2\} \qquad \{x | x > -4\}$

$\{x | x < -2\} \cap \{x | x > -4\} = \{x | -4 < x < -2\}$

68. $1 - 3x < 16$ and $1 - 3x > -16$

$\quad -3x < 15 \qquad\quad -3x > -17$

$\quad x > -5 \qquad\qquad x < \dfrac{17}{3}$

$\{x | x > -5\} \qquad \left\{x | x < \dfrac{17}{3}\right\}$

$\{x | x > -5\} \cap \left\{x | x < \dfrac{17}{3}\right\} = \left\{x | -5 < x < \dfrac{17}{3}\right\}$

69. $5 - 4x > 21$ or $7x - 2 > 19$

$\quad -4x > 16 \qquad\quad 7x > 21$

$\quad x < -4 \qquad\qquad x > 3$

$\{x | x < -4\} \qquad \{x | x > 3\}$

$\{x | x < -4\} \cup \{x | x > 3\} = \{x | x < -4 \text{ or } x > 3\}$

70. $6x + 5 < -1$ or $1 - 2x < 7$

$\quad 6x < -6 \qquad\quad -2x < 6$

$\quad x < -1 \qquad\qquad x > -3$

$\{x | x < -1\} \qquad \{x | x > -3\}$

$\{x | x < -1\} \cup \{x | x > -3\}$

$= \{x | x \text{ is a real number}\}$

71. $3 - 7x \le 31$ and $5 - 4x > 1$

$\quad -7x \le 28 \qquad\quad -4x > -4$

$\quad x \ge -4 \qquad\qquad x < 1$

$\{x | x \ge -4\} \qquad \{x | x < 1\}$

$\{x | x \ge -4\} \cap \{x | x < 1\} = \{x | -4 \le x < 1\}$

72. $9 - x \ge 7$ and $9 - 2x < 3$

$\quad -x \ge -2 \qquad\quad -2x < -6$

$\quad x \le 2 \qquad\qquad x > 3$

$\{x | x \le 2\} \qquad \{x | x > 3\}$

$\{x | x \le 2\} \cap \{x | x > 3\} = \varnothing$

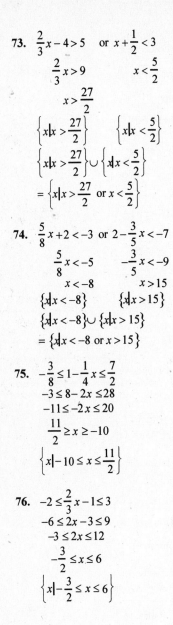

73. $\frac{2}{3}x - 4 > 5$ or $x + \frac{1}{2} < 3$

$$\frac{2}{3}x > 9 \qquad x < \frac{5}{2}$$

$$x > \frac{27}{2}$$

$$\left\{ x \Big| x > \frac{27}{2} \right\} \qquad \left\{ x \Big| x < \frac{5}{2} \right\}$$

$$\left\{ x \Big| x > \frac{27}{2} \right\} \cup \left\{ x \Big| x < \frac{5}{2} \right\}$$

$$= \left\{ x \Big| x > \frac{27}{2} \text{ or } x < \frac{5}{2} \right\}$$

74. $\frac{5}{8}x + 2 < -3$ or $2 - \frac{3}{5}x < -7$

$$\frac{5}{8}x < -5 \qquad -\frac{3}{5}x < -9$$

$$x < -8 \qquad x > 15$$

$$\{ x | x < -8 \} \qquad \{ x | x > 15 \}$$

$$\{ x | x < -8 \} \cup \{ x | x > 15 \}$$

$$= \{ x | x < -8 \text{ or } x > 15 \}$$

75. $-\frac{3}{8} \le 1 - \frac{1}{4}x \le \frac{7}{2}$

$$-3 \le 8 - 2x \le 28$$

$$-11 \le -2x \le 20$$

$$\frac{11}{2} \ge x \ge -10$$

$$\left\{ x \Big| -10 \le x \le \frac{11}{2} \right\}$$

76. $-2 \le \frac{2}{3}x - 1 \le 3$

$$-6 \le 2x - 3 \le 9$$

$$-3 \le 2x \le 12$$

$$-\frac{3}{2} \le x \le 6$$

$$\left\{ x \Big| -\frac{3}{2} \le x \le 6 \right\}$$

Objective 2.5.3 Exercises

77. Strategy
the unknown number: x
five times the difference between the number and two: $5(x - 2)$
the quotient of two times the number and three: $2x \div 3$

Solution
five times the difference between a number and two > the quotient of two times the number and three

$$5(x - 2) \ge \frac{2x}{3}$$

$$5x - 10 \ge \frac{2x}{3}$$

$$3(5x - 10) \ge 2x$$

$$15x - 30 \ge 2x$$

$$13x - 30 \ge 0$$

$$13x \ge 30$$

$$x \ge \frac{30}{13}$$

$$x \ge 2\frac{4}{13}$$

The smallest integer is 3.

78. Strategy
the unknown number: x
two times the difference between the number and eight: $2(x - 8)$
five times the sum of the number and four: $5(x + 4)$

Solution
two times the difference between the number and eight ≤ five times the sum of the number and four

$$2(x - 8) \le 5(x + 4)$$

$$2x - 16 \le 5x + 20$$

$$-3x - 16 \le 20$$

$$-3x \le 36$$

$$x \ge -12$$

The smallest number is −12.

79. Strategy
the width of the rectangle: x
the length of the rectangle: $4x + 2$
To find the maximum width, substitute the given values in the inequality $2L + 2W < 34$ and solve.

Solution

$$2L + 2W < 34$$

$$2(4x + 2) + 2x < 34$$

$$8x + 4 + 2x < 34$$

$$10x + 4 < 34$$

$$10x < 30$$

$$x < 3$$

The maximum width of the rectangle is 2 ft.

80. Strategy
the width of the rectangle: x
the length of the rectangle: $2x - 5$
To find the maximum width, substitute the given
values in the inequality $2L + 2W < 60$ and solve.

Solution
$$2L + 2W < 60$$
$$2(2x - 5) + 2x < 60$$
$$4x - 10 + 2x < 60$$
$$6x - 10 < 60$$
$$6x < 70$$
$$x < \frac{70}{6}$$
$$x < 11\frac{2}{3}$$
The maximum width of the rectangle is 11 cm.

81. Strategy
To find the four consecutive integers, write and
solve a compound inequality using x to represent
the first integer.

Solution
Lower limit of the sum < sum < Upper limit of
the sum
$$62 < x + (x + 1) + (x + 2) + (x + 3) < 78$$
$$62 < 4x + 6 < 78$$
$$62 - 6 < 4x + 6 - 6 < 78 - 6$$
$$56 < 4x < 72$$
$$\frac{56}{4} < \frac{4x}{4} < \frac{72}{4}$$
$$14 < x < 18$$
The four integers are 15, 16, 17, and 18; or 16,
17, 18, and 19; or 17, 18, 19, and 20.

82. Strategy
To find the three consecutive even integers, write
and solve a compound inequality using x to
represent the first even integer.

Solution
Lower limit of the sum < sum < Upper limit of
the sum
$$30 < x + (x + 2) + (x + 4) < 52$$
$$30 < 3x + 6 < 52$$
$$30 - 6 < 3x + 6 - 6 < 52 - 6$$
$$24 < 3x < 46$$
$$\frac{24}{3} < \frac{3x}{3} < \frac{46}{3}$$
$$8 < x < 15\frac{1}{3}$$
The three even integers are 10, 12, and 14; or 12,
14, and 16; or 14, 16, and 18.

83. Strategy
First side of the triangle: $x + 1$
Second side of the triangle: x
Third side of the triangle: $x + 2$

Solution
The perimeter of the triangle is more than 15 in.
and less than 25 in.
$$15 < P < 25$$
$$15 < (x + 1) + x + (x + 2) < 25$$
$$15 < 3x + 3 < 25$$
$$15 - 3 < 3x + 3 - 3 < 25 - 3$$
$$12 < 3x < 22$$
$$\frac{12}{3} < \frac{3x}{3} < \frac{22}{3}$$
$$4 < x < 7\frac{1}{3}$$
If $x = 5$: $5 + 1 = 6$; $5 + 2 = 7$;
$5 + 6 + 7 = 18 = $ perimeter
If $x = 6$: $6 + 1 = 7$; $6 + 2 = 8$;
$6 + 7 + 8 = 21 = $ perimeter
If $x = 7$: $7 + 1 = 8$; $7 + 2 = 9$;
$7 + 8 + 9 = 24 = $ perimeter
The lengths of the second side could be 5 in.,
6 in., or 7 in.

84. Strategy
Width of the rectangle: x
Length of the rectangle: $2x + 4$

Solution
The perimeter of the rectangle is more than 28 ft
and less than 40 ft.
$$28 < P < 40$$
$$28 < 2L + 2W < 40$$
$$28 < 2(2x + 4) + 2x < 40$$
$$28 < 4x + 8 + 2x < 40$$
$$28 < 6x + 8 < 40$$
$$28 - 8 < 6x + 8 - 8 < 40 - 8$$
$$20 < 6x < 32$$
$$\frac{20}{6} < \frac{6x}{6} < \frac{32}{6}$$
$$3\frac{2}{3} < x < 5\frac{1}{3}$$
The width of the rectangle could be 4 ft or 5 ft.

85. Strategy
To find the number of minutes, write and solve
an inequality using N to represent the number of
minutes of cellular phone time.

Solution
cost of second option $\le$ cost of first option
$$0.4N + 35 \le 99$$
$$0.4N \le 64$$
$$N \le 160$$
A customer can use a cellular phone 160 min
before the charges exceed the first option.

86. Strategy

To find the number of hours when the second plan costs you less than the first, solve an inequality using N to represent the hours of online time.

cost of second plan < cost of first plan

$(N-3)2.50 + 4.95 < 19.95$

Solution

$$2.50N - 7.50 + 4.95 < 19.95$$
$$2.50N - 2.55 < 19.95$$
$$2.50N < 22.50$$
$$N < 9$$

A customer can use AOL for 10 hours or less before the flat rate is less expensive than the second plan.

87. Strategy

To find the number of pages for which the AirTouch plan is less expensive, solve an inequality using N to represent the number of pages.

Cost of AirTouch < Cost of TopPage

$$6.95 + 0.10(x - 400) < 3.95 + 0.15(x - 400)$$
$$6.95 + 0.10x - 40 < 3.95 + 0.15x - 60$$
$$33.05 + 0.10x < -56.05 + 0.15x$$
$$23 < 0.05x$$
$$460 < x$$

AirTouch is less expensive for jobs more than 460 pages.

89. Strategy

To find the number of minutes for which a call will be cheaper to pay with coins, solve an inequality using N to represent the number of minutes.

Coins < Calling card

Solution

$$(0.70) + 0.15(N - 3) < 0.35 + 0.196 + 0.126(N - 1)$$
$$0.70 + 0.15N - 0.45 < 0.35 + 0.196 + 0.126N - 0.126$$
$$0.25 + 0.15N < 0.42 + 0.126N$$
$$0.024N < .17$$
$$N < 7.08$$

Using coins will be cheaper for 7 minutes or less.

90. Strategy

To find the number of checks that can be written using the first account rather than the second, solve an inequality using x to represent the number of checks.

First account < Second account

Solution

$$3 + 0.50(x - 10) < 8$$
$$3 + 0.5x - 5 < 8$$
$$0.5x - 2 < 8$$
$$0.5x < 10$$
$$x < 20$$

The first account will be less than the second account for less than 20 checks.

88. Strategy

To find the number of miles for which Otto Rental is less expensive than Pay Rite, solve an inequality using x to represent the number of miles after the first free 700 miles.

Otto Rental < Pay Rite

Solution

$$7(19.99) + 0.19x < 32(7)$$
$$139.93 + 0.19x < 224$$
$$0.19x < 84.07$$
$$x < 443$$
$$700 + 443 = 1143$$

Otto Rental will be less expensive than Pay Rite for up to approximately 1143 miles.

91. Strategy
To find the number of checks that have to be written for Glendale Federal to cost less than the competitor, solve an inequality using N to represent the number of checks.

Glendale account < Other account

$$8 + 0.12(N - 100) < 5 + 0.15(N - 100)$$
$$8 + 0.12N - 12 < 5 + 0.15N - 15$$
$$0.12N - 4 < 0.15N - 10$$
$$-0.03N < -6$$
$$N > 200$$

The Glendale Federal account will cost less for more than 200 checks.

92. Strategy
To find the amount of sales for which George will make at least $3200, solve an inequality using A to represent the amount.

Base pay + Commission ≥ $3200

Solution
$$1000 + 0.05A \geq 3200$$
$$0.05A \geq 2200$$
$$A \geq \$44,000$$

George needs to generate $44,000 of more in sales in order to earn $3200.

93. Strategy
To find the range of miles that a car can travel, write and solve an inequality using N to represent the range of miles.

Solution
$$22(19.5) < N < 27.5(19.5)$$
$$429 < N < 536.25$$

The range of miles is between 429 mi and 536.25 mi.

94. Strategy
To find the range of scores, write and solve an inequality using N to represent the score on the last test.

Solution
$$90 \leq \frac{85 + 88 + 90 + 98 + N}{5} \leq 100$$
$$90 \leq \frac{361 + N}{5} \leq 100$$
$$5 \cdot 90 \leq 5\left(\frac{361 + N}{5}\right) \leq 5 \cdot 100$$
$$450 \leq 361 + N \leq 500$$
$$450 - 361 \leq 361 - 361 + N \leq 500 - 361$$
$$89 \leq N \leq 139$$

Since 100 is a maximum score, the range of scores to receive an A grade is $89 \leq N \leq 100$.

Applying Concepts 2.5

95. $8x - 7 < 2x + 9$
$$6x - 7 < 9$$
$$6x < 16$$
$$x < \frac{16}{6}$$
$$x < \frac{8}{3}$$
$$\{1, 2\}$$

96. $2x + 9 \geq 5x - 4$
$$-3x + 9 \geq -4$$
$$-3x \geq -13$$
$$x \leq \frac{13}{3}$$
$$\{1, 2, 3, 4\}$$

97. $5 + 3(2 + x) > 8 + 4(x - 1)$
$$5 + 6 + 3x > 8 + 4x - 4$$
$$11 + 3x > 4 + 4x$$
$$3x > -7 + 4x$$
$$-x > -7$$
$$x < 7$$
$$\{1, 2, 3, 4, 5, 6\}$$

98. $6 + 4(2 - x) > 7 + 3(x + 5)$
$$6 + 8 - 4x > 7 + 3x + 15$$
$$14 - 4x > 22 + 3x$$
$$14 - 7x > 22$$
$$-7x > 8$$
$$x < -\frac{8}{7}$$
$$\varnothing \text{ or } \{ \; \}$$

99. $-3x < 15$ and $x + 2 < 7$
$$x > -5 \qquad x < 5$$
$$\{x | x > -5\} \cap \{x | x < 5\} = \{x | -5 < x < 5\}$$
$$\{1, 2, 3, 4\}$$

100. $3x - 2 > 1$ and $2x - 3 < 5$

$\qquad 3x > 3 \qquad\qquad 2x < 8$

$\qquad\ \ x > 1 \qquad\qquad\ \ x < 4$

$\{x | x > 1\} \qquad \{x | x < 4\}$

$\{x | x > 1\} \cap \{x | x < 4\} = \{x | 1 < x < 4\}$

$\{2, 3\}$

101. $\qquad -4 \le 3x + 8 < 16$

$-4 + (-8) \le 3x + 8 + (-8) < 16 + (-8)$

$\qquad\qquad -12 \le 3x < 8$

$\qquad\qquad \dfrac{-12}{3} \le \dfrac{3x}{3} < \dfrac{8}{3}$

$\qquad\qquad\ \ -4 \le x < \dfrac{8}{3}$

$\{1, 2\}$

102. $\qquad 5 < 7x - 3 \le 24$

$\qquad 5 + 3 < 7x - 3 + 3 \le 24 + 3$

$\qquad\qquad 8 < 7x \le 27$

$\qquad \dfrac{1}{7} \cdot 8 < \dfrac{1}{7} \cdot 7x \le \dfrac{1}{7} \cdot 27$

$\qquad\qquad \dfrac{8}{7} < x \le \dfrac{27}{7}$

$\{2, 3\}$

103. Strategy

To find the temperature range in degrees Celsius, write and solve a compound inequality.

Solution

$$77 < \frac{9}{5}C + 32 < 86$$

$$77 - 32 < \frac{9}{5}C + 32 - 32 < 86 - 32$$

$$45 < \frac{9}{5}C < 54$$

$$\frac{5}{9}(45) < \frac{5}{9}\left(\frac{9}{5}C\right) < \frac{5}{9}(54)$$

$$25 < C < 30$$

The temperature is between 25°C and 30°C.

104. Strategy

To find the value for the smaller integer, write and solve an inequality using n to represent the smaller integer and $n + 7$ to represent the larger integer. The average of the two integers is the sum of the two integers divided by 2.

Solution

$$\frac{n + (n + 7)}{2} \le -15$$

$$\frac{2n + 7}{2} \le -15$$

$$2\left(\frac{2n + 2}{2}\right) \le 2(-15)$$

$$2n + 7 \le -30$$

$$2n \le -37$$

$$n \le -18.5$$

The greatest possible value for the smaller integer is -19.

105. Strategy

To find the largest whole number of minutes the call could last, set up an inequality with N representing the number of minutes and $N - 3$ representing the number of minutes after the first 3 minutes.

Solution

$$156 + 52(N - 3) < 540$$

$$156 + 52N - 156 < 540$$

$$52N < 540$$

$$N < 10.38$$

The largest whole number of minutes the call could last is 10 min.

Section 2.6

Concept Review 2.6

1. Always true

2. Never true

$|x| < a$ is equivalent to $-a < x < a$.

3. Never true

The absolute value of a number is always positive.

4. Sometimes true

An absolute value equation may have one solution, two solutions, or no solution.

5. Never true

$|x + b| < c$ is equivalent to $-c < x + b < c$.

Objective 2.6.1 Exercises

1. $|x - 8| = 6$

$|2 - 8| = 6$

$|-6| = 6$

$\qquad 6 = 6$

Yes

2. $|2x - 5| = 9$

$|2(-2) - 5| = 9$

$|-4 - 5| = 9$

$\qquad |-9| = 9$

$\qquad\ \ 9 = 9$

Yes

3. $|3x - 4| = 7$

$|3(-1) - 4| = 7$

$|-3 - 4| = 7$

$\qquad |-7| = 7$

$\qquad\ \ 7 = 7$

Yes

4. $|6x - 1| = -5$

$|6(1) - 1| = -5$

$|6 - 1| = -5$

$\qquad |5| = -5$

$\qquad\ \ 5 \ne -5$

No. The absolute value of a number cannot be negative.

5. There are two values that have the same absolute value: a number and its opposite. Thus the solution set to any absolute value equation includes a number and its opposite.

6. To solve the absolute value equation $|x| = a$, you must rewrite the equation as two equations: $x = a$ and $x = -a$. If there is an expression such as $x + 4$ inside the absolute value signs, then the two equation will be $(x + 4) = a$ and $(x + 4) = -a$. Then you solve these two equations. The solution set of the original equation includes the solutions to each of the two equations you created.

7. $|x| = 7$

$x = 7 \qquad\qquad x = -7$

The solutions are 7 and -7.

8. $|a| = 2$

$a = 2 \qquad\qquad a = -2$

The solutions are 2 and -2.

9. $|-t| = 3$

$-t = 3 \qquad\qquad -t = -3$

$t = -3 \qquad\qquad t = 3$

The solutions are -3 and 3.

10. $|-a| = 7$

$-a = 7 \qquad\qquad -a = -7$

$a = -7 \qquad\qquad a = 7$

The solutions are -7 and 7.

11. $|-t| = -3$

There is no solution to this equation because the absolute value of a number must be non-negative.

12. $|-y| = -2$

There is no solution to this equation because the absolute value of a number must be non-negative.

13. $|x + 2| = 3$

$x + 2 = 3 \qquad\qquad x + 2 = -3$

$x = 1 \qquad\qquad x = -5$

The solutions are 1 and -5.

14. $|x + 5| = 2$

$x + 5 = 2 \qquad\qquad x + 5 = -2$

$x = -3 \qquad\qquad x = -7$

The solutions are -3 and -7.

15. $|y - 5| = 3$

$y - 5 = 3 \qquad\qquad y - 5 = -3$

$y = 8 \qquad\qquad y = 2$

The solutions are 8 and 2.

16. $|y - 8| = 4$

$y - 8 = 4 \qquad\qquad y - 8 = -4$

$y = 12 \qquad\qquad y = 4$

The solutions are 12 and 4.

17. $|a - 2| = 0$

$a - 2 = 0$

$a = 2$

The solution is 2.

18. $|a + 7| = 0$

$a + 7 = 0$

$a = -7$

The solution is -7.

19. $|x - 2| = -4$

There is no solution to this equation because the absolute value of a number must be non-negative.

20. $|x + 8| = -2$

There is no solution to this equation because the absolute value of a number must be non-negative.

21. $|2x - 5| = 4$

$2x - 5 = 4 \qquad\qquad 2x - 5 = -4$

$2x = 9 \qquad\qquad 2x = 1$

$x = \dfrac{9}{2} \qquad\qquad x = \dfrac{1}{2}$

The solutions are $\dfrac{9}{2}$ and $\dfrac{1}{2}$.

22. $|4 - 3x| = 4$

$4 - 3x = 4 \qquad\qquad 4 - 3x = -4$

$-3x = 0 \qquad\qquad -3x = -8$

$x = 0 \qquad\qquad x = \dfrac{8}{3}$

The solutions are 0 and $\dfrac{8}{3}$.

23. $|2 - 5x| = 2$

$2 - 5x = 2 \qquad\qquad 2 - 5x = -2$

$-5x = 0 \qquad\qquad -5x = -4$

$x = 0 \qquad\qquad x = \dfrac{4}{5}$

The solutions are 0 and $\dfrac{4}{5}$.

24. $|2x - 3| = 0$

$2x - 3 = 0$

$2x = 3$

$x = \dfrac{3}{2}$

The solution is $\dfrac{3}{2}$.

25. $|5x + 5| = 0$

$5x + 5 = 0$

$5x = -5$

$x = -1$

The solution is -1.

26. $|3x - 2| = -4$

There is no solution to this equation because the absolute value of a number must be non-negative.

27. $|2x+5|=-2$

There is no solution to this equation because the absolute value of a number must be non-negative.

28. $|x-2|-2=3$

$|x-2|=5$

$x-2=5$	$x-2=-5$
$x=7$	$x=-3$

The solutions are 7 and –3.

29. $|x-9|-3=2$

$|x-9|=5$

$x-9=5$	$x-9=-5$
$x=14$	$x=4$

The solutions are 14 and 4.

30. $|3a+2|-4=4$

$|3a+2|=8$

$3a+2=8$	$3a+2=-8$
$3a=6$	$3a=-10$
$a=2$	$a=-\dfrac{10}{3}$

The solutions are 2 and $-\dfrac{10}{3}$.

31. $|8-y|-3=1$

$|8-y|=4$

$8-y=4$	$8-y=-4$
$-y=-4$	$-y=-12$
$y=4$	$y=12$

The solutions are 4 and 12.

32. $|2x-3|+3=3$

$|2x-3|=0$

$2x-3=0$

$2x=3$

$x=\dfrac{3}{2}$

The solution is $\dfrac{3}{2}$.

33. $|4x-7|-5=-5$

$|4x-7|=0$

$4x-7=0$

$4x=7$

$x=\dfrac{7}{4}$

The solution is $\dfrac{7}{4}$.

34. $|2x-3|+4=-4$

$|2x-3|=-8$

There is no solution to this equation because the absolute value of a number must be non-negative.

35. $|3x-2|+1=-1$

$|3x-2|=-2$

There is no solution to this equation because the absolute value of a number must be non-negative.

36. $|6x-5|-2=4$

$|6x-5|=6$

$6x-5=6$	$6x-5=-6$
$6x=11$	$6x=-1$
$x=\dfrac{11}{6}$	$x=-\dfrac{1}{6}$

The solutions are $\dfrac{11}{6}$ and $-\dfrac{1}{6}$.

37. $|4b+3|-2=7$

$|4b+3|=9$

$4b+3=9$	$4b+3=-9$
$4b=6$	$4b=-12$
$b=\dfrac{3}{2}$	$b=-3$

The solutions are $\dfrac{3}{2}$ and –3.

38. $|3t+2|+3=4$

$|3t+2|=1$

$3t+2=1$	$3t+2=-1$
$3t=-1$	$3t=-3$
$t=-\dfrac{1}{3}$	$t=-1$

The solutions are $-\dfrac{1}{3}$ and –1.

39. $|5x-2|+5=7$

$|5x-2|=2$

$5x-2=2$	$5x-2=-2$
$5x=4$	$5x=0$
$x=\dfrac{4}{5}$	$x=0$

The solutions are $\dfrac{4}{5}$ and 0.

40. $3-|x-4|=5$

$-|x-4|=2$

$|x-4|=-2$

There is no solution to this equation because the absolute value of a number must be non-negative.

41. $2-|x-5|=4$

$-|x-5|=2$

$|x-5|=-2$

There is no solution to this equation because the absolute value of a number must be non-negative.

42. $|2x-8|+12=2$

$|2x-8|=-10$

There is no solution to this equation because the absolute value of a number must be non-negative.

43. $|3x-4|+8=3$

$|3x-4|=-5$

There is no solution to this equation because the absolute value of a number must be non-negative.

44. $2 + |3x - 4| = 5$

$|3x - 4| = 3$

$3x - 4 = 3$	$3x - 4 = -3$
$3x = 7$	$3x = 1$
$x = \dfrac{7}{3}$	$x = \dfrac{1}{3}$

The solutions are $\dfrac{7}{3}$ and $\dfrac{1}{3}$.

45. $5 + |2x + 1| = 8$

$|2x + 1| = 3$

$2x + 1 = 3$	$2x + 1 = -3$
$2x = 2$	$2x = -4$
$x = 1$	$x = -2$

The solutions are 1 and -2.

46. $5 - |2x + 1| = 5$

$-|2x + 1| = 0$

$|2x + 1| = 0$

$2x + 1 = 0$

$2x = -1$

$x = -\dfrac{1}{2}$

The solution is $-\dfrac{1}{2}$.

47. $3 - |5x + 3| = 3$

$-|5x + 3| = 0$

$|5x + 3| = 0$

$5x + 3 = 0$

$5x = -3$

$x = -\dfrac{3}{5}$

The solution is $-\dfrac{3}{5}$.

48. $8 - |1 - 3x| = -1$

$-|1 - 3x| = -9$

$|1 - 3x| = 9$

$1 - 3x = 9$	$1 - 3x = -9$
$-3x = 8$	$-3x = -10$
$x = -\dfrac{8}{3}$	$x = \dfrac{10}{3}$

The solutions are $-\dfrac{8}{3}$ and $\dfrac{10}{3}$.

Objective 2.6.2 Exercises

49. To solve an inequality of the form $|ax + b| < c$, you must rewrite it as a compound inequality. The inequality can be interpreted as "the distance from 0 is between $-c$ and c." This can be written as $-c < ac + b < c$. Solve the equivalent inequality and write the solution set.

50. To solve an inequality of the form $|ax + b| > c$, you must rewrite it as a compound inequality. The inequality can be interpreted as "the distance from 0 is greater than c." Thus $ax + b > c$ or $ax + b < -c$. Solve the equivalent compound inequality and find the union of the solution sets.

51. $|x| > 3$

$x > 3$ or $x < -3$

$\{x | x > 3\}$ $\{x | x < -3\}$

$\{x | x > 3\} \cup \{x | x < -3\} = \{x | x > 3 \text{ or } x < -3\}$

52. $|x| < 5$

$-5 < x < 5$

$\{x | -5 < x < 5\}$

53. $|x + 1| > 2$

$x + 1 > 2$ or $x + 1 < -2$

$\quad x > 1 \qquad\quad x < -3$

$\{x | x > 1\}$

$\{x | x < -3\}$

$\{x | x > 1\} \cup \{x | x < -3\} = \{x | x > 1 \text{ or } x < -3\}$

54. $|x - 2| > 1$

$x - 2 > 1$ or $x - 2 < -1$

$\quad x > 3 \qquad\quad x < 1$

$\{x | x > 3\}$ $\{x | x < 1\}$

$\{x | x > 3\} \cup \{x | x < 1\} = \{x | x > 3 \text{ or } x < 1\}$

55. $|x - 5| \le 1$

$-1 \le x - 5 \le 1$

$-1 + 5 \le x - 5 + 5 \le 1 + 5$

$\quad 4 \le x \le 6$

$\{x | 4 \le x \le 6\}$

56. $|x - 4| \le 3$

$-3 \le x - 4 \le 3$

$-3 + 4 \le x - 4 + 4 \le 3 + 4$

$\quad 1 \le x \le 7$

$\{x | 1 \le x \le 7\}$

57. $|2 - x| \ge 3$

$2 - x \le -3$ or $2 - x \ge 3$

$\quad -x \le -5 \qquad -x \ge 1$

$\quad x \ge 5 \qquad\quad x \le -1$

$\{x | x \ge 5\}$ $\{x | x \le -1\}$

$\{x | x \ge 5\} \cup \{x | x \le -1\} = \{x | x \ge 5 \text{ or } x \le -1\}$

58. $|3 - x| \ge 2$

$3 - x \ge 2$ or $3 - x \le -2$

$\quad -x \ge -1 \qquad -x \le -5$

$\quad x \le 1 \qquad\quad x \ge 5$

$\{x | x \le 1\}$ $\{x | x \ge 5\}$

$\{x | x \le 1\} \cup \{x | x \ge 5\} = \{x | x \le 1 \text{ or } x \ge 5\}$

59. $|2x+1| < 5$

$$-5 < 2x+1 < 5$$
$$-5-1 < 2x+1-1 < 5-1$$
$$-6 < 2x < 4$$
$$\frac{-6}{2} < \frac{2x}{2} < \frac{4}{2}$$
$$-3 < x < 2$$
$$\{x|-3 < x < 2\}$$

60. $|3x-2| < 4$

$$-4 < 3x-2 < 4$$
$$-4+2 < 3x-2+2 < 4+2$$
$$-2 < 3x < 6$$
$$\frac{-2}{3} < \frac{3x}{3} < \frac{6}{3}$$
$$-\frac{2}{3} < x < 2$$
$$\left\{x\left|-\frac{2}{3} < x < 2\right.\right\}$$

61. $|5x+2| > 12$

$$5x+2 > 12 \quad \text{or} \quad 5x+2 < -12$$
$$5x > 10 \qquad\qquad 5x < -14$$
$$x > 2 \qquad\qquad x < -\frac{14}{5}$$
$$\{x|x > 2\} \qquad \left\{x\left|x < -\frac{14}{5}\right.\right\}$$
$$\{x|x > 2\} \cup \left\{x\left|x < -\frac{14}{5}\right.\right\} = \left\{x\left|x > 2 \text{ or } x < -\frac{14}{5}\right.\right\}$$

62. $|7x-1| > 13$

$$7x-1 > 13 \quad \text{or} \quad 7x-1 < -13$$
$$7x > 14 \qquad\qquad 7x < -12$$
$$x > 2 \qquad\qquad x < -\frac{12}{7}$$
$$\{x|x > 2\} \qquad \left\{x\left|x < -\frac{12}{7}\right.\right\}$$
$$\{x|x > 2\} \cup \left\{x\left|x < -\frac{12}{7}\right.\right\} = \left\{x\left|x < -\frac{12}{7} \text{ or } x > 2\right.\right\}$$

63. $|4x-3| \le -2$

The absolute value of a number must be non-negative. The solution set is the empty set, $\varnothing$.

64. $|5x+1| \le -4$

The absolute value of a number must be non-negative. The solution set is the empty set, $\varnothing$.

65. $|2x+7| > -5$

$$2x+7 > -5 \quad \text{or} \quad 2x+7 < 5$$
$$2x > -12 \qquad\qquad 2x < -2$$
$$x > -6 \qquad\qquad x < -1$$
$$\{x|x > -6\} \qquad \{x|x < -1\}$$
$$\{x|x > -6\} \cup \{x|x < -1\} = \{x|x \text{ is a real number}\}$$

66. $|3x-1| > -4$

$$3x-1 > -4 \quad \text{or} \quad 3x-1 < 4$$
$$3x > -3 \qquad\qquad 3x < 5$$
$$x > -1 \qquad\qquad x < \frac{5}{3}$$
$$\{x|x > -1\} \qquad \left\{x\left|x < \frac{5}{3}\right.\right\}$$
$$\{x|x > -1\} \cup \left\{x\left|x < \frac{5}{3}\right.\right\} = \{x|x \text{ is a real number}\}$$

67. $|4-3x| \ge 5$

$$4-3x \ge 5 \quad \text{or} \quad 4-3x \le -5$$
$$-3x \ge 1 \qquad\qquad -3x \le -9$$
$$x \le -\frac{1}{3} \qquad\qquad x \ge 3$$
$$\left\{x\left|x \le -\frac{1}{3}\right.\right\} \qquad \{x|x \ge 3\}$$
$$\left\{x\left|x \le -\frac{1}{3}\right.\right\} \cup \{x|x \ge 3\} = \left\{x\left|x \le -\frac{1}{3} \text{ or } x \ge 3\right.\right\}$$

68. $|7-2x| > 9$

$$7-2x > 9 \quad \text{or} \quad 7-2x < -9$$
$$-2x > 2 \qquad\qquad -2x < -16$$
$$x < -1 \qquad\qquad x > 8$$
$$\{x|x < -1\} \qquad \{x|x > 8\}$$
$$\{x|x < -1\} \cup \{x|x > 8\} = \{x|x < -1 \text{ or } x > 8\}$$

69. $|5-4x| \le 13$

$$-13 \le 5-4x \le 13$$
$$-13-5 \le 5-5-4x \le 13-5$$
$$-18 \le -4x \le 8$$
$$\frac{-18}{-4} \ge \frac{-4x}{-4} \ge \frac{8}{-4}$$
$$\frac{9}{2} \ge x \ge -2$$
$$\left\{x\left|-2 \le x \le \frac{9}{2}\right.\right\}$$

70. $|3-7x| < 17$

$$-17 < 3-7x < 17$$
$$-17-3 < 3-3-7x < 17-3$$
$$-20 < -7x < 14$$
$$\frac{-20}{-7} > \frac{-7x}{-7} > \frac{14}{-7}$$
$$\frac{20}{7} > x > -2$$
$$\left\{x\left|-2 < x < \frac{20}{7}\right.\right\}$$

71. $|6-3x| \le 0$

$$6-3x = 0$$
$$-3x = -6$$
$$x = 2$$
$$\{x|x = 2\}$$

72. $|10 - 5x| \geq 0$

$10 - 5x \geq 0$ or $10 - 5x \leq 0$
$-5x \geq -10$ $-5x \leq -10$
$x \leq 2$ $x \geq 2$
$\{x | x \leq 2\}$ $\{x | x \geq 2\}$
$\{x | x \leq 2\} \cup \{x | x \geq 2\} = \{x | x \text{ is a real number}\}$

73. $|2 - 9x| > 20$

$2 - 9x > 20$ or $2 - 9x < -20$
$-9x > 18$ $-9x < -22$
$x < -2$ $x > \dfrac{22}{9}$
$\{x | x < -2\} \cup \left\{ x \Big| x > \dfrac{22}{9} \right\} = \left\{ x \Big| x < -2 \text{ or } x > \dfrac{22}{9} \right\}$

74. $|5x - 1| < 16$

$-16 < 5x - 1 < 16$
$-16 + 1 < 5x - 1 + 1 < 16 + 1$
$-15 < 5x < 17$
$\dfrac{-15}{5} < \dfrac{5x}{5} < \dfrac{17}{5}$
$-3 < x < \dfrac{17}{5}$
$\left\{ x \Big| -3 < x < \dfrac{17}{5} \right\}$

Objective 2.6.3 Exercises

75. Strategy

Let b represent the diameter of the bushing, T the tolerance, and d the lower and upper limits of the diameter. Solve the absolute value inequality $|d - b| \leq T$ for d.

Solution
$|d - b| \leq T$
$|d - 1.75| \leq 0.008$
$-0.008 \leq d - 1.75 \leq 0.008$
$-0.008 + 1.75 \leq d - 1.75 + 1.75 \leq 0.008 + 1.75$
$1.742 \leq d \leq 1.758$
The lower and upper limits of the diameter of the bushing are 1.742 in. and 1.758 in.

76. Strategy

Let b represent the diameter of the busing, T the tolerance, and d the lower and upper limits of the diameter. Solve the absolute value inequality $|d - b| \leq T$ for d.

Solution
$|d - b| \leq T$
$|d - 3.48| \leq 0.004$
$-0.004 \leq d - 3.48 \leq 0.004$
$-0.004 + 3.48 \leq d - 3.48 + 3.48 \leq 0.004 + 3.48$
$3.476 \leq d \leq 3.484$
The lower and upper limits of the diameter of the bushing are 3.476 in. and 3.484 in.

77. Strategy

Let p represent the prescribed amount of medication, T the tolerance, and m the lower and upper limits of the amount of medication. Solve the absolute value inequality $|m - p| \leq T$ for m.

Solution
$|m - p| \leq T$
$|m - 2.5| \leq 0.2$
$-0.2 \leq m - 2.5 \leq 0.2$
$-0.2 + 2.5 \leq m - 2.5 + 2.5 \leq 0.2 + 2.5$
$2.3 \leq m \leq 2.7$
The lower and upper limits of the amount of medicine to be given to the patient are 2.3 cc and 2.7 cc.

78. Strategy

Let r represent the diameter of the piston rod, T the tolerance, and L the lower and upper limits of the diameter. Solve the absolute value inequality $|L - r| \leq T$ for L.

Solution
$|L - r| \leq T$
$\left| L - 3\dfrac{5}{16} \right| \leq \dfrac{1}{64}$
$-\dfrac{1}{64} \leq L - 3\dfrac{5}{16} \leq \dfrac{1}{64}$
$-\dfrac{1}{64} + 3\dfrac{5}{16} \leq L - 3\dfrac{5}{16} + 3\dfrac{5}{16} \leq \dfrac{1}{64}$
$-\dfrac{1}{64} + 3\dfrac{5}{16} \leq L - 3\dfrac{5}{16} + 3\dfrac{5}{16} \leq \dfrac{1}{64} + 3\dfrac{5}{16}$
$3\dfrac{19}{64} \leq L \leq 3\dfrac{21}{64}$
The lower and upper limits of the length of the piston rod are $3\dfrac{19}{64}$ in. and $3\dfrac{21}{64}$ in.

79. Strategy

Let v represent the prescribed number of volts, T the tolerance, and m the lower and upper limits of the amount of voltage. Solve the absolute value inequality $|m - v| \leq T$ for m.

Solution
$|m - v| \leq T$
$|m - 110| \leq 16.5$
$-16.5 \leq m - 110 \leq 16.5$
$-16.5 + 110 \leq m - 110 + 110 \leq 16.5 + 110$
$93.5 \leq m \leq 126.5$
The lower and upper limits of the amount of voltage to the computer are 93.5 volts and 126.5 volts.

80. Strategy

Let v represent the prescribed number of volts, T the tolerance, and m the upper and lower limits of the amount of voltage. Solve the absolute value inequality $|m - v| \le T$ for m.

Solution

$$|m - v| \le T$$
$$|m - 220| \le 25$$
$$-25 \le m - 220 \le 25$$
$$-25 + 220 \le m - 220 + 220 \le 25 + 220$$
$$195 \le m \le 245$$

The lower and upper limits of the amount of voltage on which the motor will run are 195 volts and 245 volts.

81. Strategy

Let r represent the length of the piston rod, T the tolerance, and L the lower and upper limits of the length. Solve the absolute value inequality $|L - r| \le T$ for L.

Solution

$$|L - r| \le T$$
$$\left|L - 10\frac{3}{8}\right| \le \frac{1}{32}$$
$$-\frac{1}{32} \le L - 10\frac{3}{8} \le \frac{1}{32}$$
$$-\frac{1}{32} + 10\frac{3}{8} \le L - 10\frac{3}{8} + 10\frac{3}{8} \le \frac{1}{32} + 10\frac{3}{8}$$
$$10\frac{11}{32} \le L \le 10\frac{13}{32}$$

The lower and upper limits of the length of the piston rod are $10\frac{11}{32}$ in. and $10\frac{13}{32}$ in.

82. Strategy

Let M represent the amount of ohms, T the tolerance, and r the given amount of the resistor. Find the tolerance and solve $|M - r| \le T$ for M.

Solution

$$T = (.02)(29,000) = 580 \text{ ohms}$$
$$|M - r| \le T$$
$$|M - 29,000| \le 580$$
$$-580 \le M - 29,000 \le 580$$
$$-580 + 29,000 \le M - 29,000 + 29,000 \le 580 + 29,000$$
$$28,420 \le M \le 29,580$$

The lower and upper limits of the resistor are 28,420 ohms and 29,580 ohms.

83. Strategy

Let M represent the amount of ohms, T the tolerance, and r the given amount of the resistor. Find the tolerance and solve $|M - r| \le T$ for M.

Solution

$$T = (0.10)(15,000) = 1500 \text{ ohms}$$
$$|M - r| \le T$$
$$|M - 15,000| \le 1,500$$
$$-1,500 \le M - 15,000 \le 1,500$$
$$-1,500 + 15,000 \le M - 15,000 + 15,000 \le 1,500 + 15,000$$
$$13,500 \le M \le 16,500$$

The lower and upper limits of the resistor are 13,500 ohms and 16,500 ohms.

84. Strategy

Let M represent the amount of ohms, T the tolerance, and r the given amount of the resistor. Find the tolerance and solve $|M - r| \leq T$ for M.

Solution

$T = (.05)(25,000) = 1250$ ohms

$|M - r| \leq T$

$|M - 25,000| \leq 1250$

$-1250 \leq M - 25,000 \leq 1250$

$-1250 + 25,000 \leq M - 25,000 + 25,000 \leq 1,250 + 25,000$

$23,750 \leq M \leq 26,250$

The lower and upper limits of the resistor are 23,750 ohms and 26,250 ohms.

85. Strategy

Let M represent the amount of ohms, T the tolerance, and r the given amount of the resistor. Find the tolerance and solve $|M - r| \leq T$ for M.

Solution

$T = (.05)(56) = 2.8$

$|M - r| \leq T$

$|M - 56| \leq 2.8$

$-2.8 \leq M - 56 \leq 2.8$

$-2.8 + 56 \leq M - 56 + 56 \leq 2.8 + 56$

$53.2 \leq M \leq 58.8$

The lower and upper limits of the resistor are 53.2 ohms and 58.8 ohms.

Applying Concepts 2.6

86. $\left|\dfrac{2x - 5}{3}\right| = 7$

$\dfrac{2x - 5}{3} = 7 \qquad \dfrac{2x - 5}{3} = -7$

$2x - 5 = 21 \qquad 2x - 5 = -21$

$2x = 26 \qquad 2x = -16$

$x = 13 \qquad x = -8$

The solutions are 13 and -8.

87. $\left|\dfrac{3x - 2}{4}\right| + 5 = 6$

$\left|\dfrac{3x - 2}{4}\right| = 1$

$\dfrac{3x - 2}{4} = 1 \qquad \dfrac{3x - 2}{4} = -1$

$3x - 2 = 4 \qquad 3x - 2 = -4$

$3x = 6 \qquad 3x = -2$

$x = 2 \qquad\qquad x = -\dfrac{2}{3}$

The solutions are 2 and $-\dfrac{2}{3}$.

88. $\left|\dfrac{4x - 2}{3}\right| > 6$

$\dfrac{4x - 2}{3} > 6 \quad \text{or} \quad \dfrac{4x - 2}{3} < -6$

$4x - 2 > 18 \qquad 4x - 2 < -18$

$4x > 20 \qquad\quad 4x < -16$

$x > 5 \qquad\qquad x < -4$

$\{x | x > 5\} \qquad \{x | x < -4\}$

$\{x | x > 5\} \cup \{x | x < -4\} = \{x | x > 5 \text{ or } x < -4\}$

89. $\left|\dfrac{2x - 1}{5}\right| \leq 3$

$-3 \leq \dfrac{2x - 1}{5} \leq 3$

$5(-3) \leq 5\left(\dfrac{2x - 1}{5}\right) \leq 5(3)$

$-15 \leq 2x - 1 \leq 15$

$-15 + 1 \leq 2x - 1 + 1 \leq 15 + 1$

$-14 \leq 2x \leq 16$

$\dfrac{-14}{2} \leq \dfrac{2x}{2} \leq \dfrac{16}{2}$

$-7 \leq x \leq 8$

$\{x | -7 \leq x \leq 8\}$

90. $|x+3| = x+3$

Any value of x that makes $x + 3$ negative will result in a false equation because the left side of the equation will be positive and the right side of the equation will be negative. Therefore, the equation is true if $x + 3$ is greater than or equal to zero.

$x + 3 \geq 0$

$x \geq -3$

$\{x | x \geq -3\}$

91. $|y+6| = y+6$

Any value of y that makes $y + 6$ negative will result in a false equation because the left side of the equation will be positive and the right side of the equation will be negative. Therefore, the equation is true if $y + 6$ is greater than or equal to zero.

$y + 6 \geq 0$

$y \geq -6$

$\{y | y \geq -6\}$

92. $|a-4| = 4-a$

Any value of a that makes $4 - a$ negative will result in a false equation because the left side of the equation will be positive and the right side of the equation will be negative. Therefore, the equation is true if $4 - a$ is greater than or equal to zero.

$4 - a \geq 0$

$a \leq 4$

$\{a | a \leq 4\}$

93. $|b-7| = 7-b$

Any value of b that makes $7 - b$ negative will result in a false equation because the left side of the equation will be positive and the right side of the equation will be negative. Therefore, the equation is true if $7 - b$ is greater than or equal to zero.

$7 - b \geq 0$

$b \leq 7$

$\{b | b \leq 7\}$

94. a. $|x+y| = |x|+|y|$

Let $x = 3$ and $y = -5$.

$|3 + (-5)| = |3| + |-5|$

$|-2| = 3 + 5$

$2 = 8$ False

b. True for all real numbers x and y.

c. $|x+y| \geq |x|+|y|$

Let $x = -7$ and $y = 2$.

$|-7 + 2| \geq |-7| + |2|$

$|-5| \geq 7 + 2$

$5 \geq 9$ False

95. $|x-2| < 5$

96. $|x-j| < k$

97. a. $|x+y| \leq |x|+|y|$

b. $|x-y| \geq |x|-|y|$

c. $||x|-|y|| \geq |x|-|y|$

d. $\left|\dfrac{x}{y}\right| = \dfrac{|x|}{|y|}$, $y \neq 0$

e. $|xy| = |x||y|$

Focus on Problem Solving

1. a. The goal is to find the cost of iced tea.

b. The information that Johanna spent one-third of her allowance on a book is unnecessary.

c. Johanna spent $5 for a sandwich and tea, and one-fifth of this cost was for the iced tea. This is sufficient information for us to find the cost of iced tea.

2. a. The goal is to find the speed of the plane.

b. To find the speed, we need to know the time of travel and the distance. We do not know the distance. There is not enough information to find the speed of the plane.

3. a. The goal is to find the amount of cowhide that will cover 10 baseballs.

b. The formula for the surface area of a sphere is needed. It can be found in a reference book.

c. The radius of the baseball is all the dimensions that are needed to find the surface area of the cowhide.

4. a. The number in a baker's dozen can be found in a reference book. Multiply this number by 7 and you will find the number of donuts.

5. a. The goal is to find the size of the smallest prime number.

b. The first line indicates that the smallest prime number is 2. The rest of the information is unnecessary.

Projects and Group Activities

Venn Diagrams

1. a. 9

b. 11

c. 2

2.

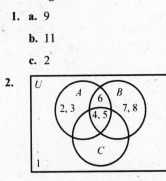

3.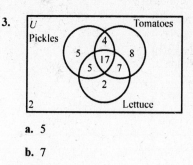

   a. 5

   b. 7

   c. 2

Electricity

1. **Strategy**
   To find the number of volts, solve the equation $V = IR$ for V using $I = 20$ amperes and $R = 100$ ohms.

   Solution
   $V = IR$
   $\quad = 20(100)$
   $\quad = 2000$
   There are 2000 volts.

2. **Strategy**
   To find the number of volts, solve the equation $V = IR$ for V using $I = 4.5$ amperes and $R = 150$ ohms.

   Solution
   $V = IR$
   $\quad = 4.5(150)$
   $\quad = 675$
   There are 675 volts.

3. **Strategy**
   To find the number of amperes, solve the equation $V = IR$ for I using $V = 100$ volts and $R = 10$ ohms.

   Solution
   $V = IR$
   $100 = I10$
   $10 = I$
   There are 10 amperes.

4. **Strategy**
   To find the amount of current, solve the equation $V = IR$ for I using $V = 115$ volts and $R = 70$ ohms.

   Solution
   $V = IR$
   $115 = I70$
   $1.64 \approx I$
   The current is approximately 1.64 amperes.

5. **Strategy**
   To find the resistance, solve the equation $V = IR$ for R using $V = 0.48$ volt and $I = 0.12$ amperes.

   Solution
   $V = IR$
   $0.48 = 0.12R$
   $4 = R$
   The resistance is 4 ohms.

6. **Strategy**
   To find the resistance, solve the equation $V = IR$ for R using $V = 1.5$ volts and $I = 120$ amperes.

   Solution
   $V = IR$
   $1.5 = 120R$
   $0.0125 = R$
   The resistance is 0.0125 ohms.

7. **Strategy**
   To find the power, solve the equation $P = VI$ for P using $V = 12$ volts and $I = 10$ amperes.

   Solution
   $P = VI$
   $\quad = 12(10)$
   $\quad = 120$
   The power is 120 watts.

8. **Strategy**
   To find the power, solve the equation $P = VI$ for P using $V = 115$ volts and $I = 2.175$ amperes.

   Solution
   $P = VI$
   $\quad = 115(2.175)$
   $\quad = 250.125$
   The power is 250.125 watts.

9. **Strategy**
   To find the current, solve the equation $P = VI$ for I using $P = 850$ watts and $V = 110$ volts.

   Solution
   $P = VI$
   $850 = 110I$
   $7.73 \approx I$
   The current is 7.73 amperes.

84   **Chapter 2:** *First-Degree Equations and Inequalities*

10. Strategy
To find the current, solve the equation
$P = VI$ for I using $P = 4500$ watts and $V = 240$ volts.

Solution
$P = VI$
$4500 = 240I$
$18.75 = I$
The current is 18.75 amperes.

11. Strategy
To find the voltage, solve the equation
$P = VI$ for V using $P = 0.5$ watt and $I = 0.08$ amperes.

Solution
$P = VI$
$0.5 = V(0.08)$
$6.25 = V$
A 6.25 volt battery is needed.

12. Strategy
To find the voltage, solve the equation
$P = VI$ for V using $P = 180$ watts and $I = 15$ amperes.

Solution
$P = VI$
$180 = V(15)$
$12 = V$
The voltage is 12 volts.

13. Strategy
To find the power, first solve the equation $V = IR$ for I using $V = 160$ volts and $R = 80$ ohms and then solve the equation $P = VI$ for P using $V = 160$ volts and I.

Solution
$V = IR$
$160 = I(80)$
$2 = I$
$P = VI$
$\quad = 160(2)$
$\quad = 320$
The power is 320 watts.

14. Strategy
To find the power, first solve the equation $V = IR$ for I using $V = 105$ volts and $R = 70$ ohms and then solve the equation $P = VI$ for P using $V = 105$ volts and I.

Solution
$V = IR$
$105 = I(70)$
$1.5 = I$
$P = VI$
$\quad = 105(1.5)$
$\quad = 157.5$
The power is 157.5 watts.

Chapter Review Exercises

1. $x + 4 = -5$
$x + 4 - 4 = -5 - 4$
$x = -9$
The solution is –9.

2. $\frac{2}{3} = x + \frac{3}{4}$
$\frac{2}{3} - \frac{3}{4} = x + \frac{3}{4} - \frac{3}{4}$
$\frac{8}{12} - \frac{9}{12} = x$
$-\frac{1}{12} = x$
The solution is $-\frac{1}{12}$.

3. $-3x = -21$
$\frac{-3x}{-3} = \frac{-21}{-3}$
$x = 7$
The solution is 7.

4. $\frac{2}{3}x = \frac{4}{9}$
$\frac{3}{2}\left(\frac{2}{3}x\right) = \frac{3}{2}\left(\frac{4}{9}\right)$
$x = \frac{2}{3}$
The solution is $\frac{2}{3}$.

5. $3y - 5 = 3 - 2y$
$3y + 2y - 5 = 3 - 2y + 2y$
$5y - 5 = 3$
$5y - 5 + 5 = 3 + 5$
$5y = 8$
$\frac{5y}{5} = \frac{8}{5}$
$y = \frac{8}{5}$
The solution is $\frac{8}{5}$.

6. $3x - 3 + 2x = 7x - 15$
$5x - 3 = 7x - 15$
$5x - 3 - 7x = 7x - 15 - 7x$
$-2x - 3 = -15$
$-2x - 3 + 3 = -15 + 3$
$-2x = -12$
$\frac{-2x}{-2} = \frac{-12}{-2}$
$x = 6$
The solution is 6.

7.
$$2(x-3) = 5(4-3x)$$
$$2x-6 = 20-15x$$
$$2x-6+15x = 20-15x+15x$$
$$17x-6 = 20$$
$$17x-6+6 = 20+6$$
$$17x = 26$$
$$\frac{17x}{17} = \frac{26}{17}$$
$$x = \frac{26}{17}$$

The solution is $\frac{26}{17}$.

8.
$$2x-(3-2x) = 4-3(4-2x)$$
$$2x-3+2x = 4-12+6x$$
$$4x-3 = -8+6x$$
$$4x-3-6x = -8+6x-6x$$
$$-2x-3 = -8$$
$$-2x-3+3 = -8+3$$
$$-2x = -5$$
$$\frac{-2x}{-2} = \frac{-5}{-2}$$
$$x = \frac{5}{2}$$

The solution is $\frac{5}{2}$.

9.
$$\frac{1}{2}x-\frac{5}{8} = \frac{3}{4}x+\frac{3}{2}$$
$$8\left(\frac{1}{2}x-\frac{5}{8}\right) = 8\left(\frac{3}{4}x+\frac{3}{2}\right)$$
$$8\left(\frac{1}{2}x\right)-8\left(\frac{5}{8}\right) = 8\left(\frac{3}{4}x\right)+8\left(\frac{3}{2}\right)$$
$$4x-5 = 6x+12$$
$$4x-5-6x = 6x+12-6x$$
$$-2x-5 = 12$$
$$-2x-5+5 = 12+5$$
$$-2x = 17$$
$$\frac{-2x}{-2} = \frac{17}{-2}$$
$$x = -\frac{17}{2}$$

The solution is $-\frac{17}{2}$.

10.
$$\frac{2x-3}{3}+2 = \frac{2-3x}{5}$$
$$15\left(\frac{2x-3}{3}+2\right) = 15\left(\frac{2-3x}{5}\right)$$
$$\frac{15(2x-3)}{3}+15(2) = \frac{15(2-3x)}{5}$$
$$5(2x-3)+30 = 3(2-3x)$$
$$10x-15+30 = 6-9x$$
$$10x+15 = 6-9x$$
$$10x+15+9x = 6-9x+9x$$
$$19x+15 = 6$$
$$19x+15-15 = 6-15$$
$$19x = -9$$
$$\frac{19x}{19} = \frac{-9}{19}$$
$$x = -\frac{9}{19}$$

The solution is $-\frac{9}{19}$.

11.
$$3x-7 > -2$$
$$3x > 5$$
$$\frac{3x}{3} > \frac{5}{3}$$
$$x > \frac{5}{3}$$

The solution is $\left(\frac{5}{3}, \infty\right)$.

12.
$$2x-9 < 8x+15$$
$$2x-8x-9 < 8x-8x+15$$
$$-6x-9 < 15$$
$$-6x-9+9 < 15+9$$
$$-6x < 24$$
$$\frac{-6x}{-6} > \frac{24}{-6}$$
$$x > -4$$

The solution is $(-4, \infty)$.

13.
$$\frac{2}{3}x-\frac{5}{8} \geq \frac{5}{4}x+3$$
$$24\left(\frac{2}{3}x-\frac{5}{8}\right) \geq 24\left(\frac{5}{4}x+3\right)$$
$$16x-15 \geq 30x+72$$
$$16x-30x-15 \geq 30x-30x+72$$
$$-14x-15 \geq 72$$
$$-14x-15+15 \geq 72+15$$
$$-14x \geq 87$$
$$\frac{-14x}{-14} \leq \frac{87}{-14}$$
$$x \leq -\frac{87}{14}$$

The solution is $\left\{x \mid x \leq -\frac{87}{14}\right\}$.

14.
$$2 - 3(x - 4) \le 4x - 2(1 - 3x)$$
$$2 - 3x + 12 \le 4x - 2 + 6x$$
$$-3x + 14 \le 10x - 2$$
$$-3x - 10x + 14 \le 10x - 10x - 2$$
$$-13x + 14 \le -2$$
$$-13x + 14 - 14 \le -2 - 14$$
$$-13x \le -16$$
$$\frac{-13x}{-13} \ge \frac{-16}{-13}$$
$$x \ge \frac{16}{13}$$

The solution is $\left\{ x \middle| x \ge \frac{16}{13} \right\}$.

15.
$$-5 < 4x - 1 < 7$$
$$-5 + 1 < 4x - 1 + 1 < 7 + 1$$
$$-4 < 4x < 8$$
$$\frac{-4}{4} < \frac{4x}{4} < \frac{8}{4}$$
$$-1 < x < 2$$

The solution is $(-1, 2)$.

16.
$$5x - 2 > 8 \quad \text{or} \quad 3x + 2 < -4$$
$$5x > 10 \qquad\qquad 3x < -6$$
$$x > 2 \qquad\qquad\quad x < -2$$
$$\{x | x > 2\} \qquad \{x | x < -2\}$$
$$\{x | x > 2\} \cup \{x | x < -2\} = \{x | x > 2 \text{ or } x < -2\}$$

The solution is $(-\infty, -2) \cup (2, \infty)$.

17.
$$3x < 4 \quad \text{and} \quad x + 2 > -1$$
$$x < \frac{4}{3} \qquad\qquad x > -3$$
$$\left\{ x \middle| x < \frac{4}{3} \right\} \qquad \{x | x > -3\}$$
$$\left\{ x \middle| x < \frac{4}{3} \right\} \cap \{x | x > -3\} = \left\{ x \middle| -3 < x < \frac{4}{3} \right\}$$

18.
$$3x - 2 > -4 \quad \text{or} \quad 7x - 5 < 3x + 3$$
$$3x > -2 \qquad\qquad 4x - 5 < 3$$
$$\frac{3x}{3} > \frac{-2}{3} \qquad\qquad 4x < 8$$
$$x > -\frac{2}{3} \qquad\qquad \frac{4x}{4} < \frac{8}{4}$$
$$\qquad\qquad\qquad\qquad x < 2$$
$$\left\{ x \middle| x > -\frac{2}{3} \right\} \qquad \{x | x < 2\}$$
$$\left\{ x \middle| x > -\frac{2}{3} \right\} \cup \{x | x < 2\} = \{x | x \text{ is any real number}\}$$

19.
$$|2x - 3| = 8$$
$$2x - 3 = 8 \quad \text{or} \quad 2x - 3 = -8$$
$$2x = 11 \qquad\qquad 2x = -5$$
$$x = \frac{11}{2} \qquad\qquad x = -\frac{5}{2}$$

The solutions are $\frac{11}{2}$ and $-\frac{5}{2}$.

20.
$$|5x + 8| = 0$$
$$5x + 8 = 0$$
$$5x = -8$$
$$x = -\frac{8}{5}$$

The solution is $-\frac{8}{5}$.

21.
$$6 + |3x - 3| = 2$$
$$|3x - 3| = -4$$

There is no solution to this equation because the absolute value of a number must be non-negative.

22.
$$|2x - 5| \le 3$$
$$-3 \le 2x - 5 < 3$$
$$-3 + 5 \le 2x - 5 + 5 \le 3 + 5$$
$$2 \le 2x \le 8$$
$$\frac{2}{2} \le \frac{2x}{2} \le \frac{8}{2}$$
$$1 \le x \le 4$$

The solution is $\{x | 1 \le x \le 4\}$.

23.
$$|4x - 5| \ge 3$$
$$4x - 5 \ge 3 \quad \text{or} \quad 4x - 5 \le -3$$
$$4x \ge 8 \qquad\qquad 4x \le 2$$
$$x \ge 2 \qquad\qquad x \le \frac{1}{2}$$
$$\{x | x \ge 2\} \qquad \left\{ x \middle| x < \frac{1}{2} \right\}$$
$$\{x | x \ge 2\} \cup \left\{ x \middle| x \le \frac{1}{2} \right\} = \left\{ x \middle| x \le \frac{1}{2} \text{ or } x \ge 2 \right\}$$

24.
$$|5x - 4| < -2$$

There is no solution to this equation because the absolute value of a number must be non-negative.

25. Strategy

Let b represent the diameter of the bushing, T the tolerance, and d the lower and upper limits of the diameter. Solve the absolute value inequality $|d - b| \le T$ for d.

Solution
$$|d - b| \le T$$
$$|d - 2.75| \le 0.003$$
$$-0.003 \le d - 2.75 \le 0.003$$
$$-0.003 + 2.75 \le d - 2.75 + 2.75 \le 0.003 + 2.75$$
$$2.747 \le d \le 2.753$$

The lower and upper limits of the diameter of the bushing are 2.747 in. and 2.753 in.

26. Strategy

Let p represent the prescribed amount of medication, T the tolerance, and m the lower and upper limits of the amount of medication. Solve the absolute value inequality $|m - p| \le T$ for m.

Solution

$|m - p| \le T$

$|m - 2| \le 0.25$

$-0.25 \le m - 2 \le 0.25$

$-0.25 + 2 \le m - 2 + 2 \le 0.25 + 2$

$1.75 \le m \le 2.25$

The lower and upper limits of the amount of medicine to be given to the patient are 1.75 cc and 2.25 cc.

27. Strategy

The smaller integer: n

The larger integer: $20 - n$

Five times the smaller integer is two more than twice the larger integer.

$5n = 2 + 2(20 - n)$

Solution

$5n = 2 + 2(20 - n)$

$5n = 2 + 40 - 2n$

$5n = 42 - 2n$

$7n = 42$

$n = 6$

$20 - n = 20 - 6 = 14$

The integers are 6 and 14.

28. Strategy

First consecutive integer: x

Second consecutive integer: $x + 1$

Third consecutive integer: $x + 2$

Five times the middle integer is twice the sum of the other two integers.

$5(x + 1) = 2[x + (x + 2)]$

Solution

$5(x + 1) = 2[x + (x + 2)]$

$5x + 5 = 2(2x + 2)$

$5x + 5 = 4x + 4$

$x + 5 = 4$

$x = -1$

$x + 1 = -1 + 1 = 0$

$x + 2 = -1 + 2 = 1$

The integers are –1, 0, and 1.

29. Strategy

Number of nickels: x

Number of dimes: $x + 3$

Number of quarters: $30 - (2x + 3) = 27 - 2x$

Coin	Number	Value	Total Value
Nickel	x	5	$5x$
Dime	$x + 3$	10	$10(x + 3)$
Quarter	$27 - 2x$	25	$25(27 - 2x)$

The sum of the total values of each type of coin equals the total value of all the coins (355 cents).

$5x + 10(x + 3) + 25(27 - 2x) = 355$

Solution

$5x + 10(x + 3) + 25(27 - 2x) = 355$

$5x + 10x + 30 + 675 - 50x = 355$

$-35x + 705 = 355$

$-35x = -350$

$x = 10$

$27 - 2x = 27 - 2(10) = 27 - 20 = 7$

There are 7 quarters in the collection.

30. Strategy

Cost per ounce of the mixture: x

	Amount	Cost	Value
Pure silver	40	\$8.00	8(40)
Alloy	200	\$3.50	3.50(200)
Mixture	240	x	$240x$

The sum of the values before mixing equals the value after mixing.

$8(40) + 3.50(200) = 240x$

Solution

$8(40) + 3.50(200) = 240x$

$320 + 700 = 240x$

$1020 = 240x$

$4.25 = x$

The mixture costs \$4.25 per ounce.

31. Strategy

Gallons of apple juice: x

	Amount	Cost	Value
Apple juice	x	3.20	$3.20x$
Cranberry juice	40	5.50	40(5.50)
Mixture	$40 + x$	4.20	4.20(40 + x)

The sum of the values before mixing equals the value after mixing.

$3.20x + 40(5.50) = 4.20(40 + x)$

Solution

$$3.20x + 40(5.50) = 4.20(40 + x)$$
$$3.20x + 220 = 168 + 4.20x$$
$$-x = -52$$
$$x = 52$$

The mixture must contain 52 gal of apple juice.

32. Strategy

Rate of the first plane: r

Rate of the second plane: $r + 80$

	Rate	Time	Distance
1st plane	r	1.75	$1.75r$
2nd plane	$r + 80$	1.75	$1.75(r + 80)$

The total distance traveled by the two planes is 1680 mi.

$1.75r + 1.75(r + 80) = 1680$

Solution

$$1.75r + 1.75(r + 80) = 1680$$
$$1.75r + 1.75r + 140 = 1680$$
$$3.5r + 140 = 1680$$
$$3.5r = 1540$$
$$r = 440$$
$$r + 80 = 440 + 80 = 520$$

The speed of the first plane is 440 mph. The speed of the second plane is 520 mph.

33. Strategy

Amount invested at 10.5%: x

Amount invested at 6.4%: $8000 - x$

	Principal	Rate	Interest
Amount at 10.5%	x	0.105	$0.105x$
Amount at 6.4%	$8000 - x$	0.064	$0.064(8000 - x)$

The sum of the interest earned by the two investments equals the total annual interest earned ($635).

$0.105x + 0.064(8000 - x) = 635$

Solution

$$0.105x + 0.064(8000 - x) = 635$$
$$0.105x + 512 - 0.064x = 635$$
$$0.041x + 512 = 635$$
$$0.041x = 123$$
$$x = 3000$$
$$8000 - x = 8000 - 3000 = 5000$$

The amount invested at 10.5% was $3000.

The amount invested at 6.4% was $5000.

34. Strategy

Pounds of 30% tin: x

Pounds of 70% tin: $500 - x$

	Amount	Percent	Quantity
30%	x	0.30	$0.30x$
70%	$500 - x$	0.70	$0.70(500 - x)$
40%	500	0.40	0.40(500)

The sum of the quantities before mixing is equal to the quantity after mixing.

$0.30x + 0.70(500 - x) = 0.40(500)$

Solution

$$0.30x + 0.70(500 - x) = 0.40(500)$$
$$0.30x + 350 - 0.70x = 200$$
$$-0.40x + 350 = 200$$
$$-0.40x = -150$$
$$x = 375$$
$$500 - x = 500 - 375 = 125$$

375 lb of 30% tin and 125 lb of 70% tin were used.

35. Strategy

To find the minimum amount of sales, write and solve an inequality using N to represent the amount of sales.

Solution

$$800 + 0.04N \geq 3000$$
$$0.04N \geq 2200$$
$$N \geq 55,000$$

The executive's amount of sales must be $55,000 or more.

36. Strategy
To find the range of scores, write and solve an inequality using N to represent the score on the last test.

Solution
$$80 \le \frac{92+66+72+88+N}{5} \le 90$$
$$80 \le \frac{318+N}{5} \le 90$$
$$5 \cdot 80 \le 5 \cdot \frac{318+N}{5} \le 5 \cdot 90$$
$$400 \le 318+N \le 450$$
$$400-318 \le 318+N-318 \le 450-318$$
$$82 \le N \le 132$$
Since 100 is the maximum score, the range of scores to receive a B grade is $82 \le N \le 100$.

Chapter Test

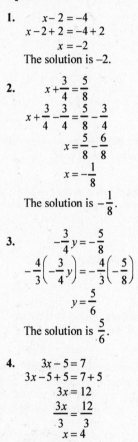

1. $x-2=-4$
$x-2+2=-4+2$
$x=-2$
The solution is –2.

2. $x+\frac{3}{4}=\frac{5}{8}$
$x+\frac{3}{4}-\frac{3}{4}=\frac{5}{8}-\frac{3}{4}$
$x=\frac{5}{8}-\frac{6}{8}$
$x=-\frac{1}{8}$
The solution is $-\frac{1}{8}$.

3. $-\frac{3}{4}y=-\frac{5}{8}$
$-\frac{4}{3}\left(-\frac{3}{4}y\right)=-\frac{4}{3}\left(-\frac{5}{8}\right)$
$y=\frac{5}{6}$
The solution is $\frac{5}{6}$.

4. $3x-5=7$
$3x-5+5=7+5$
$3x=12$
$\frac{3x}{3}=\frac{12}{3}$
$x=4$
The solution is 4.

5. $\frac{3}{4}y-2=6$
$\frac{3}{4}y-2+2=6+2$
$\frac{3}{4}y=8$
$\frac{4}{3}\left(\frac{3}{4}y\right)=\frac{4}{3}(8)$
$y=\frac{32}{3}$
The solution is $\frac{32}{3}$.

6. $2x-3-5x=8+2x-10$
$-3x-3=-2+2x$
$-3x-3+3x=-2+2x+3x$
$-3=-2+5x$
$-3+2=-2+5x+2$
$-1=5x$
$\frac{-1}{5}=\frac{5x}{5}$
$-\frac{1}{5}=x$
$x=-\frac{1}{5}$
The solution is $-\frac{1}{5}$.

7. $2[x-(2-3x)-4]=x-5$
$2[x-2+3x-4]=x-5$
$2[4x-6]=x-5$
$8x-12=x-5$
$8x-x-12=x-x-5$
$7x-12=-5$
$7x-12+12=-5+12$
$7x=7$
$\frac{7x}{7}=\frac{7}{7}$
$x=1$
The solution is 1.

8. $\frac{2}{3}x-\frac{5}{6}x=4$
$\frac{4}{6}x-\frac{5}{6}x=4$
$-\frac{1}{6}x=4$
$-6\left(-\frac{1}{6}x\right)=-6(4)$
$x=-24$
The solution is –24.

9.
$$\frac{2x+1}{3} - \frac{3x+4}{6} = \frac{5x-9}{9}$$
$$18\left(\frac{2x+1}{3} - \frac{3x+4}{6}\right) = 18\left(\frac{5x-9}{9}\right)$$
$$18\left(\frac{2x+1}{3}\right) - 18\left(\frac{3x+4}{6}\right) = 18\left(\frac{5x-9}{9}\right)$$
$$6(2x+1) - 3(3x+4) = 2(5x-9)$$
$$12x+6 - 9x - 12 = 10x - 18$$
$$3x - 6 = 10x - 18$$
$$3x - 6 - 10x = 10x - 18 - 10x$$
$$-7x - 6 = -18$$
$$-7x - 6 + 6 = -18 + 6$$
$$-7x = -12$$
$$\frac{-7x}{-7} = \frac{-12}{-7}$$
$$x = \frac{12}{7}$$

The solution is $\frac{12}{7}$.

10.
$$2x - 5 \geq 5x + 4$$
$$-3x - 5 \geq 4$$
$$-3x \geq 9$$
$$\frac{-3x}{-3} \leq \frac{9}{-3}$$
$$x \leq -3$$
$$(-\infty, -3]$$

11.
$$4 - 3(x+2) < 2(2x+3) - 1$$
$$4 - 3x - 6 < 4x + 6 - 1$$
$$-2 - 3x < 4x + 5$$
$$-7x < 7$$
$$\frac{-7x}{-7} > \frac{7}{-7}$$
$$x > -1$$
$$(-1, \infty)$$

12.
$$3x - 2 > 4 \quad \text{or} \quad 4 - 5x < 14$$
$$3x > 6 \qquad\qquad -5x < 10$$
$$x > 2 \qquad\qquad \frac{-5x}{-5} > \frac{10}{-5}$$
$$x > -2$$
$$\{x | x > 2\} \quad \{x | x > -2\}$$
$$\{x | x > 2\} \cup \{x | x > -2\} = \{x | x > -2\}$$

13.
$$4 - 3x \geq 7 \quad \text{and} \quad 2x + 3 \geq 7$$
$$-3x \geq 3 \qquad\qquad 2x \geq 4$$
$$\frac{-3x}{-3} \leq \frac{3}{-3} \qquad\qquad \frac{2x}{2} \geq \frac{4}{2}$$
$$x \leq -1 \qquad\qquad x \geq 2$$
$$\{x | x \leq -1\} \cap \{x | x \geq 2\} = \varnothing$$

14.
$$|3 - 5x| = 12$$
$$3 - 5x = 12 \qquad 3 - 5x = -12$$
$$-5x = 9 \qquad\quad -5x = -15$$
$$x = -\frac{9}{5} \qquad\quad x = 3$$

The solutions are $-\frac{9}{5}$ and 3.

15.
$$2 - |2x - 5| = -7$$
$$-|2x - 5| = -9$$
$$|2x - 5| = 9$$
$$2x - 5 = 9 \qquad 2x - 5 = -9$$
$$2x = 14 \qquad\quad 2x = -4$$
$$x = 7 \qquad\qquad x = -2$$
The solutions are 7 and –2.

16.
$$|3x - 1| \leq 2$$
$$-2 \leq 3x - 1 \leq 2$$
$$-2 + 1 \leq 3x - 1 + 1 \leq 2 + 1$$
$$-1 \leq 3x \leq 3$$
$$\frac{-1}{3} \leq \frac{3x}{3} \leq \frac{3}{3}$$
$$-\frac{1}{3} \leq x \leq 1$$
$$\left\{x \middle| -\frac{1}{3} \leq x \leq 1\right\}$$

17.
$$|2x - 1| > 3$$
$$2x - 1 > 3 \quad \text{or} \quad 2x - 1 < -3$$
$$2x > 4 \qquad\qquad 2x < -2$$
$$x > 2 \qquad\qquad x < -1$$
$$\{x | x > 2\} \cup \{x | x < -1\} = \{x | x > 2 \text{ or } x < -1\}$$

18.
$$4 + |2x - 3| = 1$$
$$|2x - 3| = -3$$
There is no solution because the absolute value of a number is always non-negative.

19. **Strategy**
To find the number of miles, write and solve an inequality using N to represent the number of miles.

Solution
cost of car A < cost of car B
$$12 + 0.10N < 24$$
$$0.10N < 12$$
$$N < 120$$
It costs less to rent from Agency A if the car is driven less than 120 mi.

20. **Strategy**
Let p represent the prescribed amount of medication, T the tolerance, and m the lower and upper limits of the given amount of medication. Solve the absolute value inequality $|m - p| \leq T$ form m.

Solution
$$|m - p| \leq T$$
$$|m - 3| \leq 0.1$$
$$-0.1 \leq m - 3 \leq 0.1$$
$$-0.1 + 3 \leq m - 3 + 3 \leq 0.1 + 3$$
$$2.9 \leq m \leq 3.1$$
The lower and upper limits of the amount of medication to be given to the patient are 2.9 cc and 3.1 cc.

21. Strategy

Number of 15¢ stamps: x

Number of 11¢ stamps: $2x$

Number of 21¢ stamps: $30 - 3x$

Stamp	Number	Value	Total Value
15¢	x	15	$15x$
11¢	$2x$	11	$11(2x)$
21¢	$30 - 3x$	21	$21(30 - 3x)$

The sum of the total values of each type of stamp equals the total value of all the stamps (440 cents).

$15x + 11(2x) + 21(30 - 3x) = 422$

Solution

$$\begin{aligned}
15x + 11(2x) + 21(30 - 3x) &= 422 \\
15x + 22x + 630 - 63x &= 422 \\
-26x + 630 &= 422 \\
-26x &= -208 \\
x &= 8
\end{aligned}$$

$30 - 3x = 30 - 3(8) = 30 - 24 = 6$

There are six 21¢ stamps.

22. Strategy

Price of hamburger mixture: x

	Amount	Cost	Value
$2.60 hamburger	100	2.60	$2.60(100)$
$4.20 hamburger	60	4.20	$4.20(60)$
Mixture	160	x	$160x$

The sum of the values before mixing equals the value after mixing.

$2.60(100) + 4.20(60) = 160x$

Solution

$$\begin{aligned}
2.60(100) + 4.20(60) &= 160x \\
260 + 252 &= 160x \\
512 &= 160x \\
3.20 &= x
\end{aligned}$$

The price of the hamburger mixture is $2.20/lb.

23. Strategy
Time jogger runs a distance: t
Time jogger returns same distance: $1\frac{45}{60} - t$

	Rate	Time	Distance
Jogger runs a distance	8	t	$8t$
Jogger returns same distance	6	$\frac{7}{4} - t$	$6\left(\frac{7}{4} - t\right)$

The jogger runs a distance and returns the same distance.

$$8t = 6\left(\frac{7}{4} - t\right)$$

Solution

$$8t = 6\left(\frac{7}{4} - t\right)$$

$$8t = \frac{21}{2} - 6t$$

$$14t = \frac{21}{2}$$

$$\frac{1}{14}(14t) = \frac{1}{14}\left(\frac{21}{2}\right)$$

$$t = \frac{3}{4}$$

The jogger ran for $\frac{3}{4}$ hour.

$$8t = 8 \cdot \frac{3}{4} = 6$$

The jogger ran a distance of 6 mi one way. The jogger ran a total distance of 12 mi.

24. Strategy
Amount invested at 7.8%: x
Amount invested at 9%: $12,000 - x$

	Principal	Rate	Interest
Amount invested at 7.8%	x	0.078	$0.078x$
Amount invested at 9%	$12,000 - x$	0.09	$0.09(12,000 - x)$

The sum of the interest earned by the two investments equals the total annual interest earned ($1020).
$0.078x + 0.09(12,000 - x) = 1020$

Solution
$$0.078x + 0.09(12,000 - x) = 1020$$
$$0.078x + 1080 - 0.09x = 1020$$
$$-0.012x = -60$$
$$x = 5000$$
$12,000 - x = 12,000 - 50000 = 7000$
The amount invested at 7.8% was $5000.
The amount invested at 9% was $7000.

25. Strategy
Ounces of pure water: x

	Amount	Percent	Quantity
Pure water	x	0	0
8% salt	60	0.08	0.08(60)
3% salt	60 + x	0.03	0.03(60 + x)

The sum of the quantities before mixing is equal to the quantity after mixing.
$0 + 0.08(60) = 0.03(60 + x)$

Solution
$$0 + 0.08(60) = 0.03(60 + x)$$
$$4.8 = 1.8 + 0.03x$$
$$3 = 0.03x$$
$$100 = x$$
There are 100 oz of pure water.

Cumulative Review Exercises

1. $-2^2 \cdot 3^3 = -(2 \cdot 2)(3 \cdot 3 \cdot 3) = -(4)(27) = -108$

2. $4 - (2 - 5)^2 \div 3 + 2 = 4 - (-3)^2 \div 3 + 2$
$$= 4 - 9 \div 3 + 2$$
$$= 4 - 3 + 2$$
$$= 1 + 2$$
$$= 3$$

3. $4 \div \dfrac{\frac{3}{8} - 1}{5} \cdot 2 = 4 \div \dfrac{-\frac{5}{8}}{5} \cdot 2$
$$= 4 \div \left(-\frac{5}{8} \cdot \frac{1}{5}\right) \cdot 2$$
$$= 4 \div \left(-\frac{1}{8}\right) \cdot 2$$
$$= 4 \cdot (-8) \cdot 2$$
$$= -32 \cdot 2$$
$$= -64$$

4. $2a^2 - (b - c)^2 = 2(2)^2 - (3 - (-1))^2$
$$= 2 \cdot 4 - (3 + 1)^2$$
$$= 2 \cdot 4 - 4^2$$
$$= 2 \cdot 4 - 16$$
$$= 8 - 16$$
$$= -8$$

5. The Commutative Property of Addition

6. $A \cap B = \{3, 9\}$

7. $3x - 2[x - 3(2 - 3x) + 5] = 3x - 2[x - 6 + 9x + 5]$
$$= 3x - 2[10x - 1]$$
$$= 3x - 20x + 2$$
$$= -17x + 2$$

8. $5[y - 2(3 - 2y) + 6] = 5[y - 6 + 4y + 6]$
$$= 5[5y]$$
$$= 25y$$

9. $4 - 3x = -2$
$$4 - 3x - 4 = -2 - 4$$
$$-3x = -6$$
$$\frac{-3x}{-3} = \frac{-6}{-3}$$
$$x = 2$$
The solution is 2.

10. $-\dfrac{5}{6}b = -\dfrac{5}{12}$
$$\left(-\frac{6}{5}\right)\left(-\frac{5}{6}\right)b = \left(-\frac{6}{5}\right)\left(-\frac{5}{12}\right)$$
$$b = \frac{1}{2}$$
The solution is $\dfrac{1}{2}$.

11. $2x + 5 = 5x + 2$
$$2x + 5 - 5x = 5x + 2 - 5x$$
$$-3x + 5 = 2$$
$$-3x + 5 - 5 = 2 - 5$$
$$-3x = -3$$
$$\frac{-3x}{-3} = \frac{-3}{-3}$$
$$x = 1$$
The solution is 1.

12. $\dfrac{5}{12}x - 3 = 7$
$$\frac{5}{12}x - 3 + 3 = 7 + 3$$
$$\frac{5}{12}x = 10$$
$$\left(\frac{12}{5}\right)\left(\frac{5}{12}\right)x = \left(\frac{12}{5}\right)10$$
$$x = 24$$
The solution is 24.

13. $2[3 - 2(3 - 2x)] = 2(3 + x)$
$$2[3 - 6 + 4x] = 6 + 2x$$
$$2[-3 + 4x] = 6 + 2x$$
$$-6 + 8x = 6 + 2x$$
$$-6 + 8x - 2x = 6 + 2x - 2x$$
$$-6 + 6x = 6$$
$$-6 + 6x + 6 = 6 + 6$$
$$6x = 12$$
$$\frac{6x}{6} = \frac{12}{6}$$
$$x = 2$$
The solution is 2.

14. $3[2x - 3(4 - x)] = 2(1 - 2x)$

$3[2x - 12 + 3x] = 2 - 4x$

$3[5x - 12] = 2 - 4x$

$15x - 36 = 2 - 4x$

$15x - 36 + 4x = 2 - 4x + 4x$

$19x - 36 = 2$

$19x - 36 + 36 = 2 + 36$

$19x = 38$

$\dfrac{19x}{19} = \dfrac{38}{19}$

$x = 2$

The solution is 2.

15.
$$\dfrac{3x - 1}{4} - \dfrac{4x - 1}{12} = \dfrac{3 + 5x}{8}$$

$$24\left(\dfrac{3x - 1}{4} - \dfrac{4x - 1}{12}\right) = 24\left(\dfrac{3 + 5x}{8}\right)$$

$$\dfrac{24(3x - 1)}{4} - \dfrac{24(4x - 1)}{12} = \dfrac{24(3 + 5x)}{8}$$

$6(3x - 1) - 2(4x - 1) = 3(3 + 5x)$

$18x - 6 - 8x + 2 = 9 + 15x$

$10x - 4 = 9 + 15x$

$10x - 4 - 15x = 9 + 15x - 15x$

$-5x - 4 = 9$

$-5x - 4 + 4 = 9 + 4$

$-5x = 13$

$\dfrac{-5x}{-5} = \dfrac{13}{-5}$

$x = -\dfrac{13}{5}$

The solution is $-\dfrac{13}{5}$.

16. $3x - 2 \ge 6x + 7$

$3x \ge 6x + 9$

$-3x \ge 9$

$x \le -3$

$\{x | x \le -3\}$

17. $5 - 2x \ge 6$ and $3x + 2 \ge 5$

     $-2x \ge 1$ $3x \ge 3$

       $x \le -\dfrac{1}{2}$ $x \ge 1$

$\left\{x \middle| x \le -\dfrac{1}{2}\right\}$ $\{x | x \ge 1\}$

$\left\{x \middle| x \le -\dfrac{1}{2}\right\} \cap \{x | x \ge 1\} = \varnothing$

18. $4x - 1 > 5$ or $2 - 3x < 8$

     $4x > 6$ $-3x < 6$

       $x > \dfrac{3}{2}$ $x > -2$

$\left\{x \middle| x > \dfrac{3}{2}\right\}$ $\{x | x > -2\}$

$\left\{x \middle| x > \dfrac{3}{2}\right\} \cup \{x | x > -2\} = \{x | x > -2\}$

19. $|3 - 2x| = 5$

$3 - 2x = 5$ $3 - 2x = -5$

$-2x = 2$ $-2x = -8$

$x = -1$ $x = 4$

The solutions are -1 and 4.

20. $3 - |2x - 3| = -8$

$-|2x - 3| = -11$

$|2x - 3| = 11$

$2x - 3 = 11$ $2x - 3 = -11$

$2x = 14$ $2x = -8$

$x = 7$ $x = -4$

The solutions are 7 and -4.

21. $|3x - 5| \le 4$

$-4 \le 3x - 5 \le 4$

$-4 + 5 \le 3x - 5 + 5 \le 4 + 5$

$1 \le 3x \le 9$

$\dfrac{1}{3} \le \dfrac{3x}{3} \le \dfrac{9}{3}$

$\dfrac{1}{3} \le x \le 3$

$\left\{x \middle| \dfrac{1}{3} \le x \le 3\right\}$

22. $|4x - 3| > 5$

$4x - 3 < -5$ or $4x - 3 > 5$

   $4x < -2$ $4x > 8$

    $x < -\dfrac{1}{2}$ $x > 2$

$\left\{x \middle| x < -\dfrac{1}{2}\right\}$ $\{x | x > 2\}$

$\left\{x \middle| x < -\dfrac{1}{2}\right\} \cup \{x | x > 2\} = \left\{x \middle| x < -\dfrac{1}{2} \text{ or } x > 2\right\}$

23. $\{x | x \ge -2\}$

24.

25. The unknown number: n

three times the number: $3n$

the sum of three times the number and six: $3n + 6$

$(3n + 6) + 3n = 6n + 6$

26. Strategy

The first integer: n

Second consecutive odd integer: $n + 2$

Third consecutive odd integer: $n + 4$

Three times the sum of the first and third

integers is fifteen more than the second integer.

Solution

$3[n + (n + 4)] = (n + 2) + 15$

$3(2n + 4) = n + 17$

$6n + 12 = n + 17$

$5n + 12 = 17$

$5n = 5$

$n = 1$

The first integer is 1.

27. Strategy
Number of 23¢ stamps: n
Number of 19¢ stamps: $2n - 5$

Stamp	Number	Value	Total Value
19¢	$2n - 5$	19	$19(2n - 5)$
23¢	n	23	$23n$

The sum of the total values of each denomination of stamp equals the total value of all the stamps (393 cents).
$19(2n - 5) + 23n = 393$

Solution
$$19(2n - 5) + 23n = 393$$
$$38n - 95 + 23n = 393$$
$$61n - 95 = 393$$
$$61n = 488$$
$$n = 8$$
$$2n - 5 = 2(8) - 5 = 16 - 5 = 11$$
There are eleven 19¢ stamps.

28. Strategy
Number of adult tickets: n
Number of children's tickets: $75 - n$

	Number	Value	Total Value
Adult tickets	n	2.25	$2.25n$
Children's tickets	$75 - n$	0.75	$0.75(75 - n)$

The sum of the total values of each denomination of ticket equals the total value of all the tickets ($128.25).
$2.25n + 0.75(75 - n) = 128.25$

Solution
$$2.25n + 0.75(75 - n) = 128.25$$
$$2.25n + 56.25 - 0.75n = 128.25$$
$$1.5n + 56.25 = 128.25$$
$$1.5n = 72$$
$$n = 48$$
48 adult tickets were sold.

29. Strategy
Slower plane: x
Faster plane: $x + 120$

	Rate	Time	Distance
Slower plane	x	2.5	$2.5x$
Faster plane	$x + 120$	2.5	$2.5(x + 120)$

The two planes travel a total distance of 1400 mi.
$2.5x + 2.5(x + 120) = 1400$

Solution
$$2.5x + 2.5(x + 120) = 1400$$
$$2.5x + 2.5x + 300 = 1400$$
$$5x + 300 = 1400$$
$$5x = 1100$$
$$x = 220$$
$$x + 120 = 220 + 120 = 340$$
The speed of the faster plane is 340 mph.

30. Strategy
Liters of 12% acid solution: x

Solution	Amount	Percent	Quantity
12%	x	0.12	$0.12x$
5%	4	0.05	$0.05(4)$
8%	$x + 4$	0.08	$0.08(x + 4)$

The sum of the quantities before mixing equals the quantity after mixing.
$0.12x + 0.05(4) = 0.08(x + 4)$

Solution
$$0.12x + 0.05(4) = 0.08(x + 4)$$
$$0.12x + 0.2 = 0.08x + 0.32$$
$$0.04x + 0.2 = 0.32$$
$$0.04x = 0.12$$
$$x = 3$$
3 L of 12% acid solution must be in the mixture.

31. Strategy
Amount invested at 9.8%: x
Amount invested at 12.8%: $10,000 - x$

	Principal	Rate	Interest
Amount at 9.8%	x	0.098	$0.098x$
Amount at 12.8%	$10,000 - x$	0.128	$0.128(10,000 - x)$

The sum of the interest earned by the two investments is equal to the total annual interest earned ($1085).
$0.098x + 0.128(10,000 - x) = 1085$

Solution
$$0.098x + 0.128(10,000 - x) = 1085$$
$$0.098x + 1280 - 0.128x = 1085$$
$$-0.03x + 1280 = 1085$$
$$-0.03x = -195$$
$$x = 6500$$
$6500 was invested at 9.8%.

Chapter 3: Linear Functions and Inequalities in Two Variables

Prep Test

1. $-4(x-3)$ [1.3.3]

2. $\sqrt{(-6)^2 + (-8)^2} = \sqrt{36+64}$ [1.2.4]
   $$= \sqrt{100}$$
   $$= 10$$

3. $\dfrac{3-(-5)}{2-6} = \dfrac{8}{-4}$ [1.2.4]
   $$= -2$$

4. $-2(-3)+5 = 6+5$ [1.3.2]
   $$= 11$$

5. $\dfrac{2(5)}{5-1} = \dfrac{10}{4}$ [1.3.2]
   $$= 2.5$$

6. $2(-1)^3 - 3(-1) + 4 = 2(-1) + 3 + 4$ [1.3.2]
   $$= -2 + 7$$
   $$= 5$$

7. $\dfrac{7+(-5)}{2} = \dfrac{2}{2}$ [1.3.2]
   $$= 1$$

8. $3x - 4(0) = 12$ [2.1.1]
   $$3x = 12$$
   $$x = 4$$

Go Figure

Since $\boxed{5} = 4$, then $\boxed{x}$ or $\boxed{y}$ would give a smaller value. Because $\textcircled{5} = 6$, then $\textcircled{x}$ or $\textcircled{y}$ would give a larger value. Finally if $y = x - 1$, then $x > y$. So the largest value is $\textcircled{x}$.

Section 3.1

Concept Review 3.1

1. Always true

2. Always true

3. Never true
   The first number is the x-coordinate and the second number is the y-coordinate.

4. Always true

5. Never true
   The point $(-2, -4)$ is in the third quadrant.

6. Always true

Objective 3.1.1 Exercises

1. A rectangular coordinate system is formed by two number lines called the x-axis and the y-axis. The x-axis is horizontal and the y-axis is vertical. The intersection of these axes is called the origin and is located at the zero point of each axis.

2. The point (a, b) lies in Quadrant I if both a and b are positive, in Quadrant II if a is negative and b is positive, in Quadrant III if both a and b are negative, and in Quadrant IV if a is positive and b is negative.

3.

4.

5. $A(0, 3)$
   $B(1, 1)$
   $C(3, -4)$
   $D(-4, 4)$

6. $A(-3, -3)$
   $B(0, 0)$
   $C(0, -3)$
   $D(2, 4)$

7.

8.

9.

10.

11. $y = x^2$

Ordered pairs:
     (–2, 4)
     (–1, 1)
     (0, 0)
     (1, 1)
     (2, 4)

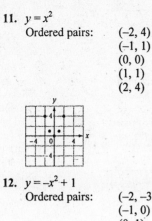

12. $y = -x^2 + 1$

Ordered pairs:
     (–2, –3)
     (–1, 0)
     (0, 1)
     (1, 0)
     (2, –3)

13. $y = |x + 1|$

Ordered pairs:
     (–5, 4)
     (–3, 2)
     (0, 1)
     (3, 4)
     (5, 6)

14. $y = -2|x|$

Ordered pairs:
     (–3, –6)
     (–1, –2)
     (0, 0)
     (1, –2)
     (3, –6)

15. $y = -x^2 + 2$

Ordered pairs:
     (–2, –2)
     (–1, 1)
     (0, 2)
     (1, 1)
     (2, –2)

16. $y = -x^2 + 4$

Ordered pairs:
     (–3, –5)
     (–1, 3)
     (0, 4)
     (1, 3)
     (3, –5)

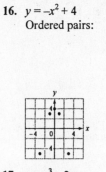

17. $y = x^3 - 2$

Ordered pairs:
     (–1, –3)
     (0, –2)
     (1, –1)
     (2, 6)

18. $y = -x^3 + 1$

Ordered pairs:
     (–1, 2)
     (0, 1)
     (1, 0)
     $\left(\dfrac{3}{2}, -\dfrac{19}{8}\right)$

Objective 3.1.2 Exercises

19. To find the distance between two points in the plane, use the distance formula

$$d = \sqrt{\left(x_2 - x_1\right)^2 + \left(y_2 - y_1\right)^2}$$. Subtract the

x-coordinates and the y-coordinates, square each difference, add the results, and take the square root of the sum.

20. The midpoint of a line segment is the point that is halfway between the two endpoints. To find its x-coordinate, divide the sum of the x-coordinates of the endpoints by 2. To find its y-coordinate, divide the sum of the y-coordinates of the endpoints by 2.

21. $d = \sqrt{(4-3)^2 + (1-5)^2}$
    $= \sqrt{1+16}$
    $d = \sqrt{17}$
    $x_m = \dfrac{3+4}{2} = \dfrac{7}{2}$
    $y_m = \dfrac{1+5}{2} = 3$

The length is $\sqrt{17}$ and the midpoint is $\left(\dfrac{7}{2}, 3\right)$.

22. $d = \sqrt{[5-(-2)]^2 + (-1-3)^2}$

$\quad = \sqrt{7^2 + (-4)^2}$

$d = \sqrt{65}$

$x_m = \dfrac{-2+5}{2} = \dfrac{3}{2}$

$y_m = \dfrac{3+(-1)}{2} = 1$

The length is $\sqrt{65}$ and the midpoint is $\left(\dfrac{3}{2}, 1\right)$.

23. $d = \sqrt{(-2-0)^2 + (4-3)^2}$

$\quad = \sqrt{4+1}$

$d = \sqrt{5}$

$x_m = \dfrac{0+(-2)}{2} = -1$

$y_m = \dfrac{3+4}{2} = \dfrac{7}{2}$

The length is $\sqrt{5}$ and the midpoint is $\left(-1, \dfrac{7}{2}\right)$.

24. $d = \sqrt{(-3-6)^2 + (-2-(-1))^2}$

$\quad = \sqrt{(-9)^2 + (-1)^2}$

$d = \sqrt{82}$

$x_m = \dfrac{6+(-3)}{2} = \dfrac{3}{2}$

$y_m = \dfrac{-1+(-2)}{2} = -\dfrac{3}{2}$

The length is $\sqrt{82}$ and the midpoint is $\left(\dfrac{3}{2}, -\dfrac{3}{2}\right)$.

25. $d = \sqrt{[2-(-3)]^2 + [-4-(-5)]^2}$

$\quad = \sqrt{5^2 + 1^2}$

$d = \sqrt{26}$

$x_m = \dfrac{-3+2}{2} = -\dfrac{1}{2}$

$y_m = \dfrac{-5+(-4)}{2} = -\dfrac{9}{2}$

The length is $\sqrt{26}$ and the midpoint is $\left(-\dfrac{1}{2}, -\dfrac{9}{2}\right)$.

26. $d = \sqrt{[-2-(-7)]^2 + [-1-(-5)]^2}$

$\quad = \sqrt{5^2 + 4^2}$

$d = \sqrt{41}$

$x_m = \dfrac{-7+(-2)}{2} = -\dfrac{9}{2}$

$y_m = \dfrac{-5+(-1)}{2} = -3$

The length is $\sqrt{41}$ and the midpoint is $\left(-\dfrac{9}{2}, -3\right)$.

27. $d = \sqrt{(-1-5)^2 + [5-(-2)]^2}$

$\quad = \sqrt{(-6)^2 + 7^2}$

$d = \sqrt{85}$

$x_m = \dfrac{5+(-1)}{2} = \dfrac{4}{2} = 2$

$y_m = \dfrac{-2+5}{2} = \dfrac{3}{2}$

The length is $\sqrt{85}$ and the midpoint is $\left(2, \dfrac{3}{2}\right)$.

28. $d = \sqrt{(6-3)^2 + [0-(-5)]^2}$

$\quad = \sqrt{3^2 + 5^2}$

$d = \sqrt{34}$

$x_m = \dfrac{6+3}{2} = \dfrac{9}{2}$

$y_m = \dfrac{-5+0}{2} = -\dfrac{5}{2}$

The length is $\sqrt{34}$ and the midpoint is $\left(\dfrac{9}{2}, -\dfrac{5}{2}\right)$.

29. $d = \sqrt{(2-5)^2 + [-5-(-5)]^2}$

$\quad = \sqrt{(-3)^2 + 0^2}$

$d = 3$

$x_m = \dfrac{5+2}{2} = \dfrac{7}{2}$

$y_m = \dfrac{-5+(-5)}{2} = -5$

The length is 3 and the midpoint is $\left(\dfrac{7}{2}, -5\right)$.

Objective 3.1.3 Exercises

30. a. The temperature can be read by looking at the x-axis. Each dotted line represents 10°C. The temperature for 25 g of cerium selenate is 50°C.

b. The number of grams can be read by looking at the y-axis. Each dotted line represents 10 grams. The number of grams of cerium selenate that corresponds to 80°C is 5.

31. a. The number of calories can be read by looking at the y-axis. Each dotted line represents an increment of 250 The number of calories for a hamburger is 275.

b. The number of milligrams can be read by looking at the x-axis. Each dotted line on the x-axis represents an increment of 100. The number of milligrams of sodium in a Big Mac is 1100.

32. a. The percentage can be read by looking at the *x*-axis, where the dotted lines represent increments of 5. Look for the point whose *x*-coordinate is 45. Then follow the horizontal dotted line to read the temperature, which is −20°F.

b. Look for −30°F on the *y*-axis, which is halfway between −20° and −40°. Then follow this dotted line to find a point. The *x*-coordinate of this point is 50. The mixture is 50% ethylene glycol.

33. a. Look for 1997 on the *x*-axis. Then look for the first point that lies above the *x*-axis. This point has an *y*-coordinate of 8 million bushels.

b. Look for 12 on the *y*-axis. Then look for the point(s) that lie above the 12. This point has an *x*-coordinate of 1999.

c. The points on the graph appear to be increasing in value for both *x*- and *y*-coordinates. We would expect the number of bushels in 2001 to be greater than in 2000.

34. Label the Millionaire households on the *x*-axis. The *y*-values go from 3.2 to 4.7, so use increments of 1 on the *y*-axis

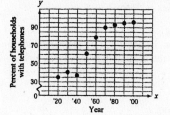

35. Label the years on the *x*-axis. The *y*-values represent percent so the values on the *y*-axis should go from 0 to 100. Since some of the values are between multiples of 10, the graph would be easier to read with increments of 5.

36. Strategy
To find the average rate of change per hour, divide the change in temperatures (58°F −34°F) by the change in hours (2PM − 6AM).

Solution
$$\text{ave} = \frac{58-34}{8} = \frac{24}{8} = 3$$
The average rate of change in temperature was 3°F per hour.

37. a. Strategy
To find the average annual rate of change, divide the change in population in millions (20.9 − 3.0) by the change in years (2000 − 1900).

Solution
$$\text{ave} = \frac{20.9-3.0}{2000-1900}$$
$$= \frac{17.9}{100}$$
$$= 0.179$$
0.179 million = 179,000
The average annual rate of change in population was 179,000 people.

b. Strategy
To find if the average annual rate of change from 1900 to 1950 was greater than or less than the change from 1950 to 2000, subtract the average annual rate of change in population from 1950 to 2000 from the average annual rate of change in population from 1900 to 1950.

Solution
For 1900 to 1950,
$$\text{ave} = \frac{7.7-3.0}{1950-1900}$$
$$= \frac{4.7}{50}$$
$$= 0.094$$
For 1950 to 2000,
$$\text{ave} = \frac{20.9-7.7}{2000-1950}$$
$$= \frac{13.2}{50}$$
$$= 0.264$$
0.094 < 0.264
The average annual rate of change in population from 1900 to 1950 was less than the average annual rate of change in population from 1950 to 2000.

c. Strategy

To find if the average annual rate of change from 1980 to 1990 in Texas was greater than or less than the change from 1980 to 1990 in California, subtract the average annual rate of change in population in Texas from 1980 to 1990 from the average annual rate of change in population in California from 1980 to 1990.

Solution

For Texas from 1980 to 1990,

$$ave = \frac{17 - 14.2}{1990 - 1980}$$
$$= \frac{2.8}{10}$$
$$= 0.28$$

For California from 1980 to 1990,

$$ave = \frac{29.8 - 23.7}{1990 - 1980}$$
$$= \frac{6.1}{10}$$
$$= 0.61$$

$0.28 < 0.61$

The average annual rate of change in population in Texas was less than the average annual rate of change in population in California.

d. Strategy

To find if the which decade had the smallest average annual rate of change, compare the average annual rate of change for each consecutive decade.

Solution

For 1850 to 1860,

$$ave = \frac{0.6 - 0.2}{1860 - 1850}$$
$$= \frac{0.4}{10}$$
$$= 0.04$$

For 1860 to 1870,

$$ave = \frac{0.8 - 0.6}{1870 - 1860}$$
$$= \frac{0.2}{10}$$
$$= 0.02$$

For 1870 to 1880,

$$ave = \frac{1.6 - 0.8}{1880 - 1870}$$
$$= \frac{0.8}{10}$$
$$= 0.08$$

The average annual rate of change for each of the subsequent years is greater than or equal to 0.06.
From 1860 to 1870 was least average annual rate of change at 20,000 people per year.

38. a. Strategy

To find the average annual rate of change, divide the change in deaths in millions (2.35 – 2.15) by the change in years (1999 – 1990).

Solution

$$ave = \frac{2.35 - 2.15}{1999 - 1990}$$
$$\approx 0.022$$

The average annual rate of change was 22,000 deaths per year.

b. Strategy

To find the average annual rate of change, divide the change in cremations in millions (595,617 – 367,975) by the change in years (1999 – 1990).

Solution

$$ave = \frac{595,617 - 367,975}{1999 - 1990}$$
$$\approx 0.025$$

The average annual rate of change was 25,000 cremations per year.

c. The number of cremations per year was greater than the number of deaths.

39. a. Strategy

To find the average annual rate of change, divide the change in fatalities (4727 – 6482) by the change in years (2000 – 1990).

Solution

$$ave = \frac{4727 - 6482}{2000 - 1990}$$
$$= -175.5$$

The average annual rate of change was –175.5 pedestrians per year.

b. The answer can be considered encouraging because it means the number of pedestrian fatalities is decreasing.

40. a. Strategy

To find the average rate of change per month, divide the change in price of gasoline ($1.53 – $1.30) by the change in months (April 2001 – January 2000).

Solution

$$ave = \frac{1.53 - 1.30}{15}$$
$$\approx 0.015$$

The average rate of change was $0.015 per month.

b. Strategy
To find the which is greater, compare the average rate of change per month of gasoline prices for January to April 2000 with that of January to April 2001.

Solution
For January to April 2000,
$$ave = \frac{1.51 - 1.30}{3}$$
$$= 0.07$$
For January to April 2001,
$$ave = \frac{1.53 - 1.47}{3}$$
$$= 0.02$$
$0.07 - 0.02 = 0.05$
The average rate of change was greater from January to April, 2000 by $0.05 per month.

41. a. Strategy
To find the average annual rate of change pr, divide the change in applications in thousands $(375 - 120)$ by the change in years $(2000 - 1990)$.

Solution
$$ave = \frac{375 - 120}{10}$$
$$= 25.5$$
The average annual rate of change 25,500 applications.

b. Strategy
To find the how much greater, compare the average annual rate of change in applications for 1995 to 2000 with that of 1990 to 1995.

Solution
For 1995 to 2000,
$$ave = \frac{375 - 175}{5}$$
$$= 40$$
For 1990 to 1995,
$$ave = \frac{175 - 120}{5}$$
$$= 11$$
$40 - 11 = 29$
The average rate of change was greater from 1995 to 2000 by 29,000 applications per year.

Applying Concepts 3.1

42. Ordered pairs:
$$\left(-2, -\frac{1}{2}\right)$$
$$(-1, -1)$$
$$\left(-\frac{1}{2}, -2\right)$$
$$\left(-\frac{1}{3}, -3\right)$$
$$\left(\frac{1}{3}, 3\right)$$
$$\left(\frac{1}{2}, 2\right)$$
$$(1, 1)$$
$$\left(2, \frac{1}{2}\right)$$

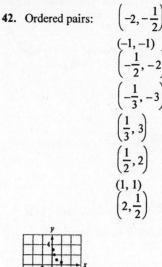

43. Ordered pairs: $(-2, 4)$
$(-1, 1)$
$(0, 0)$
$(1, 1)$
$(2, 4)$

44.

45.

46. The graph of all ordered pairs (x, y) that are 5 units from the origin is a circle of radius 5 that has its center at $(0, 0)$.

47. The graph of all ordered pairs (x, y) that are equidistant from two fixed points is a line that both is perpendicular to the line that passes through the two fixed points and also passes through the midpoint of the line segment between the two fixed points.

Section 3.2

Concept Review 3.2

1. Sometimes true
   By definition, a function cannot have different second coordinates with the same first coordinate.

2. Always true

3. Sometimes true
   The function $f(x) = \dfrac{2}{x-3}$ is not defined for $x = 3$.

4. Sometimes true
   Zero is excluded from the domain of $f(x) = \dfrac{1}{x}$ but is not excluded from the domain of $f(x) = 2x + 1$.

5. Always true

6. Never true
   By definition, the first coordinates of a function must have different values.

Objective 3.2.1 Exercises

1. A function is a set of ordered pairs in which no two ordered pairs can have the same *x*-coordinate with different *y*-coordinates.

2. The domain of a function is the set of all *x*-coordinates of the function. The range is the set of all *y*-coordinates of the function.

3. The diagram does represent a function because each number in the domain is paired with one number in the range.

4. The diagram does represent a function because each number in the domain is paired with one number in the range.

5. The diagram does represent a function because each number in the domain is paired with one number in the range.

6. The diagram does represent a function because each number in the domain is paired with one number in the range. Even though there is only one value in the range, once you choose a value in the domain, you know the number that is paired with it.

7. No, the diagram does not represent a function. The 6 in the domain is paired with two different numbers in the range.

8. No, the diagram does not represent a function. The number 3 in the domain is paired with four different numbers in the range.

9. Function

10. Function

11. Function

12. Function

13. Function

14. Function

15. Not a function

16. Not a function

17. **a.** Yes, this table defines a function because no weight occurs more than once.

    b. $29.62

18. **a.** Yes, this table defines a function because no weight occurs more than once.

    b. $10.70

19. Evaluating a function means finding the element in the range that corresponds to a specific element in the domain. To evaluate $f(x) = 3x$ for $x = 2$, substitute 2 for x:
    $$f(2) = 3 \bullet 2 = 6$$
    The value of the function when $x = 2$ is 6.

20. The value of a function is the specific value in the range (or the dependent variable) that corresponds to a chosen element in the domain (or independent variable).

21. $f(x) = 5x - 4$
    $f(3) = 5(3) - 4$
    $f(3) = 15 - 4$
    $f(3) = 11$

22. $f(x) = 5x - 4$
    $f(-2) = 5(-2) - 4$
    $f(-2) = -10 - 4$
    $f(-2) = -14$

23. $f(x) = 5x - 4$
    $f(0) = 5(0) - 4$
    $f(0) = -4$

24. $f(x) = 5x - 4$
    $f(-1) = 5(-1) - 4$
    $f(-1) = -5 - 4$
    $f(-1) = -9$

25. $G(t) = 4 - 3t$
    $G(0) = 4 - 3(0)$
    $G(0) = 4$

26. $G(t) = 4 - 3t$
    $G(-3) = 4 - 3(-3)$
    $G(-3) = 4 + 9$
    $G(-3) = 13$

27. $G(t) = 4 - 3t$
$G(-2) = 4 - 3(-2)$
$G(-2) = 4 + 6$
$G(-2) = 10$

28. $G(t) = 4 - 3t$
$G(4) = 4 - 3(4)$
$G(4) = 4 - 12$
$G(4) = -8$

29. $q(r) = r^2 - 4$
$q(3) = 3^2 - 4$
$q(3) = 9 - 4$
$q(3) = 5$

30. $q(r) = r^2 - 4$
$q(4) = 4^2 - 4$
$q(4) = 16 - 4$
$q(4) = 12$

31. $q(r) = r^2 - 4$
$q(-2) = (-2)^2 - 4$
$q(-2) = 4 - 4$
$q(-2) = 0$

32. $q(r) = r^2 - 4$
$q(-5) = (-5)^2 - 4$
$q(-5) = 25 - 4$
$q(-5) = 21$

33. $F(x) = x^2 + 3x - 4$
$F(4) = 4^2 + 3(4) - 4$
$F(4) = 16 + 12 - 4$
$F(4) = 24$

34. $F(x) = x^2 + 3x - 4$
$F(-4) = (-4)^2 + 3(-4) - 4$
$F(-4) = 16 - 12 - 4$
$F(-4) = 0$

35. $F(x) = x^2 + 3x - 4$
$F(-3) = (-3)^2 + 3(-3) - 4$
$F(-3) = 9 - 9 - 4$
$F(-3) = -4$

36. $F(x) = x^2 + 3x - 4$
$F(-6) = (-6)^2 + 3(-6) - 4$
$F(-6) = 36 - 18 - 4$
$F(-6) = 14$

37. $H(p) = \dfrac{3p}{p+2}$
$H(1) = \dfrac{3(1)}{1+2}$
$H(1) = \dfrac{3}{3}$
$H(1) = 1$

38. $H(p) = \dfrac{3p}{p+2}$
$H(-3) = \dfrac{3(-3)}{-3+2}$
$H(-3) = \dfrac{-9}{-1}$
$H(-3) = 9$

39. $H(p) = \dfrac{3p}{p+2}$
$H(t) = \dfrac{3t}{t+2}$

40. $H(p) = \dfrac{3p}{p+2}$
$H(v) = \dfrac{3v}{v+2}$

41. $s(t) = t^3 - 3t + 4$
$s(-1) = (-1)^3 - 3(-1) + 4$
$s(-1) = -1 + 3 + 4$
$s(-1) = 6$

42. $s(t) = t^3 - 3t + 4$
$s(2) = 2^3 - 3(2) + 4$
$s(2) = 8 - 6 + 4$
$s(2) = 6$

43. $s(t) = t^3 - 3t + 4$
$s(a) = a^3 - 3a + 4$

44. $s(t) = t^3 - 3t + 4$
$s(w) = w^3 - 3w + 4$

45. a. \$4.75 per game

b. \$4.00 per game

46. a. \$6.50

b. \$10.00

47. a. \$3000

b. \$950

48. a. \$29.25

b. \$26.75

49. Domain = {1, 2, 3, 4, 5}
Range = {1, 4, 7, 10, 13}

50. Domain = {2, 4, 6, 8, 10}
Range = {6, 18, 38, 66, 102}

51. Domain = {0, 2, 4, 6}
Range = {1, 2, 3, 4}

52. Domain = {0, 1, 4, 9}
Range = {1, 2, 3, 4}

53. Domain = {1, 3, 5, 7, 9}
Range = {0}

54. Domain = {−3, −2, −1, 1, 2, 3}
Range = {−4, 1, 4, 9}

55. Domain = {−2, −1, 0, 1, 2}
Range = {0, 1, 2}

56. Domain = {0, 5, 10, 15}
Range = {−5, 0, 5, 10}

57. $x = 1$

58. $x = -4$

59. $x = -8$

60. $x = 4$

61. No values are excluded.

62. No values are excluded.

63. No values are excluded.

64. No values are excluded.

65. $x = 0$

66. No values are excluded

67. No values are excluded.

68. No values are excluded.

69. No values are excluded.

70. No values are excluded.

71. $x = -2$

72. $x = 6$

73. No values are excluded.

74. $x = 2$

75. $f(x) = 4x - 3$
$f(0) = 4(0) - 3 = -3$
$f(1) = 4(1) - 3 = 1$
$f(2) = 4(2) - 3 = 5$
$f(3) = 4(3) - 3 = 9$
Range = {−3, 1, 5, 9}

76. $G(x) = 3 - 5x$
$G(-2) = 3 - 5(-2) = 13$
$G(-1) = 3 - 5(-1) = 8$
$G(0) = 3 - 5(0) = 3$
$G(1) = 3 - 5(1) = -2$
$G(2) = 3 - 5(2) = -7$
Range = {13, 8, 3, −2, −7}

77. $g(x) = 5x - 8$
$g(-3) = 5(-3) - 8 = -23$
$g(-1) = 5(-1) - 8 = -13$
$g(0) = 5(0) - 8 = -8$
$g(1) = 5(1) - 8 = -3$
$g(3) = 5(3) - 8 = 7$
Range = {−23, −13, −8, −3, 7}

78. $h(x) = 3x - 7$
$h(-4) = 3(-4) - 7 = -19$
$h(-2) = 3(-2) - 7 = -13$
$h(0) = 3(0) - 7 = -7$
$h(2) = 3(2) - 7 = -1$
$h(4) = 3(4) - 7 = 5$
Range = {−19, −13, −7, −1, 5}

79. $h(x) = x^2$
$h(-2) = (-2)^2 = 4$
$h(-1) = (-1)^2 = 1$
$h(0) = 0^2 = 0$
$h(1) = 1^2 = 1$
$h(2) = 2^2 = 4$
Range = {0, 1, 4}

80. $H(x) = 1 - x^2$
$H(-2) = 1 - (-2)^2 = -3$
$H(-1) = 1 - (-1)^2 = 0$
$H(0) = 1 - 0^2 = 1$
$H(1) = 1 - 1^2 = 0$
$H(2) = 1 - 2^2 = -3$
Range = {−3, 0, 1}

81. $f(x) = 2x^2 - 2x + 2$
$f(-4) = 2(-4)^2 - 2(-4) + 2$
$\quad = 32 + 8 + 2 = 42$
$f(-2) = 2(-2)^2 - 2(-2) + 2$
$\quad = 8 + 4 + 2 = 14$
$f(0) = 2(0)^2 - 2(0) + 2 = 2$
$f(4) = 2(4)^2 - 2(4) + 2$
$\quad = 32 - 8 + 2 = 26$
Range = {2, 14, 26, 42}

82. $G(x) = -2x^2 + 5x - 2$
$G(-3) = -2(-3)^2 + 5(-3) - 2$
$\quad = -18 - 15 - 2 = -35$
$G(-1) = -2(-1)^2 + 5(-1) - 2$
$\quad = -2 - 5 - 2 = -9$
$G(0) = -2(0)^2 + 5(0) - 2 = -2$
$G(1) = -2(1)^2 + 5(1) - 2$
$\quad = -2 + 5 - 2 = 1$
$G(3) = -2(3)^2 + 5(3) - 2$
$\quad = -18 + 15 - 2 = -5$
Range = {−35, −9, −5, −2, 1}

83. $H(x) = \dfrac{5}{1-x}$

$H(-2) = \dfrac{5}{1-(-2)} = \dfrac{5}{3}$

$H(0) = \dfrac{5}{1-0} = 5$

$H(2) = \dfrac{5}{1-2} = -5$

Range $= \left\{ -5, \dfrac{5}{3}, 5 \right\}$

84. $g(x) = \dfrac{5}{4-x}$

$g(-5) = \dfrac{4}{4-(-5)} = \dfrac{4}{9}$

$g(0) = \dfrac{4}{4-0} = 1$

$g(3) = \dfrac{4}{4-3} = 4$

Range $= \left\{ \dfrac{4}{9}, 1, 4 \right\}$

85. $f(x) = \dfrac{2}{x-4}$

$f(-2) = \dfrac{2}{-2-4} = -\dfrac{1}{3}$

$f(0) = \dfrac{2}{0-4} = -\dfrac{1}{2}$

$f(2) = \dfrac{2}{2-4} = -1$

$f(6) = \dfrac{2}{6-4} = 1$

Range $= \left\{ -1, -\dfrac{1}{2}, -\dfrac{1}{3}, 1 \right\}$

86. $g(x) = \dfrac{x}{3-x}$

$g(-2) = \dfrac{-2}{3-(-2)} = -\dfrac{2}{5}$

$g(-1) = \dfrac{-1}{3-(-1)} = -\dfrac{1}{4}$

$g(0) = \dfrac{0}{3-0} = 0$

$g(1) = \dfrac{1}{3-1} = \dfrac{1}{2}$

$g(2) = \dfrac{2}{3-2} = 2$

Range $= \left\{ -\dfrac{2}{5}, -\dfrac{1}{4}, 0, \dfrac{1}{2}, 2 \right\}$

87. $H(x) = 2 - 3x - x^2$

$H(-5) = 2 - 3(-5) - (-5)^2$

$= 2 + 15 - 25 = -8$

$H(0) = 2 - 3(0) - 0^2 = 2$

$H(5) = 2 - 3(5) - 5^2$

$= 2 - 15 - 25 = -38$

Range $= \{-38, -8, 2\}$

88. $G(x) = 4 - 3x - x^3$

$G(-3) = 4 - 3(-3) - (-3)^3$

$= 4 + 9 + 27 = 40$

$G(0) = 4 - 3(0) - 0^3 = 4$

$G(3) = 4 - 3(3) - 3^3$

$= 4 - 9 - 27 = -32$

Range $= \{-32, 4, 40\}$

Applying Concepts 3.2

89. $P(x) = 4x + 7;\ P(-2+h) - P(-2)$

$P(-2+h) - P(-2) = 4(-2+h) + 7 - [4(-2) + 7]$

$= -8 + 4h + 7 + 8 - 7$

$= 4h$

90. $G(t) = 9 - 2t;\ G(-3+h) - G(-3)$

$G(-3+h) - G(-3) = 9 - 2(-3+h) - [9 - 2(-3)]$

$= 9 + 6 - 2h - 9 - 6$

$= -2h$

91. $f(z) = 8 - 3z;\ f(-3+h) - f(-3)$

$f(-3+h) - f(-3) = 8 - 3(-3+h) - [8 - 3(-3)]$

$= 8 + 9 - 3h - 8 - 9$

$= -3h$

92. $M(n) = 5 - 2n;\ M(-6+h) - M(-6)$

$M(-6+h) - M(-6) = 5 - 2(-6+h) - [5 - 2(-6)]$

$= 5 + 12 - 2h - 5 - 12$

$= -2h$

93.   Find the value of the function

$s = f(v) = 0.017v^2$ when $v = 60$.

$s = 0.017v^2$

$s = 0.017(60)^2$

$s = 61.2$

A car will skid 61.2 feet.

94.   Find the value of the function

$P = f(v) = 0.015v^3$ when $v = 15$.

$P = 0.015v^3$

$P = 0.015(15)^3$

$P = 50.625$

50.625 watts will be produced.

95. $\{(-2, -8), (-1, 1), (0, 0), (1, 1), (2, 8)\}$

Yes, the set defines a function because each member of the domain is assigned to exactly one member of the range.

96. $\{(0, 0), (1, -1), (1, 1), (2, -2), (3, -3), (3, 3)\}$

No, this is not a function because some of the points in the domain are assigned to two values in the range.

97. a. 20 ft/s

b. 28 ft/s

98. a. 90%

b. 100%

99. a. 60°F

b. 52°F

100. a. 110 beats per minute

b. 75 beats per minute

101. a.

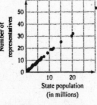

b. The 435 representatives to the House are apportioned among the states according to their populations.

102. Longitude line, also called meridians, are great circles that pass through the north and south poles. The circle that passes through Greenwich, England, has longitude 0°. Earth is divided into 360 longitude lines. However, longitude is divided into two hemispheres: 180° west of Greenwich, England, and 180° east of Greenwich, England. Latitude lines are circles that are parallel to the equator. The circle of the equator has latitude 0°. The north pole has latitude 90° north; the south pole has latitude 90° south. A nautical mile is the distance that makes up 1° of the longitude at the equator. This is approximately 6080 ft. The time zones are approximately the distance that makes up 15° of longitude. This is a result of Earth's rotation. Because Earth revolves on its axis once in 24 hours, it revolves $\frac{1}{24} \cdot 360° = 15°$ each hour.

103. This is a good class project. Have each student write down the number of miles he or she commutes to class and the number of miles on the odometer of that student's car. There are many possibilities for answers. For instance, some students may commute to school on the bus, so the miles on the odometers of their cars may have no relationship to the distance to school. Another relationship that the students might investigate is that between their overall GPA and their GPA in math classes. You might try this with and without the contribution of the math classes to overall GPA. Another possibility is the relationship between the height of a student and the score of that student on the last exam. This could lead to a discussion of statistical correlations.

104. Students will provide different examples of relations that are not functions. Examples include a person's height and that person's shoe size, and a person's age and educational level. It is not possible to give an example of a function that is not a relation because every function is a relation.

Section 3.3

Concept Review 3.3

1. Never true
The equation of a linear function is a first-degree equation. This equation has a variable in the denominator, so it is not a first-degree equation.

2. Never true
The graph of $y - 3 = 0$ is a horizontal line. The graph of a vertical line has an equation of the form $x = a$.

3. Always true

4. Always true

5. Sometimes true
The only time that this occurs is when the line passes through the point (0, 0).

6. Never true
$xy + 2 = 0$ is a second-degree equation. A linear equation is a first-degree equation.

Objective 3.3.1 Exercises

1. To graph a linear function by plotting the points, find three ordered-pair solutions of the equation. Plot these ordered pairs in a rectangular coordinate system. Draw a straight line through the points.

2. An example of a linear function is $y = 8x + 1$. An example of a nonlinear function is $y = x^2 - 2$.

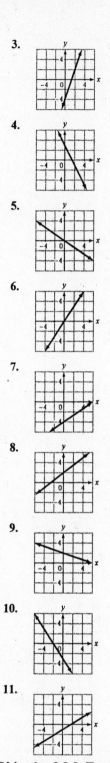

3.

4.

5.

6.

7.

8.

9.

10.

11.

Objective 3.3.2 Exercises

12. To find the *x*-intercept of the graph of an equation, let $y = 0$ in the equation and then solve the equation for *x*.

13. To find the *y*-intercept of the graph of an equation, let $x = 0$ in the equation and then solve the equation for *y*.

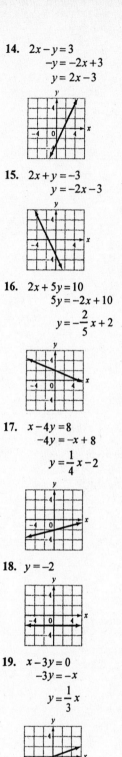

14. $2x - y = 3$
    $-y = -2x + 3$
    $y = 2x - 3$

15. $2x + y = -3$
    $y = -2x - 3$

16. $2x + 5y = 10$
    $5y = -2x + 10$
    $y = -\dfrac{2}{5}x + 2$

17. $x - 4y = 8$
    $-4y = -x + 8$
    $y = \dfrac{1}{4}x - 2$

18. $y = -2$

19. $x - 3y = 0$
    $-3y = -x$
    $y = \dfrac{1}{3}x$

20. $2x - 3y = 12$
$-3y = -2x + 12$
$y = \dfrac{2}{3}x - 4$

21. $3x - y = -2$
$-y = -3x - 2$
$y = 3x + 2$

22. $3x - 2y = 8$
$-2y = -3x + 8$
$y = \dfrac{3}{2}x - 4$

23. x-intercept:
$x - 2y = -4$
$x - 2(0) = -4$
$x = -4$

$(-4, 0)$

y-intercept
$x - 2y = -4$
$0 - 2y = -4$
$-2y = -4$
$y = 2$

$(0, 2)$

24. x-intercept:
$3x + y = 3$
$3x + 0 = 3$
$3x = 3$
$x = 1$

$(1, 0)$

y-intercept:
$3x + y = 3$
$3(0) + y = 3$
$y = 3$

$(0, 3)$

25. x-intercept:
$2x - 3y = 9$
$2x - 3(0) = 9$
$2x = 9$
$x = \dfrac{9}{2}$

$\left(\dfrac{9}{2}, 0\right)$

y-intercept:
$2x - 3y = 9$
$2(0) - 3y = 9$
$-3y = 9$
$y = -3$

$(0, -3)$

26. x-intercept:
$4x - 2y = 5$
$4x - 2(0) = 5$
$4x = 5$
$x = \dfrac{5}{4}$

$\left(\dfrac{5}{4}, 0\right)$

y-intercept:
$4x - 2y = 5$
$4(0) - 2y = 5$
$-2y = 5$
$y = -\dfrac{5}{2}$

$\left(0, -\dfrac{5}{2}\right)$

27. x-intercept:
$2x - y = 4$
$2x - 0 = 4$
$2x = 4$
$x = 2$

$(2, 0)$

y-intercept:
$2x - y = 4$
$2(0) - y = 4$
$-y = 4$
$y = -4$

$(0, -4)$

28. x-intercept:
$2x + y = 3$
$2x + 0 = 3$
$2x = 3$
$x = \dfrac{3}{2}$

$\left(\dfrac{3}{2}, 0\right)$

y-intercept:
$2x + y = 3$
$2(0) + y = 3$
$y = 3$

$(0, 3)$

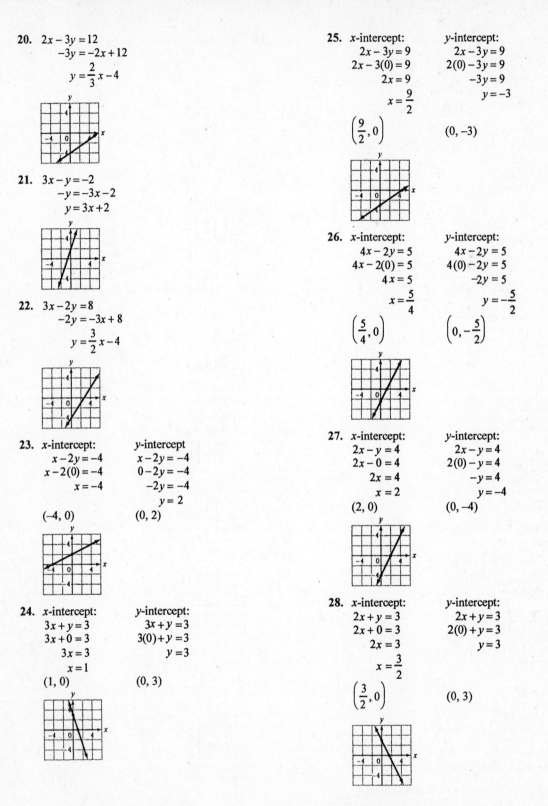

29. x-intercept: y-intercept:
$$3x + 2y = 5 \qquad 3x + 2y = 5$$
$$3x + 2(0) = 5 \qquad 3(0) + 2y = 5$$
$$3x = 5 \qquad 2y = 5$$
$$x = \frac{5}{3} \qquad y = \frac{5}{2}$$
$$\left(\frac{5}{3}, 0\right) \qquad \left(0, \frac{5}{2}\right)$$

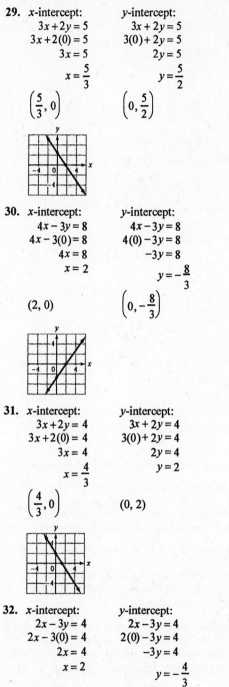

30. x-intercept: y-intercept:
$$4x - 3y = 8 \qquad 4x - 3y = 8$$
$$4x - 3(0) = 8 \qquad 4(0) - 3y = 8$$
$$4x = 8 \qquad -3y = 8$$
$$x = 2 \qquad y = -\frac{8}{3}$$
$$(2, 0) \qquad \left(0, -\frac{8}{3}\right)$$

31. x-intercept: y-intercept:
$$3x + 2y = 4 \qquad 3x + 2y = 4$$
$$3x + 2(0) = 4 \qquad 3(0) + 2y = 4$$
$$3x = 4 \qquad 2y = 4$$
$$x = \frac{4}{3} \qquad y = 2$$
$$\left(\frac{4}{3}, 0\right) \qquad (0, 2)$$

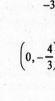

32. x-intercept: y-intercept:
$$2x - 3y = 4 \qquad 2x - 3y = 4$$
$$2x - 3(0) = 4 \qquad 2(0) - 3y = 4$$
$$2x = 4 \qquad -3y = 4$$
$$x = 2 \qquad y = -\frac{4}{3}$$
$$(2, 0) \qquad \left(0, -\frac{4}{3}\right)$$

33. x-intercept: y-intercept:
$$3x - 5y = 9 \qquad 3x - 5y = 9$$
$$3x - 5(0) = 9 \qquad 3(0) - 5y = 9$$
$$3x = 9 \qquad -5y = 9$$
$$x = 3 \qquad y = -\frac{9}{5}$$
$$(3, 0) \qquad \left(0, -\frac{9}{5}\right)$$

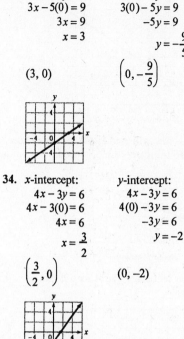

34. x-intercept: y-intercept:
$$4x - 3y = 6 \qquad 4x - 3y = 6$$
$$4x - 3(0) = 6 \qquad 4(0) - 3y = 6$$
$$4x = 6 \qquad -3y = 6$$
$$x = \frac{3}{2} \qquad y = -2$$
$$\left(\frac{3}{2}, 0\right) \qquad (0, -2)$$

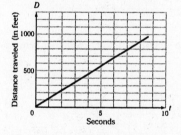

35. The roller coaster travels 500 ft. in 5 s.

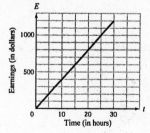

36. The tennis pro will earn \$1000 for working 25 hours.

37. The realtor will earn $4000 for selling $60,000 worth of property.

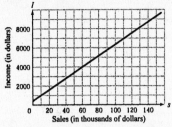

38. The line worker will earn $9.80 during an hour in which 16 transistors are produced.

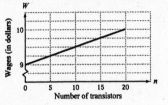

39. The caterer will charge $614 for 120 hot appetizers.

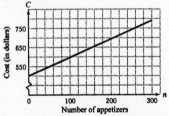

40. The tree service will charge $1810 to remove 50 trees.

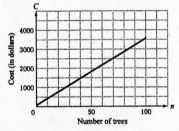

Applying Concepts 3.3

41. $s(p) = 0.80p$
    $s(p) = 0.80(200)$
    $s(p) = 160$
    The sale price is $160.

42. $m(c) = 0.25c$
    $m(c) = 0.25(150)$
    $m(c) = 37.5$
    The markup is $37.50.

43.

44.

45.

46.

47.

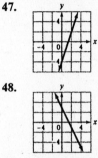

48.

49. The zero of a linear function f is the value a for which $f(a) = 0$. Because $f(a) = 0$, $y = 0$ when $x = a$, and $(a, 0)$ is the x-intercept.

50. Because the number of cricket chirps must be nonnegative, $f(C) \geq 0$, or $C \geq \dfrac{30}{7}$. The temperature must be less than 50°C (the approximate highest recorded temperature). Thus the domain is $\dfrac{30}{7} \leq C \leq 50$. The range for these values is $0 \leq y \leq 320$. The x-intercept of this function is the lowest temperature at which crickets will chirp.

51. Students answers will vary. However, you might look for the idea that the graph of an equation is a picture of all the ordered pairs (x, y) that are solutions of the equation.

52. The x-intercept of the graph of the equation $4x + 3y = 0$ is $(0, 0)$. The y-intercept of this graph is also $(0, 0)$. Therefore, the x-intercept and y-intercept are the same point. A straight line is determined by two points. Therefore, we must find another point on the line in order to graph the equation.

Section 3.4

Concept Review 3.4

1. Always true

2. Always true

3. Never true
   The slope of a vertical line is undefined.

4. Always true

Objective 3.4.1 Exercises

1. To find the slope of a line between two points, (x_1, y_1) and (x_2, y_2), subtract the y-coordinates and subtract the x-coordinates in the same order. Then divide the difference in the y-coordinates by the difference in the x-coordinates.

2. A line that has positive slope goes upward from the left to right on the coordinate axes. A line that has negative slope goes downward from left to right on the coordinate axes. A line can have zero slope. It is a horizontal line.

3. $P_1(1, 3)$, $P_2(3, 1)$
   $$m = \frac{y_2 - y_1}{x_2 - x_1} = \frac{1 - 3}{3 - 1} = \frac{-2}{2} = -1$$
   The slope is -1.

4. $P_1(2, 3)$, $P_2(5, 1)$
   $$m = \frac{y_2 - y_1}{x_2 - x_1} = \frac{1 - 3}{5 - 2} = \frac{-2}{3} = -\frac{2}{3}$$
   The slope is $-\frac{2}{3}$.

5. $P_1(-1, 4)$, $P_2(2, 5)$
   $$m = \frac{y_2 - y_1}{x_2 - x_1} = \frac{5 - 4}{2 - (-1)} = \frac{1}{3}$$
   The slope is $\frac{1}{3}$.

6. $P_1(3, -2)$, $P_2(1, 4)$
   $$m = \frac{y_2 - y_1}{x_2 - x_1} = \frac{4 - (-2)}{1 - 3} = \frac{6}{-2} = -3$$
   The slope is -3.

7. $P_1(-1, 3)$, $P_2(-4, 5)$
   $$m = \frac{y_2 - y_1}{x_2 - x_1} = \frac{5 - 3}{-4 - (-1)} = \frac{2}{-3} = -\frac{2}{3}$$
   The slope is $-\frac{2}{3}$.

8. $P_1(-1, -2)$, $P_2(-3, 2)$
   $$m = \frac{y_2 - y_1}{x_2 - x_1} = \frac{2 - (-2)}{-3 - (-1)} = \frac{4}{-2} = -2$$
   The slope is -2.

9. $P_1(0, 3)$, $P_2(4, 0)$
   $$m = \frac{y_2 - y_1}{x_2 - x_1} = \frac{0 - 3}{4 - 0} = \frac{-3}{4} = -\frac{3}{4}$$
   The slope is $-\frac{3}{4}$.

10. $P_1(-2, 0)$, $P_2(0, 3)$
    $$m = \frac{y_2 - y_1}{x_2 - x_1} = \frac{3 - 0}{0 - (-2)} = \frac{3}{2}$$
    The slope is $\frac{3}{2}$.

11. $P_1(2, 4)$, $P_2(2, -2)$
    $$m = \frac{y_2 - y_1}{x_2 - x_1} = \frac{-2 - 4}{2 - 2} = \frac{-6}{0}$$
    The slope is undefined.

12. $P_1(4, 1)$, $P_2(4, -3)$
    $$m = \frac{y_2 - y_1}{x_2 - x_1} = \frac{-3 - 1}{4 - 4} = \frac{-4}{0}$$
    The slope is undefined.

13. $P_1(2, 5)$, $P_2(-3, -2)$
    $$m = \frac{y_2 - y_1}{x_2 - x_1} = \frac{-2 - 5}{-3 - 2} = \frac{-7}{-5} = \frac{7}{5}$$
    The slope is $\frac{7}{5}$.

14. $P_1(4, 1)$, $P_2(-1, -2)$
    $$m = \frac{y_2 - y_1}{x_2 - x_1} = \frac{-2 - 1}{-1 - 4} = \frac{-3}{-5} = \frac{3}{5}$$
    The slope is $\frac{3}{5}$.

15. $P_1(2, 3)$, $P_2(-1, 3)$
    $$m = \frac{y_2 - y_1}{x_2 - x_1} = \frac{3 - 3}{-1 - 2} = \frac{0}{-3} = 0$$
    The line has zero slope.

16. $P_1(3, 4)$, $P_2(0, 4)$
    $$m = \frac{y_2 - y_1}{x_2 - x_1} = \frac{4 - 4}{0 - 3} = \frac{0}{-3} = 0$$
    The line has zero slope.

17. $P_1(0, 4)$, $P_2(-2, 5)$
    $$m = \frac{y_2 - y_1}{x_2 - x_1} = \frac{5 - 4}{-2 - 0} = \frac{1}{-2} = -\frac{1}{2}$$
    The slope is $-\frac{1}{2}$.

18. $P_1(-2, 3)$, $P_2(-2, 5)$
    $$m = \frac{y_2 - y_1}{x_2 - x_1} = \frac{5 - 3}{-2 - (-2)} = \frac{2}{0}$$
    The slope is undefined.

19. $P_1(-3, -1)$, $P_2(-3, 4)$
    $$m = \frac{y_2 - y_1}{x_2 - x_1} = \frac{4 - (-1)}{-3 - (-3)} = \frac{5}{0}$$
    The slope is undefined.

20. $P_1(-2, -5)$, $P_2(-4, -1)$
$$m = \frac{y_2 - y_1}{x_2 - x_1} = \frac{-1 - (-5)}{-4 - (-2)} = \frac{4}{-2} = -2$$
The slope is –2.

21. $m = \frac{240 - 80}{6 - 2} = \frac{160}{4} = 40$
The slope is the average speed of the motorist in miles per hour.

22. $m = \frac{9 - 6}{12 - 8} = \frac{3}{4} = 0.75$
The altitude of the plane increases at a rate of 0.75 thousand feet, or 750 feet per minute.

23. $m = \frac{13 - 6}{40 - 180} = \frac{7}{-140} = -0.05$
For each mile the car is driven, approximately 0.05 gallons of fuel is used.

24. $\frac{5 - (-34)}{2 - 8} = \frac{39}{-6} = -6.5$
The temperature of the troposphere decreases 6.5°C/km.

25. **Strategy**
Find lines that have a slope that match the rates of the runners.

Solution
Lois has the highest rate so the line with the steepest slope represents Lois. Line A has the steepest slope so it represents Lois's distance. The line which represents Tanya's distance must have a slope of $\frac{6}{1}$. Line B goes through the points (1, 6) and (0, 0) so its slope is $\frac{6}{1}$. So line B represents Tanya's distance.
In one hour the difference between Lois's and Tanya's distances is 3. Line C goes through the point (1, 3) so it represents the distance between Lois and Tanya.

26. **Strategy**
Look at the slopes of the lines to see which line represents the depth of water in each can.

Solution
Since Can 2 has a wider diameter and the water is filling both cans at the same rate, the depth of Can 1 will increase faster. Since line A has a steeper slope, it represents Can 1. Line B represents Can 2.

27. **a.** The slope for a ramp that is 6 inches high and 5 feet long is $\frac{6 \text{ inches}}{60 \text{ inches}} = \frac{1}{10}$ or 0.1.

$\frac{1}{12} = 0.0833$. Since $0.1 > 0.0833$, the ramp does not meet the ANSI requirements.

b. The slope for a ramp that is 12 inches high and 170 inches long is $\frac{12}{170}$ or 0.07. Since $0.07 < 0.08$, the ramp does meet the ANSI requirements.

28. **Strategy**
Find a length x for which $\frac{14}{x} < 0.083$.

Solution
Solve $\frac{14}{x} < 0.083$
$$14 < 0.083x$$
$$x > \frac{14}{0.083}$$
$$x > 168.7$$
The ramp must be at least 169 inches long.

Objective 3.4.2 Exercises

29.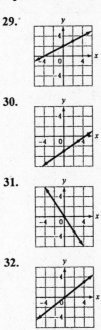

30.

31.

32.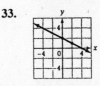

33.

34.

35. $x - 3y = 3$
    $-3y = -x + 3$
    $y = \frac{1}{3}x - 1$

36. $3x + 2y = 8$
    $2y = -3x + 8$
    $y = -\frac{3}{2}x + 4$

37. $4x + y = 2$
    $y = -4x + 2$

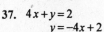

38.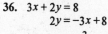

39.

40.

41.

Applying Concepts 3.4

42. $f(14) = 8$

43. increases by 2

44. decreases by 3

45. increases by $\frac{1}{2}$

46. decreases by $\frac{2}{3}$

47. $P_1 = (3, 2)$
    $P_2 = (4, 6)$
    $P_3 = (5, k)$
    P_1 to P_2: $m = \frac{6-2}{4-3} = 4$
    The slope from P_1 to P_3 and that from P_2 to P_3 must also be 4.
    Set the slope from P_1 to P_3 equal to 4.
    $\frac{2-k}{3-5} = 4$
    $\frac{2-k}{-2} = 4$
    $2 - k = -8$
    $k = 10$
    This checks out against P_2 to P_3, so $k = 10$.

48. $P_1 = (k, 1)$
    $P_2 = (0, -1)$
    $P_3 = (2, -2)$
    P_2 to P_3; $m = \frac{-2-(-1)}{2-0} = -\frac{1}{2}$
    The slope from P_1 to P_2 and that from P_1 to P_3 must also be $-\frac{1}{2}$.
    Set the slope from P_1 to P_2 equal to $-\frac{1}{2}$.
    $\frac{1-(-1)}{k-0} = -\frac{1}{2}$
    $\frac{2}{k} = -\frac{1}{2}$
    $k = -4$
    This checks out against P_1 to P_3, so $k = -4$.

49. The graph for i has a negative slope and y-intercept of 4. i and D;
    The graph for ii has negative slope and y-intercept of -4. ii and C;
    The graph for iii has zero slope and y-intercept of 2. iii and B;
    The graph of iv has a negative slope and y-intercept of 0. iv and F;
    The graph of v has a positive slope and y-intercept of 4. v and E;
    The graph of vi has a negative slope and y-intercept of -2. vi and A

50. The graphs are shown below. The graphs are different because they have different y-intercepts. They are similar because they have the same slope. The graph of $y = 2x + b$ is parallel to these lines, with y-intercept $(0, b)$.

51. Three given points lie on the same line if the slope between each pair of points is the same.

a. Let $P_1 = (2, 5)$, $P_2 = (-1, -1)$, and $P_3 = (3, 7)$. Then the slope of the line between P_1 and P_2 is $m = \dfrac{-1-5}{-1-2} = 2$, the slope of the line

between P_2 and P_3 is $m = \dfrac{7-(-1)}{3-(-1)} = 2$, and

the slope of the line between P_1 and P_3 is

$m = \dfrac{7-5}{3-2} = 2$.

Yes, the points lie on the same line.

b. Let $P_1 = (-1, 5)$, $P_2 = (0, 3)$, and $P_3 = (-3, 4)$. Then the slope of the line between P_1 and P_2

is $m = \dfrac{3-5}{0-(-1)} = -2$, the slope of the line

between P_2 and P_3 is $m = \dfrac{4-3}{-3-0} = -\dfrac{1}{3}$, and

the slope of the line between P_1 and P_3 is

$m = \dfrac{4-5}{-3-(-1)}\ \dfrac{1}{2}$.

No, the points do not lie on the same line.

Section 3.5

Concept Review 3.5

1. Always true

2. Never true
Decreasing the value of b moves the graph downward on the coordinate axes. Changing the value of m changes the slope of a line.

3. Never true
The point-slope formula is given by
$y - y_1 = m(x - x_1)$.

4. Always true

5. Never true
The line represented by the equation $y = 2x - \dfrac{1}{2}$

has slope 2 and y-intercept $-\dfrac{1}{2}$.

6. Always true

7. Never true
A horizontal line has zero slope.

Objective 3.5.1 Exercises

1. The point-slope formula is $y - y_1 = m(x - x_1)$. It is used to find the equation of a line when one point that lies on the line and the slope of the line are known. The coordinates of the known point are substituted into the formula for (x_1, y_1), and the slope is substituted for m.

2. When we know the slope and y-intercept, we can find the equation by sing the slope-intercept form, $y = mx + b$. The slope can be substituted for m, and the y-coordinate of the y-intercept can be substituted for b.

3. $m = 2$, $b = 5$
$y = mx + b$
$y = 2x + 5$
The equation of the line is $y = 2x + 5$.

4. $m = 1$, $b = 3$
$y = mx + b$
$y = x + 3$
The equation of the line is $y = x + 3$.

5. $m = \dfrac{1}{2}$, $(x_1, y_1) = (2, 3)$
$y - y_1 = m(x - x_1)$
$y - 3 = \dfrac{1}{2}(x - 2)$
$y - 3 = \dfrac{1}{2}x - 1$
$y = \dfrac{1}{2}x + 2$
The equation of the line is $y = \dfrac{1}{2}x + 2$.

6. $m = \dfrac{2}{3}$, $(x_1, y_1) = (5, 1)$
$y - y_1 = m(x - x_1)$
$y - 1 = \dfrac{2}{3}(x - 5)$
$y - 1 = \dfrac{2}{3}x - \dfrac{10}{3}$
$y = \dfrac{2}{3}x - \dfrac{7}{3}$
The equation of the line is $y = \dfrac{2}{3}x - \dfrac{7}{3}$.

7. $m = -\dfrac{5}{3}$, $(x_1, y_1) = (3, 0)$
$y - y_1 = m(x - x_1)$
$y - 0 = -\dfrac{5}{3}(x - 3)$
$y = -\dfrac{5}{3}x + 5$
The equation of the line is $y = -\dfrac{5}{3}x + 5$.

8. $m = \dfrac{3}{2}$, $(x_1, y_1) = (-2, 0)$
$y - y_1 = m(x - x_1)$
$y - 0 = \dfrac{3}{2}[x - (-2)]$
$y = \dfrac{3}{2}(x + 2)$
$y = \dfrac{3}{2}x + 3$
The equation of the line is $y = \dfrac{3}{2}x + 3$.

9. $m = -3$, $(x_1, y_1) = (-1, 7)$
    $y - y_1 = m(x - x_1)$
    $y - 7 = -3[x - (-1)]$
    $y - 7 = -3(x + 1)$
    $y - 7 = -3x - 3$
    $y = -3x + 4$
    The equation of the line is $y = -3x + 4$.

10. $m = -4$, $(x_1, y_1) = (-2, 4)$
    $y - y_1 = m(x - x_1)$
    $y - 4 = -4[x - (-2)]$
    $y - 4 = -4(x + 2)$
    $y - 4 = -4x - 8$
    $y = -4x - 4$
    The equation of the line is $y = -4x - 4$.

11. $m = \dfrac{1}{2}$, $(x_1, y_1) = (0, 0)$
    $y - y_1 = m(x - x_1)$
    $y - 0 = \dfrac{1}{2}(x - 0)$
    $y = \dfrac{1}{2}x$
    The equation of the line is $y = \dfrac{1}{2}x$.

12. $m = \dfrac{3}{4}$, $(x_1, y_1) = (0, 0)$
    $y - y_1 = m(x - x_1)$
    $y - 0 = \dfrac{3}{4}(x - 0)$
    $y = \dfrac{3}{4}x$
    The equation of the line is $y = \dfrac{3}{4}x$.

13. $m = 3$, $(x_1, y_1) = (2, -3)$
    $y - y_1 = m(x - x_1)$
    $y - (-3) = 3(x - 2)$
    $y + 3 = 3x - 6$
    $y = 3x - 9$
    The equation of the line is $y = 3x - 9$.

14. $m = 2$, $(x_1, y_1) = (4, -5)$
    $y - y_1 = m(x - x_1)$
    $y - (-5) = 2(x - 4)$
    $y + 5 = 2x - 8$
    $y = 2x - 13$
    The equation of the line is $y = 2x - 13$.

15. $m = -\dfrac{2}{3}$, $(x_1, y_1) = (3, 5)$
    $y - y_1 = m(x - x_1)$
    $y - 5 = -\dfrac{2}{3}(x - 3)$
    $y - 5 = -\dfrac{2}{3}x + 2$
    $y = -\dfrac{2}{3}x + 7$
    The equation of the line is $y = -\dfrac{2}{3}x + 7$.

16. $m = -\dfrac{4}{5}$, $(x_1, y_1) = (5, 1)$
    $y - y_1 = m(x - x_1)$
    $y - 1 = -\dfrac{4}{5}(x - 5)$
    $y - 1 = -\dfrac{4}{5}x + 4$
    $y = -\dfrac{4}{5}x + 5$
    The equation of the line is $y = -\dfrac{4}{5}x + 5$.

17. $m = -1$, $(x_1, y_1) = (0, -3)$
    $y - y_1 = m(x - x_1)$
    $y - (-3) = -1(x - 0)$
    $y + 3 = -x + 0$
    $y = -x - 3$
    The equation of the line is $y = -x - 3$.

18. $m = \dfrac{5}{6}$, $(x_1, y_1) = (2, 0)$
    $y - y_1 = m(x - x_1)$
    $y - 0 = \dfrac{5}{6}(x - 2)$
    $y = \dfrac{5}{6}x - \dfrac{5}{3}$
    The equation of the line is $y = \dfrac{5}{6}x - \dfrac{5}{3}$.

19. The slope is undefined; $(x_1, y_1) = (3, -4)$.
    The line is a vertical line. All points on the line have an abscissa of 3. The equation of the line is $x = 3$.

20. The slope is undefined; $(x_1, y_1) = (-2, 5)$.
    The line is a vertical line. All points on the line have an abscissa of -2.
    The equation of the line is $x = -2$.

21. $m = 0$, $(x_1, y_1) = (-2, -3)$
    $y - y_1 = m(x - x_1)$
    $y - (-3) = 0[x - (-2)]$
    $y + 3 = 0$
    $y = -3$
    The equation of the line is $y = -3$.

22. $m = 0$, $(x_1, y_1) = (-3, -2)$
    $y - y_1 = m(x - x_1)$
    $y - (-2) = 0[x - (-3)]$
    $y + 2 = 0$
    $y = -2$
    The equation of the line is $y = -2$.

23. $m = -2$, $(x_1, y_1) = (4, -5)$
    $y - y_1 = m(x - x_1)$
    $y - (-5) = -2(x - 4)$
    $y + 5 = -2x + 8$
    $y = -2x + 3$
    The equation of the line is $y = -2x + 3$.

24. $m = 3$, $(x_1, y_1) = (-3, 5)$

$y - y_1 = m(x - x_1)$

$y - 5 = 3[x - (-3)]$

$y - 5 = 3(x + 3)$

$y - 5 = 3x + 9$

$y = 3x + 14$

The equation of the line is $y = 3x + 14$.

25. The slope is undefined; $(x_1, y_1) = (-5, -1)$.

The line is a vertical line. All points on the line have an abscissa of -5. The equation of the line is $x = -5$.

26. The slope is undefined; $(x_1, y_1) = (0, 4)$.

The line is a vertical line. All points on the line have an abscissa of 0. The equation of the line is $x = 0$. The line is the y-axis.

Objective 3.5.2 Exercises

27. $P_1(0, 2)$, $P_2(3, 5)$

$m = \dfrac{y_2 - y_1}{x_2 - x_1} = \dfrac{5 - 2}{3 - 0} = \dfrac{3}{3} = 1$

$y - y_1 = m(x - x_1)$

$y - 2 = 1(x - 0)$

$y - 2 = x$

$y = x + 2$

The equation of the line is $y = x + 2$.

28. $P_1(0, 4)$, $P_2(1, 5)$

$m = \dfrac{y_2 - y_1}{x_2 - x_1} = \dfrac{5 - 4}{1 - 0} = \dfrac{1}{1} = 1$

$y - y_1 = m(x - x_1)$

$y - 4 = 1(x - 0)$

$y - 4 = x$

$y = x + 4$

The equation of the line is $y = x + 4$.

29. $P_1(0, -3)$, $P_2(-4, 5)$

$m = \dfrac{y_2 - y_1}{x_2 - x_1} = \dfrac{5 - (-3)}{-4 - 0} = \dfrac{8}{-4} = -2$

$y - y_1 = m(x - x_1)$

$y - (-3) = -2(x - 0)$

$y + 3 = -2x$

$y = -2x - 3$

The equation of the line is $y = -2x - 3$.

30. $P_1(0, -2)$, $P_2(-3, 4)$

$m = \dfrac{y_2 - y_1}{x_2 - x_1} = \dfrac{4 - (-2)}{-3 - 0} = \dfrac{6}{-3} = -2$

$y - y_1 = m(x - x_1)$

$y - (-2) = -2(x - 0)$

$y + 2 = -2x$

$y = -2x - 2$

The equation of the line is $y = -2x - 2$.

31. $P_1(-1, 3)$, $P_2(2, 4)$

$m = \dfrac{y_2 - y_1}{x_2 - x_1} = \dfrac{4 - 3}{2 - (-1)} = \dfrac{1}{3}$

$y - y_1 = m(x - x_1)$

$y - 3 = \dfrac{1}{3}[x - (-1)]$

$y - 3 = \dfrac{1}{3}(x + 1)$

$y - 3 = \dfrac{1}{3}x + \dfrac{1}{3}$

$y = \dfrac{1}{3}x + \dfrac{10}{3}$

The equation of the line is $y = \dfrac{1}{3}x + \dfrac{10}{3}$.

32. $P_1(-1, 1)$, $P_2(4, 4)$

$m = \dfrac{y_2 - y_1}{x_2 - x_1} = \dfrac{4 - 1}{4 - (-1)} = \dfrac{3}{5}$

$y - y_1 = m(x - x_1)$

$y - 1 = \dfrac{3}{5}[x - (-1)]$

$y - 1 = \dfrac{3}{5}(x + 1)$

$y - 1 = \dfrac{3}{5}x + \dfrac{3}{5}$

$y = \dfrac{3}{5}x + \dfrac{8}{5}$

The equation of the line is $y = \dfrac{3}{5}x + \dfrac{8}{5}$.

33. $P_1(0, 3)$, $P_2(2, 0)$

$m = \dfrac{y_2 - y_1}{x_2 - x_1} = \dfrac{0 - 3}{2 - 0} = \dfrac{-3}{2} = -\dfrac{3}{2}$

$y - y_1 = m(x - x_1)$

$y - 3 = -\dfrac{3}{2}(x - 0)$

$y - 3 = -\dfrac{3}{2}x$

$y = -\dfrac{3}{2}x + 3$

The equation of the line is $y = -\dfrac{3}{2}x + 3$.

34. $P_1(0, 4)$, $P_2(2, 0)$

$m = \dfrac{y_2 - y_1}{x_2 - x_1} = \dfrac{0 - 4}{2 - 0} = \dfrac{-4}{2} = -2$

$y - y_1 = m(x - x_1)$

$y - 4 = -2(x - 0)$

$y - 4 = -2x$

$y = -2x + 4$

The equation of the line is $y = -2x + 4$.

35. $P_1(-2,-3)$, $P_2(-1,-2)$

$$m = \frac{y_2 - y_1}{x_2 - x_1} = \frac{-2-(-3)}{-1-(-2)} = \frac{1}{1} = 1$$
$$y - y_1 = m(x - x_1)$$
$$y - (-3) = 1[x - (-2)]$$
$$y + 3 = x + 2$$
$$y = x - 1$$

The equation of the line is $y = x - 1$.

36. $P_1(4,1)$, $P_2(3,-2)$

$$m = \frac{y_2 - y_1}{x_2 - x_1} = \frac{-2-1}{3-4} = \frac{-3}{-1} = 3$$
$$y - y_1 = m(x - x_1)$$
$$y - 1 = 3(x - 4)$$
$$y - 1 = 3x - 12$$
$$y = 3x - 11$$

The equation of the line is $y = 3x - 11$.

37. $P_1(2,3)$, $P_2(5,5)$

$$m = \frac{y_2 - y_1}{x_2 - x_1} = \frac{5-3}{5-2} = \frac{2}{3}$$
$$y - y_1 = m(x - x_1)$$
$$y - 3 = \frac{2}{3}(x - 2)$$
$$y - 3 = \frac{2}{3}x - \frac{4}{3}$$
$$y = \frac{2}{3}x + \frac{5}{3}$$

The equation of the line is $y = \frac{2}{3}x + \frac{5}{3}$.

38. $P_1(7,2)$, $P_2(4,4)$

$$m = \frac{y_2 - y_1}{x_2 - x_1} = \frac{4-2}{4-7} = \frac{2}{-3} = -\frac{2}{3}$$
$$y - y_1 = m(x - x_1)$$
$$y - 2 = -\frac{2}{3}(x - 7)$$
$$y - 2 = -\frac{2}{3}x + \frac{14}{3}$$
$$y = -\frac{2}{3}x + \frac{20}{3}$$

The equation of the line is $y = -\frac{2}{3}x + \frac{20}{3}$.

39. $P_1(2,0)$, $P_2(0,-1)$

$$m = \frac{y_2 - y_1}{x_2 - x_1} = \frac{-1-0}{0-2} = \frac{-1}{-2} = \frac{1}{2}$$
$$y - y_1 = m(x - x_1)$$
$$y - 0 = \frac{1}{2}(x - 2)$$
$$y = \frac{1}{2}x - 1$$

The equation of the line is $y = \frac{1}{2}x - 1$.

40. $P_1(0,4)$, $P_2(-2,0)$

$$m = \frac{y_2 - y_1}{x_2 - x_1} = \frac{0-4}{-2-0} = \frac{-4}{-2} = 2$$
$$y - y_1 = m(x - x_1)$$
$$y - 4 = 2(x - 0)$$
$$y - 4 = 2x$$
$$y = 2x + 4$$

The equation of the line is $y = 2x + 4$.

41. $P_1(3,-4)$, $P_2(-2,-4)$

$$m = \frac{y_2 - y_1}{x_2 - x_1} = \frac{-4-(-4)}{-2-3} = \frac{0}{-5} = 0$$
$$y - y_1 = m(x - x_1)$$
$$y - (-4) = 0(x - 3)$$
$$y + 4 = 0$$
$$y = -4$$

The equation of the line is $y = -4$.

42. $P_1(-3,3)$, $P_2(-2,3)$

$$m = \frac{y_2 - y_1}{x_2 - x_1} = \frac{3-3}{-2-(-3)} = \frac{0}{1} = 0$$
$$y - y_1 = m(x - x_1)$$
$$y - 3 = 0[x - (-3)]$$
$$y - 3 = 0$$
$$y = 3$$

The equation of the line is $y = 3$.

43. $P_1(0,0)$, $P_2(4,3)$

$$m = \frac{y_2 - y_1}{x_2 - x_1} = \frac{3-0}{4-0} = \frac{3}{4}$$
$$y - y_1 = m(x - x_1)$$
$$y - 0 = \frac{3}{4}(x - 0)$$
$$y = \frac{3}{4}x$$

The equation of the line is $y = \frac{3}{4}x$.

44. $P_1(2,-5)$, $P_2(0,0)$

$$m = \frac{y_2 - y_1}{x_2 - x_1} = \frac{0-(-5)}{0-2} = \frac{5}{-2} = -\frac{5}{2}$$
$$y - y_1 = m(x - x_1)$$
$$y - (-5) = -\frac{5}{2}(x - 2)$$
$$y + 5 = -\frac{5}{2}x + 5$$
$$y = -\frac{5}{2}x$$

The equation of the line is $y = -\frac{5}{2}x$.

45. $P_1(-2,5)$, $P_2(-2,-5)$

$$m = \frac{y_2 - y_1}{x_2 - x_1} = \frac{-5-5}{-2-(-2)} = \frac{-10}{0}$$

The slope is undefined. The line is a vertical line. All points on the line have an abscissa of -2. The equation of the line is $x = -2$.

46. $P_1(3, 2)$, $P_2(3, -4)$

$$m = \frac{y_2 - y_1}{x_2 - x_1} = \frac{-4 - 2}{3 - 3} = \frac{-6}{0}$$

The slope is undefined. The line is a vertical line. All points on the line have an abscissa of 3. The equation of the line is $x = 3$.

47. $P_1(2, 1)$, $P_2(-2, -3)$

$$m = \frac{y_2 - y_1}{x_2 - x_1} = \frac{-3 - 1}{-2 - 2} = \frac{-4}{-4} = 1$$

$y - y_1 = m(x - x_1)$
$y - 1 = 1(x - 2)$
$y - 1 = x - 2$
$y = x - 1$

The equation of the line is $y = x - 1$.

48. $P_1(-3, -2)$, $P_2(1, -4)$

$$m = \frac{y_2 - y_1}{x_2 - x_1} = \frac{-4 - (-2)}{1 - (-3)} = \frac{-2}{4} = -\frac{1}{2}$$

$y - y_1 = m(x - x_1)$

$y - (-2) = -\frac{1}{2}[x - (-3)]$

$y + 2 = -\frac{1}{2}(x + 3)$

$y + 2 = -\frac{1}{2}x - \frac{3}{2}$

$y = -\frac{1}{2}x - \frac{7}{2}$

The equation of the line is $y = -\frac{1}{2}x - \frac{7}{2}$.

49. $P_1(0, 3)$, $P_2(3, 0)$

$$m = \frac{y_2 - y_1}{x_2 - x_1} = \frac{0 - 3}{3 - 0} = \frac{-3}{3} = -1$$

$y - y_1 = m(x - x_1)$
$y - 3 = -1(x - 0)$
$y - 3 = -x$
$y = -x + 3$

The equation of the line is $y = -x + 3$.

50. $P_1(1, -3)$, $P_2(-2, 4)$

$$m = \frac{y_2 - y_1}{x_2 - x_1} = \frac{4 - (-3)}{-2 - 1} = \frac{7}{-3} = -\frac{7}{3}$$

$y - y_1 = m(x - x_1)$

$y - (-3) = -\frac{7}{3}(x - 1)$

$y + 3 = -\frac{7}{3}x + \frac{7}{3}$

$y = -\frac{7}{3}x - \frac{2}{3}$

The equation of the line is $y = -\frac{7}{3}x - \frac{2}{3}$.

Objective 3.5.3 Exercises

51. Strategy
Use the slope-intercept form to determine the equation of the line.

Solution
y-intercept = 0
$m = 1200$
$y = mx + b$
$y = 1200x + 0$
The equation that represents the ascent of the plane is $y = 1200x$ where x stands for the number of minutes after take-off. To find the height of the plane when $x = 11$
$y = 1200(11)$
$y = 13,200$
The plane will be 13,200 feet in the air after 11 minutes.

52. Strategy
Use the slope-intercept form to determine the equation of the line.

Solution
y-intercept = 0
$m = 14$
$y = mx + b$
$y = 14x + 0$
The equation that represents the number of calories burned by the jogger is $y = 14x$ where x is the number of minutes run. To find the number of calories when $x = 32$
$y = 14 \cdot 32$
$y = 448$
The jogger will burn 448 calories after running 32 minutes.

53. Strategy
Use the slope-intercept form to find the equation.

Solution
The y-intercept is 4.95 because it is the charge for 0 minutes.
$b = 4.95$
$m = 0.59$
$y = mx + b$
$y = 0.59x + 4.95$
The equation for the monthly cost of the phone is $y = 0.59x + 4.95$.
To find the cost for 13 minutes of use,
$y = 0.59(13) + 4.95$
$y = 12.62$
It costs $12.62 to use the cellular phone for 13 minutes.

54. Strategy
Use the slope-intercept form of the equation.

Solution
The y-intercept is 5200 and the slope is 1000.
$y = mx + b$
$y = 1000x + 5200$
The equation representing the height in terms of time after take-off is $y = 1000x + 5200$. To find the height of the plane 8 minutes after take-off
$y = 1000 \cdot 8 + 5200$
$y = 13,200$

After 8 minutes, the height of the plane will be 13,200 feet.

55. Strategy
Use the point-slope formula.

Solution
$(x_1, y_1) = (2, 126)$, $(x_2, y_2) = (3, 189)$
$m = \dfrac{189 - 126}{3 - 2} = 63$
$y - y_1 = m(x - x_1)$
$y - y_1 = 63(x - x_1)$
$y - 126 = 63(x - 2)$
$y - 126 = 63x - 126$
$y = 63x$

The equation to approximate the number of calories in a hamburger is $y = 63x$ where x represents the ounces in the hamburger. To predict the number of calories in a 5-ounce serving of hamburger,
$y = 63 \cdot 5$
$y = 315$
A 5-ounce serving of hamburger will contain 315 calories.

56. Strategy
Use the point-slope formula.

Solution
$(x_1, y_1) = (0, 100)$, $(x_2, y_2) = (2, 93)$
$m = \dfrac{y_2 - y_1}{x_2 - x_1} = \dfrac{93 - 100}{2 - 0} = -\dfrac{7}{2}$
$y - y_1 = m(x - x_1)$
$y - 100 = -\dfrac{7}{2}(x - 0)$
$y - 100 = -\dfrac{7}{2}x$
$y = -\dfrac{7}{2}x + 100$

The equation to predict the boiling point is
$y = -\dfrac{7}{2}x + 100$ or $y = -3.5x + 100$, where x is the altitude above sea level. To predict the boiling point for an altitude of 8.85 kilometers,
$y = -\dfrac{7}{2}(8.85) + 100$
$y = -31.0 + 100 = 69$
The boiling point on the top of Mount Everest is approximately 69°C.

57. Strategy
Use the point-slope formula.

Solution
$(x_1, y_1) = (1927, 33.5)$, $(x_2, y_2) = (1997, 3.3)$
$m = \dfrac{y_2 - y_1}{x_2 - x_1} = \dfrac{3.3 - 33.5}{1997 - 1927} = \dfrac{-30.2}{70} = -0.431$
$y - y_1 = m(x - x_1)$
$y - 33.5 = -0.431(x - 1927)$
$y - 33.5 = -0.431x + 830.5$
$y = -0.431x + 864$

The equation to predict how long a flight took is $y = -0.431x + 864$ where x represents the year. To predict how long a flight between the two cities would have taken in 1967,
$y = -0.431(1967) + 864$
$= -847.8 + 864 = 16.2$
It would have taken 16.2 hours in 1967 for a plane to cross the Atlantic.

58. Strategy
Use the point-slope form where all y-values are in millions.

Solution
$(x_1, y_1) = (1991, 24)$
$m = 2.4$
$y - y_1 = m(x - x_1)$
$y - 24 = 2.4(x - 1991)$
$y - 24 = 2.4x - 4778.4$
$y = 2.4x - 4754.4$
The equation to find the number of computers in homes is $y = 2.4x - 4754.4$ where x is the year. To predict the number of computers in homes in 2001,
$y = 2.4(2001) - 4754.4$
$y = 48$

48 million computers are predicted to be in homes in the year 2001.

59. Strategy
Use the slope-intercept form of the equation.

Solution
The y-intercept is 16 gallons because 0 miles have been driven at the beginning of the trip. The slope is –0.032.
$y = mx + b$
$y = -0.032x + 16$
The equation to find the number of gallons in the tank is $y = -0.032x + 16$ where x represents the number of miles traveled. To predict the number of gallons in the tank after 150 miles,
$y = -0.032(150) + 16$
$y = 11.2$

11.2 gallons will be in the tank when 150 miles have been driven.

60. **Strategy**
Use the point-slope formula.

Solution
$(x_1, y_1) = (1000, 1480)$
$m = 0.017$
$y - y_1 = m(x - x_1)$
$y - 1480 = 0.017(x - 1000)$
$y - 1480 = 0.017x - 17$
$y = 0.017x + 1463$

The equation that can be used to approximate the speed of sound below sea level is
$y = 0.017x + 1463$. To find the speed of sound 2500 meters below sea level,
$y = 0.017(2500) + 1463$
$y = 1505.5$

The approximate speed of sound 2500 meters below sea level is 1506 m/s.

Applying Concepts 3.5

61. To find the x-intercept, set y to 0.
$0 = mx + b$
$-b = mx$
$-\dfrac{b}{m} = x$

The x-intercept is $\left(-\dfrac{b}{m}, 0\right)$.

62. Find the equation of the line.
$m = \dfrac{1 - (-1)}{2 - 4} = \dfrac{2}{-2} = -1$
$y - (-1) = -1(x - 4)$
$y + 1 = -x + 4$
$y = -x + 3$
$x = 0, \ y = -(0) + 3 = 3$
$x = 1, \ y = -1 + 3 = 2$
$x = 3, \ y = -3 + 3 = 0$

Three other points on the line are (0, 3), (1, 2), (3, 0).

63. Find the equation of the line. The two points are (1, 3) and (-1, 5).
$m = \dfrac{5 - 3}{-1 - 1} = \dfrac{2}{-2} = -1$
$y - 3 = -1(x - 1)$
$y - 3 = -x + 1$
$y = -x + 4$

The function is $f(x) = -x + 4$
$f(4) = -4 + 4 = 0$

64. Find the midpoint of the line segment.
$x_m = \dfrac{2 + (-4)}{2} = \dfrac{-2}{2} = -1$
$y_m = \dfrac{5 + 1}{2} = \dfrac{6}{2} = 3$

The midpoint is (-1, 3). Use the point-slope formula to find the equation of the line.
$y - y_1 = m(x - x_1)$
$y - 3 = -2[x - (-1)]$
$y - 3 = -2(x + 1)$
$y - 3 = -2x - 2$
$y = -2x + 1$

The equation of the line is $y = -2x + 1$.

65. If m is a given constant, changing b causes the graph of the line to move up or down.

66. The slope-intercept form of a straight line, $y = mx + b$, is the general form in which the equation of a straight line is written. Given the slope of a line and its y-intercept, the equation of the line can be written by substituting the slope for m, and the y-coordinate of the y-intercept for b, in the equation $y = mx + b$.
The point-slope formula, $y - y_1 = m(x - x_1)$, is used to find the equation of a line when the slope of the line and any point on the line other than the y-intercept are known. We substitute the known slope and the coordinates of the known point into the point-slope formula and then rewrite the equation in the slope-intercept form of a straight line.

67. The slope of any line parallel to the y-axis is undefined. In order to use the point-slope formula, we must be able to substitute the slope of the line for m. In other words, to use the point-slope formula, the slope of the line must be defined. Therefore, we cannot use the point-slope formula to find the equation of a line with undefined slope – that is, one that is parallel to the y-axis.

Section 3.6

Concept Review 3.6

1. Sometimes true
   The only time perpendicular lines have the same y-intercept is when the point of intersection of the two lines is on the y-axis.

2. Always true

3. Never true
   The product of the slopes of two perpendicular lines is equal to -1.
   $\left(\dfrac{3}{2}\right)\left(-\dfrac{3}{2}\right) = -\dfrac{9}{4}$; the lines are not perpendicular.

4. Never true
   Two lines are perpendicular if $m_1 \cdot m_2 = -1$.

5. Always true

6. Never true

The slope of a line parallel to the y-axis is undefined.

7. Always true

Objective 3.6.1 Exercises

1. We can determine whether two lines are parallel by looking at their slopes. If the slopes are equal, then the lines are parallel.

2. We can determine whether two lines are perpendicular by looking at their slopes. If one slope is the negative reciprocal of the other, then the lines are perpendicular.

3. The slope is -5. Parallel lines have the same slope.

4. The slope is $\dfrac{3}{2}$. Parallel lines have the same slope.

5. The slope is $-\dfrac{1}{4}$, the negative reciprocal of 4.

6. The slope is $\dfrac{5}{4}$, the negative reciprocal of $-\dfrac{4}{5}$.

7. $x = -2$ is a vertical line.

$y = 3$ is a horizontal line.

The lines are perpendicular.

8. $y = \dfrac{1}{2}$ is a horizontal line.

$y = -4$ is a horizontal line.

The lines are not perpendicular.

9. $x = -3$ is a vertical line.

$y = \dfrac{1}{3}$ is a horizontal line.

The lines are not parallel.

10. $x = 4$ is a vertical line.

$x = -4$ is a vertical line.

The lines are parallel.

11. $y = \dfrac{2}{3}x - 4, \ m_1 = \dfrac{2}{3}$

$y = -\dfrac{3}{2}x - 4, \ m_2 = -\dfrac{3}{2}$

$m_1 \neq m_2$

The lines are not parallel.

12. $y = -2x + \dfrac{2}{3}, \ m_1 = -2$

$y = -2x + 3, \ m_2 = -2$

$m_1 = m_2 = -2$

The lines are parallel.

13. $y = \dfrac{4}{3}x - 2, \ m_1 = \dfrac{4}{3}$

$y = -\dfrac{3}{4}x + 2, \ m_2 = -\dfrac{3}{4}$

$m_1 \cdot m_2 = \dfrac{4}{3}\left(-\dfrac{3}{4}\right) = -1$

The lines are perpendicular.

14. $y = \dfrac{1}{2}x + \dfrac{3}{2}, \ m_1 = \dfrac{1}{2}$

$y = -\dfrac{1}{2}x + \dfrac{3}{2}, \ m_2 = -\dfrac{1}{2}$

$m_1 \cdot m_2 = \dfrac{1}{2}\left(-\dfrac{1}{2}\right) = -\dfrac{1}{4}$

The lines are not perpendicular.

15. $2x + 3y = 2$

$\quad 3y = -2x + 2$

$\quad\quad y = -\dfrac{2}{3}x + \dfrac{2}{3}, \ m_1 = -\dfrac{2}{3}$

$2x + 3y = -4$

$\quad 3y = -2x - 4$

$\quad\quad y = -\dfrac{2}{3}x - \dfrac{4}{3}, \ m_2 = -\dfrac{2}{3}$

$m_1 = m_2 = -\dfrac{2}{3}$

The lines are parallel.

16. $2x - 4y = 3$

$\quad -4y = -2x + 3$

$\quad\quad y = \dfrac{1}{2}x - \dfrac{3}{4}, \ m_1 = \dfrac{1}{2}$

$2x + 4y = -3$

$\quad 4y = -2x - 3$

$\quad\quad y = -\dfrac{1}{2}x - \dfrac{3}{4}, \ m_2 = -\dfrac{1}{2}$

$m_1 \neq m_2$

The lines are not parallel.

17. $x - 4y = 2$

$\quad -4y = -x + 2$

$\quad\quad y = \dfrac{1}{4}x - \dfrac{1}{2}, \ m_1 = \dfrac{1}{4}$

$4x + y = 8$

$\quad\quad y = -4x + 8, \ m_2 = -4$

$m_1 \cdot m_2 = \dfrac{1}{4}(-4) = -1$

The lines are perpendicular.

18. $4x - 3y = 2$

$\quad -3y = -4x + 2$

$\quad\quad y = \dfrac{4}{3}x - \dfrac{2}{3}, \ m_1 = \dfrac{4}{3}$

$4x + 3y = -7$

$\quad 3y = -4x - 7$

$\quad\quad y = -\dfrac{4}{3}x - \dfrac{7}{3}, \ m_2 = -\dfrac{4}{3}$

$m_1 \cdot m_2 = \dfrac{4}{3}\left(-\dfrac{4}{3}\right) = -\dfrac{16}{9}$

The lines are not perpendicular.

19. $m_1 = \dfrac{6-2}{1-3} = \dfrac{4}{-2} = -2$

$m_2 = \dfrac{-1-3}{-1-(-1)} = \dfrac{-4}{0}$

$m_1 \neq m_2$

The lines are not parallel.

20. $m_1 = \dfrac{5-(-3)}{2-4} = \dfrac{8}{-2} = -4$

$m_2 = \dfrac{1-(-3)}{-4-(-2)} = \dfrac{4}{-2} = -2$

$m_1 \neq m_2$

The lines are not parallel.

21. $m_1 = \dfrac{-1-2}{4-(-3)} = \dfrac{-3}{7} = -\dfrac{3}{7}$

$m_2 = \dfrac{-4-3}{-2-1} = \dfrac{-7}{-3} = \dfrac{7}{3}$

$m_1 \cdot m_2 = -\dfrac{3}{7}\left(\dfrac{7}{3}\right) = -1$

The lines are perpendicular.

22. $m_1 = \dfrac{4-2}{3-(-1)} = \dfrac{2}{4} = \dfrac{1}{2}$

$m_2 = \dfrac{1-3}{-4-(-1)} = \dfrac{-2}{-3} = \dfrac{2}{3}$

$m_1 \cdot m_2 = \dfrac{1}{2}\left(\dfrac{2}{3}\right) = \dfrac{1}{3} \neq -1$

The lines are not perpendicular.

23. $m_1 = \dfrac{2-0}{0-(-5)} = \dfrac{2}{5}$

$m_2 = \dfrac{-1-1}{0-5} = \dfrac{-2}{-5} = \dfrac{2}{5}$

$m_1 = m_2 = \dfrac{2}{5}$

The lines are parallel.

24. $m_1 = \dfrac{3-5}{-3-3} = \dfrac{-2}{-6} = \dfrac{1}{3}$

$m_2 = \dfrac{4-(-5)}{-4-2} = \dfrac{9}{-6} = -\dfrac{3}{2}$

$m_1 \cdot m_2 = \dfrac{1}{3}\left(-\dfrac{3}{2}\right) = -\dfrac{1}{2} \neq -1$

The lines are not perpendicular.

25. $2x - 3y = 2$

$-3y = -2x + 2$

$y = \dfrac{2}{3}x - \dfrac{2}{3}$

$m = \dfrac{2}{3}$

$y - y_1 = m(x - x_1)$

$y - (-4) = \dfrac{2}{3}[x - (-2)]$

$y + 4 = \dfrac{2}{3}(x + 2)$

$y + 4 = \dfrac{2}{3}x + \dfrac{4}{3}$

$y = \dfrac{2}{3}x - \dfrac{8}{3}$

The equation of the line is $y = \dfrac{2}{3}x - \dfrac{8}{3}$.

26. $3x + y = -3$

$y = -3x - 3$

$m = -3$

$y - y_1 = m(x - x_1)$

$y - 2 = -3(x - 3)$

$y - 2 = -3x + 9$

$y = -3x + 11$

The equation of the line is $y = -3x + 11$.

27. $y = -3x + 4$

$m_1 = -3$

$m_1 \cdot m_2 = -1$

$-3 \cdot m_2 = -1$

$m_2 = \dfrac{1}{3}$

$y - y_1 = m(x - x_1)$

$y - 1 = \dfrac{1}{3}(x - 4)$

$y - 1 = \dfrac{1}{3}x - \dfrac{4}{3}$

$y = \dfrac{1}{3}x - \dfrac{1}{3}$

The equation of the line is $y = \dfrac{1}{3}x - \dfrac{1}{3}$.

28. $y = \dfrac{5}{2}x - 4$

$m_1 = \dfrac{5}{2}$

$m_1 \cdot m_2 = -1$

$\dfrac{5}{2} \cdot m_2 = -1$

$m_2 = -\dfrac{2}{5}$

$y - y_1 = m(x - x_1)$

$y - (-5) = -\dfrac{2}{5}(x - 2)$

$y + 5 = -\dfrac{2}{5}x + \dfrac{4}{5}$

$y = -\dfrac{2}{5}x - \dfrac{21}{5}$

The equation of the line is $y = -\dfrac{2}{5}x - \dfrac{21}{5}$.

29. $3x - 5y = 2$

$-5y = -3x + 2$

$y = \dfrac{3}{5}x - \dfrac{2}{5}$

$m_1 = \dfrac{3}{5}$

$m_1 \cdot m_2 = -1$

$\dfrac{3}{5} \cdot m_2 = -1$

$m_2 = -\dfrac{5}{3}$

$y - y_1 = m(x - x_1)$

$y - (-3) = -\dfrac{5}{3}[x - (-1)]$

$y + 3 = -\dfrac{5}{3}(x + 1)$

$y + 3 = -\dfrac{5}{3}x - \dfrac{5}{3}$

$y = -\dfrac{5}{3}x - \dfrac{14}{3}$

The equation of the line is $y = -\dfrac{5}{3}x - \dfrac{14}{3}$.

30. $2x + 4y = -1$

$4y = -2x - 1$

$y = -\dfrac{1}{2}x - \dfrac{1}{4}$

$m_1 = -\dfrac{1}{2}$

$m_1 \cdot m_2 = -1$

$-\dfrac{1}{2} \cdot m_2 = -1$

$m_2 = 2$

$y - y_1 = m(x - x_1)$

$y - 3 = 2[x - (-1)]$

$y - 3 = 2(x + 1)$

$y - 3 = 2x + 2$

$y = 2x + 5$

The equation of the line is $y = 2x + 5$.

Applying Concepts 3.6

31. Write the equations of the lines in slope-intercept form.

(1) $A_1 x + B_1 y = C_1$

$\qquad B_1 y = C_1 - A_1 x$

$\qquad y = \dfrac{C_1}{B_1} - \dfrac{A_1}{B_1}x$

(2) $A_2 x + B_2 y = C_2$

$\qquad B_2 y = C_2 - A_2 x$

$\qquad y = \dfrac{C_2}{B_2} - \dfrac{A_2}{B_2}x$

The slopes of the two lines must be the same for the lines to be parallel, so $\dfrac{A_1}{B_1} = \dfrac{A_2}{B_2}$.

32. Write the equations of the lines in slope-intercept form.

(1) $A_1 x + B_1 y = C_1$

$\qquad B_1 y = C_1 - A_1 x$

$\qquad y = \dfrac{C_1}{B_1} - \dfrac{A_1}{B_1}x$

(2) $A_2 x + B_2 y = C_2$

$\qquad B_2 y = C_2 - A_2 x$

$\qquad y = \dfrac{C_2}{B_2} - \dfrac{A_2}{B_2}x$

The slope of the second line must be the negative reciprocal of the first for the lines to be perpendicular, so $\dfrac{A_1}{B_1} = -\dfrac{B_2}{A_2}$.

33. Strategy

To find the equation of the line on the initial path
• Find the slope of the line of the string
• Find the slope of the line on the initial path which is perpendicular to the line of the string.
• Use the point slope form to find the equation of the line of the initial path.

Solution
Slope of the string,

$m_1 = \dfrac{3 - 0}{6 - 0} = \dfrac{1}{2}$

Slope of the line on the initial path,

$m_1 \cdot m_2 = -1$

$\dfrac{1}{2} \cdot m_2 = -1$

$m_2 = -2$

Equation of the line,

$y - y_1 = m(x - x_1)$

$y - 3 = -2[x - 6]$

$y - 3 = -2x + 12$

$y = -2x + 15$

The equation of the line is $y = -2x + 15$.

34. Strategy
To find the equation of the line on the initial path
• Find the slope of the line of the string
• Find the slope of the line on the initial path
which is perpendicular to the line of the string.
• Use the point slope form to find the equation of
the line of the initial path.

Solution
Slope of the string,

$$m_1 = \frac{8-0}{2-0} = 4$$

Slope of the line on the initial path,

$$m_1 \cdot m_2 = -1$$
$$4 \cdot m_2 = -1$$
$$m_2 = -\frac{1}{4}$$

Equation of the line,

$$y - y_1 = m(x - x_1)$$
$$y - 8 = -\frac{1}{4}[x - 2]$$
$$y - 8 = -\frac{1}{4}x + \frac{1}{2}$$
$$y = -\frac{1}{4}x + \frac{17}{2}$$

The equation of the line is $y = -\frac{1}{4}x + \frac{17}{2}$.

35. Strategy
Find a line perpendicular to either of the given
lines. The line must form a triangle with the
other two lines, so the line cannot go through the
point (6, –1).

Solution

Start with the line $y = -\frac{1}{2}x + 2$.

The slope of a line perpendicular to this line is 2,
and the line has the form $y = 2x + b$. Since the
line cannot go through the point (6, –1), the value
of b cannot be –13. So one possible solution is
any equation of the form $y = 2x + b$, where
$b \neq -13$.

Now consider the line $y = \frac{2}{3}x + 5$. The slope of a

line perpendicular to this line is $-\frac{3}{2}$, and the

line has the form $y = -\frac{3}{2}x + c$. Since the line

cannot go through the point (6, –1), the value of c
cannot be 8. So the other possible solution is any

equation of the form $y = -\frac{3}{2}x + c$, where $c \neq 8$.

36a. Strategy
• Find the slope of the line passing through P and
C.
• Using a slope perpendicular to the slope of the
line PC and passing through point P, define the
equation of the tangent line.

Solution
$$m = \frac{y_2 - y_1}{x_2 - x_1} = \frac{4-2}{5-3} = 1$$
The negative reciprocal of 1 is –1.
$$y - y_1 = m(x - x_1)$$
$$y - 4 = -1(x - 5)$$
$$y - 4 = -x + 5$$
$$y = -x + 9$$
The equation of the tangent line is $y = -x + 9$.

36b. The equation of the tangent line is $y = -x + 9$.
y-intercept: (0, 9)
x-intercept: (9, 0)

Section 3.7

Concept Review 3.7

1. Never true
    The solution of a linear inequality is a half-plane.

2. Always true

3. Always true

4. Never true
    The solution is a half-plane. For any value of the
    independent variable, there are an infinite
    number of values of the dependent variable.

5. Always true

6. Always true

Objective 3.7.1 Exercises

1. A half-plane is the set of points on one side of a
    line in the plane.

2. Choose a point that is not on the line
    corresponding to the inequality. If the point is a
    solution of the inequality, the half-plane
    containing the point should be shaded. If the
    point is not a solution of the inequality, the half-
    plane not containing the point should be shaded.

3. $0 > 2(0) - 7$
    $0 > -7$
    Yes

4. $0 < 5(0) + 3$
    $0 < 3$
    Yes

5. $0 \leq -\frac{2}{3}(0) - 8$
    $0 \not\leq -8$
    No

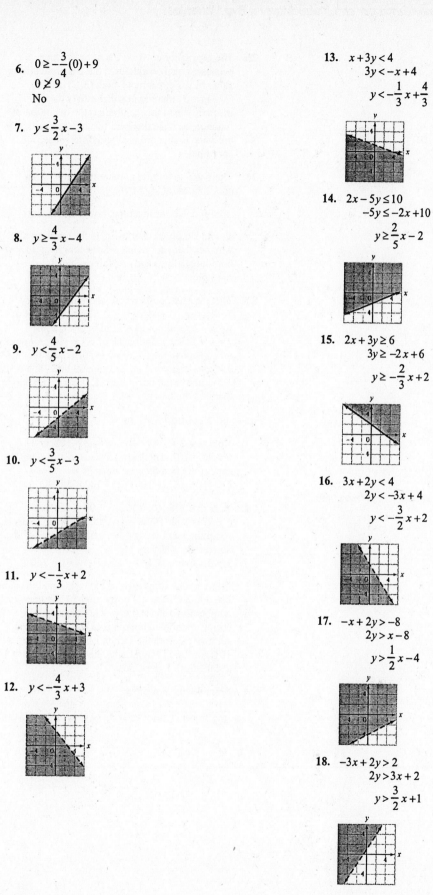

6. $0 \geq -\frac{3}{4}(0) + 9$

    $0 \not\geq 9$

    No

7. $y \leq \frac{3}{2}x - 3$

8. $y \geq \frac{4}{3}x - 4$

9. $y < \frac{4}{5}x - 2$

10. $y < \frac{3}{5}x - 3$

11. $y < -\frac{1}{3}x + 2$

12. $y < -\frac{4}{3}x + 3$

13. $x + 3y < 4$

    $3y < -x + 4$

    $y < -\frac{1}{3}x + \frac{4}{3}$

14. $2x - 5y \leq 10$

    $-5y \leq -2x + 10$

    $y \geq \frac{2}{5}x - 2$

15. $2x + 3y \geq 6$

    $3y \geq -2x + 6$

    $y \geq -\frac{2}{3}x + 2$

16. $3x + 2y < 4$

    $2y < -3x + 4$

    $y < -\frac{3}{2}x + 2$

17. $-x + 2y > -8$

    $2y > x - 8$

    $y > \frac{1}{2}x - 4$

18. $-3x + 2y > 2$

    $2y > 3x + 2$

    $y > \frac{3}{2}x + 1$

19. $y - 4 < 0$

$\quad\quad y < 4$

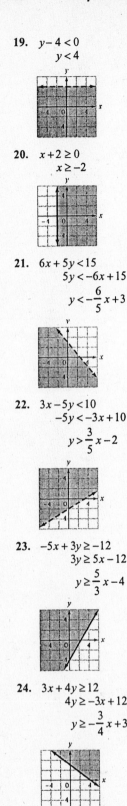

20. $x + 2 \geq 0$

$\quad\quad x \geq -2$

21. $6x + 5y < 15$

$\quad\quad 5y < -6x + 15$

$\quad\quad y < -\dfrac{6}{5}x + 3$

22. $3x - 5y < 10$

$\quad\quad -5y < -3x + 10$

$\quad\quad y > \dfrac{3}{5}x - 2$

23. $-5x + 3y \geq -12$

$\quad\quad 3y \geq 5x - 12$

$\quad\quad y \geq \dfrac{5}{3}x - 4$

24. $3x + 4y \geq 12$

$\quad\quad 4y \geq -3x + 12$

$\quad\quad y \geq -\dfrac{3}{4}x + 3$

25. The inequality $y < 3x - 1$ is not a function because, given a value of x, there is more than one value of y. For example, both $(3, 2)$ and $(3, -1)$ are ordered pairs that satisfy the inequality, and this contradicts the definition of function because there are two ordered pairs with the same first coordinate and different second coordinates.

26. There are an infinite number of points whose coordinates satisfy both $y \leq x + 3$ and $y \geq -\dfrac{1}{2}x + 1$. At this time, however, students should simply answer "yes" to the question of whether there are points whose coordinates satisfy both inequalities and cite three of them; for example, $(2, 3)$, $(6, 0)$, and $(8, -1)$.

27. There are no points whose coordinates satisfy both $y \leq x - 1$ and $y \geq x + 2$. The solution set of $y \leq x - 1$ is all points on and below the line $y = x - 1$. The solution set of $y \geq x + 2$ is all points on and above the line $y = x + 2$. Because the lines $y = x - 1$ and $y = x + 2$ are parallel lines, and $y = x + 2$ is above the line $y = x - 1$, there are no points that lie both below $y = x - 1$ and above $y = x + 2$.

Focus on Problem Solving

1. Note that $2 + 100 = 102$, $4 + 98 = 102$, and $6 + 96 = 102$. There are 25 sums of 102. Thus the sum of the first 50 even integers is
$2 + 4 + 6 + \ldots + 100 = 25 \cdot 102 = 2550$

2. Note that $1 + 101 = 102$, $3 + 99 = 102$, and $5 + 97 = 102$. There is an odd number of integers, so all the numbers will not pair. The sum will be 25 pairs of 102 plus 51.
$1 + 3 + 5 + \ldots + 101 = 25 \cdot 102 + 51 = 2601$

3. Compare the sum listed in Exercise 1 and the sum listed in Exercise 2. For the first 50 numbers, each number in Exercise 3 is one less than the corresponding number in Exercise 1, so we can subtract 50 from the sum in Exercise 1. Then add 101, for the 51st number in the sum in Exercise 3.
$2550 - 50 + 101 = 2601$.

4. From the pattern shown,
$\dfrac{1}{1 \cdot 2} + \dfrac{1}{2 \cdot 3} + \dfrac{1}{3 \cdot 4} + \ldots + \dfrac{1}{49 \cdot 50} = \dfrac{49}{50}$.

5.

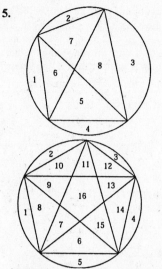

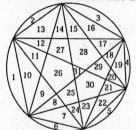

With two points, the chord divides the circle into 2 regions. With three points, the chords divide the circle into 4 or 2^2 regions. With four points, the chords divide the circle into 8 or 2^3 regions. With five points, the chords divide the circle into 16 or 2^4 regions.

Conjecture: When n points are chosen, the chords will divide the circle into 2^{n-1} regions.

With six points, the chords should divide the circle into $2^5 = 32$ regions. As you can see from the diagram, the circle is divided into 31 regions when 6 points are used. Our conjecture is not true.

6.

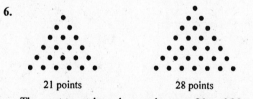

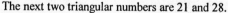

21 points   28 points

The next two triangular numbers are 21 and 28.

Projects and Group Activities

Introduction to Graphing Calculators

1. $y = 2x + 1$

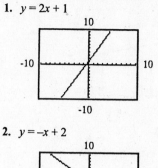

2. $y = -x + 2$

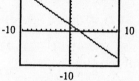

3. $3x + 2y = 6$
$$2y = -3x + 6$$
$$y = -\frac{3}{2}x + 3$$

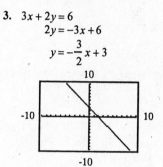

4. $y = 50x$

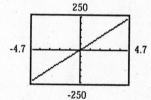

5. $y = \frac{2}{3}x - 3$

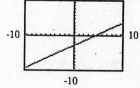

6. $4x + 3y = 75$

$3y = -4x + 75$

$y = -\dfrac{4}{3}x + 25$

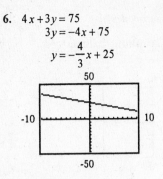

Wind-Chill Index

1. See the answer to Exercise 7.

2. Domain: {35, 30, 25, 20, 15, 10, 5, 0, –5, –10, –15, –20, –25, –30, –35}
   Range: {–59, –53, –47, –41, –35, –28, –22, –16, –10, –4, 3, 9, 15, 21, 27}

3. Yes

4. All the ordered pairs satisfy the function.

5. –65°F

6a. The *x*-intercept is (13, 0). Given a wind speed of 10 mph, the wind-chill index is 0°F when the air temperature is 13°F.

6b. The *y*-intercept is (0, –16). Given a wind speed of 10 mph, the wind-chill index is –16°F when the air temperature is 0°F.

7.

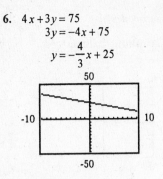

8. The points are lower on the coordinate axes. This means that when temperature remains constant and the wind speed increases the wind chill index decreases.

9. No, the lines are not parallel. At higher temperatures, the wind speed has less of an effect on the wind-chill index. At lower temperatures, the wind has more of an effect on the wind-chill index.

10a. The equation is $y = 1.425x - 38.5$, where *x* is the air temperature in degrees Fahrenheit and *y* is the wind-chill index.

10b. The *y*-intercept of this equation is (0, –38.5), vs (0, –16) for the equation $y = 1.2357x - 16$. The *y*-intercept (0, –38.5) is 22.5 units lower on the coordinate axes. Under the new formula, the wind-chill index is warmer than it was under the old formula.

Chapter Review Exercises

1. $y = \dfrac{x}{x-2}$

   $y = \dfrac{4}{4-2}$

   $y = 2$

   The ordered pair is (4, 2).

2. $x_m = \dfrac{x_1 + x_2}{2} = \dfrac{-2+3}{2} = \dfrac{1}{2}$

   $y_m = \dfrac{y_1 + y_2}{2} = \dfrac{4+5}{2} = \dfrac{9}{2}$

   Length $= \sqrt{(x_2 - x_1)^2 + (y_2 - y_1)^2}$

   $= \sqrt{[3-(-2)]^2 + (5-4)^2}$

   $= \sqrt{5^2 + 1^2}$

   $= \sqrt{26}$

   The midpoint is $\left(\dfrac{1}{2}, \dfrac{9}{2}\right)$ and the length is $\sqrt{26}$.

3. $y = x^2 - 2$
   Ordered pairs: (–2, 2)
   (–1, –1)
   (0, –2)
   (1, –1)
   (2, 2)

4.

5. $P(x) = 3x + 4$
   $P(-2) = 3(-2) + 4 = -2$

   $P(a) = 3(a) + 4$
   $P(a) = 3a + 4$

6. Domain = {–1, 0, 1, 2, 5}
   Range = {0, 2, 3}

7.
$$f(x) = x^2 - 2$$
$$f(-2) = (-2)^2 - 2 = 2$$
$$f(-1) = (-1)^2 - 2 = -1$$
$$f(0) = 0^2 - 2 = -2$$
$$f(1) = 1^2 - 2 = -1$$
$$f(2) = 2^2 - 2 = 2$$
Range = {-2, -1, 2}

8. Division by zero is undefined. Therefore, -4 must be excluded from the domain.

9. To find the x-intercept, let $y = 0$.
$$4x - 6(0) = 12$$
$$4x = 12$$
$$x = 3$$
The x-intercept is (3, 0).
To find the y-intercept, let $x = 0$.
$$4(0) - 6y = 12$$
$$-6y = 12$$
$$y = -2$$
The y-intercept is (0, -2).

10.

11.

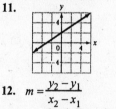

12. $m = \dfrac{y_2 - y_1}{x_2 - x_1}$

$m = \dfrac{2 - (-2)}{-1 - 3} = \dfrac{4}{-4} = -1$

13.

x-intercept	y-intercept
$3x + 2y = -4$	$3x + 2y = -4$
$3x + 2(0) = -4$	$3(0) + 2y = -4$
$3x = -4$	$2y = -4$
$x = -\dfrac{4}{3}$	$y = -2$
$\left(-\dfrac{4}{3}, 0\right)$	$(0, -2)$

14.

15. Use the point-slope form to find the equation of the line.
$$y - y_1 = m(x - x_1)$$
$$y - 4 = \frac{5}{2}[x - (-3)]$$
$$y - 4 = \frac{5}{2}(x + 3)$$
$$y - 4 = \frac{5}{2}x + \frac{15}{2}$$
$$y = \frac{5}{2}x + \frac{23}{2}$$
The equation of the line is $y = \dfrac{5}{2}x + \dfrac{23}{2}$.

16. $P_1(-2, 4)$, $P_2(4, -3)$
$$m = \frac{y_2 - y_1}{x_2 - x_1} = \frac{-3 - 4}{4 - (-2)} = \frac{-7}{6} = -\frac{7}{6}$$
$$y - y_1 = m(x - x_1)$$
$$y - 4 = -\frac{7}{6}[x - (-2)]$$
$$y - 4 = -\frac{7}{6}(x + 2)$$
$$y - 4 = -\frac{7}{6}x - \frac{7}{3}$$
$$y = -\frac{7}{6}x + \frac{5}{3}$$
The equation of the line is $y = -\dfrac{7}{6}x + \dfrac{5}{3}$.

17. $y = -3x + 4$
$$m = -3$$
$$y - y_1 = m(x - x_1)$$
$$y - (-2) = -3(x - 3)$$
$$y + 2 = -3x + 9$$
$$y = -3x + 7$$
The equation of the line is $y = -3x + 7$.

18. $2x - 3y = 4$
$$-3y = -2x + 4$$
$$y = \frac{2}{3}x - \frac{4}{3}$$
$$m = \frac{2}{3}$$
$$y - y_1 = m(x - x_1)$$
$$y - (-4) = \frac{2}{3}[x - (-2)]$$
$$y + 4 = \frac{2}{3}(x + 2)$$
$$y + 4 = \frac{2}{3}x + \frac{4}{3}$$
$$y = \frac{2}{3}x - \frac{8}{3}$$
The equation of the line is $y = \dfrac{2}{3}x - \dfrac{8}{3}$.

19. $y = -\frac{2}{3}x + 6$

$m_1 = -\frac{2}{3}$

$m_1 \cdot m_2 = -1$

$-\frac{2}{3}m_2 = -1$

$m_2 = \frac{3}{2}$

$y - y_1 = m(x - x_1)$

$y - 5 = \frac{3}{2}(x - 2)$

$y - 5 = \frac{3}{2}x - 3$

$y = \frac{3}{2}x + 2$

The equation of the line is $y = \frac{3}{2}x + 2$.

20. $4x - 2y = 7$

$-2y = -4x + 7$

$y = 2x - \frac{7}{2}$

$m_1 = 2$

$m_1 \cdot m_2 = -1$

$2m_2 = -1$

$m_2 = -\frac{1}{2}$

$y - y_1 = m(x - x_1)$

$y - (-1) = -\frac{1}{2}[x - (-3)]$

$y + 1 = -\frac{1}{2}(x + 3)$

$y + 1 = -\frac{1}{2}x - \frac{3}{2}$

$y = -\frac{1}{2}x - \frac{5}{2}$

The equation of the line is $y = -\frac{1}{2}x - \frac{5}{2}$.

21. $y \geq 2x - 3$

22. $3x - 2y < 6$

$-2y < -3x + 6$

$y > \frac{3}{2}x - 3$

23.

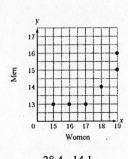

24a. $\text{ave} = \frac{28.4 - 14.1}{2000 - 1980}$

$= \frac{14.3}{20}$

$= 0.715$

The average annual rate of change was 715,000 people.

24b. For 1970 to 1980,

$\text{ave} = \frac{14.1 - 9.6}{1980 - 1970}$

$= \frac{4.5}{10}$

$= 0.45$

For 1980 to 1990,

$\text{ave} = \frac{19.8 - 14.1}{1990 - 1980}$

$= \frac{5.7}{10}$

$= 0.57$

$450,000 < 570,000$

The average annual rate of change for 1970 to 1980 was 450,000 people, which was less than the average annual rate of change from 1980 to 1990.

25.

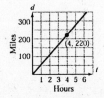

In 4 h, the car has traveled 220 miles.

26. $m = \frac{y_2 - y_1}{x_2 - x_1} = \frac{12,000 - 6000}{500 - 200} = \frac{6000}{300} = 20$

The slope is 20. The slope represents the cost per calculator manufactured. The cost of manufacturing one calculator is $20.

27. The y-intercept is $(0, 25{,}000)$.
The slope is 80.
$y = mx + b$
$y = 80x + 25{,}000$
The linear function is $y = 80x + 25{,}000$.
Predict the cost of building a house with 2000 ft^2.
$y = 80(2000) + 25{,}000$
$y = 185{,}000$
The house will cost \$185,000 to build.

Chapter Test

1. $P(x) = 2 - x^2$
Ordered pairs: $(-2, -2)$
$(-1, 1)$
$(0, 2)$
$(1, 1)$
$(2, -2)$

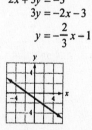

2. $y = 2x + 6$
$y = 2(-3) + 6$
$y = -6 + 6$
$y = 0$
The ordered-pair solution is $(-3, 0)$.

3.

4. $2x + 3y = -3$
$3y = -2x - 3$
$y = -\dfrac{2}{3}x - 1$

5. The equation of the vertical line that contains $(-2, 3)$ is $x = -2$.

6. $x_m = \dfrac{x_1 + x_2}{2} = \dfrac{4 + (-5)}{2} = -\dfrac{1}{2}$
$y_m = \dfrac{y_1 + y_2}{2} = \dfrac{2 + 8}{2} = 5$
$\text{Length} = \sqrt{(x_2 - x_1)^2 + (y_2 - y_1)^2}$
$= \sqrt{(-5 - 4)^2 + (8 - 2)^2}$
$= \sqrt{81 + 36}$
$= \sqrt{117}$
The midpoint is $\left(-\dfrac{1}{2}, 5\right)$ and the length is $\sqrt{117}$.

7. $P_1(-2, 3),\ P_2(4, 2)$
$m = \dfrac{y_2 - y_1}{x_2 - x_1} = \dfrac{2 - 3}{4 - (-2)} = -\dfrac{1}{6}$
The slope of the line is $-\dfrac{1}{6}$.

8. $P(x) = 3x^2 - 2x + 1$
$P(2) = 3(2)^2 - 2(2) + 1$
$P(2) = 9$

9. x-intercept: y-intercept:
$2x - 3y = 6$ $2x - 3y = 6$
$2x - 3(0) = 6$ $2(0) - 3y = 6$
$2x = 6$ $-3y = 6$
$x = 3$ $y = -2$
$(3, 0)$ $(0, -2)$

10.

11. $m = \dfrac{2}{5},\ (x_1, y_1) = (-5, 2)$

$y - 2 = \dfrac{2}{5}[x - (-5)]$

$y - 2 = \dfrac{2}{5}(x + 5)$

$y - 2 = \dfrac{2}{5}x + 2$

$y = \dfrac{2}{5}x + 4$

The equation of the line is $y = \dfrac{2}{5}x + 4$.

12. $x = 0$

13. $P_1(3, -4)$, $P_2(-2, 3)$

$$m = \frac{y_2 - y_1}{x_2 - x_1} = \frac{3 - (-4)}{-2 - 3} = \frac{3 + 4}{-5} = -\frac{7}{5}$$

$$y - y_1 = m(x - x_1)$$

$$y - (-4) = -\frac{7}{5}(x - 3)$$

$$y + 4 = -\frac{7}{5}x + \frac{21}{5}$$

$$y = -\frac{7}{5}x + \frac{1}{5}$$

The equation of the line is $y = -\frac{7}{5}x + \frac{1}{5}$.

14. A horizontal line has a slope of 0.

$$y - y_1 = m(x - x_1)$$

$$y - (-3) = 0(x - 4)$$

$$y + 3 = 0$$

$$y = -3$$

The equation of the line is $y = -3$.

15. Domain = $\{-4, -2, 0, 3\}$

Range = $\{0, 2, 5\}$

16. $y = -\frac{3}{2}x - 6$

$$m = -\frac{3}{2}$$

$$y - y_1 = m(x - x_1)$$

$$y - 2 = -\frac{3}{2}(x - 1)$$

$$y - 2 = -\frac{3}{2}x + \frac{3}{2}$$

$$y = -\frac{3}{2}x + \frac{7}{2}$$

The equation of the line is $y = -\frac{3}{2}x + \frac{7}{2}$.

17. $y = -\frac{1}{2}x - 3$

$$m_1 = -\frac{1}{2}$$

$$m_1 \cdot m_2 = -1$$

$$-\frac{1}{2}m_2 = -1$$

$$m_2 = 2$$

$$y - y_1 = m(x - x_1)$$

$$y - (-3) = 2[x - (-2)]$$

$$y + 3 = 2(x + 2)$$

$$y + 3 = 2x + 4$$

$$y = 2x + 1$$

The equation of the line is $y = 2x + 1$.

18. $3x - 4y > 8$

$$-4y > -3x + 8$$

$$y < \frac{3}{4}x - 2$$

19. Dependent variable: number of students: (y)
Independent variable: tuition cost (x)

$$m = \frac{\text{change in } y}{\text{change in } x} = \frac{-6}{20} = -\frac{3}{10}$$

$P_1(250, 100)$

Use the point-slope formula to find the equation.

$$y - y_1 = m(x - x_1)$$

$$y - 100 = -\frac{3}{10}(x - 250)$$

$$y - 100 = -\frac{3}{10}x + 75$$

$$y = -\frac{3}{10}x + 175$$

The equation that predicts the number of students for a certain tuition is $y = -\frac{3}{10}x + 175$. Predict the number of students when the tuition is $300.

$$y = -\frac{3}{10}x + 175$$

$$y = -\frac{3}{10}(300) + 175$$

$$y = 85$$

When the tuition is $300, 85 students will enroll.

20. Strategy
• Use two points on the graph to find the slope of the line.

Solution
$(x_1, y_1) = (3, 40,000)$, $(x_2, y_2) = (12, 10,000)$

$$m = \frac{y_2 - y_1}{x_2 - x_1} = \frac{10,000 - 40,000}{12 - 3} = -\frac{10,000}{3}$$

The value of the house decreases by $3333.33 per year.

21a. $\text{ave} = \frac{114.4 - 140.8}{5}$

$$= \frac{-26.4}{5}$$

$$= -5.28$$

The average rate of change was -5.28 points per month.

21b. $\text{ave} = \frac{85.5 - 114.4}{9}$

$$= \frac{-28.9}{9}$$

$$= -3.2\overline{1}$$

The average rate of change was -3.21 points per month.

Cumulative Review Exercises

1. The Commutative Property of Multiplication

2.
$$3 - \frac{x}{2} = \frac{3}{4}$$
$$4\left(3 - \frac{x}{2}\right) = \frac{3}{4}(4)$$
$$12 - 2x = 3$$
$$12 - 2x - 12 = 3 - 12$$
$$-2x = -9$$
$$x = \frac{9}{2}$$
The solution is $\frac{9}{2}$.

3.
$$2[y - 2(3 - y) + 4] = 4 - 3y$$
$$2(y - 6 + 2y + 4) = 4 - 3y$$
$$2(3y - 2) = 4 - 3y$$
$$6y - 4 = 4 - 3y$$
$$9y - 4 = 4$$
$$9y = 8$$
$$y = \frac{8}{9}$$
The solution is $\frac{8}{9}$.

4.
$$\frac{1 - 3x}{2} + \frac{7x - 2}{6} = \frac{4x + 2}{9}$$
$$18\left(\frac{1 - 3x}{2} + \frac{7x - 2}{6}\right) = 18\left(\frac{4x + 2}{9}\right)$$
$$9(1 - 3x) + 3(7x - 2) = 2(4x + 2)$$
$$9 - 27x + 21x - 6 = 8x + 4$$
$$-6x + 3 = 8x + 4$$
$$-14x = 1$$
$$x = -\frac{1}{14}$$
The solution is $-\frac{1}{14}$.

5. $x - 3 < -4$ or $2x + 2 > 3$
     $x < -1$ $2x > 1$
     $\{x \mid x < -1\}$ $x > \frac{1}{2}$
                     $\left\{x \mid x > \frac{1}{2}\right\}$

$$\{x \mid x < -1\} \cup \left\{x \mid x > \frac{1}{2}\right\} = \left\{x \mid x < -1 \text{ or } x > \frac{1}{2}\right\}$$

6.
$$8 - |2x - 1| = 4$$
$$-|2x - 1| = -4$$
$$|2x - 1| = 4$$
$2x - 1 = 4$ $2x - 1 = -4$
$2x = 5$ $2x = -3$
$x = \frac{5}{2}$ $x = -\frac{3}{2}$
The solutions are $\frac{5}{2}$ and $-\frac{3}{2}$.

7.
$$|3x - 5| < 5$$
$$-5 < 3x - 5 < 5$$
$$-5 + 5 < 3x - 5 + 5 < 5 + 5$$
$$0 < 3x < 10$$
$$\frac{1}{3}(0) < \frac{1}{3}(3x) < 10\left(\frac{1}{3}\right)$$
$$0 < x < \frac{10}{3}$$
$$\left\{x \mid 0 < x < \frac{10}{3}\right\}$$

8.
$$4 - 2(4 - 5)^3 + 2 = 4 - 2(-1)^3 + 2$$
$$= 4 + 2 + 2$$
$$= 8$$

9. $(a - b)^2 \div ab$ for $a = 4$ and $b = -2$
$$[4 - (-2)]^2 \div 4(-2) = 6^2 \div 4(-2)$$
$$= 36 \div 4(-2)$$
$$= 9 \cdot (-2)$$
$$= -18$$

10. $\{x \mid x < -2\} \cup \{x \mid x > 0\}$

11. Solve each inequality.
$3x - 1 < 4$ $x - 2 > 2$
$3x < 5$ $x > 4$
$x < \frac{5}{3}$

The solution is $\left\{x \mid x < \frac{5}{3} \text{ and } x > 4\right\}$, and there is
no such value, so the solution is the null set.

12.
$$P(x) = x^2 + 5$$
$$P(-3) = (-3)^2 + 5$$
$$P(-3) = 14$$

13.
$$y = -\frac{5}{4}x + 3$$
$$y = -\frac{5}{4}(-8) + 3$$
$$y = 10 + 3$$
$$y = 13$$
The ordered-pair solution is $(-8, 13)$.

14. $P_1(-1, 3)$, $P_2(3, -4)$
$$m = \frac{y_2 - y_1}{x_2 - x_1} = \frac{-4 - 3}{3 - (-1)} = \frac{-7}{4} = -\frac{7}{4}$$

15. $m = \dfrac{3}{2}$, $(x_1, y_1) = (-1, 5)$

$y - y_1 = m(x - x_1)$

$y - 5 = \dfrac{3}{2}[x - (-1)]$

$y - 5 = \dfrac{3}{2}(x + 1)$

$y - 5 = \dfrac{3}{2}x + \dfrac{3}{2}$

$y = \dfrac{3}{2}x + \dfrac{13}{2}$

The equation of the line is $y = \dfrac{3}{2}x + \dfrac{13}{2}$.

16. $(x_1, y_1) = (4, -2)$, $(x_2, y_2) = (0, 3)$

$m = \dfrac{y_2 - y_1}{x_2 - x_1} = \dfrac{3 - (-2)}{0 - 4} = \dfrac{3 + 2}{-4} = -\dfrac{5}{4}$

$y - y_1 = m(x - x_1)$

$y - (-2) = -\dfrac{5}{4}(x - 4)$

$y + 2 = -\dfrac{5}{4}x + 5$

$y = -\dfrac{5}{4}x + 3$

The equation of the line is $y = -\dfrac{5}{4}x + 3$.

17. $y = -\dfrac{3}{2}x + 2$, $m = -\dfrac{3}{2}$

$y - y_1 = m(x - x_1)$

$y - 4 = -\dfrac{3}{2}(x - 2)$

$y - 4 = -\dfrac{3}{2}x + 3$

$y = -\dfrac{3}{2}x + 7$

The equation of the line is $y = -\dfrac{3}{2}x + 7$.

18. $3x - 2y = 5$

$-2y = -3x + 5$

$y = \dfrac{3}{2}x - \dfrac{5}{2}$

$m_1 = \dfrac{3}{2}$

$m_1 \cdot m_2 = -1$

$\dfrac{3}{2}m_2 = -1$

$m_2 = -\dfrac{2}{3}$

$y - y_1 = m(x - x_1)$

$y - 0 = -\dfrac{2}{3}(x - 4)$

$y = -\dfrac{2}{3}x + \dfrac{8}{3}$

The equation of the line is $y = -\dfrac{2}{3}x + \dfrac{8}{3}$.

19.
x-intercept:	y-intercept:
$3x - 5y = 15$	$3x - 5y = 15$
$3x - 5(0) = 15$	$3(0) - 5y = 15$
$3x = 15$	$-5y = 15$
$x = 5$	$y = -3$
$(5, 0)$	$(0, -3)$

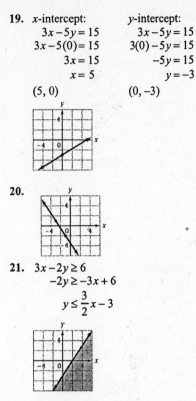

20.

21. $3x - 2y \geq 6$

$-2y \geq -3x + 6$

$y \leq \dfrac{3}{2}x - 3$

22. Strategy
• Number of nickels: $3x$
Number of quarters: x

Coin	Number	Value	Total Value
Nickels	$3x$	5	$3x(5)$
Quarters	x	25	$25x$

• The sum of the total values of each denomination of coin equals the total value of all the coins (160).
$3(x)(5) + 25x = 160$

Solution
$15x + 25x = 160$

$40x = 160$

$x = 4$

$3x = 12$

There are 12 nickels in the purse.

23. Strategy
• Rate of first plane: x
Rate of second plane: $2x$

	Rate	Time	Distance
First plane	x	3	$3x$
Second plane	$2x$	3	$3(2x)$

• The two planes travel a total distance of 1800 miles.
$3x + 3(2x) = 1800$

Solution
$$3x + 3(2x) = 1800$$
$$3x + 6x = 1800$$
$$9x = 1800$$
$$x = 200$$
$$2x = 400$$
The rate of the first plane is 200 mph and the rate of the second plane is 400 mph.

24. Strategy
• Pounds of coffee costing $3.00: x
Pounds of coffee costing $8.00: $80 - x$

	Amount	Cost	Value
$3.00 coffee	x	3.00	$3x$
$8.00 coffee	$80 - x$	8.00	$8(80 - x)$
$5.00 mixture	80	5.00	$5(80)$

• The sum of the values of each part of the mixture equals the value of the mixture.
$3x + 8(80 - x) = 5(80)$

Solution
$$3x + 640 - 8x = 400$$
$$-5x + 640 = 400$$
$$-5x = -240$$
$$x = 48$$
$$80 - x = 32$$
The mixture consists of 48 lb of $3 coffee and 32 lb of $8 coffee.

25. Strategy
To write the equation
• Use points on the graph to find the slope of the line.
• Locate the y-intercept of the line on the graph.
• Use the slope-intercept form of an equation to write the equation of the line.

Solution
$(x_1, y_1) = (0, 15,000)$, $(x_2, y_2) = (6, 0)$
The y-intercept is $(0, 15,000)$.
$$m = \frac{y_2 - y_1}{x_2 - x_1} = \frac{0 - 15,000}{6 - 0} = -2500$$
$$y = mx + b$$
$$y = -2500x + 15,000$$
The value of the truck decreases by $2500 each year.

Chapter 4: Systems of Equations and Inequalities

Prep Test

1. $6x + 5y$ [1.3.3]

2. $3x + 2y - z$ [1.3.2]
$3(-1) + 2(4) - (-2)$
$= -3 + 8 + 2$
$= 7$

3. $3x - 2(-2) = 4$ [2.1.1]
$3x + 4 = 4$
$3x = 0$
$x = 0$

4. $3x + 4(-2x - 5) = -5$ [2.1.2]
$3x - 8x - 20 = -5$
$-5x = 15$
$x = -3$

5. $0.45x + 0.06(-x + 4000) = 630$ [2.1.2]
$0.45x - 0.06x + 240 = 630$
$0.39x = 390$
$x = 1000$

6.

7. $3x - 2y = 6$ [3.3.2]
$-2y = -3x + 6$
$y = \frac{3}{2}x - 3$

8.

Go Figure

If Chris can beat Pat by 100 m, then Pat is at 900m when Chris reaches 1000 m. If Pat can beat Leslie by 10 m in a 100-meter race, then in a 1000-meter race, when Pat reaches 900m, Leslie will be 90 m behind. So then Chris will beat Leslie by 190 m.

Section 4.1

Concept Review 4.1

1. Always true

2. Always true

3. Sometimes true
A system of equations with two unknowns has one solution, an infinite number of solutions, or no solution.

4. Never true
The equations in this system would never intersect. The system has no solution.

5. Always true

6. Always true

Objective 4.1.1 Exercises

1. $3x - 2y = 2$
$3(0) - 2(-1) = 2$
$2 = 2$

$x + 2y = 6$
$0 + 2(-1) = 6$
$-2 \neq 6$
No

2. $x + y = 3$
$2 + 1 = 3$
$3 = 3$

$2x - 3y = 1$
$2(2) - 3(1) = 1$
$4 - 3 = 1$
$1 = 1$
Yes

3. $x + y = -8$
$-3 + -5 = -8$
$-8 = -8$

$2x + 5y = -31$
$2(-3) + 5(-5) = -31$
$-6 - 25 = -31$
$-31 = -31$
Yes

4. $3x - y = 4$
$3(1) - (-1) = 4$
$3 + 1 = 4$
$4 = 4$

$7x + 2y = -5$
$7(1) + 2(-1) = -5$
$7 - 2 = -5$
$5 \neq -5$
No

5. Independent

6. Dependent

7. Inconsistent

8. Independent

8. Independent

9. The solution of an independent system of linear equations in two variables is an ordered pair (x, y) that is a solution of each equation in the system.

10. A dependent system of equations has an infinite number of solutions, whereas an independent system of equations has just one solution.

11.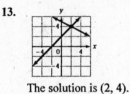

The solution is (3, –1).

12.

The solution is (–1, 2).

13.

The solution is (2, 4).

14.

The solution is (2, –1).

15.

The solution is (4, 3).

16.

The solution is (4, 4).

17.

The solution is (4, –1).

18.

The solution is (–2, 1).

19.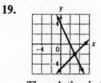

The solution is (3, –2).

20.

The solution is (–3, –2).

21.

The lines are parallel and therefore do not intersect. The system of equations has no solution. The system is inconsistent.

22.

The lines are parallel and therefore do not intersect. The system of equations has no solution. The system is inconsistent.

23.

The system of equations is dependent. The solutions are the ordered pairs $\left(x, \dfrac{2}{5}x - 2 \right)$.

24.

The system of equations is dependent. The solutions are the ordered pairs $\left(x, \dfrac{3}{2}x - 3 \right)$.

25.

The solution is $(0, -3)$.

26.

The solution is $(0, -2)$.

Objective 4.1.2 Exercises

27. When the substitution results in a false equation, such as $0 = 9$, with no variable, the system of equations is inconsistent.

28. When the substitution results in a true equation, such as $2 = 2$, with no variable, the system of equations is dependent.

29. (1) $\quad 3x - 2y = 4$
(2) $\qquad x = 2$
Substitute the value of x into equation (1).
$$3x - 2y = 4$$
$$3(2) - 2y = 4$$
$$6 - 2y = 4$$
$$-2y = -2$$
$$y = 1$$
The solution is $(2, 1)$.

30. (1) $\qquad y = -2$
(2) $\quad 2x + 3y = 4$
Substitute the value of y into equation (2).
$$2x + 3y = 4$$
$$2x + 3(-2) = 4$$
$$2x - 6 = 4$$
$$2x = 10$$
$$x = 5$$
The solution is $(5, -2)$.

31. (1) $\qquad y = 2x - 1$
(2) $\quad x + 2y = 3$
Substitute $2x - 1$ for y in equation (2).
$$x + 2y = 3$$
$$x + 2(2x - 1) = 3$$
$$x + 4x - 2 = 3$$
$$5x - 2 = 3$$
$$5x = 5$$
$$x = 1$$
Substitute into equation (1).
$$y = 2x - 1$$
$$y = 2(1) - 1$$
$$y = 2 - 1$$
$$y = 1$$
The solution is $(1, 1)$.

32. (1) $\qquad y = -x + 1$
(2) $\quad 2x - y = 5$
Substitute $-x + 1$ for y in equation (2).
$$2x - y = 5$$
$$2x - (-x + 1) = 5$$
$$2x + x - 1 = 5$$
$$3x - 1 = 5$$
$$3x = 6$$
$$x = 2$$
Substitute into equation (1).
$$y = -x + 1$$
$$y = -2 + 1$$
$$y = -1$$
The solution is $(2, -1)$.

33. (1) $\quad 4x - 3y = 5$
(2) $\qquad y = 2x - 3$
Substitute $2x - 3$ for y in equation (1).
$$4x - 3y = 5$$
$$4x - 3(2x - 3) = 5$$
$$4x - 6x + 9 = 5$$
$$-2x + 9 = 5$$
$$-2x = -4$$
$$x = 2$$
Substitute into equation (2).
$$y = 2x - 3$$
$$y = 2(2) - 3$$
$$y = 4 - 3$$
$$y = 1$$
The solution is $(2, 1)$.

34. (1) $\quad 3x + 5y = -1$
(2) $\qquad y = 2x - 8$
Substitute $2x - 8$ for y in equation (1).
$$3x + 5y = -1$$
$$3x + 5(2x - 8) = -1$$
$$3x + 10x - 40 = -1$$
$$13x - 40 = -1$$
$$13x = 39$$
$$x = 3$$
Substitute into equation (2).
$$y = 2x - 8$$
$$y = 2(3) - 8$$
$$y = 6 - 8$$
$$y = -2$$
The solution is $(3, -2)$.

35. (1) $x = 2y + 4$

(2) $4x + 3y = -17$

Substitute $2y + 4$ for x in equation (2).

$4x + 3y = -17$

$4(2y + 4) + 3y = -17$

$8y + 16 + 3y = -17$

$11y + 16 = -17$

$11y = -33$

$y = -3$

Substitute into equation (1).

$x = 2y + 4$

$x = 2(-3) + 4$

$x = -6 + 4$

$x = -2$

The solution is $(-2, -3)$.

36. (1) $3x - 2y = -11$

(2) $x = 2y - 9$

Substitute $2y - 9$ for x in equation (1).

$3x - 2y = -11$

$3(2y - 9) - 2y = -11$

$6y - 27 - 2y = -11$

$4y - 27 = -11$

$4y = 16$

$y = 4$

Substitute into equation (2).

$x = 2y - 9$

$x = 2(4) - 9$

$x = 8 - 9$

$x = -1$

The solution is $(-1, 4)$.

37. (1) $5x + 4y = -1$

(2) $y = 2 - 2x$

Substitute $2 - 2x$ for y in equation (1).

$5x + 4y = -1$

$5x + 4(2 - 2x) = -1$

$5x + 8 - 8x = -1$

$-3x + 8 = -1$

$-3x = -9$

$x = 3$

Substitute into equation (2).

$y = 2 - 2x$

$y = 2 - 2(3)$

$y = 2 - 6$

$y = -4$

The solution is $(3, -4)$.

38. (1) $3x + 2y = 4$

(2) $y = 1 - 2x$

Substitute $1 - 2x$ for y in equation (1).

$3x + 2y = 4$

$3x + 2(1 - 2x) = 4$

$3x + 2 - 4x = 4$

$-x + 2 = 4$

$-x = 2$

$x = -2$

Substitute into equation (2).

$y = 1 - 2x$

$y = 1 - 2(-2)$

$y = 1 + 4$

$y = 5$

The solution is $(-2, 5)$.

39. (1) $7x - 3y = 3$

(2) $x = 2y + 2$

Substitute $2y + 2$ for x in equation (1).

$7x - 3y = 3$

$7(2y + 2) - 3y = 3$

$14y + 14 - 3y = 3$

$11y + 14 = 3$

$11y = -11$

$y = -1$

Substitute into equation (2).

$x = 2y + 2$

$x = 2(-1) + 2$

$x = -2 + 2$

$x = 0$

The solution is $(0, -1)$.

40. (1) $3x - 4y = 6$

(2) $x = 3y + 2$

Substitute $3y + 2$ for x in equation (1).

$3x - 4y = 6$

$3(3y + 2) - 4y = 6$

$9y + 6 - 4y = 6$

$5y + 6 = 6$

$5y = 0$

$y = 0$

Substitute into equation (2).

$x = 3y + 2$

$x = 3(0) + 2$

$x = 2$

The solution is $(2, 0)$.

41. (1) $2x + 2y = 7$

(2) $y = 4x + 1$

Substitute $4x + 1$ for y in equation (1).

$2x + 2y = 7$

$2x + 2(4x + 1) = 7$

$2x + 8x + 2 = 7$

$10x + 2 = 7$

$10x = 5$

$x = \dfrac{1}{2}$

Substitute into equation (2).

$y = 4x + 1$

$y = 4\left(\dfrac{1}{2}\right) + 1$

$y = 2 + 1$

$y = 3$

The solution is $\left(\dfrac{1}{2}, 3\right)$.

42. (1) $3x + 7y = -5$

(2) $y = 6x - 5$

Substitute $6x - 5$ for y in equation (1).

$3x + 7y = -5$

$3x + 7(6x - 5) = -5$

$3x + 42x - 35 = -5$

$45x - 35 = -5$

$45x = 30$

$x = \dfrac{2}{3}$

Substitute into equation (2).

$y = 6x - 5$

$y = 6\left(\dfrac{2}{3}\right) - 5$

$y = 4 - 5$

$y = -1$

The solution is $\left(\dfrac{2}{3}, -1\right)$.

43. (1) $3x + y = 5$

(2) $2x + 3y = 8$

Solve equation (1) for y.

$3x + y = 5$

$y = -3x + 5$

Substitute into equation (2).

$2x + 3y = 8$

$2x + 3(-3x + 5) = 8$

$2x - 9x + 15 = 8$

$-7x + 15 = 8$

$-7x = -7$

$x = 1$

Substitute into equation (1).

$3x + y = 5$

$3(1) + y = 5$

$3 + y = 5$

$y = 2$

The solution is $(1, 2)$.

44. (1) $4x + y = 9$

(2) $3x - 4y = 2$

Solve equation (1) for y.

$4x + y = 9$

$y = -4x + 9$

Substitute into equation (2).

$3x - 4y = 2$

$3x - 4(-4x + 9) = 2$

$3x + 16x - 36 = 2$

$19x - 36 = 2$

$19x = 38$

$x = 2$

Substitute into equation (1).

$4x + y = 9$

$4(2) + y = 9$

$8 + y = 9$

$y = 1$

The solution is $(2, 1)$.

45. (1) $x + 3y = 5$

(2) $2x + 3y = 4$

Solve equation (1) for x.

$x + 3y = 5$

$x = -3y + 5$

Substitute into equation (2).

$2x + 3y = 4$

$2(-3y + 5) + 3y = 4$

$-6y + 10 + 3y = 4$

$-3y + 10 = 4$

$-3y = -6$

$y = 2$

Substitute into equation (1).

$x + 3y = 5$

$x + 3(2) = 5$

$x + 6 = 5$

$x = -1$

The solution is $(-1, 2)$.

46. (1) $x - 4y = 2$

(2) $2x - 5y = 1$

Solve equation (1) for x.

$x - 4y = 2$

$x = 4y + 2$

Substitute into equation (2).

$2x - 5y = 1$

$2(4y + 2) - 5y = 1$

$8y + 4 - 5y = 1$

$3y + 4 = 1$

$3y = -3$

$y = -1$

Substitute into equation (1).

$x - 4y = 2$

$x - 4(-1) = 2$

$x + 4 = 2$

$x = -2$

The solution is $(-2, -1)$.

47. (1) $3x + 4y = 14$

(2) $2x + y = 1$

Solve equation (2) for y.

$2x + y = 1$

$y = -2x + 1$

Substitute into equation (1).

$3x + 4y = 14$

$3x + 4(-2x + 1) = 14$

$3x - 8x + 4 = 14$

$-5x + 4 = 14$

$-5x = 10$

$x = -2$

Substitute into equation (2).

$2x + y = 1$

$2(-2) + y = 1$

$-4 + y = 1$

$y = 5$

The solution is $(-2, 5)$.

48. (1) $5x + 3y = 8$

(2) $3x + y = 8$

Solve equation (2) for y.

$3x + y = 8$

$y = -3x + 8$

Substitute into equation (1).

$5x + 3y = 8$

$5x + 3(-3x + 8) = 8$

$5x - 9x + 24 = 8$

$-4x + 24 = 8$

$-4x = -16$

$x = 4$

Substitute into equation (2).

$3x + y = 8$

$3(4) + y = 8$

$12 + y = 8$

$y = -4$

The solution is $(4, -4)$.

49. (1) $3x + 5y = 0$

(2) $x - 4y = 0$

Solve equation (2) for x.

$x - 4y = 0$

$x = 4y$

Substitute into equation (1).

$3x + 5y = 0$

$3(4y) + 5y = 0$

$12y + 5y = 0$

$17y = 0$

$y = 0$

Substitute into equation (2).

$x - 4y = 0$

$x - 4(0) = 0$

$x = 0$

The solution is $(0, 0)$.

50. (1) $2x - 7y = 0$

(2) $3x + y = 0$

Solve equation (2) for y.

$3x + y = 0$

$y = -3x$

Substitute into equation (1).

$2x - 7y = 0$

$2x - 7(-3x) = 0$

$2x + 21x = 0$

$23x = 0$

$x = 0$

Substitute into equation (2).

$3x + y = 0$

$3(0) + y = 0$

$y = 0$

The solution is $(0, 0)$.

51. (1) $5x - 3y = -2$

(2) $-x + 2y = -8$

Solve equation (2) for x.

$-x + 2y = -8$

$-x = -2y - 8$

$x = 2y + 8$

Substitute $2y + 8$ for x in equation (1).

$5x - 3y = -2$

$5(2y + 8) - 3y = -2$

$10y + 40 - 3y = -2$

$7y + 40 = -2$

$7y = -42$

$y = -6$

Substitute into equation (2).

$-x + 2y = -8$

$-x + 2(-6) = -8$

$-x - 12 = -8$

$-x = 4$

$x = -4$

The solution is $(-4, -6)$.

52. (1) $2x + 7y = 1$

(2) $-x + 4y = 7$

Solve equation (2) for x.

$-x + 4y = 7$

$-x = -4y + 7$

$x = 4y - 7$

Substitute $4y - 7$ for x in equation (1).

$2x + 7y = 1$

$2(4y - 7) + 7y = 1$

$8y - 14 + 7y = 1$

$15y - 14 = 1$

$15y = 15$

$y = 1$

Substitute into equation (2).

$-x + 4y = 7$

$-x + 4(1) = 7$

$-x + 4 = 7$

$-x = 3$

$x = -3$

The solution is $(-3, 1)$.

53. (1) $x + 3y = 4$

(2) $\quad x = 5 - 3y$

Substitute $5 - 3y$ for x in equation (1).

$x + 3y = 4$
$(5 - 3y) + 3y = 4$
$5 - 3y + 3y = 4$
$\qquad 5 \neq 4$

Inconsistent

54. (1) $6x + 2y = 7$

(2) $\quad y = -3x + 2$

Substitute $-3x + 2$ for y in equation (1).

$6x + 2y = 7$
$6x + 2(-3x + 2) = 7$
$6x - 6x + 4 = 7$
$\qquad 4 \neq 7$

Inconsistent

55. (1) $2x - 4y = 16$

(2) $-x + 2y = -8$

Solve equation (2) for x.

$-x + 2y = -8$
$-x = -2y - 8$
$x = 2y + 8$

Substitute $2y + 8$ for x in equation (1).

$2x - 4y = 16$
$2(2y + 8) - 4y = 16$
$4y + 16 - 4y = 16$
$\qquad 16 = 16$

The system of equations is dependent.

Solve equation (2) for y.

$-x + 2y = -8$
$2y = x - 8$
$y = \dfrac{1}{2}x - 4$

The solution is the ordered pairs $\left(x, \dfrac{1}{2}x - 4 \right)$

56. (1) $3x - 12y = -24$

(2) $-x + 4y = 8$

Solve equation (2) for x.

$-x + 4y = 8$
$-x = -4y + 8$
$x = 4y - 8$

Substitute $4y - 8$ for x in equation (1).

$3x - 12y = -24$
$3(4y - 8) - 12y = -24$
$12y - 24 - 12y = -24$
$\qquad -24 = -24$

The system of equations is dependent.

Solve equation (2) for y.

$-x + 4y = 8$
$4y = x + 8$
$y = \dfrac{1}{4}x + 2$

The solution is the ordered pairs $\left(x, \dfrac{1}{4}x + 2 \right)$

57. (1) $\quad 3x - y = 10$

(2) $6x - 2y = 5$

Solve equation (1) for y.

$3x - y = 10$
$-y = -3x + 10$
$y = 3x - 10$

Substitute $3x - 10$ for y in equation (1).

$6x - 2y = 5$
$6x - 2(3x - 10) = 5$
$6x - 6x + 20 = 5$
$\qquad 20 \neq 5$

Inconsistent

58. (1) $6x - 4y = 3$

(2) $3x - 2y = 9$

Solve equation (2) for y.

$3x - 2y = 9$
$-2y = -3x + 9$
$y = \dfrac{3}{2}x - \dfrac{9}{2}$

Substitute $\dfrac{3}{2}x - \dfrac{9}{2}$ for y in equation (1).

$6x - 4y = 3$
$6x - 4\left(\dfrac{3}{2}x - \dfrac{9}{2} \right) = 3$
$6x - 6x + 18 = 3$
$\qquad 18 \neq 3$

Inconsistent

59. (1) $\quad y = 3x + 2$

(2) $\quad y = 2x + 3$

Substitute $2x + 3$ for y in equation (1).

$y = 3x + 2$
$2x + 3 = 3x + 2$
$2x = 3x - 1$
$-x = -1$
$x = 1$

Substitute into equation (2).

$y = 2x + 3$
$y = 2(1) + 3$
$y = 2 + 3$
$y = 5$

The solution is $(1, 5)$.

60. (1) $\quad y = 3x - 7$

(2) $\quad y = 2x - 5$

Substitute $2x - 5$ for y in equation (1).

$y = 3x - 7$
$2x - 5 = 3x - 7$
$2x = 3x - 2$
$-x = -2$
$x = 2$

Substitute into equation (2).

$y = 2x - 5$
$y = 2(2) - 5$
$y = 4 - 5$
$y = -1$

The solution is $(2, -1)$.

61. (1) $x = 2y + 1$

(2) $x = 3y - 1$

Substitute $3y - 1$ for x in equation (1).

$x = 2y + 1$

$3y - 1 = 2y + 1$

$3y = 2y + 2$

$y = 2$

Substitute into equation (2).

$x = 3y - 1$

$x = 3(2) - 1$

$x = 6 - 1$

$x = 5$

The solution is (5, 2).

62. (1) $x = 4y + 1$

(2) $x = -2y - 5$

Substitute $-2y - 5$ for x in equation (1).

$x = 4y + 1$

$-2y - 5 = 4y + 1$

$-2y = 4y + 6$

$-6y = 6$

$y = -1$

Substitute into equation (2).

$x = -2y - 5$

$x = -2(-1) - 5$

$x = 2 - 5$

$x = -3$

The solution is (−3, −1).

63. (1) $y = 5x - 1$

(2) $y = 5 - x$

Substitute $5 - x$ for y in equation (1).

$y = 5x - 1$

$5 - x = 5x - 1$

$-x = 5x - 6$

$-6x = -6$

$x = 1$

Substitute into equation (2).

$y = 5 - x$

$y = 5 - 1$

$y = 4$

The solution is (1, 4).

64. (1) $y = 3 - 2x$

(2) $y = 2 - 3x$

Substitute $2 - 3x$ for y in equation (1).

$y = 3 - 2x$

$2 - 3x = 3 - 2x$

$-3x = 1 - 2x$

$-x = 1$

$x = -1$

Substitute into equation (2).

$y = 2 - 3x$

$y = 2 - 3(-1)$

$y = 2 + 3$

$y = 5$

The solution is (−1, 5).

Applying Concepts 4.1

65. Inconsistent equations have the same slope but different y-intercepts. Solve the two equations for y, and then set the slopes equal to each other.

(1) $2x - 2y = 5$

$-2y = -2x + 5$

$y = x - \dfrac{5}{2}$

(2) $kx - 2y = 3$

$-2y = -kx + 3$

$y = \dfrac{k}{2}x - \dfrac{3}{2}$

$\dfrac{k}{2} = 1$

$k = 2$

The value of k is 2.

66. Inconsistent equations have the same slope but different y-intercepts. Solve the two equations for y, and then set the slopes equal to each other.

(1) $6x - 3y = 4$

$-3y = -6x + 4$

$y = 2x - \dfrac{4}{3}$

(2) $3x - ky = 1$

$-ky = -3x + 1$

$y = \dfrac{3}{k}x - \dfrac{1}{k}$

$\dfrac{3}{k} = 2$

$3 = 2k$

$\dfrac{3}{2} = k$

The value of k is $\dfrac{3}{2}$.

67. Inconsistent equations have the same slope but different y-intercepts. Solve the two equations for y, and then set the slopes equal to each other.

(1) $x = 6y + 6$

$x - 6 = 6y$

$\dfrac{1}{6}x - 1 = y$

(2) $kx - 3y = 6$

$-3y = -kx + 6$

$y = \dfrac{k}{3}x - 2$

$\dfrac{k}{3} = \dfrac{1}{6}$

$k = \dfrac{1}{2}$

The value of k is $\dfrac{1}{2}$.

68. Inconsistent equations have the same slope but different *y*-intercepts. Solve the two equations for *y*, and then set the slopes equal to each other.

(1) $x = 2y + 2$

$x - 2 = 2y$

$\dfrac{1}{2}x - 1 = y$

(2) $kx - 8y = 2$

$-8y = -kx + 2$

$y = \dfrac{k}{8}x - \dfrac{1}{4}$

$\dfrac{k}{8} = \dfrac{1}{2}$

$k = 4$

The value of *k* is 4.

69. Strategy

Solve a system of equations using *x* to represent one number and *y* to represent the second number.

Solution

(1) $x + y = 44$

(2) $x - 8 = y$

Solve equation (1) for *y*.

$x + y = 44$

$y = -x + 44$

Substitute −*x* + 44 for *y* in equation (2).

$x - 8 = y$

$x - 8 = -x + 44$

$2x = 52$

$x = 26$

Substitute into equation (1).

$x + y = 44$

$26 + y = 44$

$y = 18$

The numbers are 26 and 18.

70. Strategy

Solve a system of equations using *x* to represent one number and *y* to represent the second number.

Solution

(1) $x + y = 76$

(2) $x - 12 = y$

Solve equation (1) for *y*.

$x + y = 76$

$y = -x + 76$

Substitute −*x* + 76 for *y* in equation (2).

$x - 12 = y$

$x - 12 = -x + 76$

$2x = 88$

$x = 44$

Substitute into equation (1).

$x + y = 76$

$44 + y = 76$

$y = 32$

The numbers are 32 and 44.

71. Strategy

Solve a system of equations using *x* to represent one number and *y* to represent the second number.

Solution

(1) $x + y = 19$

(2) $2x - 5 = y$

Solve equation (1) for *y*.

$x + y = 19$

$y = -x + 19$

Substitute −*x* + 19 for *y* in equation (2).

$2x - 5 = y$

$2x - 5 = -x + 19$

$3x = 24$

$x = 8$

Substitute into equation (1).

$x + y = 19$

$8 + y = 19$

$y = 11$

The numbers are 8 and 11.

72. Strategy

Solve a system of equations using *x* to represent one number and *y* to represent the second number.

Solution

(1) $x + y = 22$

(2) $3x + 2 = y$

Solve equation (1) for *y*.

$x + y = 22$

$y = -x + 22$

Substitute −*x* + 22 for *y* in equation (2).

$3x + 2 = y$

$3x + 2 = -x + 22$

$4x = 20$

$x = 5$

Substitute into equation (1).

$x + y = 22$

$5 + y = 22$

$y = 17$

The numbers are 5 and 17.

73.
$$\frac{2}{a}+\frac{3}{b}=4$$
$$2\left(\frac{1}{a}\right)+3\left(\frac{1}{b}\right)=4$$
(1) $2x+3y=4$
$$\frac{4}{a}+\frac{1}{b}=3$$
$$4\left(\frac{1}{a}\right)+\frac{1}{b}=3$$
(2) $4x+y=3$
Solve equation (1) for y.
$$2x+3y=4$$
$$3y=-2x+4$$
$$y=\left(-\frac{2}{3}\right)x+\frac{4}{3}$$
Substitute $-\frac{2}{3}x+\frac{4}{3}$ for y in equation (2).
$$4x+y=3$$
$$4x+\left(-\frac{2}{3}x+\frac{4}{3}\right)=3$$
$$\frac{10}{3}x+\frac{4}{3}=3$$
$$10x+4=9$$
$$10x=5$$
$$x=\frac{1}{2}$$
Substitute into equation (1).
$$2x+3y=4$$
$$2\left(\frac{1}{2}\right)+3y=4$$
$$1+3y=4$$
$$3y=3$$
$$y=1$$
Replace x by $\frac{1}{a}$.
$$x=\frac{1}{2}$$
$$\frac{1}{a}=\frac{1}{2}$$
$$2a\left(\frac{1}{a}\right)=2a\left(\frac{1}{2}\right)$$
$$2=a$$
Replace y by $\frac{1}{b}$.
$$y=1$$
$$\frac{1}{b}=1$$
$$b\left(\frac{1}{b}\right)=b(1)$$
$$1=b$$
The solution is $(2, 1)$.

74.
$$\frac{2}{a}+\frac{1}{b}=1$$
$$2\left(\frac{1}{a}\right)+\frac{1}{b}=1$$
(1) $2x+y=1$
$$\frac{8}{a}-\frac{2}{b}=0$$
$$8\left(\frac{1}{a}\right)-2\left(\frac{1}{b}\right)=0$$
(2) $8x-2y=0$
Solve equation (1) for y.
$$2x+y=1$$
$$y=-2x+1$$
Substitute $-2x+1$ for y in equation (2).
$$8x-2y=0$$
$$8x-2(-2x+1)=0$$
$$8x+4x-2=0$$
$$12x-2=0$$
$$12x=2$$
$$x=\frac{1}{6}$$
Substitute into equation (1).
$$2x+y=1$$
$$2\left(\frac{1}{6}\right)+y=1$$
$$\frac{1}{3}+y=1$$
$$y=\frac{2}{3}$$
Replace x by $\frac{1}{a}$.
$$x=\frac{1}{6}$$
$$\frac{1}{a}=\frac{1}{6}$$
$$6a\left(\frac{1}{a}\right)=6a\left(\frac{1}{6}\right)$$
$$6=a$$
Replace y by $\frac{1}{b}$.
$$y=\frac{2}{3}$$
$$\frac{1}{b}=\frac{2}{3}$$
$$3b\left(\frac{1}{b}\right)=3b\left(\frac{2}{3}\right)$$
$$3=2b$$
$$\frac{3}{2}=b$$
The solution is $\left(6,\frac{3}{2}\right)$.

75.
$$\frac{1}{a} + \frac{3}{b} = 2$$
$$\frac{1}{a} + 3\left(\frac{1}{b}\right) = 2$$
(1) $\quad x + 3y = 2$
$$\frac{4}{a} - \frac{1}{b} = 3$$
$$4\left(\frac{1}{a}\right) - \frac{1}{b} = 3$$
(2) $\quad 4x - y = 3$

Solve equation (1) for y.
$$x + 3y = 2$$
$$3y = -x + 2$$
$$y = -\frac{1}{3}x + \frac{2}{3}$$

Substitute $-\frac{1}{3}x + \frac{2}{3}$ for y in equation (2).
$$4x - y = 3$$
$$4x - \left(-\frac{1}{3}x + \frac{2}{3}\right) = 3$$
$$4x + \frac{1}{3}x - \frac{2}{3} = 3$$
$$\frac{13}{3}x = \frac{11}{3}$$
$$x = \frac{11}{13}$$

Substitute into equation (1).
$$x + 3y = 2$$
$$\frac{11}{13} + 3y = 2$$
$$3y = \frac{15}{13}$$
$$y = \frac{15}{39} = \frac{5}{13}$$

Replace x by $\frac{1}{a}$.
$$x = \frac{11}{13}$$
$$\frac{1}{a} = \frac{11}{13}$$
$$13a\left(\frac{1}{a}\right) = 13a\left(\frac{11}{13}\right)$$
$$13 = 11a$$
$$\frac{13}{11} = a$$

Replace y by $\frac{1}{b}$.
$$y = \frac{5}{13}$$
$$\frac{1}{b} = \frac{5}{13}$$
$$13b\left(\frac{1}{b}\right) = 13b\left(\frac{5}{13}\right)$$
$$13 = 5b$$
$$\frac{13}{5} = b$$

The solution is $\left(\frac{13}{11}, \frac{13}{5}\right)$.

76.
$$\frac{3}{a} + \frac{4}{b} = -1$$
$$3\left(\frac{1}{a}\right) + 4\left(\frac{1}{b}\right) = -1$$
(1) $\quad 3x + 4y = -1$
$$\frac{1}{a} + \frac{6}{b} = 2$$
$$\frac{1}{a} + 6\left(\frac{1}{b}\right) = 2$$
(2) $\quad x + 6y = 2$

Solve equation (1) for y.
$$3x + 4y = -1$$
$$4y = -3x - 1$$
$$y = -\frac{3}{4}x - \frac{1}{4}$$

Substitute $-\frac{3}{4}x - \frac{1}{4}$ for y in equation (2).
$$x + 6y = 2$$
$$x + 6\left(-\frac{3}{4}x - \frac{1}{4}\right) = 2$$
$$x - \frac{9}{2}x - \frac{3}{2} = 2$$
$$-\frac{7}{2}x - \frac{3}{2} = 2$$
$$-\frac{7}{2}x = \frac{7}{2}$$
$$x = -1$$

Substitute into equation (1).
$$3x + 4y = -1$$
$$3(-1) + 4y = -1$$
$$-3 + 4y = -1$$
$$4y = 2$$
$$y = \frac{1}{2}$$

Replace x by $\frac{1}{a}$.
$$x = -1$$
$$\frac{1}{a} = -1$$
$$-a\left(\frac{1}{a}\right) = -a(-1)$$
$$-1 = a$$

Replace y by $\frac{1}{b}$.
$$y = \frac{1}{2}$$
$$\frac{1}{b} = \frac{1}{2}$$
$$2b\left(\frac{1}{b}\right) = 2b\left(\frac{1}{2}\right)$$
$$2 = b$$

The solution is $(-1, 2)$.

77. $y = -\dfrac{1}{2}x + 2$

$y = 2x - 1$

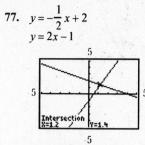

The solution is (1.20, 1.40).

78. $y = 1.2x + 2$

$y = -1.3x - 3$

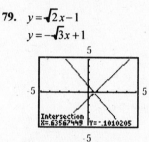

The solution is (−2.00, −0.40).

79. $y = \sqrt{2}x - 1$

$y = -\sqrt{3}x + 1$

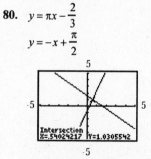

The solution is (0.64, −0.10).

80. $y = \pi x - \dfrac{2}{3}$

$y = -x + \dfrac{\pi}{2}$

The solution is (0.54, 1.03).

81. a. $y_1 = -0.0036x + 9.559$

$\quad = -0.0036(2010) + 9.559 = 2.323$

$y_2 = 0.0419x - 82.156$

$\quad = 0.0419(2010) - 82.516 = 1.703$

Since 2.323 > 1.703 the population of Orlando will not exceed the population of Pittsburgh in the year 2010.

b. $y_1 = y_2$

$-0.0036x + 9.559 = 0.0419x - 82.156$

$91.715 = 0.0455x$

$2015.7143 = x$

In 2016 the population of Orlando will first exceed the population of Pittsburgh.

c. The slope of y_1 is

$-0.0036(1,000,000) = 3600$. The slope indicates that the population of Pittsburgh is decreasing at the rate of 3600 people per year.

d. The slope of y_2 is

$0.0419(1,000,000) = 41,900$. The slope indicates that the population of Orlando is increasing at the rate of 41,900 people per year.

82. Solving the systems of equations $\begin{array}{l} a_1x + b_1y = c_1 \\ a_2x + b_2y = c_2 \end{array}$

for x yields $x = \dfrac{c_1b_2 - c_2b_1}{a_1b_2 - a_2b_1}$. Given $\dfrac{a_1}{b_1} = \dfrac{a_2}{b_2}$

implies that $a_1b_2 - a_2b_1 = 0$. Because division by zero is not allowed, the value of x cannot be determined and the system of equations is not independent.

83. The substitution method of solving a system of equations requires that a variable in one equation be replaced by an expression taken from a different equation. The Substitution Principle of Equality guarantees that the new equation will have the same solutions as the original equation.

Section 4.2

Concept Review 4.2

1. Always true

2. Always true

3. Sometimes true
   The solution of a system of three equations in three variables may be a point, a line, or a plane, or the system may not have a solution.

4. Never true
   If the system has an infinite number of solutions, it is a dependent system.

5. Never true
   The system is inconsistent and has no solutions.

Objective 4.2.1 Exercises

1. The solution to a system of equations is an ordered pair or a set of ordered pairs. 5 is not a solution to the system. It is the x-coordinate of the solution. To find the solution, substitute 5 for x into one of the equations in the system to find the y-coordinate of the solution.

2a. To eliminate x from the system of equations, multiply the first equation by 3 and the second equation by −2, or multiply the first equation by −3 and the second equation by 2. Then the coefficients of x will be opposites, and when the equations are added, the variable x will be eliminated.

b. To eliminate y from the system of equations, multiply the first equation by 2 and the second equation by 5. Then the coefficients of y will be opposites, and when the equations are added, the variable y will be eliminated.

3. (1) $x - y = 5$
(2) $x + y = 7$
Eliminate y. Add the equations.
$2x = 12$
$x = 6$
Replace x in equation (1).
$x - y = 5$
$6 - y = 5$
$-y = -1$
$y = 1$
The solution is (6, 1).

4. (1) $x + y = 1$
(2) $2x - y = 5$
Eliminate y. Add the equations.
$3x = 6$
$x = 2$
Replace x in equation (1).
$x + y = 1$
$2 + y = 1$
$y = -1$
The solution is (2, −1).

5. (1) $3x + y = 4$
(2) $x + y = 2$
Eliminate y.
$3x + y = 4$
$-1(x + y) = -1(2)$

$3x + y = 4$
$-x - y = -2$
Add the equations.
$2x = 2$
$x = 1$
Replace x in equation (2).
$x + y = 2$
$1 + y = 2$
$y = 1$
The solution is (1, 1).

6. (1) $x - 3y = 4$
(2) $x + 5y = -4$
Eliminate x.
$-1(x - 3y) = -1(4)$
$x + 5y = -4$

$-x + 3y = -4$
$x + 5y = -4$
Add the equations.
$8y = -8$
$y = -1$
Replace y in equation (2).
$x + 5y = -4$
$x + 5(-1) = -4$
$x - 5 = -4$
$x = 1$
The solution is (1, −1).

7. (1) $3x + y = 7$
(2) $x + 2y = 4$
Eliminate y.
$-2(3x + y) = -2(7)$
$x + 2y = 4$

$-6x - 2y = -14$
$x + 2y = 4$
Add the equations.
$-5x = -10$
$x = 2$
Replace x in equation (2).
$x + 2y = 4$
$2 + 2y = 4$
$2y = 2$
$y = 1$
The solution is (2, 1).

8. (1) $x - 2y = 7$
(2) $3x - 2y = 9$
Eliminate y.
$-1(x - 2y) = -1(7)$
$3x - 2y = 9$

$-x + 2y = -7$
$3x - 2y = 9$
Add the equations.
$2x = 2$
$x = 1$
Replace x in equation (1).
$x - 2y = 7$
$1 - 2y = 7$
$-2y = 6$
$y = -3$
The solution is (1, −3).

9. (1) $3x - y = 4$
    (2) $6x - 2y = 8$
    Eliminate y.
    $-2(3x - y) = -2(4)$
    $6x - 2y = 8$

    $-6x + 2y = -8$
    $6x - 2y = 8$
    Add the equations.
    $0 = 0$
    This is a true equation. The equations are dependent. The solutions are the ordered pairs $(x, 3x - 4)$.

10. (1) $x - 2y = -3$
    (2) $-2x + 4y = 6$
    Eliminate x.
    $2(x - 2y) = 2(-3)$
    $-2x + 4y = 6$

    $2x - 4y = -6$
    $-2x + 4y = 6$
    Add the equations.
    $0 = 0$
    This is a true equation. The equations are dependent. The solutions are ordered pairs $\left(x, \frac{1}{2}x + \frac{3}{2}\right)$.

11. (1) $2x + 5y = 9$
    (2) $4x - 7y = -16$
    Eliminate x.
    $-2(2x + 5y) = -2(9)$
    $4x - 7y = -16$

    $-4x - 10y = -18$
    $4x - 7y = -16$
    Add the equations.
    $-17y = -34$
    $y = 2$
    Replace y in equation (1).
    $2x + 5y = 9$
    $2x + 5(2) = 9$
    $2x + 10 = 9$
    $2x = -1$
    $x = -\frac{1}{2}$
    The solution is $\left(-\frac{1}{2}, 2\right)$.

12. (1) $8x - 3y = 21$
    (2) $4x + 5y = -9$
    Eliminate x.
    $8x - 3y = 21$
    $-2(4x + 5y) = -2(-9)$

    $8x - 3y = 21$
    $-8x - 10y = 18$
    Add the equations.
    $-13y = 39$
    $y = -3$
    Replace y in equation (1).
    $8x - 3y = 21$
    $8x - 3(-3) = 21$
    $8x + 9 = 21$
    $8x = 12$
    $x = \frac{3}{2}$
    The solution is $\left(\frac{3}{2}, -3\right)$.

13. (1) $4x - 6y = 5$
    (2) $2x - 3y = 7$
    Eliminate y.
    $4x - 6y = 5$
    $-2(2x - 3y) = -2(7)$

    $4x - 6y = 5$
    $-4x + 6y = -14$
    Add the equations.
    $0 = -9$
    This is not a true equation. The system of equations is inconsistent and therefore has no solution.

14. (1) $3x + 6y = 7$
    (2) $2x + 4y = 5$
    Eliminate x.
    $-2(3x + 6y) = -2(7)$
    $3(2x + 4y) = 3(5)$

    $-6x - 12y = -14$
    $6x + 12y = 15$
    Add the equations.
    $0 = 1$
    This is not a true equation. The system of equations is inconsistent and therefore has no solution.

15. (1) $3x - 5y = 7$

(2) $x - 2y = 3$

Eliminate x.

$3x - 5y = 7$

$-3(x - 2y) = -3(3)$

$3x - 5y = 7$

$-3x + 6y = -9$

Add the equations.

$y = -2$

Replace y in equation (2).

$x - 2y = 3$

$x - 2(-2) = 3$

$x + 4 = 3$

$x = -1$

The solution is $(-1, -2)$.

16. (1) $3x + 4y = 25$

(2) $2x + y = 10$

Eliminate y.

$3x + 4y = 25$

$-4(2x + y) = -4(10)$

$3x + 4y = 25$

$-8x - 4y = -40$

Add the equations.

$-5x = -15$

$x = 3$

Replace x in equation (2).

$2x + y = 10$

$2(3) + y = 10$

$6 + y = 10$

$y = 4$

The solution is $(3, 4)$.

17. (1) $3x + 2y = 16$

(2) $2x - 3y = -11$

Eliminate y.

$3(3x + 2y) = 3(16)$

$2(2x - 3y) = 2(-11)$

$9x + 6y = 48$

$4x - 6y = -22$

Add the equations.

$13x = 26$

$x = 2$

Replace x in equation (1).

$3x + 2y = 16$

$3(2) + 2y = 16$

$6 + 2y = 16$

$2y = 10$

$y = 5$

The solution is $(2, 5)$.

18. (1) $2x - 5y = 13$

(2) $5x + 3y = 17$

Eliminate y.

$3(2x - 5y) = 3(13)$

$5(5x + 3y) = 5(17)$

$6x - 15y = 39$

$25x + 15y = 85$

Add the equations.

$31x = 124$

$x = 4$

Replace x in equation (1).

$2x - 5y = 13$

$2(4) - 5y = 13$

$8 - 5y = 13$

$-5y = 5$

$y = -1$

The solution is $(4, -1)$.

19. (1) $4x + 4y = 5$

(2) $2x - 8y = -5$

Eliminate y.

$2(4x + 4y) = 2(5)$

$2x - 8y = -5$

$8x + 8y = 10$

$2x - 8y = -5$

Add the equations.

$10x = 5$

$x = \dfrac{1}{2}$

Replace x in equation (1).

$4x + 4y = 5$

$4\left(\dfrac{1}{2}\right) + 4y = 5$

$2 + 4y = 5$

$4y = 3$

$y = \dfrac{3}{4}$

The solution is $\left(\dfrac{1}{2}, \dfrac{3}{4}\right)$.

20. (1) $3x + 7y = 16$
$\quad$ (2) $4x - 3y = 9$
$\quad$ Eliminate y.
$\quad$ $3(3x + 7y) = 3(16)$
$\quad$ $7(4x - 3y) = 7(9)$

$\quad\quad$ $9x + 21y = 48$
$\quad$ $28x - 21y = 63$
$\quad$ Add the equations.
$\quad$ $37x = 111$
$\quad\quad$ $x = 3$
$\quad$ Replace x in equation (1).
$\quad\quad$ $3x + 7y = 16$
$\quad\quad$ $3(3) + 7y = 16$
$\quad\quad\quad$ $9 + 7y = 16$
$\quad\quad\quad\quad$ $7y = 7$
$\quad\quad\quad\quad$ $y = 1$
$\quad$ The solution is $(3, 1)$.

21. (1) $5x + 4y = 0$
$\quad$ (2) $3x + 7y = 0$
$\quad$ Eliminate x.
$\quad$ $-3(5x + 4y) = -3(0)$
$\quad\quad$ $5(3x + 7y) = 5(0)$

$\quad$ $-15x - 12y = 0$
$\quad\quad$ $15x + 35y = 0$
$\quad$ Add the equations.
$\quad$ $23y = 0$
$\quad\quad$ $y = 0$
$\quad$ Replace y in equation (1).
$\quad\quad$ $5x + 4y = 0$
$\quad$ $5x + 4(0) = 0$
$\quad\quad$ $5x = 0$
$\quad\quad\quad$ $x = 0$
$\quad$ The solution is $(0, 0)$.

22. (1) $3x - 4y = 0$
$\quad$ (2) $4x - 7y = 0$
$\quad$ Eliminate x.
$\quad$ $-4(3x - 4y) = -4(0)$
$\quad\quad$ $3(4x - 7y) = 3(0)$

$\quad$ $-12x + 16y = 0$
$\quad\quad$ $12x - 21y = 0$
$\quad$ Add the equations.
$\quad$ $-5y = 0$
$\quad\quad$ $y = 0$
$\quad$ Replace y in equation (1).
$\quad\quad$ $3x - 4y = 0$
$\quad$ $3x - 4(0) = 0$
$\quad\quad$ $3x = 0$
$\quad\quad\quad$ $x = 0$
$\quad$ The solution is $(0, 0)$.

23. (1) $3x - 6y = 6$
$\quad$ (2) $9x - 3y = 8$
$\quad$ Eliminate y.
$\quad\quad$ $3x - 6y = 6$
$\quad$ $-2(9x - 3y) = -2(8)$

$\quad\quad$ $3x - 6y = 6$
$\quad$ $-18x + 6y = -16$
$\quad$ Add the equations.
$\quad$ $-15x = -10$
$\quad\quad$ $x = \dfrac{2}{3}$
$\quad$ Replace x in the equation (1).
$\quad\quad$ $3x - 6y = 6$
$\quad$ $3\left(\dfrac{2}{3}\right) - 6y = 6$
$\quad\quad$ $2 - 6y = 6$
$\quad\quad\quad$ $-6y = 4$
$\quad\quad\quad\quad$ $y = -\dfrac{2}{3}$
$\quad$ The solution is $\left(\dfrac{2}{3}, -\dfrac{2}{3}\right)$.

24. (1) $4x - 8y = 5$
$\quad$ (2) $8x + 2y = 1$
$\quad$ Eliminate y.
$\quad\quad$ $4x - 8y = 5$
$\quad$ $4(8x + 2y) = 4(1)$

$\quad\quad$ $4x - 8y = 5$
$\quad$ $32x + 8y = 4$
$\quad$ Add the equations.
$\quad$ $36x = 9$
$\quad\quad$ $x = \dfrac{1}{4}$
$\quad$ Replace x in equation (1).
$\quad\quad$ $4x - 8y = 5$
$\quad$ $4\left(\dfrac{1}{4}\right) - 8y = 5$
$\quad\quad$ $1 - 8y = 5$
$\quad\quad\quad$ $-8y = 4$
$\quad\quad\quad\quad$ $y = -\dfrac{1}{2}$
$\quad$ The solution is $\left(\dfrac{1}{4}, -\dfrac{1}{2}\right)$.

25. (1) $5x + 2y = 2x + 1$
(2) $2x - 3y = 3x + 2$
Write the equations in the form $Ax + By = C$.
$5x + 2y = 2x + 1$
$3x + 2y = 1$

$2x - 3y = 3x + 2$
$-x - 3y = 2$
Solve the system.
$3x + 2y = 1$
$-x - 3y = 2$
Eliminate x.
$\quad 3x + 2y = 1$
$3(-x - 3y) = 3(2)$

$\quad 3x + 2y = 1$
$-3x - 9y = 6$
Add the equations.
$-7y = 7$
$\quad y = -1$
Replace y in the equation $-x - 3y = 2$.
$\quad -x - 3y = 2$
$-x - 3(-1) = 2$
$\quad -x + 3 = 2$
$\quad\quad -x = -1$
$\quad\quad\quad x = 1$
The solution is $(1, -1)$.

26. (1) $3x + 3y = y + 1$
(2) $x + 3y = 9 - x$
Write the equation in the form $Ax + By = C$.
$3x + 3y = y + 1$
$3x + 2y = 1$

$x + 3y = 9 - x$
$2x + 3y = 9$
Solve the system.
$3x + 2y = 1$
$2x + 3y = 9$
Eliminate x.
$-2(3x + 2y) = -2(1)$
$\quad 3(2x + 3y) = 3(9)$

$-6x - 4y = -2$
$\quad 6x + 9y = 27$
Add the equations.
$5y = 25$
$\quad y = 5$
Replace y in the equation $3x + 2y = 1$.
$\quad 3x + 2y = 1$
$3x + 2(5) = 1$
$3x + 10 = 1$
$\quad\quad 3x = -9$
$\quad\quad\quad x = -3$
The solution is $(-3, 5)$.

27. (1) $\frac{2}{3}x - \frac{1}{2}y = 3$
(2) $\frac{1}{3}x - \frac{1}{4}y = \frac{3}{2}$
Clear the fractions.
$6\left(\frac{2}{3}x - \frac{1}{2}y\right) = 6(3)$
$12\left(\frac{1}{3}x - \frac{1}{4}y\right) = 12\left(\frac{3}{2}\right)$

$4x - 3y = 18$
$4x - 3y = 18$
Eliminate x.
$-1(4x - 3y) = -1(18)$
$\quad 4x - 3y = 18$

$-4x + 3y = -18$
$\quad 4x - 3y = 18$
Add the equations.
$0 = 0$
This is a true equation. The equations are dependent. The solutions are the ordered pairs $\left(x, \frac{4}{3}x - 6\right)$.

28. (1) $\frac{3}{4}x + \frac{1}{3}y = -\frac{1}{2}$
(2) $\frac{1}{2}x - \frac{5}{6}y = -\frac{7}{2}$
Clear the fractions.
$12\left(\frac{3}{4}x + \frac{1}{3}y\right) = 12\left(-\frac{1}{2}\right)$
$6\left(\frac{1}{2}x - \frac{5}{6}y\right) = 6\left(-\frac{7}{2}\right)$

$9x + 4y = -6$
$3x - 5y = -21$
Eliminate x.
$\quad 9x + 4y = -6$
$-3(3x - 5y) = -3(-21)$

$\quad 9x + 4y = -6$
$-9x + 15y = 63$
Add the equations.
$19y = 57$
$\quad y = 3$
Replace y in equation (1).
$\frac{3}{4}x + \frac{1}{3}y = -\frac{1}{2}$
$\frac{3}{4}x + \frac{1}{3}(3) = -\frac{1}{2}$
$\quad \frac{3}{4}x + 1 = -\frac{1}{2}$
$\quad\quad \frac{3}{4}x = -\frac{3}{2}$
$\quad\quad\quad x = -2$
The solution is $(-2, 3)$.

29. (1) $\dfrac{2}{5}x - \dfrac{1}{3}y = 1$

(2) $\dfrac{3}{5}x + \dfrac{2}{3}y = 5$

Clear the fractions.

$15\left(\dfrac{2}{5}x - \dfrac{1}{3}y\right) = 15(1)$

$15\left(\dfrac{3}{5}x + \dfrac{2}{3}y\right) = 15(5)$

$6x - 5y = 15$
$9x + 10y = 75$

Eliminate y.
$2(6x - 5y) = 2(15)$
$9x + 10y = 75$

$12x - 10y = 30$
$9x + 10y = 75$

Add the equations.
$21x = 105$
$x = 5$

Replace x in equation (1).

$\dfrac{2}{5}x - \dfrac{1}{3}y = 1$

$\dfrac{2}{5}(5) - \dfrac{1}{3}y = 1$

$2 - \dfrac{1}{3}y = 1$

$-\dfrac{1}{3}y = -1$

$y = 3$

The solution is (5, 3).

30. (1) $\dfrac{5}{6}x + \dfrac{1}{3}y = \dfrac{4}{3}$

(2) $\dfrac{2}{3}x - \dfrac{1}{2}y = \dfrac{11}{6}$

Clear the fractions.

$6\left(\dfrac{5}{6}x + \dfrac{1}{3}y\right) = 6\left(\dfrac{4}{3}\right)$

$6\left(\dfrac{2}{3}x - \dfrac{1}{2}y\right) = 6\left(\dfrac{11}{6}\right)$

$5x + 2y = 8$
$4x - 3y = 11$

Eliminate y.
$3(5x + 2y) = 3(8)$
$2(4x - 3y) = 2(11)$

$15x + 6y = 24$
$8x - 6y = 22$

Add the equations.
$23x = 46$
$x = 2$

Replace x in equation (1).

$\dfrac{5}{6}x + \dfrac{1}{3}y = \dfrac{4}{3}$

$\dfrac{5}{6}(2) + \dfrac{1}{3}y = \dfrac{4}{3}$

$\dfrac{5}{3} + \dfrac{1}{3}y = \dfrac{4}{3}$

$\dfrac{1}{3}y = -\dfrac{1}{3}$

$y = -1$

The solution is (2, −1).

31. (1) $\frac{3}{4}x + \frac{2}{5}y = -\frac{3}{20}$

   (2) $\frac{3}{2}x - \frac{1}{4}y = \frac{3}{4}$

Clear the fractions.

(1) $\frac{3}{4}x + \frac{2}{5}y = -\frac{3}{20}$

(2) $\frac{3}{2}x - \frac{1}{4}y = \frac{3}{4}$

$15x + 8y = -3$

$6x - y = 3$

Eliminate y.

$15x + 8y = -3$

$8(6x - y) = 8(3)$

$15x + 8y = -3$

$48x - 8y = 24$

Add the equations.

$63x = 21$

$x = \frac{1}{3}$

Replace x in equation (2).

$\frac{3}{2}x - \frac{1}{4}y = \frac{3}{4}$

$\frac{3}{2}\left(\frac{1}{3}\right) - \frac{1}{4}y = \frac{3}{4}$

$\frac{1}{2} - \frac{1}{4}y = \frac{3}{4}$

$-\frac{1}{4}y = \frac{1}{4}$

$y = -1$

The solution is $\left(\frac{1}{3}, -1\right)$.

32. (1) $\frac{2}{5}x - \frac{1}{2}y = \frac{13}{2}$

   (2) $\frac{3}{4}x - \frac{1}{5}y = \frac{17}{2}$

Clear the fractions.

$10\left(\frac{2}{5}x - \frac{1}{2}y\right) = 10\left(\frac{13}{2}\right)$

$20\left(\frac{3}{4}x - \frac{1}{5}y\right) = 20\left(\frac{17}{2}\right)$

$4x - 5y = 65$

$15x - 4y = 170$

Eliminate y.

$-4(4x - 5y) = -4(65)$

$5(15x - 4y) = 5(170)$

$-16x + 20y = -260$

$75x - 20y = 850$

Add the equations.

$59x = 590$

$x = 10$

Replace x in equation (1).

$\frac{2}{5}x - \frac{1}{2}y = \frac{13}{2}$

$\frac{2}{5}(10) - \frac{1}{2}y = \frac{13}{2}$

$4 - \frac{1}{2}y = \frac{13}{2}$

$-\frac{1}{2}y = \frac{5}{2}$

$y = -5$

The solution is $(10, -5)$.

33. (1) $4x - 5y = 3y + 4$

(2) $2x + 3y = 2x + 1$

Write the equations in the form $Ax + By = C$.

$4x - 5y = 3y + 4$

$4x - 8y = 4$

$2x + 3y = 2x + 1$

$3y = 1$

Solve the system.

$4x - 8y = 4$

$3y = 1$

Solve the equation $3y = 1$ for y.

$3y = 1$

$y = \dfrac{1}{3}$

Replace y in the equation $4x - 8y = 4$.

$4x - 8y = 4$

$4x - 8\left(\dfrac{1}{3}\right) = 4$

$4x - \dfrac{8}{3} = 4$

$4x = \dfrac{20}{3}$

$x = \dfrac{5}{3}$

The solution is $\left(\dfrac{5}{3}, \dfrac{1}{3}\right)$.

34. (1) $5x - 2y = 8x - 1$

(2) $2x + 7y = 4y + 9$

Write the equations in the form $Ax + By = C$.

$5x - 2y = 8x - 1$

$-3x - 2y = -1$

$2x + 7y = 4y + 9$

$2x + 3y = 9$

Solve the system.

$-3x - 2y = -1$

$2x + 3y = 9$

Eliminate x.

$2(-3x - 2y) = 2(-1)$

$3(2x + 3y) = 3(9)$

$-6x - 4y = -2$

$6x + 9y = 27$

Add the equations.

$5y = 25$

$y = 5$

Replace y in the equation $2x + 3y = 9$.

$2x + 3y = 9$

$2x + 3(5) = 9$

$2x + 15 = 9$

$2x = -6$

$x = -3$

The solution is $(-3, 5)$.

35. (1) $2x + 5y = 5x + 1$

(2) $3x - 2y = 3y + 3$

Write the equations in the form $Ax + By = C$.

$2x + 5y = 5x + 1$

$-3x + 5y = 1$

$3x - 2y = 3y + 3$

$3x - 5y = 3$

Solve the system.

$-3x + 5y = 1$

$3x - 5y = 3$

Add the equations.

$0 = 4$

This is not a true equation. The system of equations is inconsistent and therefore has no solution.

36. If, after adding the equations, the result is a false equation, such as $0 = 7$, with no variable, the system of equations is inconsistent.

37. If, after adding the equations, the result is a true equation, such as $3 = 3$, with no variable, the system of equations is dependent.

Objective 4.2.2 Exercises

38. The graph of a linear equation in three variables is a plane.

39. The solution of an independent system of linear equations in three variables is an ordered triple of the form (x, y, z).

40. (1) $x + 2y - z = 1$

(2) $2x - y + z = 6$

(3) $x + 3y - z = 2$

Eliminate z. Add equations (1) and (2).

$x + 2y - z = 1$
$2x - y + z = 6$

(4) $3x + y = 7$

Add equations (2) and (3).

$2x - y + z = 6$
$x + 3y - z = 2$

(5) $3x + 2y = 8$

Multiply equation (4) by -1 and add to equation (5).

$-1(3x + y) = -1(7)$
$\quad 3x + 2y = 8$

$-3x - y = -7$
$\ \ 3x + 2y = 8$

$y = 1$

Replace y by 1 in equation (4).

$3x + y = 7$
$3x + 1 = 7$
$\quad 3x = 6$
$\qquad x = 2$

Replace x by 2 and y by 1 in equation (1).

$x + 2y - z = 1$
$2 + 2(1) - z = 1$
$\ \ 2 + 2 - z = 1$
$\qquad 4 - z = 1$
$\qquad\quad -z = -3$
$\qquad\quad\ \ z = 3$

The solution is $(2, 1, 3)$.

41. (1) $x + 3y + z = 6$

(2) $3x + y - z = -2$

(3) $2x + 2y - z = 1$

Eliminate z. Add equations (1) and (2).

$x + 3y + z = 6$
$3x + y - z = -2$

$4x + 4y = 4$

Multiply both sides of the equation by $\dfrac{1}{4}$.

(4) $x + y = 1$

Add equations (1) and (3).

$\ x + 3y + z = 6$
$2x + 2y - z = 1$

(5) $3x + 5y = 7$

Multiply equation (4) by -3 and add to equation (5).

$-3(x + y) = -3(1)$
$\quad 3x + 5y = 7$

$-3x - 3y = -3$
$\ \ 3x + 5y = 7$

$2y = 4$
$\ y = 2$

Replace y by 2 in equation (4).

$x + y = 1$
$x + 2 = 1$
$\quad x = -1$

Replace x by -1 and y by 2 in equation (1).

$x + 3y + z = 6$
$-1 + 3(2) + z = 6$
$\ \ -1 + 6 + z = 6$
$\qquad 5 + z = 6$
$\qquad\quad z = 1$

The solution is $(-1, 2, 1)$.

42. (1) $2x - y + 2z = 7$

(2) $\quad x + y + z = 2$

(3) $3x - y + z = 6$

Eliminate y. Add equations (1) and (2).
$2x - y + 2z = 7$
$\underline{x + y + z = 2}$

$\quad 3x + 3z = 9$

Multiply both sides of the equation by $\frac{1}{3}$.

(4) $x + z = 3$

Add equations (2) and (3).
$x + y + z = 2$
$\underline{3x - y + z = 6}$

$\quad 4x + 2z = 8$

Multiply both sides of the equation by $\frac{1}{2}$.

(5) $2x + z = 4$

Multiply equation (4) by -1 and add to equation (5).
$-1(x + z) = -1(3)$
$\quad 2x + z = 4$

$-x - z = -3$
$\underline{2x + z = 4}$
$\qquad x = 1$

Replace x by 1 in equation (4).
$x + z = 3$
$1 + z = 3$
$\quad z = 2$

Replace x by 1 and z by 2 in equation (2).
$x + y + z = 2$
$1 + y + 2 = 2$
$\quad 3 + y = 2$
$\qquad y = -1$

The solution is $(1, -1, 2)$.

43. (1) $x - 2y + z = 6$

(2) $x + 3y + z = 16$

(3) $3x - y - z = 12$

Eliminate z. Add equations (1) and (3).
$x - 2y + z = 6$
$\underline{3x - y - z = 12}$

(4) $4x - 3y = 18$

Add equations (2) and (3).
$x + 3y + z = 16$
$\underline{3x - y - z = 12}$

$\quad 4x + 2y = 28$

Multiply both sides of the equation by $\frac{1}{2}$.

(5) $2x + y = 14$

Multiply equation (5) by 3 and add to equation (4).
$3(2x + y) = 3(14)$
$\quad 4x - 3y = 18$

$6x + 3y = 42$
$\underline{4x - 3y = 18}$

$10x = 60$
$\quad x = 6$

Replace x by 6 in equation (5).
$2x + y = 14$
$2(6) + y = 14$
$\quad 12 + y = 14$
$\qquad y = 2$

Replace x by 6 and y by 2 in equation (1).
$x - 2y + z = 6$
$6 - 2(2) + z = 6$
$\quad 6 - 4 + z = 6$
$\qquad 2 + z = 6$
$\qquad\quad z = 4$

The solution is $(6, 2, 4)$.

44. (1) $3x + y = 5$

(2) $3y - z = 2$

(3) $x + z = 5$

Eliminate z. Add equations (2) and (3).

$3y - z = 2$

$x + z = 5$

(4) $x + 3y = 7$

Multiply equation (4) by -3 and add to equation (1).

$-3(x + 3y) = -3(7)$

$3x + y = 5$

$-3x - 9y = -21$

$3x + y = 5$

$-8y = -16$

$y = 2$

Replace y by 2 in equation (1).

$3x + y = 5$

$3x + 2 = 5$

$3x = 3$

$x = 1$

Replace x by 1 in equation (3).

$x + z = 5$

$1 + z = 5$

$z = 4$

The solution is (1, 2, 4).

45. (1) $2y + z = 7$

(2) $2x - z = 3$

(3) $x - y = 3$

Eliminate z. Add equations (1) and (2).

$2y + z = 7$

$2x - z = 3$

$2x + 2y = 10$

Multiply both sides of the equation by $\frac{1}{2}$.

(4) $x + y = 5$

Add equations (3) and (4).

$x - y = 3$

$x + y = 5$

$2x = 8$

$x = 4$

Replace x by 4 in equation (4).

$x + y = 5$

$4 + y = 5$

$y = 1$

Replace y by 1 in equation (1).

$2y + z = 7$

$2(1) + z = 7$

$2 + z = 7$

$z = 5$

The solution is (4, 1, 5).

46. (1) $x - y + z = 1$

(2) $2x + 3y - z = 3$

(3) $-x + 2y - 4z = 4$

Eliminate z. Add equations (1) and (2).

$x - y + z = 1$

$2x + 3y - z = 3$

(4) $3x + 2y = 4$

Multiply equation (1) by 4 and add to equation (3).

$4(x - y + z) = 4(1)$

$-x + 2y - 4z = 4$

$4x - 4y + 4z = 4$

$-x + 2y - 4z = 4$

(5) $3x - 2y = 8$

Multiply equation (4) by -1 and add to equation (5).

$-1(3x + 2y) = -1(4)$

$3x - 2y = 8$

$-3x - 2y = -4$

$3x - 2y = 8$

$-4y = 4$

$y = -1$

Replace y by -1 in equation (5).

$3x - 2y = 8$

$3x - 2(-1) = 8$

$3x + 2 = 8$

$3x = 6$

$x = 2$

Replace x by 2 and y by -1 in equation (1).

$x - y + z = 1$

$2 - (-1) + z = 1$

$3 + z = 1$

$z = -2$

The solution is (2, -1, -2).

47. (1) $2x + y - 3z = 7$

(2) $x - 2y + 3z = 1$

(3) $3x + 4y - 3z = 13$

Eliminate z. Add equations (1) and (2).

$2x + y - 3z = 7$

$x - 2y + 3z = 1$

(4) $3x - y = 8$

Add equations (2) and (3).

$x - 2y + 3z = 1$

$3x + 4y - 3z = 13$

$4x + 2y = 14$

Multiply each side of the equation by $\frac{1}{2}$.

(5) $2x + y = 7$

Add equations (4) and (5).

$3x - y = 8$

$2x + y = 7$

$5x = 15$

$x = 3$

Replace x by 3 in equation (5).

$2x + y = 7$

$2(3) + y = 7$

$6 + y = 7$

$y = 1$

Replace x by 3 and y by 1 in equation (1).

$2x + y - 3z = 7$

$2(3) + 1 - 3z = 7$

$6 + 1 - 3z = 7$

$7 - 3z = 7$

$-3z = 0$

$z = 0$

The solution is (3, 1, 0).

48. (1) $2x + 3z = 5$

(2) $3y + 2z = 3$

(3) $3x + 4y = -10$

Eliminate z. Multiply equation (1) by -2 and equation (2) by 3.

Then add the equations.

$-2(2x + 3z) = -2(5)$

$3(3y + 2z) = 3(3)$

$-4x - 6z = -10$

$9y + 6z = 9$

(4) $-4x + 9y = -1$

Multiply equation (3) by 4 and equation (4) by 3.

Then add the equations.

$4(3x + 4y) = 4(-10)$

$3(-4x + 9y) = 3(-1)$

$12x + 16y = -40$

$-12x + 27y = -3$

$43y = -43$

$y = -1$

Replace y by -1 in equation (3).

$3x + 4y = -10$

$3x + 4(-1) = -10$

$3x - 4 = -10$

$3x = -6$

$x = -2$

Replace x by -2 in equation (1).

$2x + 3z = 5$

$2(-2) + 3z = 5$

$-4 + 3z = 5$

$3z = 9$

$z = 3$

The solution is $(-2, -1, 3)$.

49. (1) $3x + 4z = 5$

(2) $2y + 3z = 2$

(3) $2x - 5y = 8$

Eliminate z. Multiply equation (1) by -3 and equation (2) by 4.
Then add the equations.
$$-3(3x + 4z) = -3(5)$$
$$4(2y + 3z) = 4(2)$$

$$-9x - 12z = -15$$
$$8y + 12z = 8$$

(4) $-9x + 8y = -7$

Multiply equation (3) by 9 and equation (4) by 2.
Then add the equations.
$$9(2x - 5y) = 9(8)$$
$$2(-9x + 8y) = 2(-7)$$

$$18x - 45y = 72$$
$$-18x + 16y = -14$$

$$-29y = 58$$
$$y = -2$$

Replace y by -2 in equation (3).
$$2x - 5y = 8$$
$$2x - 5(-2) = 8$$
$$2x + 10 = 8$$
$$2x = -2$$
$$x = -1$$

Replace x by -1 in equation (1).
$$3x + 4z = 5$$
$$3(-1) + 4z = 5$$
$$-3 + 4z = 5$$
$$4z = 8$$
$$z = 2$$

The solution is $(-1, -2, 2)$.

50. (1) $2x + 4y - 2z = 3$

(2) $x + 3y + 4z = 1$

(3) $x + 2y - z = 4$

Eliminate x. Multiply equation (2) by -2 and add to equation (1).
$$2x + 4y - 2z = 3$$
$$-2(x + 3y + 4z) = -2(1)$$

$$2x + 4y - 2z = 3$$
$$-2x - 6y - 8z = -2$$

(4) $-2y - 10z = 1$

Multiply equation (2) by -1 and add to equation (3).
$$-1(x + 3y + 4z) = -1(1)$$
$$x + 2y - z = 4$$

$$-x - 3y - 4z = -1$$
$$x + 2y - z = 4$$

(5) $-y - 5z = 3$

Multiply equation (5) by -2 and add to equation (4).
$$-2y - 10z = 1$$
$$-2(-y - 5z) = -2(3)$$

$$-2y - 10z = 1$$
$$2y + 10z = -6$$

$$0 = -5$$

This is not a true equation. The system of equations is inconsistent and therefore has no solution.

51. (1) $x - 3y + 2z = 1$

(2) $x - 2y + 3z = 5$

(3) $2x - 6y + 4z = 3$

Eliminate x. Multiply equation (1) by -1 and add to equation (2).
$$-1(x - 3y + 2z) = -1(1)$$
$$x - 2y + 3z = 5$$

$$-x + 3y - 2z = -1$$
$$x - 2y + 3z = 5$$

(4) $y + z = 4$

Multiply equation (1) by -2 and add to equation (3).
$$-2(x - 3y + 2z) = -2(1)$$
$$2x - 6y + 4z = 3$$

$$-2x + 6y - 4z = -2$$
$$2x - 6y + 4z = 3$$

$$0 = 1$$

This is not a true equation. The system of equations is inconsistent and therefore has no solution.

52. (1) $\quad 2x + y - z = 5$

    (2) $\quad x + 3y + z = 14$

    (3) $\quad 3x - y + 2z = 1$

Eliminate z. Add equations (1) and (2).

$\quad 2x + y - z = 5$

$\quad x + 3y + z = 14$

    (4) $\quad 3x + 4y = 19$

Multiply equation (1) by 2 and add to equation (3).

$\quad 2(2x + y - z) = 2(5)$

$\quad 3x - y + 2z = 1$

$\quad 4x + 2y - 2z = 10$

$\quad 3x - y + 2z = 1$

    (5) $\quad 7x + y = 11$

Multiply equation (5) by -4 and add to equation (4).

$\quad 3x + 4y = 19$

$\quad -4(7x + y) = -4(11)$

$\quad 3x + 4y = 19$

$\quad -28x - 4y = -44$

$\quad\quad -25x = -25$

$\quad\quad\quad\quad x = 1$

Replace x by 1 in equation (5).

$\quad 7x + y = 11$

$\quad 7(1) + y = 11$

$\quad 7 + y = 11$

$\quad\quad y = 4$

Replace x by 1 and y by 4 in equation (1).

$\quad 2x + y - z = 5$

$\quad 2(1) + 4 - z = 5$

$\quad 2 + 4 - z = 5$

$\quad 6 - z = 5$

$\quad -z = -1$

$\quad z = 1$

The solution is $(1, 4, 1)$.

53. (1) $\quad 3x - y - 2z = 11$

    (2) $\quad 2x + y - 2z = 11$

    (3) $\quad x + 3y - z = 8$

Eliminate z. Multiply equation (1) by -1 and add to equation (2).

$\quad -1(3x - y - 2z) = -1(11)$

$\quad 2x + y - 2z = 11$

$\quad -3x + y + 2z = -11$

$\quad 2x + y - 2z = 11$

    (4) $\quad -x + 2y = 0$

Multiply equation (3) by -2 and add to equation (1).

$\quad 3x - y - 2z = 11$

$\quad -2(x + 3y - z) = -2(8)$

$\quad 3x - y - 2z = 11$

$\quad -2x - 6y + 2z = -16$

    (5) $\quad x - 7y = -5$

Add equations (4) and (5).

$\quad -x + 2y = 0$

$\quad x - 7y = -5$

$\quad -5y = -5$

$\quad y = 1$

Replace y by 1 in equation (4).

$\quad -x + 2y = 0$

$\quad -x + 2(1) = 0$

$\quad -x + 2 = 0$

$\quad -x = -2$

$\quad x = 2$

Replace x by 2 and y by 1 in equation (3).

$\quad x + 3y - z = 8$

$\quad 2 + 3(1) - z = 8$

$\quad 2 + 3 - z = 8$

$\quad 5 - z = 8$

$\quad -z = 3$

$\quad z = -3$

The solution is $(2, 1, -3)$.

54. (1) $3x + y - 2z = 2$

(2) $x + 2y + 3z = 13$

(3) $2x - 2y + 5z = 6$

Eliminate y. Multiply equation (1) by -2 and add to equation (2).

$-2(3x + y - 2z) = -2(2)$
$x + 2y + 3z = 13$

$-6x - 2y + 4z = -4$
$x + 2y + 3z = 13$

(4) $-5x + 7z = 9$

Add equations (2) and (3).

$x + 2y + 3z = 13$
$2x - 2y + 5z = 6$

(5) $3x + 8z = 19$

Multiply equation (4) by 3 and equation (5) by 5. Then add the equations.

$3(-5x + 7z) = 3(9)$
$5(3x + 8z) = 5(19)$

$-15x + 21z = 27$
$15x + 40z = 95$

$61z = 122$
$z = 2$

Replace z by 2 in equation (5).

$3x + 8z = 19$
$3x + 8(2) = 19$
$3x + 16 = 19$
$3x = 3$
$x = 1$

Replace x by 1 and z by 2 and equation (1).

$3x + y - 2z = 2$
$3(1) + y - 2(2) = 2$
$3 + y - 4 = 2$
$y - 1 = 2$
$y = 3$

The solution is (1, 3, 2).

55. (1) $4x + 5y + z = 6$

(2) $2x - y + 2z = 11$

(3) $x + 2y + 2z = 6$

Eliminate z. Multiply equation (1) by -2 and add to equation (2).

$-2(4x + 5y + z) = -2(6)$
$2x - y + 2z = 11$

$-8x - 10y - 2z = -12$
$2x - y + 2z = 11$

(4) $-6x - 11y = -1$

Multiply equation (2) by -1 and add to equation (3).

$-1(2x - y + 2z) = -1(11)$
$x + 2y + 2z = 6$

$-2x + y - 2z = -11$
$x + 2y + 2z = 6$

(5) $-x + 3y = -5$

Multiply equation (5) by -6 and add to equation (4).

$-6x - 11y = -1$
$-6(-x + 3y) = -6(-5)$

$-6x - 11y = -1$
$6x - 18y = 30$

$-29y = 29$
$y = -1$

Replace y by -1 in equation (5).

$-x + 3y = -5$
$-x + 3(-1) = -5$
$-x - 3 = -5$
$-x = -2$
$x = 2$

Replace x by 2 and y by -1 in equation (1).

$4x + 5y + z = 6$
$4(2) + 5(-1) + z = 6$
$8 - 5 + z = 6$
$3 + z = 6$
$z = 3$

The solution is (2, -1, 3).

56. (1) $2x - y + z = 6$

   (2) $3x + 2y + z = 4$

   (3) $x - 2y + 3z = 12$

Eliminate y. Multiply equation (1) by 2 and add to equation (2).

$2(2x - y + z) = 2(6)$

$3x + 2y + z = 4$

$4x - 2y + 2z = 12$

$3x + 2y + z = 4$

   (4) $7x + 3z = 16$

Add equations (2) and (3).

$3x + 2y + z = 4$

$x - 2y + 3z = 12$

$4x + 4z = 16$

Multiply each side of the equation by $\frac{1}{4}$.

   (5) $x + z = 4$

Multiply equation (5) by -3 and add to equation (4).

$7x + 3z = 16$

$-3(x + z) = -3(4)$

$7x + 3z = 16$

$-3x - 3z = -12$

$4x = 4$

$x = 1$

Replace x by 1 in equation (5).

$x + z = 4$

$1 + z = 4$

$z = 3$

Replace x by 1 and z by 3 in equation (1).

$2x - y + z = 6$

$2(1) - y + 3 = 6$

$2 - y + 3 = 6$

$5 - y = 6$

$-y = 1$

$y = -1$

The solution is $(1, -1, 3)$.

57. (1) $3x + 2y - 3z = 8$

   (2) $2x + 3y + 2z = 10$

   (3) $x + y - z = 2$

Eliminate z. Multiply equation (1) by 2 and equation (2) by 3.

Then add the equations.

$2(3x + 2y - 3z) = 2(8)$

$3(2x + 3y + 2z) = 3(10)$

$6x + 4y - 6z = 16$

$6x + 9y + 6z = 30$

   (4) $12x + 13y = 46$

Multiply equation (3) by 2 and add to equation (2).

$2x + 3y + 2z = 10$

$2(x + y - z) = 2(2)$

$2x + 3y + 2z = 10$

$2x + 2y - 2z = 4$

   (5) $4x + 5y = 14$

Multiply equation (5) by -3 and add to equation (4).

$12x + 13y = 46$

$-3(4x + 5y) = -3(14)$

$12x + 13y = 46$

$-12x - 15y = -42$

$-2y = 4$

$y = -2$

Replace y by -2 in equation (5).

$4x + 5y = 14$

$4x + 5(-2) = 14$

$4x - 10 = 14$

$4x = 24$

$x = 6$

Replace x by 6 and y by -2 in equation (3).

$x + y - z = 2$

$6 + (-2) - z = 2$

$4 - z = 2$

$-z = -2$

$z = 2$

The solution is $(6, -2, 2)$.

58. (1) $3x - 2y + 3z = -4$

(2) $2x + y - 3z = 2$

(3) $3x + 4y + 5z = 8$

Eliminate y. Multiply equation (2) by 2 and add to equation (1).

$3x - 2y + 3z = -4$
$2(2x + y - 3z) = 2(2)$

$3x - 2y + 3z = -4$
$4x + 2y - 6z = 4$

(4) $7x - 3z = 0$

Multiply equation (2) by -4 and add to equation (3).

$-4(2x + y - 3z) = -4(2)$
$3x + 4y + 5z = 8$

$-8x - 4y + 12z = -8$
$3x + 4y + 5z = 8$

(5) $-5x + 17z = 0$

Multiply equation (4) by 5 and equation (5) by 7. Then add the equations.

$5(7x - 3z) = 5(0)$
$7(-5x + 17z) = 7(0)$

$35x - 15z = 0$
$-35x + 119z = 0$

$104z = 0$
$z = 0$

Replace z by 0 in equation (4).

$7x - 3z = 0$
$7x - 3(0) = 0$
$7x = 0$
$x = 0$

Replace x by 0 and z by 0 in equation (2).

$2x + y - 3z = 2$
$2(0) + y - 3(0) = 2$
$y = 2$

The solution is $(0, 2, 0)$.

59. (1) $3x - 3y + 4z = 6$

(2) $4x - 5y + 2z = 10$

(3) $x - 2y + 3z = 4$

Eliminate x. Multiply equation (3) by -3 and add to equation (1).

$3x - 3y + 4z = 6$
$-3(x - 2y + 3z) = -3(4)$

$3x - 3y + 4z = 6$
$-3x + 6y - 9z = -12$

(4) $3y - 5z = -6$

Multiply equation (3) by -4 and add to equation (2).

$4x - 5y + 2z = 10$
$-4(x - 2y + 3z) = -4(4)$

$4x - 5y + 2z = 10$
$-4x + 8y - 12z = -16$

(5) $3y - 10z = -6$

Multiply equation (4) by -1 and add to equation (5).

$-1(3y - 5z) = -1(-6)$
$3y - 10z = -6$

$-3y + 5z = 6$
$3y - 10z = -6$

$-5z = 0$
$z = 0$

Replace z by 0 in equation (4).

$3y - 5z = -6$
$3y - 5(0) = -6$
$3y = -6$
$y = -2$

Replace y by -2 and z by 0 in equation (3).

$x - 2y + 3z = 4$
$x - 2(-2) + 3(0) = 4$
$x + 4 = 4$
$x = 0$

The solution is $(0, -2, 0)$.

60. (1) $3x - y + 2z = 2$

(2) $4x + 2y - 7z = 0$

(3) $2x + 3y - 5z = 7$

Eliminate y. Multiply equation (1) by 2 and add to equation (2).

$2(3x - y + 2z) = 2(2)$

$4x + 2y - 7z = 0$

$6x - 2y + 4z = 4$
$4x + 2y - 7z = 0$

(4) $10x - 3z = 4$

Multiply equation (1) by 3 and add to equation (3).

$3(3x - y + 2z) = 3(2)$

$2x + 3y - 5z = 7$

$9x - 3y + 6z = 6$
$2x + 3y - 5z = 7$

(5) $11x + z = 13$

Multiply equation (5) by 3 and add to equation (4).

$10x - 3z = 4$

$3(11x + z) = 3(13)$

$10x - 3z = 4$
$33x + 3z = 39$

$43x = 43$

$x = 1$

Replace x by 1 in equation (4).

$10x - 3z = 4$

$10(1) - 3z = 4$

$10 - 3z = 4$

$-3z = -6$

$z = 2$

Replace x by 1 and z by 2 in equation (1).

$3x - y + 2z = 2$

$3(1) - y + 2(2) = 2$

$3 - y + 4 = 2$

$7 - y = 2$

$-y = -5$

$y = 5$

The solution is $(1, 5, 2)$.

61. (1) $2x + 2y + 3z = 13$

(2) $-3x + 4y - z = 5$

(3) $5x - 3y + z = 2$

Eliminate z. Multiply equation (2) by 3 and add to equation (1).

$2x + 2y + 3z = 13$

$3(-3x + 4y - z) = 3(5)$

$2x + 2y + 3z = 13$
$-9x + 12y - 3z = 15$

$-7x + 14y = 28$

Multiply each side of the equation by $\frac{1}{7}$.

(4) $-x + 2y = 4$

Add equations (2) and (3).

$-3x + 4y - z = 5$

$5x - 3y + z = 2$

(5) $2x + y = 7$

Multiply equation (4) by 2 and add to equation (5).

$2(-x + 2y) = 2(4)$

$2x + y = 7$

$-2x + 4y = 8$
$2x + y = 7$

$5y = 15$

$y = 3$

Replace y by 3 in equation (5).

$2x + y = 7$

$2x + 3 = 7$

$2x = 4$

$x = 2$

Replace x by 2 and y by 3 in equation (3).

$5x - 3y + z = 2$

$5(2) - 3(3) + z = 2$

$10 - 9 + z = 2$

$1 + z = 2$

$z = 1$

The solution is $(2, 3, 1)$.

62. (1) $2x - 3y + 7z = 0$

(2) $x + 4y - 4z = -2$

(3) $3x + 2y + 5z = 1$

Eliminate x. Multiply equation (2) by -2 and add to equation (1).

$$2x - 3y + 7z = 0$$
$$-2(x + 4y - 4z) = -2(-2)$$

$$2x - 3y + 7z = 0$$
$$-2x - 8y + 8z = 4$$

(4) $-11y + 15z = 4$

Multiply equation (2) by -3 and add to equation (3).

$$-3(x + 4y - 4z) = -3(-2)$$
$$3x + 2y + 5z = 1$$

$$-3x - 12y + 12z = 6$$
$$3x + 2y + 5z = 1$$

(5) $-10y + 17z = 7$

Multiply equation (4) by -10 and equation (5) by 11. Then add the equations.

$$-10(-11y + 15z) = -10(4)$$
$$11(-10y + 17z) = 11(7)$$

$$110y - 150z = -40$$
$$-110y + 187z = 77$$

$$37z = 37$$
$$z = 1$$

Replace z by 1 in equation (4).

$$-11y + 15z = 4$$
$$-11y + 15(1) = 4$$
$$-11y + 15 = 4$$
$$-11y = -11$$
$$y = 1$$

Replace y by 1 and z by 1 in equation (1).

$$2x - 3y + 7z = 0$$
$$2x - 3(1) + 7(1) = 0$$
$$2x - 3 + 7 = 0$$
$$2x + 4 = 0$$
$$2x = -4$$
$$x = -2$$

The solution is $(-2, 1, 1)$.

63. (1) $5x + 3y - z = 5$

(2) $3x - 2y + 4z = 13$

(3) $4x + 3y + 5z = 22$

Eliminate z. Multiply equation (1) by 4 and add to equation (2).

$$4(5x + 3y - z) = 4(5)$$
$$3x - 2y + 4z = 13$$

$$20x + 12y - 4z = 20$$
$$3x - 2y + 4z = 13$$

(4) $23x + 10y = 33$

Multiply equation (1) by 5 and add to equation (3).

$$5(5x + 3y - z) = 5(5)$$
$$4x + 3y + 5z = 22$$

$$25x + 15y - 5z = 25$$
$$4x + 3y + 5z = 22$$

(5) $29x + 18y = 47$

Multiply equation (4) by -18 and equation (5) by 10. Then add the equations.

$$-18(23x + 10y) = -18(33)$$
$$10(29x + 18y) = 10(47)$$

$$-414x - 180y = -594$$
$$290x + 180y = 470$$

$$-124x = -124$$
$$x = 1$$

Replace x by 1 in equation (4).

$$23x + 10y = 33$$
$$23(1) + 10y = 33$$
$$23 + 10y = 33$$
$$10y = 10$$
$$y = 1$$

Replace x by 1 and y by 1 in equation (1).

$$5x + 3y - z = 5$$
$$5(1) + 3(1) - z = 5$$
$$5 + 3 - z = 5$$
$$8 - z = 5$$
$$-z = -3$$
$$z = 3$$

The solution is $(1, 1, 3)$.

Applying Concepts 4.2

64. (1) $0.2x - 0.3y = 0.5$

(2) $0.3x - 0.2y = 0.5$

Multiply both sides of each equation by 10.

(1) $2x - 3y = 5$

(2) $3x - 2y = 5$

Eliminate y.

$-2(2x - 3y) = -2(5)$

$3(3x - 2y) = 3(5)$

$-4x + 6y = -10$

$9x - 6y = 15$

Add the equations.

$5x = 5$

$x = 1$

Replace x in equation (1).

$2x - 3y = 5$

$2(1) - 3y = 5$

$2 - 3y = 5$

$-3y = 3$

$y = -1$

The solution is $(1, -1)$.

65. (1) $0.4x - 0.9y = -0.1$

(2) $0.3x + 0.2y = 0.8$

Multiply both sides of each equation by 10.

(1) $4x - 9y = -1$

(2) $3x + 2y = 8$

Eliminate y.

$2(4x - 9y) = 2(-1)$

$9(3x + 2y) = 9(8)$

$8x - 18y = -2$

$27x + 18y = 72$

Add the equations.

$35x = 70$

$x = 2$

Replace x in equation (1).

$4x - 9y = -1$

$4(2) - 9y = -1$

$8 - 9y = -1$

$-9y = -9$

$y = 1$

The solution is $(2, 1)$.

66. (1) $1.25x - 0.25y = -1.5$

(2) $1.5x + 2.5y = 1$

Multiply equation (1) by 100 and equation (2) by 10.

(1) $125x - 25y = -150$

(2) $15x + 25y = 10$

Eliminate y. Add the equations.

$140x = -140$

$x = -1$

Replace x in equation (1).

$125x - 25y = -150$

$125(-1) - 25y = -150$

$-125 - 25y = -150$

$-25y = -25$

$y = 1$

The solution is $(-1, 1)$.

67. (1) $2.25x + 1.5y = 3$

(2) $1.75x + 2.25y = 1.25$

Multiply both sides of each equation by 100.

(1) $225x + 150y = 300$

(2) $175x + 225y = 125$

Eliminate y.

$3(225x + 150y) = 3(300)$

$-2(175x + 225y) = -2(125)$

$675x + 450y = 900$

$-350x - 450y = -250$

Add the equations.

$325x = 650$

$x = 2$

Replace x in equation (1).

$225x + 150y = 300$

$225(2) + 150y = 300$

$450 + 150y = 300$

$150y = -150$

$y = -1$

The solution is $(2, -1)$.

68. (1) $\quad 1.5x + 2.5y + 1.5z = 8$

    (2) $\quad 0.5x - 2.0y - 1.5z = -1$

    (3) $\quad\; 2.5x - 1.5y + 2z = 2.5$

Multiply both sides of each equation by 10.

    (1) $\quad 15x + 25y + 15z = 80$

    (2) $\quad\; 5x - 20y - 15z = -10$

    (3) $\quad 25x - 15y + 20z = 25$

Eliminate z. Add equations (1) and (2).

$$15x + 25y + 15z = 80$$
$$5x - 20y - 15z = -10$$

    (4) $\quad 20x + 5y = 70$

Multiply equation (2) by 4 and equation (3) by 3. Then add the equations.

$$4(5x - 20y - 15z) = 4(-10)$$
$$3(25x - 15y + 20z) = 3(25)$$

$$20x - 80y - 60z = -40$$
$$75x - 45y + 60z = 75$$

    (5) $\quad 95x - 125y = 35$

Multiply equation (4) by 25 and add to equation (5).

$$25(20x + 5y) = 25(70)$$
$$95x - 125y = 35$$

$$500x + 125y = 1750$$
$$95x - 125y = 35$$

$$595x = 1785$$
$$x = 3$$

Replace x by 3 in equation (4).

$$20x + 5y = 70$$
$$20(3) + 5y = 70$$
$$60 + 5y = 70$$
$$5y = 10$$
$$y = 2$$

Replace x by 3 and y by 2 in equation (1).

$$15x + 25y + 15z = 80$$
$$15(3) + 25(2) + 15z = 80$$
$$45 + 50 + 15z = 80$$
$$15z = -15$$
$$z = -1$$

The solution is $(3, 2, -1)$.

69. (1) $\quad 1.6x - 0.9y + 0.3z = 2.9$

    (2) $\quad 1.6x + 0.5y - 0.1z = 3.3$

    (3) $\quad 0.8x - 0.7y + 0.1z = 1.5$

Multiply both sides of each equation by 10.

    (1) $\quad 16x - 9y + 3z = 29$

    (2) $\quad 16x + 5x - z = 33$

    (3) $\quad\; 8x - 7y + z = 15$

Eliminate z. Add equations (2) and (3).

$$16x + 5y - z = 33$$
$$8x - 7y + z = 15$$

    (4) $\quad 24x - 2y = 48$

Multiply equation (2) by 3 and add to equation (1).

$$3(16x + 5y - z) = 3(33)$$
$$16x - 9y + 3z = 29$$

$$48x + 15y - 3z = 99$$
$$16x - 9y + 3z = 29$$

    (5) $\quad 64x + 6y = 128$

Multiply equation (4) by 3 and add to equation (5).

$$3(24x - 2y) = 3(48)$$
$$64x + 6y = 128$$

$$72x - 6y = 144$$
$$64x + 6y = 128$$

$$136x = 272$$
$$x = 2$$

Replace x by 2 in equation (4).

$$24x - 2y = 48$$
$$24(2) - 2y = 48$$
$$48 - 2y = 48$$
$$-2y = 0$$
$$y = 0$$

Replace x by 2 and y by 0 in equation (1).

$$16x - 9y + 3z = 29$$
$$16(2) - 9(0) + 3z = 29$$
$$32 - 0 + 3z = 29$$
$$3z = -3$$
$$z = -1$$

The solution is $(2, 0, -1)$.

70. Strategy

Substitute 3 for x and -2 for y in the equations. Solve for A and B.

Solution

$$Ax + 3y = 6$$
$$A(3) + 3(-2) = 6$$
$$3A - 6 = 6$$
$$3A = 12$$
$$A = 4$$
$$2x + By = -4$$
$$2(3) + B(-2) = -4$$
$$6 - 2B = -4$$
$$-2B = -10$$
$$B = 5$$

The value of A is 4. The value of B is 5.

71. Strategy

Substitute 3 for x, -2 for y, and 4 for z in the equations. Solve for A, B, and C.

Solution

$$Ax + 3y + 2z = 8$$
$$A(3) + 3(-2) + 2(4) = 8$$
$$3A - 6 + 8 = 8$$
$$3A + 2 = 8$$
$$3A = 6$$
$$A = 2$$

$$2x + By - 3z = -12$$
$$2(3) + B(-2) - 3(4) = -12$$
$$6 - 2B - 12 = -12$$
$$-2B - 6 = -12$$
$$-2B = -6$$
$$B = 3$$

$$3x - 2y + Cz = 1$$
$$3(3) - 2(-2) + C(4) = 1$$
$$9 + 4 + 4C = 1$$
$$4C + 13 = 1$$
$$4C = -12$$
$$C = -3$$

The value of A is 2. The value of B is 3. The value of C is -3.

72. Strategy

The distance between a point and a line is the perpendicular distance from the point to the line. To find the perpendicular distance:

Find the equation of the line that passes through $(3, 1)$ and is perpendicular to $y = x$.

Solve the system to find the point of intersection between the given line and the perpendicular line.

Find the distance between $(3, 1)$ and the solution of the system.

Solution

$$m_1 m_2 = -1 \qquad y - y_1 = m(x - x_1)$$
$$1 \cdot m_2 = -1 \qquad y - 1 = -1(x - 3)$$
$$m_2 = -1 \qquad y - 1 = -x + 3$$
$$(1) \quad y = -x + 4$$

The equation of the line that is perpendicular to $y = x$ and passes through $(3, 1)$ is $y = -x + 4$.

(1) $y = -x + 4$

(2) $y = x$

Replace y by x in equation (1).
$$y = -x + 4$$
$$x = -x + 4$$
$$2x = 4$$
$$x = 2$$

Replace x by 2 in equation (2).
$$y = x$$
$$y = 2$$

The solution of the system is $(2, 2)$.
$$(x_1, y_1) = (3, 1), \ (x_2, y_2) = (2, 2)$$
$$d = \sqrt{(x_1 - x_2)^2 + (y_1 - y_2)^2}$$
$$= \sqrt{(3 - 2)^2 + (1 - 2)^2}$$
$$= \sqrt{1^2 + (-1)^2}$$
$$= \sqrt{1 + 1} = \sqrt{2}$$

The distance between $y = x$ and $(3, 1)$ is $\sqrt{2}$.

73. Strategy
Solve a system of equations using x to represent the number of nickels, y to represent the number of dimes, and z to represent the number of quarters.

Solution
$$(1) \qquad x+y+z = 30$$
$$(2) \quad 5x+10y+25z = 325$$
Eliminate x by multiplying equation (1) by (−5) and adding equation (2).
$$-5x-5y-5z = -150$$
$$\underline{5x+10y+25z = 325}$$
$$(3) \quad 5y+20z = 175$$
Solve equation (3) for y in terms of z.
$$(3) \quad 5y+20z = 175$$
$$5y = -20z+175$$
$$y = -4z+35$$
Replace y by $-4z + 35$ in equation (1) and solve for x in terms of z.
$$x+y+z = 30$$
$$x+(-4z+35)+z = 30$$
$$x-4z+35+z = 30$$
$$x-3z+35 = 30$$
$$x = 3z-5$$
The number of nickels is $3z - 5$, the number of dimes is $-4z + 35$, and the number of quarters is z, where $z = 2, 3, 4, 5, 6, 7,$ or 8. All other values of z make the number of nickels or dimes negative, which is not possible.

74.
$$(1) \quad \frac{1}{x}-\frac{2}{y} = 3$$
$$(2) \quad \frac{2}{x}+\frac{3}{y} = -1$$
Clear the fractions.
$$xy\left(\frac{1}{x}-\frac{2}{y}\right) = xy\cdot 3$$
$$xy\left(\frac{2}{x}+\frac{3}{y}\right) = xy\cdot(-1)$$
$$y-2x = 3xy$$
$$2y+3x = -xy$$
Eliminate y.
$$-2y+4x = -6xy$$
$$2y+3x = -xy$$
$$7x = -7xy$$
$$y = -1$$
Substitute y into equation (2).
$$\frac{2}{x}+\frac{3}{y} = -1$$
$$\frac{2}{x}+\frac{3}{-1} = -1$$
$$\frac{2}{x} = 2$$
$$x = 1$$
The solution is $(1, -1)$.

75.
$$(1) \quad \frac{1}{x}+\frac{2}{y} = 3$$
$$(2) \quad \frac{1}{x}-\frac{3}{y} = -2$$
Clear the fractions.
$$xy\left(\frac{1}{x}+\frac{2}{y}\right) = xy\cdot 3$$
$$xy\left(\frac{1}{x}-\frac{3}{y}\right) = xy\cdot(-2)$$
$$y+2x = 3xy$$
$$y-3x = -2xy$$
Eliminate y.
$$y+2x = 3xy$$
$$-y+3x = 2xy$$
$$5x = 5xy$$
$$y = 1$$
Substitute y into equation (2).
$$\frac{1}{x}-\frac{3}{y} = -2$$
$$\frac{1}{x}-\frac{3}{1} = -2$$
$$\frac{1}{x} = 1$$
$$x = 1$$
The solution is $(1, 1)$.

76.
$$(1) \quad \frac{3}{x}+\frac{2}{y} = 1$$
$$(2) \quad \frac{2}{x}+\frac{4}{y} = -2$$
Clear fractions.
$$xy\left(\frac{3}{x}+\frac{2}{y}\right) = xy\cdot 1$$
$$xy\left(\frac{2}{x}+\frac{4}{y}\right) = xy\cdot(-2)$$
$$3y+2x = xy$$
$$2y+4x = -2xy$$
Eliminate x.
$$-6y-4x = -2xy$$
$$2y+4x = -2xy$$
$$-4y = -4xy$$
$$x = 1$$
Substitute x into equation (2).
$$\frac{2}{x}+\frac{4}{y} = -2$$
$$2+\frac{4}{y} = -2$$
$$\frac{4}{y} = -4$$
$$y = -1$$
The solution is $(1, -1)$.

77. (1) $\dfrac{3}{x}-\dfrac{5}{y}=-\dfrac{3}{2}$

(2) $\dfrac{1}{x}-\dfrac{2}{y}=-\dfrac{2}{3}$

Clear fractions.

$2xy\left(\dfrac{3}{x}-\dfrac{5}{y}\right)=2xy\left(-\dfrac{3}{2}\right)$

$3xy\left(\dfrac{1}{x}-\dfrac{2}{y}\right)=3xy\left(-\dfrac{2}{3}\right)$

$6y-10x=-3xy$

$3y-6x=-2xy$

Eliminate y.

$6y-10x=-3xy$

$-6y+12x=4xy$

$2x=xy$

$y=2$

Substitute y into equation (2).

$\dfrac{1}{x}-\dfrac{2}{y}=-\dfrac{2}{3}$

$\dfrac{1}{x}-\dfrac{2}{2}=-\dfrac{2}{3}$

$\dfrac{1}{x}=\dfrac{1}{3}$

$x=3$

The solution is (3, 2).

78. Solve each equation for y.

$\dfrac{1}{x}-\dfrac{2}{y}=3$ $\dfrac{2}{x}+\dfrac{3}{y}=-1$

$-\dfrac{2}{y}=3-\dfrac{1}{x}$ $\dfrac{3}{y}=-1-\dfrac{2}{x}$

Reciprocate both sides.

$-\dfrac{y}{2}=\dfrac{1}{3-\frac{1}{x}}$ $\dfrac{y}{3}=-\dfrac{1}{1+\frac{2}{x}}$

$y=\dfrac{-2}{3-\frac{1}{x}}$ $y=-\dfrac{3}{1+\frac{2}{x}}$

Reduce.

$y=\dfrac{2x}{1-3x}$ $y=\dfrac{-3x}{x+2}$

79a. The graph of $x=3$ in an xyz-coordinate system is a plane parallel to the yz plane at $x=3$.

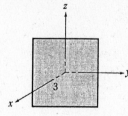

b. The graph of $y=4$ in an xyz-coordinate system is a plane parallel to the xz-plane at $y=4$.

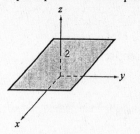

c. The graph of $z=2$ in an xyz-coordinate system is a plane at $z=2$.

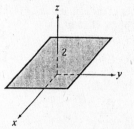

d. The graph of $y=x$ in an xyz-coordinate system is a vertical plane perpendicular to the xy-plane and 45° from the xz- and yz-planes.

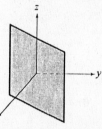

80a. The system of equations has no solution; it is inconsistent. See Figures A, B, C, and D.

b. The system of equations has infinitely many solutions; it is an independent system whose solution is a point in space. See Figure E.

c. The system of equations had infinitely many solutions; it is a dependent system. See Figures F, G, and H.

Section 4.3

Concept Review 4.3

1. Always true

2. Sometimes true
If $D=0$, the system cannot be solved by Cramer's Rule.

3. Sometimes true
A square matrix has the same number of rows and columns. A matrix may have different numbers of rows and columns.

4. Sometimes true
Only square matrices have an associated determinant.

5. Always true

Objective 4.3.1 Exercises

1. The determinant associated with the 2 x 2 matrix $\begin{bmatrix} a & b \\ c & d \end{bmatrix}$ is $\begin{vmatrix} a & b \\ c & d \end{vmatrix}$. Its value is $ad - bc$.

2. The cofactor of a given element in a matrix is $(-1)^{i+j}$ times the minor of that element, where i is the row number of the element and j is the column number of the element.

3. $\begin{vmatrix} 2 & -1 \\ 3 & 4 \end{vmatrix} = 2(4) - 3(-1) = 8 + 3 = 11$

4. $\begin{vmatrix} 5 & 1 \\ -1 & 2 \end{vmatrix} = 5(2) - (-1)(1) = 10 + 1 = 11$

5. $\begin{vmatrix} 6 & -2 \\ -3 & 4 \end{vmatrix} = 6(4) - (-3)(-2) = 24 - 6 = 18$

6. $\begin{vmatrix} -3 & 5 \\ 1 & 7 \end{vmatrix} = -3(7) - 1(5) = -21 - 5 = -26$

7. $\begin{vmatrix} 3 & 6 \\ 2 & 4 \end{vmatrix} = 3(4) - 2(6) = 12 - 12 = 0$

8. $\begin{vmatrix} 5 & -10 \\ 1 & -2 \end{vmatrix} = 5(-2) - 1(-10) = -10 + 10 = 0$

9. $\begin{vmatrix} 1 & -1 & 2 \\ 3 & 2 & 1 \\ 1 & 0 & 4 \end{vmatrix} = 1\begin{vmatrix} 2 & 1 \\ 0 & 4 \end{vmatrix} + 1\begin{vmatrix} 3 & 1 \\ 1 & 4 \end{vmatrix} + 2\begin{vmatrix} 3 & 2 \\ 1 & 0 \end{vmatrix}$
$= 1(8 - 0) + 1(12 - 1) + 2(0 - 2)$
$= 8 + 11 - 4 = 15$

10. $\begin{vmatrix} 4 & 1 & 3 \\ 2 & -2 & 1 \\ 3 & 1 & 2 \end{vmatrix} = 4\begin{vmatrix} -2 & 1 \\ 1 & 2 \end{vmatrix} - 1\begin{vmatrix} 2 & 1 \\ 3 & 2 \end{vmatrix} + 3\begin{vmatrix} 2 & -2 \\ 3 & 1 \end{vmatrix}$
$= 4(-4 - 1) - 1(4 - 3) + 3(2 + 6)$
$= 4(-5) - 1(1) + 3(8)$
$= -20 - 1 + 24 = 3$

11. $\begin{vmatrix} 3 & -1 & 2 \\ 0 & 1 & 2 \\ 3 & 2 & -2 \end{vmatrix} = 3\begin{vmatrix} 1 & 2 \\ 2 & -2 \end{vmatrix} + 1\begin{vmatrix} 0 & 2 \\ 3 & -2 \end{vmatrix} + 2\begin{vmatrix} 0 & 1 \\ 3 & 2 \end{vmatrix}$
$= 3(-2 - 4) + 1(0 - 6) + 2(0 - 3)$
$= 3(-6) + 1(-6) + 2(-3)$
$= -18 - 6 - 6 = -30$

12. $\begin{vmatrix} 4 & 5 & -2 \\ 3 & -1 & 5 \\ 2 & 1 & 4 \end{vmatrix} = 4\begin{vmatrix} -1 & 5 \\ 1 & 4 \end{vmatrix} - 5\begin{vmatrix} 3 & 5 \\ 2 & 4 \end{vmatrix} - 2\begin{vmatrix} 3 & -1 \\ 2 & 1 \end{vmatrix}$
$= 4(-4 - 5) - 5(12 - 10) - 2(3 + 2)$
$= 4(-9) - 5(2) - 2(5)$
$= -36 - 10 - 10 = -56$

13. $\begin{vmatrix} 4 & 2 & 6 \\ -2 & 1 & 1 \\ 2 & 1 & 3 \end{vmatrix} = 4\begin{vmatrix} 1 & 1 \\ 1 & 3 \end{vmatrix} - 2\begin{vmatrix} -2 & 1 \\ 2 & 3 \end{vmatrix} + 6\begin{vmatrix} -2 & 1 \\ 2 & 1 \end{vmatrix}$
$= 4(3 - 1) - 2(-6 - 2) + 6(-2 - 2)$
$= 4(2) - 2(-8) + 6(-4)$
$= 8 + 16 - 24 = 0$

14. $\begin{vmatrix} 3 & 6 & -3 \\ 4 & -1 & 6 \\ -1 & -2 & 3 \end{vmatrix} = 3\begin{vmatrix} -1 & 6 \\ -2 & 3 \end{vmatrix} - 6\begin{vmatrix} 4 & 6 \\ -1 & 3 \end{vmatrix} - 3\begin{vmatrix} 4 & -1 \\ -1 & -2 \end{vmatrix}$
$= 3(-3 + 12) - 6(12 + 6) - 3(-8 - 1)$
$= 3(9) - 6(18) - 3(-9)$
$= 27 - 108 + 27 = -54$

Objective 4.3.2 Exercises

15. If the system of two equations is written as $\begin{aligned} a_{11}x + a_{12}y &= b_1 \\ a_{21}x + a_{22}y &= b_2 \end{aligned}$ then $x = \dfrac{D_x}{D}$ and $y = \dfrac{D_y}{D}$, where
$$D = \begin{vmatrix} a_{11} & a_{12} \\ a_{21} & a_{22} \end{vmatrix}, \ D_x = \begin{vmatrix} b_1 & a_{12} \\ b_2 & a_{22} \end{vmatrix}, \ D_y = \begin{vmatrix} a_{11} & b_1 \\ a_{21} & b_2 \end{vmatrix}$$
and $D \neq 0$.

16. Cramer's rule cannot be used when the coefficient matrix is 0 because this matrix is used in the denominators $\left(\dfrac{D_x}{D} \text{ and } \dfrac{D_y}{D} \right)$ in the expressions for x and y.

17. $\begin{aligned} 2x - 5y &= 26 \\ 5x + 3y &= 3 \end{aligned}$
$D = \begin{vmatrix} 2 & -5 \\ 5 & 3 \end{vmatrix} = 31, \ D_x = \begin{vmatrix} 26 & -5 \\ 3 & 3 \end{vmatrix} = 93,$
$D_y = \begin{vmatrix} 2 & 26 \\ 5 & 3 \end{vmatrix} = -124$
$x = \dfrac{D_x}{D} = \dfrac{93}{31} = 3 \quad y = \dfrac{D_y}{D} = \dfrac{-124}{31} = -4$
The solution is (3, -4).

18. $\begin{aligned} 3x + 7y &= 15 \\ 2x + 5y &= 11 \end{aligned}$
$D = \begin{vmatrix} 3 & 7 \\ 2 & 5 \end{vmatrix} = 1, \ D_x = \begin{vmatrix} 15 & 7 \\ 11 & 5 \end{vmatrix} = -2,$
$D_y = \begin{vmatrix} 3 & 15 \\ 2 & 11 \end{vmatrix} = 3$
$x = \dfrac{D_x}{D} = \dfrac{-2}{1} = -2 \quad y = \dfrac{D_y}{D} = \dfrac{3}{1} = 3$
The solution is (-2, 3).

19. $x - 4y = 8$
$3x + 7y = 5$

$D = \begin{vmatrix} 1 & -4 \\ 3 & 7 \end{vmatrix} = 19, \; D_x = \begin{vmatrix} 8 & -4 \\ 5 & 7 \end{vmatrix} = 76,$

$D_y = \begin{vmatrix} 1 & 8 \\ 3 & 5 \end{vmatrix} = -19$

$x = \dfrac{D_x}{D} = \dfrac{76}{19} = 4 \quad y = \dfrac{D_y}{D} = \dfrac{-19}{19} = -1$

The solution is $(4, -1)$.

20. $5x + 2y = -5$
$3x + 4y = 11$

$D = \begin{vmatrix} 5 & 2 \\ 3 & 4 \end{vmatrix} = 14, \; D_x = \begin{vmatrix} -5 & 2 \\ 11 & 4 \end{vmatrix} = -42,$

$D_y = \begin{vmatrix} 5 & -5 \\ 3 & 11 \end{vmatrix} = 70$

$x = \dfrac{D_x}{D} = \dfrac{-42}{14} = -3 \quad y = \dfrac{D_y}{D} = \dfrac{70}{14} = 5$

The solution is $(-3, 5)$.

21. $2x + 3y = 4$
$6x - 12y = -5$

$D = \begin{vmatrix} 2 & 3 \\ 6 & -12 \end{vmatrix} = -42, \; D_x = \begin{vmatrix} 4 & 3 \\ -5 & -12 \end{vmatrix} = -33,$

$D_y = \begin{vmatrix} 2 & 4 \\ 6 & -5 \end{vmatrix} = -34$

$x = \dfrac{D_x}{D} = \dfrac{-33}{-42} = \dfrac{11}{14} \quad y = \dfrac{D_y}{D} = \dfrac{-34}{-42} = \dfrac{17}{21}$

The solution is $\left(\dfrac{11}{14}, \dfrac{17}{21} \right)$.

22. $5x + 4y = 3$
$15x - 8y = -21$

$D = \begin{vmatrix} 5 & 4 \\ 15 & -8 \end{vmatrix} = -100, \; D_x = \begin{vmatrix} 3 & 4 \\ -21 & -8 \end{vmatrix} = 60,$

$D_y = \begin{vmatrix} 5 & 3 \\ 15 & -21 \end{vmatrix} = -150$

$x = \dfrac{D_x}{D} = \dfrac{60}{-100} = -\dfrac{3}{5}$

$y = \dfrac{D_y}{D} = \dfrac{-150}{-100} = \dfrac{3}{2}$

The solution is $\left(-\dfrac{3}{5}, \dfrac{3}{2} \right)$.

23. $2x + 5y = 6$
$6x - 2y = 1$

$D = \begin{vmatrix} 2 & 5 \\ 6 & -2 \end{vmatrix} = -34, \; D_x = \begin{vmatrix} 6 & 5 \\ 1 & -2 \end{vmatrix} = -17,$

$D_y = \begin{vmatrix} 2 & 6 \\ 6 & 1 \end{vmatrix} = -34$

$x = \dfrac{D_x}{D} = \dfrac{-17}{-34} = \dfrac{1}{2} \quad y = \dfrac{D_y}{D} = \dfrac{-34}{-34} = 1$

The solution is $\left(\dfrac{1}{2}, 1 \right)$.

24. $7x + 3y = 4$
$5x - 4y = 9$

$D = \begin{vmatrix} 7 & 3 \\ 5 & -4 \end{vmatrix} = -43, \; D_x = \begin{vmatrix} 4 & 3 \\ 9 & -4 \end{vmatrix} = -43,$

$D_y = \begin{vmatrix} 7 & 4 \\ 5 & 9 \end{vmatrix} = 43$

$x = \dfrac{D_x}{D} = \dfrac{-43}{-43} = 1 \quad y = \dfrac{D_y}{D} = \dfrac{43}{-43} = -1$

The solution is $(1, -1)$.

25. $-2x + 3y = 7$
$4x - 6y = 9$

$D = \begin{vmatrix} -2 & 3 \\ 4 & -6 \end{vmatrix} = 0$

Since $D = 0$, $\dfrac{D_x}{D}$ is undefined. The system cannot be solved by Cramer's Rule.

26. $9x + 6y = 7$
$3x + 2y = 4$

$D = \begin{vmatrix} 9 & 6 \\ 3 & 2 \end{vmatrix} = 0$

Since $D = 0$, $\dfrac{D_x}{D}$ is undefined. The system cannot be solved by Cramer's Rule.

27. $2x - 5y = -2$
$3x - 7y = -3$

$D = \begin{vmatrix} 2 & -5 \\ 3 & -7 \end{vmatrix} = 1, \; D_x = \begin{vmatrix} -2 & -5 \\ -3 & -7 \end{vmatrix} = -1,$

$D_y = \begin{vmatrix} 2 & -2 \\ 3 & -3 \end{vmatrix} = 0$

$x = \dfrac{D_x}{D} = \dfrac{-1}{1} = -1 \quad y = \dfrac{D_y}{D} = \dfrac{0}{1} = 0$

The solution is $(-1, 0)$.

28. $8x + 7y = -3$
$2x + 2y = 5$

$D = \begin{vmatrix} 8 & 7 \\ 2 & 2 \end{vmatrix} = 2, \; D_x = \begin{vmatrix} -3 & 7 \\ 5 & 2 \end{vmatrix} = -41,$

$D_y = \begin{vmatrix} 8 & -3 \\ 2 & 5 \end{vmatrix} = 46$

$x = \dfrac{D_x}{D} = \dfrac{-41}{2} \quad y = \dfrac{D_y}{D} = \dfrac{46}{2} = 23$

The solution is $\left(-\dfrac{41}{2}, 23 \right)$.

29. $2x - y + 3z = 9$
$x + 4y + 4z = 5$
$3x + 2y + 2z = 5$

$$D = \begin{vmatrix} 2 & -1 & 3 \\ 1 & 4 & 4 \\ 3 & 2 & 2 \end{vmatrix} = -40,$$

$$D_x = \begin{vmatrix} 9 & -1 & 3 \\ 5 & 4 & 4 \\ 5 & 2 & 2 \end{vmatrix} = -40,$$

$$D_y = \begin{vmatrix} 2 & 9 & 3 \\ 1 & 5 & 4 \\ 3 & 5 & 2 \end{vmatrix} = 40,$$

$$D_z = \begin{vmatrix} 2 & -1 & 9 \\ 1 & 4 & 5 \\ 3 & 2 & 5 \end{vmatrix} = -80$$

$x = \dfrac{D_x}{D} = \dfrac{-40}{-40} = 1$ $y = \dfrac{D_y}{D} = \dfrac{40}{-40} = -1$

$z = \dfrac{D_z}{D} = \dfrac{-80}{-40} = 2$

The solution is $(1, -1, 2)$.

30. $3x - 2y + z = 2$
$2x + 3y + 2z = -6$
$3x - y + z = 0$

$$D = \begin{vmatrix} 3 & -2 & 1 \\ 2 & 3 & 2 \\ 3 & -1 & 1 \end{vmatrix} = -4,$$

$$D_x = \begin{vmatrix} 2 & -2 & 1 \\ -6 & 3 & 2 \\ 0 & -1 & 1 \end{vmatrix} = 4,$$

$$D_y = \begin{vmatrix} 3 & 2 & 1 \\ 2 & -6 & 2 \\ 3 & 0 & 1 \end{vmatrix} = 8,$$

$$D_z = \begin{vmatrix} 3 & -2 & 2 \\ 2 & 3 & -6 \\ 3 & -1 & 0 \end{vmatrix} = -4$$

$x = \dfrac{D_x}{D} = \dfrac{4}{-4} = -1$ $y = \dfrac{D_y}{D} = \dfrac{8}{-4} = -2$

$z = \dfrac{D_z}{D} = \dfrac{-4}{-4} = 1$

The solution is $(-1, -2, 1)$.

31. $3x - y + z = 11$
$x + 4y - 2z = -12$
$2x + 2y - z = -3$

$$D = \begin{vmatrix} 3 & -1 & 1 \\ 1 & 4 & -2 \\ 2 & 2 & -1 \end{vmatrix} = -3,$$

$$D_x = \begin{vmatrix} 11 & -1 & 1 \\ -12 & 4 & -2 \\ -3 & 2 & -1 \end{vmatrix} = -6,$$

$$D_y = \begin{vmatrix} 3 & 11 & 1 \\ 1 & -12 & -2 \\ 2 & -3 & -1 \end{vmatrix} = 6,$$

$$D_z = \begin{vmatrix} 3 & -1 & 11 \\ 1 & 4 & -12 \\ 2 & 2 & -3 \end{vmatrix} = -9$$

$x = \dfrac{D_x}{D} = \dfrac{-6}{-3} = 2$ $y = \dfrac{D_y}{D} = \dfrac{6}{-3} = -2$

$z = \dfrac{D_z}{D} = \dfrac{-9}{-3} = 3$

The solution is $(2, -2, 3)$.

32. $x + 2y + 3z = 8$
$2x - 3y + z = 5$
$3x - 4y + 2z = 9$

$$D = \begin{vmatrix} 1 & 2 & 3 \\ 2 & -3 & 1 \\ 3 & -4 & 2 \end{vmatrix} = -1,$$

$$D_x = \begin{vmatrix} 8 & 2 & 3 \\ 5 & -3 & 1 \\ 9 & -4 & 2 \end{vmatrix} = 3,$$

$$D_y = \begin{vmatrix} 1 & 8 & 3 \\ 2 & 5 & 1 \\ 3 & 9 & 2 \end{vmatrix} = 2,$$

$$D_z = \begin{vmatrix} 1 & 2 & 8 \\ 2 & -3 & 5 \\ 3 & -4 & 9 \end{vmatrix} = -5$$

$x = \dfrac{D_x}{D} = \dfrac{3}{-1} = -3$ $y = \dfrac{D_y}{D} = \dfrac{2}{-1} = -2$

$z = \dfrac{D_z}{D} = \dfrac{-5}{-1} = 5$

The solution is $(-3, -2, 5)$.

33. $4x - 2y + 6z = 1$
$3x + 4y + 2z = 1$
$2x - y + 3z = 2$

$$D = \begin{vmatrix} 4 & -2 & 6 \\ 3 & 4 & 2 \\ 2 & -1 & 3 \end{vmatrix} = 0$$

Since $D = 0$, $\dfrac{D_x}{D}$ is undefined. The system cannot be solved by Cramer's Rule.

34. $x - 3y + 2z = 1$
$2x + y - 2z = 3$
$3x - 9y + 6z = -3$

$$D = \begin{vmatrix} 1 & -3 & 2 \\ 2 & 1 & -2 \\ 3 & -9 & 6 \end{vmatrix} = 0$$

Since $D = 0$, $\dfrac{D_x}{D}$ is undefined. The system cannot be solved by Cramer's Rule.

35. $5x - 4y + 2z = 4$
$3x - 5y + 3z = -4$
$3x + y - 5z = 12$

$$D = \begin{vmatrix} 5 & -4 & 2 \\ 3 & -5 & 3 \\ 3 & 1 & -5 \end{vmatrix} = 50,$$

$$D_x = \begin{vmatrix} 4 & -4 & 2 \\ -4 & -5 & 3 \\ 12 & 1 & -5 \end{vmatrix} = 136,$$

$$D_y = \begin{vmatrix} 5 & 4 & 2 \\ 3 & -4 & 3 \\ 3 & 12 & -5 \end{vmatrix} = 112,$$

$$D_z = \begin{vmatrix} 5 & -4 & 4 \\ 3 & -5 & -4 \\ 3 & 1 & 12 \end{vmatrix} = -16$$

$x = \dfrac{D_x}{D} = \dfrac{136}{50} = \dfrac{68}{25}$ $y = \dfrac{D_y}{D} = \dfrac{112}{50} = \dfrac{56}{25}$

$z = \dfrac{D_z}{D} = \dfrac{-16}{50} = -\dfrac{8}{25}$

The solution is $\left(\dfrac{68}{25}, \dfrac{56}{25}, -\dfrac{8}{25} \right)$.

36. $2x + 4y + z = 7$
$x + 3y - z = 1$
$3x + 2y - 2z = 5$

$$D = \begin{vmatrix} 2 & 4 & 1 \\ 1 & 3 & -1 \\ 3 & 2 & -2 \end{vmatrix} = -19,$$

$$D_x = \begin{vmatrix} 7 & 4 & 1 \\ 1 & 3 & -1 \\ 5 & 2 & -2 \end{vmatrix} = -53,$$

$$D_y = \begin{vmatrix} 2 & 7 & 1 \\ 1 & 1 & -1 \\ 3 & 5 & -2 \end{vmatrix} = 1,$$

$$D_z = \begin{vmatrix} 2 & 4 & 7 \\ 1 & 3 & 1 \\ 3 & 2 & 5 \end{vmatrix} = -31$$

$x = \dfrac{D_x}{D} = \dfrac{-53}{-19} = \dfrac{53}{19}$ $y = \dfrac{D_y}{D} = \dfrac{1}{-19} = -\dfrac{1}{19}$

$z = \dfrac{D_z}{D} = \dfrac{-31}{-19} = \dfrac{31}{19}$

The solution is $\left(\dfrac{53}{19}, -\dfrac{1}{19}, \dfrac{31}{19} \right)$.

Objective 4.3.3 Exercises

37. To write the augmented matrix of a system of three equations in three unknowns in which each equation is of the form $ax + by + cz = d$, write the coefficients of x in the first column, the coefficients of y in the second column, and coefficients of z in the third column, and the constants in the fourth column of the matrix. It is common practice to draw a vertical line between the coefficients of the variables and the constant terms. The first row of the matrix represents equation 1, the second row represents equation 2, and the third row represents equation 3 of the system.

38. The matrix is not in row echelon form because a_{32} is not a zero and a_{33} is not a one.

39. $\begin{bmatrix} 2 & -4 & | & 1 \\ 3 & -7 & | & -1 \end{bmatrix}$

$\dfrac{1}{2}R_1 \rightarrow \begin{bmatrix} 1 & -2 & | & \dfrac{1}{2} \\ 3 & -7 & | & -1 \end{bmatrix}$

$-3R_1 + R_2 \rightarrow \begin{bmatrix} 1 & -2 & | & \dfrac{1}{2} \\ 0 & -1 & | & -\dfrac{5}{2} \end{bmatrix}$

$-1R_2 \rightarrow \begin{bmatrix} 1 & -2 & | & \dfrac{1}{2} \\ 0 & 1 & | & \dfrac{5}{2} \end{bmatrix}$

40. $\begin{bmatrix} 4 & 2 & | & -2 \\ 7 & 4 & | & -1 \end{bmatrix}$

$\frac{1}{4}R_1 \rightarrow \begin{bmatrix} 1 & \frac{1}{2} & | & -\frac{1}{2} \\ 7 & 4 & | & -1 \end{bmatrix}$

$-7R_1 + R_2 \rightarrow \begin{bmatrix} 1 & \frac{1}{2} & | & -\frac{1}{2} \\ 0 & \frac{1}{2} & | & \frac{5}{2} \end{bmatrix}$

$2R_2 \rightarrow \begin{bmatrix} 1 & \frac{1}{2} & | & -\frac{1}{2} \\ 0 & 1 & | & 5 \end{bmatrix}$

41. $\begin{bmatrix} 5 & -2 & | & 3 \\ -7 & 3 & | & 1 \end{bmatrix}$

$\begin{bmatrix} 5 & -2 & | & 3 \\ -7 & 3 & | & 1 \end{bmatrix}$

$\frac{1}{5}R_1 \rightarrow \begin{bmatrix} 1 & -\frac{2}{5} & | & \frac{3}{5} \\ -7 & 3 & | & 1 \end{bmatrix}$

$7R_1 + R_2 \rightarrow \begin{bmatrix} 1 & -\frac{2}{5} & | & \frac{3}{5} \\ 0 & \frac{1}{5} & | & \frac{26}{5} \end{bmatrix}$

$5R_2 \rightarrow \begin{bmatrix} 1 & -\frac{2}{5} & | & \frac{3}{5} \\ 0 & 1 & | & 26 \end{bmatrix}$

42. $\begin{bmatrix} 2 & 5 & | & -4 \\ 3 & 1 & | & 2 \end{bmatrix}$

$\frac{1}{2}R_1 \rightarrow \begin{bmatrix} 1 & \frac{5}{2} & | & -2 \\ 3 & 1 & | & 2 \end{bmatrix}$

$-3R_1 + R_2 \rightarrow \begin{bmatrix} 1 & \frac{5}{2} & | & -2 \\ 0 & -\frac{13}{2} & | & 8 \end{bmatrix}$

$-\frac{2}{13}R_2 \rightarrow \begin{bmatrix} 1 & \frac{5}{2} & | & -2 \\ 0 & 1 & | & -\frac{16}{13} \end{bmatrix}$

43. $\begin{bmatrix} 1 & 4 & 1 & | & -2 \\ 3 & 11 & -1 & | & 2 \\ 2 & 3 & 1 & | & 4 \end{bmatrix}$

$\begin{matrix} -3R_1 + R_2 \rightarrow \\ -2R_1 + R_3 \rightarrow \end{matrix} \begin{bmatrix} 1 & 4 & 1 & | & -2 \\ 0 & -1 & -4 & | & 8 \\ 0 & -5 & -1 & | & 8 \end{bmatrix}$

$-1R_2 \rightarrow \begin{bmatrix} 1 & 4 & 1 & | & -2 \\ 0 & 1 & 4 & | & -8 \\ 0 & -5 & -1 & | & 8 \end{bmatrix}$

$5R_2 + R_3 \rightarrow \begin{bmatrix} 1 & 4 & 1 & | & -2 \\ 0 & 1 & 4 & | & -8 \\ 0 & 0 & 19 & | & -32 \end{bmatrix}$

$\frac{1}{19}R_3 \rightarrow \begin{bmatrix} 1 & 4 & 1 & | & -2 \\ 0 & 1 & 4 & | & -8 \\ 0 & 0 & 1 & | & -\frac{32}{19} \end{bmatrix}$

44. $\begin{bmatrix} 1 & 2 & 2 & | & -1 \\ -4 & -10 & -1 & | & 3 \\ 3 & 4 & 2 & | & -2 \end{bmatrix}$

$\begin{matrix} 4R_1 + R_2 \rightarrow \\ -3R_1 + R_3 \rightarrow \end{matrix} \begin{bmatrix} 1 & 2 & 2 & | & -1 \\ 0 & -2 & 7 & | & -1 \\ 0 & -2 & -4 & | & 1 \end{bmatrix}$

$-\frac{1}{2}R_2 \rightarrow \begin{bmatrix} 1 & 2 & 2 & | & -1 \\ 0 & 1 & -\frac{7}{2} & | & \frac{1}{2} \\ 0 & -2 & -4 & | & 1 \end{bmatrix}$

$2R_2 + R_3 \rightarrow \begin{bmatrix} 1 & 2 & 2 & | & -1 \\ 0 & 1 & -\frac{7}{2} & | & \frac{1}{2} \\ 0 & 0 & -11 & | & 2 \end{bmatrix}$

$-\frac{1}{11}R_3 \rightarrow \begin{bmatrix} 1 & 2 & 2 & | & -1 \\ 0 & 1 & -\frac{7}{2} & | & \frac{1}{2} \\ 0 & 0 & 1 & | & -\frac{2}{11} \end{bmatrix}$

45. $\begin{bmatrix} -2 & 6 & -1 & | & 3 \\ 1 & -2 & 2 & | & 1 \\ 3 & -6 & 7 & | & 6 \end{bmatrix}$

$-\dfrac{1}{2}R_1 \rightarrow \begin{bmatrix} 1 & -3 & \dfrac{1}{2} & | & -\dfrac{3}{2} \\ 1 & -2 & 2 & | & 1 \\ 3 & -6 & 7 & | & 6 \end{bmatrix}$

$\begin{matrix} -1R_1 + R_2 \rightarrow \\ -3R_1 + R_3 \rightarrow \end{matrix} \begin{bmatrix} 1 & -3 & \dfrac{1}{2} & | & -\dfrac{3}{2} \\ 0 & 1 & \dfrac{3}{2} & | & \dfrac{5}{2} \\ 0 & 3 & \dfrac{11}{2} & | & \dfrac{21}{2} \end{bmatrix}$

$-3R_2 + R_3 \rightarrow \begin{bmatrix} 1 & -3 & \dfrac{1}{2} & | & -\dfrac{3}{2} \\ 0 & 1 & \dfrac{3}{2} & | & \dfrac{5}{2} \\ 0 & 0 & 1 & | & 3 \end{bmatrix}$

46. $\begin{bmatrix} 2 & 6 & 10 & | & 3 \\ 3 & 8 & 15 & | & 0 \\ 1 & 2 & 3 & | & -1 \end{bmatrix}$

$\dfrac{1}{2}R_1 \rightarrow \begin{bmatrix} 1 & 3 & 5 & | & \dfrac{3}{2} \\ 3 & 8 & 15 & | & 0 \\ 1 & 2 & 3 & | & -1 \end{bmatrix}$

$\begin{matrix} -3R_1 + R_2 \rightarrow \\ -1R_1 + R_3 \rightarrow \end{matrix} \begin{bmatrix} 1 & 3 & 5 & | & \dfrac{3}{2} \\ 0 & -1 & 0 & | & -\dfrac{9}{2} \\ 0 & -1 & -2 & | & -\dfrac{5}{2} \end{bmatrix}$

$-1R_2 \rightarrow \begin{bmatrix} 1 & 3 & 5 & | & \dfrac{3}{2} \\ 0 & 1 & 0 & | & \dfrac{9}{2} \\ 0 & -1 & -2 & | & -\dfrac{5}{2} \end{bmatrix}$

$R_2 + R_3 \rightarrow \begin{bmatrix} 1 & 3 & 5 & | & \dfrac{3}{2} \\ 0 & 1 & 0 & | & \dfrac{9}{2} \\ 0 & 0 & -2 & | & 2 \end{bmatrix}$

$-\dfrac{1}{2}R_3 \rightarrow \begin{bmatrix} 1 & 3 & 5 & | & \dfrac{3}{2} \\ 0 & 1 & 0 & | & \dfrac{9}{2} \\ 0 & 0 & 1 & | & -1 \end{bmatrix}$

47. Writing the augmented matrix as a system of equations,

$$x - y + 3z = -2$$
$$y - z = 1$$
$$z = 3$$

Using substitution,

$$y - 3 = 1$$
$$y = 4$$
$$x - 4 + 3(3) = -2$$
$$x = -7$$

The solution is $(-7, 4, 3)$.

48. Writing the augmented matrix as a system of equations,

$$x - 3y + 2z = 4$$
$$y - 2z = 3$$
$$z = -1$$

Using substitution,

$$y - 2(-1) = 3$$
$$y = 1$$
$$x - 3(1) + 2(-1) = 4$$
$$x = 9$$

The solution is $(9, 1, -1)$.

49.
$$3x + y = 6$$
$$2x - y = -1$$

$$\begin{bmatrix} 3 & 1 & | & 6 \\ 2 & -1 & | & -1 \end{bmatrix}$$

$$\frac{1}{3}R_1 \rightarrow \begin{bmatrix} 1 & \frac{1}{3} & | & 2 \\ 2 & -1 & | & -1 \end{bmatrix}$$

$$-2R_1 + R_2 \rightarrow \begin{bmatrix} 1 & \frac{1}{3} & | & 2 \\ 0 & -\frac{5}{3} & | & -5 \end{bmatrix}$$

$$-\frac{3}{5}R_2 \rightarrow \begin{bmatrix} 1 & \frac{1}{3} & | & 2 \\ 0 & 1 & | & 3 \end{bmatrix}$$

$$x + \left(\frac{1}{3}\right)y = 2$$
$$y = 3$$
$$x + \left(\frac{1}{3}\right)(3) = 2$$
$$x + 1 = 2$$
$$x = 1$$

The solution is $(1, 3)$.

50.
$$2x + y = 3$$
$$x - 4y = 6$$

$$\begin{bmatrix} 2 & 1 & | & 3 \\ 1 & -4 & | & 6 \end{bmatrix}$$

$$R_1 \leftrightarrow R_2 \begin{bmatrix} 1 & -4 & | & 6 \\ 2 & 1 & | & 3 \end{bmatrix}$$

$$-2R_1 + R_2 \rightarrow \begin{bmatrix} 1 & -4 & | & 6 \\ 0 & 9 & | & -9 \end{bmatrix}$$

$$\frac{1}{9}R_2 \rightarrow \begin{bmatrix} 1 & -4 & | & 6 \\ 0 & 1 & | & -1 \end{bmatrix}$$

$$x - 4y = 6$$
$$y = -1$$
$$x - 4(-1) = 6$$
$$x + 4 = 6$$
$$x = 2$$

The solution is $(2, -1)$.

51.
$$x - 3y = 8$$
$$3x - y = 0$$

$$\begin{bmatrix} 1 & -3 & | & 8 \\ 3 & -1 & | & 0 \end{bmatrix}$$

$$-3R_1 + R_2 \rightarrow \begin{bmatrix} 1 & -3 & | & 8 \\ 0 & 8 & | & -24 \end{bmatrix}$$

$$\frac{1}{8}R_2 \rightarrow \begin{bmatrix} 1 & 3 & | & 8 \\ 0 & 1 & | & -3 \end{bmatrix}$$

$$x - 3y = 8$$
$$y = -3$$
$$x - 3(-3) = 8$$
$$x + 9 = 8$$
$$x = -1$$

The solution is $(-1, -3)$.

52.
$$2x + 3y = 16$$
$$x - 4y = -14$$

$$\begin{bmatrix} 2 & 3 & | & 16 \\ 1 & -4 & | & -14 \end{bmatrix}$$

$$R_1 \leftrightarrow R_2 \begin{bmatrix} 1 & -4 & | & -14 \\ 2 & 3 & | & 16 \end{bmatrix}$$

$$-2R_1 + R_2 \rightarrow \begin{bmatrix} 1 & -4 & | & -14 \\ 0 & 11 & | & 44 \end{bmatrix}$$

$$\frac{1}{11}R_2 \rightarrow \begin{bmatrix} 1 & -4 & | & -14 \\ 0 & 1 & | & 4 \end{bmatrix}$$

$$x - 4y = -14$$
$$y = 4$$
$$x - 4(4) = -14$$
$$x - 16 = -14$$
$$x = 2$$

The solution is $(2, 4)$.

53.
$$y = 4x - 10$$
$$2y = 5x - 11$$

$$4x - y = 10$$
$$5x - 2y = 11$$

$$\begin{bmatrix} 4 & -1 & | & 10 \\ 5 & -2 & | & 11 \end{bmatrix}$$

$$\frac{1}{4}R_1 \rightarrow \begin{bmatrix} 1 & -\frac{1}{4} & | & \frac{5}{2} \\ 5 & -2 & | & 11 \end{bmatrix}$$

$$-5R_1 + R_2 \rightarrow \begin{bmatrix} 1 & -\frac{1}{4} & | & \frac{5}{2} \\ 0 & -\frac{3}{4} & | & -\frac{3}{2} \end{bmatrix}$$

$$-\frac{4}{3}R_2 \rightarrow \begin{bmatrix} 1 & -\frac{1}{4} & | & \frac{5}{2} \\ 0 & 1 & | & 2 \end{bmatrix}$$

$$x - \left(\frac{1}{4}\right)y = \frac{5}{2}$$
$$y = 2$$
$$x - \left(\frac{1}{4}\right)(2) = \frac{5}{2}$$
$$x - \frac{1}{2} = \frac{5}{2}$$
$$x = 3$$

The solution is $(3, 2)$.

54. $2y = 4 - 3x$
$y = 1 - 2x$

$3x + 2y = 4$
$2x + y = 1$

$\begin{bmatrix} 3 & 2 & | & 4 \\ 2 & 1 & | & 1 \end{bmatrix}$

$\frac{1}{3}R_1 \rightarrow \begin{bmatrix} 1 & \frac{2}{3} & | & \frac{4}{3} \\ 2 & 1 & | & 1 \end{bmatrix}$

$-2R_1 + R_2 \rightarrow \begin{bmatrix} 1 & \frac{2}{3} & | & \frac{4}{3} \\ 0 & -\frac{1}{3} & | & -\frac{5}{3} \end{bmatrix}$

$-3R_2 \rightarrow \begin{bmatrix} 1 & \frac{2}{3} & | & \frac{4}{3} \\ 0 & 1 & | & 5 \end{bmatrix}$

$x + \left(\frac{2}{3}\right)y = \frac{4}{3}$
$y = 5$

$x + \left(\frac{2}{3}\right)(5) = \frac{4}{3}$

$x + \frac{10}{3} = \frac{4}{3}$

$x = -2$

The solution is $(-2, 5)$.

55. $2x - y = -4$
$y = 2x - 8$

$2x - y = -4$
$2x - y = 8$

$\begin{bmatrix} 2 & -1 & | & -4 \\ 2 & -1 & | & 8 \end{bmatrix}$

$-\frac{1}{2}R_1 \rightarrow \begin{bmatrix} 1 & -\frac{1}{2} & | & -2 \\ 2 & -1 & | & 8 \end{bmatrix}$

$-2R_1 + R_2 \rightarrow \begin{bmatrix} 1 & -\frac{1}{2} & | & -2 \\ 0 & 0 & | & 12 \end{bmatrix}$

$x - \frac{1}{2}y = -2$
$0 = 12$

This is not a true equation. The system of equations is inconsistent.

56. $3x - 2y = -8$
$y = \frac{3}{2}x - 2$

$3x - 2y = -8$
$3x - 2y = 4$

$\begin{bmatrix} 3 & -2 & | & -8 \\ 3 & -2 & | & 4 \end{bmatrix}$

$\frac{1}{3}R_1 \rightarrow \begin{bmatrix} 1 & -\frac{2}{3} & | & -\frac{8}{3} \\ 3 & -2 & | & 4 \end{bmatrix}$

$-3R_1 + R_2 \rightarrow \begin{bmatrix} 1 & -\frac{2}{3} & | & -\frac{8}{3} \\ 0 & 0 & | & 12 \end{bmatrix}$

$x - \frac{2}{3}y = -\frac{8}{3}$
$0 = 12$

This is not a true equation. The system of equations is inconsistent.

57. $4x - 3y = -14$
$3x + 4y = 2$

$\begin{bmatrix} 4 & -3 & | & -14 \\ 3 & 4 & | & 2 \end{bmatrix}$

$\frac{1}{4}R_1 \rightarrow \begin{bmatrix} 1 & -\frac{3}{4} & | & -\frac{7}{2} \\ 3 & 4 & | & 2 \end{bmatrix}$

$-3R_1 + R_2 \rightarrow \begin{bmatrix} 1 & -\frac{3}{4} & | & -\frac{7}{2} \\ 0 & \frac{25}{4} & | & \frac{25}{2} \end{bmatrix}$

$\frac{4}{25}R_2 \rightarrow \begin{bmatrix} 1 & -\frac{3}{4} & | & -\frac{7}{2} \\ 0 & 1 & | & 2 \end{bmatrix}$

$x - \left(\frac{3}{4}\right)y = -\frac{7}{2}$
$y = 2$

$x - \left(\frac{3}{4}\right)(2) = -\frac{7}{2}$

$x - \frac{3}{2} = -\frac{7}{2}$

$x = -2$

The solution is $(-2, 2)$.

58. $5x + 2y = 3$
$3x + 4y = 13$

$\begin{bmatrix} 5 & 2 & | & 3 \\ 3 & 4 & | & 13 \end{bmatrix}$

$\frac{1}{5}R_1 \rightarrow \begin{bmatrix} 1 & \frac{2}{5} & | & \frac{3}{5} \\ 3 & 4 & | & 13 \end{bmatrix}$

$-3R_1 + R_2 \rightarrow \begin{bmatrix} 1 & \frac{2}{5} & | & \frac{3}{5} \\ 0 & \frac{14}{5} & | & \frac{56}{5} \end{bmatrix}$

$\frac{5}{14}R_2 \rightarrow \begin{bmatrix} 1 & \frac{2}{5} & | & \frac{3}{5} \\ 0 & 1 & | & 4 \end{bmatrix}$

$x + \left(\frac{2}{5}\right)y = \frac{3}{5}$
$\qquad\qquad y = 4$
$x + \left(\frac{2}{5}\right)(4) = \frac{3}{5}$
$\qquad x + \frac{8}{5} = \frac{3}{5}$
$\qquad\qquad x = -1$

The solution is $(-1, 4)$.

59. $5x + 4y + 3z = -9$
$x - 2y + 2z = -6$
$x - y - z = 3$

$\begin{bmatrix} 5 & 4 & 3 & | & -9 \\ 1 & -2 & 2 & | & -6 \\ 1 & -1 & -1 & | & 3 \end{bmatrix}$

$R_1 \leftrightarrow R_2 \begin{bmatrix} 1 & -2 & 2 & | & -6 \\ 5 & 4 & 3 & | & -9 \\ 1 & -1 & -1 & | & 3 \end{bmatrix}$

$\begin{matrix} -5R_1 + R_2 \rightarrow \\ -1R_1 + R_2 \rightarrow \end{matrix} \begin{bmatrix} 1 & -2 & 2 & | & -6 \\ 0 & 14 & -7 & | & 21 \\ 0 & 1 & -3 & | & 9 \end{bmatrix}$

$\frac{1}{14}R_2 \rightarrow \begin{bmatrix} 1 & -2 & 2 & | & -6 \\ 0 & 1 & -\frac{1}{2} & | & \frac{3}{2} \\ 0 & 1 & -3 & | & 9 \end{bmatrix}$

$-1R_2 + R_3 \rightarrow \begin{bmatrix} 1 & -2 & 2 & | & -6 \\ 0 & 1 & -\frac{1}{2} & | & \frac{3}{2} \\ 0 & 0 & -\frac{5}{2} & | & \frac{15}{2} \end{bmatrix}$

$-\frac{2}{5}R_3 \rightarrow \begin{bmatrix} 1 & -2 & 2 & | & -6 \\ 0 & 1 & -\frac{1}{2} & | & \frac{3}{2} \\ 0 & 0 & 1 & | & -3 \end{bmatrix}$

$x - 2y + 2z = -6$
$y - \left(\frac{1}{2}\right)z = \frac{3}{2}$
$\qquad\qquad z = -3$

$y - \left(\frac{1}{2}\right)(-3) = \frac{3}{2}$
$\qquad y + \frac{3}{2} = \frac{3}{2}$
$\qquad\qquad y = 0$
$x - 2(0) + 2(-3) = -6$
$\qquad\qquad x - 6 = -6$
$\qquad\qquad\qquad x = 0$

The solution is $(0, 0, -3)$.

60.
$$x - y - z = 0$$
$$3x - y + 5z = -10$$
$$x + y - 4z = 12$$

$$\begin{bmatrix} 1 & -1 & -1 & | & 0 \\ 3 & -1 & 5 & | & -10 \\ 1 & 1 & -4 & | & 12 \end{bmatrix}$$

$$\begin{matrix} -3R_1 + R_2 \to \\ -1R_1 + R_3 \to \end{matrix} \begin{bmatrix} 1 & -1 & -1 & | & 0 \\ 0 & 2 & 8 & | & -10 \\ 0 & 2 & -3 & | & 12 \end{bmatrix}$$

$$\frac{1}{2}R_2 \to \begin{bmatrix} 1 & -1 & -1 & | & 0 \\ 0 & 1 & 4 & | & -5 \\ 0 & 2 & -3 & | & 12 \end{bmatrix}$$

$$-2R_2 + R_3 \to \begin{bmatrix} 1 & -1 & -1 & | & 0 \\ 0 & 1 & 4 & | & -5 \\ 0 & 0 & -11 & | & -22 \end{bmatrix}$$

$$-\frac{1}{11}R_3 \to \begin{bmatrix} 1 & -1 & -1 & | & 0 \\ 0 & 1 & 4 & | & -5 \\ 0 & 0 & 1 & | & 2 \end{bmatrix}$$

$$x - y - z = 0$$
$$y + 4z = -5$$
$$z = -2$$

$$y + 4(-2) = -5$$
$$y - 8 = -5$$
$$y = 3$$

$$x - 3 - (-2) = 0$$
$$x - 3 + 2 = 0$$
$$x - 1 = 0$$
$$x = 1$$

The solution is $(1, 3, -2)$.

61.
$$5x - 5y + 2z = 8$$
$$2x + 3y - z = 0$$
$$x + 2y - z = 0$$

$$\begin{bmatrix} 5 & -5 & 2 & | & 8 \\ 2 & 3 & -1 & | & 0 \\ 1 & 2 & -1 & | & 0 \end{bmatrix}$$

$$R_1 \leftrightarrow R_3 \begin{bmatrix} 1 & 2 & -1 & | & 0 \\ 2 & 3 & -1 & | & 0 \\ 5 & -5 & 2 & | & 8 \end{bmatrix}$$

$$\begin{matrix} -2R_1 + R_2 \to \\ -5R_1 + R_3 \to \end{matrix} \begin{bmatrix} 1 & 2 & -1 & | & 0 \\ 0 & -1 & 1 & | & 0 \\ 0 & -15 & 7 & | & 8 \end{bmatrix}$$

$$-1R_2 \to \begin{bmatrix} 1 & 2 & -1 & | & 0 \\ 0 & 1 & -1 & | & 0 \\ 0 & -15 & 7 & | & 8 \end{bmatrix}$$

$$15R_2 + R_3 \to \begin{bmatrix} 1 & 2 & -1 & | & 0 \\ 0 & 1 & -1 & | & 0 \\ 0 & 0 & -8 & | & 8 \end{bmatrix}$$

$$-\frac{1}{8}R_3 \to \begin{bmatrix} 1 & 2 & -1 & | & 0 \\ 0 & 1 & -1 & | & 0 \\ 0 & 0 & 1 & | & -1 \end{bmatrix}$$

$$x + 2y - z = 0$$
$$y - z = 0$$
$$z = -1$$

$$y - (-1) = 0$$
$$y + 1 = 0$$
$$y = -1$$

$$x + 2(-1) - (-1) = 0$$
$$x - 2 + 1 = 0$$
$$x - 1 = 0$$
$$x = 1$$

The solution is $(1, -1, -1)$.

62. $2x+y-5z=3$
$3x+2y+z=15$
$5x-y-z=5$

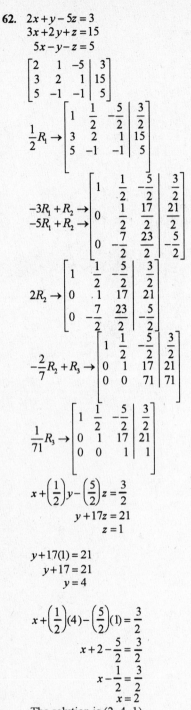

$$\begin{bmatrix} 2 & 1 & -5 & 3 \\ 3 & 2 & 1 & 15 \\ 5 & -1 & -1 & 5 \end{bmatrix}$$

$\frac{1}{2}R_1 \to \begin{bmatrix} 1 & \frac{1}{2} & -\frac{5}{2} & \frac{3}{2} \\ 3 & 2 & 1 & 15 \\ 5 & -1 & -1 & 5 \end{bmatrix}$

$\begin{matrix} -3R_1+R_2 \to \\ -5R_1+R_2 \to \end{matrix} \begin{bmatrix} 1 & \frac{1}{2} & -\frac{5}{2} & \frac{3}{2} \\ 0 & \frac{1}{2} & \frac{17}{2} & \frac{21}{2} \\ 0 & -\frac{7}{2} & \frac{23}{2} & -\frac{5}{2} \end{bmatrix}$

$2R_2 \to \begin{bmatrix} 1 & \frac{1}{2} & -\frac{5}{2} & \frac{3}{2} \\ 0 & 1 & 17 & 21 \\ 0 & -\frac{7}{2} & \frac{23}{2} & -\frac{5}{2} \end{bmatrix}$

$-\frac{2}{7}R_2+R_3 \to \begin{bmatrix} 1 & \frac{1}{2} & -\frac{5}{2} & \frac{3}{2} \\ 0 & 1 & 17 & 21 \\ 0 & 0 & 71 & 71 \end{bmatrix}$

$\frac{1}{71}R_3 \to \begin{bmatrix} 1 & \frac{1}{2} & -\frac{5}{2} & \frac{3}{2} \\ 0 & 1 & 17 & 21 \\ 0 & 0 & 1 & 1 \end{bmatrix}$

$x+\left(\frac{1}{2}\right)y-\left(\frac{5}{2}\right)z=\frac{3}{2}$
$y+17z=21$
$z=1$

$y+17(1)=21$
$y+17=21$
$y=4$

$x+\left(\frac{1}{2}\right)(4)-\left(\frac{5}{2}\right)(1)=\frac{3}{2}$
$x+2-\frac{5}{2}=\frac{3}{2}$
$x-\frac{1}{2}=\frac{3}{2}$
$x=2$

The solution is $(2, 4, 1)$.

63. $2x+3y+z=5$
$3x+3y+3z=10$
$4x+6y+2z=5$

$$\begin{bmatrix} 2 & 1 & 3 & 5 \\ 3 & 3 & 3 & 10 \\ 4 & 6 & 2 & 5 \end{bmatrix}$$

$\frac{1}{2}R_1 \to \begin{bmatrix} 1 & \frac{1}{2} & \frac{3}{2} & \frac{5}{2} \\ 3 & 3 & 3 & 10 \\ 4 & 6 & 2 & 5 \end{bmatrix}$

$\begin{matrix} -3R_1+R_2 \to \\ -4R_1+R_2 \to \end{matrix} \begin{bmatrix} 1 & \frac{1}{2} & \frac{3}{2} & \frac{5}{2} \\ 0 & -\frac{3}{2} & \frac{3}{2} & \frac{5}{2} \\ 0 & 0 & 0 & -5 \end{bmatrix}$

$x+\left(\frac{3}{2}\right)y+\left(\frac{1}{2}\right)z=\frac{5}{2}$
$-\left(\frac{3}{2}\right)y+\left(\frac{3}{2}\right)z=\frac{5}{2}$
$0=-5$

This is not a true equation. The system of equations is inconsistent.

64. $x-2y+3z=2$
$2x+y+2z=5$
$2x-4y+6z=-4$

$$\begin{bmatrix} 1 & -2 & 3 & 2 \\ 2 & 1 & 2 & 5 \\ 2 & -4 & 6 & -4 \end{bmatrix}$$

$\begin{matrix} -2R_1+R_2 \to \\ -2R_1+R_3 \to \end{matrix} \begin{bmatrix} 1 & -2 & 3 & 2 \\ 0 & 5 & -4 & 1 \\ 0 & 0 & 0 & -8 \end{bmatrix}$

$x-2y+3z=2$
$5y-4z=1$
$0=-8$

This is not a true equation. The system of equations is inconsistent.

65. $3x + 2y + 3z = 2$
$6x - 2y + z = 1$
$3x + 4y + 2z = 3$

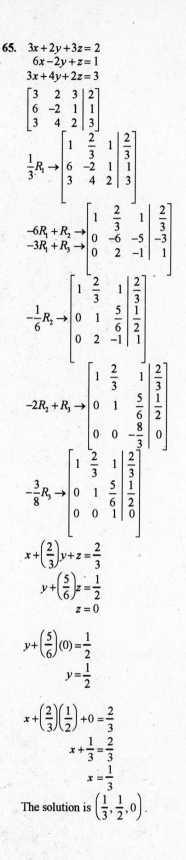

$x + \left(\dfrac{2}{3}\right)y + z = \dfrac{2}{3}$

$y + \left(\dfrac{5}{6}\right)z = \dfrac{1}{2}$

$z = 0$

$y + \left(\dfrac{5}{6}\right)(0) = \dfrac{1}{2}$

$y = \dfrac{1}{2}$

$x + \left(\dfrac{2}{3}\right)\left(\dfrac{1}{2}\right) + 0 = \dfrac{2}{3}$

$x + \dfrac{1}{3} = \dfrac{2}{3}$

$x = \dfrac{1}{3}$

The solution is $\left(\dfrac{1}{3}, \dfrac{1}{2}, 0\right)$.

66. $2x + 3y - 3z = -1$
$2x + 3y + 3z = 3$
$4x - 4y + 3z = 4$

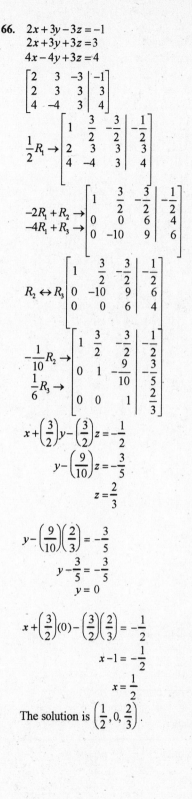

$x + \left(\dfrac{3}{2}\right)y - \left(\dfrac{3}{2}\right)z = -\dfrac{1}{2}$

$y - \left(\dfrac{9}{10}\right)z = -\dfrac{3}{5}$

$z = \dfrac{2}{3}$

$y - \left(\dfrac{9}{10}\right)\left(\dfrac{2}{3}\right) = -\dfrac{3}{5}$

$y - \dfrac{3}{5} = -\dfrac{3}{5}$

$y = 0$

$x + \left(\dfrac{3}{2}\right)(0) - \left(\dfrac{3}{2}\right)\left(\dfrac{2}{3}\right) = -\dfrac{1}{2}$

$x - 1 = -\dfrac{1}{2}$

$x = \dfrac{1}{2}$

The solution is $\left(\dfrac{1}{2}, 0, \dfrac{2}{3}\right)$.

67.
$$5x - 5y - 5z = 2$$
$$5x + 5y - 5z = 6$$
$$10x + 10y + 5z = 3$$

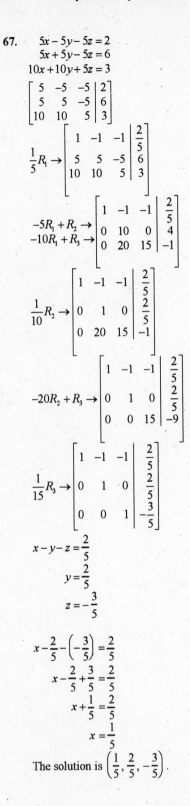

$$\begin{bmatrix} 5 & -5 & -5 & | & 2 \\ 5 & 5 & -5 & | & 6 \\ 10 & 10 & 5 & | & 3 \end{bmatrix}$$

$$\frac{1}{5}R_1 \rightarrow \begin{bmatrix} 1 & -1 & -1 & | & \frac{2}{5} \\ 5 & 5 & -5 & | & 6 \\ 10 & 10 & 5 & | & 3 \end{bmatrix}$$

$$\begin{matrix} -5R_1 + R_2 \rightarrow \\ -10R_1 + R_3 \rightarrow \end{matrix} \begin{bmatrix} 1 & -1 & -1 & | & \frac{2}{5} \\ 0 & 10 & 0 & | & 4 \\ 0 & 20 & 15 & | & -1 \end{bmatrix}$$

$$\frac{1}{10}R_2 \rightarrow \begin{bmatrix} 1 & -1 & -1 & | & \frac{2}{5} \\ 0 & 1 & 0 & | & \frac{2}{5} \\ 0 & 20 & 15 & | & -1 \end{bmatrix}$$

$$-20R_2 + R_3 \rightarrow \begin{bmatrix} 1 & -1 & -1 & | & \frac{2}{5} \\ 0 & 1 & 0 & | & \frac{2}{5} \\ 0 & 0 & 15 & | & -9 \end{bmatrix}$$

$$\frac{1}{15}R_3 \rightarrow \begin{bmatrix} 1 & -1 & -1 & | & \frac{2}{5} \\ 0 & 1 & 0 & | & \frac{2}{5} \\ 0 & 0 & 1 & | & -\frac{3}{5} \end{bmatrix}$$

$$x - y - z = \frac{2}{5}$$
$$y = \frac{2}{5}$$
$$z = -\frac{3}{5}$$

$$x - \frac{2}{5} - \left(-\frac{3}{5}\right) = \frac{2}{5}$$
$$x - \frac{2}{5} + \frac{3}{5} = \frac{2}{5}$$
$$x + \frac{1}{5} = \frac{2}{5}$$
$$x = \frac{1}{5}$$

The solution is $\left(\frac{1}{5}, \frac{2}{5}, -\frac{3}{5}\right)$.

68.
$$3x - 2y + 2z = 5$$
$$6x + 3y - 4z = -1$$
$$3x - y + 2z = 4$$

$$\begin{bmatrix} 3 & -2 & 2 & | & 5 \\ 6 & 3 & -4 & | & -1 \\ 3 & -1 & 2 & | & 4 \end{bmatrix}$$

$$\frac{1}{3}R_1 \rightarrow \begin{bmatrix} 1 & -\frac{2}{3} & \frac{2}{3} & | & \frac{5}{3} \\ 6 & 3 & -4 & | & -1 \\ 3 & -1 & 2 & | & 4 \end{bmatrix}$$

$$\begin{matrix} -6R_1 + R_2 \rightarrow \\ -3R_1 + R_3 \rightarrow \end{matrix} \begin{bmatrix} 1 & -\frac{2}{3} & \frac{2}{3} & | & \frac{5}{3} \\ 0 & 7 & -8 & | & -11 \\ 0 & 1 & 0 & | & -1 \end{bmatrix}$$

$$R_2 + R_3 \rightarrow \begin{bmatrix} 1 & -\frac{2}{3} & \frac{2}{3} & | & \frac{5}{3} \\ 0 & 1 & 0 & | & -1 \\ 0 & 7 & -8 & | & -11 \end{bmatrix}$$

$$-7R_2 + R_3 \rightarrow \begin{bmatrix} 1 & -\frac{2}{3} & \frac{2}{3} & | & \frac{5}{3} \\ 0 & 1 & 0 & | & -1 \\ 0 & 0 & -8 & | & -4 \end{bmatrix}$$

$$-\frac{1}{8}R_3 \rightarrow \begin{bmatrix} 1 & -\frac{2}{3} & \frac{2}{3} & | & \frac{5}{3} \\ 0 & 1 & 0 & | & -1 \\ 0 & 0 & 1 & | & \frac{1}{2} \end{bmatrix}$$

$$x - \left(\frac{2}{3}\right)y + \left(\frac{2}{3}\right)z = \frac{5}{3}$$
$$y = -1$$
$$z = \frac{1}{2}$$

$$x - \left(\frac{2}{3}\right)(-1) + \left(\frac{2}{3}\right)\left(\frac{1}{2}\right) = \frac{5}{3}$$
$$x + \frac{2}{3} + \frac{1}{3} = \frac{5}{3}$$
$$x + 1 = \frac{5}{3}$$
$$x = \frac{2}{3}$$

The solution is $\left(\frac{2}{3}, -1, \frac{1}{2}\right)$.

69. $4x + 4y - 3z = 3$
$8x + 2y + 3z = 0$
$4x - 4y + 6z = -3$

$$\begin{bmatrix} 4 & 4 & -3 & | & 3 \\ 8 & 2 & 3 & | & 0 \\ 4 & -4 & 6 & | & -3 \end{bmatrix}$$

$$\frac{1}{4}R_1 \to \begin{bmatrix} 1 & 1 & -\frac{3}{4} & | & \frac{3}{4} \\ 8 & 2 & 3 & | & 0 \\ 4 & -4 & 6 & | & -3 \end{bmatrix}$$

$$\begin{matrix} -8R_1 + R_2 \to \\ -4R_1 + R_3 \to \end{matrix} \begin{bmatrix} 1 & 1 & -\frac{3}{4} & | & \frac{3}{4} \\ 0 & -6 & 9 & | & -6 \\ 0 & -8 & 9 & | & -6 \end{bmatrix}$$

$$-\frac{1}{6}R_2 \to \begin{bmatrix} 1 & 1 & -\frac{3}{4} & | & \frac{3}{4} \\ 0 & 1 & -\frac{3}{2} & | & 1 \\ 0 & -8 & 9 & | & -6 \end{bmatrix}$$

$$8R_2 + R_3 \to \begin{bmatrix} 1 & 1 & -\frac{3}{4} & | & \frac{3}{4} \\ 0 & 1 & -\frac{3}{2} & | & 1 \\ 0 & 0 & -3 & | & 2 \end{bmatrix}$$

$$-\frac{1}{3}R_3 \to \begin{bmatrix} 1 & 1 & -\frac{3}{4} & | & \frac{3}{4} \\ 0 & 1 & -\frac{3}{2} & | & 1 \\ 0 & 0 & 1 & | & -\frac{2}{3} \end{bmatrix}$$

$$x + y - \left(\frac{3}{4}\right)z = \frac{3}{4}$$
$$y - \left(\frac{3}{2}\right)z = 1$$
$$z = -\frac{2}{3}$$

$$y - \left(\frac{3}{2}\right)\left(-\frac{2}{3}\right) = 1$$
$$y + 1 = 1$$
$$y = 0$$

$$x + 0 - \left(\frac{3}{4}\right)\left(-\frac{2}{3}\right) = \frac{3}{4}$$
$$x + \frac{1}{2} = \frac{3}{4}$$
$$x = \frac{1}{4}$$

The solution is $\left(\frac{1}{4}, 0, -\frac{2}{3}\right)$.

Applying Concepts 4.3

70. $\begin{vmatrix} 3 & 2 \\ 4 & x \end{vmatrix} = -11$

$3x - 4(2) = -11$
$3x - 8 = -11$
$3x = -3$
$x = -1$
The solution is -1.

71. $\begin{vmatrix} 1 & 0 & 2 \\ 4 & 3 & -1 \\ 0 & 2 & x \end{vmatrix} = -24$

Expand the minors of the first row.
$1(3x + 2) - 0 + 2(8 - 0) = -24$
$3x + 2 + 16 = -24$
$3x + 18 = -24$
$3x = -42$
$x = -14$
The solution is -14.

72. $\begin{vmatrix} -2 & 1 & 3 \\ 0 & x & 4 \\ -1 & 2 & -3 \end{vmatrix} = -24$

Expand by minors of the first column.
$-2(-3x - 8) - 0 + (-1)(4 - 3x) = -24$
$6x + 16 - (4 - 3x) = -24$
$6x + 16 - 4 + 3x = -24$
$9x + 12 = -24$
$9x = -36$
$x = -4$
The solution is -4.

73. If all the elements in one row or one column of a 2×2 matrix are zeros, the value of the determinant of the matrix is 0.
For example,
$$\begin{vmatrix} a_1 & 0 \\ b_1 & 0 \end{vmatrix} = a_1(0) - (0)b_1 = 0 - 0 = 0$$

74. If all the elements in one row or one column of a 3×3 matrix are zeros, the value of the determinant of the matrix is 0.
For example,
$$\begin{vmatrix} 0 & 0 & 0 \\ b_1 & b_2 & b_3 \\ c_1 & c_2 & c_3 \end{vmatrix}$$
Expanding by minors of the first row results in $0 - 0 + 0 = 0$.

75. a.
$$\begin{vmatrix} x & x & a \\ y & y & b \\ z & z & c \end{vmatrix}$$

Expand by minors of the first row.
$x(cy - bz) - x(cy - bz) + a(yz - yz)$
$= cxy - bxz - cxy + bxz + ayz - ayz$
$= 0$

b. If two columns of a determinant contain identical elements, the value of the determinant is 0.

76. Show that $\begin{vmatrix} a & b \\ c & d \end{vmatrix} = -\begin{vmatrix} c & d \\ a & b \end{vmatrix}$

First evaluate $\begin{vmatrix} a & b \\ c & d \end{vmatrix} = ad - bc$.

Next evaluate $-\begin{vmatrix} c & d \\ a & b \end{vmatrix} = -bc - (-ad) = -bc + ad$.

$ad - bc = -bc + ad$

77. $A = \dfrac{1}{2}\left\{ \begin{vmatrix} x_1 & x_2 \\ y_1 & y_2 \end{vmatrix} + \begin{vmatrix} x_2 & x_3 \\ y_2 & y_3 \end{vmatrix} + \begin{vmatrix} x_3 & x_4 \\ y_3 & y_4 \end{vmatrix} + \ldots + \begin{vmatrix} x_n & x_1 \\ y_n & y_1 \end{vmatrix} \right\}$

$A = \dfrac{1}{2}\left\{ \begin{vmatrix} 9 & 26 \\ -3 & 6 \end{vmatrix} + \begin{vmatrix} 26 & 18 \\ 6 & 21 \end{vmatrix} + \begin{vmatrix} 18 & 16 \\ 21 & 10 \end{vmatrix} + \begin{vmatrix} 16 & 1 \\ 10 & 11 \end{vmatrix} + \begin{vmatrix} 1 & 9 \\ 11 & -3 \end{vmatrix} \right\}$

$A = \dfrac{1}{2}(132 + 438 - 156 + 166 - 102) = 239$

The area of the polygon is 239 ft^2.

78. Start with the system of equations $\begin{array}{l} 3x - 2y = 12 \\ 2x + 5y = -11 \end{array}$. Multiply the second equation by 3, add it to the first equation, and replace the second equation by the new equation. The resulting system of equations is $\begin{array}{l} 3x - 2y = 12 \\ 9x + 13y = -21 \end{array}$. The graph of each system of equations follows.

This is an illustration of the third elementary row operation. Multiplying an equation, adding it to another equation, and then replacing an equation with the new equation does not change the solution of a system of equations.

79. The last row of this matrix indicates $0x + 0y + 0z = -3$. This equation is not true for any values of x, y, and z. Therefore, the system of equations has no solution.

Section 4.4

Concept Review 4.4

1. Never true
The rate up the river is $(y - x)$ mph.

2. Never true
The speed of the plane relative to an observer on the ground is 450 mph.

3. Always true

4. Sometimes true
There are a number of combinations of coins that would total $.70.

Objective 4.4.1 Exercises

1. Strategy
Rate of the plane in calm air: p
Rate of the wind: w

	Rate	Time	Distance
With wind	$p+w$	2	$2(p+w)$
Against wind	$p-w$	2	$2(p-w)$

• The distance traveled with the wind is 320 mi.
The distance traveled against the wind is 280 mi.
$2(p+w)=320$
$2(p-w)=280$

Solution
$2(p+w)=320$
$2(p-w)=280$

$\frac{1}{2}\cdot 2(p+w)=\frac{1}{2}\cdot 320$
$\frac{1}{2}\cdot 2(p-w)=\frac{1}{2}\cdot 280$

$p+w=160$
$p-w=140$

$2p=300$
$p=150$

$p+w=160$
$150+w=160$
$w=10$
The rate of the plane in calm air is 150 mph. The rate of the wind is 10 mph.

2. Strategy
Rate of the plane in calm air: p
Rate of the wind: w

	Rate	Time	Distance
With wind	$p+w$	4	$4(p+w)$
Against wind	$p-w$	4	$4(p-w)$

• The distance traveled with the wind is 2100 mi.
The distance traveled against the wind is 1760 mi.
$4(p+w)=2100$
$4(p-w)=1760$

Solution
$4(p+w)=2100$
$4(p-w)=1760$

$\frac{1}{4}\cdot 4(p+w)=\frac{1}{4}\cdot 2100$
$\frac{1}{4}\cdot 4(p-w)=\frac{1}{4}\cdot 1760$

$p+w=525$
$p-w=440$

$2p=965$
$p=482.5$

$p+w=525$
$482.5+w=525$
$w=42.5$
The rate of the plane in calm air is 482.5 mph.
The rate of the wind is 42.5 mph.

3. Strategy
Rate of the cabin cruiser in calm water: x
Rate of the current: y

	Rate	Time	Distance
With current	$x + y$	3	$3(x + y)$
Against current	$x - y$	4	$4(x - y)$

• The distance traveled with the current is 48 mi.
The distance traveled against the current is 48 mi.
$$3(x + y) = 48$$
$$4(x - y) = 48$$

Solution
$$3(x + y) = 48$$
$$4(x - y) = 48$$

$$\frac{1}{3} \cdot 3(x + y) = \frac{1}{3} \cdot 48$$
$$\frac{1}{4} \cdot 4(x - y) = \frac{1}{4} \cdot 48$$

$$x + y = 16$$
$$x - y = 12$$

$$2x = 28$$
$$x = 14$$

$$x + y = 16$$
$$14 + y = 16$$
$$y = 2$$

The rate of the cabin cruiser in calm water is 14 mph. The rate of the current is 2 mph.

4. Strategy
Rate of the motorboat in calm water: x
Rate of the current: y

	Rate	Time	Distance
With current	$x + y$	2	$2(x + y)$
Against current	$x - y$	3	$3(x - y)$

• The distance traveled with the current is 48 mi.
The distance traveled against the current is 48 mi.
$$2(x + y) = 48$$
$$3(x - y) = 48$$

Solution
$$2(x + y) = 48$$
$$3(x - y) = 48$$

$$\frac{1}{2} \cdot 2(x + y) = \frac{1}{2} \cdot 48$$
$$\frac{1}{3} \cdot 3(x - y) = \frac{1}{3} \cdot 48$$

$$x + y = 24$$
$$x - y = 16$$

$$2x = 40$$
$$x = 20$$

$$x + y = 24$$
$$20 + y = 24$$
$$y = 4$$

The rate of the motorboat in calm water is 20 mph. The rate of the current is 4 mph.

5. Strategy
Rate of the plane in calm air: x
Rate of the wind: y

	Rate	Time	Distance
With wind	$x+y$	2.5	$2.5(x+y)$
Against wind	$x-y$	3	$3(x-y)$

• The distance traveled with the wind is 450 mi.
The distance traveled against the wind is 450 mi.
$2.5(x+y) = 450$
$3(x-y) = 450$

Solution
$2.5(x+y) = 450$
$3(x-y) = 450$

$\dfrac{1}{2.5} \cdot 2.5(x+y) = \dfrac{1}{2.5} \cdot 450$

$\dfrac{1}{3} \cdot 3(x-y) = \dfrac{1}{3} \cdot 450$

$x+y = 180$
$x-y = 150$

$2x = 330$
$x = 165$

$x+y = 180$
$165+y = 180$
$y = 15$

The rate of the plane in calm air is 165 mph.
The rate of the wind is 15 mph.

6. Strategy
Rate of the plane in calm air: x
Rate of the wind: y

	Rate	Time	Distance
With wind	$x+y$	2	$2(x+y)$
Against wind	$x-y$	3	$3(x-y)$

• The distance traveled with the wind is 600 mi.
The distance traveled against the wind is 600 mi.
$2(x+y) = 600$
$3(x-y) = 600$

Solution
$2(x+y) = 600$
$3(x-y) = 600$

$\dfrac{1}{2} \cdot 2(x+y) = \dfrac{1}{2} \cdot 600$

$\dfrac{1}{3} \cdot 3(x-y) = \dfrac{1}{3} \cdot 600$

$x+y = 300$
$x-y = 200$

$2x = 500$
$x = 250$

$x+y = 300$
$250+y = 300$
$y = 50$

The rate of the plane in calm air is 250 mph. The rate of the wind is 50 mph.

7. Strategy
The rate of the boat in calm water: x
The rate of the current: y

	Rate	Time	Distance
With current	$x+y$	4	$4(x+y)$
Against current	$x-y$	4	$4(x-y)$

• The distance traveled with the current is 88 km. The distance traveled against the current is 64 km.
$$4(x+y)=88$$
$$4(x-y)=64$$

Solution
$$4(x+y)=88$$
$$4(x-y)=64$$

$$\frac{1}{4}\cdot 4(x+y)=\frac{1}{4}\cdot 88$$
$$\frac{1}{4}\cdot 4(x-y)=\frac{1}{4}\cdot 64$$

$$x+y=22$$
$$x-y=16$$

$$2x=38$$
$$x=19$$

$$x+y=22$$
$$19+y=22$$
$$y=3$$

The rate of the boat in calm water is 19 km/h.
The rate of the current is 3 km/h.

8. Strategy
Rate of the team in calm water: x
Rate of the current: y

	Rate	Time	Distance
With current	$x+y$	2	$2(x+y)$
Against current	$x-y$	2	$2(x-y)$

• The distance traveled with the current is 18 km. The distance traveled against the current is 12 km.
$$2(x+y)=18$$
$$2(x-y)=12$$

Solution
$$2(x+y)=18$$
$$2(x-y)=12$$

$$\frac{1}{2}\cdot 2(x+y)=\frac{1}{2}\cdot 18$$
$$\frac{1}{2}\cdot 2(x-y)=\frac{1}{2}\cdot 12$$

$$x+y=9$$
$$x-y=6$$

$$2x=15$$
$$x=7.5$$

$$x+y=9$$
$$7.5+y=9$$
$$y=1.5$$

The rate of the team in calm water is 7.5 km/h.
The rate of the current is 1.5 km/h.

9. Strategy
   Rate of the plane in calm air: x
   Rate of the wind: y

	Rate	Time	Distance
With wind	$x+y$	3	$3(x+y)$
Against wind	$x-y$	4	$4(x-y)$

   • The distance traveled with the wind is 360 mi.
   The distance traveled against the wind is 360 mi.
   $3(x+y) = 360$
   $4(x-y) = 360$

   Solution
   $3(x+y) = 360$
   $4(x-y) = 360$

   $\frac{1}{3} \cdot 3(x+y) = \frac{1}{3} \cdot 360$

   $\frac{1}{4} \cdot 4(x-y) = \frac{1}{4} \cdot 360$

   $x+y = 120$
   $x-y = 90$

   $2x = 210$
   $x = 105$

   $x+y = 120$
   $105+y = 120$
   $y = 15$

   The rate of the plane in calm air is 105 mph. The rate of the wind is 15 mph.

10. Strategy
    Rate of the plane in calm air: x
    Rate of the wind: y

	Rate	Time	Distance
With wind	$x+y$	4	$4(x+y)$
Against wind	$x-y$	5	$5(x-y)$

    • The distance traveled with the wind is 1000 mi.
    The distance traveled against the wind is 1000 mi.
    $4(x+y) = 1000$
    $5(x-y) = 1000$

    Solution
    $4(x+y) = 1000$
    $5(x-y) = 1000$

    $\frac{1}{4} \cdot 4(x+y) = \frac{1}{4} \cdot 1000$

    $\frac{1}{5} \cdot 5(x-y) = \frac{1}{5} \cdot 1000$

    $x+y = 250$
    $x-y = 200$

    $2x = 450$
    $x = 225$

    $x+y = 250$
    $225+y = 250$
    $y = 25$

    The rate of the plane in calm air is 225 mph.
    The rate of the wind is 25 mph.

11. Strategy
Rate of the boat in calm water: x
Rate of the current: y

	Rate	Time	Distance
With current	$x+y$	3	$3(x+y)$
Against current	$x-y$	3.6	$3.6(x-y)$

• The distance traveled with the current is 54 mi.
The distance traveled against the current is 54 mi.

$3(x+y)=54$
$3.6(x-7)=54$

Solution
$3(x+y)=54$
$3.6(x-y)=54$

$$\frac{1}{3}\cdot 3(x+y)=\frac{1}{3}\cdot 54$$

$$\frac{1}{3.6}\cdot 3.6(x-y)=\frac{1}{3.6}\cdot 54$$

$x+y=18$
$x-y=15$

$2x=33$
$x=16.5$

$x+y=18$
$16.5+y=18$
$y=1.5$

The rate of the boat in calm water is 16.5 mph.
The rate of the current is 1.5 mph.

12. Strategy
Rate of the plane in calm water: x
Rate of the wind: y

	Rate	Time	Distance
With wind	$x+y$	6.25	$6.25(x+y)$
Against wind	$x-y$	7.25	$7.25(x-y)$

• The distance traveled with the wind is 3625 mi.
The distance traveled against the wind is 3625 mi.

$6.25(x+y)=3625$
$7.25(x-y)=3625$

Solution
$6.25(x+y)=3625$
$7.25(x-y)=3625$

$$\frac{1}{6.25}\cdot 6.25(x+y)=\frac{1}{6.25}\cdot 3625$$

$$\frac{1}{7.25}\cdot 7.25(x-y)=\frac{1}{7.25}\cdot 3625$$

$x+y=580$
$x-y=500$

$2x=1080$
$x=540$

$x+y=580$
$540+y=580$
$y=40$

The rate of the plane in calm air is 540 mph.
The rate of the wind is 40 mph.

Objective 4.4.2 Exercises

13. Strategy
   Cost of redwood: x
   Cost of pine: y
   First purchase:

	Amount	Cost	Total Value
Redwood	50	x	$50x$
Pine	90	y	$90y$

   Second Purchase:

	Amount	Cost	Total Value
Redwood	200	x	$200x$
Pine	100	y	$100y$

   • The first purchase cost $31.20.
   The second purchase cost $78.
   $$50x + 90y = 31.20$$
   $$200x + 100y = 78$$

   Solution
   $$50x + 90y = 31.20$$
   $$200x + 100y = 78$$

   $$-4(50x + 90y) = -4(31.20)$$
   $$200x + 100y = 78$$

   $$-200x - 360y = -124.80$$
   $$200x + 100y = 78$$

   $$-260y = -46.80$$
   $$y = 0.18$$

   $$50x + 90y = 31.20$$
   $$50x + 90(0.18) = 31.20$$
   $$50x + 16.20 = 31.20$$
   $$50x = 15$$
   $$x = 0.30$$
   The cost of the pine is $.18 per foot.
   The cost of the redwood is $.30 per foot.

14. Strategy
   Cost of the cinnamon tea: x
   Cost of the spice tea: y
   First mixture:

	Amount	Cost	Total Value
Cinnamon	10	x	$10x$
Spice	5	y	$5y$

   Second mixture:

	Amount	Cost	Total Value
Cinnamon	12	x	$12x$
Spice	8	y	$8y$

   • The first mixture costs $40.
   The second mixture costs $54.
   $$10x + 5y = 40$$
   $$12x + 8y = 54$$

   Solution
   $$10x + 5y = 40$$
   $$12x + 8y = 54$$

   $$8(10x + 5y) = 8(40)$$
   $$-5(12x + 8y) = -5(54)$$

   $$80x + 40y = 320$$
   $$-60x - 40y = -270$$

   $$20x = 50$$
   $$x = 2.5$$

   $$10x + 5y = 40$$
   $$10(2.5) + 5y = 40$$
   $$25 + 5y = 40$$
   $$5y = 15$$
   $$y = 3$$
   The cost of the cinnamon tea is $2.50/lb.
   The cost of the spice tea is $3.00/lb.

15. Strategy
Cost per unit of electricity: x
Cost per unit of gas: y
First month:

	Amount	Rate	Total Value
Electricity	400	x	$400x$
Gas	120	y	$120y$

Second month:

	Amount	Rate	Total Value
Electricity	350	x	$350x$
Gas	200	y	$200y$

• The total cost for the first month was $147.20.
The total cost for the second month was $144.
$$400x + 120y = 147.20$$
$$350x + 200y = 144$$

Solution
$$400x + 120y = 147.20$$
$$350x + 200y = 144$$

$$-5(400x + 120y) = -5(147.20)$$
$$3(350x + 200y) = 3(144)$$

$$-2000x - 600y = -736$$
$$1050x + 600y = 432$$

$$-950x = -304$$
$$x = 0.32$$

$$400x + 120y = 147.20$$
$$400(0.32) + 120y = 147.20$$
$$128 + 120y = 147.20$$
$$120y = 19.2$$
$$y = 0.16$$

The cost per unit of gas is $.16.

16. Strategy
Cost per yard of nylon carpet: x
Cost per yard of wool carpet: y
First purchase:

	Amount	Unit Cost	Value
Nylon	20	x	$20x$
Wool	28	y	$28y$

Second purchase:

	Amount	Unit Cost	Value
Nylon	15	x	$15x$
Wool	20	y	$20y$

• The first purchase cost $1360.
The second purchase cost $990.
$$20x + 28y = 1360$$
$$15x + 20y = 990$$

Solution
$$20x + 28y = 1360$$
$$15x + 20y = 990$$

$$-3(20x + 28y) = -3(1360)$$
$$4(15x + 20y) = 4(990)$$

$$-60x - 84y = -4080$$
$$60x + 80y = 3960$$

$$-4y = -120$$
$$y = 30$$
The cost of the wool carpet is $30/yd.

17. Strategy
    Number of quarters in the bank: q
    Number of dimes in the bank: d
    Coins in the bank now:

Coin	Number	Value	Total Value
Quarter	q	25	$25q$
Dime	d	10	$10d$

    Coins in the bank if the quarters were dimes and the dimes were quarters:

Coin	Number	Value	Total Value
Quarter	d	25	$25d$
Dime	q	10	$10q$

    • The value of the quarters and dimes in the bank is $6.90.
    The value of the quarters and dimes in the bank would be $7.80.
    $$25q + 10d = 690$$
    $$10q + 25d = 780$$

    Solution
    $$25q + 10d = 690$$
    $$10q + 25d = 780$$

    $$5(25q + 10d) = 5(690)$$
    $$-2(10q + 25d) = -2(780)$$

    $$125q + 50d = 3450$$
    $$-20q - 50d = -1560$$

    $$105q = 1890$$
    $$q = 18$$
    There are 18 quarters in the bank.

18. Strategy
    Number of nickels in the bank: n
    Number of dimes in the bank: d
    Coins in the bank now:

Coin	Number	Value	Total Value
Nickel	n	5	$5n$
Dime	d	10	$10d$

    Coins in the bank if the nickels were dimes and the dimes were nickels:

Coin	Number	Value	Total Value
Nickel	d	5	$5d$
Dime	n	10	$10n$

    • The value of the nickels and dimes in the bank is $2.50.
    The value of the nickels and dimes in the bank would be $3.20.
    $$5n + 10d = 250$$
    $$10n + 5d = 320$$

    Solution
    $$5n + 10d = 250$$
    $$10n + 5d = 320$$

    $$-1(5n + 10d) = -1(250)$$
    $$2(10n + 5d) = 2(320)$$

    $$-5n - 10d = -250$$
    $$20n + 10d = 640$$

    $$15n = 390$$
    $$n = 26$$
    There are 26 nickels in the bank.

19. Strategy

Number of mountain bikes to be manufactured: t
Number of trail bikes to be manufactured: s
Cost of materials:

Type of Bicycle	Number	Cost	Total Cost
Mountain	t	70	$70t$
Trail	s	50	$50s$

Cost of labor:

Type of Bicycle	Number	Cost	Total Cost
Mountain	t	80	$80t$
Trail	s	40	$40s$

• The company has budgeted $2500 for material.
The company has budgeted $2600 for labor.
$70t + 50s = 2500$
$80t + 40s = 2600$

Solution
$70t + 50s = 2500$
$80t + 40s = 2600$

$4(70t + 50s) = 4(2500)$
$-5(80t + 40s) = -5(2600)$

$280t + 200s = 10,000$
$-400t - 200s = -13,000$

$-120t = -3000$
$t = 25$

The company plans to manufacture 25 mountain bikes during the week.

20. Strategy

Number of black-and-white monitors to be manufactured: b
Number of color monitors to be manufactured: c
Cost of materials:

Type of monitor	Number	Cost	Total Cost
B & W	b	40	$40b$
Color	c	160	$160c$

Cost of labor:

Type of monitor	Number	Cost	Total Cost
B & W	b	60	$60b$
Color	c	100	$100c$

• The company has budgeted $8400 for materials.
The company has budgeted $5600 for labor.
$40b + 160c = 8400$
$60b + 100c = 5600$

Solution
$40b + 160c = 8400$
$60b + 100c = 5600$

$6(40b + 160c) = 6(8400)$
$-4(60b + 100c) = -4(5600)$

$240b + 960c = 50,400$
$-240b - 400c = -22,400$

$560c = 28,000$
$c = 50$

The company plans to manufacture 50 color monitors during the week.

21. Strategy

Amount of the first powder to be used: x

Amount of the second powder to be used: y

Vitamin B_1:

	Amount	Percent	Quantity
1st powder	x	0.25	$0.25x$
2nd powder	y	0.15	$0.15y$

Vitamin B_2:

	Amount	Percent	Quantity
1st powder	x	0.15	$0.15x$
2nd powder	y	0.20	$0.20y$

• The mixture contains 117.5 mg of vitamin B_1.

The mixture contains 120 mg of vitamin B_2.

$0.25x + 0.15y = 117.5$

$0.15x + 0.20y = 120$

Solution

$0.25x + 0.15y = 117.5$

$0.15x + 0.20y = 120$

$-4(0.25x + 0.15y) = -4(117.5)$

$3(0.15x + 0.20y) = 3(120)$

$-1.0x - 0.60y = -470$

$0.45x + 0.60y = 360$

$-0.55x = -110$

$x = 200$

$0.25x + 0.15y = 117.5$

$0.25(200) + 0.15y = 117.5$

$50 + 0.15y = 117.5$

$0.15y = 67.5$

$y = 450$

The pharmacist should use 200 mg of the first powder and 450 mg of the second powder.

22. Strategy

Amount of first alloy to be used: x

Amount of second alloy to be used: y

Gold:

	Amount	Percent	Quantity
1st alloy	x	0.10	$0.10x$
2nd alloy	y	0.30	$0.30y$

Lead:

	Amount	Percent	Quantity
1st alloy	x	0.15	$0.15x$
2nd alloy	y	0.40	$0.40y$

• The resulting alloy contains 60 g of gold.

The resulting alloy contains 88 g of lead.

$0.10x + 0.30y = 60$

$0.15x + 0.40y = 88$

Solution

$0.10x + 0.30y = 60$

$0.15x + 0.40y = 88$

$3(0.10x + 0.30y) = 3(60)$

$-2(0.15x + 0.40y) = -2(88)$

$0.30x + 0.90y = 180$

$-0.30x - 0.80y = -176$

$0.10y = 4$

$y = 40$

$0.10x + 0.30y = 60$

$0.10x + 0.30(40) = 60$

$0.10x + 12 = 60$

$0.10x = 48$

$x = 480$

The chemist should use 480 g of the first alloy and 40 g of the second alloy.

23. Strategy

Cost of a Model II computer: x

Cost of a Model VI computer: y

Cost of a Model IX computer: z

First shipment:

Computer	Number	Cost	Total Cost
Model II	4	x	$4x$
Model VI	6	y	$6y$
Model IX	10	z	$10z$

Second shipment:

Computer	Number	Cost	Total Cost
Model II	8	x	$8x$
Model VI	3	y	$3y$
Model IX	5	z	$5z$

Third Shipment:

Computer	Number	Cost	Total Cost
Model II	2	x	$2x$
Model VI	9	y	$9y$
Model IX	5	z	$5z$

• The bill for the first shipment was $114,000.
The bill for the second shipment was $72,000.
The bill for the third shipment was $81,000.

$$4x + 6y + 10z = 114,000$$
$$8x + 3y + 5z = 72,000$$
$$2x + 9y + 5z = 81,000$$

Solution

$$4x + 6y + 10z = 114,000$$
$$8x + 3y + 5z = 72,000$$
$$2x + 9y + 5z = 81,000$$

$$4x + 6y + 10z = 114,000$$
$$-2(8x + 3y + 5z) = -2(72,000)$$

$$4x + 6y + 10z = 114,000$$
$$-16x - 6y - 10z = -144,000$$

$$-12x = -30,000$$
$$x = 2500$$

$$4x + 6y + 10z = 114,000$$
$$-2(2x + 9y + 5z) = -2(81,000)$$

$$4x + 6y + 10z = 114,000$$
$$-4x - 18y - 10z = 162,000$$

$$-12y = -48,000$$
$$y = 4000$$

$$4x + 6y + 10z = 114,000$$
$$4(2500) + 6(4000) + 10z = 114,000$$
$$10,000 + 24,000 + 10z = 114,000$$
$$34,000 + 10z = 114,000$$
$$10z = 80,000$$
$$z = 8000$$

The manufacturer charges $2500 for a Model II, $4000 for a Model VI, and $8000 for a Model IX computer.

24. Strategy

Cost of one blanket: b

Cost of one cot: c

Cost of one lantern: l

First week:

Item	Number	Cost	Total Cost
blanket	15	b	$15b$
cot	5	c	$5c$
lantern	10	l	$10l$

Second week:

Item	Number	Cost	Total Cost
blanket	20	b	$20b$
cot	10	c	$10c$
lantern	15	l	$15l$

Third week:

Item	Number	Cost	Total Cost
blanket	10	b	$10b$
cot	15	c	$15c$
lantern	5	l	$5l$

• The bill for the first week was $1250.

The bill for the second week was $2000.

The bill for the third week was $1625.

$$15b + 5c + 10l = 1250$$
$$20b + 10c + 15l = 2000$$
$$10b + 15c + 5l = 1625$$

Solution

$$15b + 5c + 10l = 1250$$
$$20b + 10c + 15l = 2000$$
$$10b + 15c + 5l = 1625$$

$$-2(15b + 5c + 10l) = -2(1250)$$
$$20b + 10c + 15l = 2000$$

$$-30b - 10c - 20l = -2500$$
$$20b + 10c + 15l = 2000$$

$$-10b - 5l = -500$$

$$-3(15b + 5c + 10l) = -3(1250)$$
$$10b + 15c + 5l = 1625$$

$$-45b - 15c - 30l = -3750$$
$$10b + 15c + 5l = 1625$$
$$-35b - 25l = -2125$$

$$-5(-10b - 5l) = -5(-500)$$
$$-35b - 25l = -2125$$

$$50b + 25l = 2500$$
$$-35b - 25l = -2125$$

$$15b = 375$$
$$b = 25$$

$$-10b - 5l = -500$$
$$-10(25) - 5l = -500$$
$$-250 - 5l = -500$$
$$-5l = -250$$
$$l = 50$$

$$15b + 5c + 10l = 1250$$
$$15(25) + 5c + 10(50) = 1250$$
$$375 + 5c + 500 = 1250$$
$$5c + 875 = 1250$$
$$5c = 375$$
$$c = 75$$

Each blanket costs $25, a cot costs $75, and a lantern costs $50.

25. Strategy
Amount earning 9% interest: x
Amount earning 7% interest: y
Amount earning 5% interest: z

Interest Rate	Amount deposited	Amount earned
9%	x	$0.09x$
7%	y	$0.07y$
5%	z	$0.05z$

• The total amount deposited is $18,000.
The total interest earned is $1340.
$$x+y+z=18,000$$
$$x=2z$$
$$0.09x+0.07y+0.05z=1340$$

Solution
$$x+y+z=18,000$$
$$x=2z$$
$$0.09x+0.07y+0.05z=1340$$

$$x+y+z=18,000$$
$$2z+y+z=18,000$$
$$3z+y=18,000$$

$$0.09x+0.07y+0.05z=1340$$
$$0.09(2z)+0.07y+0.05z=1340$$
$$0.18z+0.07y+0.05z=1340$$
$$0.23z+0.07y=1340$$

$$0.23z+0.07y=1340$$
$$-0.07(3z+y)=-0.07(18,000)$$

$$0.23z+0.07y=1340$$
$$-0.21z-0.07y=-1260$$
$$0.02z=80$$
$$z=4000$$

$$x=2z$$
$$x=2(4000)$$
$$x=8000$$

$$x+y+z=18,000$$
$$8000+y+4000=18,000$$
$$12,000+y=18,000$$
$$y=6000$$

The amounts deposited in each account are $8000 at 9% interest, $6000 at 7% interest, and $4000 at 5% interest.

26. Strategy
Amount earning 9% interest: x
Amount earning 6% interest: y
Amount earning 4% interest: z

Interest Rate	Amount deposited	Amount earned
9%	x	$0.09x$
6%	y	$0.06y$
4%	z	$0.04z$

• The total amount deposited is $15,000.
The total interest earned is $980.
$$x+y+z=15,000$$
$$y=z+2000$$
$$0.09x+0.06y+0.04z=980$$

Solution
$$x+y+z=15,000$$
$$y=z+2000$$
$$0.09x+0.06y+0.04z=980$$

$$x+y+z=15,000$$
$$x+(z+2000)+z=15,000$$
$$x+2z+2000=15,000$$
$$x+2z=13,000$$

$$0.09x+0.06y+0.04z=980$$
$$0.09x+0.06(z+2000)+0.04z=980$$
$$0.09x+0.06z+120+0.04z=980$$
$$0.09x+0.1z+120=980$$
$$0.09x+0.1z=860$$

$$x+2z=13,000$$
$$-20(0.09x+0.1z)=-20(860)$$

$$x+2z=13,000$$
$$-1.8x-2z=-17,200$$

$$-0.8x=-4200$$
$$x=5250$$

$$x+2z=13,000$$
$$5250+2z=13,000$$
$$2z=7750$$
$$z=3875$$

$$y=z+2000$$
$$y=3875+2000$$
$$y=5875$$

The amounts deposited in each account are $5250 at 9% interest, $5875 at 6% interest, and $3875 at 4% interest.

27. Strategy

The sum of d_1 and d_3 is equal to the length of the rod, which is 15 in.

$w_1 = 5$, $w_2 = 1$, and $w_3 = 3$ so the equation that ensures the mobile will balance is $5d_1 = d_2 + 3d_3$.

$d_1 + d_3 = 15$
$5d_1 = d_2 + 3d_3$
$d_3 = 3d_2$

Solution

$d_1 + d_3 = 15$
$5d_1 = d_2 + 3d_3$
$d_3 = 3d_2$

$5d_1 = d_2 + 3d_3$
$5d_1 = d_2 + 3(3d_2)$
$5d_1 = d_2 + 9d_2$
$5d_1 = 10d_2$
$5d_1 - 10d_2 = 0$

$d_1 + d_3 = 15$
$d_1 + 3d_2 = 15$

$5d_1 - 10d_2 = 0$
$-5(d_1 + 3d_2) = -5(15)$

$5d_1 - 10d_2 = 0$
$-5d_1 - 15d_2 = -75$
$-25d_2 = -75$
$d_2 = 3$

$d_3 = 3d_2$
$d_3 = 3(3)$
$d_3 = 9$

$d_1 + d_3 = 15$
$d_1 + 9 = 15$
$d_1 = 6$

The distances are
$d_1 = 6$ in., $d_2 = 3$ in., and $d_3 = 9$ in.

28. Strategy

The sum of d_1 and d_3 is equal to the length of the rod, which is 20 in.

$w_1 = 3$, $w_2 = 2$, and $w_3 = 3$ so the equation that ensures the mobile will balance is
$3d_1 + 2d_2 = 3d_3$
$d_1 + d_3 = 20$
$d_3 = 2d_2$

Solution

$d_1 + d_3 = 20$
$d_1 + 2d_2 = 20$
$d_1 = 20 - 2d_2$

$3d_1 + 2d_2 = 3d_3$
$3d_1 + 2d_2 = 3(2d_2)$
$3d_1 + 2d_2 = 6d_2$
$3d_1 = 4d_2$
$d_1 = \frac{4}{3}d_2$

$20 - 2d_2 = \frac{4}{3}d_2$
$20 = \frac{10}{3}d_2$
$d_2 = 6$

$d_3 = 2d_2$
$d_3 = 2(6)$
$d_3 = 12$

$d_1 + d_3 = 20$
$d_1 + 12 = 20$
$d_1 = 8$

The distances are $d_1 = 8$ in., $d_2 = 6$ in., and $d_3 = 12$ in.

29. Strategy

Number of nickels in the bank: n
Number of dimes in the bank: d
Number of quarters in the bank: q
Coins in the bank:

Coin	Number	Value	Total Value
Nickel	n	5	$5n$
Dime	d	10	$10d$
Quarter	q	25	$25q$

• The value of the nickels, dimes, and quarters in the bank is 200 cents.

$$n+d+q=19$$
$$5n+10d+25q=200$$
$$n=2d$$

Solution

$$n+d+q=19$$
$$5n+10d+25q=200$$
$$n=2d$$

$$n+d+q=19$$
$$2d+d+q=19$$
$$3d+q=19$$

$$5n+10d+25q=200$$
$$5(2d)+10d+25q=200$$
$$10d+10d+25q=200$$
$$20d+25q=200$$

$$-25(3d+q)=-25(19)$$
$$20d+25q=200$$

$$-75d-25q=-475$$
$$20d+25q=200$$

$$-55d=-275$$
$$d=5$$

$$n=2d$$
$$n=10$$

$$n+d+q=19$$
$$10+5+q=19$$
$$15+q=19$$
$$q=4$$

There are 10 nickels, 5 dimes, and 4 quarters in the bank.

30. Strategy

Number of nickels in the bank: n
Number of dimes in the bank: d
Number of quarters in the bank: q
Coins in the bank now:

Coin	Number	Value	Total Value
Nickel	n	5	$5n$
Dime	d	10	$10d$
Quarter	q	25	$25q$

Coins in the bank if nickels were dimes and dimes were nickels:

Coin	Number	Value	Total Value
Nickel	d	5	$5d$
Dime	n	10	$10n$
Quarter	q	25	$25q$

Coins in the bank if quarters were dimes and dimes were quarters:

Coin	Number	Value	Total Value
Nickel	n	5	$5n$
Dime	q	10	$10q$
Quarter	d	25	$25d$

• The value of the nickels, dimes, and quarters in the bank is 400 cents.
• The value of the nickels, dimes, and quarters would be 375 cents if the nickels were dimes and dimes were nickels.
• The value of the nickels, dimes, and quarters would be 625 cents if the quarters were dimes and the dimes were quarters.

$$5n+10d+25q=400$$
$$10n+5d+25q=375$$
$$5n+25d+10q=625$$

Solution

$$5n + 10d + 25q = 400$$
$$10n + 5d + 25q = 375$$
$$5n + 25d + 10q = 625$$

$$-2(5n + 10d + 25q) = -2(400)$$
$$10n + 5d + 25q = 375$$

$$-10n - 20d - 50q = -800$$
$$10n + 5d + 25q = 375$$

$$-15d - 25q = -425$$

$$10n + 5d + 25q = 375$$
$$-2(5n + 25d + 10q) = -2(625)$$

$$10n + 5d + 25q = 375$$
$$-10n - 50d - 20q = -1250$$

$$-45d + 5q = -875$$

$$-3(-15d - 25q) = -3(-425)$$
$$-45d + 5q = -875$$

$$45d + 75q = 1275$$
$$-45d + 5q = -875$$
$$80q = 400$$
$$q = 5$$

$$-45d + 5q = -875$$
$$-45d + 5(5) = -875$$
$$-45d + 25 = -875$$
$$-45d = -900$$
$$d = 20$$

$$5n + 10d + 25q = 400$$
$$5n + 10(20) + 25(5) = 400$$
$$5n + 200 + 125 = 400$$
$$5n + 325 = 400$$
$$5n = 75$$
$$n = 15$$

There are 15 nickels, 20 dimes, and 5 quarters in the bank.

31. Strategy

Amount invested at 9%: x
Amount invested at 12%: y
Amount invested at 8%: z

Interest Rate	Amount deposited	Amount earned
9%	x	$0.09x$
12%	y	$0.12y$
8%	z	$0.08z$

• The total amount invested is \$33,000.
$$x + y + z = 33,000$$
$$0.09x + 0.12y + 0.08z = 3290$$
$$y = x + z - 5000$$

Solution

$$x + y + z = 33,000$$
$$x + (x + z - 5000) + z = 33,000$$
$$2x + 2z - 5000 = 33,000$$
$$2x + 2z = 38,000$$

$$0.09x + 0.12y + 0.08z = 3290$$
$$0.09x + 0.12(x + z - 5000) + 0.08z = 3290$$
$$0.09x + 0.12x + 0.12z - 600 + 0.08z = 3290$$
$$0.21x + 0.2z - 600 = 3290$$
$$0.21x + 0.2z = 3890$$

$$2x + 2z = 38,000$$
$$-10(0.21x + 0.2z) = -10(3890)$$

$$2x + 2z = 38,000$$
$$-2.1x - 2z = -38,900$$
$$-0.1x = -900$$
$$x = 9000$$

$$2x + 2z = 38,000$$
$$2(9000) + 2z = 38,000$$
$$18,000 + 2z = 38,000$$
$$2z = 20,000$$
$$z = 10,000$$

$$y = x + z - 5000$$
$$y = 9000 + 10,000 - 5000$$
$$y = 14,000$$

The amounts invested are \$9000 at 9% interest, \$14,000 at 12% interest, and \$10,000 at 8% interest.

32. Strategy

Number of elementary students: g

Number of secondary students: s

Number of college students: c

$$g + s + c = 69$$
$$c = s + 1$$
$$g + 7 = s + c$$

Solution

$$g + s + c = 69$$
$$c = s + 1$$
$$g = s + c + 7$$

$$g + s + c = 69$$
$$-s + c = 1$$
$$g - s - c = 7$$

$$g + s + c = 69$$
$$g - s - c = 7$$
$$2g = 76$$
$$g = 38$$

$$38 + s + c = 69$$
$$-s + c = 1$$

$$s + c = 31$$
$$-s + c = 1$$
$$2c = 32$$
$$c = 16$$

$$c = s + 1$$
$$16 = s + 1$$
$$15 = s$$

There are 38 million students in elementary school, 15 million students in secondary school and 16 million students in college.

33. Strategy

Number of Las Vegas, Nevada hotels: n

Number of Orlando, Florida hotels: f

Number of Los Angeles-Long Beach, California hotels: c

$$n + f + c = 1268$$
$$c = n + f + 38$$
$$n = f - 85$$

Solution

$$n + f + c = 1268$$
$$c = n + f + 38$$
$$n = f - 85$$

$$c = n + f + 38$$
$$c = (f - 85) + f + 38$$
$$c = 2f - 47$$

$$n + f + c = 1268$$
$$(f - 85) + f + (2f - 47) = 1268$$
$$4f - 132 = 1268$$
$$4f = 1400$$
$$f = 350$$

$$n = f - 85$$
$$n = 350 - 85$$
$$n = 265$$

$$n + f + c = 1268$$
$$265 + 350 + c = 1268$$
$$c + 615 = 1268$$
$$c = 653$$

There are 265 hotels in Las Vegas, 350 hotels in Orlando and 653 hotels in Los Angeles-Long Beach.

34. Strategy
   Numerical job decline for farmers: f
   Numerical job decline for
   typists/word processors: t
   Numerical job decline for clerks: c
   $f + t + c = 663$
   $\quad f = t + c - 117$
   $\quad c = f - 95$

Solution
   $f + t + c = 663$
   $\quad f = t + c - 117$
   $\quad c = f - 95$

   $f = t + c - 117$
   $f = t + (f - 95) - 117$
   $f = t + f - 212$
   $t = 212$

   $\qquad f + t + c = 663$
   $f + 212 + f - 95 = 663$
   $\quad 2f + 117 = 663$
   $\qquad 2f = 546$
   $\qquad f = 273$

   $c = f - 95$
   $c = 273 - 95$
   $c = 178$
   The numerical job decline for farmers will be
   273 thousand, 212 thousand for
   typists/word processors, and 178 thousand for
   clerks.

Applying Concepts 4.4

35. Strategy
   Write and solve a system of equations using x
   and y to represent the measures of the two
   angles.

Solution
   $x + y = 90$
   $\quad y = 8x + 9$

   $x + (8x + 9) = 90$
   $\quad 9x + 9 = 90$
   $\quad 9x = 81$
   $\quad x = 9$

   $x + y = 90$
   $9 + y = 90$
   $\quad y = 81$
   The measures of the two angles are 9 and
   81 degrees.

36. Strategy
   Write and solve a system of equations using x
   and y to represent the measures of the two
   angles.

Solution
   $x + y = 180$
   $\quad y = 3x + 40$

   $x + (3x + 40) = 180$
   $\quad 4x + 40 = 180$
   $\quad 4x = 140$
   $\quad x = 35$

   $x + y = 180$
   $35 + y = 180$
   $\quad y = 145$
   The measures of the two angles are 35 and
   145 degrees.

37. Strategy

• Number of nickels in the bank: n
Number of dimes in the bank: d
Number of quarters in the bank: q
Coins in the bank now:

Coin	Number	Value	Total Value
Nickel	n	5	$5n$
Dime	d	10	$10d$
Quarter	q	25	$25q$

Coins in the bank if nickels were dimes and dimes were nickels:

Coin	Number	Value	Total Value
Nickel	d	5	$5d$
Dime	n	10	$10n$
Quarter	q	25	$25q$

Coins in the bank if quarters were dimes and dimes were quarters:

Coin	Number	Value	Total Value
Nickel	n	5	$5n$
Dime	q	10	$10q$
Quarter	d	25	$25d$

• The value of the nickels, dimes, and quarters in the bank is 350 cents.
• The value of the nickels, dimes, and quarters would be 425 cents if the nickels were dimes and the dimes were nickels.
• The value of the nickels, dimes, and quarters would be 425 cents if the dimes were quarters and the quarters were dimes.

Solution

$5n + 10d + 25q = 350$
$10n + 5d + 25q = 425$
$5n + 25d + 10q = 425$

$5n + 10d + 25q = 350$
$-(5n + 25d + 10q) = -(425)$

$5n + 10d + 25q = 350$
$-5n - 25d - 10q = -425$

$-15d + 15q = -75$

$-2(5n + 10d + 25q) = -2(350)$
$10n + 5d + 25q = 425$

$-10n - 20d - 50q = -700$
$10n + 5d + 25q = 425$

$-15d - 25q = -275$

$-15d - 25q = -275$
$-(-15d + 15q) = -(-75)$

$-15d - 25q = -275$
$15d - 15q = 75$
$-40q = -200$
$q = 5$

$-15d + 15q = -75$
$-15d + 15(5) = -75$
$-15d + 75 = -75$
$-15d = -150$
$d = 10$

$5n + 10d + 25q = 350$
$5n + 10(10) + 25(5) = 350$
$5n + 100 + 125 = 350$
$5n + 225 = 350$
$5n = 125$
$n = 25$

There are 25 nickels, 10 dimes, and 5 quarters in the bank.

38. a. No. The slopes of all the equations are positive.

b. Because the slope of the line is greatest for the Iceland ($m = 19.9$), we know that the payments are increasing most rapidly in the Iceland. Because the slope of the line is smallest for Ireland ($m = 5.5$), we know that the payments are increasing least rapidly in Ireland.

c. In 1987, Korea's per capita, out-of-pocket, health care payments were $154.

d. A graphing utility can be used to find the point of intersection for each system of equations. The abscissa is the year, and the ordinate is the per capita spending on health care.

    (1) The per capita spending on health care was the same in Australia and Denmark in 1984. The per capita spending on health care during that year was $126.

    (2) The per capita spending on health care was the same in Canada and Finland in 1987. The per capita spending on health care during that year was $172.

    (3) The per capita spending on health care was the same in New Zealand and the United Kingdom in 1983. The per capita spending on health care during that year was $53.

39. The article "Matrix Mathematics: How to Win at Monopoly" is a report on an attempt to determine an optimal strategy for playing Monopoly. The technique was to solve a system of 123 equations with 123 variables. One of the conclusions of the analysis is that the B&O railroad is the railroad on which a player is most likely to land.

Section 4.5

Concept Review 4.5

1. Sometimes true
The solution set of a system of inequalities can be a portion of the plane or the empty set.

2. Sometimes true
The solution set may be a portion of the plane.

3. Always true

Objective 4.5.1 Exercises

1. Check the ordered pair $(5, 1)$ in the system of inequalities

$$
\begin{array}{c|c}
2(5)-1 & 4 \\
10-1 & 4 \\
9 & 4
\end{array}
$$

$9 > 4$
The ordered pair $(5, 1)$ is not a solution.

Check the ordered pair $(-3, -5)$ in the system of inequalities.

$$
\begin{array}{c|c}
2(-3)-(-5) & 4 \\
-6+5 & 4 \\
-1 & 4
\end{array}
\qquad
\begin{array}{c|c}
-3-3(-5) & 6 \\
-3+15 & 6 \\
12 & 6
\end{array}
$$

$-1 < 4$ and $12 \geq 6$
The ordered pair $(-3, -5)$ is a solution.

2. Check the ordered pair $(-2, 3)$ in the system of inequalities.

$$
\begin{array}{c|c}
3(-2)-2(3) & 6 \\
-6-6 & 6 \\
-12 & 6
\end{array}
$$

$-12 < 6$
The ordered pair $(-2, 3)$ is not a solution.

Check the ordered pair $(3, -2)$ in the system of inequalities.

$$
\begin{array}{c|c}
3(3)-2(-2) & 6 \\
9+4 & 6 \\
13 & 6
\end{array}
\qquad
\begin{array}{c|c}
3+-2 & 5 \\
1 & 5
\end{array}
$$

$13 \geq 6$ and $1 < 5$
The ordered pair $(3, -2)$ is a solution.

3. The solution set of a system of linear inequalities in two variables is the intersection of the solutions sets of the individual inequalities.

4. The slopes of the lines must be equal.

5. Solve each inequality for y.

$$
\begin{array}{ll}
x-y \geq 3 & x+y \leq 5 \\
-y \geq -x+3 & y \leq -x+5 \\
y \leq x-3 &
\end{array}
$$

6. Solve each inequality for y.

$$
\begin{array}{ll}
2x-y < 4 & x+y < 5 \\
-y < -2x+4 & y < -x+5 \\
y > 2x-4 &
\end{array}
$$

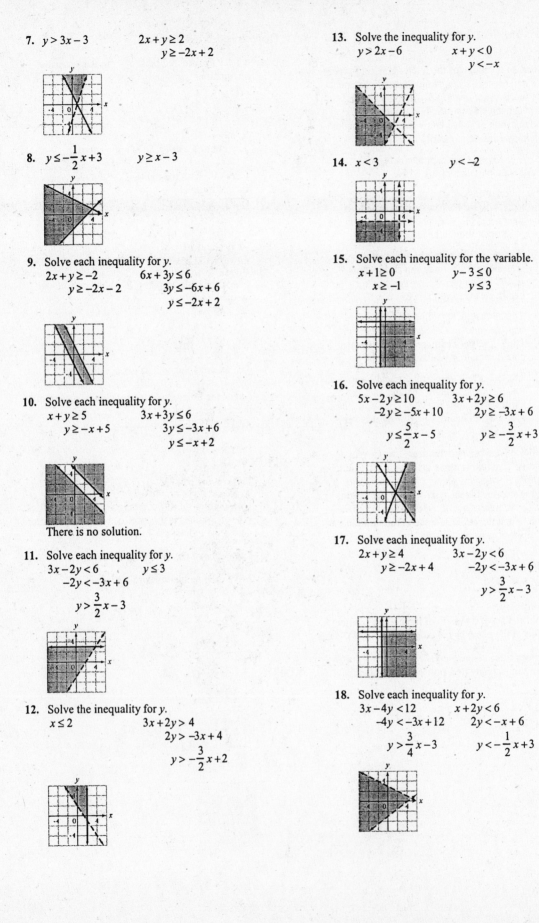

7. $y > 3x - 3$ $2x + y \geq 2$
$y \geq -2x + 2$

8. $y \leq -\dfrac{1}{2}x + 3$ $y \geq x - 3$

9. Solve each inequality for y.
$2x + y \geq -2$ $6x + 3y \leq 6$
$y \geq -2x - 2$ $3y \leq -6x + 6$
$y \leq -2x + 2$

10. Solve each inequality for y.
$x + y \geq 5$ $3x + 3y \leq 6$
$y \geq -x + 5$ $3y \leq -3x + 6$
$y \leq -x + 2$

There is no solution.

11. Solve each inequality for y.
$3x - 2y < 6$ $y \leq 3$
$-2y < -3x + 6$
$y > \dfrac{3}{2}x - 3$

12. Solve the inequality for y.
$x \leq 2$ $3x + 2y > 4$
$2y > -3x + 4$
$y > -\dfrac{3}{2}x + 2$

13. Solve the inequality for y.
$y > 2x - 6$ $x + y < 0$
$y < -x$

14. $x < 3$ $y < -2$

15. Solve each inequality for the variable.
$x + 1 \geq 0$ $y - 3 \leq 0$
$x \geq -1$ $y \leq 3$

16. Solve each inequality for y.
$5x - 2y \geq 10$ $3x + 2y \geq 6$
$-2y \geq -5x + 10$ $2y \geq -3x + 6$
$y \leq \dfrac{5}{2}x - 5$ $y \geq -\dfrac{3}{2}x + 3$

17. Solve each inequality for y.
$2x + y \geq 4$ $3x - 2y < 6$
$y \geq -2x + 4$ $-2y < -3x + 6$
$y > \dfrac{3}{2}x - 3$

18. Solve each inequality for y.
$3x - 4y < 12$ $x + 2y < 6$
$-4y < -3x + 12$ $2y < -x + 6$
$y > \dfrac{3}{4}x - 3$ $y < -\dfrac{1}{2}x + 3$

19. Solve each inequality for y.

$x - 2y \le 6$ $\qquad$ $2x + 3y \le 6$

$-2y \le -x + 6$ $\qquad$ $3y \le -2x + 6$

$y \ge \dfrac{1}{2}x - 3$ $\qquad$ $y \le -\dfrac{2}{3}x + 2$

20. Solve each inequality for y.

$x - 3y > 6$ $\qquad$ $2x + y > 5$

$-3y > -x + 6$ $\qquad$ $y > -2x + 5$

$y < \dfrac{1}{3}x - 2$

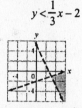

21. Solve each inequality for y.

$x - 2y \le 4$ $\qquad$ $3x + 2y \le 8$

$-2y \le -x + 4$ $\qquad$ $2y \le -3x + 8$

$y \ge \dfrac{1}{2}x - 2$ $\qquad$ $y \le -\dfrac{3}{2}x + 4$

$y \ge \dfrac{1}{2}x - 2$

$y \le -\dfrac{3}{2}x + 4$

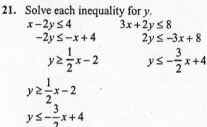

22. Solve each inequality for y.

$3x - 2y < 0$ $\qquad$ $5x + 3y > 9$

$2y < -3x$ $\qquad$ $3y > -5x + 9$

$y > \dfrac{3}{2}x$ $\qquad$ $y > -\dfrac{5}{3}x + 3$

$y > \dfrac{3}{2}x$

$y > -\dfrac{5}{3}x + 3$

Applying Concepts 4.5

23. Solve each inequality for y.

$2x + 3y \le 15$ $\qquad$ $3x - y \le 6$

$3y \le -2x + 15$ $\qquad$ $-y \le -3x + 6$

$y \le -\dfrac{2}{3}x + 5$ $\qquad$ $y \ge 3x - 6$

$y \le -\dfrac{2}{3}x + 5$

$y \ge 3x - 6$

$y \ge 0$

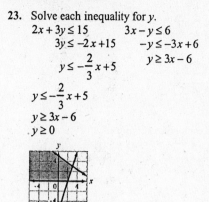

24. Solve each inequality for y.

$x + y \le 6$ $\qquad$ $x - y \le 2$

$y \le -x + 6$ $\qquad$ $-y \le -x + 2$

$\qquad\qquad$ $y \ge x - 2$

$y \le -x + 6$

$y \ge x - 2$

$x \ge 0$

25. Solve each inequality for y.

$x - y \le 5$ $\qquad$ $2x - y \ge 6$ $\qquad$ $y \ge 0$

$-y \le -x + 5$ $\qquad$ $-y \ge -2x + 6$

$y \ge x - 5$ $\qquad$ $y \le 2x - 6$

26. Solve each inequality for y.

$x - 3y \le 6$ $\qquad$ $5x - 2y \ge 4$ $\qquad$ $y \ge 0$

$-3y \le -x + 6$ $\qquad$ $-2y \ge -5x + 4$

$y \ge \dfrac{1}{3}x - 2$ $\qquad$ $y \le \dfrac{5}{2}x - 2$

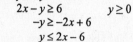

27. Solve each inequality for y.

$$2x - y \le 4 \qquad 3x + y < 1 \qquad y \le 0$$
$$-y \le -2x + 4 \qquad y < 1 - 3x$$
$$y \ge 2x - 4$$

28. Solve each inequality for y.

$$x - y \le 4 \qquad 2x + 3y > 6 \qquad x \ge 0$$
$$-y \le -x + 4 \qquad 3y > -2x + 6$$
$$y \ge x - 4 \qquad y > -\frac{2}{3}x + 2$$

Focus on Problem Solving

1.

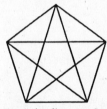

From the diagram, 5 teams will require 10 games in which every team plays every other team once.

2. The table of results is reproduced here for up to five teams.

Number of teams	Number of Games	Possible Pattern
1	0	1
2	1	0 + 1
3	3	1 + 2
4	6	1 + 2 + 3
5	10	1 + 2 + 3 + 4

Note the pattern. For n teams, the number of games is the sum of the first $n - 1$ whole numbers.

3. Assuming that the pattern holds, the number of games scheduled for 15 teams is
Number of games = $1 + 2 + 3 + 4 + 5 + 6 + 7 + 8 + 9 + 10 + 11 + 12 + 13 + 14 = 105$
If 15 teams are to play each other once, 105 games must be scheduled.

4. By continuing this reasoning, Team C had already played Team A and Team B, so there are 12 teams left for Team C to play. Consequently, you must schedule at least $14 + 13 + 12$ games. Continuing with this argument, when we get to the two last teams, there will be 1 game left to play. Therefore, the total number of games to be played is $14 + 13 + 12 + 11 + 10 + 9 + 8 + 7 + 6 + 5 + 4 + 3 + 2 + 1 = 105$. This is the same result obtained in Exercise 3.

5. Answers will vary.

6. For n teams, the total number of games that must be scheduled is the sum of the first $n - 1$ triangular numbers.

Projects and Group Activities

Using a Graphing Calculator to Solve a System of Equations

1. Cost to make bread at home: $190 + 0.95x$
Cost to buy bread at store: $1.98x$
Y1 = 1.98X
Y2 = 190 + 0.95X
Xmin = 0, Xmax = 250
Ymin = 0, Ymax = 500
X = 185 Y = 366.3
The break even point is 185 loaves.

2. Cost to use wash clothes at home: $295 + 0.25x$
Cost to use wash clothes at laundromat: $1.75x$
Y1 = 1.75X
Y2 = 295 + 0.25X
Xmin = 0, Xmax = 300
Ymin = 0, Ymax = 500
X = 197 Y = 344.5
The break even point is 197 loads.

3. a. Cost to use dry clothes at home: $260 + 0.40x$
Cost to use dry clothes at laundromat: $1.75x$
$Y1 = 1.75X$
$Y2 = 260 + 0.40X$
Xmin = 0, Xmax = 250
Ymin = 0, Ymax = 400
X = 193 Y = 337.04
The break even point is 193 loads

b. The y-coordinate is approximately 337.04.
This is the cost of doing approximately 193
loads of clothes either at the laundromat or
after purchasing the dryer.

4. a. Interest earned at 6.25%: $0.0625(7500 - x)$
Interest earned at 5.75%: $0.0575x$
$Y1 = 0.0575X$
$Y2 = 0.0625(7500 - X)$
Xmin = 0, Xmax = 4000
Ymin = 0, Ymax = 400
X = 3906.25 Y = 224.61
$7500 - x = 7500 - 3906.25 = 3593.75$
There must be $3593.75 at 6.25% and
$3906.25 at 5.75%.

b. The y-coordinate is approximately 224.61.
This is the amount of interest earned on each
account if the money is invested such that
both accounts earn the same amount of
interest.

Solving a First-Degree Equation with a Graphing Calculator

1. $3x - 1 = 5x + 1$
$y = 3x - 1$
$y = 5x + 1$

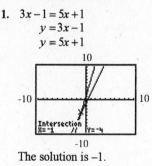

The solution is -1.

2. $3x + 2 = 4$
$y = 3x + 2$
$y = 4$

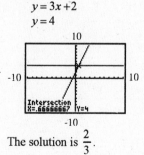

The solution is $\dfrac{2}{3}$.

3. $3 + 2(2x - 4) = 5(x - 3)$
$y = 3 + 2(2x - 4)$
$y = 5(x - 3)$

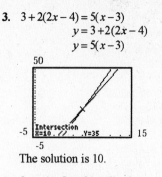

The solution is 10.

4. $2x - 4 = 5x - 3(x + 2) + 2$
$y = 2x - 4$
$y = 5x - 3(x + 2) + 2$

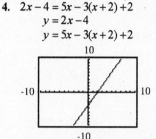

The solution is all real numbers.

5. Simplify the right side of the equation.
$5x - 3(x + 2) + 2 = 5x - 3x - 6 + 2$
$\qquad\qquad\qquad\qquad = 2x - 4$
Problem 4 relates to an identity since any
replacement for x will result in a true equation.

6. $2x - 10 = 1.8x + 3.6$
$y = 2x - 10$
$y = 1.8x + 3.6$
Use the viewing window
[67.5, 68.5] by [123, 127].

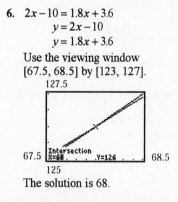

The solution is 68.

Chapter Review Exercises

1. (1) $2x - 6y = 15$
(2) $x = 3y + 8$
Substitute $3y + 8$ for x in equation (1).
$2(3y + 8) - 6y = 15$
$\quad 6y + 16 - 6y = 15$
$\qquad\qquad\quad 16 = 15$
This is not a true equation. The lines are parallel
and the system is inconsistent.

2. (1) $3x + 12y = 18$

(2) $x + 4y = 6$

Solve equation (2) for x.

$x + 4y = 6$

$x = -4y + 6$

Substitute into equation (1).

$3x + 12y = 18$

$3(-4y + 6) + 12y = 18$

$-12y + 18 + 12y = 18$

$18 = 18$

This is a true equation. The equations are dependent. The solutions are the ordered pairs $\left(x, -\frac{1}{4}x + \frac{3}{2} \right)$.

3. (1) $3x + 2y = 2$

(2) $x + y = 3$

Eliminate y. Multiply equation (2) by -2 and add to equation (1).

$3x + 2y = 2$

$-2(x + y) = 3(-2)$

$3x + 2y = 2$

$-2x - 2y = -6$

Add the equations.

$x = -4$

Replace x in equation (2).

$x + y = 3$

$-4 + y = 3$

$y = 7$

The solution is $(-4, 7)$.

4. (1) $5x - 15y = 30$

(2) $x - 3y = 6$

Eliminate x. Multiply equation (2) by -5 and add to equation (1).

$5x - 15y = 30$

$-5(x - 3y) = 6(-5)$

$5x - 15y = 30$

$-5x + 15y = -30$

Add the equations.

$0 = 0$

This is a true equation. The equations are dependent. The solutions are the ordered pairs $\left(x, \frac{1}{3}x - 2 \right)$.

5. (1) $3x + y = 13$

(2) $2y + 3z = 5$

(3) $x + 2z = 11$

Eliminate y. Multiply equation (1) by -2 and add to equation (2).

$-2(3x + y) = 13(-2)$

$2y + 3z = 5$

$-6x - 2y = -26$

$2y + 3z = 5$

(4) $-6x + 3z = -21$

Multiply equation (3) by 6 and add to equation (4).

$6(x + 2z) = 6(11)$

$-6x + 3z = -21$

$6x + 12z = 66$

$-6x + 3z = -21$

$15z = 45$

$z = 3$

Replace z by 3 in equation (3).

$x + 2z = 11$

$x + 2(3) = 11$

$x + 6 = 11$

$x = 5$

Replace x by 5 in equation (1).

$3x + y = 13$

$3(5) + y = 13$

$15 + y = 13$

$y = -2$

The solution is $(5, -2, 3)$.

6. (1) $3x - 4y - 2z = 17$

(2) $4x - 3y + 5z = 5$

(3) $5x - 5y + 3z = 14$

Eliminate z. Multiply equation (1) by 5 and equation (2) by 2 and add the new equations.

$5(3x - 4y - 2z) = 17(5)$
$2(4x - 3y + 5z) = 5(2)$

$15x - 20y - 10z = 85$
$8x - 6y + 10z = 10$

(4) $23x - 26y = 95$

Multiply equation (1) by 3 and equation (3) by 2 and add the new equations.

$3(3x - 4y - 2z) = (17)3$
$2(5x - 5y + 3z) = (14)2$

$9x - 12y - 6z = 51$
$10x - 10y + 6z = 28$

(5) $19x - 22y = 79$

Multiply equation (4) by -11 and equation (5) by 13 and add the new equations.

$-11(23x - 26y) = 95(-11)$
$13(19x - 22y) = 79(13)$

$-253x + 286y = -1045$
$247x - 286y = 1027$

$-6x = -18$
$x = 3$

Substitute x for 3 in equation (4).

$23x - 26y = 95$
$23(3) - 26y = 95$
$69 - 26y = 95$
$-26y = 26$
$y = -1$

Substitute x by 3 and y by -1 in equation (1).

$3x - 4y - 2z = 17$
$3(3) - 4(-1) - 2z = 17$
$9 + 4 - 2z = 17$
$-2z = 4$
$z = -2$

The solution is $(3, -1, -2)$.

7. $\begin{vmatrix} 6 & 1 \\ 2 & 5 \end{vmatrix} = 6(5) - 2(1) = 30 - 2 = 28$

8. $\begin{vmatrix} 1 & 5 & -2 \\ -2 & 1 & 4 \\ 4 & 3 & -8 \end{vmatrix} = 1\begin{vmatrix} 1 & 4 \\ 3 & -8 \end{vmatrix} - 5\begin{vmatrix} -2 & 4 \\ 4 & -8 \end{vmatrix} - 2\begin{vmatrix} -2 & 1 \\ 4 & 3 \end{vmatrix}$

$= 1(-8 - 12) - 5(16 - 16) - 2(-6 - 4)$
$= 1(-20) - 5(0) - 2(-10)$
$= -20 - 0 + 20$
$= 0$

9. $2x - y = 7$
$3x + 2y = 7$

$D = \begin{vmatrix} 2 & -1 \\ 3 & 2 \end{vmatrix} = 7$

$D_x = \begin{vmatrix} 7 & -1 \\ 7 & 2 \end{vmatrix} = 21$

$D_y = \begin{vmatrix} 2 & 7 \\ 3 & 7 \end{vmatrix} = -7$

$x = \dfrac{D_x}{D} = \dfrac{21}{7} = 3$

$y = \dfrac{D_y}{D} = \dfrac{-7}{7} = -1$

The solution is $(3, -1)$.

10. $3x - 4y = 10$
$2x + 5y = 15$

$D = \begin{vmatrix} 3 & -4 \\ 2 & 5 \end{vmatrix} = 23$

$D_x = \begin{vmatrix} 10 & -4 \\ 15 & 5 \end{vmatrix} = 110$

$D_y = \begin{vmatrix} 3 & 10 \\ 2 & 15 \end{vmatrix} = 25$

$x = \dfrac{D_x}{D} = \dfrac{110}{23}$

$y = \dfrac{D_y}{D} = \dfrac{25}{23}$

The solution is $\left(\dfrac{110}{23}, \dfrac{25}{23} \right)$.

11. $x + y + z = 0$
$x + 2y + 3z = 5$
$2x + y + 2z = 3$

$D = \begin{vmatrix} 1 & 1 & 1 \\ 1 & 2 & 3 \\ 2 & 1 & 2 \end{vmatrix} = 2$

$D_x = \begin{vmatrix} 0 & 1 & 1 \\ 5 & 2 & 3 \\ 3 & 1 & 2 \end{vmatrix} = -2$

$D_y = \begin{vmatrix} 1 & 0 & 1 \\ 1 & 5 & 3 \\ 2 & 3 & 2 \end{vmatrix} = -6$

$D_z = \begin{vmatrix} 1 & 1 & 0 \\ 1 & 2 & 5 \\ 2 & 1 & 3 \end{vmatrix} = 8$

$x = \dfrac{D_x}{D} = \dfrac{-2}{2} = -1$

$y = \dfrac{D_y}{D} = \dfrac{-6}{2} = -3$

$z = \dfrac{D_z}{D} = \dfrac{8}{2} = 4$

The solution is $(-1, -3, 4)$.

12. $x + 3y + z = 6$
$2x + y - z = 12$
$x + 2y - z = 13$

$$D = \begin{vmatrix} 1 & 3 & 1 \\ 2 & 1 & -1 \\ 1 & 2 & -1 \end{vmatrix} = 7$$

$$D_x = \begin{vmatrix} 6 & 3 & 1 \\ 12 & 1 & -1 \\ 13 & 2 & -1 \end{vmatrix} = 14$$

$$D_y = \begin{vmatrix} 1 & 6 & 1 \\ 2 & 12 & -1 \\ 1 & 13 & -1 \end{vmatrix} = 21$$

$$D_z = \begin{vmatrix} 1 & 3 & 6 \\ 2 & 1 & 12 \\ 1 & 2 & 13 \end{vmatrix} = -35$$

$x = \dfrac{D_x}{D} = \dfrac{14}{7} = 2$

$y = \dfrac{D_y}{D} = \dfrac{21}{7} = 3$

$z = \dfrac{D_z}{D} = \dfrac{-35}{7} = -5$

The solution is $(2, 3, -5)$.

13.   (1) $x - 2y + z = 7$

(2) $3x - z = -1$

(3) $3y + z = 1$

Eliminate z. Add equations (2) and (3).
$3x - z = -1$
$3y + z = 1$

(4) $3x + 3y = 0$

Multiply equation (1) by -1 and add to equation (3).
$-(x - 2y + z) = -7$
$3y + z = 1$

$-x + 2y - z = -7$
$3y + z = 1$

(5) $-x + 5y = -6$

Multiply equation (4) by $\dfrac{1}{3}$ and add to equation (5).

$\dfrac{1}{3}(3x + 3y) = \dfrac{1}{3}(0)$
$-x + 5y = -6$

$x + y = 0$
$-x + 5y = -6$

$6y = -6$
$y = -1$

Replace y in equation (5).
$-x + 5y = -6$
$-x + 5(-1) = -6$
$-x - 5 = -6$
$-x = -1$
$x = 1$

Replace x in equation (2).
$3x - z = -1$
$3(1) - z = -1$
$3 - z = -1$
$-z = -4$
$z = 4$

The solution is $(1, -1, 4)$.

14. $3x - 2y = 2$
$-2x + 3y = 1$

$$D = \begin{vmatrix} 3 & -2 \\ -2 & 3 \end{vmatrix} = 5$$

$$D_x = \begin{vmatrix} 2 & -2 \\ 1 & 3 \end{vmatrix} = 8$$

$$D_y = \begin{vmatrix} 3 & 2 \\ -2 & 1 \end{vmatrix} = 7$$

$x = \dfrac{D_x}{D} = \dfrac{8}{5}$

$y = \dfrac{D_y}{D} = \dfrac{7}{5}$

The solution is $\left(\dfrac{8}{5}, \dfrac{7}{5} \right)$.

15. $2x - 2y - 6z = 1$
$4x + 2y + 3z = 1$
$2x - 3y - 3z = 3$

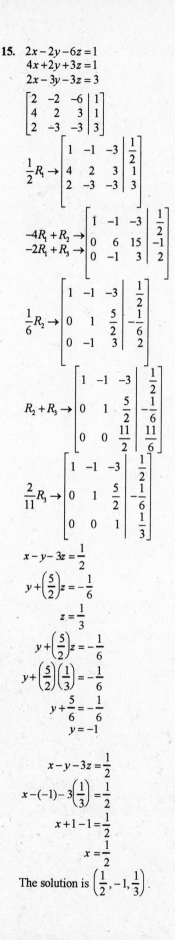

$$\begin{bmatrix} 2 & -2 & -6 & | & 1 \\ 4 & 2 & 3 & | & 1 \\ 2 & -3 & -3 & | & 3 \end{bmatrix}$$

$\frac{1}{2}R_1 \rightarrow \begin{bmatrix} 1 & -1 & -3 & | & \frac{1}{2} \\ 4 & 2 & 3 & | & 1 \\ 2 & -3 & -3 & | & 3 \end{bmatrix}$

$\begin{matrix} -4R_1 + R_2 \rightarrow \\ -2R_1 + R_3 \rightarrow \end{matrix} \begin{bmatrix} 1 & -1 & -3 & | & \frac{1}{2} \\ 0 & 6 & 15 & | & -1 \\ 0 & -1 & 3 & | & 2 \end{bmatrix}$

$\frac{1}{6}R_2 \rightarrow \begin{bmatrix} 1 & -1 & -3 & | & \frac{1}{2} \\ 0 & 1 & \frac{5}{2} & | & -\frac{1}{6} \\ 0 & -1 & 3 & | & 2 \end{bmatrix}$

$R_2 + R_3 \rightarrow \begin{bmatrix} 1 & -1 & -3 & | & \frac{1}{2} \\ 0 & 1 & \frac{5}{2} & | & -\frac{1}{6} \\ 0 & 0 & \frac{11}{2} & | & \frac{11}{6} \end{bmatrix}$

$\frac{2}{11}R_3 \rightarrow \begin{bmatrix} 1 & -1 & -3 & | & \frac{1}{2} \\ 0 & 1 & \frac{5}{2} & | & -\frac{1}{6} \\ 0 & 0 & 1 & | & \frac{1}{3} \end{bmatrix}$

$x - y - 3z = \frac{1}{2}$

$y + \left(\frac{5}{2}\right)z = -\frac{1}{6}$

$z = \frac{1}{3}$

$y + \left(\frac{5}{2}\right)z = -\frac{1}{6}$

$y + \left(\frac{5}{2}\right)\left(\frac{1}{3}\right) = -\frac{1}{6}$

$y + \frac{5}{6} = -\frac{1}{6}$

$y = -1$

$x - y - 3z = \frac{1}{2}$

$x - (-1) - 3\left(\frac{1}{3}\right) = \frac{1}{2}$

$x + 1 - 1 = \frac{1}{2}$

$x = \frac{1}{2}$

The solution is $\left(\frac{1}{2}, -1, \frac{1}{3}\right)$.

16.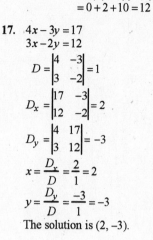

$\begin{vmatrix} 3 & -2 & 5 \\ 4 & 6 & 3 \\ 1 & 2 & 1 \end{vmatrix} = 3\begin{vmatrix} 6 & 3 \\ 2 & 1 \end{vmatrix} + 2\begin{vmatrix} 4 & 3 \\ 1 & 1 \end{vmatrix} + 5\begin{vmatrix} 4 & 6 \\ 1 & 2 \end{vmatrix}$

$= 3(6-6) + 2(4-3) + 5(8-6)$

$= 3(0) + 2(1) + 5(2)$

$= 0 + 2 + 10 = 12$

17. $4x - 3y = 17$
$3x - 2y = 12$

$D = \begin{vmatrix} 4 & -3 \\ 3 & -2 \end{vmatrix} = 1$

$D_x = \begin{vmatrix} 17 & -3 \\ 12 & -2 \end{vmatrix} = 2$

$D_y = \begin{vmatrix} 4 & 17 \\ 3 & 12 \end{vmatrix} = -3$

$x = \dfrac{D_x}{D} = \dfrac{2}{1} = 2$

$y = \dfrac{D_y}{D} = \dfrac{-3}{1} = -3$

The solution is $(2, -3)$.

18.
$$3x + 2y - z = -1$$
$$x + 2y + 3z = -1$$
$$3x + 4y + 6z = 0$$

$$\begin{bmatrix} 3 & 2 & -1 & | & -1 \\ 1 & 2 & 3 & | & -1 \\ 3 & 4 & 6 & | & 0 \end{bmatrix}$$

$$R_1 \leftrightarrow R_2 \begin{bmatrix} 1 & 2 & 3 & | & -1 \\ 3 & 2 & -1 & | & -1 \\ 3 & 4 & 6 & | & 0 \end{bmatrix}$$

$$\begin{matrix} -3R_1 + R_2 \to \\ -3R_1 + R_3 \to \end{matrix} \begin{bmatrix} 1 & 2 & 3 & | & -1 \\ 0 & 1 & \frac{5}{2} & | & -\frac{1}{2} \\ 0 & -2 & -3 & | & 3 \end{bmatrix}$$

$$2R_2 + R_3 \to \begin{bmatrix} 1 & 2 & 3 & | & -1 \\ 0 & 1 & \frac{5}{2} & | & -\frac{1}{2} \\ 0 & 0 & 2 & | & 2 \end{bmatrix}$$

$$\frac{1}{2}R_3 \to \begin{bmatrix} 1 & 2 & 3 & | & -1 \\ 0 & 1 & \frac{5}{2} & | & -\frac{1}{2} \\ 0 & 0 & 1 & | & 1 \end{bmatrix}$$

$$x + 2y + 3z = -1$$
$$y + \frac{5}{2}z = -\frac{1}{2}$$
$$z = 1$$

$$y + \left(\frac{5}{2}\right)z = -\frac{1}{2}$$
$$y + \frac{5}{2}(1) = -\frac{1}{2}$$
$$y + \frac{5}{2} = -\frac{1}{2}$$
$$y = -3$$

$$x + 2y + 3z = -1$$
$$x + 2(-3) + 3(1) = -1$$
$$x - 6 + 3 = -1$$
$$x - 3 = -1$$
$$x = 2$$

The solution is $(2, -3, 1)$.

19.

The solution is $(0, 3)$.

20.

The two equations represent the same line. The solutions are the ordered pairs $(x, 2x - 4)$.

21. Solve each inequality for y.

$$x + 3y \le 6 \qquad 2x - y \ge 4$$
$$3y \le -x + 6 \qquad -y \ge -2x + 4$$
$$y \le -\frac{1}{3}x + 2 \qquad y \le 2x - 4$$

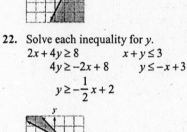

22. Solve each inequality for y.

$$2x + 4y \ge 8 \qquad x + y \le 3$$
$$4y \ge -2x + 8 \qquad y \le -x + 3$$
$$y \ge -\frac{1}{2}x + 2$$

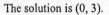

23. Strategy

Rate of the cabin cruiser in calm water: x
Rate of the current: y

	Rate	Time	Distance
With current	$x + y$	3	$3(x + y)$
Against current	$x - y$	5	$5(x - y)$

• The distance traveled with the current is 60 mi.
The distance traveled against the current is 60 mi.
$$3(x + y) = 60$$
$$5(x - y) = 60$$

Solution
$$3(x + y) = 60$$
$$5(x - y) = 60$$

$$\frac{1}{3} \cdot 3(x + y) = \frac{1}{3}(60)$$
$$\frac{1}{5} \cdot 5(x - y) = \frac{1}{5}(60)$$

$$x + y = 20$$
$$x - y = 12$$

$$2x = 32$$
$$x = 16$$

$$x + y = 20$$
$$16 + y = 20$$
$$y = 4$$

The rate of the cabin cruiser in calm water is 16 mph. The rate of the current is 4 mph.

24. Strategy
Rate of the plane in calm air: p
Rate of the wind: w

	Rate	Time	Distance
With wind	$p+w$	3	$3(p+w)$
Against wind	$p-w$	4	$4(p-w)$

• The distance traveled with the wind is 600 mi.
The distance traveled against the wind is 600 mi.
$3(p+w)=600$
$4(p-w)=600$

Solution
$3(p+w)=600$
$4(p-w)=600$

$\frac{1}{3}\cdot 3(p+w)=\frac{1}{3}(600)$
$\frac{1}{4}\cdot 4(p-w)=\frac{1}{4}(600)$

$p+w=200$
$p-w=150$

$2p=350$
$p=175$

$p+w=200$
$175+w=200$
$w=25$
The rate of the plane in calm air is 175 mph.
The rate of the wind is 25 mph.

25. Strategy
Number of children's tickets sold Friday: x
Number of adult's tickets sold Friday: y
Friday:

	Number	Value	Total Value
Children	x	5	$5x$
Adults	y	8	$8y$

Saturday:

	Number	Value	Total Value
Children	$3x$	5	$5(3x)$
Adults	$\frac{1}{2}y$	8	$8\left(\frac{1}{2}y\right)$

• The total receipts for Friday were \$2500.
The total receipts for Saturday were \$2500.
$5x+8y=2500$
$5(3x)+8\left(\frac{1}{2}y\right)=2500$

Solution
$5x+8y=2500$
$15x+4y=2500$

$5x+8y=2500$
$-2(15x+4y)=-2(2500)$

$5x+8y=2500$
$-30x-8y=-5000$

$-25x=-2500$
$x=100$
The number of children attending on Friday was 100.

26. Strategy

Amount of meat to cook: x

Amount of potatoes to cook: y

Amount of green beans to cook: z

Calories	Amount	Calories	Total Calories
Meat	x	50	$50x$
Potatoes	y	9	$9y$
Beans	z	12	$12z$

Protein	Amount	Protein	Total Protein
Meat	x	20	$20x$
Potatoes	y	1	$1y$
Beans	z	2	$2z$

Sodium	Amount	Sodium	Total Sodium
Meat	x	16	$16x$
Potatoes	y	3	$3y$
Beans	z	17	$17z$

The chef wants the meal to contain 243 cal, 73 g of protein and 131 mg of sodium.

$$50x + 9y + 12z = 243$$
$$20x + 1y + 2z = 73$$
$$16x + 3y + 17z = 131$$

Solution

$$50x + 9y + 12z = 243$$
$$20x + 1y + 2z = 73$$
$$16x + 3y + 17z = 131$$

$$50x + 9y + 12z = 243$$
$$-9(20x + 1y + 2z) = -9(73)$$

$$50x + 9y + 12z = 243$$
$$-180x - 9y - 18z = -657$$

$$-130x - 6z = -414$$

$$50x + 9y + 12z = 243$$
$$-3(16x + 3y + 17z) = -3(131)$$

$$50x + 9y + 12z = 243$$
$$-48x - 9y - 51z = -393$$

$$2x - 39z = -150$$

$$-130x - 6z = -414$$
$$65(2x - 39z) = 65(-150)$$

$$-130x - 6z = -414$$
$$130x - 2535z = -9750$$
$$-2541z = -10,164$$
$$\frac{-2541z}{-2541} = \frac{-10,164}{-2541}$$
$$z = 4$$

$$2x - 39z = -150$$
$$2x - 39(4) = -150$$
$$2x - 156 = -150$$
$$2x = 6$$
$$x = 3$$

$$20x + 1y + 2z = 73$$
$$20(3) + y + 2(4) = 73$$
$$60 + y + 8 = 73$$
$$y = 5$$

3 oz of meat, 5 oz of potatoes, and 4 oz of green beans should be prepared.

Chapter Test

1. (1) $3x + 2y = 4$

   (2) $\quad\quad x = 2y - 1$

   Substitute $2y - 1$ for x in equation (1).
   $3(2y-1) + 2y = 4$
   $\quad 6y - 3 + 2y = 4$
   $\quad\quad\quad\quad 8y = 7$
   $\quad\quad\quad\quad\, y = \dfrac{7}{8}$

   Substitute into equation (2).
   $x = 2y - 1$
   $x = 2\left(\dfrac{7}{8}\right) - 1$
   $x = \dfrac{7}{4} - 1 = \dfrac{3}{4}$

   The solution is $\left(\dfrac{3}{4}, \dfrac{7}{8}\right)$.

2. (1) $5x + 2y = -23$

   (2) $\quad 2x + y = -10$

   Solve equation (2) for y.
   $2x + y = -10$
   $\quad\quad y = -2x - 10$
   Substitute $-2x - 10$ for y in equation (1).
   $\quad\quad\quad 5x + 2y = -23$
   $5x + 2(-2x - 10) = -23$
   $\quad 5x - 4x - 20 = -23$
   $\quad\quad\quad x - 20 = -23$
   $\quad\quad\quad\quad\quad x = -3$
   Substitute into equation (2).
   $\quad\, 2x + y = -10$
   $2(-3) + y = -10$
   $\quad -6 + y = -10$
   $\quad\quad\quad\, y = -4$
   The solution is $(-3, -4)$.

3. (1) $y = 3x - 7$

   (2) $y = -2x + 3$

   Substitute equation (2) into equation (1).
   $-2x + 3 = 3x - 7$
   $\quad -5x + 3 = -7$
   $\quad\quad\, -5x = -10$
   $\quad\quad\quad\quad x = 2$
   Substitute into equation (1).
   $y = 3x - 7$
   $y = 3(2) - 7 = 6 - 7 = -1$
   The solution is $(2, -1)$.

4. $3x + 4y = -2$
   $2x + 5y = 1$

   $\begin{bmatrix} 3 & 4 & | & -2 \\ 2 & 5 & | & 1 \end{bmatrix}$

   $-1R_2 + R_1 \rightarrow \begin{bmatrix} 1 & -1 & | & -3 \\ 2 & 5 & | & 1 \end{bmatrix}$

   $-2R_1 + R_2 \rightarrow \begin{bmatrix} 1 & -1 & | & -3 \\ 0 & 7 & | & 7 \end{bmatrix}$

   $\dfrac{1}{7}R_2 \rightarrow \begin{bmatrix} 1 & -1 & | & -3 \\ 0 & 1 & | & 1 \end{bmatrix}$

   $x - y = -3$
   $\quad\quad y = 1$
   $x - 1 = -3$
   $\quad\quad x = -2$
   The solution is $(-2, 1)$.

5. (1) $4x - 6y = 5$

   (2) $6x - 9y = 4$

   Multiply equation (1) by -3. Multiply
   equation (2) by 2. Add the new equations.
   $-3(4x - 6y) = -3(5)$
   $\quad 2(6x - 9y) = 2(4)$

   $-12x + 18y = -15$
   $\quad 12x - 18y = 8$

   $\quad\quad\quad\quad 0 = -7$
   This is not a true equation. The system of
   equations is inconsistent and therefore has no
   solution.

6. (1) $3x - y = 2x + y - 1$

   (2) $5x + 2y = y + 6$

   Write the equation in the form $Ax + By = C$.

   (3) $x - 2y = -1$

   (4) $5x + y = 6$

   Multiply equation (4) by 2 and add to
   equation (3).
   $\quad\, x - 2y = -1$
   $2(5x + y) = 2(6)$

   $\quad\quad x - 2y = -1$
   $\quad 10x + 2y = 12$

   $\quad\quad\quad 11x = 11$
   $\quad\quad\quad\quad x = 1$
   Substitute into equation (4).
   $\quad 5x + y = 6$
   $5(1) + y = 6$
   $\quad\quad\quad y = 1$
   The solution is $(1, 1)$.

7. (1) $2x + 4y - z = 3$

   (2) $x + 2y + z = 5$

   (3) $4x + 8y - 2z = 7$

   Eliminate z. Add equations (1) and (2).

   $2x + 4y - z = 3$
   $x + 2y + z = 5$

   (4) $3x + 6y = 8$

   Multiply equation (2) by 2 and add to equation (3).

   $2(x + 2y + z) = 2(5)$
   $4x + 8y - 2z = 7$

   $2x + 4y + 2z = 10$
   $4x + 8y - 2z = 7$

   (5) $6x + 12y = 17$

   Multiply equation (4) by -2 and add to equation (5).

   $-2(3x + 6y) = -2(8)$
   $6x + 12y = 17$

   $-6x - 12y = -16$
   $6x + 12y = 17$
   $0 = 1$

   This is not a true equation. The system of equations is inconsistent and therefore has no solution.

8. $x - y - z = 5$
   $2x + z = 2$
   $3y - 2z = 1$

   $$\begin{bmatrix} 1 & -1 & -1 & | & 5 \\ 2 & 0 & 1 & | & 2 \\ 0 & 3 & -2 & | & 1 \end{bmatrix}$$

   $$-2R_1 + R_2 \rightarrow \begin{bmatrix} 1 & -1 & -1 & | & 5 \\ 0 & 2 & 3 & | & -8 \\ 0 & 3 & -2 & | & 1 \end{bmatrix}$$

   $$R_2 \leftrightarrow R_3 \begin{bmatrix} 1 & -1 & -1 & | & 5 \\ 0 & 3 & -2 & | & 1 \\ 0 & 2 & 3 & | & -8 \end{bmatrix}$$

   $$-1R_3 + R_2 \rightarrow \begin{bmatrix} 1 & -1 & -1 & | & 5 \\ 0 & 1 & -5 & | & 9 \\ 0 & 2 & 3 & | & -8 \end{bmatrix}$$

   $$-2R_2 + R_3 \rightarrow \begin{bmatrix} 1 & -1 & -1 & | & 5 \\ 0 & 1 & -5 & | & 9 \\ 0 & 0 & 13 & | & -26 \end{bmatrix}$$

   $$\frac{1}{13}R_3 \rightarrow \begin{bmatrix} 1 & -1 & -1 & | & 5 \\ 0 & 1 & -5 & | & 9 \\ 0 & 0 & 1 & | & -2 \end{bmatrix}$$

   $x - y - z = 5$
   $y - 5z = 9$
   $z = -2$

   $y - 5z = 9$
   $y - 5(-2) = 9$
   $y + 10 = 9$
   $y = -1$

   $x - y - z = 5$
   $x - (-1) - (-2) = 5$
   $x + 1 + 2 = 5$
   $x + 3 = 5$
   $x = 2$

   The solution is $(2, -1, -2)$.

9. $\begin{vmatrix} 3 & -1 \\ -2 & 4 \end{vmatrix} = 3(4) - (-2)(-1) = 12 - 2 = 10$

10. $\begin{vmatrix} 1 & -2 & 3 \\ 3 & 1 & 1 \\ 2 & -1 & -2 \end{vmatrix} = 1\begin{vmatrix} 1 & 1 \\ -1 & -2 \end{vmatrix} - (-2)\begin{vmatrix} 3 & 1 \\ 2 & -2 \end{vmatrix} + 3\begin{vmatrix} 3 & 1 \\ 2 & -1 \end{vmatrix}$

$= 1(-2 - (-1)) + 2(-6 - 2) + 3(-3 - 2)$
$= 1(-2 + 1) + 2(-8) + 3(-5)$
$= -1 - 16 - 15$
$= -32$

11. $x - y = 3$
$2x + y = -4$

$$D = \begin{vmatrix} 1 & -1 \\ 2 & 1 \end{vmatrix} = 3$$

$$D_x = \begin{vmatrix} 3 & -1 \\ -4 & 1 \end{vmatrix} = -1$$

$$D_y = \begin{vmatrix} 1 & 3 \\ 2 & -4 \end{vmatrix} = -10$$

$$x = \frac{D_x}{D} = -\frac{1}{3}$$

$$y = \frac{D_y}{D} = -\frac{10}{3}$$

The solution is $\left(-\frac{1}{3}, -\frac{10}{3}\right)$.

12. $x - y + z = 2$
$2x - y - z = 1$
$x + 2y - 3z = -4$

$$D = \begin{vmatrix} 1 & -1 & 1 \\ 2 & -1 & -1 \\ 1 & 2 & -3 \end{vmatrix} = 5$$

$$D_x = \begin{vmatrix} 2 & -1 & 1 \\ 1 & -1 & -1 \\ -4 & 2 & -3 \end{vmatrix} = 1$$

$$D_y = \begin{vmatrix} 1 & 2 & 1 \\ 2 & 1 & -1 \\ 1 & -4 & -3 \end{vmatrix} = -6$$

$$D_z = \begin{vmatrix} 1 & -1 & 2 \\ 2 & -1 & 1 \\ 1 & 2 & -4 \end{vmatrix} = 3$$

$$x = \frac{D_x}{D} = \frac{1}{5}$$

$$y = \frac{D_y}{D} = -\frac{6}{5}$$

$$z = \frac{D_z}{D} = \frac{3}{5}$$

The solution is $\left(\frac{1}{5}, -\frac{6}{5}, \frac{3}{5}\right)$.

13. $3x + 2y + 2z = 2$
$x - 2y - z = 1$
$2x - 3y - 3z = -3$

$$D = \begin{vmatrix} 3 & 2 & 2 \\ 1 & -2 & -1 \\ 2 & -3 & -3 \end{vmatrix} = 13$$

$$D_x = \begin{vmatrix} 2 & 2 & 2 \\ 1 & -2 & -1 \\ -3 & -3 & -3 \end{vmatrix} = 0$$

$$D_y = \begin{vmatrix} 3 & 2 & 2 \\ 1 & 1 & -1 \\ 2 & -3 & 3 \end{vmatrix} = -26$$

$$D_z = \begin{vmatrix} 3 & 2 & 2 \\ 1 & -2 & 1 \\ 2 & -3 & -3 \end{vmatrix} = 39$$

$$\frac{D_x}{D} = \frac{0}{13} = 0$$

$$\frac{D_y}{D} = \frac{-26}{13} = -2$$

$$\frac{D_z}{D} = \frac{39}{13} = 3$$

The solution is $(0, -2, 3)$.

14.

The solution is $(3, 4)$.

15.

The solution is $(-5, 0)$.

16. Solve each inequality for y.

$2x - y < 3 \qquad\qquad 4x + 3y < 11$
$\quad -y < -2x + 3 \qquad\qquad 3y < -4x + 11$
$\qquad y > 2x - 3 \qquad\qquad\quad y < -\frac{4}{3}x + \frac{11}{3}$

$y > 2x - 3$
$y < -\frac{4}{3}x + \frac{11}{3}$

17. Solve each inequality for y.

$x + y > 2$ $\qquad$ $2x - y < -1$

$\quad y > -x + 2$ $\qquad$ $-y < -2x - 1$

$\qquad\qquad\qquad\qquad y > 1 + 2x$

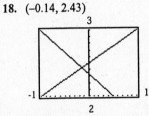

18. $(-0.14, 2.43)$

19. Strategy

• Rate of the plane in calm air: x

Rate of the wind: y

	Rate	Time	Distance
With wind	$x + y$	2	$2(x + y)$
Against wind	$x - y$	2.8	$2.8(x - y)$

• The distance traveled with the wind is 350 mi. The distance traveled against the wind is 350 mi.

$2(x + y) = 350$

$2.8(x - y) = 350$

Solution

$2(x + y) = 350$

$2.8(x - y) = 350$

$$\frac{1}{2} \cdot 2(x + y) = \frac{1}{2} \cdot 350$$

$$\frac{1}{2.8} \cdot 2.8(x - y) = \frac{1}{2.8} \cdot 350$$

$x + y = 175$

$x - y = 125$

$2x = 300$

$\quad x = 150$

$\quad\quad x + y = 175$

$150 + y = 175$

$\quad\quad\quad y = 25$

The rate of the plane in calm air is 150 mph. The rate of the wind is 25 mph.

20. Strategy

Cost per yard of cotton: x

Cost per yard of wool: y

First purchase:

	Amount	Cost	Total Value
Cotton	60	x	$60x$
Wool	90	y	$90y$

Second purchase:

	Amount	Cost	Total Value
Cotton	80	x	$80x$
Wool	20	y	$20y$

• The total cost of the first purchase was $1800. The total cost of the second purchase was $1000.

$60x + 90y = 1800$

$80x + 20y = 1000$

Solution

$-4(60x + 90y) = -4(1800)$

$\quad 3(80x + 20y) = 3(1000)$

$-240x - 360y = -7200$

$\quad 240x + 60y = 3000$

$-300y = -4200$

$\quad\quad y = 14$

$60x + 90(14) = 1800$

$\quad 60x + 1260 = 1800$

$\quad\quad\quad\quad 60x = 540$

$\quad\quad\quad\quad\quad x = 9$

The cost per yard of cotton is $9.00. The cost per yard of wool is $14.00.

Cumulative Review Exercises

1.

$$\frac{3}{2}x - \frac{3}{8} + \frac{1}{4}x = \frac{7}{12}x - \frac{5}{6}$$

$$24\left(\frac{3}{2}x - \frac{3}{8} + \frac{1}{4}x\right) = 24\left(\frac{7}{12}x - \frac{5}{6}\right)$$

$$36x - 9 + 6x = 14x - 20$$

$$42x - 9 = 14x - 20$$

$$28x - 9 = -20$$

$$28x = -11$$

$$x = -\frac{11}{28}$$

The solution is $-\dfrac{11}{28}$.

2. $(x_1, y_1) = (2, -1)$, $(x_2, y_2) = (3, 4)$

$$m = \frac{y_2 - y_1}{x_2 - x_1} = \frac{4 - (-1)}{3 - 2} = \frac{5}{1} = 5$$

$$y - y_1 = m(x - x_1)$$

$$y - (-1) = 5(x - 2)$$

$$y + 1 = 5x - 10$$

$$y = 5x - 11$$

The equation of the line is $y = 5x - 11$.

3. $3[x-2(5-2x)-4x]+6 = 3(x-10+4x-4x)+6$
$$= 3(x-10)+6$$
$$= 3x-30+6$$
$$= 3x-24$$

4. $a=4,\ b=8,\ c=-2$
$a+bc \div 2 = 4+8(-2) \div 2$
$$= 4-16 \div 2$$
$$= 4-8$$
$$= -4$$

5. $2x-3<9$ or $5x-1<4$
Solve each inequality.
$2x-3<9$ or $5x-1<4$
   $2x<12$ $5x<5$
     $x<6$ $x<1$
is the same as $\{x|x<6\} \cup \{x|x<1\}$, which is
$\{x|x<6\}$.

6. $|x-2|-4<2$
   $|x-2|<6$

    $-6<x-2<6$
$-6+2<x-2+2<6+2$
     $-4<x<8$
$\{x|-4<x<8\}$

7. $|2x-3|>5$
Solve each inequality.
$2x-3<-5$ or $2x-3>5$
   $2x<-2$ $2x>8$
     $x<-1$ $x>4$
This is the set $\{x|x<-1\} \cup \{x|x>4\}$ or
$\{x|x<-1 \text{ or } x>4\}$.

8. $f(x)=3x^3-2x^2+1$
$f(-3)=3(-3)^3-2(-3)^2+1$
$f(-3)=3(-27)-2(9)+1$
$f(-3)=-98$

9. The range is the set of numbers found by
substituting in the set of numbers in the domain.
$f(-2)=3(-2)^2-2(-2)=16$
$f(-1)=3(-1)^2-2(-1)=5$
$f(0)=3(0)^2-2(0)=0$
$f(1)=3(1)^2-2(1)=1$
$f(2)=3(2)^2-2(2)=8$
The range is $\{0, 1, 5, 8, 16\}$.

10. $F(x)=x^2-3$
$F(2)=2^2-3=1$

11. $f(x)=3x-4$
$f(2+h)=3(2+h)-4$
$$=6+3h-4$$
$$=2+3h$$

       $f(2)=3(2)-4=2$
$f(2+h)-f(2)=2+3h-2=3h$

12. $\{x|x \le 2\} \cap \{x|x>-3\}$

13. Slope $= -\dfrac{2}{3}$, Point $= (-2, 3)$

$y-3=-\dfrac{2}{3}[x-(-2)]$

$y-3=-\dfrac{2}{3}(x+2)$

$y=-\dfrac{2}{3}x-\dfrac{4}{3}+3$

$y=-\dfrac{2}{3}x+\dfrac{5}{3}$

14. The slope of the line $2x-3y=7$ is found by
rearranging the equation as follows:
$-3y=7-2x$
$$y=-\dfrac{7}{3}+\dfrac{2}{3}x$$
Slope $= \dfrac{2}{3}$

The perpendicular line has slope $= -\dfrac{3}{2}$.
The line is found using
$y-2=-\dfrac{3}{2}[x-(-1)]$

$y=-\dfrac{3}{2}(x+1)+2$

$y=-\dfrac{3}{2}x-\dfrac{3}{2}+2$

$y=-\dfrac{3}{2}x+\dfrac{1}{2}$

15. The distance between points is
$\sqrt{(x_2-x_1)^2+(y_2-y_1)^2}$.
$d=\sqrt{[2-(-4)^2]+(0-2)^2}$
$d=\sqrt{6^2+(-2)^2}$
$d=\sqrt{36+4}$
$d=\sqrt{40}$
$d=2\sqrt{10}$

16. The midpoint is found using $\left(\dfrac{x_1+x_2}{2}, \dfrac{y_1+y_2}{2}\right)$.
Midpoint $=\left(\dfrac{-4+3}{2}, \dfrac{3+5}{2}\right)$
$$=\left(-\dfrac{1}{2}, 4\right)$$

17. $2x - 5y = 10$

$\quad -5y = -2x + 10$

$\quad y = \dfrac{2}{5}x - 2$

The y-intercept is -2.

The slope is $\dfrac{2}{5}$.

18. $3x - 4y \geq 8$

$\quad -4y \geq -3x + 8$

$\quad y \leq \dfrac{3}{4}x - 2$

The y-intercept is -2. The slope is $\dfrac{3}{4}$.

19. (1) $\quad 3x - 2y = 7$

(2) $\qquad y = 2x - 1$

Solve by the substitution method.

$3x - 2(2x - 1) = 7$

$\quad 3x - 4x + 2 = 7$

$\qquad -x + 2 = 7$

$\qquad\quad -x = 5$

$\qquad\quad\ x = -5$

Substitute -5 for x in equation (2).

$y = 2x - 1$

$y = 2(-5) - 1 = -10 - 1 = -11$

The solution is $(-5, -11)$.

20. (1) $\quad 3x + 2z = 1$

(2) $\quad 2y - z = 1$

(3) $\quad x + 2y = 1$

Multiply equation (2) by -1 and add to equation (3).

$-1(2y - z) = -1(1)$

$\quad x + 2y = 1$

$-2y + z = -1$

$\ \ x + 2y = 1$

(4) $\ x + z = 0$

Multiply equation (4) by -2 and add to equation (1).

$(-2)(x + z) = -2(0)$

$\quad 3x + 2z = 1$

$-2x - 2z = 0$

$\ \ 3x + 2z = 1$

$\qquad x = 1$

Substitute 1 for x in equation (4).

$x + z = 0$

$1 + z = 0$

$\quad\ z = -1$

Substitute 1 for x in equation (3).

$x + 2y = 1$

$1 + 2y = 1$

$\quad\ 2y = 0$

$\qquad y = 0$

The solution is $(1, 0, -1)$.

21. $\begin{vmatrix} 2 & -5 & 1 \\ 3 & 1 & 2 \\ 6 & -1 & 4 \end{vmatrix} = 2\begin{vmatrix} 1 & 2 \\ -1 & 4 \end{vmatrix} - 3\begin{vmatrix} -5 & 1 \\ -1 & 4 \end{vmatrix} + 6\begin{vmatrix} -5 & 1 \\ 1 & 2 \end{vmatrix}$

$= 2(4 + 2) - 3(-20 + 1) + 6(-10 - 1)$

$= 2(6) - 3(-19) + 6(-11)$

$= 12 + 57 - 66$

$= 3$

22.

The solution is $(2, 0)$.

23. $D = \begin{vmatrix} 4 & -3 \\ 3 & -2 \end{vmatrix} = 4(-2) - 3(-3) = 1$

$D_x = \begin{vmatrix} 17 & -3 \\ 12 & -2 \end{vmatrix} = 17(-2) - 12(-3) = 2$

$D_y = \begin{vmatrix} 4 & 17 \\ 3 & 12 \end{vmatrix} = 4(12) - 3(17) = -3$

$x = \dfrac{D_x}{D} = \dfrac{2}{1} = 2$

$y = \dfrac{D_y}{D} = \dfrac{-3}{1} = -3$

The solution is $(2, -3)$.

24. Solve each inequality for y.

$$3x - 2y \geq 4 \qquad\qquad x + y < 3$$
$$-2y \geq -3x + 4 \qquad\quad y < -x + 3$$
$$y \leq \frac{3}{2}x - 2$$

25. Strategy

• The unknown number of quarters: x
The unknown number of dimes: $3x$
The unknown number of nickels: $40 - (x + 3x)$

	Number	Value	Total Value
Quarters	x	25	$25x$
Dimes	$3x$	10	$10(3x)$
Nickels	$40 - 4x$	5	$5(40 - 4x)$

• The sum of the total values of the denominations is \$4.10 (410 cents).

$$25x + 10(3x) + 5(40 - 4x) = 410$$

Solution

$$25x + 10(3x) + 5(40 - 4x) = 410$$
$$25x + 30x + 200 - 20x = 410$$
$$35x + 200 = 410$$
$$35x = 210$$
$$x = 6$$
$$40 - 4x = 40 - 4(6) = 40 - 24 = 16$$

There are 16 nickels in the purse.

26. Strategy

The unknown amount of pure water: x

	Amount	Percent	Quantity
Water	x	0	$0x$
4%	100	0.04	$100(0.04)$
2.5%	$100 + x$	0.025	$(100 + x)(0.025)$

The sum of the quantities before mixing equals the quantity after mixing.

$$0 \cdot x + 100(0.04) = (100 + x)0.025$$

Solution

$$0 \cdot x + 100(0.04) = (100 + x)0.025$$
$$0 + 4 = 2.5 + 0.025x$$
$$1.5 = 0.025x$$
$$60 = x$$

The amount of water that should be added is 60 ml.

27. Strategy

Rate of the plane in calm air: x
Rate of the wind: y

	Rate	Time	Distance
With wind	$x + y$	2	$2(x + y)$
Against wind	$x - y$	3	$3(x - y)$

• The distance traveled with the wind is 150 mi. The distance traveled against the wind is 150 mi.

$$2(x + y) = 150$$
$$3(x - y) = 150$$

Solution

$$2(x + y) = 150$$
$$3(x - y) = 150$$

$$\frac{1}{2} \cdot 2(x + y) = \frac{1}{2} \cdot 150$$
$$\frac{1}{3} \cdot 3(x - y) = \frac{1}{3} \cdot 150$$

$$x + y = 75$$
$$x - y = 50$$

$$2x = 125$$
$$x = 62.5$$

$$x + y = 75$$
$$62.5 + y = 75$$
$$y = 12.5$$

The rate of the wind is 12.5 mph.

28. Strategy

Cost per pound of hamburger: x
Cost per pound of steak: y
First purchase:

	Amount	Cost	Value
Hamburger	100	x	$100x$
Steak	50	y	$50y$

Second purchase:

	Amount	Cost	Value
Hamburger	150	x	$150x$
Steak	100	y	$100y$

• The total cost of the first purchase is $490.
The total cost of the second purchase is $860.

$100x + 50y = 490$
$150x + 100y = 860$

Solution
$100x + 50y = 490$
$150x + 100y = 860$

$3(100x + 50y) = 3(490)$
$-2(150x + 100y) = -2(860)$

$300x + 150y = 1470$
$-300x - 200y = -1720$

$-50y = -250$
$y = 5$

The cost per pound of steak is $5.

29. Strategy

Let M be the number of ohms, T the tolerance, and r the given amount of resistance. Find the tolerance and solve $|M - r| \le T$ for M.

Solution
$T = 0.15 \cdot 12{,}000 = 1800$ ohms

$|M - 12{,}000| \le 1800$
$-1800 \le M - 12{,}000 \le 1800$
$-1800 + 12{,}000 \le M - 12{,}000 + 12{,}000$
$\le 1800 + 12{,}000$
$10{,}200 \le M \le 13{,}800$

The lower and upper limits of the resistance are 10,200 ohms and 13,800 ohms.

30. The slope of the line is
$$\frac{5000 - 1000}{100 - 0} = \frac{4000}{100} = 40$$

The slope represents the marginal income or the income generated per number of sales. The account executive earns $40 for each $1000 of sales.

Chapter 5: Polynomials and Exponents

Prep Test

1. $-4(3y) = -12y$ [1.3.3]

2. $(-2)^3 = -8$ [1.2.3]

3. $-4a - 8b + 7a = 3a - 8b$ [1.3.3]

4. $\begin{aligned} 3x - 2[y - 4(x+1) + 5] &\quad [1.3.3] \\ &= 3x - 2[y - 4x - 4 + 5] \\ &= 3x - 2[y - 4x + 1] \\ &= 3x - 2y + 8x - 2 \\ &= 11x - 2y - 2 \end{aligned}$

5. $-(x - y) = -x + y$ [1.3.3]

6. $40 = 2 \cdot 2 \cdot 2 \cdot 5$ [1.2.2]

7. 4 [1.2.2]

8. $\begin{aligned} x^3 - 2x^2 + x + 5 &\quad [1.3.2] \\ &= (-2)^3 - 2(-2)^2 + (-2) + 5 \\ &= -8 - 2(4) - 2 + 5 \\ &= -8 - 8 + 3 \\ &= -13 \end{aligned}$

9. $\begin{aligned} 3x + 1 &= 0 \quad [2.1.1] \\ 3x &= -1 \\ x &= -\frac{1}{3} \end{aligned}$

Go Figure

First it is important to note that the distance traveled is the same whether I am late, early, or on time. Use the $d = rt$ formula, where the distance is the same for both late and early. The rate for arriving late is 57, and the time, in hours, is $t + \frac{1}{3}$. The rate for arriving early is 64, and the time, in hours is $t - \frac{1}{4}$. Since the distances are equal,

$$57\left(t + \frac{1}{3}\right) = 64\left(t - \frac{1}{4}\right)$$
$$57t + 19 = 64t - 16$$
$$35 = 7t$$
$$5 = t$$

Now, the distance traveled is

$$57\left(t + \frac{1}{3}\right) = 57\left(5 + \frac{1}{3}\right) = 304 \text{ miles}$$

So to arrive just in time, find the rate
$$d = rt$$
$$304 = r(5)$$
$$60.8 = r$$

I need to travel at 60.8 mph to arrive just in time.

Section 5.1

Concept Review 5.1

1. Never true
   $$2^{-4} = \frac{1}{2^4} = \frac{1}{16}$$

2. Never true
   For example, $(-2)^{-1} = \frac{1}{-2} = -\frac{1}{2}$

3. Never true
   $$(2 + 3)^{-1} = 5^{-1} = \frac{1}{5}$$

4. Never true
   When multiplying two numbers with the same base, the rule is to add the exponents.

5. Never true
   There is no rule to add two numbers with the same base.

Objective 5.1.1 Exercises

1. To multiply two exponential expressions with the same base, add the exponents. The base remains unchanged.

2. Write each expression in factored form. Rearrange the factors using the Commutative Property of Multiplication and group factors using the Associative Property of Multiplication. Multiply the coefficients and multiply variables with like bases by adding the exponents.
   $$\begin{aligned} (2a^3b^2)(3a^2b) &= (2 \cdot a^3 \cdot b^2)(3 \cdot a^2 \cdot b) \\ &= (2 \cdot 3)(a^3 \cdot a^2)(b^2 \cdot b) \\ &= 6a^5b^3 \end{aligned}$$

3. $(ab^3)(a^3b) = a^4b^4$

4. $(-2ab^4)(-3a^2b^4) = 6a^3b^8$

5. $(9xy^2)(-2x^2y^2) = -18x^3y^4$

6. $(x^2y)^2 = x^4y^2$

7. $(x^4y^4)^4 = x^8y^{16}$

8. $(-2ab^2)^3 = (-2)^3a^3b^6 = -8a^3b^6$

9. $(-3x^2y^3)^4 = (-3)^4x^8y^{12} = 81x^8y^{12}$

10. $(2^2a^2b^3)^3 = 2^6a^6b^9 = 64a^6b^9$

11. $(3^3a^5b^3)^2 = 3^6a^{10}b^6 = 729a^{10}b^6$

12. $(xy)(x^2y)^4 = (xy)(x^8y^4) = x^9y^5$

13. $(x^2y^2)(xy^3)^3 = (x^2y^2)(x^3y^9) = x^5y^{11}$

14. $[(2x)^4]^2 = (2x)^8 = 2^8 x^8 = 256x^8$

15. $[(3x)^3]^2 = (3x)^6 = 3^6 x^6 = 729x^6$

16. $[(x^2 y)^4]^5 = (x^2 y)^{20} = x^{40} y^{20}$

17. $[(ab)^3]^6 = (ab)^{18} = a^{18} b^{18}$

18. $[(2ab)^3]^2 = (2ab)^6 = 2^6 a^6 b^6 = 64a^6 b^6$

19. $[(2xy)^3]^4 = (2xy)^{12} = 2^{12} x^{12} y^{12} = 4096 x^{12} y^{12}$

20. $[(3x^2 y^3)^2]^2 = (3x^2 y^3)^4 = 3^4 x^8 y^{12} = 81x^8 y^{12}$

21. $[(2a^4 b^3)^3]^2 = (2a^4 b^3)^6 = 2^6 a^{24} b^{18} = 64a^{24} b^{18}$

22. $y^n \cdot y^{2n} = y^{n+2n} = y^{3n}$

23. $x^n \cdot x^{n+1} = x^{n+n+1} = x^{2n+1}$

24. $y^{2n} y^{4n+1} = y^{2n+4n+1} = y^{6n+1}$

25. $y^{3n} \cdot y^{3n-2} = y^{3n+3n-2} = y^{6n-2}$

26. $(a^n)^{2n} = a^{n \cdot 2n} = a^{2n^2}$

27. $(a^n)^{3n} = a^{3n^2}$

28. $(y^{2n})^3 = y^{6n}$

29. $(x^{3n})^5 = x^{15n}$

30. $(b^{2n})^{4n} = b^{8n^2}$

31. $(2xy)(-3x^2 yz)(x^2 y^3 z^3) = -6x^5 y^5 z^4$

32. $(x^2 z^4)(2xyz^4)(-3x^3 y^2) = -6x^6 y^3 z^8$

33. $(3b^5)(2ab^2)(-2ab^2 c^2) = -12a^2 b^9 c^2$

34. $(-c^3)(-2a^2 bc)(3a^2 b) = 6a^4 b^2 c^4$

35. $(-2x^2 y^3 z)(3x^2 yz^4) = -6x^4 y^4 z^5$

36. $(2a^2 b)^3 (-3ab^4)^2 = (2^3 a^6 b^3)[(-3)^2 a^2 b^8]$
$\qquad = (8a^6 b^3)(9a^2 b^8)$
$\qquad = 72a^8 b^{11}$

37. $(-3ab^3)^3 (-2^2 a^2 b)^2 = [(-3)^3 a^3 b^9][(-2^2)^2 a^4 b^2]$
$\qquad = (-27a^3 b^9)(16a^4 b^2)$
$\qquad = -432a^7 b^{11}$

38. $(4ab)^2 (-2ab^2 c^3)^3 = (4^2 a^2 b^2)[(-2)^3 a^3 b^6 c^9]$
$\qquad = (16a^2 b^2)(-8a^3 b^6 c^9)$
$\qquad = -128a^5 b^8 c^9$

39. $(-2ab^2)(-3a^4 b^5)^3 = (-2ab^2)[(-3)^3 a^{12} b^{15}]$
$\qquad = (-2ab^2)(-27a^{12} b^{15})$
$\qquad = 54a^{13} b^{17}$

Objective 5.1.2 Exercises

40. To divide two exponential expressions with the same base, subtract the exponent of the divisor from the exponent of the dividend. The base remains unchanged.

41. If a variable has a negative exponent, write the expression in the denominator of a fraction whose numerator is 1 and change the sign of the exponent. For example, $x^{-3} = \dfrac{1}{x^3}$. If the expression is in the denominator of a fraction, write it in the numerator of the fraction and change the sign of the exponent. For example, $\dfrac{1}{x^{-5}} = \dfrac{x^5}{1} = x^5$.

42. $\dfrac{x^3}{x^{12}} = x^{3-12} = x^{-9} = \dfrac{1}{x^9}$

43. $\dfrac{a^8}{a^5} = a^{8-5} = a^3$

44. $\dfrac{x^3 y^6}{x^3 y^3} = x^{3-3} y^{6-3} = x^0 y^3 = y^3$

45. $\dfrac{a^7 b}{a^2 b^4} = a^{7-2} b^{1-4} = a^5 b^{-3} = \dfrac{a^5}{b^3}$

46. $2^{-3} = \dfrac{1}{2^3} = \dfrac{1}{8}$

47. $\dfrac{1}{3^{-5}} = 3^5 = 243$

48. $\dfrac{1}{x^{-4}} = x^4$

49. $\dfrac{1}{y^{-3}} = y^3$

50. $\dfrac{2x^{-2}}{y^4} = \dfrac{2}{x^2 y^4}$

51. $\dfrac{a^3}{4b^{-2}} = \dfrac{a^3 b^2}{4}$

52. $x^{-4} \cdot x^4 = x^0 = 1$

53. $x^{-3} \cdot x^{-5} = x^{-8} = \dfrac{1}{x^8}$

54. $(3x^{-2})^2 = 3^2 x^{-4} = \dfrac{9}{x^4}$

55. $(5x^2)^{-3} = 5^{-3} x^{-6} = \dfrac{1}{5^3 x^6} = \dfrac{1}{125x^6}$

56. $\dfrac{x^{-3}}{x^2} = x^{-5} = \dfrac{1}{x^5}$

57. $\dfrac{x^4}{x^{-5}} = x^9$

58. $a^{-2} \cdot a^4 = a^2$

59. $a^{-5} \cdot a^7 = a^2$

60. $(x^2 y^{-4})^2 = x^4 y^{-8} = \dfrac{x^4}{y^8}$

61. $(x^3 y^5)^{-2} = x^{-6} y^{-10} = \dfrac{1}{x^6 y^{10}}$

62. $(2a^{-1})^{-2}(2a^{-1})^4 = (2^{-2} a^2)(2^4 a^{-4})$
$$= 2^2 a^{-2}$$
$$= \dfrac{4}{a^2}$$

63. $(3a)^{-3}(9a^{-1})^{-2} = (3a)^{-3}(3^2 a^{-1})^{-2}$
$$= (3^{-3} a^{-3})(3^{-4} a^2)$$
$$= 3^{-7} a^{-1}$$
$$= \dfrac{1}{3^7 a}$$
$$= \dfrac{1}{2187 a}$$

64. $(x^{-2} y)^2 (xy)^{-2} = (x^{-4} y^2)(x^{-2} y^{-2})$
$$= x^{-6} y^0$$
$$= \dfrac{1}{x^6}$$

65. $(x^{-1} y^2)^{-3}(x^2 y^{-4})^{-3} = (x^3 y^{-6})(x^{-6} y^{12})$
$$= x^{-3} y^6$$
$$= \dfrac{y^6}{x^3}$$

66. $\dfrac{6^2 a^{-2} b^3}{3ab^4} = \dfrac{36}{3a^3 b} = \dfrac{12}{a^3 b}$

67. $\left(\dfrac{x^2 y^{-1}}{xy}\right)^{-4} = \left(\dfrac{x}{y^2}\right)^{-4} = \dfrac{x^{-4}}{y^{-8}} = \dfrac{y^8}{x^4}$

68. $\dfrac{-48ab^{10}}{32a^4 b^3} = -\dfrac{3b^7}{2a^3}$

69. $\dfrac{a^2 b^3 c^7}{a^6 bc^5} = \dfrac{b^2 c^2}{a^4}$

70. $\dfrac{(-4x^2 y^3)^2}{(2xy^2)^3} = \dfrac{(-4)^2 x^4 y^6}{2^3 x^3 y^6} = \dfrac{16 x^4 y^6}{8 x^3 y^6} = 2x$

71. $\dfrac{(-3a^2 b^3)^2}{(-2ab^4)^3} = \dfrac{(-3)^2 a^4 b^6}{(-2)^3 a^3 b^{12}} = \dfrac{9 a^4 b^6}{-8 a^3 b^{12}} = -\dfrac{9a}{8b^6}$

72. $\left(\dfrac{x^{-3} y^{-4}}{x^{-2} y}\right)^{-2} = \left(\dfrac{1}{xy^5}\right)^{-2} = \dfrac{1^{-2}}{x^{-2} y^{-10}} = x^2 y^{10}$

73. $\left(\dfrac{a^{-2} b}{a^3 b^{-4}}\right)^2 = \left(\dfrac{b^5}{a^5}\right)^2 = \dfrac{b^{10}}{a^{10}}$

74. $\dfrac{-x^{5n}}{x^{2n}} = -x^{5n-2n} = -x^{3n}$

75. $\dfrac{y^{2n}}{-y^{8n}} = -\dfrac{1}{y^{8n-2n}} = -\dfrac{1}{y^{6n}}$

76. $\dfrac{a^{3n-2} b^{n+1}}{a^{2n+1} b^{2n+2}} = \dfrac{a^{3n-2-(2n+1)}}{b^{2n+2-(n+1)}}$
$$= \dfrac{a^{3n-2-2n-1}}{b^{2n+2-n-1}}$$
$$= \dfrac{a^{n-3}}{b^{n+1}}$$

77. $\dfrac{x^{2n-1} y^{n-3}}{x^{n+4} y^{n+3}} = x^{2n-1-(n+4)} y^{n-3-(n+3)}$
$$= x^{2n-1-n-4} y^{n-3-n-3}$$
$$= x^{n-5} y^{-6}$$
$$= \dfrac{x^{n-5}}{y^6}$$

78. $\dfrac{(2a^{-3} b^{-2})^3}{(a^{-4} b^{-1})^{-2}} = \dfrac{2^3 a^{-9} b^{-6}}{a^8 b^2} = \dfrac{8}{a^{17} b^8}$

79. $\dfrac{(3x^{-2} y)^{-2}}{(4xy^{-2})^{-1}} = \dfrac{3^{-2} x^4 y^{-2}}{4^{-1} x^{-1} y^2} = \dfrac{4x^5}{9y^4}$

80. $\left(\dfrac{4^{-2} xy^{-3}}{x^{-3} y}\right)^3 \left(\dfrac{8^{-1} x^{-2} y}{x^4 y^{-1}}\right)^{-2}$
$$= (4^{-2} x^4 y^{-4})^3 (8^{-1} x^{-6} y^2)^{-2}$$
$$= (4^{-6} x^{12} y^{-12})(8^2 x^{12} y^{-4})$$
$$= \dfrac{8^2 x^{24} y^{-16}}{4^6}$$
$$= \dfrac{64 x^{24}}{4096 y^{16}}$$
$$= \dfrac{x^{24}}{64 y^{16}}$$

81. $\left(\dfrac{9ab^{-2}}{8a^{-2} b}\right)^{-2} \left(\dfrac{3a^{-2} b}{2a^2 b^{-2}}\right)^3 = \left(\dfrac{9a^3 b^{-3}}{8}\right)^{-2} \left(\dfrac{3a^{-4} b^3}{2}\right)^3$
$$= \dfrac{9^{-2} a^{-6} b^6}{8^{-2}} \cdot \dfrac{3^3 a^{-12} b^9}{2^3}$$
$$= \dfrac{8^2 \cdot 3^3 a^{-18} b^{15}}{9^2 \cdot 2^3}$$
$$= \dfrac{64 \cdot 27 b^{15}}{81 \cdot 8 a^{18}}$$
$$= \dfrac{8b^{15}}{3a^{18}}$$

82. $[(xy^{-2})^3]^{-2} = (x^3 y^{-6})^{-2} = x^{-6} y^{12} = \dfrac{y^{12}}{x^6}$

83. $[(x^{-2} y^{-1})^2]^{-3} = (x^{-4} y^{-2})^{-3} = x^{12} y^6$

84. $\left[\left(\dfrac{x}{y^2}\right)^{-2}\right]^3 = \left(\dfrac{x^{-2}}{y^{-4}}\right)^3 = \left(\dfrac{y^4}{x^2}\right)^3 = \dfrac{y^{12}}{x^6}$

85. $\left[\left(\dfrac{a^2}{b}\right)^{-1}\right]^2 = \left(\dfrac{a^{-2}}{b^{-1}}\right)^2 = \left(\dfrac{b}{a^2}\right)^2 = \dfrac{b^2}{a^4}$

Objective 5.1.3 Exercises

86. $0.00000467 = 4.67 \times 10^{-6}$

87. $0.00000005 = 5 \times 10^{-8}$

88. $0.00000000017 = 1.7 \times 10^{-10}$

89. $4,300,000 = 4.3 \times 10^6$

90. $200,000,000,000 = 2 \times 10^{11}$

91. $9,800,000,000 = 9.8 \times 10^9$

92. $1.23 \times 10^{-7} = 0.000000123$

93. $6.2 \times 10^{-12} = 0.0000000000062$

94. $8.2 \times 10^{15} = 8,200,000,000,000,000$

95. $6.34 \times 10^5 = 634,000$

96. $3.9 \times 10^{-2} = 0.039$

97. $4.35 \times 10^9 = 4,350,000,000$

98. $(3 \times 10^{-12})(5 \times 10^{16}) = (3)(5) \times 10^{-12+16}$
$\qquad\qquad = 15 \times 10^4$
$\qquad\qquad = 1.5 \times 10^5$

99. $(8.9 \times 10^{-5})(3.2 \times 10^{-6}) = (8.9)(3.2) \times 10^{-5+(-6)}$
$\qquad\qquad\qquad = 28.48 \times 10^{-11}$
$\qquad\qquad\qquad = 2.848 \times 10^{-10}$

100. $(0.0000065)(3,200,000,000,000)$
$\qquad = (6.5 \times 10^{-6})(3.2 \times 10^{12})$
$\qquad = (6.5)(3.2) \times 10^{-6+12}$
$\qquad = 20.8 \times 10^6$
$\qquad = 2.08 \times 10^7$

101. $(480,000)(0.0000000096)$
$\qquad = (4.8 \times 10^5)(9.6 \times 10^{-9})$
$\qquad = (4.8)(9.6) \times 10^{5+(-9)}$
$\qquad = 46.08 \times 10^{-4}$
$\qquad = 4.608 \times 10^{-3}$

102. $\dfrac{9 \times 10^{-3}}{6 \times 10^5} = 1.5 \times 10^{-3-5}$
$\qquad\qquad = 1.5 \times 10^{-8}$

103. $\dfrac{2.7 \times 10^4}{3 \times 10^{-6}} = 0.9 \times 10^{4-(-6)}$
$\qquad\qquad = 0.9 \times 10^{10}$
$\qquad\qquad = 9 \times 10^9$

104. $\dfrac{0.0089}{500,000,000} = \dfrac{8.9 \times 10^{-3}}{5 \times 10^8}$
$\qquad\qquad\qquad = 1.78 \times 10^{-3-8}$
$\qquad\qquad\qquad = 1.78 \times 10^{-11}$

105. $\dfrac{4800}{0.00000024} = \dfrac{4.8 \times 10^3}{2.4 \times 10^{-7}}$
$\qquad\qquad\qquad = 2 \times 10^{3-(-7)}$
$\qquad\qquad\qquad = 2 \times 10^{10}$

106. $\dfrac{0.00056}{0.000000000004} = \dfrac{5.6 \times 10^{-4}}{4 \times 10^{-12}}$
$\qquad\qquad\qquad = 1.4 \times 10^{-4-(-12)}$
$\qquad\qquad\qquad = 1.4 \times 10^8$

107. $\dfrac{0.000000346}{0.0000005} = \dfrac{3.46 \times 10^{-7}}{5 \times 10^{-7}}$
$\qquad\qquad\qquad = 0.692 \times 10^{-7-(-7)}$
$\qquad\qquad\qquad = 0.692 \times 10^0 = 6.92 \times 10^{-1}$

108. $\dfrac{(3.2 \times 10^{-11})(2.9 \times 10^{15})}{8.1 \times 10^{-3}}$
$\qquad = \dfrac{(3.2)(2.9) \times 10^{-11+15-(-3)}}{8.1}$
$\qquad = 1.14567901 \times 10^7$

109. $\dfrac{(6.9 \times 10^{27})(8.2 \times 10^{-13})}{4.1 \times 10^{15}}$
$\qquad = \dfrac{(6.9)(8.2) \times 10^{27+(-13)-15}}{4.1}$
$\qquad = 13.8 \times 10^{-1}$
$\qquad = 1.38$

110. $\dfrac{(0.00000004)(84,000)}{(0.0003)(1,400,000)}$
$\qquad = \dfrac{4 \times 10^{-8} \times 8.4 \times 10^4}{3 \times 10^{-4} \times 1.4 \times 10^6}$
$\qquad = \dfrac{(4)(8.4) \times 10^{-8+4-(-4)-6}}{(3)(1.4)}$
$\qquad = 8 \times 10^{-6}$

111. $\dfrac{(720)(0.0000000039)}{(26,000,000,000)(0.018)}$
$\qquad = \dfrac{7.2 \times 10^2 \times 3.9 \times 10^{-9}}{2.6 \times 10^{10} \times 1.8 \times 10^{-2}}$
$\qquad = \dfrac{(7.2)(3.9) \times 10^{2+(-9)-10-(-2)}}{(2.6)(1.8)}$
$\qquad = 6 \times 10^{-15}$

Objective 5.1.4 Exercises

112. Strategy

To find the number of arithmetic operations:
• Find the reciprocal of 5×10^{-7}, which is the number of operations performed in one second.
• Write the number of seconds in one hour (3600) in scientific notation.
• Multiply the number of arithmetic operations per second by the number of seconds in one hour.

Solution

$$\frac{1}{5 \times 10^{-7}} = \frac{1}{5} \times 10^7$$

$$60 \cdot 60 = 3600 = 3.6 \times 10^3$$

$$\left(\frac{1}{5} \times 10^7\right)(3.6 \times 10^3) = \frac{1}{5} \times 3.6 \times 10^{10}$$

$$= 0.72 \times 10^{10}$$

$$= 7.2 \times 10^9$$

The computer can perform 7.2×10^9 operations in one hour.

113. Strategy

To find the number of arithmetic operations:
• Find the reciprocal of 2×10^{-9}, which is the number of operations performed in one second.
• Write the number of seconds in one minute (60) in scientific notation.
• Multiply the number of arithmetic operations per second by the number of seconds in one minute.

Solution

$$\frac{1}{2 \times 10^{-9}} = \frac{1}{2} \times 10^9$$

$$60 = 6 \times 10$$

$$\left(\frac{1}{2} \times 10^9\right)(6 \times 10) = \frac{1}{2} \times 6 \times 10^{10}$$

$$= 3 \times 10^{10}$$

The computer can perform 3×10^{10} operations in one minute.

114. Strategy

To find the distance traveled:
Write the number of seconds in 8 h in scientific notation.
Use the equation $d = rt$, where r is the speed of light and t is the number of seconds in 8 h.

Solution

$$8 \cdot 60 \cdot 60 = 28,800 = 2.88 \times 10^4$$

$$d = rt$$

$$d = (3 \times 10^8)(2.88 \times 10^4)$$

$$d = 3 \times 2.88 \times 10^{12}$$

$$d = 8.64 \times 10^{12}$$

Light travels 8.64×10^{12} m in 8 h.

115. Strategy

To find the distance traveled:
Write the number of seconds in one day in scientific notation.
Use the equation $d = rt$, where r is the speed of light and t is the number of seconds in one day.

Solution

$$r = 3 \times 10^8$$

$$24 \cdot 60 \cdot 60 = 86,400 = 8.64 \times 10^4$$

$$d = rt$$

$$d = (3 \times 10^8)(8.64 \times 10^4)$$

$$d = 3 \times 8.64 \times 10^{12}$$

$$d = 25.92 \times 10^{12}$$

$$d = 2.592 \times 10^{13}$$

Light travels 2.592×10^{13} m in one day.

116. Strategy

To find the time for one revolution:
Write the number of seconds in one minute (60) in scientific notation.
Divide the number of revolutions per minute by the number of seconds in one minute.
Find the reciprocal of the number of revolutions per second, which is the number of seconds per revolution.

Solution

$$60 = 6 \times 10$$

$$\frac{4 \times 10^8}{6 \times 10} = 0.\overline{6} \times 10^7$$

$$\frac{1}{0.\overline{6} \times 10^7} = \frac{1}{0.6} \times 10^{-7}$$

$$= 1.5 \times 10^{-7}$$

The high-speed centrifuge can make one revolution in 1.5×10^{-7} s.

117. Strategy

To find the number of times heavier the proton is, divide the mass of the proton by the mass of the electron.

Solution

$$\frac{1.673 \times 10^{-27}}{9.109 \times 10^{-31}} = 0.183664508 \times 10^4$$

$$= 1.83664508 \times 10^3$$

The proton is 1.83664508×10^3 times heavier than the electron.

118. Strategy

To find the number of times heavier the sun is, divide the mass of the sun by the mass of Earth.

Solution

$$\frac{2 \times 10^{30}}{5.9 \times 10^{24}} = 0.33898305 \times 10^6$$

$$= 3.3898305 \times 10^5$$

The sun is 3.3898305×10^5 times heavier than Earth.

119. Strategy
To find the rate, divide the number of miles by the time.

Solution
$$\frac{119 \times 10^6}{11} = 1.08\overline{1} \times 10^7 \text{ mi/min}$$

The signals traveled at $1.08\overline{1} \times 10^7$ mi/min.

120. Strategy
To find the time, use the equation $d = rt$, where r is the speed of light and d is the distance to the Earth from the sun.

Solution
$$d = rt$$
$$9.3 \times 10^7 = (1.86 \times 10^5)t$$
$$\frac{9.3 \times 10^7}{1.86 \times 10^5} = t$$
$$5 \times 10^2 = t$$

Light travels to Earth from the sun in 5×10^2 s.

121. Strategy
To find the weight of one seed:
Write the number of seeds per ounce in scientific notation.
Find the reciprocal of the number of seeds per ounce, which is the number of ounces per seed.

Solution
$$31,000,000 = 3.1 \times 10^7$$
$$\frac{1}{3.1 \times 10^7} = 0.32258065 \times 10^{-7}$$
$$= 3.2258065 \times 10^{-8}$$

The weight of one orchid seed is 3.2258065×10^{-8} oz.

122. Strategy
To find the rate, divide the debt by the number of citizens.

Solution
$$\frac{6.6 \times 10^{12}}{3 \times 10^8} = 2 \times 10^4$$

Each American would have to pay 2×10^4 dollars.

123. Strategy
To find the time, use the equation $d = rt$, where r is the speed of the satellite and d is the distance to Saturn.

Solution
$$d = rt$$
$$8.86 \times 10^8 = (1 \times 10^5)t$$
$$\frac{8.86 \times 10^8}{1 \times 10^5} = t$$
$$8.86 \times 10^3 = t$$

It will take the satellite 8.86×10^3 h to reach Saturn.

124. Strategy
To find the surface area, use the formula $SA = 4\pi r^2$, where r is the radius.

Solution
$$r = 0.5(3 \times 10^4) = 1.5 \times 10^4$$
$$SA = 4\pi r^2$$
$$= 4\pi(1.5 \times 10^4)^2$$
$$= 4\pi(1.5)^2 \times 10^8$$
$$= 4\pi(2.25) \times 10^8$$
$$= 28.2743339 \times 10^8$$
$$= 2.82743339 \times 10^9$$

The surface area of Neptune is 2.82743339×10^9 mi^2.

125. Strategy
To find the volume, use the formula $V = \frac{4}{3}\pi r^3$, where $r = 1.5 \times 10^{-4}$ mm.

Solution
$$V = \frac{4}{3}\pi r^3$$
$$= \frac{4}{3}\pi(1.5 \times 10^{-4})^3$$
$$= \frac{4}{3}\pi(1.5)^3 \times 10^{-12}$$
$$= 14.1371669 \times 10^{-12}$$
$$= 1.41371669 \times 10^{-11}$$

The volume of the cell is $1.41371669 \times 10^{-11}$ mm^3.

126. Strategy
To find the weight of one atom, find the reciprocal of the number of atoms per gram, which is the number of grams per atom.

Solution
$$\frac{1}{6.023 \times 10^{23}} = 0.166030217 \times 10^{-23}$$
$$= 1.66030217 \times 10^{-24}$$

The weight of one atom of hydrogen is $1.66030217 \times 10^{-24}$ g.

127. Strategy
To find the time:
Write the speed of the space ship in scientific notation.
Use the equation $d = rt$, where r is the speed of the space ship and d is the distance across the galaxy.

Solution
$$25,000 = 2.5 \times 10^4$$
$$d = rt$$
$$5.6 \times 10^{10} = (2.5 \times 10^4)t$$
$$\frac{5.6 \times 10^{19}}{2.5 \times 10^4} = t$$
$$2.24 \times 10^{15} = t$$
The space ship travels across the galaxy in 2.24×10^{15} h.

Applying Concepts 5.1

128. $\frac{1}{3}x - 1$

Yes, the expression is a polynomial.

129. $\frac{3}{x} - 1$

No, the expression is not a polynomial because there is a variable in the denominator.

130. $5\sqrt{x} + 2$

No, the expression is not a polynomial because there is a variable under a radical.

131. $\sqrt{5}x + 2$

Yes, the expression is a polynomial.

132. $\frac{1}{4y^2} + \frac{1}{3y}$

No, the expression is not a polynomial because there is a variable in the denominator.

133. $x + \sqrt{3}$

Yes, the expression is a polynomial.

134.
$$(2x^3 + 3x^2 + kx + 5) - (x^3 + x^2 - 5x - 2) = x^3 + 2x^2 + 3x + 7$$
$$(2x^3 + 3x^2 + kx + 5) + (-x^3 - x^2 + 5x + 2) = x^3 + 2x^2 + 3x + 7$$
$$x^3 + 2x^2 + (k+5)x + 7 = x^3 + 2x^2 + 3x + 7$$
$$k + 5 = 3$$
$$k = -2$$

135.
$$(6x^3 + kx^2 - 2x - 1) - (4x^3 - 3x^2 + 1) = 2x^3 - x^2 - 2x - 2$$
$$(6x^3 + kx^2 - 2x - 1) + (-4x^3 + 3x^2 - 1) = 2x^3 - x^2 - 2x - 2$$
$$2x^3 + (k+3)x^2 - 2x - 2 = 2x^3 - x^2 - 2x - 2$$
$$k + 3 = -1$$
$$k = -4$$

136. Strategy
To find the perimeter, replace the variables L and W in the equation $P = 2L + 2W$ by the given values and solve for P.

Solution
$$P = 2L + 2W$$
$$P = 2(3x^n) + 2(x^n)$$
$$P = 6x^n + 2x^n$$
$$P = 8x^n$$
The perimeter is $8x^n$.

137. Strategy
To find the perimeter, replace the variables a, b, and c in the equation $P = a + b + c$ by the given values and solve for P.

Solution
$$P = a + b + c$$
$$P = 4x^n + 3x^n + 3x^n$$
$$P = 10x^n$$
The perimeter is $10x^n$.

138. Strategy
To find the area, replace the variables L and W in the equation $A = L \cdot W$ by the given values and solve for A.

Solution
$A = L \cdot W$
$A = (4ab)(6ab)$
$A = 24a^2b^2$
The area is $24a^2b^2$.

139. Strategy
To find the area, replace the variables b and h in the equation $A = \dfrac{1}{2}bh$ by the given values and solve for A.

Solution
$A = \dfrac{1}{2}bh$
$A = \dfrac{1}{2}(8xy)(5xy)$
$A = 4xy(5xy)$
$A = 20x^2y^2$
The area is $20x^2y^2$.

140. $\dfrac{4m^4}{n^{-2}} + \left(\dfrac{n^{-1}}{m^2}\right)^{-2} = 4m^4n^2 + (m^{-2}n^{-1})^{-2}$
$$= 4m^4n^2 + m^4n^2$$
$$= 5m^4n^2$$

141. $\dfrac{5x^3}{y^{-6}} + \left(\dfrac{x^{-1}}{y^2}\right)^{-3} = 5x^3y^6 + (x^{-1}y^{-2})^{-3}$
$$= 5x^3y^6 + x^3y^6$$
$$= 6x^3y^6$$

142. $\left(\dfrac{3a^{-2}b}{a^{-4}b^{-1}}\right)^2 \div \left(\dfrac{a^{-1}b}{9a^2b^3}\right)^{-1}$
$$= (3a^2b^2)^2 \div \left(\dfrac{a^{-3}b^{-2}}{9}\right)^{-1}$$
$$= 9a^4b^4 \div \dfrac{a^3b^2}{9^{-1}}$$
$$= 9a^4b^4 \div 9a^3b^2$$
$$= \dfrac{9a^4b^4}{9a^3b^2}$$
$$= ab^2$$

143. $\left(\dfrac{2m^3n^{-2}}{4m^4n}\right)^{-2} \div \left(\dfrac{mn^5}{m^{-1}n^3}\right)^3$
$$= \left(\dfrac{m^{-1}n^{-3}}{2}\right)^{-2} \div (m^2n^2)^3$$
$$= \dfrac{m^2n^6}{2^{-2}} \div m^6n^6$$
$$= 2^2m^2n^6 \div m^6n^6$$
$$= \dfrac{4m^2n^6}{m^6n^6}$$
$$= \dfrac{4}{m^4}$$

144. $(2+3)^{-2} \neq 2^{-2} + 3^{-2}$
$$5^{-2} \neq \dfrac{1}{2^2} + \dfrac{1}{3^2}$$
$$\dfrac{1}{25} \neq \dfrac{1}{4} + \dfrac{1}{9}$$
$$\dfrac{1}{25} \neq \dfrac{13}{36}$$

145. No, let $a = -1$, and $b = 1$. Then $a < b$, but
$a^{-1} = \dfrac{1}{-1} = -1 < b^{-1} = \dfrac{1}{1} = 1$ because $-1 < 1$.

146. a. $2x + 3x = 5x^2$ incorrect
$2x + 3x = 5x$ correct
The Distributive Property was used incorrectly.

b. $a - (b - c) = a - b - c$ incorrect
$a - (b - c) = a - b + c$ correct
The Distributive Property was used incorrectly.

c. $x^0 = 0$ incorrect
$x^0 = 1$ unless $x = 0$, correct
The definition of zero as an exponent was used incorrectly.

d. $(x^4)^5 = x^9$ incorrect
$(x^4)^5 = x^{20}$ correct
The Rule for Simplifying the Power of an Exponential Expression was used incorrectly.

e. $x^2 \cdot x^3 = x^6$ incorrect
$x^2 \cdot x^3 = x^5$ correct
The Rule for Multiplying Exponential Expressions was used incorrectly.

f. $b^{m+n} = b^m + b^n$ incorrect
$b^{m+n} = b^m \cdot b^n$ correct
The Rule for Multiplying Exponential Expressions was used incorrectly.

Section 5.2

Concept Review 5.2

1. Always true

2. Never true
   The leading coefficient is the coefficient of the term with the highest degree. The leading coefficient is –3.

3. Always true

4. Always true

5. Sometimes true
   The sum of $-x^2 + 2x - 3$ and $x^2 + 5x - 10$ is the binomial $7x - 13$.

6. Never true
   A polynomial function does not have a variable raised to a negative power.

Objective 5.2.1 Exercises

1. The degree of a polynomial in one variable is the greatest of the degrees of any of its terms.
   $x^3 - 2x^2 + 4$ and $7 + 5x - 6x^3$ are third-degree polynomials.

2. To evaluate a polynomial function, replace the variable by its value and simplify.

3. $P(3) = 3(3)^2 - 2(3) - 8$
   $P(3) = 13$

4. $P(-5) = -3(-5)^2 - 5(-5) + 8$
   $P(-5) = -42$

5. $R(2) = 2(2)^3 - 3(2)^2 + 4(2) - 2$
   $R(2) = 10$

6. $R(-1) = -(-1)^3 + 2(-1)^2 - 3(-1) + 4$
   $R(-1) = 10$

7. $f(-1) = (-1)^4 - 2(-1)^2 - 10$
   $f(-1) = -11$

8. $f(2) = (2)^5 - 2(2)^3 + 4(2)$
   $f(2) = 24$

9. $L(s) = 0.641s^2$
   $L(6) = 0.641(6)^2$
   $L(6) = 23.076$
   The length of the wave is 23.1 m.

10. $s(t) = 2.735t^2$
    $s(3) = 2.735(3)^2$
    $s(3) = 24.615$
    An object will fall 24.615 feet in 3 seconds.

11. $T(n) = n^2 - n$
    $T(8) = (8)^2 - 8$
    $T(8) = 56$
    The league must schedule 56 games.

12. $T(n) = \frac{1}{2}n^2 - \frac{3}{2}n$
    $T(10) = \frac{1}{2}(10)^2 - \frac{3}{2}(10)$
    $T(10) = 35$
    A decagon has 35 diagonals.

13. $M(r) = 6.14r^2 + 6.14r + 2.094$
    $M(6) = 6.14(6)^2 + 6.14(6) + 2.094$
    $M(6) = 259.974$
    260 in^3 of meringue are needed.

14. When $0 < x < 1$, x^3 is less than x^2 and x is less than 1, therefore $x^3 + x < x^2 + 1$. So $f(x) > g(x)$.

15. Polynomial: (a) –1 (b) 8 (c) 2

16. Polynomial: (a) 3 (b) –7 (c) 4

17. Not a polynomial.

18. Not a polynomial.

19. Not a polynomial.

20. Not a polynomial.

21. Polynomial: (a) 3 (b) π (c) 5

22. Polynomial: (a) –4 (b) $-\sqrt{7}$ (c) 5

23. Polynomial: (a) –5 (b) 2 (c) 3

24. Polynomial: (a) –1 (b) 0 (c) 6

25. Polynomial: (a) 14 (b) 14 (c) 0

26. Not a polynomial.

27.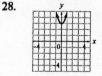

28.

29.

30.

31.

32.

Objective 5.2.2 Exercises

33. The additive inverse of a polynomial is the polynomial that has the same terms but the sign of each term has been changed to its opposite.

34. **a.** To add two polynomials, combine like terms.

    b. To subtract two polynomials, add the additive inverse of the second polynomial to the first polynomial.

35. $5x^2 + 2x - 7$
$x^2 - 8x + 12$
$\overline{6x^2 - 6x + 5}$

36. $3x^2 - 2x + 7$
$-3x^2 + 2x - 12$
$\overline{ - 5}$

37. $x^2 - 3x + 8$
$-2x^2 + 3x - 7$
$\overline{-x^2 + 1}$

38. $2x^2 + 3x - 7$
$-5x^2 + 8x + 1$
$\overline{-3x^2 + 11x - 6}$

39. $(3y^2 - 7y) + (2y^2 - 8y + 2)$
$= (3y^2 + 2y^2) + (-7y - 8y) + 2$
$= 5y^2 - 15y + 2$

40. $(-2y^2 - 4y - 12) + (5y^2 - 5y)$
$= (-2y^2 + 5y^2) + (-4y - 5y) - 12$
$= 3y^2 - 9y - 12$

41. $(2a^2 - 3a - 7) - (-5a^2 - 2a - 9)$
$= (2a^2 + 5a^2) + (-3a + 2a) + (-7 + 9)$
$= 7a^2 - a + 2$

42. $(3a^2 - 9a) - (-5a^2 + 7a - 6)$
$= (3a^2 + 5a^2) + (-9a - 7a) + 6$
$= 8a^2 - 16a + 6$

43. $P(x) + R(x) = (3x^3 - 4x^2 - x + 1) + (2x^3 + 5x - 8)$
$= 5x^3 - 4x^2 + 4x - 7$

44. $P(x) - R(x) = (5x^3 - 3x - 7) - (2x^3 - 3x^2 + 8)$
$= (5x^3 - 3x - 7) + (-2x^3 + 3x^2 - 8)$
$= 3x^3 + 3x^2 - 3x - 15$

45. $P(x) + R(x) = (x^{2n} + 7x^n - 3) + (-x^{2n} + 2x^n + 8)$
$= 9x^n + 5$

46. $P(x) - R(x) = (2x^{2n} - x^n - 1) - (5x^{2n} + 7x^n + 1)$
$= (2x^{2n} - x^n - 1) + (-5x^{2n} - 7x^n - 1)$
$= -3x^{2n} - 8x^n - 2$

47. $S(x) = P(x) + R(x)$
$= (3x^4 - 3x^3 - x^2) + (3x^3 - 7x^2 + 2x)$
$= 3x^4 - 8x^2 + 2x$

48. $S(x) = P(x) + R(x)$
$= (3x^4 - 2x + 1) + (3x^5 - 5x - 8)$
$= 3x^5 + 3x^4 - 7x - 7$

49. $D(x) = P(x) - R(x)$
$= (x^2 + 2x + 1) - (2x^3 - 3x^2 + 2x - 7)$
$= (x^2 + 2x + 1) + (-2x^3 + 3x^2 - 2x + 7)$
$= -2x^3 + 4x^2 + 8$

50. $D(x) = P(x) - R(x)$
$= (2x^4 - 2x^2 + 1) - (3x^3 - 2x^2 + 3x + 8)$
$= (2x^4 - 2x^2 + 1) + (-3x^3 + 2x^2 - 3x - 8)$
$= 2x^4 - 3x^3 - 3x - 7$

Applying Concepts 5.2

51.

$x = 1.5$

52.

$x = 1.9$

53.

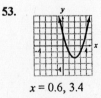

$x = 0.6, 3.4$

54.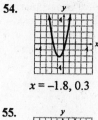

$x = -1.8, 0.3$

57.

$x = -0.6, 1.6$

55.

$x = -1.9, 0.35, 1.5$

58.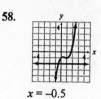

$x = -0.5$

56.

$x = 0.8$

59.
$$(2x^3 + 3x^2 + kx + 5) - (x^3 + x^2 - 5x - 2) = x^3 + 2x^2 + 3x + 7$$
$$(2x^3 - x^3) + (3x^2 - x^2) + (kx + 5x) + (5 + 2) = x^3 + 2x^2 + 3x + 7$$
$$x^3 + 2x^2 + (k + 5)x + 7 = x^3 + 2x^2 + 3x + 7$$
$$(k + 5)x = 3x$$
$$k + 5 = 3$$
$$k = -2$$

60.
$$(6x^3 + kx^2 - 2x - 1) - (4x^3 - 3x^2 + 1) = 2x^3 - x^2 - 2x - 2$$
$$(6x^3 - 4x^3) + (kx^2 + 3x^2) + (-2x) + (-1 - 1) = 2x^3 - x^2 - 2x - 2$$
$$2x^3 + (k + 3)x^2 - 2x - 2 = 2x^3 - x^2 - 2x - 2$$
$$(k + 3)x^2 = -x^2$$
$$k + 3 = -1$$
$$k = -4$$

61. The degree of $P(x) + Q(x)$ will be 4.
Example:
$$P(x) = 2x^3 + 4x^2 - 3x + 9$$
$$Q(x) = x^4 - 5x + 1$$
$$P(x) + Q(x) = x^4 + 2x^3 + 4x^2 - 8x + 10,$$
a fourth-degree polynomial.

62. The degree of $P(x) - Q(x)$ will be 5.
Example:
$$P(x) = 10x^5 - x^4 + 3x^2 - 1$$
$$Q(x) = -x^4 + x^3 + x^2 + 2x + 5$$
$$P(x) - Q(x) = 10x^5 - x^3 + 2x^2 - 2x - 6,$$
a fifth-degree polynomial.

63. Strategy
Determine the midpoint of the beam, x, and substitute x into $D(x)$ to determine the deflection.

Solution
Length of beam = 10 ft
Midpoint of beam = 5
$$D(x) = 0.005x^4 - 0.1x^3 + 0.5x^2$$
$$D(5) = 0.005(5)^4 - 0.1(5)^3 + 0.5(5)^2$$
$$D(5) = 3.125$$
The maximum deflection of the beam is 3.125 in.

64. $P(x) = 2x^3 - 4x^2 - 2x + c$
$$3 = 2(2)^3 - 4(2)^2 - 2(2) + c$$
$$3 = 16 - 16 - 4 + c$$
$$3 = -4 + c$$
$$7 = c$$
The value of c is 7.

65. $P(x) = 4x^4 - 3x^2 + 6x + c$

$-3 = 4(-1)^4 - 3(-1)^2 + 6(-1) + c$

$-3 = 4 - 3 - 6 + c$

$-3 = -5 + c$

$2 = c$

The value of c is 2.

66.

The graph of k is the graph of f moved 2 units to the right.

67.

The graph of k is the graph of f moved 2 units down.

68. a. $f(x) = \dfrac{1}{8820} x^2 + 25$

$f(1000) = \dfrac{1}{8820}(1000)^2 + 25 \approx 138.4$

The height of the cables is approximately 138.4 ft.

b. $f(x) = \dfrac{1}{8820} x^2 + 25$

$f(1500) = \dfrac{1}{8820}(1500)^2 + 25 \approx 280.1$

The height of the cables is approximately 280.1 ft.

69. A spline is a piecewise polynomial approximation to a function f. Thus a cubic spline is a piecewise cubic polynomial approximation to a function. The interval on which f is defined is partitioned, and a cubic polynomial that approximates f on that interval is determined. The cubic spline defined by

$$c(x) = \begin{cases} -2x^3 - x^2 & -1 \le x \le 0 \\ 2x^3 - x^2 & 0 \le x \le 1 \end{cases}$$

is an approximation to $f(x) = x^4$ on the interval $-1 \le x \le 1$. The graph is shown below.

The graph of f is a solid graph; c is shown as a dotted graph.

70. Numbers that can be represented in a regular geometric form are called polygonal numbers. They are also called figurative numbers. Examples of triangular, square, and pentagonal numbers follow.

71. The graphs of $f(x) = x^2$, $g(x) = (x-3)^2$, and $h(x) = x^2 - 3$ are all graphs of the parabola whose equation is $f(x) = x^2$. The graph of g is shifted 3 units to the right; the graph of h is shifted three units down. See accompanying diagram.

Section 5.3

Concept Review 5.3

1. Always true

2. Sometimes true
   A third-degree polynomial is a cubic function.
   $f(x) = x^3 - 2$ is a cubic function with two terms.

3. Always true

4. Sometimes true
   $(x-2)(x+2) = x^2 - 4$ is an example of a product of two binomials that is not a trinomial.

5. Always true

6. Always true

Objective 5.3.1 Exercises

1. The Distributive Property is used to multiply expressions when one or both of the expressions have more than one term.

2. Use the Distributive Property to multiply each term of the polynomial by the monomial. In multiplying each term, multiply the coefficients; multiply variables with like bases by adding the exponents.

3. $2x(x-3) = 2x^2 - 6x$

4. $2a(2a+4) = 4a^2 + 8a$

5. $3x^2(2x^2 - x) = 6x^4 - 3x^3$

6. $-4y^2(4y - 6y^2) = -16y^3 + 24y^4$

7. $3xy(2x - 3y) = 6x^2y - 9xy^2$

8. $-4ab(5a - 3b) = -20a^2b + 12ab^2$

9. $x^n(x+1) = x^{n+1} + x^n$

10. $y^n(y^{2n}-3)=y^{3n}-3y^n$

11. $x^n(x^n+y^n)=x^{2n}+x^ny^n$

12. $x-2x(x-2)=x-2x^2+4x=-2x^2+5x$

13. $2b+4b(2-b)=2b+8b-4b^2=-4b^2+10b$

14. $-2y(3-y)+2y^2=-6y+2y^2+2y^2=4y^2-6y$

15. $-2a^2(3a^2-2a+3)=-6a^4+4a^3-6a^2$

16. $4b(3b^3-12b^2-6)=12b^4-48b^3-24b$

17. $3b(3b^4-3b^2+8)=9b^5-9b^3+24b$

18. $(2x^2-3x-7)(-2x^2)=-4x^4+6x^3+14x^2$

19. $-5x^2(4-3x+3x^2+4x^3)$
$=-20x^2+15x^3-15x^4-20x^5$
$=-20x^5-15x^4+15x^3-20x^2$

20. $-2y^2(3-2y-3y^2+2y^3)$
$=-6y^2+4y^3+6y^4-4y^5$
$=-4y^5+6y^4+4y^3-6y^2$

21. $-2x^2y(x^2-3xy+2y^2)=-2x^4y+6x^3y^2-4x^2y^3$

22. $3ab^2(3a^2-2ab+4b^2)$
$=9a^3b^2-6a^2b^3+12ab^4$

23. $x^n(x^{2n}+x^n+x)=x^{3n}+x^{2n}+x^{n+1}$

24. $x^{2n}(x^{2n-2}+x^{2n}+x)=x^{4n-2}+x^{4n}+x^{2n+1}$

25. $a^{n+1}(a^n-3a+2)=a^{2n+1}-3a^{n+2}+2a^{n+1}$

26. $a^{n+4}(a^{n-2}+5a^2-3)=a^{2n+2}+5a^{n+6}-3a^{n+4}$

27. $2y^2-y[3-2(y-4)-y]=2y^2-y[3-2y+8-y]$
$=2y^2-y[11-3y]$
$=2y^2-11y+3y^2$
$=5y^2-11y$

28. $3x^2-x[x-2(3x-4)]=3x^2-x[x-6x+8]$
$=3x^2-x[-5x+8]$
$=3x^2+5x^2-8x$
$=8x^2-8x$

29. $2y-3[y-2y(y-3)+4y]$
$=2y-3[y-2y^2+6y+4y]$
$=2y-3[11y-2y^2]$
$=2y-33y+6y^2$
$=6y^2-31y$

30. $4a^2-2a[3-a(2-a+a^2)]$
$=4a^2-2a[3-2a+a^2-a^3]$
$=4a^2-6a+4a^2-2a^3+2a^4$
$=2a^4-2a^3+8a^2-6a$

Objective 5.3.2 Exercises

31. $(5x-7)(3x-8)=15x^2-40x-21x+56$
$=15x^2-61x+56$

32. $(2x-3y)(2x+5y)=4x^2+10xy-6xy-15y^2$
$=4x^2+4xy-15y^2$

33. $(7x-3y)(2x-9y)=14x^2-63xy-6xy+27y^2$
$=14x^2-69xy+27y^2$

34. $(2a-3b)(5a+4b)=10a^2+8ab-15ab-12b^2$
$=10a^2-7ab-12b^2$

35. $(3a-5b)(a+7b)=3a^2+21ab-5ab-35b^2$
$=3a^2+16ab-35b^2$

36. $(5a+2b)(3a+7b)=15a^2+35ab+6ab+14b^2$
$=15a^2+41ab+14b^2$

37. $(5x+9y)(3x+2y)=15x^2+10xy+27xy+18y^2$
$=15x^2+37xy+18y^2$

38. $(3x-7y)(7x+2y)=21x^2+6xy-49xy-14y^2$
$=21x^2-43xy-14y^2$

39. $(5x-9y)(6x-5y)=30x^2-25xy-54xy+45y^2$
$=30x^2-79xy+45y^2$

40. $(xy+4)(xy-3)=x^2y^2-3xy+4xy-12$
$=x^2y^2+xy-12$

41. $(xy-5)(2xy+7)=2x^2y^2+7xy-10xy-35$
$=2x^2y^2-3xy-35$

42. $(2x^2-5)(x^2-5)=2x^4-10x^2-5x^2+25$
$=2x^4-15x^2+25$

43. $(x^2-4)(x^2-6)=x^4-6x^2-4x^2+24$
$=x^4-10x^2+24$

44. $(5x^2-5y)(2x^2-y)=10x^4-5x^2y-10x^2y+5y^2$
$=10x^4-15x^2y+5y^2$

45. $(x^2-2y^2)(x^2+4y^2)$
$=x^4+4x^2y^2-2x^2y^2-8y^4$
$=x^4+2x^2y^2-8y^4$

46. $(x^n+2)(x^n-3)=x^{2n}-3x^n+2x^n-6$
$=x^{2n}-x^n-6$

47. $(x^n-4)(x^n-5)=x^{2n}-5x^n-4x^n+20$
$=x^{2n}-9x^n+20$

48. $(2a^n-3)(3a^n+5)=6a^{2n}+10a^n-9a^n-15$
$=6a^{2n}+a^n-15$

49. $(5b^n - 1)(2b^n + 4) = 10b^{2n} + 20b^n - 2b^n - 4$
$= 10b^{2n} + 18b^n - 4$

50. $(2a^n - b^n)(3a^n + 2b^n)$
$= 6a^{2n} + 4a^n b^n - 3a^n b^n - 2b^{2n}$
$= 6a^{2n} + a^n b^n - 2b^{2n}$

51. $(3x^n + b^n)(x^n + 2b^n)$
$= 3x^{2n} + 6x^n b^n + x^n b^n + 2b^{2n}$
$= 3x^{2n} + 7x^n b^n + 2b^{2n}$

52.
$$
\begin{array}{r}
x^2 - 3x + 7 \\
\times \qquad x - 2 \\
\hline
-2x^2 + 6x - 14 \\
x^3 - 3x^2 + 7x \\
\hline
x^3 - 5x^2 + 13x - 14
\end{array}
$$

53.
$$
\begin{array}{r}
x^2 + 5x - 8 \\
\times \qquad x + 3 \\
\hline
3x^2 + 15x - 24 \\
x^3 + 5x^2 - 8x \\
\hline
x^3 + 8x^2 + 7x - 24
\end{array}
$$

54.
$$
\begin{array}{r}
x^3 \qquad - 3x + 4 \\
\times \qquad x + 5 \\
\hline
5x^3 \qquad - 15x + 20 \\
x^4 \qquad - 3x^2 + 4x \\
\hline
x^4 + 5x^3 - 3x^2 - 11x + 20
\end{array}
$$

55.
$$
\begin{array}{r}
a^3 - 3a^2 \quad + 7 \\
\times \qquad a + 2 \\
\hline
2a^3 - 6a^2 \quad + 14 \\
a^4 - 3a^3 \qquad + 7a \\
\hline
a^4 - a^3 - 6a^2 + 7a + 14
\end{array}
$$

56.
$$
\begin{array}{r}
5a^2 - 6ab + 4b^2 \\
\times \qquad 2a - 3b \\
\hline
-15a^2 b + 18ab^2 - 12b^3 \\
10a^3 - 12a^2 b + 8ab^2 \\
\hline
10a^3 - 27a^2 b + 26ab^2 - 12b^3
\end{array}
$$

57.
$$
\begin{array}{r}
2a^2 - 5ab - 3b^2 \\
\times \qquad 3a + b \\
\hline
2a^2 b - 5ab^2 - 3b^3 \\
6a^3 - 15a^2 b - 9ab^2 \\
\hline
6a^3 - 13a^2 b - 14ab^2 - 3b^3
\end{array}
$$

58.
$$
\begin{array}{r}
y^3 - 5y^2 - 3 \\
\times \qquad 2y^2 - 1 \\
\hline
-y^3 + 5y^2 + 3 \\
2y^5 - 10y^4 \qquad - 6y^2 \\
\hline
2y^5 - 10y^4 - y^3 - y^2 + 3
\end{array}
$$

59.
$$
\begin{array}{r}
3b^2 - 3b + 6 \\
\times \qquad 2b^2 \qquad - 3 \\
\hline
-9b^2 + 9b - 18 \\
6b^4 - 6b^3 + 12b^2 \\
\hline
6b^4 - 6b^3 + 3b^2 + 9b - 18
\end{array}
$$

60.
$$
\begin{array}{r}
2x^4 - 3x^3 \qquad - 2x + 9 \\
\times \qquad 2x - 5 \\
\hline
-10x^4 + 15x^3 \qquad + 10x - 45 \\
4x^5 - 6x^4 \qquad - 4x^2 + 18x \\
\hline
4x^5 - 16x^4 + 15x^3 - 4x^2 + 28x - 45
\end{array}
$$

61.
$$
\begin{array}{r}
3a^4 \qquad - 3a^2 + 2a - 5 \\
\times \qquad 2a - 5 \\
\hline
-15a^4 \qquad + 15a^2 - 10a + 25 \\
6a^5 \qquad - 6a^3 + 4a^2 - 10a \\
\hline
6a^5 - 15a^4 - 6a^3 + 19a^2 - 20a + 25
\end{array}
$$

62.
$$
\begin{array}{r}
x^2 + 2x - 3 \\
\times \qquad x^2 - 5x + 7 \\
\hline
7x^2 + 14x - 21 \\
-5x^3 - 10x^2 + 15x \\
x^4 + 2x^3 - 3x^2 \\
\hline
x^4 - 3x^3 - 6x^2 + 29x - 21
\end{array}
$$

63.
$$
\begin{array}{r}
x^2 - 3x + 1 \\
\times \qquad x^2 - 2x + 7 \\
\hline
7x^2 - 21x + 7 \\
-2x^3 + 6x^2 - 2x \\
x^4 - 3x^3 + x^2 \\
\hline
x^4 - 5x^3 + 14x^2 - 23x + 7
\end{array}
$$

64. $(a - 2)(2a - 3)(a + 7)$
$= (2a^2 - 3a - 4a + 6)(a + 7)$
$= (2a^2 - 7a + 6)(a + 7)$
$$
\begin{array}{r}
= \quad 2a^2 - 7a + 6 \\
\times \qquad a + 7 \\
\hline
14a^2 - 49a + 42 \\
2a^3 - 7a^2 + 6a \\
\hline
2a^3 + 7a^2 - 43a + 42
\end{array}
$$

65. $(b - 3)(3b - 2)(b - 1)$
$= (3b^2 - 2b - 9b + 6)(b - 1)$
$= (3b^2 - 11b + 6)(b - 1)$
$$
\begin{array}{r}
= \quad 3b^2 - 11b + 6 \\
\times \qquad b - 1 \\
\hline
-3b^2 + 11b - 6 \\
3b^3 - 11b^2 + 6b \\
\hline
3b^3 - 14b^2 + 17b - 6
\end{array}
$$

66.
$$x^n - 2x^n y^n + 3y^n$$
$$\times \qquad\qquad x^n + y^n$$
$$\overline{x^n y^n - 2x^n y^{2n} + 3y^{2n}}$$
$$\underline{x^{2n} - 2x^{2n} y^n + 3x^n y^n}$$
$$x^{2n} - 2x^{2n} y^n + 4x^n y^n - 2x^n y^{2n} + 3y^{2n}$$

67.
$$x^{2n} - 3x^n y^n - y^{2n}$$
$$\times \qquad\qquad x^n - y^n$$
$$\overline{-x^{2n} y^n + 3x^n y^{2n} + y^{3n}}$$
$$\underline{x^{3n} - 3x^{2n} y^n - x^n y^{2n}}$$
$$x^{3n} - 4x^{2n} y^n + 2x^n y^{2n} + y^{3n}$$

Objective 5.3.3 Exercises

68. $(a-4)(a+4) = a^2 - 16$

69. $(b-7)(b+7) = b^2 - 49$

70. $(3x-2)(3x+2) = 9x^2 - 4$

71. $(b-11)(b+11) = b^2 - 121$

72. $(3a+5b)^2 = 9a^2 + 30ab + 25b^2$

73. $(5x-4y)^2 = 25x^2 - 40xy + 16y^2$

74. $(x^2-3)^2 = x^4 - 6x^2 + 9$

75. $(x^2+y^2)^2 = x^4 + 2x^2 y^2 + y^4$

76. $(10+b)(10-b) = 100 - b^2$

77. $(2a-3b)(2a+3b) = 4a^2 - 9b^2$

78. $(5x-7y)(5x+7y) = 25x^2 - 49y^2$

79. $(x^2+1)(x^2-1) = x^4 - 1$

80. $(x^2+y^2)(x^2-y^2) = x^4 - y^4$

81. $(2x^n+y^n)^2 = 4x^{2n} + 4x^n y^n + y^{2n}$

82. $(a^n+5b^n)^2 = a^{2n} + 10a^n b^n + 25b^{2n}$

83. $(5a-9b)(5a+9b) = 25a^2 - 81b^2$

84. $(3x+7y)(3x-7y) = 9x^2 - 49y^2$

85. $(2x^n-5)(2x^n+5) = 4x^{2n} - 25$

86. $(4y+1)(4y-1) = 16y^2 - 1$

87. $(6-x)(6+x) = 36 - x^2$

88. $(2x^2-3y^2)^2 = 4x^4 - 12x^2 y^2 + 9y^4$

89. $(3a-4b)^2 = 9a^2 - 24ab + 16b^2$

90. $(2x^2+5)^2 = 4x^4 + 20x^2 + 25$

91. $(3x^n+2)^2 = 9x^{2n} + 12x^n + 4$

92. $(4b^n-3)^2 = 16b^{2n} - 24b^n + 9$

93. $(x^n+3)(x^n-3) = x^{2n} - 9$

94. $(x^n+y^n)(x^n-y^n) = x^{2n} - y^{2n}$

95. $(x^n-1)^2 = x^{2n} - 2x^n + 1$

96. $(a^n-b^n)^2 = a^{2n} - 2a^n b^n + b^{2n}$

97. $(2x^n+5y^n)^2 = 4x^{2n} + 20x^n y^n + 25y^{2n}$

Objective 5.3.4 Exercises

98. Strategy
To find the area, replace the variables L and W in the equation $A = L \cdot W$ by the given values and solve for A.

Solution
$A = L \cdot W$
$A = (3x+3)(x-4)$
$A = 3x^2 - 12x + 3x - 12$
$A = 3x^2 - 9x - 12$
The area is $(3x^2 - 9x - 12)$ ft^2.

99. Strategy
To find the area, replace the variables b and h in the equation $A = \frac{1}{2}bh$ by the given values and solve for A.

Solution
$A = \frac{1}{2}bh$
$A = \frac{1}{2}(x+2)(2x-3)$
$A = \left(\frac{1}{2}x+1\right)(2x-3)$
$A = x^2 - \frac{3}{2}x + 2x - 3$
$A = x^2 + \frac{x}{2} - 3$
The area is $\left(x^2 + \frac{x}{2} - 3\right)$ ft^2.

100. Strategy

To find the area, add the area of the small rectangle to the area of the large rectangle.

Large rectangle:

Length $= L_1 = x + 5$

Width $= W_1 = x - 2$

Small rectangle:

Length $= L_2 = 5$

Width $= W_2 = 2$

Solution

$A = $ Area of the large rectangle $+$

(area of the small rectangle)

$A = (L_1 \cdot W_1) + (L_2 \cdot W_2)$

$A = (x + 5)(x - 2) + (5)(2)$

$A = x^2 - 2x + 5x - 10 + 10$

$A = x^2 + 3x$

The area is $(x^2 + 3x)\, \mathrm{m}^2$.

101. Strategy

To find the area, subtract the four small rectangles from the large rectangle.

Large rectangle:

Length $= L_1 = x + 8$

Width $= W_1 = x + 4$

Small rectangles:

Length $= L_2 = 2$

Width $= W_2 = 2$

Solution

$A = $ Area of the large rectangle $- 4$(area of small rectangle)

$A = (L_1 \cdot W_1) - 4(L_2 \cdot W_2)$

$A = (x + 8)(x + 4) - 4(2)(2)$

$A = x^2 + 4x + 8x + 32 - 16$

$A = x^2 + 12x + 16$

The area is $(x^2 + 12x + 16)\, \mathrm{ft}^2$.

102. Strategy

Length of the trough: 6

Width of the trough: $10 - 2x$

Height of the trough: x

To find the volume, replace the variables L, W, and H in the equation $V = LWH$ and solve for V.

Solution

$V = LWH$

$V = 6(10 - 2x)(x)$

$V = (60 - 12x)x$

$V = 60x - 12x^2$

The volume is $(-12x^2 + 60x)\, \mathrm{m}^3$.

103. Strategy

Length of the box: $18 - 2x$
Width of the box: $18 - 2x$
Height of the box: x
To find the volume, replace the variables L, W, and H in the equation $V = LWH$ and solve for V.

Solution
$V = LWH$
$V = (18 - 2x)(18 - 2x)x$
$V = (324 - 36x - 36x + 4x^2)x$
$V = (324 - 72x + 4x^2)x$
$V = 324x - 72x^2 + 4x^3$
The volume is $(4x^3 - 72x^2 + 324x)$ in^3.

104. Strategy

To find the volume, replace the variable s in the equation $V = s^3$ with its given value and solve for V.

Solution
$V = s^3$
$V = (x - 2)^3$
$V = (x - 2)(x - 2)(x - 2)$
$V = (x^2 - 4x + 4)(x - 2)$
$V = x^3 - 6x^2 + 12x - 8$
The volume is $(x^3 - 6x^2 + 12x - 8)$ cm^3.

105. Strategy

To find the volume, replace the variables, L, W, and H in the equation $V = L \cdot W \cdot H$ by the given values and solve for V.

Solution
$V = L \cdot W \cdot H$
$V = (2x + 3)(x - 5)(x)$
$V = (2x^2 - 7x - 15)(x)$
$V = 2x^3 - 7x^2 - 15x$
The volume is $(2x^3 - 7x^2 - 15x)$ cm^3.

106. Strategy

To find the volume, subtract the volume of the small rectangular solid from the volume of the large rectangular solid.
Large rectangular solid:
Length = $L_1 = x + 2$
Width = $W_1 = 2x$
Height = $H_1 = x$
Small rectangular solid:
Length = $L_2 = x$
Width = $W_2 = 2x$
Height = $H_2 = 2$

Solution
$V = (L_1 \cdot W_1 \cdot H_1) - (L_2 \cdot W_2 \cdot H_2)$
$V = (x + 2)(2x)(x) - (x)(2x)(2)$
$V = (2x^2 + 4x)(x) - (2x^2)(2)$
$V = 2x^3 + 4x^2 - 4x^2$
$V = 2x^3$
The volume is $2x^3$ in^3.

107. Strategy

To find the volume, add the volume of the small rectangular solid to the volume of the large rectangular solid.
Large rectangular solid:
Length = $L_1 = 3x + 4$
Width = $W_1 = x + 6$
Height = $H_1 = x$
Small rectangular solid:
Length = $L_2 = x + 4$
Width = $W_2 = x + 6$
Height = $H_2 = x$

Solution
$V = (L_1 \cdot W_1 \cdot H_1) + (L_2 \cdot W_2 \cdot H_2)$
$V = (3x + 4)(x + 6)(x) + (x + 4)(x + 6)(x)$
$V = (3x^2 + 22x + 24)(x) + (x^2 + 10x + 24)(x)$
$V = 3x^3 + 22x^2 + 24x + x^3 + 10x^2 + 24x$
$V = 4x^3 + 32x^2 + 48x$
The volume is $(4x^3 + 32x^2 + 48x)$ cm^3.

Applying Concepts 5.3

108.

$\dfrac{(2x + 1)^5}{(2x + 1)^3} = (2x + 1)^{5-3}$

$= (2x + 1)^2$
$= (2x + 1)(2x + 1)$
$= 4x^2 + 4x + 1$

109.

$\dfrac{(3x - 5)^6}{(3x - 5)^4} = (3x - 5)^{6-4}$

$= (3x - 5)^2$
$= (3x - 5)(3x - 5)$
$= 9x^2 - 30x + 25$

110. $(a-b)^2 - (a+b)^2 = (a-b)(a-b) - (a+b)(a+b)$
$$= (a^2 - 2ab + b^2) - (a^2 + 2ab + b^2)$$
$$= (a^2 - 2ab + b^2) + (-a^2 - 2ab - b^2)$$
$$= -4ab$$

111. $(x+2y)^2 + (x+2y)(x-2y) = (x+2y)(x+2y) + (x+2y)(x-2y)$
$$= (x^2 + 4xy + 4y^2) + (x^2 - 4y^2)$$
$$= 2x^2 + 4xy$$

112. $(4y+3)^2 - (3y+4)^2 = (4y+3)(4y+3) - (3y+4)(3y+4)$
$$= (16y^2 + 24y + 9) - (9y^2 + 24y + 16)$$
$$= (16y^2 + 24y + 9) + (-9y^2 - 24y - 16)$$
$$= 7y^2 - 7$$

113. $2x^2(3x^3 + 4x - 1) - 5x^2(x^2 - 3) = (6x^5 + 8x^3 - 2x^2) - (5x^4 - 15x^2)$
$$= (6x^5 + 8x^3 - 2x^2) + (-5x^4 + 15x^2)$$
$$= 6x^5 - 5x^4 + 8x^3 + 13x^2$$

114. $(2b+3)(b-4) + (3+b)(3-2b) = (2b^2 - 8b + 3b - 12) + (9 - 6b + 3b - 2b^2)$
$$= (2b^2 - 5b - 12) + (9 - 3b - 2b^2)$$
$$= -8b - 3$$

115. $(3x-2y)^2 - (2x-3y)^2 = (3x-2y)(3x-2y) - (2x-3y)(2x-3y)$
$$= (9x^2 - 12xy + 4y^2) - (4x^2 - 12xy + 9y^2)$$
$$= (9x^2 - 12xy + 4y^2) + (-4x^2 + 12xy - 9y^2)$$
$$= 5x^2 - 5y^2$$

116. $[x+(y+1)][x-(y+1)] = x^2 - (y+1)^2$
$$= x^2 - (y^2 + 2y + 1)$$
$$= x^2 - y^2 - 2y - 1$$

117. $[x^2(2y-1)]^2 = x^{2 \cdot 2}(2y-1)^2$
$$= x^4(4y^2 - 4y + 1)$$
$$= 4x^4y^2 - 4x^4y + x^4$$

118. $\qquad (5x-k)(3x+k) = 15x^2 + 4x - k^2$
$$15x^2 + 5kx - 3kx - k^2 = 15x^2 + 4x - k^2$$
$$15x^2 + 2kx - k^2 = 15x^2 + 4x - k^2$$
$$2kx = 4x$$
$$2k = 4$$
$$k = 2$$

119. $\qquad (kx-7)(kx+2) = k^2x^2 + 5x - 14$
$$k^2x^2 + 2kx - 7kx - 14 = k^2x^2 + 5x - 14$$
$$k^2x^2 - 5kx - 14 = k^2x^2 + 5x - 14$$
$$-5kx = 5x$$
$$-5k = 5$$
$$k = -1$$

120. $\dfrac{a^m}{a^n}$, $m = n + 1$
$$\frac{a^{n+1}}{a^n} = a^{(n+1)-n} = a^1 = a$$

121. $\dfrac{a^m}{a^n}$, $m = n+2$

$$\dfrac{a^{n+2}}{a^n} = a^{(n+2)-n} = a^2$$

122. $(2x+3)(x-4) = 2x^2 - 8x + 3x - 12$
$$= 2x^2 - 5x - 12$$

123. $(x+7)(2x-3) = 2x^2 - 3x + 14x - 21$
$$= 2x^2 + 11x - 21$$

124. $(9a^2 - 2ab) - (4a+b)(2a-b)$
$$= (9a^2 - 2ab) - (8a^2 - 4ab + 2ab - b^2)$$
$$= (9a^2 - 2ab) - (8a^2 - 2ab - b^2)$$
$$= (9a^2 - 2ab) + (-8a^2 + 2ab + b^2)$$
$$= a^2 + b^2$$

125. $(6x^2 + 12xy - 2y^2) - (5x-y)(x+3y)$
$$= (6x^2 + 12xy - 2y^2) - (5x^2 + 15xy - xy - 3y^2)$$
$$= (6x^2 + 12xy - 2y^2) - (5x^2 + 14xy - 3y^2)$$
$$= (6x^2 + 12xy - 2y^2) + (-5x^2 - 14xy + 3y^2)$$
$$= x^2 - 2xy + y^2$$

126. Find the value of n.
$$5(n-1) = 2(3n-2)$$
$$5n - 5 = 6n - 4$$
$$-n - 5 = -4$$
$$-n = 1$$
$$n = -1$$
Substitute the value of n into the expression.
$$(3n^4)^3 = [3(-1)^4]^3 = [3(1)]^3 = 3^3 = 27$$

127. Find the value of n.
$$3(2n-1) = 5(n-1)$$
$$6n - 3 = 5n - 5$$
$$n - 3 = -5$$
$$n = -2$$
Substitute the value of n into the expression.
$$(-2n^3)^2 = [-2(-2)^3]^2 = [-2(-8)]^2 = 16^2 = 256$$

Section 5.4

Concept Review 5.4

1. Sometimes true

For example, 1 and x are monomials but $\dfrac{1}{x}$ is

not a monomial.

2. Sometimes true
The method works only for divisors of the form $x + a$.

3. Always true

4. Always true

Objective 5.4.1 Exercises

1. The degree of the quotient of two polynomials is equal to the degree of the dividend minus the degree of the divisor.

2. You can check the result of dividing two polynomials by multiplying the quotient by the divisor and then adding the remainder. The result should be equal to the dividend.

3.
$$\begin{array}{r} x+8 \\ x-5\overline{)x^2+3x-40} \\ \underline{x^2-5x} \\ 8x-40 \\ \underline{8x-40} \\ 0 \end{array}$$

$$(x^2 + 3x - 40) \div (x-5) = x + 8$$

4.
$$\begin{array}{r} x-12 \\ x-2\overline{)x^2-14x+24} \\ \underline{x^2-2x} \\ -12x+24 \\ \underline{-12x+24} \\ 0 \end{array}$$

$$(x^2 - 14x + 24) \div (x-2) = x - 12$$

5.
$$\begin{array}{r} x^2 \\ x-3\overline{)x^3-3x^2+0x+2} \\ \underline{x^3-3x^2} \\ 2 \end{array}$$

$$(x^3 - 3x^2 + 2) \div (x-3) = x^2 + \dfrac{2}{x-3}$$

6.
$$\begin{array}{r} x^2 \\ x+4\overline{)x^3+4x^2+0x-8} \\ \underline{x^3+4x^2} \\ -8 \end{array}$$

$$(x^3 + 4x^2 - 8) \div (x+4) = x^2 - \dfrac{8}{x+4}$$

7.
$$\begin{array}{r} 3x+5 \\ 2x+1\overline{)6x^2+13x+8} \\ \underline{6x^2+3x} \\ 10x+8 \\ \underline{10x+5} \\ 3 \end{array}$$

$$(6x^2 + 13x + 8) \div (2x+1) = 3x + 5 + \dfrac{3}{2x+1}$$

8.
$$\begin{array}{r} 4x+7 \\ 3x-2\overline{)12x^2+13x-14} \\ \underline{12x^2-8x} \\ 21x-14 \\ \underline{21x-14} \\ 0 \end{array}$$

$$(12x^2 + 13x - 14) \div (3x-2) = 4x + 7$$

9.
$$
\begin{array}{r}
5x+7 \\
2x-1 \overline{)10x^2+9x-5} \\
\underline{10x^2-5x} \\
14x-5 \\
\underline{14x-7} \\
2
\end{array}
$$

$$(10x^2+9x-5)\div(2x-1)=5x+7+\frac{2}{2x-1}$$

10.
$$
\begin{array}{r}
6x-5 \\
3x+2 \overline{)18x^2-3x+2} \\
\underline{18x^2+12x} \\
-15x+2 \\
\underline{-15x-10} \\
12
\end{array}
$$

$$(18x^2-3x+2)\div(3x+2)=6x-5+\frac{12}{3x+2}$$

11.
$$
\begin{array}{r}
4x^2+6x+9 \\
2x-3 \overline{)8x^3+0x^2+0x-9} \\
\underline{8x^3-12x^2} \\
12x^2+0x \\
\underline{12x^2-18x} \\
18x-9 \\
\underline{18x-27} \\
18
\end{array}
$$

$$(8x^3-9)\div(2x-3)=4x^2+6x+9+\frac{18}{2x-3}$$

12.
$$
\begin{array}{r}
16x^2-8x+4 \\
4x+2 \overline{)64x^3+0x^2+0x+4} \\
\underline{64x^3+32x^2} \\
-32x^2+0x \\
\underline{-32x^2-16x} \\
16x+4 \\
\underline{16x+8} \\
-4
\end{array}
$$

$$(64x^3+4)\div(4x+2)=16x^2-8x+4-\frac{4}{4x+2}$$

$$=16x^2-8x+4-\frac{2}{2x+1}$$

13.
$$
\begin{array}{r}
3x^2+1 \\
2x^2-5 \overline{)6x^4+0x^3-13x^2+0x-4} \\
\underline{6x^4-15x^2} \\
2x^2+0x-4 \\
\underline{2x^2-5} \\
1
\end{array}
$$

$$(6x^4-13x^2-4)\div(2x^2-5)=3x^2+1+\frac{1}{2x^2-5}$$

14.
$$
\begin{array}{r}
4x^2-5 \\
3x^2+1 \overline{)12x^4+0x^3-11x^2+0x+10} \\
\underline{12x^4+4x^2} \\
-15x^2+0x+10 \\
\underline{-15x^2-5} \\
15
\end{array}
$$

$$(12x^4-11x^2+10)\div(3x^2+1)=4x^2-5+\frac{15}{3x^2+1}$$

15.
$$
\begin{array}{r}
x^2-3x-10 \\
3x+1 \overline{)3x^3-8x^2-33x-10} \\
\underline{3x^3+x^2} \\
-9x^2-33x \\
\underline{-9x^2-3x} \\
-30x-10 \\
\underline{-30x-10} \\
0
\end{array}
$$

$$\frac{3x^3-8x^2-33x-10}{3x+1}=x^2-3x-10$$

16.
$$
\begin{array}{r}
2x^2-9x+10 \\
4x-1 \overline{)8x^3-38x^2+49x-10} \\
\underline{8x^3-2x^2} \\
-36x^2+49x \\
\underline{-36x^2+9x} \\
40x-10 \\
\underline{40x-10} \\
0
\end{array}
$$

$$\frac{8x^3-38x^2+49x-10}{4x-1}=2x^2-9x+10$$

17.
$$
\begin{array}{r}
-x^2+2x-1 \\
x-3 \overline{)-x^3+5x^2-7x+4} \\
\underline{-x^3+3x^2} \\
2x^2-7x \\
\underline{2x^2-6x} \\
-x+4 \\
\underline{-x+3} \\
1
\end{array}
$$

$$\frac{4-7x+5x^2-x^3}{x-3}=-x^2+2x-1+\frac{1}{x-3}$$

18.
$$
\begin{array}{r}
x^2-2x+4 \\
2x+1 \overline{)2x^3-3x^2+6x+4} \\
\underline{2x^3+x^2} \\
-4x^2+6x \\
\underline{-4x^2-2x} \\
8x+4 \\
\underline{8x+4} \\
0
\end{array}
$$

$$\frac{4+6x-3x^2+2x^3}{2x+1}=x^2-2x+4$$

19.
$$
\begin{array}{r}
2x^3 \ \ -3x^2 \ +x \ -4 \\
x-5\overline{\smash{\big)}2x^4-13x^3+16x^2-9x+20} \\
\underline{2x^4-10x^3} \\
-3x^3+16x^2 \\
\underline{-3x^3+15x^2} \\
x^2-9x \\
\underline{x^2-5x} \\
-4x+20 \\
\underline{-4x+20} \\
0
\end{array}
$$

$$\frac{16x^2-13x^3+2x^4-9x+20}{x-5}=2x^3-3x^2+x-4$$

20.
$$
\begin{array}{r}
3x^3 \ -x^2 \ +x-1 \\
x+2\overline{\smash{\big)}3x^4+5x^3-x^2+x-2} \\
\underline{3x^4+6x^3} \\
-x^3-x^2 \\
\underline{-x^3-2x^2} \\
x^2+x \\
\underline{x^2+2x} \\
-x-2 \\
\underline{-x-2} \\
0
\end{array}
$$

$$\frac{x+3x^4-x^2+5x^3-2}{x+2}=3x^3-x^2+x-1$$

21.
$$
\begin{array}{r}
x-4 \\
x^2+1\overline{\smash{\big)}x^3-4x^2+2x-1} \\
\underline{x^3 \ \ +x} \\
-4x^2+x-1 \\
\underline{-4x^2 \ -4} \\
x+3
\end{array}
$$

$$\frac{x^3-4x^2+2x-1}{x^2+1}=x-4+\frac{x+3}{x^2+1}$$

22.
$$
\begin{array}{r}
3x-2 \\
x^2+5\overline{\smash{\big)}3x^3-2x^2+0x-8} \\
\underline{3x^3 \ \ +15x} \\
-2x^2-15x-8 \\
\underline{-2x^2 \ -10} \\
-15x+2
\end{array}
$$

$$\frac{3x^3-2x^2-8}{x^2+5}=3x-2-\frac{15x-2}{x^2+5}$$

23.
$$
\begin{array}{r}
2x-3 \\
x^2-1\overline{\smash{\big)}2x^3-3x^2-x+4} \\
\underline{2x^3 \ \ -2x} \\
-3x^2+x+4 \\
\underline{-3x^2 \ +3} \\
x+1
\end{array}
$$

$$\frac{2x^3-x+4-3x^2}{x^2-1}=2x-3+\frac{x+1}{x^2-1}$$
$$=2x-3+\frac{1}{x-1}$$

24.
$$
\begin{array}{r}
5x-3 \\
x^2+3\overline{\smash{\big)}5x^3-3x^2+0x+2} \\
\underline{5x^3 \ \ +15x} \\
-3x^2-15x+2 \\
\underline{-3x^2 \ -9} \\
-15x+11
\end{array}
$$

$$\frac{2-3x^2+5x^3}{x^2+3}=5x-3-\frac{15x-11}{x^2+3}$$

25.
$$
\begin{array}{r}
3x+1 \\
2x^2-3\overline{\smash{\big)}6x^3+2x^2+x+4} \\
\underline{6x^3 \ \ -9x} \\
2x^2+10x+4 \\
\underline{2x^2 \ -3} \\
10x+7
\end{array}
$$

$$\frac{6x^3+2x^2+x+4}{2x^2-3}=3x+1+\frac{10x+7}{2x^2-3}$$

26.
$$
\begin{array}{r}
3x+2 \\
3x^2+2\overline{\smash{\big)}9x^3+6x^2+2x+1} \\
\underline{9x^3 \ \ +6x} \\
6x^2-4x+1 \\
\underline{6x^2 \ +4} \\
-4x-3
\end{array}
$$

$$\frac{9x^3+6x^2+2x+1}{3x^2+2}=3x+2-\frac{4x+3}{3x^2+2}$$

Objective 5.4.2 Exercises

27.
$$
\begin{array}{r|rrr}
-1 & 2 & -6 & -8 \\
& & -2 & 8 \\
\hline
& 2 & -8 & 0
\end{array}
$$
$$(2x^2-6x-8)\div(x+1)=2x-8$$

28.
$$
\begin{array}{r|rrr}
-5 & 3 & 19 & 20 \\
& & -15 & -20 \\
\hline
& 3 & 4 & 0
\end{array}
$$
$$(3x^2+19x+20)\div(x+5)=3x+4$$

29.

```
1 | 3   0   -4
        3    3
    3   3   -1
```

$(3x^2-4)\div(x-1)=3x+3-\dfrac{1}{x-1}$

30.

```
2 | 4   0   -8
        8   16
    4   8    8
```

$(4x^2-8)\div(x-2)=4x+8+\dfrac{8}{x-2}$

31.

```
-4 | 1   0   -9
        -4   16
     1  -4    7
```

$(x^2-9)\div(x+4)=x-4+\dfrac{7}{x+4}$

32.

```
-5 | 1   0   -49
        -5    25
     1  -5   -24
```

$(x^2-49)\div(x+5)=x-5-\dfrac{24}{x+5}$

33.

```
-2 | 1   0   12
        -2    4
     1  -2   16
```

$(2x^2+24)\div(2x+4)=x-2+\dfrac{16}{x+2}$

34.

```
-3 | 3   0   -15
        -9    27
     3  -9    12
```

$(3x^2-15)\div(x+3)=3x-9+\dfrac{12}{x+3}$

35.

```
-1 | 2  -1   6   9
        -2   3  -9
     2  -3   9   0
```

$(2x^3-x^2+6x+9)\div(x+1)=2x^2-3x+9$

36.

```
-2 | 3  10   6  -4
        -6  -8   4
     3   4  -2   0
```

$(3x^3+10x^2+6x-4)\div(x+2)=3x^2+4x-2$

37.

```
3 | 1  -6  11  -6
        3  -9   6
    1  -3   2   0
```

$(x^3-6x^2+11x-6)\div(x-3)=x^2-3x+2$

38.

```
-1 | 1  -4   1   6
        -1   5  -6
     1  -5   6   0
```

$(x^3-4x^2+x+6)\div(x+1)=x^2-5x+6$

39.

```
-2 | 1  -3   6   -9
        -2  10  -32
     1  -5  16  -41
```

$(6x-3x^2+x^3-9)\div(x+2)$
$=x^2-5x+16-\dfrac{41}{x+2}$

40.

```
3 | 1   4  -5   5
       3  21  48
    1   7  16  53
```

$(5-5x+4x^2+x^3)\div(x-3)$
$=x^2+7x+16+\dfrac{53}{x-3}$

41.

```
-1 | 1   0   1  -2
        -1   1  -2
     1  -1   2  -4
```

$(x^3+x-2)\div(x+1)=x^2-x+2-\dfrac{4}{x+1}$

42.

```
2 | 1   0   2   5
       2   4  12
    1   2   6  17
```

$(x^3+2x+5)\div(x-2)=x^2+2x+6+\dfrac{17}{x-2}$

43.

```
2 | 4   0  -1  -18
       8  16   30
    4   8  15   12
```

$(18+x-4x^3)\div(2-x)=4x^2+8x+15+\dfrac{12}{x-2}$

44.

```
-3 | 1  -3   0   12
        -3  18  -54
     1  -6  18  -42
```

$(12-3x^2+x^3)\div(3+x)=x^2-6x+18-\dfrac{42}{x+3}$

45.

```
5 | 2  -13  16  -9   20
       10  -15   5  -20
    2   -3   1  -4    0
```

$\dfrac{16x^2-13x^3+2x^4-9x+20}{x-5}=2x^3-3x^2+x-4$

46.

2	1	2	−1	−10	15
		2	8	14	8
	1	4	7	4	23

$$\frac{2x^3 - x^2 - 10x + 15 + x^4}{x - 2}$$
$$= x^3 + 4x^2 + 7x + 4 + \frac{23}{x - 2}$$

47.

2	3	−4	8	−5	−5
		6	4	24	38
	3	2	12	19	33

$$\frac{5 + 5x - 8x^2 + 4x^3 - 3x^4}{2 - x}$$
$$= 3x^3 + 2x^2 + 12x + 19 + \frac{33}{x - 2}$$

48.

3	2	−9	5	13	−3
		6	−9	−12	3
	2	−3	−4	1	0

$$\frac{3 - 13x - 5x^2 + 9x^3 - 2x^4}{3 - x}$$
$$= 2x^3 - 3x^2 - 4x + 1$$

49.

−1	3	3	−1	3	2
		−3	0	1	−4
	3	0	−1	4	−2

$$\frac{3x^4 + 3x^3 - x^2 + 3x + 2}{x + 1}$$
$$= 3x^3 - x + 4 - \frac{2}{x + 1}$$

50.

−3	4	12	−1	−1	2
		−12	0	3	−6
	4	0	−1	2	−4

$$\frac{4x^4 + 12x^3 - x^2 - x + 2}{x + 3}$$
$$= 4x^3 - x + 2 - \frac{4}{x + 3}$$

51.

3	2	0	−1	0	2
		6	18	51	153
	2	6	17	51	155

$$\frac{2x^4 - x^2 + 2}{x - 3}$$
$$= 2x^3 + 6x^2 + 17x + 51 + \frac{155}{x - 3}$$

52.

−2	1	−3	0	0	−30
		−2	10	−20	40
	1	−5	10	−20	10

$$\frac{x^4 - 3x^3 - 30}{x + 2}$$
$$= x^3 - 5x^2 + 10x - 20 + \frac{10}{x + 2}$$

53.

−5	1	0	0	125
		−5	25	−125
	1	−5	25	0

$$\frac{x^3 + 125}{x + 5} = x^2 - 5x + 25$$

54.

−7	1	0	0	343
		−7	49	−343
	1	−7	49	0

$$\frac{x^3 + 343}{x + 7} = x^2 - 7x + 49$$

Objective 5.4.3 Exercises

55.

3	2	−3	−1
		6	9
	2	3	8

$P(3) = 8$

56.

2	3	−5	−1
		6	2
	3	1	1

$Q(2) = 1$

57.

4	1	−2	3	−1
		4	8	44
	1	2	11	43

$R(4) = 43$

58.

3	1	4	−3	2
		3	21	54
	1	7	18	56

$F(3) = 56$

59.

−2	2	−4	3	−1
		−4	16	−38
	2	−8	19	−39

$P(-2) = -39$

60.

−3	3	1	−4	2
		−9	24	−60
	3	−8	20	−58

$R(-3) = -58$

61.

2	1	3	-2	4	-9
		2	10	16	40
	1	5	8	20	31

$Q(2) = 31$

62.

3	1	-2	-3	-1	7
		3	3	0	-3
	1	1	0	-1	4

$Y(3) = 4$

63.

-3	2	-1	0	-2	-5
		-6	21	-63	195
	2	-7	21	-65	190

$F(-3) = 178$

64.

-2	1	-2	0	4	-2
		-2	8	-16	24
	1	-4	8	-12	22

$Q(-2) = 22$

65.

5	1	0	0	-3
		5	25	125
	1	5	25	122

$P(5) = 122$

66.

-4	4	0	0	5
		-16	64	-256
	4	-16	64	-251

$S(-4) = -251$

67.

-3	4	0	-3	0	5
		-12	36	-99	297
	4	-12	33	-99	302

$R(-3) = 302$

68.

-4	2	0	1	0	-3
		-8	32	-132	528
	2	-8	33	-132	525

$P(-4) = 525$

69.

2	1	0	-4	-2	5	-2
		2	4	0	-4	2
	1	2	0	-2	1	0

$Q(2) = 0$

70.

3	2	4	0	-1	0	4
		6	30	90	267	801
	2	10	30	89	267	805

$T(3) = 805$

Applying Concepts 5.4

71.
$$\require{enclose}
\begin{array}{r}
x - y \\
3x+2y \enclose{longdiv}{3x^2 - xy - 2y^2} \\
\underline{3x^2 + 2xy} \\
-3xy - 2y^2 \\
\underline{-3xy - 2y^2} \\
0
\end{array}$$

$$\frac{3x^2 - xy - 2y^2}{3x + 2y} = x - y$$

72.
$$\begin{array}{r}
3x + 2y \\
4x+y \enclose{longdiv}{12x^2 + 11xy + 2y^2} \\
\underline{12x^2 + 3xy} \\
8xy + 2y^2 \\
\underline{8xy + 2y^2} \\
0
\end{array}$$

$$\frac{12x^2 + 11xy + 2y^2}{4x + y} = 3x + 2y$$

73.
$$\begin{array}{r}
a^2 + ab + b^2 \\
a-b \enclose{longdiv}{a^3 + 0a^2 b + 0ab^2 - b^3} \\
\underline{a^3 - a^2 b} \\
a^2 b + 0ab^2 \\
\underline{a^2 b - ab^2} \\
ab^2 - b^3 \\
\underline{ab^2 - b^3} \\
0
\end{array}$$

$$\frac{a^3 - b^3}{a - b} = a^2 + ab + b^2$$

74.
$$\begin{array}{r}
a^3 - a^2 b + ab^2 - b^3 \\
a+b \enclose{longdiv}{a^4 + 0a^3 b + 0a^2 b^2 + 0ab^3 + b^4} \\
\underline{a^4 + a^3 b} \\
-a^3 b + 0a^2 b^2 \\
\underline{-a^3 b - a^2 b^2} \\
a^2 b^2 + 0ab^3 \\
\underline{a^2 b^2 + ab^3} \\
-ab^3 + b^4 \\
\underline{-ab^3 - b^4} \\
2b^4
\end{array}$$

$$\frac{a^4 + b^4}{a + b} = a^3 - a^2 b + ab^2 - b^3 + \frac{2b^4}{a + b}$$

75.

$$\begin{array}{r} x^4 - x^3y + x^2y^2 - xy^3 + y^4 \\ x+y \overline{\smash{\big)}\, x^5 + 0x^4y + 0x^3y^2 + 0x^2y^3 + 0xy^4 + y^5} \end{array}$$

$$\begin{array}{r} x^5 + x^4y \\ \hline -x^4y + 0x^3y^2 \\ -x^4y - x^3y^2 \\ \hline x^3y^2 + 0x^2y^3 \\ x^3y^2 + x^2y^3 \\ \hline -x^2y^3 + 0xy^4 \\ -x^2y^3 - xy^4 \\ \hline xy^4 + y^5 \\ xy^4 + y^5 \\ \hline 0 \end{array}$$

$$\frac{x^5 + y^5}{x+y} = x^4 - x^3y + x^2y^2 - xy^3 + y^4$$

76.

$$\begin{array}{r} x^5 + x^4y + x^3y^2 + x^2y^3 + xy^4 + y^5 \\ x-y \overline{\smash{\big)}\, x^6 + 0x^5y + 0x^4y^2 + 0x^3y^3 + 0x^2y^4 + 0xy^5 - y^6} \end{array}$$

$$\begin{array}{r} x^6 - x^5y \\ \hline x^5y + 0x^4y^2 \\ x^5y - x^4y^2 \\ \hline x^4y^2 + 0x^3y^3 \\ x^4y^2 - x^3y^3 \\ \hline x^3y^3 + 0x^2y^4 \\ x^3y^3 - x^2y^4 \\ \hline x^2y^4 + 0xy^5 \\ x^2y^4 - xy^5 \\ \hline xy^5 - y^6 \\ xy^5 - y^6 \\ \hline 0 \end{array}$$

$$\frac{x^6 - y^6}{x-y} = x^5 + x^4y + x^3y^2 + x^2y^3 + xy^4 + y^5$$

77.

$$\begin{array}{r|rrrr} 3 & 1 & -3 & -1 & k \\ & & 3 & 0 & -3 \\ \hline & 1 & 0 & -1 & k-3 \end{array}$$

$k - 3 = 0$
$\quad k = 3$
The remainder is zero when k equals 3.

78.

$$\begin{array}{r|rrrr} 2 & 1 & -2 & 1 & k \\ & & 2 & 0 & 2 \\ \hline & 1 & 0 & 1 & k+2 \end{array}$$

$k + 2 = 0$
$\quad k = -2$
The remainder is zero when k equals -2.

79.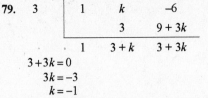

$3 + 3k = 0$
$3k = -3$
$k = -1$

The remainder is zero when k equals -1.

80.

1	1	0	k	$k-1$
		1	1	$k+1$
	1	1	$k+1$	$2k$

$2k = 0$
$k = 0$

The remainder is zero when k equals 0.

81. Note: (Quotient)(Divisor)+Remainder = Dividend
$$(\text{Quotient})(\text{Divisor}) = \text{Dividend} - \text{Remainder}$$
$$\text{Divisor} = \frac{\text{Dividend} - \text{Remainder}}{\text{Quotient}}$$

Therefore, $\text{Divisor} = \dfrac{(x^2 + x + 2) - 14}{x + 4}$

$$= \frac{x^2 + x - 12}{x + 4}$$

$$
\begin{array}{r}
x - 3 \\
x+4 \overline{)\, x^2 + x - 12} \\
\underline{x^2 + 4x} \\
-3x - 12 \\
\underline{-3x - 12} \\
0
\end{array}
$$

The polynomial is $x - 3$.

Check: $(x + 4)(x - 3) + 14 = x^2 + x - 12 + 14$
$$= x^2 + x + 2$$

Section 5.5

Concept Review 5.5

1. Always true

2. Sometimes true
   There are some trinomials that are nonfactorable over the integers.

3. Sometimes true
   There are some trinomials that are nonfactorable over the integers.

4. Sometimes true
   Some polynomials do not have a common binomial factor after grouping.

Objective 5.5.1 Exercises

1. The GCF of two monomials is the product of all common factors, each with its smallest exponent. The GCF of $7x^2y$ and $2xy^3$ is xy.

2. To factor a polynomial means to write the polynomial as a product of prime polynomials.

3. The GCF of $6a^2$ and $15a$ is $3a$.
   $6a^2 - 15a = 3a(2a - 5)$

4. The GCF of $32b^2$ and $12b$ is $4b$.
   $32b^2 + 12b = 4b(8b + 3)$

5. The GCF of $4x^3$ and $3x^2$ is x^2.
   $4x^3 - 3x^2 = x^2(4x - 3)$

6. The GCF of $12a^5b^2$ and $16a^4b$ is $4a^4b$.
   $12a^5b^2 + 16a^4b = 4a^4b(3ab + 4)$

7. There is no common factor.
   $3a^2 - 10b^3$ is nonfactorable over the integers.

8. There is no common factor.
   $9x^2 + 14y^4$ is nonfactorable over the integers.

9. The GCF of x^5, x^3, and x is x.
   $x^5 - x^3 - x = x(x^4 - x^2 - 1)$

10. The GCF of y^4, $3y^2$, and $2y$ is y.
    $y^4 - 3y^2 - 2y = y(y^3 - 3y - 2)$

11. The GCF of $16x^2$, $12x$ and 24 is 4.
$16x^2 - 12x + 24 = 4(4x^2 - 3x + 6)$

12. The GCF of $2x^5$, $3x^4$, and $4x^2$ is x^2.
$2x^5 + 3x^4 - 4x^2 = x^2(2x^3 + 3x^2 - 4)$

13. The GCF of $5b^2$, $10b^3$, and $25b^4$ is $5b^2$.
$5b^2 - 10b^3 + 25b^4 = 5b^2(1 - 2b + 5b^2)$

14. The GCF of x^2y^4, x^2y, and $4x^2$ is x^2.
$x^2y^4 - x^2y - 4x^2 = x^2(y^4 - y - 4)$

15. The GCF of x^{2n} and x^n is x^n.
$x^{2n} - x^n = x^n(x^n - 1)$

16. The GCF of $a^{5n} + a^{2n}$ is a^{2n}.
$a^{5n} + a^{2n} = a^{2n}(a^{3n} + 1)$

17. The GCF of x^{3n} and x^{2n} is x^{2n}.
$x^{3n} - x^{2n} = x^{2n}(x^n - 1)$

18. The GCF of y^{4n} and y^{2n} is y^{2n}.
$y^{4n} + y^{2n} = y^{2n}(y^{2n} + 1)$

19. The GCF of a^{2n+2} and a^2 is a^2.
$a^{2n+2} + a^2 = a^2(a^{2n} + 1)$

20. The GCF of b^{n+5} and b^5 is b^5.
$b^{n+5} - b^5 = b^5(b^n - 1)$

21. The GCF of $12x^2y^2$, $18x^3y$, and $24x^2y$ is $6x^2y$.
$12x^2y^2 - 18x^3y + 24x^2y = 6x^2y(2y - 3x + 4)$

22. The GCF of $14a^4b^4$, $42a^3b^3$, and $28a^3b^2$
is $14a^3b^2$.
$14a^4b^4 - 42a^3b^3 + 28a^3b^2$
$= 14a^3b^2(ab^2 - 3b + 2)$

23. The GCF of $16a^2b^4$, $4a^2b^2$, and $24a^3b^2$ is
$4a^2b^2$.
$-16a^2b^4 - 4a^2b^2 + 24a^3b^2$
$= 4a^2b^2(-4b^2 - 1 + 6a)$

24. The GCF of $10x^2y$, $20x^2y^2$, and $30x^2y^3$
is $10x^2y$.
$10x^2y + 20x^2y^2 + 30x^2y^3$
$= 10x^2y(1 + 2y + 3y^2)$

25. The GCF of y^{2n+2}, y^{n+2}, and y^2 is y^2.
$y^{2n+2} + y^{n+2} - y^2$
$= y^2(y^{2n} + y^n - 1)$

26. The GCF of a^{2n+2}, a^{2n+1}, and a^n is a^n.
$a^{2n+2} + a^{2n+1} + a^n$
$= a^n(a^{n+2} + a^{n+1} + 1)$

Objective 5.5.2 Exercises

27. $x(a+2) - 2(a+2) = (a+2)(x-2)$

28. $3(x+y) + a(x+y) = (x+y)(3+a)$

29. $a(x-2) - b(2-x) = a(x-2) + b(x-2)$
$= (x-2)(a+b)$

30. $3(a-7) - b(7-a) = 3(a-7) + b(a-7)$
$= (a-7)(3+b)$

31. $x^2 + 3x + 2x + 6 = x(x+3) + 2(x+3)$
$= (x+3)(x+2)$

32. $x^2 - 5x + 4x - 20 = x(x-5) + 4(x-5)$
$= (x-5)(x+4)$

33. $xy + 4y - 2x - 8 = y(x+4) - 2(x+4)$
$= (x+4)(y-2)$

34. $ab + 7b - 3a - 21 = b(a+7) - 3(a+7)$
$= (a+7)(b-3)$

35. $ax + bx - ay - by = x(a+b) - y(a+b)$
$= (a+b)(x-y)$

36. $2ax - 3ay - 2bx + 3by = a(2x-3y) - b(2x-3y)$
$= (2x-3y)(a-b)$

37. $x^2y - 3x^2 - 2y + 6 = x^2(y-3) - 2(y-3)$
$= (y-3)(x^2-2)$

38. $a^2b + 3a^2 + 2b + 6 = a^2(b+3) + 2(b+3)$
$= (b+3)(a^2+2)$

39. $6 + 2y + 3x^2 + x^2y = 2(3+y) + x^2(3+y)$
$= (3+y)(2+x^2)$

40. $15 + 3b - 5a^2 - a^2b = 3(5+b) - a^2(5+b)$
$= (5+b)(3-a^2)$

41. $2ax^2 + bx^2 - 4ay - 2by = x^2(2a+b) - 2y(2a+b)$
$= (2a+b)(x^2-2y)$

42. $4a^2x + 2a^2y - 6bx - 3by$
$= 2a^2(2x+y) - 3b(2x+y)$
$= (2x+y)(2a^2-3b)$

43. $x^ny - 5x^n + y - 5 = x^n(y-5) + (y-5)$
$= (y-5)(x^n+1)$

44. $a^nx^n + 2a^n + x^n + 2 = a^n(x^n+2) + (x^n+2)$
$= (x^n+2)(a^n+1)$

45. $x^3 + x^2 + 2x + 2 = x^2(x+1) + 2(x+1)$
$= (x+1)(x^2+2)$

46. $y^3 - y^2 + 3y - 3 = y^2(y-1) + 3(y-1)$
$= (y-1)(y^2+3)$

47. $2x^3 - x^2 + 4x - 2 = x^2(2x - 1) + 2(2x - 1)$
$= (2x - 1)(x^2 + 2)$

48. $2y^3 - y^2 + 6y - 3 = y^2(2y - 1) + 3(2y - 1)$
$= (2y - 1)(y^2 + 3)$

49. A quadratic trinomial is a trinomial of the form $ax^2 + bx + c$, where a and b are nonzero coefficients and x is a nonzero constant. To factor a quadratic trinomial means to express the trinomial as a product of two binomials.

50. A polynomial is nonfactorable over the integers if the polynomial cannot be written as the product of other polynomials that have only integer coefficients and constants.

Objective 5.5.3 Exercises

51. $x^2 - 8x + 15 = (x - 5)(x - 3)$

52. $x^2 + 12x + 20 = (x + 10)(x + 2)$

53. $a^2 + 12a + 11 = (a + 11)(a + 1)$

54. $a^2 + a - 72 = (a + 9)(a - 8)$

55. $b^2 + 2b - 35 = (b + 7)(b - 5)$

56. $a^2 + 7a + 6 = (a + 6)(a + 1)$

57. $y^2 - 16y + 39 = (y - 3)(y - 13)$

58. $y^2 - 18y + 72 = (y - 6)(y - 12)$

59. $b^2 + 4b - 32 = (b + 8)(b - 4)$

60. $x^2 + x - 132 = (x + 12)(x - 11)$

61. $a^2 - 15a + 56 = (a - 7)(a - 8)$

62. $x^2 + 15x + 50 = (x + 10)(x + 5)$

63. $y^2 + 13y + 12 = (y + 12)(y + 1)$

64. $b^2 - 6b - 16 = (b - 8)(b + 2)$

65. $x^2 + 4x - 5 = (x + 5)(x - 1)$

66. $a^2 - 3ab + 2b^2 = (a - 2b)(a - b)$

67. $a^2 + 11ab + 30b^2 = (a + 6b)(a + 5b)$

68. $a^2 + 8ab - 33b^2 = (a + 11b)(a - 3b)$

69. $x^2 - 14xy + 24y^2 = (x - 12y)(x - 2y)$

70. $x^2 + 5xy + 6y^2 = (x + 2y)(x + 3y)$

71. $y^2 + 2xy - 63x^2 = (y + 9x)(y - 7x)$

72. $y^2 - 13y + 12 = (y - 12)(y - 1)$

73. $x^2 - 35x - 36 = (x - 36)(x + 1)$

74. $x^2 + 7x - 18 = (x - 2)(x + 9)$

75. $a^2 + 13a + 36 = (a + 9)(a + 4)$

76. There are no binomial factors whose product is $x^2 - 5x + 7$. The trinomial is nonfactorable over the integers.

77. There are no binomial factors whose product $x^2 - 7x - 12$. The trinomial is nonfactorable over the integers.

Objective 5.5.4 Exercises

78. $2x^2 + 7x + 3 = (2x + 1)(x + 3)$

79. $2x^2 - 11x - 40 = (2x + 5)(x - 8)$

80. $6y^2 + 5y - 6 = (2y + 3)(3y - 2)$

81. $4y^2 - 15y + 9 = (4y - 3)(y - 3)$

82. $6b^2 - b - 35 = (2b - 5)(3b + 7)$

83. $2a^2 + 13a + 6 = (2a + 1)(a + 6)$

84. $3y^2 - 22y + 39 = (3y - 13)(y - 3)$

85. There are no binomial factors whose product is $12y^2 - 13y - 72$. The trinomial is nonfactorable over the integers.

86. There are no binomial factors whose product is $6a^2 - 26a + 15$. The trinomial is nonfactorable over the integers.

87. $5x^2 + 26x + 5 = (5x + 1)(x + 5)$

88. $4a^2 - a - 5 = (4a - 5)(a + 1)$

89. $11x^2 - 122x + 11 = (11x - 1)(x - 11)$

90. $11y^2 - 47y + 12 = (11y - 3)(y - 4)$

91. $12x^2 - 17x + 5 = (12x - 5)(x - 1)$

92. $12x^2 - 40x + 25 = (6x - 5)(2x - 5)$

93. $8y^2 - 18y + 9 = (4y - 3)(2y - 3)$

94. There are no binomial factors whose product is $4x^2 + 9x + 10$. The trinomial is nonfactorable over the integers.

95. There are no binomial factors whose product is $6a^2 - 5a - 2$. The trinomial is nonfactorable over the integers.

96. $10x^2 - 29x + 10 = (5x - 2)(2x - 5)$

97. There are no binomial factors whose product is $2x^2 + 5x + 12$. The trinomial is nonfactorable over the integers.

98. There are no binomial factors whose product is $4x^2 - 6x + 1$. The trinomial is nonfactorable over the integers.

99. $6x^2 + 5xy - 21y^2 = (2x - 3y)(3x + 7y)$

100. $6x^2 + 41xy - 7y^2 = (6x - y)(x + 7y)$

101. $4a^2 + 43ab + 63b^2 = (4a + 7b)(a + 9b)$

102. $7a^2 + 46ab - 21b^2 = (7a - 3b)(a + 7b)$

103. $10x^2 - 23xy + 12y^2 = (5x - 4y)(2x - 3y)$

104. $18x^2 + 27xy + 10y^2 = (6x + 5y)(3x + 2y)$

105. $24 + 13x - 2x^2 = (8 - x)(3 + 2x)$

106. $6 - 7x - 5x^2 = (2 + x)(3 - 5x)$

107. There are no binomial factors whose product is $8 - 13x + 6x^2$. The trinomial is nonfactorable over the integers.

108. There are no binomial factors whose product is $30 + 17a - 20a^2$. The trinomial is nonfactorable over the integers.

109. $15 - 14a - 8a^2 = (3 - 4a)(5 + 2a)$

110. $35 - 6b - 8b^2 = (7 - 4b)(5 + 2b)$

111. The GCF of $5y^4$, $29y^3$, and $20y^2$ is y^2.
$5y^4 - 29y^3 + 20y^2 = y^2(5y^2 - 29y + 20)$
$= y^2(5y - 4)(y - 5)$

112. The GCF of $30a^2$, $85ab$, and $60b^2$ is 5.
$30a^2 + 85ab + 60b^2 = 5(6a^2 + 17ab + 12b^2)$
$= 5(2a + 3b)(3a + 4b)$

113. The GCF of $4x^3$, $10x^2y$ and $24xy^2$ is $2x$
$4x^3 + 10x^2y - 24xy^2 = 2x(2x^2 + 5xy - 12y^2)$
$= 2x(2x - 3y)(x + 4y)$

114. The GCF of $8a^4$, $37a^3b$, and $15a^2b^2$ is a^2.
$8a^4 + 37a^3b - 15a^2b^2 = a^2(8a^2 + 37ab - 15b^2)$
$= a^2(8a - 3b)(a + 5b)$

115. The GCF of 100, $5x$, and $5x^2$ is 5.
$100 - 5x - 5x^2 = 5(20 - x - x^2)$
$= 5(5 + x)(4 - x)$

116. The GCF of $50x^2$, $25x^3$, and $12x^4$ is x^2.
$50x^2 + 25x^3 - 12x^4 = x^2(50 + 25x - 12x^2)$
$= x^2(5 + 4x)(10 - 3x)$

117. The GCF of $320x$, $8x^2$, and $4x^3$ is $4x$.
$320x - 8x^2 - 4x^3 = 4x(80 - 2x - x^2)$
$= 4x(10 + x)(8 - x)$

118. The GCF of $96y$, $16xy$, and $2x^2y$ is $2y$.
$96y - 16xy - 2x^2y = 2y(48 - 8x - x^2)$
$= 2y(12 + x)(4 - x)$

119. The GCF of $20x^2$, $38x^3$, and $30x^4$ is $2x^2$.
$20x^2 - 38x^3 - 30x^4 = 2x^2(10 - 19x - 15x^2)$
$= 2x^2(5 + 3x)(2 - 5x)$

120. The GCF of $4x^2y^2$, $32xy$, and 60 is 4.
$4x^2y^2 - 32xy + 60 = 4(x^2y^2 - 8xy + 15)$
$= 4(xy - 3)(xy - 5)$

121. The GCF of a^4b^4, $3a^3b^3$, and $10a^2b^2$ is a^2b^2.
$a^4b^4 - 3a^3b^3 - 10a^2b^2 = a^2b^2(a^2b^2 - 3ab - 10)$
$= a^2b^2(ab - 5)(ab + 2)$

122. The GCF of $2a^2b^4$, $9ab^3$, and $18b^2$ is b^2.
$2a^2b^4 + 9ab^3 - 18b^2 = b^2(2a^2b^2 + 9ab - 18)$
$= b^2(2ab - 3)(ab + 6)$

123. The GCF of $90a^2b^2$, $45ab$, and 10 is 5.
$90a^2b^2 + 45ab + 10 = 5(18a^2b^2 + 9ab + 2)$

124. The GCF of $3x^3y^2$, $12x^2y$, and $96x$ is $3x$.
$3x^3y^2 + 12x^2y - 96x = 3x(x^2y^2 + 4xy - 32)$
$= 3x(xy + 8)(xy - 4)$

125. There is no common factor.
$4x^4 - 45x^2 + 80$ is nonfactorable over the integers.

126. There is no common factor.
$x^4 + 2x^2 + 15$ is nonfactorable over the integers.

127. The GCF of $2a^5$, $14a^3$, and $20a$ is $2a$.
$2a^5 + 14a^3 + 20a = 2a(a^4 + 7a^2 + 10)$
$= 2a(a^2 + 5)(a^2 + 2)$

128. The GCF of $3b^6$, $9b^4$, and $30b^2$ is $3b^2$.
$3b^6 - 9b^4 - 30b^2 = 3b^2(b^4 - 3b^2 - 10)$
$= 3b^2(b^2 - 5)(b^2 + 2)$

129. The GCF of $3x^4y^2$, $39x^2y^2$, and $120y^2$ is $3y^2$.
$3x^4y^2 - 39x^2y^2 + 120y^2 = 3y^2(x^4 - 13x^2 + 40)$
$= 3y^2(x^2 - 5)(x^2 - 8)$

130. The GCF of $2x^4y$, $7x^3y$, and $30x^2y$ is x^2y.
$2x^4y - 7x^3y - 30x^2y = x^2y(2x^2 - 7x - 30)$
$= x^2y(2x + 5)(x - 6)$

131. The GCF of $45a^2b^2$, $6ab^2$, and $72b^2$ is $3b^2$.
$45a^2b^2 + 6ab^2 - 72b^2 = 3b^2(15a^2 + 2a - 24)$
$= 3b^2(3a + 4)(5a - 6)$

132. The GCF of $16x^2y^3$, $36x^2y^2$,
and $20x^2y$ is $4x^2y$.
$$16x^2y^3 + 36x^2y^2 + 20x^2y = 4x^2y(4y^2 + 9y + 5)$$
$$= 4x^2y(4y + 5)(y + 1)$$

133. The GCF of $36x^3y$, $24x^2y^2$, and $45xy^3$ is $3xy$.
$$36x^3y + 24x^2y^2 - 45xy^3$$
$$= 3xy(12x^2 + 8xy - 15y^2)$$
$$= 3xy(6x - 5y)(2x + 3y)$$

134. The GCF of $12a^3b$, $70a^2b^2$, and $12ab^3$ is $2ab$.
$$12a^3b - 70a^2b^2 - 12ab^3$$
$$= 2ab(6a^2 - 35ab - 6b^2)$$
$$= 2ab(6a + b)(a - 6b)$$

135. The GCF of $48a^2b^2$, $36ab^3$, and $54b^4$ is $6b^2$.
$$48a^2b^2 - 36ab^3 - 54b^4$$
$$= 6b^2(8a^2 - 6ab - 9b^2)$$
$$= 6b^2(2a - 3b)(4a + 3b)$$

136. The GCF of x^{3n}, $10x^{2n}$, and $16x^n$ is x^n.
$$x^{3n} + 10x^{2n} + 16x^n = x^n(x^{2n} + 10x^n + 16)$$
$$= x^n(x^n + 8)(x^n + 2)$$

137. The GCF of $10x^{2n}$, $25x^n$, and 60 is 5.
$$10x^{2n} + 25x^n - 60 = 5(2x^{2n} + 5x^n - 12)$$
$$= 5(2x^n - 3)(x^n + 4)$$

Applying Concepts 5.5

138. $2a^3b - ab^3 - a^2b^2 = 2a^3b - a^2b^2 - ab^3$
$$= ab(2a^2 - ab - b^2)$$
$$= ab(2a + b)(a - b)$$

139. $3x^3y - xy^3 - 2x^2y^2 = 3x^3y - 2x^2y^2 - xy^3$
$$= xy(3x^2 - 2xy - y^2)$$
$$= xy(3x + y)(x - y)$$

140. $2y^3 + 2y^5 - 24y = 2y^5 + 2y^3 - 24y$
$$= 2y(y^4 + y^2 - 12)$$
$$= 2y(y^2 + 4)(y^2 - 3)$$

141. $9b^3 + 3b^5 - 30b = 3b^5 + 9b^3 - 30b$
$$= 3b(b^4 + 3b^2 - 10)$$
$$= 3b(b^2 + 5)(b^2 - 2)$$

142. $x^2 + kx + 8$

Factors of 8	Sum
1, 8	9
–1, –8	–9
2, 4	6
–2, –4	–6

The possible integer values of k are 6, –6, 9, and –9.

143. $x^2 + kx - 6$

Factors of –6	Sum
1, –6	–5
–1, 6	5
2, –3	–1
–2, 3	1

The possible integer values of k are 5, –5, 1, and –1.

144. $2x^2 - kx + 3$
$$2x^2 + (-k)x + 3$$

Factors of 2	Factors of 3
1, 2	1, 3
	–1, –3

Trial Factors	Middle Term
$(x + 1)(2x + 3)$	$3x + 2x = 5x$
$(x + 3)(2x + 1)$	$x + 6x = 7x$
$(x - 1)(2x - 3)$	$-3x - 2x = -5x$
$(x - 3)(2x - 1)$	$-x - 6x = -7x$

The possible integer values of $-k$ are 7, –7, 5, and –5. The possible integer values of k are –5, –7, 5, and 7.

145. $2x^2 - kx - 5$
$$2x^2 + (-k)x - 5$$

Factors of 2	Factors of –5
1, 2	1, –5
	–1, 5

Trial Factors	Middle Term
$(x + 1)(2x - 5)$	$-5x + 2x = -3x$
$(x - 5)(2x + 1)$	$x - 10x = -9x$
$(x - 1)(2x + 5)$	$5x - 2x = 3x$
$(x + 5)(2x - 1)$	$-x + 10x = 9x$

The possible integer values of $-k$ are 3, –3, 9, and –9.
The possible integer values of k are 3, 9, –3, and –9.

146. $3x^2 + kx + 5$

Factors of 3	Factors of 5
1, 3	1, 5
	–1, –5

Trial Factors	Middle Term
$(x + 1)(3x + 5)$	$5x + 3x = 8x$
$(x + 5)(3x + 1)$	$x + 15x = 16x$
$(x - 1)(3x - 5)$	$-5x - 3x = -8x$
$(x - 5)(3x - 1)$	$-x - 15x = -16x$

The possible integer values of k are 8, 16, –8, and –16.

147. $2x^2 + kx - 3$

Factors of 2	Factors of –3
1, 2	1, –3
	–1, 3

Trial Factors	Middle Term
$(x+1)(2x-3)$	$-3x + 2x = -x$
$(x-3)(2x+1)$	$x - 6x = -5x$
$(x-1)(2x+3)$	$3x - 2x = x$
$(x+3)(2x-1)$	$-x + 6x = 5x$

The possible integer values of k are –1, –5, 1, and 5.

148. **a.** The area of the square is
base · height $= 2x \cdot 2x = 4x^2$.
The area of the circle is πx^2.

The shaded area is equal to the area of the square minus the area of the circle.
Shaded area $= 4x^2 - \pi x^2$
$= x^2(4 - \pi)$

b. The area of the larger circle is πR^2.
The area of the smaller circle is πr^2.
The shaded area is equal to the area of the larger circle minus the area of the smaller circle.
Shaded area $= \pi R^2 - \pi r^2$
$= \pi(R^2 - r^2)$
$= \pi(R - r)(R + r)$

c. The area of the rectangle is
base · height $= 4x \cdot 2x = 8x^2$.
The area of the circle is πx^2.
The shaded area is equal to the area of the rectangle minus the area of the circle.
Shaded area $= 8x^2 - \pi x^2$
$= x^2(8 - \pi)$

Section 5.6

Concept Review 5.6

1. Never true
$a^2 b^2 c^2$ is a monomial.

2. Never true
$a^3 + b^3 = (a + b)(a^2 - ab + b^2)$

3. Never true
The difference of two perfect cubes is always factorable. For example,
$8^2 - x^3 = 2^3 - x^3$
$= (2 - x)(4 + 2x + x^2)$

4. Always true

5. Never true
$b^3 + 1$ is the sum of two perfect cubes.
$b^3 + 1^3 = (b + 1)(b^2 - b + 1)$

Objective 5.6.1 Exercises

1. $4; 25x^6; 100x^4y^4$

2. $9; 49b^{12}; 64a^{16}b^2$

3. $4z^4$

4. $6d^5$

5. $9a^2b^3$

6. $5mn^6$

7. The factors of the difference of two perfect squares are the sum and difference of the square roots of the perfect squares.

8. A perfect-square trinomial is the square of a binomial.

9. $x^2 - 16 = x^2 - 4^2$
$= (x + 4)(x - 4)$

10. $y^2 - 49 = y^2 - 7^2$
$= (y + 7)(y - 7)$

11. $4x^2 - 1 = (2x)^2 - 1^2$
$= (2x + 1)(2x - 1)$

12. $81x^2 - 4 = (9x)^2 - 2^2$
$= (9x + 2)(9x - 2)$

13. $b^2 - 2b + 1 = (b - 1)^2$

14. $a^2 + 14a + 49 = (a + 7)^2$

15. $16x^2 - 40x + 25 = (4x - 5)^2$

16. $49x^2 + 28x + 4 = (7x + 2)^2$

17. $x^2y^2 - 100 = (xy)^2 - 10^2$
$= (xy + 10)(xy - 10)$

18. $a^2 b^2 - 25 = (ab)^2 - 5^2$
$= (ab + 5)(ab - 5)$

19. $x^2 + 4$ is nonfactorable over the integers.

20. $a^2 + 16$ is nonfactorable over the integers.

21. $x^2 + 6xy + 9y^2 = (x + 3y)^2$

22. $4x^2y^2 + 12xy + 9 = (2xy + 3)^2$

23. $4x^2 - y^2 = (2x)^2 - 4^2 = (2x + y)(2x - y)$

24. $49a^2 - 16b^4 = (7a)^2 - (4b^2)^2$
$= (7a + 4b^2)(7a - 4b^2)$

25. $a^{2n} - 1 = (a^n)^2 - 1^2$
$\quad = (a^n + 1)(a^n - 1)$

26. $b^{2n} - 16 = (b^n)^2 - 4^2$
$\quad = (b^n + 4)(b^n - 4)$

27. $a^2 + 4a + 4 = (a+2)^2$

28. $b^2 - 18b + 81 = (b-9)^2$

29. $x^2 - 12x + 36 = (x-6)^2$

30. $y^2 - 6y + 9 = (y-3)^2$

31. $16x^2 - 121 = (4x)^2 - 11^2$
$\quad = (4x+11)(4x-11)$

32. $49y^2 - 36 = (7y)^2 - 6^2$
$\quad = (7y+6)(7y-6)$

33. $1 - 9a^2 = 1^2 - (3a)^2$
$\quad = (1+3a)(1-3a)$

34. $16 - 81y^2 = 4^2 - (9y)^2$
$\quad = (4+9y)(4-9y)$

35. $4a^2 + 4a - 1$ is nonfactorable over the integers.

36. $9x^2 + 12x - 4$ is nonfactorable over the integers.

37. $b^2 + 7b + 14$ is nonfactorable over the integers.

38. $y^2 - 5y + 25$ is nonfactorable over the integers.

39. $25 - a^2b^2 = 5^2 - (ab)^2$
$\quad = (5+ab)(5-ab)$

40. $64 - x^2y^2 = 8^2 - (xy)^2$
$\quad = (8+xy)(8-xy)$

41. $25a^2 - 40ab + 16b^2 = (5a - 4b)^2$

42. $4a^2 - 36ab + 81b^2 = (2a - 9b)^2$

43. $x^{2n} + 6x^n + 9 = (x^n + 3)^2$

44. $y^{2n} - 16y^n + 64 = (y^n - 8)^2$

Objective 5.6.2 Exercises

45. $8;\ x^9;\ 27c^{15}d^{18}$

46. $27;\ y^{12};\ m^3n^6$

47. $2x^3$

48. $3y^5$

49. $4a^2b^6$

50. $5c^4d$

51. $x^3 - 27 = x^3 - 3^3$
$\quad = (x-3)(x^2 + 3x + 9)$

52. $y^3 + 125 = y^3 + 5^3$
$\quad = (y+5)(y^2 - 5y + 25)$

53. $8x^3 - 1 = (2x)^3 - 1^3$
$\quad = (2x-1)(4x^2 + 2x + 1)$

54. $64a^3 + 27 = (4a)^3 + 3^3$
$\quad = (4a+3)(16a^2 - 12a + 9)$

55. $x^3 - y^3 = (x-y)(x^2 + xy + y^2)$

56. $x^3 - 8y^3 = x^3 - (2y)^3$
$\quad = (x-2y)(x^2 + 2xy + 4y^2)$

57. $m^3 + n^3 = (m+n)(m^2 - mn + n^2)$

58. $27a^3 + b^3 = (3a)^3 + b^3$
$\quad = (3a+b)(9a^2 - 3ab + b^2)$

59. $64x^3 + 1 = (4x)^3 + 1^3$
$\quad = (4x+1)(16x^2 - 4x + 1)$

60. $1 - 125b^3 = 1^3 - (5b)^3$
$\quad = (1 - 5b)(1 + 5b + 25b^2)$

61. $27x^3 - 8y^3 = (3x)^3 - (2y)^3$
$\quad = (3x-2y)(9x^2 + 6xy + 4y^2)$

62. $64x^3 + 27y^3 = (4x)^3 + (3y)^3$
$\quad = (4x+3y)(16x^2 - 12xy + 9y^2)$

63. $x^3y^3 + 64 = (xy)^3 + 4^3$
$\quad = (xy+4)(x^2y^2 - 4xy + 16)$

64. $8x^3y^3 + 27 = (2xy)^3 + 3^3$
$\quad = (2xy+3)(4x^2y^2 - 6xy + 9)$

65. $16x^3 - y^3$ is nonfactorable over the integers.

66. $27x^3 - 8y^3 = (3x)^3 - (2y)^3$
$\quad = (3x-2y)(9x^2 + 6xy + 4y^2)$

67. $8x^3 - 9y^3$ is nonfactorable over the integers.

68. $27a^3 - 16$ is nonfactorable over the integers.

69. $(a-b)^3 - b^3$
$\quad = [(a-b) - b][(a-b)^2 + b(a-b) + b^2]$
$\quad = (a-2b)(a^2 - 2ab + b^2 + ab - b^2 + b^2)$
$\quad = (a-2b)(a^2 - ab + b^2)$

70. $a^3 + (a+b)^3$
$\quad = [a + (a+b)][a^2 - a(a+b) + (a+b)^2]$
$\quad = (2a+b)(a^2 - a^2 - ab + a^2 + 2ab + b^2)$
$\quad = (2a+b)(a^2 + ab + b^2)$

71. $x^{6n}+y^{3n}=(x^{2n})^3+(y^n)^3$
$\quad = (x^{2n}+y^n)(x^{4n}-x^{2n}y^n+y^{2n})$

72. $x^{3n}+y^{3n}=(x^n)^3+(y^n)^3$
$\quad = (x^n+y^n)(x^{2n}-x^ny^n+y^{2n})$

73. A polynomial is quadratic in form if it can be written in the form $au^2+bu+c,\ a\neq0$.

74. No, not all polynomials that are quadratic in form factor. For example, x^4-6x^2+14 does not factor.

Objective 5.6.3 Exercises

75. Let $u=xy$.
$x^2y^2-8xy+15=u^2-8u+15$
$\quad = (u-3)(u-5)$
$\quad = (xy-3)(xy-5)$

76. Let $u=xy$.
$x^2y^2-8xy-33=u^2-8u-33$
$\quad = (u-11)(u+3)$
$\quad = (xy-11)(xy+3)$

77. Let $u=xy$.
$x^2y^2-17xy+60=u^2-17u+60$
$\quad = (u-5)(u-12)$
$\quad = (xy-5)(xy-12)$

78. Let $u=ab$.
$a^2b^2+10ab+24=u^2+10u+24$
$\quad = (u+4)(u+6)$
$\quad = (ab+4)(ab+6)$

79. Let $u=x^2$.
$x^4-9x^2+18=u^2-9u+18$
$\quad = (u-6)(u-3)$
$\quad = (x^2-6)(x^2-3)$

80. Let $u=y^2$.
$y^4-6y^2-16=u^2-6u-16$
$\quad = (u-8)(u+2)$
$\quad = (y^2-8)(y^2+2)$

81. Let $u=b^2$.
$b^4-13b^2-90=u^2-13u-90$
$\quad = (u-18)(u+5)$
$\quad = (b^2-18)(b^2+5)$

82. Let $u=a^2$.
$a^4+14a^2+45=u^2+14u+45$
$\quad = (u+9)(u+5)$
$\quad = (a^2+9)(a^2+5)$

83. Let $u=x^2y^2$.
$x^4y^4-8x^2y^2+12=u^2-8u+12$
$\quad = (u-6)(u-2)$
$\quad = (x^2y^2-6)(x^2y^2-2)$

84. Let $u=a^2b^2$.
$a^4b^4+11a^2b^2-26=u^2+11u-26$
$\quad = (u+13)(u-2)$
$\quad = (a^2b^2+13)(a^2b^2-2)$

85. Let $u=x^n$.
$x^{2n}+3x^n+2=u^2+3u+2$
$\quad = (u+2)(u+1)$
$\quad = (x^n+2)(x^n+1)$

86. Let $u=a^n$.
$a^{2n}-a^n-12=u^2-u-12$
$\quad = (u-4)(u+3)$
$\quad = (a^n-4)(a^n+3)$

87. Let $u=xy$.
$3x^2y^2-14xy+15=3u^2-14u+15$
$\quad = (3u-5)(u-3)$
$\quad = (3xy-5)(xy-3)$

88. Let $u=xy$.
$5x^2y^2-59xy+44=5u^2-59u+44$
$\quad = (5u-4)(u-11)$
$\quad = (5xy-4)(xy-11)$

89. Let $u=ab$.
$6a^2b^2-23ab+21=6u^2-23u+21$
$\quad = (2u-3)(3u-7)$
$\quad = (2ab-3)(3ab-7)$

90. Let $u=ab$.
$10a^2b^2+3ab-7=10u^2+3u-7$
$\quad = (u+1)(10u-7)$
$\quad = (ab+1)(10ab-7)$

91. Let $u=x^2$.
$2x^4-13x^2-15=2u^2-13u-15$
$\quad = (2u-15)(u+1)$
$\quad = (2x^2-15)(x^2+1)$

92. Let $u=x^2$.
$3x^4+20x^2+32=3u^2+20u+32$
$\quad = (3u+8)(u+4)$
$\quad = (3x^2+8)(x^2+4)$

93. Let $u=x^n$.
$2x^{2n}-7x^n+3=2u^2-7u+3$
$\quad = (2u-1)(u-3)$
$\quad = (2x^n-1)(x^n-3)$

94. Let $u=x^n$.
$4x^{2n}+8x^n-5=4u^2+8u-5$
$\quad = (2u-1)(2u+5)$
$\quad = (2x^n-1)(2x^n+5)$

95. Let $u = a^n$.
$$6a^{2n} + 19a^n + 10 = 6u^2 + 19u + 10$$
$$= (2u + 5)(3u + 2)$$
$$= (2a^n + 5)(3a^n + 2)$$

Objective 5.6.4 Exercises

96. $5x^2 + 10x + 5 = 5(x^2 + 2x + 1)$
$$= 5(x + 1)^2$$

97. $12x^2 - 36x + 27 = 3(4x^2 - 12x + 9)$
$$= 3(2x - 3)^2$$

98. $3x^4 - 81x = 3x(x^3 - 27)$
$$= 3x(x - 3)(x^2 + 3x + 9)$$

99. $27a^4 - a = a(27a^3 - 1)$
$$= a(3a - 1)(9a^2 + 3a + 1)$$

100. $7x^2 - 28 = 7(x^2 - 4)$
$$= 7(x + 2)(x - 2)$$

101. $20x^2 - 5 = 5(4x^2 - 1)$
$$= 5(2x + 1)(2x - 1)$$

102. $y^4 - 10y^3 + 21y^2 = y^2(y^2 - 10y + 21)$
$$= y^2(y - 7)(y - 3)$$

103. $y^5 + 6y^4 - 55y^3 = y^3(y^2 + 6y - 55)$
$$= y^3(y + 11)(y - 5)$$

104. $x^4 - 16 = (x^2 + 4)(x^2 - 4)$
$$= (x^2 + 4)(x + 2)(x - 2)$$

105. $16x^4 - 81 = (4x^2 + 9)(4x^2 - 9)$
$$= (4x^2 + 9)(2x + 3)(2x - 3)$$

106. $8x^5 - 98x^3 = 2x^3(4x^2 - 49)$
$$= 2x^3(2x + 7)(2x - 7)$$

107. $16a - 2a^4 = 2a(8 - a^3)$
$$= 2a(2 - a)(4 + 2a + a^2)$$

108. $x^3y^3 - x^3 = x^3(y^3 - 1)$
$$= x^3(y - 1)(y^2 + y + 1)$$

109. $x^3 + 2x^2 - x - 2 = x^2(x + 2) - 1(x + 2)$
$$= (x + 2)(x^2 - 1)$$
$$= (x + 2)(x + 1)(x - 1)$$

110. $2x^3 - 3x^2 - 8x + 12 = x^2(2x - 3) - 4(2x - 3)$
$$= (2x - 3)(x^2 - 4)$$
$$= (2x - 3)(x + 2)(x - 2)$$

111. $2x^3 + 4x^2 - 3x - 6 = 2x^2(x + 2) - 3(x + 2)$
$$= (x + 2)(2x^2 - 3)$$

112. $3x^3 - 3x^2 + 4x - 4 = 3x^2(x - 1) + 4(x - 1)$
$$= (x - 1)(3x^2 + 4)$$

113. $x^3 + x^2 - 16x - 16 = x^2(x + 1) - 16(x + 1)$
$$= (x + 1)(x^2 - 16)$$
$$= (x + 1)(x + 4)(x - 4)$$

114. $4x^3 + 8x^2 - 9x - 18 = 4x^2(x + 2) - 9(x + 2)$
$$= (x + 2)(4x^2 - 9)$$
$$= (x + 2)(2x + 3)(2x - 3)$$

115. $a^3b^6 - b^3 = b^3(a^3b^3 - 1)$
$$= b^3(ab - 1)(a^2b^2 + ab + 1)$$

116. $x^6y^6 - x^3y^3 = x^3y^3(x^3y^3 - 1)$
$$= x^3y^3(xy - 1)(x^2y^2 + xy + 1)$$

117. $x^4 - 2x^3 - 35x^2 = x^2(x^2 - 2x - 35)$
$$= x^2(x - 7)(x + 5)$$

118. $x^4 + 15x^3 - 56x^2 = x^2(x^2 + 15x - 56)$

119. $4x^2 + 4x - 1$ is nonfactorable over the integers.

120. $8x^4 - 40x^3 + 50x^2 = 2x^2(4x^2 - 20x + 25)$
$$= 2x^2(2x - 5)^2$$

121. $6x^5 + 74x^4 + 24x^3 = 2x^3(3x^2 + 37x + 12)$
$$= 2x^3(3x + 1)(x + 12)$$

122. $x^4 - y^4 = (x^2 + y^2)(x^2 - y^2)$
$$= (x^2 + y^2)(x + y)(x - y)$$

123. $16a^4 - b^4 = (4a^2 + b^2)(4a^2 - b^2)$
$$= (4a^2 + b^2)(2a + b)(2a - b)$$

124. $x^6 + y^6 = (x^2)^3 + (y^2)^3$
$$= (x^2 + y^2)(x^4 - x^2y^2 + y^4)$$

125. $x^4 - 5x^2 - 4$ is nonfactorable over the integers.

126. $a^4 - 25a^2 - 144$ is nonfactorable over the integers.

127. $3b^5 - 24b^2 = 3b^2(b^3 - 8)$
$$= 3b^2(b - 2)(b^2 + 2b + 4)$$

128. $16a^4 - 2a = 2a(8a^3 - 1)$
$$= 2a(2a - 1)(4a^2 + 2a + 1)$$

129. $x^4y^2 - 5x^3y^3 + 6x^2y^4 = x^2y^2(x^2 - 5xy + 6y^2)$
$$= x^2y^2(x - 3y)(x - 2y)$$

130. $a^4b^2 - 8a^3b^3 - 48a^2b^4 = a^2b^2(a^2 - 8ab - 48b^2)$
$$= a^2b^2(a + 4b)(a - 12b)$$

131. $16x^3y + 4x^2y^2 - 42xy^3$
$$= 2xy(8x^2 + 2xy - 21y^2)$$
$$= 2xy(4x + 7y)(2x - 3y)$$

132. $24a^2b^2 - 14ab^3 - 90b^4$
$= 2b^2(12a^2 - 7ab - 45b^2)$
$= 2b^2(4a - 9b)(3a + 5b)$

133. $x^3 - 2x^2 - x + 2 = x^2(x-2) - (x-2)$
$= (x-2)(x^2-1)$
$= (x-2)(x+1)(x-1)$

134. $x^3 - 2x^2 - 4x + 8 = x^2(x-2) - 4(x-2)$
$= (x-2)(x^2-4)$
$= (x-2)(x+2)(x-2)$
$= (x-2)^2(x+2)$

135. $8xb - 8x - 4b + 4 = 4(2xb - 2x - b + 1)$
$= 4[2x(b-1) - (b-1)]$
$= 4(b-1)(2x-1)$

136. $4xy + 8x + 4y + 8 = 4(xy + 2x + y + 2)$
$= 4[x(y+2) + (y+2)]$
$= 4(x+1)(y+2)$

137. $4x^2y^2 - 4x^2 - 9y^2 + 9$
$= 4x^2(y^2-1) - 9(y^2-1)$
$= (y^2-1)(4x^2-9)$
$= (y+1)(y-1)(2x+3)(2x-3)$

138. $4x^4 - x^2 - 4x^2y^2 + y^2$
$= x^2(4x^2-1) - y^2(4x^2-1)$
$= (4x^2-1)(x^2-y^2)$
$= (2x+1)(2x-1)(x+y)(x-y)$

139. $x^5 - 4x^3 - 8x^2 + 32$
$= x^3(x^2-4) - 8(x^2-4)$
$= (x^2-4)(x^3-8)$
$= (x+2)(x-2)(x-2)(x^2+2x+4)$
$= (x+2)(x-2)^2(x^2+2x+4)$

140. $x^6y^3 + x^3 - x^3y^3 - 1$
$= x^3(x^3y^3+1) - (x^3y^3+1)$
$= (x^3y^3+1)(x^3-1)$
$= (xy+1)(x^2y^2-xy+1)(x-1)(x^2+x+1)$

141. $a^{2n+2} - 6a^{n+2} + 9a^2 = a^2(a^{2n} - 6a^n + 9)$
$= a^2(a^n-3)^2$

142. $x^{2n+1} + 2x^{n+1} + x = x(x^{2n} + 2x^n + 1)$
$= x(x^n+1)^2$

143. $2x^{n+2} - 7x^{n+1} + 3x^n = x^n(2x^2 - 7x + 3)$
$= x^n(2x-1)(x-3)$

144. $3b^{n+2} + 4b^{n+1} - 4b^n = b^n(3b^2 + 4b - 4)$
$= b^n(3b-2)(b+2)$

Applying Concepts 5.6

145. $4x^2 - kx + 25 = (2x+5)^2$ or $(2x-5)^2$
$(2x+5)(2x+5) = 4x^2 + 20x + 25$
$(2x-5)(2x-5) = 4x^2 - 20x + 25$
The possible values of $-k$ are 20 and -20.
The possible values of k are -20 and 20.

146. $9x^2 - kx + 1 = (3x+1)^2$ or $(3x-1)^2$
$(3x+1)(3x+1) = 9x^2 + 6x + 1$
$(3x-1)(3x-1) = 9x^2 - 6x + 1$
The possible values of $-k$ are 6 and -6.
The possible values of k are -6 and 6.

147. $16x^2 + kxy + y^2 = (4x+y)^2$ or $(4x-y)^2$
$(4x+y)(4x+y) = 16x^2 + 8xy + y^2$
$(4x-y)(4x-y) = 16x^2 - 8xy + y^2$
The possible values of k are 8 and -8.

148. $49x^2 + kxy + 64y^2 = (7x+8y)^2$ or $(7x-8y)^2$
$(7x+8y)(7x+8y) = 49x^2 + 112x + 64y^2$
$(7x-8y)(7x-8y) = 49x^2 - 112x + 64y^2$
The possible values of k are 112 and -112.

149. $ax^3 + b - bx^3 - a = (ax^3 - bx^3) + (b-a)$
$= x^3(a-b) + [-(a-b)]$
$= x^3(a-b) - (a-b)$
$= (a-b)(x^3-1)$
$= (a-b)(x^3-1^3)$
$= (a-b)(x-1)(x^2+x+1)$

150. $xy^2 - 2b - x + 2by^2 = (xy^2 - x) + (-2b + 2by^2)$
$= x(y^2-1) + 2b(-1+y^2)$
$= x(y^2-1) + 2b(y^2-1)$
$= (y^2-1)(x+2b)$
$= (y^2-1^2)(x+2b)$
$= (y+1)(y-1)(x+2b)$

151.
$$y^{8n} - 2y^{4n} + 1 = (y^{4n} - 1)^2$$
$$= [(y^{2n})^2 - 1][(y^{2n})^2 - 1]$$
$$= (y^{2n} + 1)(y^{2n} - 1)(y^{2n} + 1)(y^{2n} - 1)$$
$$= (y^{2n} + 1)^2 (y^{2n} - 1)^2$$
$$= (y^{2n} + 1)^2 [(y^n)^2 - 1]^2$$
$$= (y^{2n} + 1)^2 [(y^n + 1)(y^n - 1)]^2$$
$$= (y^{2n} + 1)^2 (y^n + 1)^2 (y^n - 1)^2$$

152.
$$x^{6n} - 1 = [(x^{3n})^2 - 1^2]$$
$$= (x^{3n} + 1)(x^{3n} - 1)$$
$$= [(x^n)^3 + 1^3][(x^n)^3 - 1^3]$$
$$= (x^n + 1)(x^{2n} - x^n + 1)(x^n - 1)(x^{2n} + x^n + 1)$$

153. One number is a perfect square less than 63: 1, 4, 9, 16, 25, 36, 49
One number is a prime number less than 63: 2, 3, 5, 7, 11, 13, 17, 19, 23, 29, 31, 37, 41, 43, 47, 53, 59, 61
The product of the numbers is 63: $9 \cdot 7 = 63$
$9 + 7 = 16$
The sum of the numbers is 16.

154. $250 = 2 \cdot 5 \cdot 5 \cdot 5 = 2 \cdot 5^3$
The exponents of the factors of a perfect square are even.
$(2 \cdot 5^3) \cdot (2 \cdot 5) = 2^2 \cdot 5^4$
The smallest whole number is $2 \cdot 5 = 10$.

155. Perfect squares less than 500

1	144
4	169
9	196
16	225
25	256
36	289
49	324
64	361
81	400
100	441
121	484

The palindromic perfect squares less than 500 are 1, 4, 9, 121, and 484.

156. Strategy
To find the number of cubic centimeters of dough left over, subtract the volume of dough in the cookie from the volume of dough in the square piece of dough. The formula for the volume of a rectangular solid is $V = LWH$. The formula for the volume of a cylinder is $V = \pi r^2 h$.

Solution
$$LWH - \pi r^2 h$$
$$= x \cdot x \cdot 1 - \pi \left(\frac{1}{2} x\right)^2 (1)$$
$$= x^2 - \pi \left(\frac{1}{4} x^2\right)$$
$$= x^2 - \frac{1}{4} \pi x^2$$
$$= x^2 - \frac{1}{4} (3.14) x^2$$
$$= x^2 - 0.785 x^2$$
$$= 0.215 x^2$$
$0.215 x^2$ cm^3 of dough is left over.

157.
$$x^4 + 64$$
$$= (x^4 + 16x^2 + 64) - 16x^2$$
$$= (x^2 + 8)(x^2 + 8) - 16x^2$$
$$= (x^2 + 8)^2 - 16x^2$$
$$= (x^2 + 8 - 4x)(x^2 + 8 + 4x)$$
$$= (x^2 - 4x + 8)(x^2 + 4x + 8)$$

158.
$$x^4 + 4$$
$$= (x^4 + 4x^2 + 4) - 4x^2$$
$$= (x^2 + 2)(x^2 + 2) - 4x^2$$
$$= (x^2 + 2)^2 - 4x^2$$
$$= (x^2 + 2 - 2x)(x^2 + 2 + 2x)$$
$$= (x^2 - 2x + 2)(x^2 + 2x + 2)$$

159. No, a third-degree polynomial cannot have factors $x - 1$, $x + 1$, $x - 3$, and $x + 4$ because the leading term in the product of these factors must be a fourth-degree term.

Section 5.7

Concept Review 5.7

1. Always true

2. Always true

3. Sometimes true
   The equation $(x-2)(x+3)(x-1) = 0$ has three solutions.

4. Sometimes true
   The Principle of Zero Products can be used only if the second-degree equation can be factored.

5. Sometimes true
   If $n = 1$, then $n + 1 = 2$, and $n + 3 = 4$, which are even integers.

6. Never true
   To solve an equation by the Principle of Zero Products, the equation must be set equal to zero.

Objective 5.7.1 Exercises

1. A quadratic equation is an equation of the form $ax^2 + bx + c = 0$, $a \neq 0$. A quadratic equation has a term of degree 2. In a linear equation, the highest exponent on a variable is 1.
   $x^2 + 3x - 7 = 0$ is an example of a quadratic equation.
   $2x + 4 = 0$ is an example of a linear equation.

2. Write the quadratic equation in standard form. Factor the trinomial. Since the product of the factors is equal to zero, by the Principle of Zero Products, it must be that one of the factors is equal to zero. Therefore, we can set each factor equal to zero. Solve these equations for the variable. The values of the variable are the solutions of the quadratic equation.

3. $(y+4)(y+6) = 0$
   $y + 4 = 0 \qquad y + 6 = 0$
   $\quad y = -4 \qquad y = -6$
   The solutions are -4 and -6.

4. $(a-5)(a-2) = 0$
   $a - 5 = 0 \quad a - 2 = 0$
   $\quad a = 5 \qquad a = 2$
   The solutions are 5 and 2.

5. $x(x-7) = 0$
   $x = 0 \quad x - 7 = 0$
   $\qquad\quad x = 7$
   The solutions are 0 and 7.

6. $b(b+8) = 0$
   $b = 0 \quad b + 8 = 0$
   $\qquad\quad b = -8$
   The solutions are 0 and -8.

7. $3z(2z+5) = 0$
   $3z = 0 \quad 2z + 5 = 0$
   $\quad z = 0 \qquad 2z = -5$
   $\qquad\qquad\qquad z = -\dfrac{5}{2}$
   The solutions are 0 and $-\dfrac{5}{2}$.

8. $4y(3y-2) = 0$
   $4y = 0 \quad 3y - 2 = 0$
   $\quad y = 0 \qquad 3y = 2$
   $\qquad\qquad\qquad y = \dfrac{2}{3}$
   The solutions are 0 and $\dfrac{2}{3}$.

9. $(2x+3)(x-7) = 0$
   $2x + 3 = 0 \qquad x - 7 = 0$
   $\quad 2x = -3 \qquad x = 7$
   $\quad x = -\dfrac{3}{2}$
   The solutions are $-\dfrac{3}{2}$ and 7.

10. $(4a-1)(a+9) = 0$
    $4a - 1 = 0 \quad a + 9 = 0$
    $\quad 4a = 1 \qquad a = -9$
    $\quad a = \dfrac{1}{4}$
    The solutions are $\dfrac{1}{4}$ and -9.

11. $b^2 - 49 = 0$
    $b^2 - 7^2 = 0$
    $(b+7)(b-7) = 0$
    $b + 7 = 0 \quad b - 7 = 0$
    $\quad b = -7 \qquad b = 7$
    The solutions are 7 and -7.

12. $4z^2 - 1 = 0$
    $(2z)^2 - 1^2 = 0$
    $(2z+1)(2z-1) = 0$
    $2z + 1 = 0 \qquad 2z - 1 = 0$
    $\quad 2z = -1 \qquad 2z = 1$
    $\quad z = -\dfrac{1}{2} \qquad z = \dfrac{1}{2}$
    The solutions are $\dfrac{1}{2}$ and $-\dfrac{1}{2}$.

13. $9t^2 - 16 = 0$
    $(3t)^2 - 4^2 = 0$
    $(3t+4)(3t-4) = 0$
    $3t + 4 = 0 \qquad 3t - 4 = 0$
    $\quad 3t = -4 \qquad 3t = 4$
    $\quad t = -\dfrac{4}{3} \qquad t = \dfrac{4}{3}$
    The solutions are $\dfrac{4}{3}$ and $-\dfrac{4}{3}$.

14. $x^2 + x - 6 = 0$
$(x+3)(x-2) = 0$
$x+3 = 0 \quad x-2 = 0$
$x = -3 \quad x = 2$
The solutions are 2 and –3.

15. $y^2 + 4y - 5 = 0$
$(y+5)(y-1) = 0$
$y+5 = 0 \quad y-1 = 0$
$y = -5 \quad y = 1$
The solutions are –5 and 1.

16. $a^2 - 8a + 16 = 0$
$(a-4)^2 = 0$
$(a-4)(a-4) = 0$
$a-4 = 0 \quad a-4 = 0$
$a = 4 \quad a = 4$
The solution is 4.

17. $2b^2 - 5b - 12 = 0$
$(2b+3)(b-4) = 0$
$2b+3 = 0 \quad b-4 = 0$
$2b = -3 \quad b = 4$
$b = -\dfrac{3}{2}$
The solutions are $-\dfrac{3}{2}$ and 4.

18. $t^2 - 8t = 0$
$t(t-8) = 0$
$t = 0 \quad t-8 = 0$
$t = 8$
The solutions are 0 and 8.

19. $x^2 - 9x = 0$
$x(x-9) = 0$
$x = 0 \quad x-9 = 0$
$x = 9$
The solutions are 0 and 9.

20. $2y^2 - 10y = 0$
$2y(y-5) = 0$
$2y = 0 \quad y-5 = 0$
$y = 0 \quad y = 5$
The solutions are 0 and 5.

21. $3a^2 - 12a = 0$
$3a(a-4) = 0$
$3a = 0 \quad a-4 = 0$
$a = 0 \quad a = 4$
The solutions are 0 and 4.

22. $b^2 - 4b = 32$
$b^2 - 4b - 32 = 0$
$(b-8)(b+4) = 0$
$b-8 = 0 \quad b+4 = 0$
$b = 8 \quad b = -4$
The solutions are 8 and –4.

23. $z^2 - 3z = 28$
$z^2 - 3z - 28 = 0$
$(z-7)(z+4) = 0$
$z-7 = 0 \quad z+4 = 0$
$z = 7 \quad z = -4$
The solutions are 7 and –4.

24. $2x^2 - 5x = 12$
$2x^2 - 5x - 12 = 0$
$(2x+3)(x-4) = 0$
$2x+3 = 0 \quad x-4 = 0$
$2x = -3 \quad x = 4$
$x = -\dfrac{3}{2}$
The solutions are $-\dfrac{3}{2}$ and 4.

25. $3t^2 + 13t = 10$
$3t^2 + 13t - 10 = 0$
$(3t-2)(t+5) = 0$
$3t-2 = 0 \quad t+5 = 0$
$3t = 2 \quad t = -5$
$t = \dfrac{2}{3}$
The solutions are $\dfrac{2}{3}$ and –5.

26. $4y^2 - 19y = 5$
$4y^2 - 19y - 5 = 0$
$(4y+1)(y-5) = 0$
$4y+1 = 0 \quad y-5 = 0$
$4y = -1 \quad y = 5$
$y = -\dfrac{1}{4}$
The solutions are $-\dfrac{1}{4}$ and 5.

27. $5b^2 - 17b = -6$
$5b^2 - 17b + 6 = 0$
$(5b-2)(b-3) = 0$
$5b-2 = 0 \quad b-3 = 0$
$5b = 2 \quad b = 3$
$b = \dfrac{2}{5}$
The solutions are $\dfrac{2}{5}$ and 3.

28. $6a^2 + a = 2$
$6a^2 + a - 2 = 0$
$(2a-1)(3a+2) = 0$
$2a-1 = 0 \quad 3a+2 = 0$
$2a = 1 \quad 3a = -2$
$a = \dfrac{1}{2} \quad a = -\dfrac{2}{3}$
The solutions are $\dfrac{1}{2}$ and $-\dfrac{2}{3}$.

29.
$$8x^2 - 10x = 3$$
$$8x^2 - 10x - 3 = 0$$
$$(2x - 3)(4x + 1) = 0$$
$$2x - 3 = 0 \quad 4x + 1 = 0$$
$$2x = 3 \quad 4x = -1$$
$$x = \frac{3}{2} \quad x = -\frac{1}{4}$$
The solutions are $\frac{3}{2}$ and $-\frac{1}{4}$.

30.
$$z(z - 1) = 20$$
$$z^2 - z = 20$$
$$z^2 - z - 20 = 0$$
$$(z - 5)(z + 4) = 0$$
$$z - 5 = 0 \quad z + 4 = 0$$
$$z = 5 \quad z = -4$$
The solutions are 5 and –4.

31.
$$y(y - 2) = 35$$
$$y^2 - 2y = 35$$
$$y^2 - 2y - 35 = 0$$
$$(y - 7)(y + 5) = 0$$
$$y - 7 = 0 \quad y + 5 = 0$$
$$y = 7 \quad y = -5$$
The solutions are 7 and –5.

32.
$$t(t + 1) = 42$$
$$t^2 + t = 42$$
$$t^2 + t - 42 = 0$$
$$(t + 7)(t - 6) = 0$$
$$t + 7 = 0 \quad t - 6 = 0$$
$$t = -7 \quad t = 6$$
The solutions are –7 and 6.

33.
$$x(x - 12) = -27$$
$$x^2 - 12x = -27$$
$$x^2 - 12x + 27 = 0$$
$$(x - 9)(x - 3) = 0$$
$$x - 9 = 0 \quad x - 3 = 0$$
$$x = 9 \quad x = 3$$
The solutions are 9 and 3.

34.
$$x(2x - 5) = 12$$
$$2x^2 - 5x = 12$$
$$2x^2 - 5x - 12 = 0$$
$$(2x + 3)(x - 4) = 0$$
$$2x + 3 = 0 \quad x - 4 = 0$$
$$2x = -3 \quad x = 4$$
$$x = -\frac{3}{2}$$
The solutions are $-\frac{3}{2}$ and 4.

35.
$$y(3y - 2) = 8$$
$$3y^2 - 2y = 8$$
$$3y^2 - 2y - 8 = 0$$
$$(3y + 4)(y - 2) = 0$$
$$3y + 4 = 0 \quad y - 2 = 0$$
$$3y = -4 \quad y = 2$$
$$y = -\frac{4}{3}$$
The solutions are $-\frac{4}{3}$ and 2.

36.
$$2b^2 - 6b = b - 3$$
$$2b^2 - 7b = -3$$
$$2b^2 - 7b + 3 = 0$$
$$(2b - 1)(b - 3) = 0$$
$$2b - 1 = 0 \quad b - 3 = 0$$
$$2b = 1 \quad b = 3$$
$$b = \frac{1}{2}$$
The solutions are $\frac{1}{2}$ and 3.

37.
$$3a^2 - 4a = 20 - 15a$$
$$3a^2 + 11a = 20$$
$$3a^2 + 11a - 20 = 0$$
$$(3a - 4)(a + 5) = 0$$
$$3a - 4 = 0 \quad a + 5 = 0$$
$$3a = 4 \quad a = -5$$
$$a = \frac{4}{3}$$
The solutions are $\frac{4}{3}$ and –5.

38.
$$2t^2 + 5t = 6t + 15$$
$$2t^2 - t = 15$$
$$2t^2 - t - 15 = 0$$
$$(2t + 5)(t - 3) = 0$$
$$2t + 5 = 0 \quad t - 3 = 0$$
$$2t = -5 \quad t = 3$$
$$t = -\frac{5}{2}$$
The solutions are $-\frac{5}{2}$ and 3.

39.
$$(y + 5)(y - 7) = -20$$
$$y^2 - 2y - 35 = -20$$
$$y^2 - 2y - 15 = 0$$
$$(y - 5)(y + 3) = 0$$
$$y - 5 = 0 \quad y + 3 = 0$$
$$y = 5 \quad y = -3$$
The solutions are 5 and –3.

40. $(x+2)(x-6)=20$
$x^2-4x-12=20$
$x^2-4x-32=0$
$(x-8)(x+4)=0$
$x-8=0 \quad x+4=0$
$\quad x=8 \qquad x=-4$
The solutions are 8 and –4.

41. $(b+5)(b+10)=6$
$b^2+15b+50=6$
$b^2+15b+44=0$
$(b+11)(b+4)=0$
$b+11=0 \qquad b+4=0$
$\quad b=-11 \qquad b=-4$
The solutions are –11 and –4.

42. $(a-9)(a-1)=-7$
$a^2-10a+9=-7$
$a^2-10a+16=0$
$(a-2)(a-8)=0$
$a-2=0 \quad a-8=0$
$\quad a=2 \qquad a=8$
The solutions are 2 and 8.

43. $(t-3)^2=1$
$t^2-6t+9=1$
$t^2-6t+8=0$
$(t-2)(t-4)=0$
$t-2=0 \quad t-4=0$
$\quad t=2 \qquad t=4$
The solutions are 2 and 4.

44. $(y-4)^2=4$
$y^2-8y+16=4$
$y^2-8y+12=0$
$(y-6)(y-2)=0$
$y-6=0 \quad y-2=0$
$\quad y=6 \qquad y=2$
The solutions are 6 and 2.

45. $(3-x)^2+x^2=5$
$9-6x+x^2+x^2=5$
$2x^2-6x+9=5$
$2x^2-6x+4=0$
$2(x^2-3x+2)=0$
$2(x-1)(x-2)=0$
$x-1=0 \quad x-2=0$
$\quad x=1 \qquad x=2$
The solutions are 1 and 2.

46. $(2-b)^2+b^2=10$
$4-4b+b^2+b^2=10$
$2b^2-4b+4=10$
$2b^2-4b-6=0$
$2(b^2-2b-3)=0$
$2(b-3)(b+1)=0$
$b-3=0 \quad b+1=0$
$\quad b=3 \qquad b=-1$
The solutions are 3 and –1.

47. $(a-1)^2=3a-5$
$a^2-2a+1=3a-5$
$a^2-5a+1=-5$
$a^2-5a+6=0$
$(a-2)(a-3)=0$
$a-2=0 \quad a-3=0$
$\quad a=2 \qquad a=3$
The solutions are 2 and 3.

48. $2x^3+x^2-8x-4=0$
$x^2(2x+1)-4(2x+1)=0$
$\quad (2x+1)(x^2-4)=0$
$(2x+1)(x+2)(x-2)=0$
$2x+1=0 \quad x+2=0 \quad x-2=0$
$\quad 2x=-1 \qquad x=-2 \qquad x=2$
$\quad x=-\dfrac{1}{2}$
The solutions are $-\dfrac{1}{2}$, –2 and 2.

49. $x^3+4x^2-x-4=0$
$x^2(x+4)-1(x+4)=0$
$\quad (x+4)(x^2-1)=0$
$(x+4)(x+1)(x-1)=0$
$x+4=0 \quad x+1=0 \quad x-1=0$
$\quad x=-4 \qquad x=-1 \qquad x=1$
The solutions are –4, –1, and 1.

50. $12x^3-8x^2-3x+2=0$
$4x^2(3x-2)-1(3x-2)=0$
$\quad (3x-2)(4x^2-1)=0$
$(3x-2)(2x+1)(2x-1)=0$
$3x-2=0 \quad 2x+1=0 \quad 2x-1=0$
$\quad 3x=2 \qquad 2x=-1 \qquad 2x=1$
$\quad x=\dfrac{2}{3} \qquad x=-\dfrac{1}{2} \qquad x=\dfrac{1}{2}$
The solutions are $\dfrac{2}{3}$, $-\dfrac{1}{2}$, and $\dfrac{1}{2}$.

51. $f(c)=1$
$c^2-3c+3=1$
$c^2-3c+2=0$
$(c-2)(c-1)=0$
$c-2=0 \quad c-1=0$
$\quad c=2 \qquad c=1$
The values of c are 1 and 2.

52.
$$f(c) = 3$$
$$c^2 + 4c - 2 = 3$$
$$c^2 + 4c - 5 = 0$$
$$(c+5)(c-1) = 0$$
$$c+5 = 0 \quad c-1 = 0$$
$$c = -5 \quad c = 1$$
The values of c are -5 and 1.

53.
$$f(c) = -4$$
$$2c^2 - c - 5 = -4$$
$$2c^2 - c - 1 = 0$$
$$(2c+1)(c-1) = 0$$
$$2c+1 = 0 \quad c-1 = 0$$
$$2c = -1 \quad c = 1$$
$$c = -\frac{1}{2}$$
The values of c are $-\frac{1}{2}$ and 1.

54.
$$f(c) = -3$$
$$6c^2 - 5c - 9 = -3$$
$$6c^2 - 5c - 6 = 0$$
$$(3c+2)(2c-3) = 0$$
$$3c+2 = 0 \quad 2c-3 = 0$$
$$3c = -2 \quad 2c = 3$$
$$c = -\frac{2}{3} \quad c = \frac{3}{2}$$
The values of c are $-\frac{2}{3}$ and $\frac{3}{2}$.

55.
$$f(c) = 2$$
$$4c^2 - 4c + 3 = 2$$
$$4c^2 - 4c + 1 = 0$$
$$(2c-1)(2c-1) = 0$$
$$2c-1 = 0 \quad 2c-1 = 0$$
$$2c = 1 \quad 2c = 1$$
$$c = \frac{1}{2} \quad c = \frac{1}{2}$$
The value of c is $\frac{1}{2}$.

56.
$$f(c) = 3$$
$$c^2 - 6c + 12 = 3$$
$$c^2 - 6c + 9 = 0$$
$$(c-3)(c-3) = 0$$
$$c-3 = 0 \quad c-3 = 0$$
$$c = 3 \quad c = 3$$
The value of c is 3.

57.
$$f(c) = -5$$
$$c^3 + 9c^2 - c - 14 = -5$$
$$c^3 + 9c^2 - c - 9 = 0$$
$$c^2(c+9) - (c+9) = 0$$
$$(c+9)(c^2 - 1) = 0$$
$$(c+9)(c+1)(c-1) = 0$$
$$c+9 = 0 \quad c+1 = 0 \quad c-1 = 0$$
$$c = -9 \quad c = -1 \quad c = 1$$
The values of c are -9, -1, and 1.

58.
$$f(c) = 1$$
$$c^3 + 3c^2 - 4c - 11 = 1$$
$$c^3 + 3c^2 - 4c - 12 = 0$$
$$c^2(c+3) - 4(c+3) = 0$$
$$(c+3)(c^2 - 4) = 0$$
$$(c+3)(c+2)(c-2) = 0$$
$$c+3 = 0 \quad c+2 = 0 \quad c-2 = 0$$
$$c = -3 \quad c = -2 \quad c = 2$$
The values of c are -3, -2, and 2.

Objective 5.7.2 Exercises

59. Strategy
This is an integer problem.
The unknown integer is n.
The sum of the integer and its square is 90.
$$n + n^2 = 90$$

Solution
$$n + n^2 = 90$$
$$n^2 + n - 90 = 0$$
$$(n+10)(n-9) = 0$$
$$n+10 = 0 \quad n-9 = 0$$
$$n = -10 \quad n = 9$$
The integer is -10 or 9.

60. Strategy
This is an integer problem.
The unknown integer is n.
The sum of the integer and its square is 132.
$$n + n^2 = 132$$

Solution
$$n + n^2 = 132$$
$$n^2 + n - 132 = 0$$
$$(n+12)(n-11) = 0$$
$$n+12 = 0 \quad n-11 = 0$$
$$n = -12 \quad n = 11$$
The integer is -12 or 11.

61. Strategy
This is an integer problem.
The first positive integer is n.
The next consecutive positive integer is $n + 1$.
The sum of the squares of the two consecutive positive integers is equal to 145.
$$n^2 + (n+1)^2 = 145$$

Solution
$$n^2 + (n+1)^2 = 145$$
$$n^2 + n^2 + 2n + 1 = 145$$
$$2n^2 + 2n - 144 = 0$$
$$2(n^2 + n - 72) = 0$$
$$2(n+9)(n-8) = 0$$
$$n + 9 = 0 \quad n - 8 = 0$$
$$n = -9 \qquad n = 8$$
The solutions −9 and −8 are not possible because they are not positive. The integers are 8 and 9.

62. Strategy
This is an integer problem.
The first integer: n
The next consecutive positive odd integer: $n + 2$
The sum of the squares of the two integers is 290.
$$n^2 + (n+2)^2 = 290$$

Solution
$$n^2 + (n+2)^2 = 290$$
$$n^2 + n^2 + 4n + 4 = 290$$
$$2n^2 + 4n - 286 = 0$$
$$2(n^2 + 2n - 143) = 0$$
$$2(n+13)(n-11) = 0$$
$$n + 13 = 0 \qquad n - 11 = 0$$
$$n = -13 \qquad n = 11$$
$$n + 2 = -13 + 2 = -11 \quad n + 2 = 11 + 2 = 13$$
The solutions −13 and −11 are not possible because they are not positive. The integers are 11 and 13.

63. Strategy
This is an integer problem.
The unknown integer is n.
The sum of the cube of the integer and the product of the integer and twelve is equal to seven times the square of the integer.
$$x^3 + 12x = 7x^2$$

Solution
$$x^3 + 12x = 7x^2$$
$$x^3 - 7x^2 + 12x = 0$$
$$x(x^2 - 7x + 12) = 0$$
$$x(x-3)(x-4) = 0$$
$$x = 0 \quad x - 3 = 0 \quad x - 4 = 0$$
$$x = 3 \qquad x = 4$$
The integer is 0, 3, or 4.

64. Strategy
This is an integer problem.
The unknown integer is n.
The sum of the cube of the integer and the product of the integer and seven is equal to eight times the square of the integer.
$$n^3 + 7n = 8n^2$$

Solution
$$n^3 + 7n = 8n^2$$
$$n^3 - 8n^2 + 7n = 0$$
$$n(n^2 - 8n + 7) = 0$$
$$n(n-1)(n-7) = 0$$
$$n = 0 \quad n - 1 = 0 \quad n - 7 = 0$$
$$n = 1 \qquad n = 7$$
The integer is 0, 1, or 7.

65. Strategy
This is a geometry problem.
The width of the rectangle: x
The length of the rectangle: $2x + 5$
The area of the rectangle is 168 in^2. Use the equation for the area of a rectangle ($A = L \cdot W$).

Solution
$$A = L \cdot W$$
$$168 = (2x+5)x$$
$$168 = 2x^2 + 5x$$
$$0 = 2x^2 + 5x - 168$$
$$0 = (2x+21)(x-8)$$
$$2x + 21 = 0 \qquad x - 8 = 0$$
$$2x = -21 \qquad x = 8$$
$$x = -\frac{21}{2}$$
Since the width cannot be negative, $-\frac{21}{2}$ cannot be a solution.
$$2x + 5 = 2(8) + 5 = 21$$
The width is 8 in. The length is 21 in.

66. Strategy
This is a geometry problem.
The length of the rectangle: x
The width of the rectangle: $x - 5$
The area of the rectangle is 300 ft^2.
Use the equation for the area of a rectangle ($A = L \cdot W$)

Solution
$$A = L \cdot W$$
$$300 = x(x-5)$$
$$300 = x^2 - 5x$$
$$0 = x^2 - 5x - 300$$
$$0 = (x-20)(x+15)$$
$$x - 20 = 0 \qquad x + 15 = 0$$
$$x = 20 \qquad x = -15$$
Since the length cannot be negative, −15 cannot be a solution.
$$x - 5 = 20 - 5 = 15$$
The length is 20 ft. The width is 15 ft.

67. Strategy

Length of the trough: 6
Width of the trough: $10 - 2x$
Height of the trough: x
The volume of the trough is 72 m^3.
Use the equation for the volume of a rectangular solid ($V = LWH$).

Solution

$$V = LWH$$
$$72 = 6(10 - 2x)(x)$$
$$72 = (60 - 12x)x$$
$$72 = 60x - 12x^2$$
$$12x^2 - 60x + 72 = 0$$
$$12(x^2 - 5x + 6) = 0$$
$$12(x - 3)(x - 2) = 0$$
$$x - 3 = 0 \quad x - 2 = 0$$
$$x = 3 \qquad x = 2$$

The value of x should be 2 m or 3 m.

68. Strategy

To find the number of sides of the polygon, substitute 54 for D in the equation and solve for n.

Solution

$$54 = \frac{n(n - 3)}{2}$$
$$108 = n(n - 3)$$
$$108 = n^2 - 3n$$
$$n^2 - 3n - 108 = 0$$
$$(n + 9)(n - 12) = 0$$
$$n + 9 = 0 \quad n - 12 = 0$$
$$n = -9 \qquad n = 12$$

Since the number of sides cannot be negative, -9 cannot be a solution. The polygon has 12 sides.

69. Strategy

To find the velocity of the rocket, substitute 500 for s in the equation and solve for v.

Solution

$$v^2 = 20s$$
$$v^2 = 20(500)$$
$$v^2 = 10,000$$
$$v^2 - 10,000 = 0$$
$$(v - 100)(v + 100) = 0$$
$$v - 100 = 0 \quad v + 100 = 0$$
$$v = 100 \qquad v = -100$$

Since the rocket is traveling in the direction it was launched, the velocity is not negative, so -100 is not a solution. The velocity of the rocket is 100 m/s.

70. Strategy

This is a geometry problem.
The base of the triangle: $13 + x$
The height of the triangle: $9 + x$
Use the Pythagorean Theorem to solve for x ($a^2 + b^2 = c^2$, where a and b are legs of the triangle and c is the hypotenuse).

Solution

$$a^2 + b^2 = c^2$$
$$(13 + x)^2 + (9 + x)^2 = (20)^2$$
$$(169 + 13x + 13x + x^2) + (81 + 9x + 9x + x^2) = 400$$
$$169 + 26x + x^2 + 81 + 18x + x^2 = 400$$
$$2x^2 + 44x + 250 = 400$$
$$2x^2 + 44x - 150 = 0$$
$$2(x^2 + 22x - 75) = 0$$
$$2(x + 25)(x - 3) = 0$$
$$x + 25 = 0 \quad x - 3 = 0$$
$$x = -25 \qquad x = 3$$

Since the length x cannot be negative, -25 is not a solution. The value of x must be 3 ft.

71. Strategy

This is a geometry problem.
The height of the triangle: x
The base of the triangle: $3x$
The area of the triangle is 24 cm^2. Use the equation for the area of a triangle $\left(A = \frac{1}{2}bh\right)$.

Solution

$$A = \frac{1}{2}bh$$
$$24 = \frac{1}{2}(3x)x$$
$$24 = \frac{1}{2}(3x^2)$$
$$48 = 3x^2$$
$$0 = 3x^2 - 48$$
$$0 = 3(x^2 - 16)$$
$$0 = 3(x + 4)(x - 4)$$
$$x + 4 = 0 \quad x - 4 = 0$$
$$x = -4 \qquad x = 4$$

Since the height cannot be negative, -4 cannot be a solution.
$3x = 3(4) = 12$
The height is 4 cm. The base is 12 cm.

72. **Strategy**
This is a geometry problem.
The base of the triangle: x
The height of the triangle: $2x + 4$
The area of the triangle is 35 cm^2. Use the equation for the area of a triangle $\left(A = \frac{1}{2}bh \right)$.

Solution
$$A = \frac{1}{2}bh$$
$$35 = \frac{1}{2}x(2x + 4)$$
$$35 = \frac{1}{2}(2x^2 + 4x)$$
$$35 = x^2 + 2x$$
$$0 = x^2 + 2x - 35$$
$$0 = (x + 7)(x - 5)$$
$$x + 7 = 0 \qquad x - 5 = 0$$
$$x = -7 \qquad x = 5$$

Since the base of a triangle cannot be negative, –7 cannot be a solution.
$2x + 4 = 2(5) + 4 = 14$
The height of the triangle is 14 cm.

73. **Strategy**
To find the time for the object to reach the ground, replace the variables d and v in the equation by their given values and solve for t.

Solution
$$d = vt + 16t^2$$
$$480 = 16t + 16t^2$$
$$0 = 16t^2 + 16t - 480$$
$$0 = 16(t^2 + t - 30)$$
$$0 = t^2 + t - 30$$
$$0 = (t + 6)(t - 5)$$
$$t + 6 = 0 \qquad t - 5 = 0$$
$$t = -6 \qquad t = 5$$

Since the time cannot be a negative number, –6 is not a solution. The time is 5 s.

74. **Strategy**
To find the time for the object to drop to the bottom of the well, replace the variables d and v in the equation by their given values and solve for t.

Solution
$$d = vt + 16t^2$$
$$624 = 8t + 16t^2$$
$$0 = 16t^2 + 8t - 624$$
$$0 = 8(2t^2 + t - 78)$$
$$0 = 2t^2 + t - 78$$
$$0 = (2t + 13)(t - 6)$$
$$2t + 13 = 0 \qquad t - 6 = 0$$
$$2t = -13 \qquad t = 6$$
$$t = -\frac{13}{2}$$

Since the time cannot be a negative number, $-\frac{13}{2}$ is not a solution. The time is 6 s.

75. **Strategy**
Increase in length and width: x
Length of the larger rectangle: $6 + x$
Width of the larger rectangle: $3 + x$
Use the equation $A = L \cdot W$.

Solution
Smaller rectangle:
$$A = L \cdot W$$
$$A = 6 \cdot 3 = 18$$
Larger rectangle:
$$A = L \cdot W$$
$$18 + 70 = (6 + x)(3 + x)$$
$$88 = 18 + 9x + x^2$$
$$0 = x^2 + 9x - 70$$
$$0 = (x + 14)(x - 5)$$
$$x + 14 = 0 \qquad x - 5 = 0$$
$$x = -14 \qquad x = 5$$

Since an increase in length and width cannot be a negative number, –14 is not a solution.
Length = $6 + x = 6 + 5 = 11$
Width = $3 + x = 3 + 5 = 8$
The length of the larger rectangle is 11 cm. The width is 8 cm.

76. Strategy

Increase in length and width: x
Width of larger rectangle: $4 + x$
Length of larger rectangle: $8 + x$
Use the equation $A = L \cdot W$

Solution
Smaller rectangle:
$A = L \cdot W$
$A = 8 \cdot 4 = 32$
Larger rectangle:
$$A = L \cdot W$$
$$32 + 64 = (8 + x)(4 + x)$$
$$96 = 32 + 12x + x^2$$
$$0 = x^2 + 12x - 64$$
$$0 = (x + 16)(x - 4)$$
$$x + 16 = 0 \qquad x - 4 = 0$$
$$x = -16 \qquad x = 4$$

Since an increase in length and width cannot be a negative number, –16 is not a solution.
Width $= 4 + x = 4 + 4 = 8$
Length $= 8 + x = 8 + 4 = 12$
The width of the larger rectangle is 8 cm. The length is 12 cm.

Applying Concepts 5.7

77. Strategy

Solve the equation $n(n + 6) = 16$ for n, and then substitute the values of n into the expression $3n^2 + 2n - 1$ and evaluate.

Solution
$$n(n + 6) = 16$$
$$n^2 + 6n = 16$$
$$n^2 + 6n - 16 = 0$$
$$(n + 8)(n - 2) = 0$$
$$n + 8 = 0 \qquad n - 2 = 0$$
$$n = -8 \qquad n = 2$$

$3n^2 + 2n - 1$	$3n^2 + 2n - 1$
$= 3(-8)^2 + 2(-8) - 1$	$= 3(2)^2 + 2(2) - 1$
$= 3(64) + 2(-8) - 1$	$= 3(4) + 2(2) - 1$
$= 192 - 16 - 1$	$= 12 + 4 - 1$
$= 175$	$= 15$

$3n^2 + 2n - 1$ is equal to 175 or 15.

78. Strategy

Solve the equation $(y - 1)(y + 2) = 4$ for y, and then substitute the values of y into the expression $4y^2 - y + 3$ and evaluate.

Solution
$$(y - 1)(y + 2) = 4$$
$$y^2 + y - 2 = 4$$
$$y^2 + y - 6 = 0$$
$$(y + 3)(y - 2) = 0$$
$$y + 3 = 0 \qquad y - 2 = 0$$
$$y = -3 \qquad y = 2$$

$4y^2 - y + 3$	$4y^2 - y + 3$
$= 4(-3)^2 - (-3) + 3$	$= 4(2)^2 - (2) + 3$
$= 4(9) - (-3) + 3$	$= 4(4) - 2 + 3$
$= 36 + 3 + 3$	$= 16 - 2 + 3$
$= 42$	$= 17$

$4y^2 - y + 3$ is equal to 17 or 42.

79. Strategy

Solve the equation $6a(a - 1) = 36$ for a, and then substitute the values of a into the expression $-a^2 + 5a - 2$ and evaluate.

Solution
$$6a(a - 1) = 36$$
$$6a^2 - 6a = 36$$
$$6a^2 - 6a - 36 = 0$$
$$(a + 2)(6a - 18) = 0$$
$$a + 2 = 0 \qquad 6a - 18 = 0$$
$$a = -2 \qquad a = 3$$

$-a^2 + 5a - 2$	$-a^2 + 5a - 2$
$= -(-2)^2 + 5(-2) - 2$	$= -(3)^2 + 5(3) - 2$
$= -(4) + 5(-2) - 2$	$= -(9) + 5(3) - 2$
$= -4 - 10 - 2$	$= -9 + 15 - 2$
$= -16$	$= 4$

$-a^2 + 5a - 2$ is equal to –16 or 4.

80. Strategy

Length of the garden: x
Width of the garden: $22 - x$
The formula for the area of a rectangle is $A = L \cdot W$.

Solution
$$A = LW$$
$$120 = x(22 - x)$$
$$120 = 22x - x^2$$
$$0 = 22x - x^2 - 120$$
$$0 = x^2 - 22x + 120$$
$$0 = (x - 12)(x - 10)$$
$$x - 12 = 0 \qquad x - 10 = 0$$
$$x = 12 \qquad x = 10$$

The solution 10 is not possible since then the width would be greater than the length $(22 - x = 22 - 10 = 12)$.
Width $= 22 - x = 22 - 12 = 10$
The length is 12 m and the width is 10 m.

81. Strategy
Width of rectangular piece of cardboard: x
Length of rectangular piece of cardboard: $x + 10$
Width of cardboard box: $x - 4$
Length of cardboard box: $(x + 10) - 4 = x + 6$
Height of cardboard box: 2
The formula for the volume of a rectangular solid is $V = LWH$.

Solution
$$V = LWH$$
$$112 = (x+6)(x-4)(2)$$
$$56 = (x+6)(x-4)$$
$$56 = x^2 + 2x - 24$$
$$0 = x^2 + 2x - 80$$
$$0 = (x+10)(x-8)$$
$$x + 10 = 0 \qquad x - 8 = 0$$
$$x = -10 \qquad x = 8$$

Since width cannot be a negative number, -10 is not a solution.
Length $= x + 10 = 8 + 10 = 18$
The length is 18 in. The width is 8 in.

82. Strategy
The area of one side: width × height
The area of a second side: width × length
The area of a third side: length × height
Find three numbers for the length, width, and height such that the product of the width and height is 16, the product of the width and length is 20, and the product of the length and height is 80.
Use the equation $V = LWH$.

Solution
By trial and error, the width is 2 cm, the height is 8 cm, and the length is 10 cm.
width × height $= 2 × 8 = 16$
width × length $= 2 × 10 = 20$
height × length $= 8 × 10 = 80$
$V = LWH = 2 \cdot 8 \cdot 10 = 160$
The volume is 160 cm^3.

83.
$$(x-3)(x-2)(x+1) = 0$$
$$(x^2 - 5x + 6)(x+1) = 0$$
$$(x^3 - 5x^2 + 6x) + (x^2 - 5x + 6) = 0$$
$$x^3 - 4x^2 + x + 6 = 0$$

84. The error is in the division step in step 4.
Because $a - b = 0$, dividing by $a - b$ is equivalent to dividing by 0, which is undefined.

Focus on Problem Solving

1. False
0 is a real number, and $0^2 = 0$ is not positive.

2. True

3. True

4. False
Let $x = -4$ and $y = 2$. Then the expression $(-4)^2 < 2^2$ is not true.

5. False
It is impossible to construct a triangle with $a = 2$, $b = 3$, and $c = 10$. In a triangle, the sum of two sides must be greater than the third side.

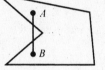

6. False
The product of $\sqrt{3} \cdot \sqrt{3} = 3$.

7. False
For $n = 4$, $1 \cdot 2 \cdot 3 \cdot 4 + 1 = 25$. The number is not a prime number.

8. False
Part of AB is outside the polygon.

9. True

10. False
If the points are selected so that $AC + CD < DB$, a triangle cannot be formed.

Projects and Group Activities

Reverse Polish Notation

1. 12 [ENTER] 6 [÷]

2. 7 [ENTER] 5 [×] 6 [+]

3. 9 [ENTER] 3 [+] 4 [÷]

4. 5 [ENTER] 7 [+] 2 [ENTER] 4 [+] [÷]

5. 6 [ENTER] 7 [×] 10 [×]

6. 1 [ENTER] 4 [ENTER] 5 [×] [+] 7 [÷]

7. $18 ÷ 2 = 9$

8. $6 + 5 \; 3 \; 3 = 21$

9. $3 × 5 + 4 = 19$

10. $[7 + (4 × 5)] ÷ 3 = 9$

11. $228 ÷ [6 + (9 × 12)] = 2$

12. $1 + [1 ÷ (1 + 3)] = 1.25$

Pythagorean Triples

1. **a.** $5^2 + 7^2 = 25 + 49 = 74 \neq 81 = 9^2$
   5, 7, and 9 are not a Pythagorean triple.

   b. $8^2 + 15^2 = 64 + 225 = 289 = 17^2$
   8, 15, and 17 are a Pythagorean triple.

   c. $11^2 + 60^2 = 121 + 3600 = 3721 = 61^2$
   11, 60, and 61 are a Pythagorean triple.

   d. $28^2 + 45^2 = 784 + 2025 = 2809 = 53^2$
   28, 45, and 53 are a Pythagorean triple.

2. $a = m^2 - n^2$
   $b = 2mn$
   $c = m^2 + n^2$

   a. $m = 3, n = 1$
   $a = 3^2 - 1^2 = 8$
   $b = 2(3)(1) = 6$
   $c = 3^2 + 1^2 = 10$
   The Pythagorean triple is 6, 8, and 10.

   b. $m = 5, n = 2$
   $a = 5^2 - 2^2 = 21$
   $b = 2(5)(2) = 20$
   $c = 5^2 + 2^2 = 29$
   The Pythagorean triple is 20, 21, and 29.

   c. $m = 4, n = 2$
   $a = 4^2 - 2^2 = 12$
   $b = 2(4)(2) = 16$
   $c = 4^2 + 2^2 = 20$
   The Pythagorean triple is 12, 16, and 20.

   d. $m = 6, n = 1$
   $a = 6^2 - 1^2 = 35$
   $b = 2(6)(1) = 12$
   $c = 6^2 + 1^2 = 37$
   The Pythagorean triple is 12, 35, and 37.

3. $a = m^2 - n^2 = 11$
   $b = 2mn = 60$
   $c = m^2 + n^2 = 61$

   $m^2 - n^2 = 11$
   $m^2 + n^2 = 61$
   $\quad 2m^2 = 72$
   $\quad\quad m^2 = 36$
   $\quad\quad\quad m = 6$
   −6 is not a solution since m and n must be positive.

   $2mn = 60$
   $2(6)n = 60$
   $\quad 12n = 60$
   $\quad\quad n = 5$
   So $m = 6$ and $n = 5$ generate the Pythagorean triple 11, 60, and 61.

4. $a^2 = (m^2 - n^2)^2$
   $\quad = (m^2 - n^2)(m^2 - n^2)$
   $\quad = m^4 - 2m^2n^2 + n^4$

   $b^2 = (2mn)^2 = 4m^2n^2$

   $c^2 = (m^2 + n^2)^2$
   $\quad = (m^2 + n^2)(m^2 + n^2)$
   $\quad = m^4 + 2m^2n^2 + n^4$

   $a^2 + b^2 = m^4 - 2m^2n^2 + n^4 + 4m^2n^2$
   $\quad\quad\quad = m^4 + 2m^2n^2 + n^4$
   $\quad\quad\quad = c^2$

5. Using the Pythagorean triple 3, 4, and 5, the rope could have been held as shown in the diagram below.

6. It is not possible. The formula $b = 2mn$ ensures that one number will be even.

Astronomical Distances and Scientific Notation

1. $1.86 \times 10^5 \dfrac{\text{mi}}{\text{s}} \cdot \dfrac{60\text{s}}{1\text{min}} \cdot \dfrac{60\text{min}}{1\text{h}} \cdot \dfrac{24\text{h}}{1\text{day}} \cdot \dfrac{365\text{day}}{1\text{yr}}$
   $= 5.83416 \times 10^{12} \text{mi}$
   One light year is 5.83416×10^{12} mi.

2. 25 trillion mi $= 2.5 \times 10^{13}$ mi
   $\dfrac{2.5 \times 10^{13}}{5.83416 \times 10^{12}} \approx 4.29$
   The distance is 4.29 light years.

3. $5.83416 \times 10^{12} \cdot 2.8 \times 10^8$
   $= 1.6335648 \times 10^{21}$
   The distance is 1.6335648×10^{21} mi.

4. $\dfrac{1.8228 \times 10^{12}}{9.3 \times 10^7} = 1.96 \times 10^4$
   The distance is 1.96×10^4 A.U.

5. $\dfrac{5.865696 \times 10^{12}}{9.3 \times 10^7} \approx 63{,}000$
   One light-year is approximately 63,000 A.U.

6. Mercury, Venus, Earth, Mars, Jupiter, Saturn Uranus, Neptune, Pluto.

7. Jupiter, Saturn, Neptune, Uranus, Earth, Venus, Mars, Mercury, Pluto

8. When comparing two numbers written in scientific notation, the number with the higher exponent on 10 is the larger number. If the exponents on 10 are the same, compare the numbers between 1 and 10; the number with a larger number between 1 and 10 is the larger number.

Chapter Review Exercises

1. $(3x^2 - 2x - 6) + (-x^2 - 3x + 4) = 2x^2 - 5x - 2$

2. $(5x^2 - 8xy + 2y^2) - (x^2 - 3y^2)$
$= (5x^2 - 8xy + 2y^2) + (-x^2 + 3y^2)$
$= 4x^2 - 8xy + 5y^2$

3. $(5x^2yz^4)(2xy^3z^{-1})(7x^{-2}y^{-2}z^3) = 70xy^2z^6$

4. $(2x^{-1}y^2z^5)^4(-3x^3yz^{-3})$
$= (16x^{-4}y^8z^{20})(-3x^3yz^{-3})$
$= -48x^{-1}y^9z^{17}$
$= -\dfrac{48y^9z^{17}}{x}$

5. $\dfrac{3x^4yz^{-1}}{-12xy^3z^2} = -\dfrac{x^3}{4y^2z^3}$

6. $\dfrac{(2a^4b^{-3}c^2)^3}{(2a^3b^2c^{-1})^4} = \dfrac{8a^{12}b^{-9}c^6}{16a^{12}b^8c^{-4}}$
$= \dfrac{1}{2}a^{12-12}b^{-9-8}c^{6-(-4)}$
$= \dfrac{1}{2}b^{-17}c^{10}$
$= \dfrac{c^{10}}{2b^{17}}$

7. $93{,}000{,}000 = 9.3 \times 10^7$

8. $2.54 \times 10^{-3} = 0.00254$

9. $\dfrac{3 \times 10^{-3}}{15 \times 10^2} = \dfrac{3}{15} \times \dfrac{10^{-3}}{10^2} = 0.2 \times 10^{-5} = 2 \times 10^{-6}$

10. $P(-2) = 2(-2)^3 - (-2) + 7$
$P(-2) = -16 + 2 + 7$
$P(-2) = -7$

11. $y = x^2 + 1$

12. **a.** 3

   b. 8

   c. 5

13.

-3	-2	2	0	-4
		6	-24	72
	-2	8	-24	68

$P(-3) = 68$

14.

$$\begin{array}{r} 5x+4 \\ 3x-2\overline{)15x^2+ 2x-2} \\ \underline{15x^2-10x} \\ 12x-2 \\ \underline{12x-8} \\ 6 \end{array}$$

$\dfrac{15x^2+2x-2}{3x-2} = 5x+4+\dfrac{6}{3x-2}$

15.

$$\begin{array}{r} 2x-3 \\ 6x+1\overline{)12x^2-16x-7} \\ \underline{12x^2+ 2x} \\ -18x-7 \\ \underline{-18x-3} \\ -4 \end{array}$$

$\dfrac{12x^2-16x-7}{6x+1} = 2x-3-\dfrac{4}{6x+1}$

16.

-6	4	27	10	2
		-24	-18	48
	4	3	-8	50

$\dfrac{4x^3+27x^2+10x+2}{x+6} = 4x^2+3x-8+\dfrac{50}{x+6}$

17.

4	1	0	0	0	-4
		4	16	64	256
	1	4	16	64	252

$\dfrac{x^4-4}{x-4} = x^3+4x^2+16x+64+\dfrac{252}{x-4}$

18. $4x^2y(3x^3y^2 + 2xy - 7y^3)$
$= 12x^5y^3 + 8x^3y^2 - 28x^2y^4$

19. $a^{2n+3}(a^n - 5a + 2) = a^{3n+3} - 5a^{2n+4} + 2a^{2n+3}$

20. $5x^2 - 4x[x - (3x+2) + x]$
$= 5x^2 - 4x(x - 3x - 2 + x)$
$= 5x^2 - 4x(-x - 2)$
$= 5x^2 + 4x^2 + 8x$
$= 9x^2 + 8x$

21. $(x^{2n} - x)(x^{n+1} - 3) = x^{3n+1} - 3x^{2n} - x^{n+2} + 3x$

22.

$$
\begin{array}{r}
x^3 - 3x^2 - 5x + 1 \\
\times x + 6 \\
\hline
6x^3 - 18x^2 - 30x + 6 \\
x^4 - 3x^3 - 5x^2 + x \\
\hline
x^4 + 3x^3 - 23x^2 - 29x + 6
\end{array}
$$

$(x+6)(x^3 - 3x^2 - 5x + 1)$
$= x^4 + 3x^3 - 23x^2 - 29x + 6$

23. $(x-4)(3x+2)(2x-3)$
$= (x-4)(6x^2 - 5x - 6)$
$= 6x^3 - 5x^2 - 6x - 24x^2 + 20x + 24$
$= 6x^3 - 29x^2 + 14x + 24$

24. $(5a+2b)(5a-2b) = 25a^2 - 4b^2$

25. $(4x-3y)^2 = 16x^2 - 24xy + 9y^2$

26. The GCF of $18a^5b^2$, $12a^3b^3$, and $30a^2b$
is $6a^2b$.
$18a^5b^2 - 12a^3b^3 + 30a^2b$
$= 6a^2b(3a^3b - 2ab^2 + 5)$

27. The GCF of $5x^{n+5}$, x^{n+3}, and $4x^2$ is x^2.
$5x^{n+5} + x^{n+3} + 4x^2 = x^2(5x^{n+3} + x^{n+1} + 4)$

28. $x(y-3) + 4(3-y) = x(y-3) + 4[(-1)(y-3)]$
$= x(y-3) - 4(y-3)$
$= (y-3)(x-4)$

29. $2ax + 4bx - 3ay - 6by = 2x(a+2b) - 3y(a+2b)$
$= (a+2b)(2x-3y)$

30. $x^2 + 12x + 35 = (x+5)(x+7)$

31. $12 + x - x^2 = (3+x)(4-x)$

32. $x^2 - 16x + 63 = (x-7)(x-9)$

33. $6x^2 - 31x + 18 = (3x-2)(2x-9)$

34. $24x^2 + 61x - 8 = (8x-1)(3x+8)$

35. Let $u = xy$.
$x^2y^2 - 9 = u^2 - 9$
$= (u+3)(u-3)$
$= (xy+3)(xy-3)$

36. $4x^2 + 12xy + 9y^2 = (2x+3y)^2$

37. Let $u = x^n$.
$x^{2n} - 12x^n + 36 = u^2 - 12u + 36$
$= (u-6)^2$
$= (x^n - 6)^2$

38. $36 - a^{2n} = 6^2 - (a^n)^2 = (6+a^n)(6-a^n)$

39. $64a^3 - 27b^3 = (4a)^3 - (3b)^3$
$= (4a - 3b)(16a^2 + 12ab + 9b^2)$

40. $8 - y^{3n} = (2)^3 - (y^n)^3 = (2 - y^n)(4 + 2y^n + y^{2n})$

41. Let $u = x^2$.
$15x^4 + x^2 - 6 = 15u^2 + u - 6$
$= (3u+2)(5u-3)$
$= (3x^2 + 2)(5x^2 - 3)$

42. Let $u = x^4$.
$36x^8 - 36x^4 + 5 = 36u^2 - 36u + 5$
$= (6u-5)(6u-1)$
$= (6x^4 - 5)(6x^4 - 1)$

43. Let $u = x^2y^2$.
$21x^4y^4 + 23x^2y^2 + 6 = 21u^2 + 23u + 6$
$= (7u+3)(3u+2)$
$= (7x^2y^2 + 3)(3x^2y^2 + 2)$

44. $3a^6 - 15a^4 - 18a^2 = 3a^2(a^4 - 5a^2 - 6)$
$= 3a^2(a^2 - 6)(a^2 + 1)$

45. $x^{4n} - 8x^{2n} + 16 = (x^{2n} - 4)^2$
$= [(x^n + 2)(x^n - 2)]^2$
$= (x^n + 2)^2(x^n - 2)^2$

46. $3a^4b - 3ab^4 = 3ab(a^3 - b^3)$
$= 3ab(a - b)(a^2 + ab + b^2)$

47. $x^3 - x^2 - 6x = 0$
$x(x^2 - x - 6) = 0$
$x(x-3)(x+2) = 0$
$x = 0 \quad x - 3 = 0 \quad x + 2 = 0$
$ x = 3 \qquad x = -2$
The solutions are 0, 3, and –2.

48.
$6x^2 + 60 = 39x$
$6x^2 - 39x + 60 = 0$
$3(2x^2 - 13x + 20) = 0$
$3(2x - 5)(x - 4) = 0$
$2x - 5 = 0 \quad x - 4 = 0$
$2x = 5 \qquad x = 4$
$x = \dfrac{5}{2}$

The solutions are $\dfrac{5}{2}$ and 4.

49.
$x^3 - 16x = 0$
$x(x^2 - 16) = 0$
$x(x+4)(x-4) = 0$
$x = 0 \quad x + 4 = 0 \quad x - 4 = 0$
$ x = -4 \qquad x = 4$
The solutions are 0, –4, and 4.

50. $y^3 + y^2 - 36y - 36 = 0$

$y^2(y+1) - 36(y+1) = 0$

$(y+1)(y^2 - 36) = 0$

$(y+1)(y+6)(y-6) = 0$

$y+1 = 0 \quad y+6 = 0 \quad y-6 = 0$

$y = -1 \quad\quad y = -6 \quad\quad y = 6$

The solutions are -1, -6, and 6.

51. Strategy

To find how far Earth is from the Great Galaxy of Andromeda, use the equation $d = rt$, where $r = 5.9 \times 10^{12}$ mph and $t = 2.2 \times 10^6$ years .

$2.2 \times 10^6 \times 24 \times 365 = 1.9272 \times 10^{10}$

Solution

$d = r \cdot t$

$\quad = (5.9 \times 10^{12})(1.9272 \times 10^{10})$

$\quad = 5.9 \times 1.9272 \times 10^{22}$

$\quad = 11.37048 \times 10^{22}$

$\quad = 1.137048 \times 10^{23}$

The distance from Earth to the Great Galaxy of Andromeda is 1.137048×10^{23} mi.

52. Strategy

To find how much power is generated by the sun, divide the amount of horsepower that Earth receives by the proportion that this is of the power generated by the sun.

Solution

$\dfrac{2.4 \times 10^{14}}{2.2 \times 10^{-7}} = \dfrac{2.4}{2.2} \times \dfrac{10^{14}}{10^{-7}} = 1.09 \times 10^{21}$

The sun generates 1.09×10^{21} horsepower.

53. Strategy

To find the area, replace the variables L and W in the equation $A = LW$ by the given values and solve for A.

Solution

$A = L \cdot W$

$A = (5x+3)(2x-7) = 10x^2 - 29x - 21$

The area is $(10x^2 - 29x - 21)$ cm^2.

54. Strategy

This is a geometry problem.

To find the volume, replace the variable s in the equation $V = s^3$ by the given value and solve for V.

Solution

$V = s^3$

$V = (3x-1)^3$

$V = (3x-1)(9x^2 - 6x + 1)$

$V = 27x^3 - 18x^2 + 3x - 9x^2 + 6x - 1$

$V = 27x^3 - 27x^2 + 9x - 1$

The volume is $(27x^3 - 27x^2 + 9x - 1)$ ft^3.

55. Strategy

To find the area, subtract the area of the small square from the area of the large rectangle.

Large rectangle:

$L_1 = 3x - 2$

$W_1 = (x+4) + x$

Small square:

side $= x$

Solution

$A = $ Area of large rectangle $-$ Area of square

$A = L_1 W_1 - s^2$

$A = (3x-2)[(x+4)+x] - x^2$

$A = (3x-2)(2x+4) - x^2$

$A = 6x^2 + 8x - 8 - x^2$

$A = 5x^2 + 8x - 8$

The area is $(5x^2 + 8x - 8)$ in^2.

56. Strategy

This is an integer problem.

The first even integer: n

The next consecutive even integer: $n + 2$

The sum of the squares of the 2 consecutive even integers is 52.

$n^2 + (n+2)^2 = 52$

Solution

$n^2 + (n+2)^2 = 52$

$n^2 + n^2 + 4n + 4 = 52$

$2n^2 + 4n - 48 = 0$

$2(n^2 + 2n - 24) = 0$

$2(n+6)(n-4) = 0$

$n + 6 = 0 \quad\quad\quad n - 4 = 0$

$n = -6 \quad\quad\quad\quad n = 4$

$n + 2 = -6 + 2 = -4 \quad n + 2 = 4 + 2 = 6$

The two integers are -6 and -4, or 4 and 6.

57. Strategy

This is an integer problem.

The unknown integer is n.

The sum of this number and its square is 56.

Solution

$n^2 + n = 56$

$n^2 + n - 56 = 0$

$(n+8)(n-7) = 0$

$n + 8 = 0 \quad n - 7 = 0$

$n = -8 \quad\quad n = 7$

The integer is -8 or 7.

58. Strategy

This is a geometry problem.

Width of the rectangle: x

Length of the rectangle: $2x + 2$

The area of the rectangle is 60 m^2.

Use the equation for the area of a rectangle $(A = LW)$.

Solution

$A = LW$

$60 = (2x + 2)(x)$

$60 = 2x^2 + 2x$

$0 = 2x^2 + 2x - 60$

$0 = 2(x^2 + x - 30)$

$0 = 2(x + 6)(x - 5)$

$x + 6 = 0 \quad x - 5 = 0$

$\quad x = -6 \quad\quad x = 5$

Since the width of a rectangle cannot be negative, -6 cannot be a solution.

$2x + 2 = 2(5) + 2 = 10 + 2 = 12$

The length of the rectangle is 12 m.

Chapter Test

1. $(6x^3 - 7x^2 + 6x - 7) - (4x^3 - 3x^2 + 7)$

$= (6x^3 - 7x^2 + 6x - 7) + (-4x^3 + 3x^2 - 7)$

$= 2x^3 - 4x^2 + 6x - 14$

2. $(-4a^2b)^3(-ab^4) = (-64a^6b^3)(-ab^4) = 64a^7b^7$

3. $\dfrac{(2a^{-4}b^2)^3}{4a^{-2}b^{-1}} = \dfrac{8a^{-12}b^6}{4a^{-2}b^{-1}}$

$= 2a^{-12-(-2)}b^{6-(-1)}$

$= 2a^{-10}b^7$

$= \dfrac{2b^7}{a^{10}}$

4. $0.000000501 = 5.01 \times 10^{-7}$

5. Strategy

To find the number of seconds in one week in scientific notation:

Multiply the number of seconds in a minute (60) by the minutes in an hour (60) by the hours in a day (24) by the days in a week (7).

Convert that product to scientific notation.

Solution

$60 \times 60 \times 24 \times 7 = 604{,}800 = 6.048 \times 10^5$

The number of seconds in a week is 6.048×10^5.

6. $(2x^{-3}y)^{-4} = 2^{-4}x^{12}y^{-4} = \dfrac{x^{12}}{2^4y^4} = \dfrac{x^{12}}{16y^4}$

7. $-5x[3 - 2(2x - 4) - 3x] = -5x[3 - 4x + 8 - 3x]$

$= -5x[-7x + 11]$

$= 35x^2 - 55x$

8. $(3a + 4b)(2a - 7b) = 6a^2 - 13ab - 28b^2$

9.

$$
\begin{array}{r}
3t^3 - 4t^2 + 1 \\
\times \quad\quad 2t^2 - 5 \\
\hline
-15t^3 + 20t^2 - 5 \\
6t^5 - 8t^4 \quad\quad + 2t^2 \\
\hline
6t^5 - 8t^4 - 15t^3 + 22t^2 - 5
\end{array}
$$

10. $(3z - 5)^2 = 9z^2 - 30z + 25$

11.

$$
\begin{array}{r}
2x^2 + 3x + 5 \\
2x - 3 \overline{) 4x^3 + 0x^2 + x - 15} \\
\underline{4x^3 - 6x^2} \\
6x^2 + x \\
\underline{6x^2 - 9x} \\
10x - 15 \\
\underline{10x - 15} \\
0
\end{array}
$$

$(4x^3 + x - 15) \div (2x - 3) = 2x^2 + 3x + 5$

12.

$$
\begin{array}{c|cccc}
3 & 1 & -5 & 5 & 5 \\
& & 3 & -6 & -3 \\
\hline
& 1 & -2 & -1 & 2
\end{array}
$$

$(x^3 - 5x^2 + 5x + 5) \div (x - 3) = x^2 - 2x - 1 + \dfrac{2}{x - 3}$

13. $P(2) = 3(2)^2 - 8(2) + 1$

$P(2) = 12 - 16 + 1$

$P(2) = -3$

14.

$$
\begin{array}{c|cccc}
-2 & -1 & 0 & 4 & -8 \\
& & 2 & -4 & 0 \\
\hline
& -1 & 2 & 0 & -8
\end{array}
$$

$P(-2) = -8$

15. Let $u = a^2$.

$6a^4 - 13a^2 - 5 = 6u^2 - 13u - 5$

$= (2u - 5)(3u + 1)$

$= (2a^2 - 5)(3a^2 + 1)$

16. $12x^3 + 12x^2 - 45x = 3x(4x^2 + 4x - 15)$

$= 3x(2x - 3)(2x + 5)$

17. $16x^2 - 25 = (4x - 5)(4x + 5)$

18. $16t^2 + 24t + 9 = (4t + 3)^2$

19. $27x^3 - 8 = (3x)^3 - (2)^3 = (3x - 2)(9x^2 + 6x + 4)$

20. $6x^2 - 4x - 3xa + 2a = 2x(3x - 2) - a(3x - 2)$

$= (3x - 2)(2x - a)$

21.
$$6x^2 = x + 1$$
$$6x^2 - x - 1 = 0$$
$$(2x - 1)(3x + 1) = 0$$
$$2x - 1 = 0 \quad 3x + 1 = 0$$
$$2x = 1 \quad 3x = -1$$
$$x = \frac{1}{2} \quad x = -\frac{1}{3}$$
The solutions are $\frac{1}{2}$ and $-\frac{1}{3}$.

22.
$$6x^3 + x^2 - 6x - 1 = 0$$
$$x^2(6x + 1) - 1(6x + 1) = 0$$
$$(x^2 - 1)(6x + 1) = 0$$
$$(x + 1)(x - 1)(6x + 1) = 0$$
$$x + 1 = 0 \quad x - 1 = 0 \quad 6x + 1 = 0$$
$$x = -1 \quad x = 1 \quad 6x = -1$$
$$x = -\frac{1}{6}$$
The solutions are -1, 1, and $-\frac{1}{6}$.

23. Strategy
This is a geometry problem.
To find the area of the rectangle, replace the variables L and W in the equation $A = LW$ by the given values and solve for A.

Solution
$$A = LW$$
$$A = (5x + 1)(2x - 1)$$
$$A = 10x^2 - 3x - 1$$
The area of the rectangle is $(10x^2 - 3x - 1)$ ft^2.

24. Strategy
To find the time:
Use the equation $d = rt$, where d is the distance from Earth to the moon and r is the average velocity.

Solution
$$d = rt$$
$$2.4 \times 10^5 = (2 \times 10^4)t$$
$$\frac{2.4 \times 10^5}{2 \times 10^4} = t$$
$$1.2 \times 10 = t$$
$$12 = t$$
It takes 12 h for the space vehicle to reach the moon.

Cumulative Review Exercises

1.
$$8 - 2[-3 - (-1)]^2 + 4 = 8 - 2[-3 + 1]^2 + 4$$
$$= 8 - 2[-2]^2 + 4$$
$$= 8 - 2(4) + 4$$
$$= 8 - 8 + 4$$
$$= 0 + 4$$
$$= 4$$

2. $\dfrac{2(4) - (-2)}{-2 - 6} = \dfrac{8 + 2}{-8} = \dfrac{10}{-8} = -\dfrac{5}{4}$

3. The Inverse Property of Addition

4. $2x - 4[x - 2(3 - 2x) + 4] = 2x - 4[x - 6 + 4x + 4]$
$$= 2x - 4(5x - 2)$$
$$= 2x - 20x + 8$$
$$= -18x + 8$$

5.
$$\frac{2}{3} - y = \frac{5}{6}$$
$$\frac{2}{3} - \frac{2}{3} - y = \frac{5}{6} - \frac{2}{3}$$
$$-y = \frac{1}{6}$$
$$(-1)(-y) = (-1)\frac{1}{6}$$
$$y = -\frac{1}{6}$$

6.
$$8x - 3 - x = -6 + 3x - 8$$
$$7x - 3 = 3x - 14$$
$$7x - 3 - 3x = 3x - 14 - 3x$$
$$4x - 3 = -14$$
$$4x - 3 + 3 = -14 + 3$$
$$4x = -11$$
$$\frac{4x}{4} = -\frac{11}{4}$$
$$x = -\frac{11}{4}$$

7.
$$\begin{array}{r|rrrr} 3 & 1 & 0 & 0 & -3 \\ & & 3 & 9 & 27 \\ \hline & 1 & 3 & 9 & 24 \end{array}$$
$$\frac{x^3 - 3}{x - 3} = x^2 + 3x + 9 + \frac{24}{x - 3}$$

8.
$$3 - |2 - 3x| = -2$$
$$-|2 - 3x| = -5$$
$$|2 - 3x| = 5$$
$$2 - 3x = 5 \quad 2 - 3x = -5$$
$$-3x = 3 \quad -3x = -7$$
$$x = -1 \quad x = \frac{7}{3}$$
The solutions are -1 and $\frac{7}{3}$.

9. $P(-2) = 3(-2)^2 - 2(-2) + 2$
$$P(-2) = 12 + 4 + 2$$
$$P(-2) = 18$$

10. $x = -2$

11. $f(x) = 3x^2 - 4$
$$f(-2) = 3(-2)^2 - 4 = 8$$
$$f(-1) = 3(-1)^2 - 4 = -1$$
$$f(0) = 3(0)^2 - 4 = -4$$
$$f(1) = 3(1)^2 - 4 = -1$$
$$f(2) = 3(2)^2 - 4 = 8$$
Range = $\{-4, -1, 8\}$

12. $m = \dfrac{y_2 - y_1}{x_2 - x_1} = \dfrac{2-3}{4-(-2)} = -\dfrac{1}{6}$

13. Use the point-slope form.

$y - y_1 = m(x - x_1)$

$y - 2 = -\dfrac{3}{2}[x - (-1)]$

$y - 2 = -\dfrac{3}{2}(x + 1)$

$y - 2 = -\dfrac{3}{2}x - \dfrac{3}{2}$

$y = -\dfrac{3}{2}x + \dfrac{1}{2}$

14. $3x + 2y = 4$

$2y = -3x + 4$

$y = -\dfrac{3}{2}x + 2$

$m_1 = -\dfrac{3}{2}$

$m_1 \cdot m_2 = -1$

$-\dfrac{3}{2} \cdot m_2 = -1$

$m_2 = \dfrac{2}{3}$

Now use the point-slope formula to find the equation of the line.

$y - y_1 = m(x - x_1)$

$y - 4 = \dfrac{2}{3}[x - (-2)]$

$y - 4 = \dfrac{2}{3}(x + 2)$

$y - 4 = \dfrac{2}{3}x + \dfrac{4}{3}$

$y = \dfrac{2}{3}x + \dfrac{16}{3}$

The equation of the perpendicular line is
$y = \dfrac{2}{3}x + \dfrac{16}{3}$.

15. $2x - 3y = 2$

$x + y = -3$

$D = \begin{vmatrix} 2 & -3 \\ 1 & 1 \end{vmatrix} = 2 - (-3) = 5$

$D_x = \begin{vmatrix} 2 & -3 \\ -3 & 1 \end{vmatrix} = 2 - 9 = -7$

$D_y = \begin{vmatrix} 2 & 2 \\ 1 & -3 \end{vmatrix} = -6 - 2 = -8$

$x = \dfrac{D_x}{D} = -\dfrac{7}{5}$

$y = \dfrac{D_y}{D} = -\dfrac{8}{5}$

The solution is $\left(-\dfrac{7}{5}, -\dfrac{8}{5}\right)$.

16. (1) $\quad x - y + z = 0$

(2) $\quad 2x + y - 3z = -7$

(3) $\quad -x + 2y + 2z = 5$

Add equations (1) and (3) to eliminate x.

$\begin{array}{r} x - y + z = 0 \\ -x + 2y + 2z = 5 \\ \hline y + 3z = 5 \end{array}$

Add -2 times equation (1) and equation (2) to eliminate x.

$\begin{array}{r} -2x + 2y - 2z = 0 \\ 2x + y - 3z = -7 \\ \hline 3y - 5z = -7 \end{array}$

Now solve the system in two variables.

$y + 3z = 5$

$3y - 5z = -7$

Add -3 times the first of these equations to the second.

$\begin{array}{r} -3y - 9z = -15 \\ 3y - 5z = -7 \\ \hline -14z = -22 \end{array}$

$z = \dfrac{11}{7}$

Next find y.

$y + 3z = 5$

$y + 3\left(\dfrac{11}{7}\right) = 5$

$y + \dfrac{33}{7} = 5$

$y = \dfrac{2}{7}$

Replace y and z in equation (1) and solve for x.

$x - \dfrac{2}{7} + \dfrac{11}{7} = 0$

$x = -\dfrac{9}{7}$

The solution is $\left(-\dfrac{9}{7}, \dfrac{2}{7}, \dfrac{11}{7}\right)$.

17.

x-intercept: y-intercept:

$3x - 4y = 12$ $3x - 4y = 12$

$3x - 4(0) = 12$ $3(0) - 4y = 12$

$3x = 12$ $-4y = 12$

$x = 4$ $y = -3$

The x-intercept is $(4, 0)$.
The y-intercept is $(0, -3)$.

18. $-3x + 2y < 6$

$\quad\quad 2y < 3x + 6$

$\quad\quad y < \dfrac{3}{2}x + 3$

19.

The lines intersect at $(1, -1)$.

20. Solve each inequality for y.

$2x + y < 3 \quad\quad\quad -6x + 3y \geq 4$

$\quad y < 3 - 2x \quad\quad\quad 3y \geq 4 + 6x$

$\quad\quad\quad\quad\quad\quad\quad\quad y \geq \dfrac{4}{3} + 2x$

21. $(4a^{-2}b^3)(2a^3b^{-1})^{-2} = (4a^{-2}b^3)(2^{-2}a^{-6}b^2)$

$\quad\quad\quad\quad\quad\quad\quad\quad\quad = 4 \cdot 2^{-2} a^{-2-6} b^{3+2}$

$\quad\quad\quad\quad\quad\quad\quad\quad\quad = 4 \cdot \dfrac{1}{4} a^{-8} b^5$

$\quad\quad\quad\quad\quad\quad\quad\quad\quad = \dfrac{b^5}{a^8}$

22. $\dfrac{(5x^3y^{-3}z)^{-2}}{y^4z^{-2}} = \dfrac{5^{-2}x^{-6}y^6z^{-2}}{y^4z^{-2}}$

$\quad\quad\quad\quad\quad\quad\quad = 5^{-2}x^{-6}y^{6-4}z^{-2-(-2)}$

$\quad\quad\quad\quad\quad\quad\quad = \dfrac{1}{25}x^{-6}y^2$

$\quad\quad\quad\quad\quad\quad\quad = \dfrac{y^2}{25x^6}$

23. $3 - (3 - 3^{-1})^{-1} = 3 - \left(3 - \dfrac{1}{3}\right)^{-1}$

$\quad\quad\quad\quad\quad\quad\quad = 3 - \left(\dfrac{8}{3}\right)^{-1}$

$\quad\quad\quad\quad\quad\quad\quad = 3 - \dfrac{3}{8}$

$\quad\quad\quad\quad\quad\quad\quad = \dfrac{21}{8}$

24.
$$
\begin{array}{r}
2x^2 - 3x + 1 \\
\times \quad\quad 2x + 3 \\
\hline
6x^2 - 9x + 3 \\
4x^3 - 6x^2 + 2x \quad\quad \\
\hline
4x^3 \quad\quad\quad - 7x + 3
\end{array}
$$

25. $-4x^3 + 14x^2 - 12x = -2x(2x^2 - 7x + 6)$

$\quad\quad\quad\quad\quad\quad\quad\quad\quad = -2x(2x - 3)(x - 2)$

26. $a(x - y) - b(y - x) = a(x - y) + b(x - y)$

$\quad\quad\quad\quad\quad\quad\quad\quad = (x - y)(a + b)$

27. $x^4 - 16 = (x^2 + 4)(x^2 - 4)$

$\quad\quad\quad\quad = (x^2 + 4)(x + 2)(x - 2)$

28. $2x^3 - 16 = 2(x^3 - 8)$

$\quad\quad\quad\quad = 2(x - 2)(x^2 + 2x + 4)$

29. Strategy

Smaller integer: x

Larger integer: $24 - x$

The difference between four times the smaller and nine is 3 less than twice the larger.

$4x - 9 = 2(24 - x) - 3$

Solution

$4x - 9 = 2(24 - x) - 3$

$4x - 9 = 48 - 2x - 3$

$4x - 9 = 45 - 2x$

$6x - 9 = 45$

$6x = 54$

$x = 9$

$24 - x = 15$

The integers are 9 and 15.

30. Strategy

The number of ounces of pure gold: x

	Amount	Cost	Value
Pure gold	x	360	$360x$
Alloy	80	120	$80(120)$
Mixture	$x + 80$	200	$200(x + 80)$

The sum of the values before mixing equals the value after mixing.

$360x + 80(120) = 200(x + 80)$

Solution

$360x + 80(120) = 200(x + 80)$

$360x + 9600 = 200x + 16{,}000$

$160x + 9600 = 16{,}000$

$160x = 6400$

$x = 40$

40 oz of pure gold must be mixed with the alloy.

31. Strategy

Faster cyclist: x

Slower cyclist: $\dfrac{2}{3}x$

	Rate	Time	Distance
Faster cyclist	x	2	$2x$
Slower cyclist	$\frac{2}{3}x$	2	$2\left(\frac{2}{3}x\right)$

The sum of the distances is 25 mi.

Solution

$$2x+2\left(\frac{2}{3}x\right)=25$$
$$2x+\frac{4}{3}x=25$$
$$\frac{10}{3}x=25$$
$$x=7.5$$
$$\frac{2}{3}x=5$$

The slower cyclist travels at 5 mph, the faster cyclist at 7.5 mph.

32. Strategy

Amount invested at 10%: x

	Principal	Rate	Interest
Amount at 7.5%	3000	0.07	0.075(3000)
Amount at 10%	x	0.10	$0.10x$
Amount at 9%	$3000+x$	0.09	$0.09(3000+x)$

The amount of interest earned at 9% equals the total amount of the interest earned at 7.5% and 10%.
$0.075(3000)+0.10x=0.09(3000+x)$

Solution
$$0.075(3000)+0.10x=0.09(3000+x)$$
$$225+0.10x=270+0.09x$$
$$0.01x+225=270$$
$$0.01x=45$$
$$x=4500$$

The additional investment is $4500.

33. $m=\dfrac{y_2-y_1}{x_2-x_1}=\dfrac{300-100}{6-2}=\dfrac{200}{4}$

$m=50$

The slope represents the average speed of travel in miles per hour. The average speed was 50 mph.

Chapter 6: Rational Expressions

Prep Test

1. 50   [1.2.2]

2. $-\dfrac{3}{8}\cdot\dfrac{4}{9}=-\dfrac{1}{6}$ [1.2.2]

3. $-\dfrac{4}{5}\div\dfrac{8}{15}=-\dfrac{4}{5}\cdot\dfrac{15}{8}=-\dfrac{3}{2}$ [1.2.2]

4. $-\dfrac{5}{6}+\dfrac{7}{8}=-\dfrac{20}{24}+\dfrac{21}{24}=\dfrac{1}{24}$ [1.2.2]

5. $-\dfrac{3}{8}-\left(-\dfrac{7}{12}\right)=-\dfrac{9}{24}+\dfrac{14}{24}=\dfrac{5}{24}$ [1.2.2]

6. $\dfrac{\dfrac{2}{3}-\dfrac{1}{4}}{\dfrac{1}{8}-2}=\dfrac{\dfrac{8}{12}-\dfrac{3}{12}}{\dfrac{1}{8}-\dfrac{16}{8}}$ [1.2.4]

   $=\dfrac{\dfrac{5}{12}}{-\dfrac{15}{8}}$

   $=\dfrac{5}{12}\cdot\left(-\dfrac{8}{15}\right)$

   $=-\dfrac{2}{9}$

7. $\dfrac{2(2)-3}{(2)^2-2+1}=\dfrac{4-3}{4-1}=\dfrac{1}{3}$ [1.3.2]

8. $4(2x+1)=3(x-2)$ [2.1.2]
   $8x+4=3x-6$
   $5x=-10$
   $x=-2$

9. $10\left(\dfrac{t}{2}+\dfrac{t}{5}\right)=10(1)$ [2.1.2]
   $5t+2t=10$
   $7t=10$
   $t=\dfrac{10}{7}$

10. Strategy
    Rate of the second plane: r
    Rate of the first plane: $r-20$

	Rate	Time	Distance
2nd plane	r	2.	$2\cdot r$
1st plane	$r-20$	2.	$2\cdot(r-20)$

The total distance traveled by the two planes is 480 mi.
$2r+2(r-20)=480$

Solution
$2r+2(r-20)=480$
$2r+2r-40=480$
$4r=520$
$r=130$
$r-20=130-20=110$
The rate of the first plane is 110 mph.
The rate of the second plane is 130 mph.

Go Figure

If 6 machines can fill 12 boxes in 7 minutes, then dividing by 6, each machine can fill 2 boxes in 7 minutes, or each machine can fill $\dfrac{2}{7}$ of a box per minute. To find the number of boxes that can be filled by 14 machines, multiply the output of each machine, $\dfrac{2}{7}$, by 14, or $\dfrac{2}{7}\cdot14=4$. That means that fourteen machines can fill 4 boxes per minute. Multiply by 12 minutes, $4\cdot12=48$. Fourteen machines can fill 48 boxes of cereal in 12 minutes.

Section 6.1

Concept Review 6.1

1. Never true
   A rational expression is the quotient of polynomials. $x^{1/2}-2x+4$ is not a polynomial.

2. Sometimes true
   Values of x that make the denominator zero are excluded from the domain of a rational function.

3. Always true

4. Always true

5. Never true
   The quotient $\dfrac{a+4}{a+4}=1$. The correct solution is $\dfrac{1}{a+2}$.

6. Sometimes true
   The expression is not true for $a=0$.

Objective 6.1.1 Exercises

1. A rational function is a function that is written in terms of an expression in which the numerator and denominator are polynomials. An example is

$$f(x) = \frac{x^2 - 2x + 3}{7x - 4}.$$

2. The domain of a rational function excludes all numbers for which the value of the polynomial in the denominator is zero.

3. $f(x) = \frac{2}{x - 3}$

$f(4) = \frac{2}{4 - 3} = \frac{2}{1}$

$f(4) = 2$

4. $f(x) = \frac{-7}{5 - x}$

$f(-2) = \frac{-7}{5 - (-2)} = \frac{-7}{7}$

$f(-2) = -1$

5. $f(x) = \frac{x - 2}{x + 4}$

$f(-2) = \frac{-2 - 2}{-2 + 4} = \frac{-4}{2}$

$f(-2) = -2$

6. $f(x) = \frac{x - 3}{2x - 1}$

$f(3) = \frac{3 - 3}{2(3) - 1} = \frac{0}{5}$

$f(3) = 0$

7. $f(x) = \frac{1}{x^2 - 2x + 1}$

$f(-2) = \frac{1}{(-2)^2 - 2(-2) + 1} = \frac{1}{9}$

$f(-2) = \frac{1}{9}$

8. $f(x) = \frac{-3}{x^2 - 4x + 2}$

$f(-1) = \frac{-3}{(-1)^2 - 4(-1) + 2} = \frac{-3}{7}$

$f(-1) = -\frac{3}{7}$

9. $f(x) = \frac{x - 2}{2x^2 + 3x + 8}$

$f(3) = \frac{3 - 2}{2(3)^2 + 3(3) + 8} = \frac{1}{35}$

$f(3) = \frac{1}{35}$

10. $f(x) = \frac{x^2}{3x^2 - 3x + 5}$

$f(4) = \frac{4^2}{3(4)^2 - 3(4) + 5} = \frac{16}{41}$

$f(4) = \frac{16}{41}$

11. $f(x) = \frac{x^2 - 2x}{x^3 - x + 4}$

$f(-1) = \frac{(-1)^2 - 2(-1)}{(-1)^3 - (-1) + 4} = \frac{3}{4}$

$f(-1) = \frac{3}{4}$

12. $f(x) = \frac{8 - x^2}{x^3 - x^2 + 4}$

$f(-3) = \frac{8 - (-3)^2}{(-3)^3 - (-3)^2 + 4} = \frac{-1}{-32}$

$f(-3) = \frac{1}{32}$

13. $x - 3 = 0$

$x = 3$

The domain of $H(x)$ is $\{x | x \neq 3\}$

14. $x + 2 = 0$

$x = -2$

The domain of $G(x)$ is $\{x | x \neq -2\}$

15. $x + 4 = 0$

$x = -4$

The domain $f(x)$ is $\{x | x \neq -4\}$

16. $x - 5 = 0$

$x = 5$

The domain of $g(x)$ is $\{x | x \neq 5\}$

17. $3x + 9 = 0$

$3x = -9$

$x = -3$

The domain of $R(x)$ is $\{x | x \neq -3\}$

18. $6 - 2x = 0$

$-2x = -6$

$x = 3$

The domain of $p(x)$ is $\{x | x \neq 3\}$

19. $(x - 4)(x + 2) = 0$

$x - 4 = 0 \qquad x + 2 = 0$

$x = 4 \qquad x = -2$

The domain of $q(x)$ is $\{x | x \neq -2, x \neq 4\}$

20. $(x + 1)(x + 5) = 0$

$x + 1 = 0 \qquad x + 5 = 0$

$x = -1 \qquad x = -5$

The domain of $h(x)$ is $\{x | x \neq -5, x \neq -1\}$

21. $(2x+5)(3x-6)=0$
 $2x+5=0 \qquad 3x-6=0$
 $2x=-5 \qquad\quad 3x=6$
 $x=-\dfrac{5}{2} \qquad\quad x=2$

 The domain of $V(x)$ is $\left\{x\middle| x\neq-\dfrac{5}{2},\, x\neq 2\right\}$.

22. $(4x+8)(3x-1)=0$
 $4x+8=0 \qquad 3x-1=0$
 $4x=-8 \qquad\quad 3x=1$
 $x=-2 \qquad\quad x=\dfrac{1}{3}$

 The domain of $F(x)$ is $\left\{x\middle| x\neq-2,\, x\neq\dfrac{1}{3}\right\}$.

23. $x=0$
 The domain of $f(x)$ is $\{x| x\neq 0\}$

24. $x^2=0$
 $\sqrt{x^2}=\sqrt{0}$
 $x=0$
 The domain of $g(x)$ is $\{x| x\neq 0\}$

25. The domain must exclude values of x for which $x^2+1=0$. This is not possible, because $x^2\geq 0$, and a positive number added to a number equal to or greater than zero cannot equal zero. Therefore, there are no real numbers that must be excluded from the domain of k.
 The domain of $k(x)$ is $\{x| x \text{ is a real number}\}$

26. The domain must exclude values of x for which $2x^2+3=0$. this is not possible, because $2x^2\geq 0$, and a positive number added to a number equal to or greater than zero cannot equal zero. Therefore, there are no real numbers that must be excluded from the domain of P.
 The domain of $P(x)$ is $\{x| x \text{ is a real number}\}$

27. $x^2+x-6=0$
 $(x+3)(x-2)=0$
 $x+3=0 \qquad x-2=0$
 $x=-3 \qquad\quad x=2$
 The domain of $f(x)$ is $\{x| x\neq-3,\, x\neq 2\}$

28. $x^2+4x-5=0$
 $(x+5)(x-1)=0$
 $x+5=0 \qquad x-1=0$
 $x=-5 \qquad\quad x=1$
 The domain of $G(x)$ is $\{x| x\neq-5,\, x\neq 1\}$

29. $x^2+2x-24=0$
 $(x+6)(x-4)=0$
 $x+6=0 \qquad x-4=0$
 $x=-6 \qquad\quad x=4$
 The domain of $A(x)$ is $\{x| x\neq-6,\, x\neq 4\}$

30. $x^2-4=0$
 $(x-2)(x+2)=0$
 $x-2=0 \qquad x+2=0$
 $x=2 \qquad\quad x=-2$
 The domain of $h(x)$ is $\{x| x\neq 2,\, x\neq-2\}$

31. The domain must exclude values of x for which $3x^2+12=0$. This is not possible, because $3x^2\geq 0$, and a positive number added to a number equal to or greater than zero cannot equal zero. Therefore, there are no real numbers that must be excluded from the domain of f.
 The domain of $f(x)$ is $\{x| x \text{ is a real number}\}$

32. The domain must exclude values of x for which $5x^2+1=0$. This is not possible, because $5x^2\geq 0$, and a positive number added to a number equal to or greater than zero cannot equal zero. Therefore, there are no real numbers that must be excluded from the domain of g.
 The domain of $g(x)$ is $\{x| x \text{ is a real number}\}$

33. $6x^2-13x+6=0$
 $(2x-3)(3x-2)=0$
 $2x-3=0 \qquad 3x-2=0$
 $x=\dfrac{3}{2} \qquad\quad x=\dfrac{2}{3}$
 The domain of $G(x)$ is $\left\{x\middle| x\neq\dfrac{3}{2},\, x\neq\dfrac{2}{3}\right\}$.

34. $x(x-2)(x-3)=0$
 $x=0 \qquad x-2=0 \quad x-3=0$
 $\qquad\qquad x=2 \qquad x=3$
 The domain of $A(x)$ is $\{x| x\neq 0,\, x\neq 2,\, x\neq 3\}$

35. $2x^3+9x^2-5x=0$
 $x(2x^2+9x-5)=0$
 $x(2x-1)(x+5)=0$
 $x=0 \qquad 2x-1=0 \qquad x+5=0$
 $\qquad\qquad x=\dfrac{1}{2} \qquad\quad x=-5$
 The domain of $f(x)$ is $\left\{x\middle| x\neq 0,\, x\neq\dfrac{1}{2},\, x\neq-5\right\}$.

36. $2x^3+2x^2-24x=0$
 $2x(x^2+x-12)=0$
 $2x(x+4)(x-3)=0$
 $2x=0 \qquad x+4=0 \qquad x-3=0$
 $x=0 \qquad\quad x=-4 \qquad\quad x=3$
 The domain of $H(x)$ is $\{x| x\neq 0,\, x\neq-4,\, x\neq 3\}$

Objective 6.1.2 Exercises

37. A rational function is in simplest form when the numerator and denominator have no common factors other than 1.

38. The expressions are not equal for all values of x.

The expression $\dfrac{x(x-2)}{2(x-2)}$ is undefined for $x=2$,

but $\dfrac{x}{2}$ has the value 1 for $x=2$.

39. $\dfrac{4-8x}{4} = \dfrac{4(1-2x)}{4} = 1-2x$

40. $\dfrac{8y+2}{2} = \dfrac{2(4y+1)}{2} = 4y+1$

41. $\dfrac{6x^2-2x}{2x} = \dfrac{2x(3x-1)}{2x} = 3x-1$

42. $\dfrac{3y-12y^2}{3y} = \dfrac{3y(1-4y)}{3y} = 1-4y$

43. $\dfrac{8x^2(x-3)}{4x(x-3)} = \dfrac{8x^2}{4x} = 2x$

44. $\dfrac{16y^4(y+8)}{12y^3(y+8)} = \dfrac{16y^4}{12y^3} = \dfrac{4y}{3}$

45. $\dfrac{2x-6}{3x-x^2} = \dfrac{2(x-3)}{x(3-x)} = \dfrac{2}{-x} = -\dfrac{2}{x}$

46. $\dfrac{3a^2-6a}{12-6a} = \dfrac{3a(a-2)}{6(2-a)} = \dfrac{3a}{-6} = -\dfrac{a}{2}$

47. $\dfrac{6x^3-15x^2}{12x^2-30x} = \dfrac{3x^2(2x-5)}{6x(2x-5)} = \dfrac{3x^2}{6x} = \dfrac{x}{2}$

48. $\dfrac{-36a^2-48a}{18a^3+24a^2} = \dfrac{-12a(3a+4)}{6a^2(3a+4)} = \dfrac{-12a}{6a^2} = -\dfrac{2}{a}$

49. $\dfrac{a^2+4a}{4a-16} = \dfrac{a(a+4)}{4(a-4)}$

The expression is in simplest form.

50. $\dfrac{3x-6}{x^2+2x} = \dfrac{3(x-2)}{x(x+2)}$

The expression is in simplest form.

51. $\dfrac{16x^3-8x^2+12x}{4x} = \dfrac{4x(4x^2-2x+3)}{4x}$

$\qquad\qquad = 4x^2-2x+3$

52. $\dfrac{3x^3y^3-12x^2y^2+15xy}{3xy} = \dfrac{3xy(x^2y^2-4xy+5)}{3xy}$

$\qquad\qquad = x^2y^2-4xy+5$

53. $\dfrac{-10a^4-20a^3+30a^2}{-10a^2} = \dfrac{-10a^2(a^2+2a-3)}{-10a^2}$

$\qquad\qquad = a^2+2a-3$

54. $\dfrac{-7a^5-14a^4+21a^3}{-7a^3} = \dfrac{-7a^3(a^2+2a-3)}{-7a^3}$

$\qquad\qquad = a^2+2a-3$

55. $\dfrac{3x^{3n}-9x^{2n}}{12x^{2n}} = \dfrac{3x^{2n}(x^n-3)}{12x^{2n}} = \dfrac{x^n-3}{4}$

56. $\dfrac{8a^n}{4a^{2n}-8a^n} = \dfrac{8a^n}{4a^n(a^n-2)} = \dfrac{2}{a^n-2}$

57. $\dfrac{x^2-7x+12}{x^2-9x+20} = \dfrac{(x-3)(x-4)}{(x-4)(x-5)} = \dfrac{x-3}{x-5}$

58. $\dfrac{x^2-x-20}{x^2-2x-15} = \dfrac{(x+4)(x-5)}{(x+3)(x-5)} = \dfrac{x+4}{x+3}$

59. $\dfrac{x^2-xy-2y^2}{x^2-3xy+2y^2} = \dfrac{(x+y)(x-2y)}{(x-y)(x-2y)} = \dfrac{x+y}{x-y}$

60. $\dfrac{2x^2+7xy-4y^2}{4x^2-4xy+y^2} = \dfrac{(x+4y)(2x-y)}{(2x-y)(2x-y)} = \dfrac{x+4y}{2x-y}$

61. $\dfrac{6-x-x^2}{3x^2-10x+8} = \dfrac{(3+x)(2-x)}{(3x-4)(x-2)}$

$\qquad = \dfrac{-1(x+3)}{1(3x-4)}$

$\qquad = -\dfrac{x+3}{3x-4}$

62. $\dfrac{3x^2+10x-8}{8-14x+3x^2} = \dfrac{(3x-2)(x+4)}{(2-3x)(4-x)}$

$\qquad = \dfrac{-1(x+4)}{1(4-x)}$

$\qquad = -\dfrac{x+4}{4-x}$

63. $\dfrac{14-19x-3x^2}{3x^2-23x+14} = \dfrac{(7+x)(2-3x)}{(3x-2)(x-7)}$

$\qquad = \dfrac{-1(7+x)}{1(x-7)}$

$\qquad = -\dfrac{x+7}{x-7}$

64. $\dfrac{x^2+x-12}{x^2-x-12} = \dfrac{(x+4)(x-3)}{(x+3)(x-4)}$

The expression is in simplest form.

65. $\dfrac{a^2-7a+10}{a^2+9a+14} = \dfrac{(a-5)(a-2)}{(a+7)(a+2)}$

The expression is in simplest form.

66. $\dfrac{x^2-2x}{x^2+2x} = \dfrac{x(x-2)}{x(x+2)} = \dfrac{x-2}{x+2}$

67. $\dfrac{a^2-b^2}{a^3+b^3} = \dfrac{(a+b)(a-b)}{(a+b)(a^2-ab+b^2)} = \dfrac{a-b}{a^2-ab+b^2}$

68. $\dfrac{x^4-y^4}{x^2+y^2} = \dfrac{(x^2+y^2)(x^2-y^2)}{x^2+y^2}$

$\qquad = x^2-y^2$

$\qquad = (x+y)(x-y)$

69. $\dfrac{x^3+y^3}{3x^3-3x^2y+3xy^2} = \dfrac{(x+y)(x^2-xy+y^2)}{3x(x^2-xy+y^2)}$

$\qquad = \dfrac{x+y}{3x}$

70. $\dfrac{3x^3+3x^2+3x}{9x^3-9} = \dfrac{3x(x^2+x+1)}{9(x^3-1)}$

$\qquad = \dfrac{3x(x^2+x+1)}{9(x-1)(x^2+x+1)}$

$\qquad = \dfrac{3x}{9(x-1)}$

$\qquad = \dfrac{x}{3(x-1)}$

71. $\dfrac{x^3-4xy^2}{3x^3-2x^2y-8xy^2} = \dfrac{x(x^2-4y^2)}{x(3x^2-2xy-8y^2)}$

$\qquad = \dfrac{x(x+2y)(x-2y)}{x(3+4y)(x-2y)}$

$\qquad = \dfrac{x+2y}{3x+4y}$

72. $\dfrac{4a^2-8ab+4b^2}{4a^2-4b^2} = \dfrac{4(a^2-2ab+b^2)}{4(a^2-b^2)}$

$\qquad = \dfrac{4(a-b)(a-b)}{4(a+b)(a-b)}$

$\qquad = \dfrac{4(a-b)}{4(a+b)}$

$\qquad = \dfrac{a-b}{a+b}$

73. $\dfrac{4x^3-14x^2+12x}{24x+4x^2-8x^3} = \dfrac{2x(2x^2-7x+6)}{4x(6+x-2x^2)}$

$\qquad = \dfrac{2x(2x-3)(x-2)}{4x(3+2x)(2-x)}$

$\qquad = \dfrac{2x(2x-3)(-1)}{4x(3+2x)(1)}$

$\qquad = -\dfrac{2x-3}{2(2x+3)}$

74. $\dfrac{6x^3-15x^2-75x}{150x+30x^2-12x^3} = \dfrac{3x(2x^2-5x-25)}{6x(25+5x-2x^2)}$

$\qquad = \dfrac{3x(2x+5)(x-5)}{6x(5+2x)(5-x)}$

$\qquad = \dfrac{3x(1)(-1)}{6x(1)(1)}$

$\qquad = -\dfrac{1}{2}$

75. $\dfrac{x^2-4}{a(x+2)-b(x+2)} = \dfrac{(x+2)(x-2)}{(x+2)(a-b)}$

$\qquad = \dfrac{(1)(x-2)}{(1)(a-b)}$

$\qquad = \dfrac{x-2}{a-b}$

76. $\dfrac{x^2(a-2)-a+2}{ax^2-ax} = \dfrac{x^2(a-2)-(a-2)}{ax(x-1)}$

$\qquad = \dfrac{(a-2)(x^2-1)}{ax(x-1)}$

$\qquad = \dfrac{(a-2)(x+1)(x-1)}{ax(x-1)}$

$\qquad = \dfrac{(a-2)(x+1)(1)}{ax(1)}$

$\qquad = \dfrac{(a-2)(x+1)}{ax}$

77. $\dfrac{x^4+3x^2+2}{x^4-1} = \dfrac{(x^2+1)(x^2+2)}{(x^2+1)(x^2-1)}$

$\qquad = \dfrac{(x^2+1)(x^2+2)}{(x^2+1)(x+1)(x-1)}$

$\qquad = \dfrac{(1)(x^2+2)}{(1)(x+1)(x-1)}$

$\qquad = \dfrac{x^2+2}{(x+1)(x-1)}$

78. $\dfrac{x^4-2x^2-3}{x^4+2x^2+1} = \dfrac{(x^2+1)(x^2-3)}{(x^2+1)(x^2+1)}$

$\qquad = \dfrac{(1)(x^2-3)}{(1)(x^2+1)}$

$\qquad = \dfrac{x^2-3}{x^2+1}$

79. $\dfrac{x^2y^2+4xy-21}{x^2y^2-10xy+21} = \dfrac{(xy+7)(xy-3)}{(xy-3)(xy-7)}$

$\qquad = \dfrac{(xy+7)(1)}{(1)(xy-7)}$

$\qquad = \dfrac{xy+7}{xy-7}$

80. $\dfrac{6x^2y^2+11xy+4}{9x^2y^2+9xy-4} = \dfrac{(2xy+1)(3xy+4)}{(3xy+4)(3xy-1)}$

$\qquad = \dfrac{(2xy+1)(1)}{(1)(3xy-1)}$

$\qquad = \dfrac{2xy+1}{3xy-1}$

81. $\dfrac{a^{2n}-a^n-2}{a^{2n}+3a^n+2} = \dfrac{(a^n+1)(a^n-2)}{(a^n+1)(a^n+2)}$

$\qquad = \dfrac{(1)(a^n-2)}{(1)(a^n+2)}$

$\qquad = \dfrac{a^n-2}{a^n+2}$

82. $\dfrac{a^{2n}+a^n-12}{a^{2n}-2a^n-3} = \dfrac{(a^n+4)(a^n-3)}{(a^n+1)(a^n-3)}$

$\qquad = \dfrac{(a^n+4)(1)}{(a^n+1)(1)}$

$\qquad = \dfrac{a^n+4}{a^n+1}$

Applying Concepts 6.1

83. $h(x) = \dfrac{x+2}{x-3}$

    $h(2.9) = -49$

    $h(2.99) = -499$

    $h(2.999) = -4999$

    $h(2.9999) = -49,999$

    As x becomes closer to 3, the values of $h(x)$ decrease.

84. $h(x) = \dfrac{x+2}{x-3}$

    $h(3.1) = 51$

    $h(3.01) = 501$

    $h(3.001) = 5001$

    $h(3.0001) = 50,001$

    As x becomes closer to 3, the values of $h(x)$ increase.

85. **a.**

    b. The ordered pair (2000, 51) means that when the distance between the object and the lens is 2000 m, the distance between the lens and the film is 51 mm.

    c. For $x = 50$, the expression $\dfrac{50x}{x-50}$ is undefined. For $0 \le x < 50$, $f(x)$ is negative, and distance cannot be negative. Therefore, the domain is $x > 50$.

    d. For $x > 1000$, $f(x)$ changes very little for large changes in x.

86. If $F(x) = \dfrac{g(x)}{h(x)}$ and $g(a) = h(a) = 0$ for some value of a, then $F(x)$ is not in simplest form. Because $g(a) = h(a) = 0$, $x - a$ is a factor of both $g(x)$ and $h(x)$. Thus $F(x)$ is not in simplest form.

87. Let $x - a$ be a common factor of the numerator and denominator of a rational expression. Then

$$\frac{f(x)(x-a)}{g(x)(x-a)} = \frac{f(x)}{g(x)} \cdot \frac{x-a}{x-a}$$

$$= \frac{f(x)}{g(x)} \cdot 1$$

$$= \frac{f(x)}{g(x)}$$

These operations are valid as long as $x \ne a$. If $x = a$, then $x - a = 0$ and $\dfrac{x-a}{x-a}$ is undefined.

Section 6.2

Concept Review 6.2

1. Always true

2. Always true

3. Never true
    To add fractions with the same denominator, add the numerators.
$$\frac{3}{x+y} + \frac{2}{x+y} = \frac{3+2}{x+y} = \frac{5}{x+y}$$

4. Always true

Objective 6.2.1 Exercises

1. To multiply two rational expressions, find the product of the numerators and the product of the numerators and the product of the denominators. Then simplify by dividing the numerator and denominator by their common factors.

2. To divide two rational expressions, multiply the first rational expression by the reciprocal of the second rational expression.

3. $\dfrac{27a^2 b^5}{16xy^2} \cdot \dfrac{20x^2 y^3}{9a^2 b} = \dfrac{27a^2 b^5 \cdot 20x^2 y^3}{16xy^2 \cdot 9a^2 b}$

    $= \dfrac{15b^4 xy}{4}$

4. $\dfrac{15x^2 y^4}{24ab^3} \cdot \dfrac{28a^2 b^4}{35xy^4} = \dfrac{15x^2 y^4 \cdot 28a^2 b^4}{24ab^3 \cdot 35xy^4} = \dfrac{abx}{2}$

5. $\dfrac{3x-15}{4x^2 -2x} \cdot \dfrac{20x^2 -10x}{15x-75} = \dfrac{3(x-5)}{2x(2x-1)} \cdot \dfrac{10x(2x-1)}{15(x-5)}$

    $= \dfrac{3(x-5) \cdot 10x(2x-1)}{2x(2x-1) \cdot 15(x-5)}$

    $= \dfrac{3(1) \cdot 10x(1)}{2x(1) \cdot 15(1)}$

    $= 1$

6. $\dfrac{2x^2 +4x}{8x^2 -40x} \cdot \dfrac{6x^3 -30x^2}{3x^2 +6x} = \dfrac{2x(x+2)}{8x(x-5)} \cdot \dfrac{6x^2 (x-5)}{3x(x+2)}$

    $= \dfrac{2x(x+2) \cdot 6x^2 (x-5)}{8x(x-5) \cdot 3x(x+2)}$

    $= \dfrac{2x(1) \cdot 6x^2 (1)}{8x(1) \cdot 3x(1)}$

    $= \dfrac{x}{2}$

7. $\dfrac{x^2 y^3}{x^2-4x-5} \cdot \dfrac{2x^2-13x+15}{x^4 y^3}$

$= \dfrac{x^2 y^3}{(x+1)(x-5)} \cdot \dfrac{(2x-3)(x-5)}{x^4 y^3}$

$= \dfrac{x^2 y^3 \cdot (2x-3)(x-5)}{(x+1)(x-5) \cdot x^4 y^3}$

$= \dfrac{x^2 y^3 \cdot (2x-3)(1)}{(x+1)(1) \cdot x^4 y^3}$

$= \dfrac{2x-3}{x^2(x+1)}$

8. $\dfrac{2x^2-5x+3}{x^6 y^3} \cdot \dfrac{x^4 y^4}{2x^2-x-3}$

$= \dfrac{(x-1)(2x-3)}{x^6 y^3} \cdot \dfrac{x^4 y^4}{(x+1)(2x-3)}$

$= \dfrac{(x-1)(2x-3) \cdot x^4 y^4}{x^6 y^3 \cdot (x+1)(2x-3)}$

$= \dfrac{(x-1)(1) \cdot x^4 y^4}{x^6 y^3 \cdot (x+1)(1)}$

$= \dfrac{y(x-1)}{x^2(x+1)}$

9. $\dfrac{x^2-3x+2}{x^2-8x+15} \cdot \dfrac{x^2+x-12}{8-2x-x^2}$

$= \dfrac{(x-1)(x-2)}{(x-3)(x-5)} \cdot \dfrac{(x+4)(x-3)}{(4+x)(2-x)}$

$= \dfrac{(x-1)(x-2)(x+4)(x-3)}{(x-3)(x-5)(4+x)(2-x)}$

$= \dfrac{(x-1)(-1)(1)(1)}{(1)(x-5)(1)(1)}$

$= -\dfrac{x-1}{x-5}$

10. $\dfrac{x^2+x-6}{12+x-x^2} \cdot \dfrac{x^2+x-20}{x^2-4x+4}$

$= \dfrac{(x+3)(x-2)}{(3+x)(4-x)} \cdot \dfrac{(x+5)(x-4)}{(x-2)(x-2)}$

$= \dfrac{(x+3)(x-2)(x+5)(x-4)}{(3+x)(4-x)(x-2)(x-2)}$

$= \dfrac{(1)(1)(x+5)(-1)}{(1)(1)(1)(x-2)}$

$= -\dfrac{x+5}{x-2}$

11. $\dfrac{x^{n+1}+2x^n}{4x^2-6x} \cdot \dfrac{8x^2-12x}{x^{n+1}-x^n} = \dfrac{x^n(x+2)}{2x(2x-3)} \cdot \dfrac{4x(2x-3)}{x^n(x-1)}$

$= \dfrac{x^n(x+2) \cdot 4x(2x-3)}{2x(2x-3) \cdot x^n(x-1)}$

$= \dfrac{x^n(x+2) \cdot 4x(1)}{2x(1) \cdot x^n(x-1)}$

$= \dfrac{2(x+2)}{x-1}$

12. $\dfrac{x^{2n}+2x^n}{x^{n+1}+2x} \cdot \dfrac{x^2-3x}{x^{n+1}-3x^n} = \dfrac{x^n(x^n+2)}{x(x^n+2)} \cdot \dfrac{x(x-3)}{x^n(x-3)}$

$= \dfrac{x^n(x^n+2) \cdot x(x-3)}{x(x^n+2) \cdot x^n(x-3)}$

$= \dfrac{x^n(1) \cdot x(1)}{x(1) \cdot x^n(1)}$

$= 1$

13. $\dfrac{12+x-6x^2}{6x^2+29x+28} \cdot \dfrac{2x^2+x-21}{4x^2-9}$

$= \dfrac{(4+3x)(3-2x)}{(2x+7)(3x+4)} \cdot \dfrac{(2x+7)(x-3)}{(2x+3)(2x-3)}$

$= \dfrac{(4+3x)(3-2x)(2x+7)(x-3)}{(2x+7)(3x+4)(2x+3)(2x-3)}$

$= \dfrac{(1)(-1)(1)(x-3)}{(1)(1)(2x+3)(1)}$

$= -\dfrac{x-3}{2x+3}$

14. $\dfrac{x^2+5x+4}{4+x-3x^2} \cdot \dfrac{3x^2+2x-8}{x^2+4x}$

$= \dfrac{(x+1)(x+4)}{(1+x)(4-3x)} \cdot \dfrac{(x+2)(3x-4)}{x(x+4)}$

$= \dfrac{(x+1)(x+4)(x+2)(3x-4)}{(1+x)(4-3x) \cdot x(x+4)}$

$= \dfrac{(1)(1)(x+2)(-1)}{(1)(1) \cdot x(1)}$

$= -\dfrac{x+2}{x}$

15. $\dfrac{x^{2n}-x^n-6}{x^{2n}+x^n-2} \cdot \dfrac{x^{2n}-5x^n-6}{x^{2n}-2x^n-3}$

$= \dfrac{(x^n+2)(x^n-3)}{(x^n+2)(x^n-1)} \cdot \dfrac{(x^n+1)(x^n-6)}{(x^n+1)(x^n-3)}$

$= \dfrac{(x^n+2)(x^n-3)(x^n+1)(x^n-6)}{(x^n+2)(x^n-1)(x^n+1)(x^n-3)}$

$= \dfrac{(1)(1)(1)(x^n-6)}{(1)(x^n-1)(1)(1)}$

$= \dfrac{x^n-6}{x^n-1}$

16. $\dfrac{x^{2n}+3x^n+2}{x^{2n}-x^n-6} \cdot \dfrac{x^{2n}+x^n-12}{x^{2n}-1}$

$= \dfrac{(x^n+1)(x^n+2)}{(x^n+2)(x^n-3)} \cdot \dfrac{(x^n+4)(x^n-3)}{(x^n+1)(x^n-1)}$

$= \dfrac{(x^n+1)(x^n+2)(x^n+4)(x^n-3)}{(x^n+2)(x^n-3)(x^n+1)(x^n-1)}$

$= \dfrac{(1)(1)(x^n+4)(1)}{(1)(1)(1)(x^n-1)}$

$= \dfrac{x^n+4}{x^n-1}$

17. $\dfrac{x^3 - y^3}{2x^2 + xy - 3y^2} \cdot \dfrac{2x^2 + 5xy + 3y^2}{x^2 + xy + y^2}$

$= \dfrac{(x-y)(x^2 + xy + y^2)}{(2x+3y)(x-y)} \cdot \dfrac{(2x+3y)(x+y)}{x^2 + xy + y^2}$

$= \dfrac{(x-y)(x^2 + xy + y^2)(2x+3y)(x+y)}{(2x+3y)(x-y)(x^2 + xy + y^2)}$

$= \dfrac{(1)(1)(1)(x+y)}{(1)(1)(1)}$

$= x + y$

18. $\dfrac{x^4 - 5x^2 + 4}{3x^2 - 4x - 4} \cdot \dfrac{3x^2 - 10x - 8}{x^2 - 4}$

$= \dfrac{(x^2 - 1)(x^2 - 4)}{(3x+2)(x-2)} \cdot \dfrac{(3x+2)(x-4)}{(x+2)(x-2)}$

$= \dfrac{(x+1)(x-1)(x+2)(x-2)}{(3x+2)(x-2)} \cdot \dfrac{(3x+2)(x-4)}{(x+2)(x-2)}$

$= \dfrac{(x+1)(x-1)(x+2)(x-2)(3x+2)(x-4)}{(3x+2)(x-2)(x+2)(x-2)}$

$= \dfrac{(x+1)(x-1)(1)(1)(1)(x-4)}{(1)(x-2)(1)(1)}$

$= \dfrac{(x+1)(x-1)(x-4)}{x-2}$

19. $\dfrac{6x^2 y^4}{35a^2 b^5} \div \dfrac{12x^3 y^3}{7a^4 b^5} = \dfrac{6x^2 y^4}{35a^2 b^5} \cdot \dfrac{7a^4 b^5}{12x^3 y^3}$

$= \dfrac{6x^2 y^4 \cdot 7a^4 b^5}{35a^2 b^5 \cdot 12x^3 y^3}$

$= \dfrac{a^2 y}{10x}$

20. $\dfrac{12a^4 b^7}{13x^2 y^2} \div \dfrac{18a^5 b^6}{26xy^3} = \dfrac{12a^4 b^7}{13x^2 y^2} \cdot \dfrac{26xy^3}{18a^5 b^6}$

$= \dfrac{12a^4 b^7 \cdot 26xy^3}{13x^2 y^2 \cdot 18a^5 b^6}$

$= \dfrac{4by}{3ax}$

21. $\dfrac{2x - 6}{6x^2 - 15x} \div \dfrac{4x^2 - 12x}{18x^3 - 45x^2}$

$= \dfrac{2x - 6}{6x^2 - 15x} \cdot \dfrac{18x^3 - 45x^2}{4x^2 - 12x}$

$= \dfrac{2(x-3)}{3x(2x-5)} \cdot \dfrac{9x^2(2x-5)}{4x(x-3)}$

$= \dfrac{2(x-3) \cdot 9x^2(2x-5)}{3x(2x-5) \cdot 4x(x-3)}$

$= \dfrac{2(1) \cdot 9x^2(1)}{3x(1) \cdot 4x(1)}$

$= \dfrac{3}{2}$

22. $\dfrac{4x^2 - 4y^2}{6x^2 y^2} \div \dfrac{3x^2 + 3xy}{2x^2 y - 2xy^2}$

$= \dfrac{4x^2 - 4y^2}{6x^2 y^2} \cdot \dfrac{2x^2 y - 2xy^2}{3x^2 + 3xy}$

$= \dfrac{4(x^2 - y^2)}{6x^2 y^2} \cdot \dfrac{2xy(x-y)}{3x(x+y)}$

$= \dfrac{4(x+y)(x-y)}{6x^2 y^2} \cdot \dfrac{2xy(x-y)}{3x(x+y)}$

$= \dfrac{4(x+y)(x-y) \cdot 2xy(x-y)}{6x^2 y^2 \cdot 3x(x+y)}$

$= \dfrac{4(1)(x-y) \cdot 2xy(x-y)}{6x^2 y^2 \cdot 3x(1)}$

$= \dfrac{4(x-y)^2}{9x^2 y}$

23. $\dfrac{2x^2 - 2y^2}{14x^2 y^4} \div \dfrac{x^2 + 2xy + y^2}{35xy^3}$

$= \dfrac{2x^2 - 2y^2}{14x^2 y^4} \cdot \dfrac{35xy^3}{x^2 + 2xy + y^2}$

$= \dfrac{2(x^2 - y^2)}{14x^2 y^4} \cdot \dfrac{35xy^3}{(x+y)(x+y)}$

$= \dfrac{2(x+y)(x-y)}{14x^2 y^4} \cdot \dfrac{35xy^3}{(x+y)(x+y)}$

$= \dfrac{2(x+y)(x-y) \cdot 35xy^3}{14x^2 y^4 (x+y)(x+y)}$

$= \dfrac{2(1)(x-y) \cdot 35xy^3}{14x^2 y^4 (1)(x+y)}$

$= \dfrac{5(x-y)}{xy(x+y)}$

24. $\dfrac{8x^3 + 12x^2 y}{4x^2 - 9y^2} \div \dfrac{16x^2 y^2}{4x^2 - 12xy + 9y^2}$

$= \dfrac{8x^3 + 12x^2 y}{4x^2 - 9y^2} \cdot \dfrac{4x^2 - 12xy + 9y^2}{16x^2 y^2}$

$= \dfrac{4x^2(2x+3y)}{(2x+3y)(2x-3y)} \cdot \dfrac{(2x-3y)(2x-3y)}{16x^2 y^2}$

$= \dfrac{4x^2(2x+3y)(2x-3y)(2x-3y)}{(2x+3y)(2x-3y) \cdot 16x^2 y^2}$

$= \dfrac{4x^2(1)(1)(2x-3y)}{(1)(1)16x^2 y^2}$

$= \dfrac{2x - 3y}{4y^2}$

25. $\dfrac{2x^2-5x-3}{2x^2+7x+3} \div \dfrac{2x^2-3x-20}{2x^2-x-15}$

$= \dfrac{2x^2-5x-3}{2x^2+7x+3} \cdot \dfrac{2x^2-x-15}{2x^2-3x-20}$

$= \dfrac{(2x+1)(x-3)}{(2x+1)(x+3)} \cdot \dfrac{(2x+5)(x-3)}{(2x+5)(x-4)}$

$= \dfrac{(1)(x-3)(1)(x-3)}{(1)(x+3)(1)(x-4)}$

$= \dfrac{(x-3)^2}{(x+3)(x-4)}$

26. $\dfrac{3x^2-10x-8}{6x^2+13x+6} \div \dfrac{2x^2-9x+10}{4x^2-4x-15}$

$= \dfrac{3x^2-10x-8}{6x^2+13x+6} \cdot \dfrac{4x^2-4x-15}{2x^2-9x+10}$

$= \dfrac{(3x+2)(x-4)}{(2x+3)(3x+2)} \cdot \dfrac{(2x+3)(2x-5)}{(2x-5)(x-2)}$

$= \dfrac{(3x+2)(x-4)(2x+3)(2x-5)}{(2x+3)(3x+2)(2x-5)(x-2)}$

$= \dfrac{(1)(x-4)(1)(1)}{(1)(1)(1)(x-2)}$

$= \dfrac{x-4}{x-2}$

27. $\dfrac{x^2-8x+15}{x^2+2x-35} \div \dfrac{15-2x-x^2}{x^2+9x+14}$

$= \dfrac{x^2-8x+15}{x^2+2x-35} \cdot \dfrac{x^2+9x+14}{15-2x-x^2}$

$= \dfrac{(x-3)(x-5)}{(x+7)(x-5)} \cdot \dfrac{(x+2)(x+7)}{(5+x)(3-x)}$

$= \dfrac{(x-3)(x-5)(x+2)(x+7)}{(x+7)(x-5)(5+x)(3-x)}$

$= \dfrac{(-1)(1)(x+2)(1)}{(1)(1)(5+x)(1)}$

$= -\dfrac{x+2}{x+5}$

28. $\dfrac{2x^2+13x+20}{8-10x-3x^2} \div \dfrac{6x^2-13x-5}{9x^2-3x-2}$

$= \dfrac{2x^2+13x+20}{8-10x-3x^2} \cdot \dfrac{9x^2-3x-2}{6x^2-13x-5}$

$= \dfrac{(2x+5)(x+4)}{(4+x)(2-3x)} \cdot \dfrac{(3x+1)(3x-2)}{(3x+1)(2x-5)}$

$= \dfrac{(2x+5)(x+4)(3x+1)(3x-2)}{(4+x)(2-3x)(3x+1)(2x-5)}$

$= \dfrac{(2x+5)(1)(1)(-1)}{(1)(1)(1)(2x-5)}$

$= -\dfrac{2x+5}{2x-5}$

29. $\dfrac{x^{2n}+x^n}{2x-2} \div \dfrac{4x^n+4}{x^{n+1}-x^n} = \dfrac{x^{2n}+x^n}{2x-2} \cdot \dfrac{x^{n+1}-x^n}{4x^n+4}$

$= \dfrac{x^n(x^n+1)}{2(x-1)} \cdot \dfrac{x^n(x-1)}{4(x^n+1)}$

$= \dfrac{x^n(x^n+1) \cdot x^n(x-1)}{2(x-1) \cdot 4(x^n+1)}$

$= \dfrac{x^n(1) \cdot x^n(1)}{2(1) \cdot 4(1)}$

$= \dfrac{x^{2n}}{8}$

30. $\dfrac{x^{2n}-4}{4x^n+8} \div \dfrac{x^{n+1}-2x}{4x^3-12x^2}$

$= \dfrac{x^{2n}-4}{4x^n+8} \cdot \dfrac{4x^3-12x^2}{x^{n+1}-2x}$

$= \dfrac{(x^n+2)(x^n-2)}{4(x^n+2)} \cdot \dfrac{4x^2(x-3)}{x(x^n-2)}$

$= \dfrac{(x^n+2)(x^n-2) \cdot 4x^2(x-3)}{4(x^n+2) \cdot x(x^n-2)}$

$= \dfrac{(1)(1) \cdot 4x^2(x-3)}{4(1) \cdot x(1)}$

$= x(x-3)$

31. $\dfrac{2x^2-13x+21}{2x^2+11x+15} \div \dfrac{2x^2+x-28}{3x^2+4x-15}$

$= \dfrac{2x^2-13x+21}{2x^2+11x+15} \cdot \dfrac{3x^2+4x-15}{2x^2+x-28}$

$= \dfrac{(2x-7)(x-3)}{(2x+5)(x+3)} \cdot \dfrac{(3x-5)(x+3)}{(2x-7)(x+4)}$

$= \dfrac{(2x-7)(x-3)(3x-5)(x+3)}{(2x+5)(x+3)(2x-7)(x+4)}$

$= \dfrac{(1)(x-3)(3x-5)(1)}{(2x+5)(1)(1)(x+4)}$

$= \dfrac{(x-3)(3x-5)}{(2x+5)(x+4)}$

32. $\dfrac{2x^2-13x+15}{2x^2-3x-35} \div \dfrac{6x^2+x-12}{6x^2+13x-28}$

$= \dfrac{2x^2-13x+15}{2x^2-3x-35} \cdot \dfrac{6x^2+13x-28}{6x^2+x-12}$

$= \dfrac{(2x-3)(x-5)}{(2x+7)(x-5)} \cdot \dfrac{(2x+7)(3x-4)}{(2x+3)(3x-4)}$

$= \dfrac{(2x-3)(x-5)(2x+7)(3x-4)}{(2x+7)(x-5)(2x+3)(3x-4)}$

$= \dfrac{(2x-3)(1)(1)(1)}{(1)(1)(2x+3)(1)}$

$= \dfrac{2x-3}{2x+3}$

33. $\dfrac{14+17x-6x^2}{3x^2+14x+8} \div \dfrac{4x^2-49}{2x^2+15x+28}$

$= \dfrac{14+17x-6x^2}{3x^2+14x+8} \cdot \dfrac{2x^2+15x+28}{4x^2-49}$

$= \dfrac{(2+3x)(7-2x)}{(3x+2)(x+4)} \cdot \dfrac{(2x+7)(x+4)}{(2x+7)(2x-7)}$

$= \dfrac{(2+3x)(7-2x)(2x+7)(x+4)}{(3x+2)(x+4)(2x+7)(2x-7)}$

$= \dfrac{(1)(-1)(1)(1)}{(1)(1)(1)(1)}$

$= -1$

34. $\dfrac{16x^2-9}{6-5x-4x^2} \div \dfrac{16x^2+24x+9}{4x^2+11x+6}$

$= \dfrac{16x^2-9}{6-5x-4x^2} \cdot \dfrac{4x^2+11x+6}{16x^2+24x+9}$

$= \dfrac{(4x+3)(4x-3)}{(2+x)(3-4x)} \cdot \dfrac{(x+2)(4x+3)}{(4x+3)(4x+3)}$

$= \dfrac{(4x+3)(4x-3)(x+2)(4x+3)}{(2+x)(3-4x)(4x+3)(4x+3)}$

$= \dfrac{(1)(-1)(1)(1)}{(1)(1)(1)(1)}$

$= -1$

35. $\dfrac{2x^{2n}-x^n-6}{x^{2n}-x^n-2} \div \dfrac{2x^{2n}+x^n-3}{x^{2n}-1}$

$= \dfrac{2x^{2n}-x^n-6}{x^{2n}-x^n-2} \cdot \dfrac{x^{2n}-1}{2x^{2n}+x^n-3}$

$= \dfrac{(2x^n+3)(x^n-2)}{(x^n+1)(x^n-2)} \cdot \dfrac{(x^n+1)(x^n-1)}{(2x^n+3)(x^n-1)}$

$= \dfrac{(2x^n+3)(x^n-2)(x^n+1)(x^n-1)}{(x^n+1)(x^n-2)(2x^n+3)(x^n-1)}$

$= \dfrac{(1)(1)(1)(1)}{(1)(1)(1)(1)}$

$= 1$

36. $\dfrac{x^{4n}-1}{x^{2n}+x^n-2} \div \dfrac{x^{2n}+1}{x^{2n}+3x^n+2}$

$= \dfrac{x^{4n}-1}{x^{2n}+x^n-2} \cdot \dfrac{x^{2n}+3x^n+2}{x^{2n}+1}$

$= \dfrac{(x^{2n}+1)(x^{2n}-1)}{(x^n+2)(x^n-1)} \cdot \dfrac{(x^n+1)(x^n+2)}{x^{2n}+1}$

$= \dfrac{(x^{2n}+1)(x^n+1)(x^n-1)}{(x^n+2)(x^n-1)} \cdot \dfrac{(x^n+1)(x^n+2)}{x^{2n}+1}$

$= \dfrac{(x^{2n}+1)(x^n+1)(x^n-1)(x^n+1)(x^n+2)}{(x^n+2)(x^n-1)(x^{2n}+1)}$

$= \dfrac{(1)(x^n+1)(1)(x^n+1)(1)}{(1)(1)(1)}$

$= (x^n+1)^2$

37. $\dfrac{6x^2+6x}{3x+6x^2+3x^3} \div \dfrac{x^2-1}{1-x^3}$

$= \dfrac{6x^2+6x}{3x+6x^2+3x^3} \cdot \dfrac{1-x^3}{x^2-1}$

$= \dfrac{6x(x+1)}{3x(1+2x+x^2)} \cdot \dfrac{(1-x)(1+x+x^2)}{(x+1)(x-1)}$

$= \dfrac{6x(x+1)}{3x(1+x)(1+x)} \cdot \dfrac{(1-x)(1+x+x^2)}{(x+1)(x-1)}$

$= \dfrac{6x(x+1)(1-x)(1+x+x^2)}{3x(1+x)(1+x)(x+1)(x-1)}$

$= \dfrac{6x(1)(-1)(1+x+x^2)}{3x(1)(1+x)(x+1)(1)}$

$= -\dfrac{2(1+x+x^2)}{(x+1)^2}$

38. $\dfrac{x^3+y^3}{2x^3+2x^2y} \div \dfrac{3x^3-3x^2y+3xy^2}{6x^2-6y^2}$

$= \dfrac{x^3+y^3}{2x^3+2x^2y} \cdot \dfrac{6x^2-6y^2}{3x^3-3x^2y+3xy^2}$

$= \dfrac{(x+y)(x^2-xy+y^2)}{2x^2(x+y)} \cdot \dfrac{6(x^2-y^2)}{3x(x^2-xy+y^2)}$

$= \dfrac{(x+y)(x^2-xy+y^2)}{2x^2(x+y)} \cdot \dfrac{6(x+y)(x-y)}{3x(x^2-xy+y^2)}$

$= \dfrac{(x+y)(x^2-xy+y^2)\cdot 6(x+y)(x-y)}{2x^2(x+y)\cdot 3x(x^2-xy+y^2)}$

$= \dfrac{(1)(1)\cdot 6(x+y)(x-y)}{2x^2(1)\cdot 3x(1)}$

$= \dfrac{(x+y)(x-y)}{x^3}$

Objective 6.2.2 Exercises

39. The LCM is $12x^2y^4$

$\dfrac{3}{4x^2y} = \dfrac{3}{4x^2y} \cdot \dfrac{3y^3}{3y^3} = \dfrac{9y^3}{12x^2y^4}$

$\dfrac{17}{12xy^4} = \dfrac{17}{12xy^4} \cdot \dfrac{x}{x} = \dfrac{17x}{12x^2y^4}$

40. The LCM is $240a^5b^3$.

$\dfrac{5}{16a^3b^3} = \dfrac{5}{16a^3b^3} \cdot \dfrac{15a^2}{15a^2} = \dfrac{75a^2}{240a^5b^3}$

$\dfrac{7}{30a^5b} = \dfrac{7}{30a^5b} \cdot \dfrac{8b^2}{8b^2} = \dfrac{56b^2}{240a^5b^3}$

41. The LCM is $(2x-3)(2x+3)$.

$\dfrac{3x}{2x-3} = \dfrac{3x}{2x-3} \cdot \dfrac{2x+3}{2x+3} = \dfrac{6x^2+9x}{(2x-3)(2x+3)}$

$\dfrac{5x}{2x+3} = \dfrac{5x}{2x+3} \cdot \dfrac{(2x-3)}{(2x-3)} = \dfrac{10x^2-15x}{(2x-3)(2x+3)}$

42. The LCM is $(7y-3)(7y+3)$.

$$\frac{2}{7y-3}=\frac{2}{7y-3}\cdot\frac{7y+3}{7y+3}=\frac{14y+6}{(7y-3)(7y+3)}$$

$$\frac{-3}{7y+3}=\frac{-3}{7y+3}\cdot\frac{7y-3}{7y-3}=\frac{-21y+9}{(7y-3)(7y+3)}$$

43. The LCM is $(x+3)(x-3)$.

$$\frac{2x}{x^2-9}=\frac{2x}{(x-3)(x+3)}$$

$$\frac{x+1}{x-3}=\frac{x+1}{x-3}\cdot\frac{x+3}{x+3}=\frac{x^2+4x+3}{(x-3)(x+3)}$$

44. The LCM is $4(x+4)(x-4)$.

$$\frac{3x}{x^2-16}=\frac{3x}{(x+4)(x-4)}\cdot\frac{4}{4}=\frac{12x}{4(x+4)(x-4)}$$

$$\frac{2x}{4x-16}=\frac{2x}{4(x-4)}\cdot\frac{x+4}{x+4}=\frac{2x^2+8x}{4(x+4)(x-4)}$$

45. The LCM is $(x+1)(x-1)^2$.

$$\frac{3x}{x^2-1}=\frac{3x}{(x+1)(x-1)}\cdot\frac{x-1}{x-1}=\frac{3x^2-3x}{(x+1)(x-1)^2}$$

$$\frac{5x}{x^2-2x+1}=\frac{5x}{(x-1)^2}\cdot\frac{x+1}{x+1}=\frac{5x^2+5x}{(x+1)(x-1)^2}$$

46. The LCM is $(x+3)(x-2)(x+2)$.

$$\frac{2x}{x^2+x-6}=\frac{2x}{(x+3)(x-2)}\cdot\frac{x+2}{x+2}$$
$$=\frac{2x^2+4x}{(x+3)(x-2)(x+2)}$$

$$\frac{-4x}{x^2+5x+6}=\frac{-4x}{(x+3)(x+2)}\cdot\frac{x-2}{x-2}$$
$$=-\frac{4x^2-8x}{(x+3)(x-2)(x+2)}$$

47. The LCM is $2xy$.

$$\frac{3}{2xy}-\frac{7}{2xy}-\frac{9}{2xy}=\frac{3-7-9}{2xy}=-\frac{13}{2xy}$$

48. The LCM is $4x^2$.

$$-\frac{3}{4x^2}+\frac{8}{4x^2}-\frac{3}{4x^2}=\frac{-3+8-3}{4x^2}=\frac{2}{4x^2}=\frac{1}{2x^2}$$

49. The LCM is x^2-3x+2.

$$\frac{x}{x^2-3x+2}-\frac{2}{x^2-3x+2}=\frac{x-2}{x^2-3x+2}$$
$$=\frac{(1)}{(1)(x-1)}$$
$$=\frac{1}{x-1}$$

50. The LCM is $3x^2+x-10$.

$$\frac{3x}{3x^2+x-10}-\frac{5}{3x^2+x-10}=\frac{3x-5}{3x^2+x-10}$$
$$=\frac{(1)}{(1)(x+2)}$$
$$=\frac{1}{x+2}$$

51. The LCM is $10x^2y$.

$$\frac{3}{2x^2y}-\frac{8}{5x}-\frac{9}{10xy}$$
$$=\frac{3}{2x^2y}\cdot\frac{5}{5}-\frac{8}{5x}\cdot\frac{2xy}{2xy}-\frac{9}{10xy}\cdot\frac{x}{x}$$
$$=\frac{15-16xy-9x}{10x^2y}$$

52. The LCM is $30a^2b^2$.

$$\frac{2}{5ab}-\frac{3}{10a^2b}+\frac{4}{15ab^2}$$
$$=\frac{2}{5ab}\cdot\frac{6ab}{6ab}-\frac{3}{10a^2b}\cdot\frac{3b}{3b}+\frac{4}{15ab^2}\cdot\frac{2a}{2a}$$
$$=\frac{12ab-9b+8a}{30a^2b^2}$$

53. The LCM is $30xy$.

$$\frac{2}{3x}-\frac{3}{2xy}+\frac{4}{5xy}-\frac{5}{6x}$$
$$=\frac{2}{3x}\cdot\frac{10y}{10y}-\frac{3}{2xy}\cdot\frac{15}{15}+\frac{4}{5xy}\cdot\frac{6}{6}-\frac{5}{6x}\cdot\frac{5y}{5y}$$
$$=\frac{20y-45+24-25y}{30xy}$$
$$=\frac{-5y-21}{30xy}$$
$$=-\frac{5y+21}{30xy}$$

54. The LCM is $40ab$.

$$\frac{3}{4ab}-\frac{2}{5a}+\frac{3}{10b}-\frac{5}{8ab}$$
$$=\frac{3}{4ab}\cdot\frac{10}{10}-\frac{2}{5a}\cdot\frac{8b}{8b}+\frac{3}{10b}\cdot\frac{4a}{4a}-\frac{5}{8ab}\cdot\frac{5}{5}$$
$$=\frac{30-16b+12a-25}{40ab}$$
$$=\frac{12a+5-16b}{40ab}$$

55. The LCM is $36x$.

$$\frac{2x-1}{12x}-\frac{3x+4}{9x}=\frac{2x-1}{12x}\cdot\frac{3}{3}-\frac{3x+4}{9x}\cdot\frac{4}{4}$$
$$=\frac{(6x-3)-(12x+16)}{36x}$$
$$=\frac{6x-3-12x-16}{36x}$$
$$=\frac{-6x-19}{36x}$$
$$=-\frac{6x+19}{36x}$$

56. The LCM is $12x$.

$$\frac{3x-4}{6x} - \frac{2x-5}{4x} = \frac{3x-4}{6x} \cdot \frac{2}{2} - \frac{2x-5}{4x} \cdot \frac{3}{3}$$

$$= \frac{(6x-8)-(6x-15)}{12x}$$

$$= \frac{6x-8-6x+15}{12x}$$

$$= \frac{7}{12x}$$

57. The LCM is $12x^2y^2$.

$$\frac{3x+2}{4x^2y} - \frac{y-5}{6xy^2} = \frac{3x+2}{4x^2y} \cdot \frac{3y}{3y} - \frac{y-5}{6xy^2} \cdot \frac{2x}{2x}$$

$$= \frac{(9xy+6y)-(2xy-10x)}{12x^2y^2}$$

$$= \frac{9xy+6y-2xy+10x}{12x^2y^2}$$

$$= \frac{10x+7xy+6y}{12x^2y^2}$$

58. The LCM is $10x^2y^2$.

$$\frac{2y-4}{5xy^2} + \frac{3-2x}{10x^2y} = \frac{2y-4}{5xy^2} \cdot \frac{2x}{2x} + \frac{3-2x}{10x^2y} \cdot \frac{y}{y}$$

$$= \frac{4xy-8x+(3y-2xy)}{10x^2y^2}$$

$$= \frac{4xy-8x+3y-2xy}{10x^2y^2}$$

$$= \frac{2xy-8x+3y}{10x^2y^2}$$

59. The LCM is $(x-3)(x-5)$.

$$\frac{2x}{x-3} - \frac{3x}{x-5} = \frac{2x}{x-3} \cdot \frac{x-5}{x-5} - \frac{3x}{x-5} \cdot \frac{x-3}{x-3}$$

$$= \frac{(2x^2-10x)-(3x^2-9x)}{(x-3)(x-5)}$$

$$= \frac{2x^2-10x-3x^2+9x}{(x-3)(x-5)}$$

$$= \frac{-x^2-x}{(x-3)(x-5)}$$

$$= -\frac{x^2+x}{(x-3)(x-5)}$$

60. The LCM is $(a-2)(a+1)$.

$$\frac{3a}{a-2} - \frac{5a}{a+1} = \frac{3a}{a-2} \cdot \frac{a+1}{a+1} - \frac{5a}{a+1} \cdot \frac{a-2}{a-2}$$

$$= \frac{(3a^2+3a)-(5a^2-10a)}{(a-2)(a+1)}$$

$$= \frac{3a^2+3a-5a^2+10a}{(a-2)(a+1)}$$

$$= \frac{-2a^2+13a}{(a-2)(a+1)}$$

$$= \frac{-(2a^2-13a)}{(a-2)(a+1)}$$

$$= -\frac{2a^2-13a}{(a-2)(a+1)}$$

61. $3-2a = -(2a-3)$
The LCM is $2a-3$.

$$\frac{3}{2a-3} + \frac{2a}{3-2a} = \frac{3}{2a-3} + \frac{2a}{3-2a} \cdot \frac{-1}{-1}$$

$$= \frac{3-2a}{2a-3}$$

$$= \frac{(-1)}{(1)}$$

$$= -1$$

62. The LCM is $(2x-5)(5x-2)$.

$$\frac{x}{2x-5} - \frac{2}{5x-2} = \frac{x}{2x-5} \cdot \frac{5x-2}{5x-2} - \frac{2}{5x-2} \cdot \frac{2x-5}{2x-5}$$

$$= \frac{(5x^2-2x)-(4x-10)}{(2x-5)(5x-2)}$$

$$= \frac{5x^2-2x-4x+10}{(2x-5)(5x-2)}$$

$$= \frac{5x^2-6x+10}{(2x-5)(5x-2)}$$

63. $x^2-25 = (x+5)(x-5)$
The LCM is $(x+5)(x-5)$.

$$\frac{3}{x+5} + \frac{2x+7}{x^2-25} = \frac{3}{x+5} \cdot \frac{x-5}{x-5} + \frac{2x+7}{(x-5)(x+5)}$$

$$= \frac{3x-15}{(x+5)(x-5)} + \frac{2x+7}{(x-5)(x+5)}$$

$$= \frac{(3x-15)+(2x+7)}{(x-5)(x+5)}$$

$$= \frac{3x-15+2x+7}{(x-5)(x+5)}$$

$$= \frac{5x-8}{(x-5)(x+5)}$$

64. $4-x = -(x-4)$
$x^2-16 = (x+4)(x-4)$
The LCM is $(x+4)(x-4)$.

$$\frac{x}{4-x} - \frac{4}{x^2-16}$$

$$= \frac{x}{4-x} \cdot \frac{-1}{-1} \cdot \frac{x+4}{x+4} - \frac{4}{(x+4)(x-4)}$$

$$= \frac{-x^2-4x}{(x+4)(x-4)} - \frac{4}{(x+4)(x-4)}$$

$$= \frac{-x^2-4x-4}{(x+4)(x-4)}$$

$$= -\frac{x^2+4x+4}{(x+4)(x-4)}$$

$$= -\frac{(x+2)^2}{(x+4)(x-4)}$$

65. The LCM is $x(x-4)$.

$$\frac{2}{x}-3-\frac{10}{x-4}=\frac{2}{x}\cdot\frac{x-4}{x-4}-3\cdot\frac{x(x-4)}{x(x-4)}-\frac{10}{x-4}\cdot\frac{x}{x}$$

$$=\frac{(2x-8)-3x(x-4)-10x}{x(x-4)}$$

$$=\frac{2x-8-3x^2+12x-10x}{x(x-4)}$$

$$=\frac{-3x^2+4x-8}{x(x-4)}$$

$$=-\frac{3x^2-4x+8}{x(x-4)}$$

66. The LCM is $a(a-3)$.

$$\frac{6a}{a-3}-5+\frac{3}{a}=\frac{6a}{a-3}\cdot\frac{a}{a}-5\cdot\frac{a(a-3)}{a(a-3)}+\frac{3}{a}\cdot\frac{a-3}{a-3}$$

$$=\frac{6a^2-5a(a-3)+3a-9}{a(a-3)}$$

$$=\frac{6a^2-5a^2+15a+3a-9}{a(a-3)}$$

$$=\frac{a^2+18a-9}{a(a-3)}$$

67. The LCM is $2x(2x-3)$.

$$\frac{1}{2x-3}-\frac{5}{2x}+1$$

$$=\frac{1}{2x-3}\cdot\frac{2x}{2x}-\frac{5}{2x}\cdot\frac{2x-3}{2x-3}+\frac{2x(2x-3)}{2x(2x-3)}$$

$$=\frac{2x-5(2x-3)+4x^2-6x}{2x(2x-3)}$$

$$=\frac{2x-10x+15+4x^2-6x}{2x(2x-3)}$$

$$=\frac{4x^2-14x+15}{2x(2x-3)}$$

68. $5-6x=-(6x-5)$

The LCM is $x(6x-5)$.

$$\frac{5}{x}-\frac{5x}{5-6x}+2$$

$$=\frac{5}{x}\cdot\frac{6x-5}{6x-5}-\frac{(-5x)}{6x-5}\cdot\frac{x}{x}+2\cdot\frac{x(6x-5)}{x(6x-5)}$$

$$=\frac{30x-25+5x^2+2x(6x-5)}{x(6x-5)}$$

$$=\frac{30x-25+5x^2+12x^2-10x}{x(6x-5)}$$

$$=\frac{17x^2+20x-25}{x(6x-5)}$$

69. $x^2-1=(x+1)(x-1)$

$x^2+2x+1=(x+1)^2$

The LCM is $(x-1)(x+1)^2$.

$$\frac{3}{x^2-1}+\frac{2x}{x^2+2x+1}$$

$$=\frac{3}{(x+1)(x-1)}\cdot\frac{x+1}{x+1}+\frac{2x}{(x+1)^2}\cdot\frac{x-1}{x-1}$$

$$=\frac{3x+3+2x^2-2x}{(x+1)^2(x-1)}$$

$$=\frac{2x^2+x+3}{(x-1)(x+1)^2}$$

70. $x^2-6x+9=(x-3)^2$

$x^2-9=(x+3)(x-3)$

The LCM is $(x+3)(x-3)^2$.

$$\frac{1}{x^2-6x+9}-\frac{1}{x^2-9}$$

$$=\frac{1}{(x-3)^2}\cdot\frac{x+3}{x+3}-\frac{1}{(x+3)(x-3)}\cdot\frac{x-3}{x-3}$$

$$=\frac{x+3-(x-3)}{(x+3)(x-3)^2}$$

$$=\frac{x+3-x+3}{(x-3)^2(x+3)}$$

$$=\frac{6}{(x-3)^2(x+3)}$$

71. $x^2-9=(x+3)(x-3)$

The LCM is $(x+3)(x-3)$.

$$\frac{x}{x+3}-\frac{3-x}{x^2-9}=\frac{x}{x+3}\cdot\frac{x-3}{x-3}-\frac{3-x}{(x+3)(x-3)}$$

$$=\frac{x^2-3x-(3-x)}{(x+3)(x-3)}$$

$$=\frac{x^2-3x-3+x}{(x+3)(x-3)}$$

$$=\frac{x^2-2x-3}{(x+3)(x-3)}$$

$$=\frac{(x-3)(x+1)}{(x+3)(x-3)}$$

$$=\frac{(1)(x+1)}{(x+3)(1)}$$

$$=\frac{x+1}{x+3}$$

72. $x^2 + 4x + 4 = (x+2)^2$

The LCM is $(x+2)^2$.

$$\frac{1}{x+2} - \frac{3x}{x^2+4x+4} = \frac{1}{x+2} \cdot \frac{x+2}{x+2} - \frac{3x}{(x+2)^2}$$

$$= \frac{x+2-3x}{(x+2)^2}$$

$$= \frac{-2x+2}{(x+2)^2}$$

$$= -\frac{2x-2}{(x+2)^2}$$

$$= -\frac{2(x-1)}{(x+2)^2}$$

73. $x^2 + 8x + 15 = (x+5)(x+3)$

The LCM is $(x+5)(x+3)$.

$$\frac{2x-3}{x+5} - \frac{x^2-4x-19}{x^2+8x+15}$$

$$= \frac{2x-3}{x+5} \cdot \frac{x+3}{x+3} - \frac{x^2-4x-19}{(x+5)(x+3)}$$

$$= \frac{2x^2+3x-9-(x^2-4x-19)}{(x+3)(x+5)}$$

$$= \frac{2x^2+3x-9-x^2+4x+19}{(x+3)(x+5)}$$

$$= \frac{x^2+7x+10}{(x+3)(x+5)}$$

$$= \frac{(x+2)(x+5)}{(x+3)(x+5)}$$

$$= \frac{(x+2)(1)}{(x+3)(1)}$$

$$= \frac{x+2}{x+3}$$

74. $x^2 + 2x - 8 = (x+4)(x-2)$

The LCM is $(x+4)(x-2)$.

$$\frac{-3x^2+8x+2}{x^2+2x-8} - \frac{2x-5}{x+4}$$

$$= \frac{-3x^2+8x+2}{(x+4)(x-2)} - \frac{2x-5}{x+4} \cdot \frac{x-2}{x-2}$$

$$= \frac{-3x^2+8x+2-(2x-5)(x-2)}{(x+4)(x-2)}$$

$$= \frac{-3x^2+8x+2-(2x^2-9x+10)}{(x+4)(x-2)}$$

$$= \frac{-3x^2+8x+2-2x^2+9x-10}{(x+4)(x-2)}$$

$$= \frac{-5x^2+17x-8}{(x+4)(x-2)}$$

$$= \frac{-(5x^2-17x+8)}{(x+4)(x-2)}$$

$$= -\frac{5x^2-17x+8}{(x+4)(x-2)}$$

75. $x^{2n} - 1 = (x^n+1)(x^n-1)$

The LCM is $(x^n+1)(x^n-1)$.

$$\frac{x^n}{x^{2n}-1} - \frac{2}{x^n+1}$$

$$= \frac{x^n}{(x^n+1)(x^n-1)} - \frac{2}{x^n+1} \cdot \frac{x^n-1}{x^n-1}$$

$$= \frac{x^n-2(x^n-1)}{(x^n+1)(x^n-1)}$$

$$= \frac{x^n-2x^n+2}{(x^n+1)(x^n-1)}$$

$$= \frac{-x^n+2}{(x^n+1)(x^n-1)}$$

$$= \frac{-(x^n-2)}{(x^n+1)(x^n-1)}$$

$$= -\frac{x^n-2}{(x^n+1)(x^n-1)}$$

76. $x^{2n} - 1 = (x^n+1)(x^n-1)$

The LCM is $(x^n+1)(x^n-1)$.

$$\frac{2}{x^n-1} + \frac{x^n}{x^{2n}-1}$$

$$= \frac{2}{x^n-1} \cdot \frac{x^n+1}{x^n+1} + \frac{x^n}{(x^n+1)(x^n-1)}$$

$$= \frac{2x^n+2+x^n}{(x^n+1)(x^n-1)}$$

$$= \frac{3x^n+2}{(x^n+1)(x^n-1)}$$

77. $4x^2 - 9 = (2x+3)(2x-3)$

$3 - 2x = -(2x-3)$

The LCM is $(2x+3)(2x-3)$.

$$\frac{2x-2}{4x^2-9} - \frac{5}{3-2x}$$

$$= \frac{2x-2}{(2x+3)(2x-3)} - \frac{(-5)}{2x-3} \cdot \frac{2x+3}{2x+3}$$

$$= \frac{2x-2+5(2x+3)}{(2x-3)(2x+3)}$$

$$= \frac{2x-2+10x+15}{(2x+3)(2x-3)}$$

$$= \frac{12x+13}{(2x+3)(2x-3)}$$

78. $4x^2 - 36 = 4(x^2 - 9) = 4(x+3)(x-3)$

The LCM is $4(x+3)(x-3)$.

$$\frac{x^2+4}{4x^2-36} - \frac{13}{x+3}$$

$$= \frac{x^2+4}{4(x+3)(x-3)} - \frac{13}{x+3} \cdot \frac{4(x-3)}{4(x-3)}$$

$$= \frac{x^2+4-52(x-3)}{4(x+3)(x-3)}$$

$$= \frac{x^2+4-52x+156}{4(x+3)(x-3)}$$

$$= \frac{x^2-52x+160}{4(x+3)(x-3)}$$

79. $2x^2 - x - 3 = (2x-3)(x+1)$

The LCM is $(2x-3)(x+1)$.

$$\frac{x-2}{x+1} - \frac{3-12x}{2x^2-x-3}$$

$$= \frac{x-2}{x+1} \cdot \frac{2x-3}{2x-3} - \frac{3-12x}{(2x-3)(x+1)}$$

$$= \frac{(x-2)(2x-3)-(3-12x)}{(2x-3)(x+1)}$$

$$= \frac{2x^2-7x+6-3+12x}{(2x-3)(x+1)}$$

$$= \frac{2x^2+5x+3}{(2x-3)(x+1)}$$

$$= \frac{(x+1)(2x+3)}{(2x-3)(x+1)}$$

$$= \frac{2x+3}{2x-3}$$

80. $4x^2 + 9x + 2 = (4x+1)(x+2)$

The LCM is $(4x+1)(x+2)$.

$$\frac{3x-4}{4x+1} + \frac{3x+6}{4x^2+9x+2}$$

$$= \frac{3x-4}{4x+1} \cdot \frac{x+2}{x+2} + \frac{3x+6}{(4x+1)(x+2)}$$

$$= \frac{3x^2+2x-8+3x+6}{(4x+1)(x+2)}$$

$$= \frac{3x^2+5x-2}{(4x+1)(x+2)}$$

$$= \frac{(x+2)(3x-1)}{(x+2)(4x+1)}$$

$$= \frac{3x-1}{4x+1}$$

81. $x^2 + x - 6 = (x+3)(x-2)$

$x^2 + 4x + 3 = (x+3)(x+1)$

The LCM is $(x+3)(x-2)(x+1)$.

$$\frac{x+1}{x^2+x-6} - \frac{x+2}{x^2+4x+3} = \frac{x+1}{(x+3)(x-2)} \cdot \frac{x+1}{x+1} - \frac{x+2}{(x+3)(x+1)} \cdot \frac{x-2}{x-2}$$

$$= \frac{x^2+2x+1-(x^2-4)}{(x+3)(x-2)(x+1)}$$

$$= \frac{x^2+2x+1-x^2+4}{(x+3)(x-2)(x+1)}$$

$$= \frac{2x+5}{(x+3)(x-2)(x+1)}$$

82. $x^2 + x - 12 = (x+4)(x-3)$

$x^2 + 7x + 12 = (x+4)(x+3)$

The LCM is $(x+4)(x-3)(x+3)$.

$$\frac{x+1}{x^2+x-12} - \frac{x-3}{x^2+7x+12} = \frac{x+1}{(x+4)(x-3)} \cdot \frac{x+3}{x+3} - \frac{x-3}{(x+4)(x+3)} \cdot \frac{x-3}{x-3}$$

$$= \frac{x^2+4x+3-(x^2-6x+9)}{(x+4)(x-3)(x+3)}$$

$$= \frac{x^2+4x+3-x^2+6x-9}{(x+4)(x-3)(x+3)}$$

$$= \frac{10x-6}{(x+4)(x-3)(x+3)}$$

83. $2x^2 + 11x + 12 = (2x + 3)(x + 4)$

$2x^2 - 3x - 9 = (2x + 3)(x - 3)$

The LCM is $(x + 4)(2x + 3)(x - 3)$.

$$\frac{x-1}{2x^2+11x+12} + \frac{2x}{2x^2-3x-9} = \frac{x-1}{(2x+3)(x+4)} \cdot \frac{x-3}{x-3} + \frac{2x}{(2x+3)(x-3)} \cdot \frac{x+4}{x+4}$$

$$= \frac{x^2-4x+3+2x^2+8x}{(x+4)(2x+3)(x-3)}$$

$$= \frac{3x^2+4x+3}{(x+4)(2x+3)(x-3)}$$

84. $4x^2 + 4x - 3 = (2x + 3)(2x - 1)$

$6x^2 + x - 2 = (2x - 1)(3x + 2)$

The LCM is $(2x + 3)(2x - 1)(3x + 2)$.

$$\frac{x-2}{4x^2+4x-3} + \frac{3-2x}{6x^2+x-2} = \frac{x-2}{(2x+3)(2x-1)} \cdot \frac{3x+2}{3x+2} + \frac{3-2x}{(2x-1)(3x+2)} \cdot \frac{2x+3}{2x+3}$$

$$= \frac{3x^2-4x-4+9-4x^2}{(2x+3)(2x-1)(3x+2)}$$

$$= \frac{-x^2-4x+5}{(2x+3)(2x-1)(3x+2)}$$

$$= -\frac{x^2+4x-5}{(2x+3)(2x-1)(3x+2)}$$

85. $x^2 + x - 12 = (x + 4)(x - 3)$

The LCM is $(x + 4)(x - 3)$.

$$\frac{x}{x-3} - \frac{2}{x+4} - \frac{14}{x^2+x-12}$$

$$= \frac{x}{x-3} \cdot \frac{x+4}{x+4} - \frac{2}{x+4} \cdot \frac{x-3}{x-3} - \frac{14}{(x+4)(x-3)}$$

$$= \frac{x^2+4x-2x+6-14}{(x+4)(x-3)}$$

$$= \frac{x^2+2x-8}{(x+4)(x-3)}$$

$$= \frac{(x+4)(x-2)}{(x+4)(x-3)}$$

$$= \frac{x-2}{x-3}$$

86. $x^2 + x - 2 = (x + 2)(x - 1)$

The LCM is $(x + 2)(x - 1)$.

$$\frac{x^2}{x^2+x-2} + \frac{3}{x-1} - \frac{4}{x+2}$$

$$= \frac{x^2}{(x+2)(x-1)} + \frac{3}{x-1} \cdot \frac{x+2}{x+2} - \frac{4}{x+2} \cdot \frac{x-1}{x-1}$$

$$= \frac{x^2+3x+6-4(x-1)}{(x+2)(x-1)}$$

$$= \frac{x^2+3x+6-4x+4}{(x+2)(x-1)}$$

$$= \frac{x^2-x+10}{(x+2)(x-1)}$$

87. $x^2 + 3x - 18 = (x + 6)(x - 3)$

$3 - x = -(x - 3)$

The LCM is $(x + 6)(x - 3)$.

$$\frac{x^2+6x}{x^2+3x-18} - \frac{2x-1}{x+6} + \frac{x-2}{3-x}$$

$$= \frac{x^2+6x}{(x+6)(x-3)} - \frac{2x-1}{x+6} \cdot \frac{x-3}{x-3} + \frac{-(x-2)}{x-3} \cdot \frac{x+6}{x+6}$$

$$= \frac{x^2+6x-(2x-1)(x-3)-(x-2)(x+6)}{(x+6)(x-3)}$$

$$= \frac{x^2+6x-2x^2+7x-3-x^2-4x+12}{(x+6)(x-3)}$$

$$= \frac{-2x^2+9x+9}{(x+6)(x-3)}$$

$$= \frac{-(2x^2-9x-9)}{(x+6)(x-3)}$$

$$= -\frac{2x^2-9x-9}{(x+6)(x-3)}$$

88. $x^2 - 2x - 15 = (x - 5)(x + 3)$
$5 - x = -(x - 5)$
The LCM is $(x - 5)(x + 3)$.

$$\frac{2x^2 - 2x}{x^2 - 2x - 15} - \frac{2}{x + 3} + \frac{x}{5 - x}$$

$$= \frac{2x^2 - 2x}{(x - 5)(x + 3)} - \frac{2}{x + 3} \cdot \frac{x - 5}{x - 5} + \frac{-x}{x - 5} \cdot \frac{x + 3}{x + 3}$$

$$= \frac{2x^2 - 2x - 2x + 10 - x^2 - 3x}{(x - 5)(x + 3)}$$

$$= \frac{x^2 - 7x + 10}{(x - 5)(x + 3)}$$

$$= \frac{(x - 5)(x - 2)}{(x - 5)(x + 3)}$$

$$= \frac{x - 2}{x + 3}$$

89. $6x^2 + 11x - 10 = (3x - 2)(2x + 5)$
$2 - 3x = -(3x - 2)$
The LCM is $(3x - 2)(2x + 5)$.

$$\frac{4 - 20x}{6x^2 + 11x - 10} - \frac{4}{2 - 3x} + \frac{x}{2x + 5} = \frac{4 - 20x}{(3x - 2)(2x + 5)} - \frac{(-4)}{3x - 2} \cdot \frac{2x + 5}{2x + 5} + \frac{x}{2x + 5} \cdot \frac{3x - 2}{3x - 2}$$

$$= \frac{4 - 20x + 8x + 20 + 3x^2 - 2x}{(3x - 2)(2x + 5)}$$

$$= \frac{3x^2 - 14x + 24}{(3x - 2)(2x + 5)}$$

90. $8x^2 + 2x - 1 = (2x + 1)(4x - 1)$
The LCM is $(2x + 1)(4x - 1)$.

$$\frac{x}{4x - 1} + \frac{2}{2x + 1} + \frac{6}{8x^2 + 2x - 1} = \frac{x}{4x - 1} \cdot \frac{2x + 1}{2x + 1} + \frac{2}{2x + 1} \cdot \frac{4x - 1}{4x - 1} + \frac{6}{(2x + 1)(4x - 1)}$$

$$= \frac{2x^2 + x + 8x - 2 + 6}{(2x + 1)(4x - 1)}$$

$$= \frac{2x^2 + 9x + 4}{(2x + 1)(4x - 1)}$$

$$= \frac{(2x + 1)(x + 4)}{(2x + 1)(4x - 1)}$$

$$= \frac{x + 4}{4x - 1}$$

91. $x^4 - 1 = (x+1)(x-1)(x^2+1)$
$x^2 - 1 = (x+1)(x-1)$
The LCM is $(x+1)(x-1)(x^2+1)$.

$$\frac{2x^2}{x^4-1} - \frac{1}{x^2-1} + \frac{1}{x^2+1} = \frac{2x^2}{(x+1)(x-1)(x^2+1)} - \frac{1}{(x+1)(x-1)} \cdot \frac{x^2+1}{x^2+1} + \frac{1}{x^2+1} \cdot \frac{(x+1)(x-1)}{(x+1)(x-1)}$$

$$= \frac{2x^2 - (x^2+1) + x^2 - 1}{(x+1)(x-1)(x^2+1)}$$

$$= \frac{2x^2 - x^2 - 1 + x^2 - 1}{(x+1)(x-1)(x^2+1)}$$

$$= \frac{2x^2 - 2}{(x+1)(x-1)(x^2+1)}$$

$$= \frac{2(x^2-1)}{(x+1)(x-1)(x^2+1)}$$

$$= \frac{2(x+1)(x-1)}{(x+1)(x-1)(x^2+1)}$$

$$= \frac{2}{x^2+1}$$

92. $x^4 - 16 = (x^2+4)(x+2)(x-2)$
$x^2 - 4 = (x+2)(x-2)$
The LCM is $(x^2+4)(x+2)(x-2)$.

$$\frac{x^2-12}{x^4-16} + \frac{1}{x^2-4} - \frac{1}{x^2+4} = \frac{x^2-12}{(x^2+4)(x+2)(x-2)} + \frac{1}{(x+2)(x-2)} \cdot \frac{x^2+4}{x^2+4} - \frac{1}{x^2+4} \cdot \frac{(x+2)(x-2)}{(x+2)(x-2)}$$

$$= \frac{x^2-12 + x^2+4 - (x^2-4)}{(x^2+4)(x+2)(x-2)}$$

$$= \frac{x^2-12 + x^2+4 - x^2+4}{(x^2+4)(x+2)(x-2)}$$

$$= \frac{x^2-4}{(x^2+4)(x+2)(x-2)}$$

$$= \frac{(x+2)(x-2)}{(x^2+4)(x+2)(x-2)}$$

$$= \frac{1}{x^2+4}$$

Applying Concepts 6.2

93. $\dfrac{(x+1)^2}{1-2x} \cdot \dfrac{2x-1}{x+1} = \dfrac{(x+1)(x+1)(2x-1)}{(1-2x)(x+1)}$
$\qquad\qquad\qquad\quad = -(x+1)$
$\qquad\qquad\qquad\quad = -x-1$

94. $\left(\dfrac{2m}{3}\right)^2 \div \left(\dfrac{m^2}{6} + \dfrac{m}{2}\right) = \dfrac{2^2 m^2}{3^2} \div \left(\dfrac{m^2}{6} + \dfrac{3m}{6}\right)$

$$= \frac{4m^2}{9} \div \frac{m^2+3m}{6}$$

$$= \frac{4m^2}{9} \cdot \frac{6}{m^2+3m}$$

$$= \frac{4m^2 \cdot 6}{9m(m+3)}$$

$$= \frac{8m}{3(m+3)}$$

95. $\left(\dfrac{y-2}{x^2}\right)^3 \cdot \left(\dfrac{x}{2-y}\right)^2 = \dfrac{(y-2)^3}{x^6} \cdot \dfrac{x^2}{(2-y)^2}$

$\qquad\qquad = \dfrac{(y-2)(y-2)(y-2)x^2}{x^6(2-y)(2-y)}$

$\qquad\qquad = \dfrac{y-2}{x^4}.$

96. $\dfrac{b+3}{b-1} \div \dfrac{b+3}{b-2} \cdot \dfrac{b-1}{b+4} = \dfrac{b+3}{b-1} \cdot \dfrac{b-2}{b+3} \cdot \dfrac{b-1}{b+4}$

$\qquad\qquad = \dfrac{(b+3)(b-2)(b-1)}{(b-1)(b+3)(b+4)}$

$\qquad\qquad = \dfrac{b-2}{b+4}$

97. $\left(\dfrac{y+1}{y-1}\right)^2 - 1 = \left(\dfrac{y+1}{y-1}+1\right)\left(\dfrac{y+1}{y-1}-1\right)$

$\qquad\qquad = \left(\dfrac{y+1}{y-1}+\dfrac{y-1}{y-1}\right)\left(\dfrac{y+1}{y-1}-\dfrac{y-1}{y-1}\right)$

$\qquad\qquad = \left(\dfrac{y+1+y-1}{y-1}\right)\left(\dfrac{y+1-y+1}{y-1}\right)$

$\qquad\qquad = \left(\dfrac{2y}{y-1}\right)\left(\dfrac{2}{y-1}\right)$

$\qquad\qquad = \dfrac{4y}{(y-1)^2}$

98. $\left(\dfrac{1}{3}-\dfrac{2}{a}\right) \div \left(\dfrac{3}{a}-2+\dfrac{a}{4}\right) = \left(\dfrac{a}{3a}-\dfrac{6}{3a}\right) \div \left(\dfrac{12}{4a}-\dfrac{8a}{4a}+\dfrac{a^2}{4a}\right)$

$\qquad\qquad = \left(\dfrac{a-6}{3a}\right) \div \left(\dfrac{12-8a+a^2}{4a}\right)$

$\qquad\qquad = \dfrac{a-6}{3a} \cdot \dfrac{4a}{a^2-8a+12}$

$\qquad\qquad = \dfrac{(a-6)4a}{3a(a-2)(a-6)}$

$\qquad\qquad = \dfrac{4}{3(a-2)}$

99. $\dfrac{3x^2+6x}{4x^2-16} \cdot \dfrac{2x+8}{x^2+2x} \div \dfrac{3x-9}{5x-20} = \dfrac{3x^2+6x}{4x^2-16} \cdot \dfrac{2x+8}{x^2+2x} \cdot \dfrac{5x-20}{3x-9}$

$\qquad\qquad = \dfrac{3x(x+2) \cdot 2(x+4) \cdot 5(x-4)}{4(x+2)(x-2) \cdot x(x+2) \cdot 3(x-3)}$

$\qquad\qquad = \dfrac{5(x+4)(x-4)}{2(x+2)(x-2)(x-3)}$

100. $\dfrac{5y^2-20}{3y^2-12y} \cdot \dfrac{9y^3+6y^2}{2y^2-4y} \div \dfrac{y^3+2y^2}{2y^2-8y} = \dfrac{5y^2-20}{3y^2-12y} \cdot \dfrac{9y^3+6y^2}{2y^2-4y} \cdot \dfrac{2y^2-8y}{y^3+2y^2}$

$\qquad\qquad = \dfrac{5(y+2)(y-2) \cdot 3y^2(3y+2) \cdot 2y(y-4)}{3y(y-4) \cdot 2y(y-2) \cdot y^2(y+2)}$

$\qquad\qquad = \dfrac{5(3y+2)}{y}$

101. $\dfrac{a^2+a-6}{4+11a-3a^2}\cdot\dfrac{15a^2-a-2}{4a^2+7a-2}\div\dfrac{6a^2-7a-3}{4-17a+4a^2}=\dfrac{a^2+a-6}{4+11a-3a^2}\cdot\dfrac{15a^2-a-2}{4a^2+7a-2}\cdot\dfrac{4-17a+4a^2}{6a^2-7a-3}$

$$=\dfrac{(a+3)(a-2)(5a-2)(3a+1)(4-a)(1-4a)}{(4-a)(1+3a)(4a-1)(a+2)(3a+1)(2a-3)}$$

$$=-\dfrac{(a+3)(a-2)(5a-2)}{(a+2)(3a+1)(2a-3)}$$

102. $\dfrac{25x-x^3}{x^4-1}\cdot\dfrac{3-x-4x^2}{2x^2+7x-15}\div\dfrac{4x^3-23x^2+15x}{3-5x+2x^2}=\dfrac{25x-x^3}{x^4-1}\cdot\dfrac{3-x-4x^2}{2x^2+7x-15}\cdot\dfrac{3-5x+2x^2}{4x^3-23x^2+15x}$

$$=\dfrac{x(5-x)(5+x)(3-4x)(1+x)(3-2x)(1-x)}{(x^2+1)(x-1)(x+1)(2x-3)(x+5)\cdot x(4x-3)(x-5)}$$

$$=\dfrac{1}{x^2+1}$$

103. $\left(\dfrac{x+1}{2x-1}-\dfrac{x-1}{2x+1}\right)\cdot\left(\dfrac{2x-1}{x}-\dfrac{2x-1}{x^2}\right)$

$$=\left[\dfrac{(x+1)(2x+1)}{(2x-1)(2x+1)}-\dfrac{(x-1)(2x-1)}{(2x+1)(2x-1)}\right]\cdot\left[\dfrac{x(2x-1)}{x^2}-\dfrac{2x-1}{x^2}\right]$$

$$=\dfrac{2x^2+3x+1-(2x^2-3x+1)}{(2x-1)(2x+1)}\cdot\dfrac{2x^2-x-(2x-1)}{x^2}$$

$$=\dfrac{6x}{(2x-1)(2x+1)}\cdot\dfrac{2x^2-3x+1}{x^2}$$

$$=\dfrac{6x(2x-1)(x-1)}{x^2(2x-1)(2x+1)}$$

$$=\dfrac{6(x-1)}{x(2x+1)}$$

104. $\left(\dfrac{y-2}{3y+1}-\dfrac{y+2}{3y-1}\right)\cdot\left(\dfrac{3y+1}{y}-\dfrac{3y-1}{y^2}\right)$

$$=\left[\dfrac{(y-2)(3y-1)}{(3y+1)(3y-1)}-\dfrac{(y+2)(3y+1)}{(3y-1)(3y+1)}\right]\cdot\left[\dfrac{y(3y+1)}{y^2}-\dfrac{3y-1}{y^2}\right]$$

$$=\dfrac{3y^2-7y+2-(3y^2+7y+2)}{(3y+1)(3y-1)}\cdot\dfrac{3y^2+y-(3y-1)}{y^2}$$

$$=\dfrac{-14y}{(3y+1)(3y-1)}\cdot\dfrac{3y^2-2y+1}{y^2}$$

$$=\dfrac{-14y(3y^2-2y+1)}{y^2(3y+1)(3y-1)}$$

$$=-\dfrac{14(3y^2-2y+1)}{y(3y+1)(3y-1)}$$

105. $\dfrac{1}{3}+\dfrac{1}{5}\neq\dfrac{1}{3+5}$

$\dfrac{5}{15}+\dfrac{3}{15}\neq\dfrac{1}{8}$

$\dfrac{8}{15}\neq\dfrac{1}{8}$

106. $\dfrac{1}{3}-\dfrac{1}{5}\neq\dfrac{1}{3-5}$

$\dfrac{5}{15}-\dfrac{3}{15}\neq\dfrac{1}{-2}$

$\dfrac{2}{15}\neq-\dfrac{1}{2}$

107. $\dfrac{3x+6y}{xy}=\dfrac{3x}{xy}+\dfrac{6y}{xy}=\dfrac{3}{y}+\dfrac{6}{x}$

108. $\dfrac{5a+8b}{ab}=\dfrac{5a}{ab}+\dfrac{8b}{ab}=\dfrac{5}{b}+\dfrac{8}{a}$

109. $\dfrac{4a^2+3ab}{a^2b^2}=\dfrac{4a^2}{a^2b^2}+\dfrac{3ab}{a^2b^2}=\dfrac{4}{b^2}+\dfrac{3}{ab}$

110. **a.** $2\pi r^2 + \dfrac{710}{r} = \dfrac{2\pi r^3 + 710}{r}$

b.

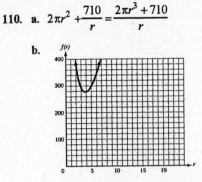

c. The point whose coordinates are (7, 409) means that when the radius of the can is 7 cm, the surface area of the can is 409 cm^3.

d. The radius of the can that has a minimum surface area is approximately 3.8 cm.

e. $h = \dfrac{355}{\pi r^2}$

$h = \dfrac{355}{\pi(3.8)^2} \approx 7.8$

The height of the can that has a minimum surface area is 7.8 cm.

f. $f(r) = 2\pi r^2 + \dfrac{710}{r}$

$f(3.8) = 2\pi(3.8)^2 + \dfrac{710}{3.8} \approx 277.6$

The minimum surface area is 277.6 cm^3.

111. **a.** $2x^2 + \dfrac{528}{x} = \dfrac{2x^3 + 528}{x}$

b.

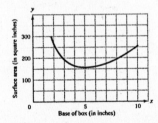

c. The point whose coordinates are (4, 164) means that when the base of the box is 4 in., 164 in^2 of cardboard will be needed.

d. The base of the box that uses the minimum amount of cardboard is 5.1 in.

e. $f(x) = 2x^2 + \dfrac{528}{x}$

$f(5.1) = 2(5.1)^2 + \dfrac{528}{5.1} \approx 155.5$ in^2

112. An advantage of using the LCM of the denominators is that unnecessary operations are avoided. A disadvantage of using the LCM is that it is necessary to determine it.

113. When fractions are incorrectly added as in the inaccurate calculation $\dfrac{1}{5} + \dfrac{2}{3} = \dfrac{1+2}{5+3} = \dfrac{3}{8}$, the incorrect sum is always between the two fractions being added. Here is proof based on a, b, c, and d being positive real numbers. Assume $\dfrac{a}{b} < \dfrac{c}{d}$.

Then $ad < bc$. Now consider $\dfrac{a+c}{b+d}$.

$\dfrac{a+c}{b+d} = \dfrac{a+c}{b+d} \cdot \dfrac{d}{d} = \dfrac{ad+cd}{bd+d^2}$
$< \dfrac{bc+cd}{bd+d^2} = \dfrac{c(b+d)}{d(b+d)} = \dfrac{c}{d}$

Therefore, $\dfrac{a+c}{b+c} < \dfrac{c}{d}$.

$\dfrac{a+c}{b+d} = \dfrac{a+c}{b+d} \cdot \dfrac{a}{a} = \dfrac{a^2+ac}{ab+ad}$
$> \dfrac{a^2+ac}{ab+bc} = \dfrac{a(a+c)}{b(a+c)} = \dfrac{a}{b}$

Therefore, $\dfrac{a+c}{b+d} > \dfrac{a}{b}$.

Section 6.3

Concept Review 6.3

1. Sometimes true
The numerator of a complex fraction may contain a number, a variable, a fraction, or more than one fraction.

2. Always true

3. Always true

4. Never true
$$\dfrac{c^{-1}}{a^{-1} + b^{-1}} = \dfrac{\frac{1}{c}}{\frac{1}{a} + \frac{1}{b}} = \dfrac{\frac{1}{c}}{\frac{b+a}{ab}} = \dfrac{ab}{c(b+a)}$$

Objective 6.3.1 Exercises

1. A complex fraction is a fraction whose numerator or denominator contains one or more fractions.

2. The general goal is to have no fractions in the numerator or denominator. The resulting fraction is then written in simplest form.

3. The LCM is 3.
$$\dfrac{2 - \frac{1}{3}}{4 + \frac{11}{3}} = \dfrac{2 - \frac{1}{3}}{4 + \frac{11}{3}} \cdot \dfrac{3}{3} = \dfrac{2 \cdot 3 - \frac{1}{3} \cdot 3}{4 \cdot 3 + \frac{11}{3} \cdot 3} = \dfrac{6-1}{12+11} = \dfrac{5}{23}$$

4. The LCM is 2.
$$\dfrac{3 + \frac{5}{2}}{8 - \frac{7}{2}} = \dfrac{3 + \frac{5}{2}}{8 - \frac{7}{2}} \cdot \dfrac{2}{2} = \dfrac{3 \cdot 2 + \frac{5}{2} \cdot 2}{8 \cdot 2 - \frac{7}{2} \cdot 2} = \dfrac{6+5}{16-7} = \dfrac{11}{9}$$

5. The LCM is 6.
$$\dfrac{3 - \frac{2}{3}}{5 + \frac{5}{6}} = \dfrac{3 - \frac{2}{3}}{5 + \frac{5}{6}} \cdot \dfrac{6}{6} = \dfrac{3 \cdot 6 - \frac{2}{3} \cdot 6}{5 \cdot 6 + \frac{5}{6} \cdot 6} = \dfrac{18-4}{30+5} = \dfrac{14}{35} = \dfrac{2}{5}$$

6. The LCM of x and x^2 is x^2.

$$\frac{1+\frac{1}{x}}{1-\frac{1}{x^2}} = \frac{1+\frac{1}{x}}{1-\frac{1}{x^2}} \cdot \frac{x^2}{x^2}$$

$$= \frac{1 \cdot x^2 + \frac{1}{x} \cdot x^2}{1 \cdot x^2 - \frac{1}{x^2} \cdot x^2}$$

$$= \frac{x^2 + x}{x^2 - 1}$$

$$= \frac{x(x+1)}{(x+1)(x-1)}$$

$$= \frac{x}{x-1}$$

7. The LCM of y^2 and y is y^2.

$$\frac{\frac{1}{y^2}-1}{1+\frac{1}{y}} = \frac{\frac{1}{y^2}-1}{1+\frac{1}{y}} \cdot \frac{y^2}{y^2}$$

$$= \frac{\frac{1}{y^2} \cdot y^2 - 1 \cdot y^2}{1 \cdot y^2 + \frac{1}{y} \cdot y^2}$$

$$= \frac{1-y^2}{y^2 + y}$$

$$= \frac{(1+y)(1-y)}{y(y+1)}$$

$$= \frac{1-y}{y}$$

8. The LCM is a.

$$\frac{a-2}{\frac{4}{a}-a} = \frac{a-2}{\frac{4}{a}-a} \cdot \frac{a}{a}$$

$$= \frac{a \cdot a - 2 \cdot a}{\frac{4}{a} \cdot a - a \cdot a}$$

$$= \frac{a^2 - 2a}{4 - a^2}$$

$$= \frac{a(a-2)}{(2+a)(2-a)}$$

$$= -\frac{a}{a+2}$$

9. The LCM is a.

$$\frac{\frac{25}{a}-a}{5+a} = \frac{\frac{25}{a}-a}{5+a} \cdot \frac{a}{a}$$

$$= \frac{\frac{25}{a} \cdot a - a \cdot a}{5 \cdot a + a \cdot a}$$

$$= \frac{25 - a^2}{5a + a^2}$$

$$= \frac{(5+a)(5-a)}{a(5+a)}$$

$$= \frac{5-a}{a}$$

10. The LCM is a^2 and a is a^2.

$$\frac{\frac{1}{a^2}-\frac{1}{a}}{\frac{1}{a^2}+\frac{1}{a}} = \frac{\frac{1}{a^2}-\frac{1}{a}}{\frac{1}{a^2}+\frac{1}{a}} \cdot \frac{a^2}{a^2}$$

$$= \frac{\frac{1}{a^2} \cdot a^2 - \frac{1}{a} \cdot a^2}{\frac{1}{a^2} \cdot a^2 + \frac{1}{a} \cdot a^2}$$

$$= \frac{1-a}{1+a}$$

$$= \frac{-(a-1)}{a+1}$$

$$= -\frac{a-1}{a+1}$$

11. The LCM of b, 2, and b^2 is $2b^2$.

$$\frac{\frac{1}{b}+\frac{1}{2}}{\frac{4}{b^2}-1} = \frac{\frac{1}{b}+\frac{1}{2}}{\frac{4}{b^2}-1} \cdot \frac{2b^2}{2b^2}$$

$$= \frac{\frac{1}{b} \cdot 2b^2 + \frac{1}{2} \cdot 2b^2}{\frac{4}{b^2} \cdot 2b^2 - 1 \cdot 2b^2}$$

$$= \frac{2b + b^2}{8 - 2b^2}$$

$$= \frac{b(2+b)}{2(4-b^2)}$$

$$= \frac{b(2+b)}{2(2+b)(2-b)}$$

$$= \frac{b}{2(2-b)}$$

12. The LCM is $x+2$.

$$\frac{2-\frac{4}{x+2}}{5-\frac{10}{x+2}} = \frac{2-\frac{4}{x+2}}{5-\frac{10}{x+2}} \cdot \frac{x+2}{x+2}$$

$$= \frac{2(x+2) - \frac{4}{x+2} \cdot (x+2)}{5(x+2) - \frac{10}{x+2} \cdot (x+2)}$$

$$= \frac{2x+4-4}{5x+10-10}$$

$$= \frac{2x}{5x}$$

$$= \frac{2}{5}$$

13. The LCM is $2x-3$.

$$\frac{4+\frac{12}{2x-3}}{5+\frac{15}{2x-3}} = \frac{4+\frac{12}{2x-3}}{5+\frac{15}{2x-3}} \cdot \frac{2x-3}{2x-3}$$

$$= \frac{4(2x-3) + \frac{12}{2x-3}(2x-3)}{5(2x-3) + \frac{15}{2x-3}(2x-3)}$$

$$= \frac{8x-12+12}{10x-15+15}$$

$$= \frac{8x}{10x}$$

$$= \frac{4}{5}$$

14. The LCM is $2a - 3$.

$$\frac{\frac{3}{2a-3}+2}{\frac{-6}{2a-3}-4} = \frac{\frac{3}{2a-3}+2}{\frac{-6}{2a-3}-4} \cdot \frac{2a-3}{2a-3}$$

$$= \frac{\frac{3}{2a-3}\cdot(2a-3)+2(2a-3)}{\frac{-6}{2a-3}\cdot(2a-3)-4(2a-3)}$$

$$= \frac{3+4a-6}{-6-8a+12}$$

$$= \frac{4a-3}{-8a+6}$$

$$= \frac{4a-3}{-2(4a-3)}$$

$$= -\frac{1}{2}$$

15. The LCM is $b - 5$.

$$\frac{\frac{-5}{b-5}-3}{\frac{10}{b-5}+6} = \frac{\frac{-5}{b-5}-3}{\frac{10}{b-5}+6} \cdot \frac{b-5}{b-5}$$

$$= \frac{\frac{-5}{b-5}\cdot(b-5)-3(b-5)}{\frac{10}{b-5}\cdot(b-5)+6(b-5)}$$

$$= \frac{-5-3b+15}{10+6b-30}$$

$$= \frac{-3b+10}{6b-20}$$

$$= \frac{-3b+10}{2(3b-10)}$$

$$= -\frac{1}{2}$$

16. The LCM of x and $x + 1$ is $x(x+1)$.

$$\frac{\frac{x}{x+1}-\frac{1}{x}}{\frac{x}{x+1}+\frac{1}{x}} = \frac{\frac{x}{x+1}-\frac{1}{x}}{\frac{x}{x+1}+\frac{1}{x}} \cdot \frac{x(x+1)}{x(x+1)}$$

$$= \frac{\frac{x}{x+1}\cdot x(x+1)-\frac{1}{x}\cdot x(x+1)}{\frac{x}{x+1}\cdot x(x+1)+\frac{1}{x}\cdot x(x+1)}$$

$$= \frac{x^2-(x+1)}{x^2+(x+1)}$$

$$= \frac{x^2-x-1}{x^2+x+1}$$

17. The LCM of $a - 1$ and a is $a(a-1)$.

$$\frac{\frac{2a}{a-1}-\frac{3}{a}}{\frac{1}{a-1}+\frac{2}{a}} = \frac{\frac{2a}{a-1}-\frac{3}{a}}{\frac{1}{a-1}+\frac{2}{a}} \cdot \frac{a(a-1)}{a(a-1)}$$

$$= \frac{\frac{2a}{a-1}\cdot a(a-1)-\frac{3}{a}\cdot a(a-1)}{\frac{1}{a-1}\cdot a(a-1)+\frac{2}{a}\cdot a(a-1)}$$

$$= \frac{2a^2-3(a-1)}{a+2(a-1)}$$

$$= \frac{2a^2-3a+3}{a+2a-2}$$

$$= \frac{2a^2-3a+3}{3a-2}$$

18. The LCM of x and x^2 is x^2.

$$\frac{\frac{3}{x}}{\frac{9}{x^2}} = \frac{\frac{3}{x}}{\frac{9}{x^2}} \cdot \frac{x^2}{x^2} = \frac{3x}{9} = \frac{x}{3}$$

19. The LCM of $3x - 2$ and $9x^2 - 4$ is $(3x+2)(3x-2)$.

$$\frac{\frac{x}{3x-2}}{\frac{x}{9x^2-4}} = \frac{\frac{x}{3x-2}}{\frac{x}{(3x+2)(3x-2)}}$$

$$= \frac{\frac{x}{3x-2}}{\frac{x}{(3x+2)(3x-2)}} \cdot \frac{(3x+2)(3x-2)}{(3x+2)(3x-2)}$$

$$= \frac{x(3x+2)}{x}$$

$$= 3x+2$$

20. The LCM of $4a^2b$ and $16ab^2$ is $16a^2b^2$.

$$\frac{\frac{a^2-b^2}{4a^2b}}{\frac{a+b}{16ab^2}} = \frac{\frac{(a+b)(a-b)}{4a^2b}}{\frac{a+b}{16ab^2}}$$

$$= \frac{\frac{(a+b)(a-b)}{4a^2b}}{\frac{a+b}{16ab^2}} \cdot \frac{16a^2b^2}{16a^2b^2}$$

$$= \frac{(a+b)(a-b)4b}{(a+b)a}$$

$$= \frac{4b(a-b)}{a}$$

21. The LCM of x and x^2 is x^2.

$$\frac{1-\frac{1}{x}-\frac{6}{x^2}}{1-\frac{4}{x}+\frac{3}{x^2}} = \frac{1-\frac{1}{x}-\frac{6}{x^2}}{1-\frac{4}{x}+\frac{3}{x^2}} \cdot \frac{x^2}{x^2}$$

$$= \frac{1\cdot x^2-\frac{1}{x}\cdot x^2-\frac{6}{x^2}\cdot x^2}{1\cdot x^2-\frac{4}{x}\cdot x^2+\frac{3}{x^2}\cdot x^2}$$

$$= \frac{x^2-x-6}{x^2-4x+3}$$

$$= \frac{(x+2)(x-3)}{(x-1)(x-3)}$$

$$= \frac{x+2}{x-1}$$

22. The LCM of x and x^2 is x^2.

$$\frac{1-\frac{3}{x}-\frac{10}{x^2}}{1+\frac{11}{x}+\frac{18}{x^2}} = \frac{1-\frac{3}{x}-\frac{10}{x^2}}{1+\frac{11}{x}+\frac{18}{x^2}} \cdot \frac{x^2}{x^2}$$

$$= \frac{1\cdot x^2-\frac{3}{x}\cdot x^2-\frac{10}{x^2}\cdot x^2}{1\cdot x^2+\frac{11}{x}\cdot x^2+\frac{18}{x^2}\cdot x^2}$$

$$= \frac{x^2-3x-10}{x^2+11x+18}$$

$$= \frac{(x+2)(x-5)}{(x+2)(x+9)}$$

$$= \frac{x-5}{x+9}$$

23. The LCM of x^2 and x is x^2.

$$\frac{\frac{15}{x^2}-\frac{2}{x}-1}{\frac{4}{x^2}-\frac{5}{x}+4}=\frac{\frac{15}{x^2}-\frac{2}{x}-1}{\frac{4}{x^2}-\frac{5}{x}+4}\cdot\frac{x^2}{x^2}$$

$$=\frac{\frac{15}{x^2}\cdot x^2-\frac{2}{x}\cdot x^2-1\cdot x^2}{\frac{4}{x^2}\cdot x^2-\frac{5}{x}\cdot x^2+4\cdot x^2}$$

$$=\frac{15-2x-x^2}{4-5x+4x^2}$$

$$=-\frac{(x-3)(x+5)}{4x^2-5x+4}$$

24. The LCM is $3x-4$.

$$\frac{1-\frac{2x}{3x-4}}{x-\frac{32}{3x-4}}=\frac{1-\frac{2x}{3x-4}}{x-\frac{32}{3x-4}}\cdot\frac{3x-4}{3x-4}$$

$$=\frac{1\cdot(3x-4)-\frac{2x}{3x-4}\cdot(3x-4)}{x(3x-4)-\frac{32}{3x-4}\cdot(3x-4)}$$

$$=\frac{3x-4-2x}{3x^2-4x-32}$$

$$=\frac{x-4}{(3x+8)(x-4)}$$

$$=\frac{1}{3x+8}$$

25. The LCM is $3x+10$.

$$\frac{1-\frac{12}{3x+10}}{x-\frac{8}{3x+10}}=\frac{1-\frac{12}{3x+10}}{x-\frac{8}{3x+10}}\cdot\frac{3x+10}{3x+10}$$

$$=\frac{1\cdot(3x+10)-\frac{12}{3x+10}\cdot(3x+10)}{x(3x+10)-\frac{8}{3x+10}\cdot(3x+10)}$$

$$=\frac{3x+10-12}{3x^2+10x-8}$$

$$=\frac{3x-2}{(x+4)(3x-2)}$$

$$=\frac{1}{x+4}$$

26. The LCM is $x-4$.

$$\frac{x-1+\frac{2}{x-4}}{x+3+\frac{6}{x-4}}=\frac{x-1+\frac{2}{x-4}}{x+3+\frac{6}{x-4}}\cdot\frac{x-4}{x-4}$$

$$=\frac{(x-1)(x-4)+\frac{2}{x-4}\cdot(x-4)}{(x+3)(x-4)+\frac{6}{x-4}\cdot(x-4)}$$

$$=\frac{x^2-5x+4+2}{x^2-x-12+6}$$

$$=\frac{x^2-5x+6}{x^2-x-6}$$

$$=\frac{(x-2)(x-3)}{(x+2)(x-3)}$$

$$=\frac{x-2}{x+2}$$

27. The LCM is $x+2$.

$$\frac{x-5-\frac{18}{x+2}}{x+7+\frac{6}{x+2}}=\frac{x-5-\frac{18}{x+2}}{x+7+\frac{6}{x+2}}\cdot\frac{x+2}{x+2}$$

$$=\frac{(x-5)(x+2)-\frac{18}{x+2}\cdot(x+2)}{(x+7)(x+2)+\frac{6}{x+2}\cdot(x+2)}$$

$$=\frac{x^2-3x-10-18}{x^2+9x+14+6}$$

$$=\frac{x^2-3x-28}{x^2+9x+20}$$

$$=\frac{(x+4)(x-7)}{(x+4)(x+5)}$$

$$=\frac{x-7}{x+5}$$

28. The LCM is $2x+3$.

$$\frac{x-4+\frac{9}{2x+3}}{x+3-\frac{5}{2x+3}}=\frac{x-4+\frac{9}{2x+3}}{x+3-\frac{5}{2x+3}}\cdot\frac{2x+3}{2x+3}$$

$$=\frac{(x-4)(2x+3)+\frac{9}{2x+3}\cdot(2x+3)}{(x+3)(2x+3)-\frac{5}{2x+3}\cdot(2x+3)}$$

$$=\frac{2x^2-5x-12+9}{2x^2+9x+9-5}$$

$$=\frac{2x^2-5x-3}{2x^2+9x+4}$$

$$=\frac{(2x+1)(x-3)}{(2x+1)(x+4)}$$

$$=\frac{x-3}{x+4}$$

29. The LCM is $a(a-2)$.

$$\frac{\frac{1}{a}-\frac{3}{a-2}}{\frac{2}{a}+\frac{5}{a-2}}=\frac{\frac{1}{a}-\frac{3}{a-2}}{\frac{2}{a}+\frac{5}{a-2}}\cdot\frac{a(a-2)}{a(a-2)}$$

$$=\frac{\frac{1}{a}\cdot a(a-2)-\frac{3}{a-2}\cdot a(a-2)}{\frac{2}{a}\cdot a(a-2)+\frac{5}{a-2}\cdot a(a-2)}$$

$$=\frac{a-2-3a}{2a-4+5a}$$

$$=\frac{-2a-2}{7a-4}$$

$$=\frac{-(2a+2)}{7a-4}$$

$$=-\frac{2a+2}{7a-4}$$

$$=-\frac{2(a+1)}{7a-4}$$

30. The LCM is $b(b+3)$.

$$\dfrac{\frac{2}{b}-\frac{5}{b+3}}{\frac{3}{b}+\frac{3}{b+3}}=\dfrac{\frac{2}{b}-\frac{5}{b+3}}{\frac{3}{b}+\frac{3}{b+3}}\cdot\dfrac{b(b+3)}{b(b+3)}$$

$$=\dfrac{\frac{2}{b}\cdot b(b+3)-\frac{5}{b+3}\cdot b(b+3)}{\frac{3}{b}\cdot b(b+3)+\frac{3}{b+3}\cdot b(b+3)}$$

$$=\dfrac{2b+6-5b}{3b+9+3b}$$

$$=\dfrac{-3b+6}{6b+9}$$

$$=\dfrac{-3(b-2)}{3(2b+3)}$$

$$=-\dfrac{b-2}{2b+3}$$

31. The LCM of y^2, xy, and x^2 is x^2y^2.

$$\dfrac{\frac{1}{y^2}-\frac{1}{xy}-\frac{2}{x^2}}{\frac{1}{y^2}-\frac{3}{xy}+\frac{2}{x^2}}=\dfrac{\frac{1}{y^2}-\frac{1}{xy}-\frac{2}{x^2}}{\frac{1}{y^2}-\frac{3}{xy}+\frac{2}{x^2}}\cdot\dfrac{x^2y^2}{x^2y^2}$$

$$=\dfrac{\frac{1}{y^2}\cdot x^2y^2-\frac{1}{xy}\cdot x^2y^2-\frac{2}{x^2}\cdot x^2y^2}{\frac{1}{y^2}\cdot x^2y^2-\frac{3}{xy}\cdot x^2y^2+\frac{2}{x^2}\cdot x^2y^2}$$

$$=\dfrac{x^2-xy-2y^2}{x^2-3xy+2y^2}$$

$$=\dfrac{(x+y)(x-2y)}{(x-y)(x-2y)}$$

$$=\dfrac{x+y}{x-y}$$

32. The LCM of b^2, ab, and a^2 is a^2b^2.

$$\dfrac{\frac{2}{b^2}-\frac{5}{ab}-\frac{3}{a^2}}{\frac{2}{b^2}+\frac{7}{ab}+\frac{3}{a^2}}=\dfrac{\frac{2}{b^2}-\frac{5}{ab}-\frac{3}{a^2}}{\frac{2}{b^2}+\frac{7}{ab}+\frac{3}{a^2}}\cdot\dfrac{a^2b^2}{a^2b^2}$$

$$=\dfrac{\frac{2}{b^2}\cdot a^2b^2-\frac{5}{ab}\cdot a^2b^2-\frac{3}{a^2}\cdot a^2b^2}{\frac{2}{b^2}\cdot a^2b^2+\frac{7}{ab}\cdot a^2b^2+\frac{3}{a^2}\cdot a^2b^2}$$

$$=\dfrac{2a^2-5ab-3b^2}{2a^2+7ab+3b^2}$$

$$=\dfrac{(2a+b)(a-3b)}{(2a+b)(a+3b)}$$

$$=\dfrac{a-3b}{a+3b}$$

33. The LCM is $(x+1)(x-1)$.

$$\dfrac{\frac{x-1}{x+1}-\frac{x+1}{x-1}}{\frac{x-1}{x+1}+\frac{x+1}{x-1}}$$

$$=\dfrac{\frac{x-1}{x+1}-\frac{x+1}{x-1}}{\frac{x-1}{x+1}+\frac{x+1}{x-1}}\cdot\dfrac{(x+1)(x-1)}{(x+1)(x-1)}$$

$$=\dfrac{\frac{x-1}{x+1}\cdot(x+1)(x-1)-\frac{x+1}{x-1}\cdot(x+1)(x-1)}{\frac{x-1}{x+1}\cdot(x+1)(x-1)+\frac{x+1}{x-1}\cdot(x+1)(x-1)}$$

$$=\dfrac{(x-1)(x-1)-(x+1)(x+1)}{(x-1)(x-1)+(x+1)(x+1)}$$

$$=\dfrac{x^2-2x+1-(x^2+2x+1)}{x^2-2x+1+x^2+2x+1}$$

$$=\dfrac{x^2-2x+1-x^2-2x-1}{2x^2+2}$$

$$=\dfrac{-4x}{2(x^2+1)}$$

$$=-\dfrac{2x}{x^2+1}$$

34. The LCM is $(y+2)(y-2)$.

$$\dfrac{\frac{y}{y+2}-\frac{y}{y-2}}{\frac{y}{y+2}+\frac{y}{y-2}}$$

$$=\dfrac{\frac{y}{y+2}-\frac{y}{y-2}}{\frac{y}{y+2}+\frac{y}{y-2}}\cdot\dfrac{(y+2)(y-2)}{(y+2)(y-2)}$$

$$=\dfrac{\frac{y}{y+2}\cdot(y+2)(y-2)-\frac{y}{y-2}\cdot(y+2)(y-2)}{\frac{y}{y+2}\cdot(y+2)(y-2)+\frac{y}{y-2}\cdot(y+2)(y-2)}$$

$$=\dfrac{y(y-2)-y(y+2)}{y(y-2)+y(y+2)}$$

$$=\dfrac{y^2-2y-y^2-2y}{y^2-2y+y^2+2y}$$

$$=\dfrac{-4y}{2y^2}$$

$$=-\dfrac{2}{y}$$

35. The LCM is x.

$$4-\dfrac{2}{2-\frac{3}{x}}=4-\dfrac{2}{2-\frac{3}{x}}\cdot\dfrac{x}{x}$$

$$=4-\dfrac{2\cdot x}{2\cdot x-\frac{3}{x}\cdot x}$$

$$=4-\dfrac{2x}{2x-3}$$

The LCM is $2x-3$.

$$4-\dfrac{2x}{2x-3}=4\cdot\dfrac{2x-3}{2x-3}-\dfrac{2x}{2x-3}$$

$$=\dfrac{4(2x-3)-2x}{2x-3}$$

$$=\dfrac{8x-12-2x}{2x-3}$$

$$=\dfrac{6x-12}{2x-3}$$

$$=\dfrac{6(x-2)}{2x-3}$$

Applying Concepts 6.3

36. $\dfrac{x^{-1}+y^{-1}}{x^{-1}-y^{-1}} = \dfrac{\frac{1}{x}+\frac{1}{y}}{\frac{1}{x}-\frac{1}{y}}$

The LCM is xy.

$\dfrac{\frac{1}{x}+\frac{1}{y}}{\frac{1}{x}-\frac{1}{y}} \cdot \dfrac{xy}{xy} = \dfrac{y+x}{y-x}$

37. $\dfrac{x^{-1}}{y^{-1}}+\dfrac{y}{x} = \dfrac{\frac{1}{x}}{\frac{1}{y}}+\dfrac{y}{x}$

$= \dfrac{\frac{1}{x}}{\frac{1}{y}} \cdot \dfrac{xy}{xy}+\dfrac{y}{x}$

$= \dfrac{y}{x}+\dfrac{y}{x}$

$= \dfrac{y+y}{x}$

$= \dfrac{2y}{x}$

38. $\dfrac{x^{-1}+y}{x^{-1}-y} = \dfrac{\frac{1}{x}+y}{\frac{1}{x}-y} = \dfrac{\frac{1}{x}+y}{\frac{1}{x}-y} \cdot \dfrac{x}{x} = \dfrac{1+xy}{1-xy}$

39. $\dfrac{x-\frac{1}{x}}{1+\frac{1}{x}} = \dfrac{x-\frac{1}{x}}{1+\frac{1}{x}} \cdot \dfrac{x}{x}$

$= \dfrac{x \cdot x - \frac{1}{x} \cdot x}{1 \cdot x + \frac{1}{x} \cdot x}$

$= \dfrac{x^2-1}{x+1}$

$= \dfrac{(x+1)(x-1)}{x+1}$

$= x-1$

40. $1-\dfrac{1}{1-\frac{1}{b-2}} = 1-\dfrac{1}{1-\frac{1}{b-2}} \cdot \dfrac{b-2}{b-2}$

$= 1-\dfrac{1(b-2)}{1(b-2)-1}$

$= 1-\dfrac{b-2}{b-2-1}$

$= 1-\dfrac{b-2}{b-3}$

$= \dfrac{b-3}{b-3}-\dfrac{b-2}{b-3}$

$= \dfrac{b-3-(b-2)}{b-3}$

$= \dfrac{-1}{b-3}$

$= -\dfrac{1}{b-3}$

$= \dfrac{1}{3-b}$

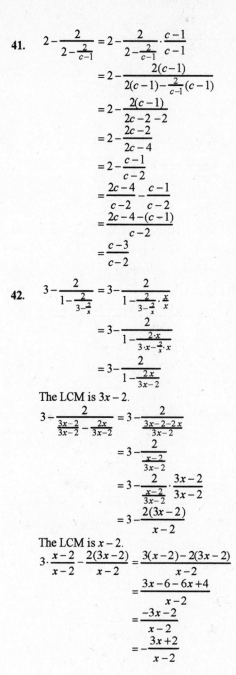

41. $2-\dfrac{2}{2-\frac{2}{c-1}} = 2-\dfrac{2}{2-\frac{2}{c-1}} \cdot \dfrac{c-1}{c-1}$

$= 2-\dfrac{2(c-1)}{2(c-1)-\frac{2}{c-1}(c-1)}$

$= 2-\dfrac{2(c-1)}{2c-2-2}$

$= 2-\dfrac{2c-2}{2c-4}$

$= 2-\dfrac{c-1}{c-2}$

$= \dfrac{2c-4}{c-2}-\dfrac{c-1}{c-2}$

$= \dfrac{2c-4-(c-1)}{c-2}$

$= \dfrac{c-3}{c-2}$

42. $3-\dfrac{2}{1-\frac{2}{3-\frac{2}{x}}} = 3-\dfrac{2}{1-\frac{2}{3-\frac{2}{x}} \cdot \frac{x}{x}}$

$= 3-\dfrac{2}{1-\frac{2 \cdot x}{3 \cdot x - \frac{2}{x} \cdot x}}$

$= 3-\dfrac{2}{1-\frac{2x}{3x-2}}$

The LCM is $3x-2$.

$3-\dfrac{2}{\frac{3x-2}{3x-2}-\frac{2x}{3x-2}} = 3-\dfrac{2}{\frac{3x-2-2x}{3x-2}}$

$= 3-\dfrac{2}{\frac{x-2}{3x-2}}$

$= 3-\dfrac{2}{\frac{x-2}{3x-2}} \cdot \dfrac{3x-2}{3x-2}$

$= 3-\dfrac{2(3x-2)}{x-2}$

The LCM is $x-2$.

$3 \cdot \dfrac{x-2}{x-2}-\dfrac{2(3x-2)}{x-2} = \dfrac{3(x-2)-2(3x-2)}{x-2}$

$= \dfrac{3x-6-6x+4}{x-2}$

$= \dfrac{-3x-2}{x-2}$

$= -\dfrac{3x+2}{x-2}$

43. $a + \dfrac{a}{2 + \dfrac{1}{1 - \frac{2}{a}}} = a + \dfrac{a}{2 + \dfrac{1}{1 - \frac{2}{a}} \cdot \dfrac{a}{a}}$

$= a + \dfrac{a}{2 + \dfrac{1 \cdot a}{1 \cdot a - \frac{2}{a} \cdot a}}$

$= a + \dfrac{a}{2 + \dfrac{a}{a - 2}}$

The LCM is $a - 2$.

$a + \dfrac{a}{\dfrac{2(a-2)}{a-2} + \dfrac{a}{a-2}} = a + \dfrac{a}{\dfrac{2a - 4 + a}{a - 2}}$

$= a + \dfrac{a}{\dfrac{3a - 4}{a - 2}}$

$= a + \dfrac{a}{\dfrac{3a - 4}{a - 2}} \cdot \dfrac{a - 2}{a - 2}$

$= a + \dfrac{a(a - 2)}{3a - 4}$

The LCM is $3a - 4$.

$a \dfrac{(3 - 4)}{3a - 4} + \dfrac{a(a - 2)}{3a - 4} = \dfrac{3a^2 - 4a + a^2 - 2a}{3a - 4}$

$= \dfrac{4a^2 - 6a}{3a - 4}$

$= \dfrac{2a(2a - 3)}{3a - 4}$

44. $a - \dfrac{1}{2 - \dfrac{2}{2 - \frac{2}{a}}} = a - \dfrac{1}{2 - \dfrac{2}{2 - \frac{2}{a}} \cdot \dfrac{a}{a}}$

$= a - \dfrac{1}{2 - \dfrac{2a}{2a - 2}}$

$= a - \dfrac{1}{2 - \dfrac{2a}{2(a - 1)}}$

$= a - \dfrac{1}{2 - \dfrac{a}{a - 1}}$

$= a - \dfrac{1}{2 - \dfrac{a}{a - 1}} \cdot \dfrac{a - 1}{a - 1}$

$= a - \dfrac{a - 1}{2(a - 1) - a}$

$= a - \dfrac{a - 1}{2a - 2 - a}$

$= a - \dfrac{a - 1}{a - 2}$

The LCM is $a - 2$.

$\dfrac{a(a - 2)}{a - 2} - \dfrac{a - 1}{a - 2} = \dfrac{a^2 - 2a - a + 1}{a - 2} = \dfrac{a^2 - 3a + 1}{a - 2}$

45. $\dfrac{\frac{1}{x+h} - \frac{1}{x}}{h} = \dfrac{\frac{1}{x+h} - \frac{1}{x}}{h} \cdot \dfrac{x(x+h)}{x(x+h)}$

$= \dfrac{\frac{1}{x+h} \cdot x(x+h) - \frac{1}{x} \cdot x(x+h)}{hx(x+h)}$

$= \dfrac{x - (x + h)}{hx(x + h)}$

$= \dfrac{-h}{hx(x + h)}$

$= -\dfrac{1}{x(x + h)}$

46. $\dfrac{\frac{1}{(x+h)^2} - \frac{1}{x^2}}{h}$

$= \dfrac{\frac{1}{(x+h)^2} - \frac{1}{x^2}}{h} \cdot \dfrac{x^2(x+h)^2}{x^2(x+h)^2}$

$= \dfrac{\frac{1}{(x+h)^2} \cdot x^2(x+h)^2 - \frac{1}{x^2} \cdot x^2(x+h)^2}{hx^2(x+h)^2}$

$= \dfrac{x^2 - (x+h)^2}{hx^2(x+h)^2}$

$= \dfrac{x^2 - (x^2 + 2xh + h^2)}{hx^2(x+h)^2}$

$= \dfrac{-2xh - h^2}{hx^2(x+h)^2}$

$= \dfrac{h(-2x - h)}{hx^2(x+h)^2}$

$= \dfrac{-2x - h}{x^2(x+h)^2}$

$= -\dfrac{2x + h}{x^2(x+h)^2}$

47. Strategy
The first even integer: n
The second consecutive even integer: $n + 2$
The third consecutive even integer: $n + 4$
Add the reciprocals of the three integers.

Solution
$$\frac{1}{n} + \frac{1}{n+2} + \frac{1}{n+4}$$
$$= \frac{1}{n} \cdot \frac{(n+2)(n+4)}{(n+2)(n+4)} + \frac{1}{n+2} \cdot \frac{n(n+4)}{n(n+4)} + \frac{1}{n+4} \cdot \frac{n(n+2)}{n(n+2)}$$
$$= \frac{(n+2)(n+4) + n(n+4) + n(n+2)}{n(n+2)(n+4)}$$
$$= \frac{n^2 + 6n + 8 + n^2 + 4n + n^2 + 2n}{n^3 + 6n^2 + 8n}$$
$$= \frac{3n^2 + 12n + 8}{n(n+2)(n+4)}$$

48. $R = \dfrac{1}{\frac{1}{R_1} + \frac{1}{R_2} + \frac{1}{R_3}} = \dfrac{1}{\frac{1}{2} + \frac{1}{4} + \frac{1}{8}}$

The denominator is $\dfrac{1}{2} + \dfrac{1}{4} + \dfrac{1}{8} = \dfrac{4}{8} + \dfrac{2}{8} + \dfrac{1}{8} = \dfrac{7}{8}$.

$R = \dfrac{1}{\frac{7}{8}} = \dfrac{8}{7}$

The total resistance is $\dfrac{8}{7}$.

49. a. $\dfrac{Cx}{\left(1 - \frac{1}{(x+1)^{60}}\right)} = \dfrac{Cx}{\left(\frac{(x+1)^{60} - 1}{(x+1)^{60}}\right)} = \dfrac{Cx(x+1)^{60}}{(x+1)^{60} - 1}$

b.
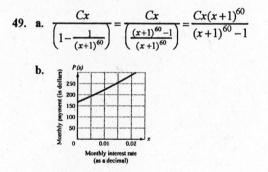

c. $12(0) = 0$
$12(0.025) = 0.3$
The interval of annual interest rates is 0% to 30%.

d. The ordered pair (0.004, 386.66) means that when the monthly interest rate on a car loan is 0.5%, the monthly payment on the loan is \$386.66.

e. The monthly payment with a loan amount of \$20,000 and an annual interest rate of 8% is \$406.

50. A continued fraction is a fraction of the form $a_0 + \cfrac{a_1}{a_2 + \cfrac{a_3}{a_4 + \cfrac{a_5}{a_6 + \ldots}}}$. The nth convergent of a continued fraction is

the value of the fraction for n terms.

A continued fraction that can be used to approximate $\sqrt{2}$ is given by $1 + \cfrac{1}{2 + \cfrac{1}{2 + \cfrac{1}{2 + \ldots}}}$.

Section 6.4

Concept Review 6.4

1. Never true
   An equation must have an equals sign.

2. Sometimes true
   The variable expression cannot be zero.

3. Always true

4. Sometimes true
   If the variable in the denominator is equivalent to zero, clearing the equation of the variable will not result in an equivalent equation.

5. Always true

Objective 6.4.1 Exercises

1. In simplifying a rational expression, the denominator is factored (as is the numerator); any factors common to the numerator and denominator are eliminated. In solving a rational equation, we clear the denominators by multiplying each side of the equation by the LCM of the denominators. The result is an equation that does not contain any fractions.

2. It is necessary to check the solution of a rational equation because multiplying each side of an equation by a variable expression may produce an equation with different solutions from the original equation.

3. $\dfrac{x}{2} + \dfrac{5}{6} = \dfrac{x}{3}$

   $12\left(\dfrac{x}{2} + \dfrac{5}{6}\right) = 12\left(\dfrac{x}{3}\right)$

   $12 \cdot \dfrac{x}{2} + 12 \cdot \dfrac{5}{6} = 4x$

   $6x + 10 = 4x$

   $10 = -2x$

   $-5 = x$

   The solution is -5.

4. $\dfrac{x}{5} - \dfrac{2}{9} = \dfrac{x}{15}$

   $45\left(\dfrac{x}{5} - \dfrac{2}{9}\right) = 45\left(\dfrac{x}{15}\right)$

   $45 \cdot \dfrac{x}{5} - 45 \cdot \dfrac{2}{9} = 3x$

   $9x - 10 = 3x$

   $-10 = -6x$

   $\dfrac{5}{3} = x$

   The solution is $\dfrac{5}{3}$.

5. $1 - \dfrac{3}{y} = 4$

   $y\left(1 - \dfrac{3}{y}\right) = y \cdot 4$

   $y \cdot 1 - y \cdot \dfrac{3}{y} = 4y$

   $y - 3 = 4y$

   $-3 = 3y$

   $-1 = y$

   The solution is -1.

6. $7 + \dfrac{6}{y} = 5$

   $y\left(7 + \dfrac{6}{y}\right) = y \cdot 5$

   $y \cdot 7 + y \cdot \dfrac{6}{y} = 5y$

   $7y + 6 = 5y$

   $6 = -2y$

   $-3 = y$

   The solution is -3.

7. $\dfrac{8}{2x-1} = 2$

   $(2x-1) \cdot \dfrac{8}{2x-1} = (2x-1)2$

   $8 = 4x - 2$

   $10 = 4x$

   $\dfrac{5}{2} = x$

   The solution is $\dfrac{5}{2}$.

8. $3 = \dfrac{18}{3x-4}$

   $(3x-4)3 = (3x-4) \cdot \dfrac{18}{3x-4}$

   $9x - 12 = 18$

   $9x = 30$

   $x = \dfrac{10}{3}$

   The solution is $\dfrac{10}{3}$.

9. $\dfrac{4}{x-4} = \dfrac{2}{x-2}$

   $\dfrac{4}{x-4} \cdot (x-4)(x-2) = \dfrac{2}{x-2} \cdot (x-4)(x-2)$

   $4(x-2) = 2(x-4)$

   $4x - 8 = 2x - 8$

   $2x - 8 = -8$

   $2x = 0$

   $x = 0$

   The solution is 0.

10.
$$\frac{x}{3} = \frac{x+1}{7}$$
$$\frac{x}{3} \cdot 21 = \frac{x+1}{7} \cdot 21$$
$$7x = (x+1)3$$
$$7x = 3x+3$$
$$4x = 3$$
$$x = \frac{3}{4}$$
The solution is $\frac{3}{4}$.

11.
$$\frac{x-2}{5} = \frac{1}{x+2}$$
$$5(x+2)\left(\frac{x-2}{5}\right) = \frac{1}{x+2} \cdot 5(x+2)$$
$$(x+2)(x-2) = 5$$
$$x^2 - 4 = 5$$
$$x^2 - 9 = 0$$
$$(x+3)(x-3) = 0$$
The solutions are –3 and 3.

12.
$$\frac{x+4}{10} = \frac{6}{x-3}$$
$$10(x-3) \cdot \frac{x+4}{10} = \frac{6}{x-3} \cdot 10(x-3)$$
$$(x-3)(x+4) = 6(10)$$
$$x^2 + x - 12 = 60$$
$$x^2 + x - 72 = 0$$
$$(x+9)(x-8) = 0$$
The solutions are –9 and 8.

13.
$$\frac{3}{x-2} = \frac{4}{x}$$
$$x(x-2) \cdot \frac{3}{x-2} = x(x-2) \cdot \frac{4}{x}$$
$$3x = (x-2)4$$
$$3x = 4x-8$$
$$-x = -8$$
$$x = 8$$
The solution is 8.

14.
$$\frac{5}{x} = \frac{2}{x+3}$$
$$x(x+3) \cdot \frac{5}{x} = x(x+3) \cdot \frac{2}{x+3}$$
$$(x+3)5 = 2x$$
$$5x + 15 = 2x$$
$$15 = -3x$$
$$-5 = x$$
The solution is –5.

15.
$$\frac{3}{x-4} + 2 = \frac{5}{x-4}$$
$$(x-4)\left(\frac{3}{x-4} + 2\right) = (x-4)\frac{5}{x-4}$$
$$(x-4) \cdot \frac{3}{x-4} + (x-4)2 = 5$$
$$3 + 2x - 8 = 5$$
$$2x - 5 = 5$$
$$2x = 10$$
$$x = 5$$
The solution is 5.

16.
$$\frac{5}{y+3} - 2 = \frac{7}{y+3}$$
$$(y+3)\left(\frac{5}{y+3} - 2\right) = (y+3) \cdot \frac{7}{y+3}$$
$$(y+3) \cdot \frac{5}{y+3} - (y+3)2 = 7$$
$$5 - 2y - 6 = 7$$
$$-2y - 1 = 7$$
$$-2y = 8$$
$$y = -4$$
The solution is –4.

17.
$$\frac{8}{x-5} = \frac{3}{x}$$
$$\frac{8}{x-5} \cdot x(x-5) = \frac{3}{x} \cdot x(x-5)$$
$$8x = 3(x-5)$$
$$8x = 3x - 15$$
$$5x = -15$$
$$x = -3$$
The solution is –3.

18.
$$\frac{16}{2-x} = \frac{4}{x}$$
$$\frac{16}{2-x} \cdot x(2-x) = \frac{4}{x} \cdot x(2-x)$$
$$16x = 4(2-x)$$
$$16x = 8 - 4x$$
$$20x = 8$$
$$x = \frac{8}{20}$$
$$x = \frac{2}{5}$$
The solution is $\frac{2}{5}$.

19.
$$5 + \frac{8}{a-2} = \frac{4a}{a-2}$$
$$(a-2)\left(5 + \frac{8}{a-2}\right) = (a-2) \cdot \frac{4a}{a-2}$$
$$(a-2)5 + (a-2) \cdot \frac{8}{a-2} = 4a$$
$$5a - 10 + 8 = 4a$$
$$5a - 2 = 4a$$
$$-2 = -a$$
$$2 = a$$
2 does not check as a solution. The equation has no solution.

20.

$$\frac{-4}{a-4} = 3 - \frac{a}{a-4}$$

$$(a-4)\frac{-4}{a-4} = (a-4)\left(3 - \frac{a}{a-4}\right)$$

$$-4 = (a-4)3 - (a-4)\frac{a}{a-4}$$

$$-4 = 3a - 12 - a$$

$$-4 = 2a - 12$$

$$8 = 2a$$

$$4 = a$$

4 does not check as a solution. The equation has no solution.

21.

$$\frac{x}{2} + \frac{20}{x} = 7$$

$$2x\left(\frac{x}{2} + \frac{20}{x}\right) = 7(2x)$$

$$2x\left(\frac{x}{2}\right) + 2x\left(\frac{20}{x}\right) = 14x$$

$$x^2 + 40 = 14x$$

$$x^2 - 14x + 40 = 0$$

$$(x-10)(x-4) = 0$$

$$x - 10 = 0 \qquad x - 4 = 0$$

$$x = 10 \qquad x = 4$$

The solutions are 10 and 4.

22.

$$3x = \frac{4}{x} - \frac{13}{2}$$

$$2x(3x) = \left(\frac{4}{x} - \frac{13}{2}\right)(2x)$$

$$6x^2 = \frac{4}{x}(2x) - \frac{13}{2}(2x)$$

$$6x^2 = 8 - 13x$$

$$6x^2 + 13x - 8 = 0$$

$$(2x-1)(3x+8) = 0$$

$$2x - 1 = 0 \qquad 3x + 8 = 0$$

$$2x = 1 \qquad 3x = -8$$

$$x = \frac{1}{2} \qquad x = -\frac{8}{3}$$

The solutions are $\frac{1}{2}$ and $-\frac{8}{3}$.

23.

$$\frac{6}{x-5} = \frac{1}{x}$$

$$\frac{6}{x-5} \cdot x(x-5) = \frac{1}{x} \cdot x(x-5)$$

$$6x = x - 5$$

$$5x = -5$$

$$x = -1$$

The solution is –1.

24.

$$\frac{8}{x-2} = \frac{4}{x+1}$$

$$\frac{8}{x-2} \cdot (x-2)(x+1) = \frac{4}{x+1} \cdot (x-2)(x+1)$$

$$8(x+1) = 4(x-2)$$

$$8x + 8 = 4x - 8$$

$$4x + 8 = -8$$

$$4x = -16$$

$$x = -4$$

The solution is –4.

25.

$$\frac{x}{x+2} = \frac{6}{x+5}$$

$$(x+2)(x+5)\frac{x}{x+2} = (x+2)(x+5)\frac{6}{x+5}$$

$$x(x+5) = 6(x+2)$$

$$x^2 + 5x = 6x + 12$$

$$x^2 - x - 12 = 0$$

$$(x-4)(x+3) = 0$$

$$x - 4 = 0 \qquad x + 3 = 0$$

$$x = 4 \qquad x = -3$$

The solutions are 4 and –3.

26.

$$\frac{x}{x-2} = \frac{3}{x-4}$$

$$(x-2)(x-4)\frac{x}{x-2} = \frac{3}{x-4}(x-2)(x-4)$$

$$x(x-4) = 3(x-2)$$

$$x^2 - 4x = 3x - 6$$

$$x^2 - 7x + 6 = 0$$

$$(x-6)(x-1) = 0$$

$$x - 6 = 0 \qquad x - 1 = 0$$

$$x = 6 \qquad x = 1$$

The solutions are 6 and 1.

27.

$$-\frac{5}{x+7} + 1 = \frac{4}{x+7}$$

$$\frac{-5}{x+7} + 1 = \frac{4}{x+7}$$

$$(x+7)\left(\frac{-5}{x+7} + 1\right) = (x+7) \cdot \frac{4}{x+7}$$

$$(x+7) \cdot \frac{-5}{x+7} + (x+7)(1) = 4$$

$$-5 + x + 7 = 4$$

$$x + 2 = 4$$

$$x = 2$$

The solution is 2.

28.

$$5 - \frac{2}{2x-5} = \frac{3}{2x-5}$$

$$(2x-5)\left(5 - \frac{2}{2x-5}\right) = (2x-5) \cdot \frac{3}{2x-5}$$

$$(2x-5)5 - (2x-5) \cdot \frac{2}{2x-5} = 3$$

$$10x - 25 - 2 = 3$$

$$10x - 27 = 3$$

$$10x = 30$$

$$x = 3$$

The solution is 3.

29.
$$\frac{2}{4y^2-9}+\frac{1}{2y-3}=\frac{3}{2y+3}$$

$$\frac{2}{(2y+3)(2y-3)}+\frac{1}{2y-3}=\frac{3}{2y+3}$$

$$(2y+3)(2y-3)\left(\frac{2}{(2y+3)(2y-3)}+\frac{1}{2y-3}\right)=(2y+3)(2y-3)\frac{3}{2y+3}$$

$$(2y+3)(2y-3)\frac{2}{(2y+3)(2y-3)}+(2y+3)(2y-3)\frac{1}{2y-3}=(2y-3)3$$

$$2+2y+3=6y-9$$
$$2y+5=6y-9$$
$$-4y+5=-9$$
$$-4y=-14$$
$$y=\frac{7}{2}$$

The solution is $\frac{7}{2}$.

30.
$$\frac{5}{x-2}-\frac{2}{x+2}=\frac{3}{x^2-4}$$

$$\frac{5}{x-2}-\frac{2}{x+2}=\frac{3}{(x+2)(x-2)}$$

$$(x+2)(x-2)\left(\frac{5}{x-2}-\frac{2}{x+2}\right)=(x+2)(x-2)\frac{3}{(x+2)(x-2)}$$

$$(x+2)(x-2)\frac{5}{x-2}-(x+2)(x-2)\frac{2}{x+2}=3$$

$$(x+2)5-(x-2)2=3$$
$$5x+10-2x+4=3$$
$$3x+14=3$$
$$3x=-11$$
$$x=-\frac{11}{3}$$

The solution is $-\frac{11}{3}$.

31.
$$\frac{5}{x^2-7x+12}=\frac{2}{x-3}+\frac{5}{x-4}$$

$$\frac{5}{(x-3)(x-4)}=\frac{2}{x-3}+\frac{5}{x-4}$$

$$(x-3)(x-4)\frac{5}{(x-3)(x-4)}=(x-3)(x-4)\left(\frac{2}{x-3}+\frac{5}{x-4}\right)$$

$$5=(x-3)(x-4)\frac{2}{x-3}+(x-3)(x-4)\frac{5}{x-4}$$

$$5=(x-4)2+(x-3)5$$
$$5=2x-8+5x-15$$
$$5=7x-23$$
$$28=7x$$
$$4=x$$

4 does not check as a solution. The equation has no solution.

32.
$$\frac{9}{x^2+7x+10}=\frac{5}{x+2}-\frac{3}{x+5}$$
$$\frac{9}{(x+2)(x+5)}=\frac{5}{x+2}-\frac{3}{x+5}$$
$$(x+2)(x+5)\frac{9}{(x+2)(x+5)}=(x+2)(x+5)\left(\frac{5}{x+2}-\frac{3}{x+5}\right)$$
$$9=(x+2)(x+5)\frac{5}{x+2}-(x+2)(x+5)\frac{3}{x+5}$$
$$9=(x+5)5-(x+2)3$$
$$9=5x+25-3x-6$$
$$9=2x+19$$
$$-10=2x$$
$$-5=x$$

-5 does not check as a solution. The equation has no solution.

Objective 6.4.2 Exercises

33. The gardener can mow $\frac{1}{20}$ of the lawn in 1 min.

34. It takes less than 2 h, because the first person can complete the task in that time when working alone.

35. Strategy
Unknown time to process the data working together: t

	Rate	Time	Part
First computer	$\frac{1}{2}$	t	$\frac{t}{2}$
Second computer	$\frac{1}{3}$	t	$\frac{t}{3}$

The sum of the part of the task completed by the first computer and the part of the task completed by the second computer is 1.
$$\frac{t}{2}+\frac{t}{3}=1$$

Solution
$$\frac{t}{2}+\frac{t}{3}=1$$
$$6\left(\frac{t}{2}+\frac{t}{3}\right)=6(1)$$
$$3t+2t=6$$
$$5t=6$$
$$t=1.2$$
With both computers, it would take 1.2 h to process the data.

36. Strategy
Unknown time for second student to build the computer: t

	Rate	Time	Part
First student	$\frac{1}{20}$	7.5	$\frac{7.5}{20}$
Second student	$\frac{1}{t}$	7.5	$\frac{7.5}{t}$

The sum of the part of the task completed by the first student and the part of the task completed by the second student is 1.
$$\frac{7.5}{20}+\frac{7.5}{t}=1$$

Solution
$$\frac{7.5}{20}+\frac{7.5}{t}=1$$
$$20t\left(\frac{7.5}{20}+\frac{7.5}{t}\right)=20t(1)$$
$$7.5t+150=20t$$
$$150=12.5t$$
$$12=t$$
The second student can build the computer alone in 12 h.

37. Strategy

Unknown time to heat the water working together: t

	Rate	Time	Part
First panel	$\frac{1}{30}$	t	$\frac{t}{30}$
Second panel	$\frac{1}{45}$	t	$\frac{t}{45}$

The sum of the part of the task completed by the first panel and the part of the task completed by the second panel is 1.

$$\frac{t}{30} + \frac{t}{45} = 1$$

Solution

$$\frac{t}{30} + \frac{t}{45} = 1$$
$$90\left(\frac{t}{30} + \frac{t}{45}\right) = 90(1)$$
$$3t + 2t = 90$$
$$5t = 90$$
$$t = 18$$

With both panels working, it would take 18 min to raise the temperature 1°.

38. Strategy

Unknown time to landscape the lawn working together: t

	Rate	Time	Part
First gardener	$\frac{1}{36}$	t	$\frac{t}{36}$
Second gardener	$\frac{1}{45}$	t	$\frac{t}{45}$

The sum of the part of the task completed by the first gardener and the part of the task completed by the second gardener is 1.

$$\frac{t}{36} + \frac{t}{45} = 1$$

Solution

$$\frac{t}{36} + \frac{t}{45} = 1$$
$$180\left(\frac{t}{36} + \frac{t}{45}\right) = 180(1)$$
$$5t + 4t = 180$$
$$9t = 180$$
$$t = 20$$

With both gardeners working, it would take 20 h to landscape the lawn.

39. Strategy

Unknown time to wire the telephone lines working together: t

	Rate	Time	Part
First member	$\frac{1}{5}$	t	$\frac{t}{5}$
Second member	$\frac{1}{7.5}$	t	$\frac{t}{7.5}$

The sum of the part of the task completed by the first member and the part of the task completed by the second member is 1.

$$\frac{t}{5} + \frac{t}{7.5} = 1$$

Solution

$$\frac{t}{5} + \frac{t}{7.5} = 1$$
$$15\left(\frac{t}{5} + \frac{t}{7.5}\right) = 15(1)$$
$$3t + 2t = 15$$
$$5t = 15$$
$$t = 3$$

With both members working together, it would take 3 h to wire the telephone lines.

40. Strategy

Time for the water to be disposed if both pumps were working: t

	Rate	Time	Part
First pump	$\frac{1}{3}$	t	$\frac{t}{3}$
Second pump	$\frac{1}{4.5}$	t	$\frac{t}{4.5}$

The sum of the parts of the task completed by each pump must equal 1.

$$\frac{t}{3} + \frac{t}{4.5} = 1$$

Solution

$$\frac{t}{3} + \frac{t}{4.5} = 1$$
$$9\left(\frac{t}{3} + \frac{t}{4.5}\right) = 9(1)$$
$$3t + 2t = 9$$
$$5t = 9$$
$$t = 1.8$$

It would take 1.8 h to dispose of 9000 gal if both pumps were working.

41. Strategy

Time for the new machine to package the transistors: t

Time for the old machine to package the transistors: $4t$

	Rate	Time	Part
New machine	$\frac{1}{t}$	8	$\frac{8}{t}$
Old machine	$\frac{1}{4t}$	8	$\frac{8}{4t}$

The sum of the parts of the task completed by each machine must equal 1.

$$\frac{8}{t}+\frac{8}{4t}=1$$

Solution

$$\frac{8}{t}+\frac{8}{4t}=1$$
$$4t\left(\frac{8}{t}+\frac{8}{4t}\right)=4t(1)$$
$$32+8=4t$$
$$40=4t$$
$$10=t$$

Working alone, the new machine would take 10 h to package the transistors.

42. Strategy

Time for the man-made snow and snow falling naturally: t

	Rate	Time	Part
Man-made	$\frac{1}{12}$	t	$\frac{t}{12}$
Naturally	$\frac{1}{36}$	t	$\frac{t}{36}$

The sum of the parts of the task completed by each machine must equal 1.

$$\frac{t}{12}+\frac{t}{36}=1$$

Solution

$$\frac{t}{12}+\frac{t}{36}=1$$
$$36\left(\frac{t}{12}+\frac{t}{36}\right)=36(1)$$
$$3t+t=36$$
$$4t=36$$
$$t=9$$

It would take snowing naturally and man-made snow making 9 h to open the run.

43. Strategy

Time for the smaller printer to print the payroll: t

	Rate	Time	Part
Large printer	$\frac{1}{40}$	10	$\frac{10}{40}$
Smaller printer	$\frac{1}{t}$	60	$\frac{60}{t}$

The sum of the parts of the task completed by each printer must equal 1.

$$\frac{10}{40}+\frac{60}{t}=1$$

Solution

$$\frac{10}{40}+\frac{60}{t}=1$$
$$40t\left(\frac{10}{40}+\frac{60}{t}\right)=40t(1)$$
$$10t+2400=40t$$
$$2400=30t$$
$$80=t$$

Working alone, the smaller printer would take 80 min to print the payroll.

44. Strategy

Time for the experienced bricklayer to do the job: t

Time for the inexperienced bricklayer to do the job: $2t$

	Rate	Time	Part
Experienced bricklayer	$\frac{1}{t}$	8	$\frac{8}{t}$
Inexperienced bricklayer	$\frac{1}{2t}$	20	$\frac{20}{2t}$

The sum of the parts of the task completed by each bricklayer must equal 1.

$$\frac{8}{t}+\frac{20}{2t}=1$$

Solution

$$\frac{8}{t}+\frac{20}{2t}=1$$
$$2t\left(\frac{8}{t}+\frac{20}{2t}\right)=2t(1)$$
$$16+20=2t$$
$$36=2t$$
$$18=t$$

Working alone, the experienced bricklayer can do the job in 18 h.

45. Strategy

Time for the apprentice to shingle the roof: t

	Rate	Time	Part
Roofer	$\frac{1}{12}$	3	$\frac{3}{12}$
Apprentice	$\frac{1}{t}$	15	$\frac{15}{t}$

The sum of the part of the task completed by the roofer and the part of the task completed by the apprentice is 1.

$$\frac{3}{12}+\frac{15}{t}=1$$

Solution

$$\frac{3}{12}+\frac{15}{t}=1$$
$$12t\left(\frac{3}{12}+\frac{15}{t}\right)=12t(1)$$
$$3t+180=12t$$
$$180=9t$$
$$20=t$$

It would take the apprentice 20 h to shingle the roof.

46. Strategy

Time for the apprentice to do the job alone: t

	Rate	Time	Part
Welder	$\frac{1}{25}$	10	$\frac{10}{25}$
Apprentice	$\frac{1}{t}$	27	$\frac{27}{t}$

The sum of the part of the job completed by the welder and the part of the job completed by the apprentice is 1.

$$\frac{10}{25}+\frac{27}{t}=1$$

Solution

$$\frac{10}{25}+\frac{27}{t}=1$$
$$25t\left(\frac{10}{25}+\frac{27}{t}\right)=25t(1)$$
$$10t+675=25t$$
$$675=15t$$
$$45=t$$

It would take the apprentice 45 h to do the job alone.

47. Strategy

Time, in seconds, to address envelopes working together: t

	Rate	Time	Part
First clerk	$\frac{1}{30}$	t	$\frac{t}{30}$
Second clerk	$\frac{1}{40}$	t	$\frac{t}{40}$

The sum of the parts of the job completed by each clerk is 1.

$$\frac{t}{30}+\frac{t}{40}=1$$

Solution

$$\frac{t}{30}+\frac{t}{40}=1$$
$$120\left(\frac{t}{30}+\frac{t}{40}\right)=120(1)$$
$$40t+30t=120$$
$$70t=120$$
$$t=\frac{12}{7}$$

Addressing 140 envelopes,

$$140\cdot\frac{12}{7}=240$$

Converting from seconds to minutes,

$$\frac{240}{60}=40$$

It would take 40 min to address 140 envelopes if both clerks worked at the same time.

48. Strategy

Unknown time to fill the bottles working together: t

	Rate	Time	Part
First machine	$\frac{1}{12}$	t	$\frac{t}{12}$
Second machine	$\frac{1}{15}$	t	$\frac{t}{15}$
Third machine	$\frac{1}{20}$	t	$\frac{t}{20}$

The sum of the parts of the task completed by each machine must equal 1.

$$\frac{t}{12}+\frac{t}{15}+\frac{t}{20}=1$$

Solution

$$\frac{t}{12}+\frac{t}{15}+\frac{t}{20}=1$$
$$60\left(\frac{t}{12}+\frac{t}{15}+\frac{t}{20}\right)=60(1)$$
$$5t+4t+3t=60$$
$$12t=60$$
$$t=5$$

When all three machines are working, it will take 5 h to fill the bottles.

49. Strategy

Unknown time to fill the bathtub working together: t

	Rate	Time	Part
Faucets	$\frac{1}{10}$	t	$\frac{t}{10}$
Drain	$\frac{1}{15}$	t	$\frac{t}{15}$

The part of the task completed by the faucets minus the part of the task completed by the drain is 1.

$$\frac{t}{10} - \frac{t}{15} = 1$$

Solution

$$\frac{t}{10} - \frac{t}{15} = 1$$
$$30\left(\frac{t}{10} - \frac{t}{15}\right) = 30(1)$$
$$3t - 2t = 30$$
$$t = 30$$

In 30 min, the bathtub will start to overflow.

50. Strategy

Unknown time to empty the tank working together: t

	Rate	Time	Part
Inlet pipe	$\frac{1}{30}$	t	$\frac{t}{30}$
Outlet pipe	$\frac{1}{20}$	t	$\frac{t}{20}$

The part of the task completed by the outlet pipe minus the part of the task completed by the inlet pipe is 1.

$$\frac{t}{20} - \frac{t}{30} = 1$$

Solution

$$\frac{t}{20} - \frac{t}{30} = 1$$
$$60\left(\frac{t}{20} - \frac{t}{30}\right) = 60(1)$$
$$3t - 2t = 60$$
$$t = 60$$

It would take 60 min to empty the tank.

51. Strategy

Unknown time to fill the tank working together: t

	Rate	Time	Part
First inlet pipe	$\frac{1}{12}$	t	$\frac{t}{12}$
Second inlet pipe	$\frac{1}{20}$	t	$\frac{t}{20}$
Outlet pipe	$\frac{1}{10}$	t	$\frac{t}{10}$

The sum of the parts of the task completed by the inlet pipes minus the part of the task completed by the outlet pipe is 1.

$$\frac{t}{12} + \frac{t}{20} - \frac{t}{10} = 1$$

Solution

$$\frac{t}{12} + \frac{t}{20} - \frac{t}{10} = 1$$
$$60\left(\frac{t}{12} + \frac{t}{20} - \frac{t}{10}\right) = 60(1)$$
$$5t + 3t - 6t = 60$$
$$2t = 60$$
$$t = 30$$

When all three pipes are open, it will take 30 h to fill the tank.

52. Strategy

Unknown time to fill the tank working together: t

	Rate	Time	Part
First inlet pipe	$\frac{1}{6}$	t	$\frac{t}{6}$
Second inlet pipe	$\frac{1}{12}$	t	$\frac{t}{12}$
Outlet pipe	$\frac{1}{24}$	t	$\frac{t}{24}$

The sum of the parts of the task completed by the inlet pipes minus the part of the task completed by the outlet pipe is 1.

$$\frac{t}{6} + \frac{t}{12} - \frac{t}{24} = 1$$

Solution

$$\frac{t}{6} + \frac{t}{12} - \frac{t}{24} = 1$$
$$24\left(\frac{t}{6} + \frac{t}{12} - \frac{t}{24}\right) = 24(1)$$
$$4t + 2t - t = 24$$
$$5t = 24$$
$$t = 4.8$$

When all three pipes are open, it will take 4.8 h to fill the tank.

Objective 6.4.3 Exercises

53. Strategy

Rate of the first skater: r

Rate of the second skater: $r - 3$

	Distance	Rate	Time
First skater	15	r	$\frac{15}{r}$
Second skater	12	$r - 3$	$\frac{12}{r-3}$

The time of the first skater is equal to the time of the second skater.

$$\frac{15}{r} = \frac{12}{r-3}$$

Solution

$$\frac{15}{r} = \frac{12}{r-3}$$
$$r(r-3)\frac{15}{r} = r(r-3)\frac{12}{r-3}$$
$$(r-3)(15) = (r)(12)$$
$$15r - 45 = 12r$$
$$3r = 45$$
$$r = 15$$
$$r - 3 = 12$$

The first skater's rate is 15 mph, and the second skater's rate is 12 mph.

54. Strategy

Rate of the corporate jet: r

Rate of the commercial jet: $r + 120$

	Distance	Rate	Time
Corporate jet	1260	r	$\frac{1260}{r}$
Commercial jet	1620	$r + 120$	$\frac{1620}{r+120}$

The time the corporate jet travels equals the time the commercial jet travels.

$$\frac{1260}{r} = \frac{1620}{r+20}$$

Solution

$$\frac{1260}{r} = \frac{1620}{r+120}$$
$$r(r+120)\frac{1260}{r} = r(r+120)\frac{1620}{r+120}$$
$$(r+120)(1260) = 1620r$$
$$1260r + 151{,}200 = 1620r$$
$$151{,}200 = 360r$$
$$420 = r$$
$$r + 120 = 420 + 120 = 540$$

The rate of the corporate jet is 420 mph. The rate of the commercial jet is 540 mph.

55. Strategy

Rate of the freight train: r

Rate of the passenger train: $r + 14$

	Distance	Rate	Time
Freight train	225	r	$\frac{225}{r}$
Passenger train	295	$r + 14$	$\frac{295}{r+14}$

The time the freight train travels equals the time the passenger train travels.

$$\frac{225}{r} = \frac{295}{r+14}$$

Solution

$$\frac{225}{r} = \frac{295}{r+14}$$
$$r(r+14)\frac{225}{r} = r(r+14)\frac{295}{r+14}$$
$$(r+14)(225) = 295r$$
$$225r + 3150 = 295r$$
$$3150 = 70r$$
$$45 = r$$
$$r + 14 = 45 + 14 = 59$$

The rate of the freight train is 45 mph. The rate of the passenger train is 59 mph.

56. Strategy

Rate of the runner: r

Rate of the bicyclist: $r + 7$

	Distance	Rate	Time
Runner	16	r	$\frac{16}{r}$
Bicyclist	30	$r + 7$	$\frac{30}{r+7}$

The time the runner travels equals the time the bicyclist travels.

$$\frac{16}{r} = \frac{30}{r+7}$$

Solution

$$\frac{16}{r} = \frac{30}{r+7}$$
$$r(r+7)\frac{16}{r} = r(r+7)\frac{30}{r+7}$$
$$(r+7)(16) = 30r$$
$$16r + 112 = 30r$$
$$112 = 14r$$
$$8 = r$$

The rate of the runner is 8 mph.

57. Strategy
Rate by foot: r
Rate by bicycle: $4r$

	Distance	Rate	Time
By foot	5	r	$\frac{5}{r}$
By bicycle	40	$4r$	$\frac{40}{4r}$

The total time spent walking and cycling was 5 h.
$$\frac{5}{r}+\frac{40}{4r}=5$$

Solution
$$\frac{5}{r}+\frac{40}{4r}=5$$
$$4r\left(\frac{5}{r}+\frac{40}{4r}\right)=4r(5)$$
$$20+40=20r$$
$$60=20r$$
$$3=r$$
$$4r=4(3)=12$$
The cyclist was riding 12 mph.

58. Strategy
Rate of the car: r
Rate of the plane: $9r$

	Distance	Rate	Time
Car	32	r	$\frac{32}{r}$
Plane	576	$9r$	$\frac{576}{9r}$

The total time for the trip was 3 h.
$$\frac{32}{r}+\frac{576}{9r}=3$$

Solution
$$\frac{32}{r}+\frac{576}{9r}=3$$
$$9r\left(\frac{32}{r}+\frac{576}{9r}\right)=9r(3)$$
$$288+576=27r$$
$$864=27r$$
$$32=r$$
$$9r=9(32)=288$$
The rate of the plane was 288 mph.

59. Strategy
Rate by foot: r
Rate by car: $12r$

	Distance	Rate	Time
By foot	4	r	$\frac{4}{r}$
By car	72	$12r$	$\frac{72}{12r}$

The total time spent riding and walking was 2.5 h.
$$\frac{4}{r}+\frac{72}{12r}=2.5$$

Solution
$$\frac{4}{r}+\frac{72}{12r}=2.5$$
$$12r\left(\frac{4}{r}+\frac{72}{12r}\right)=12r(2.5)$$
$$48+72=30r$$
$$120=30r$$
$$4=r$$
The motorist walks at the rate of 4 mph.

60. Strategy
Rate by helicopter: r
Rate by jet: $4r$

	Distance	Rate	Time
Helicopter	105	r	$\frac{105}{r}$
Jet	735	$4r$	$\frac{735}{4r}$

The total time for the trip was 2.2 h.
$$\frac{105}{r}+\frac{735}{4r}=2.2$$

Solution
$$\frac{105}{r}+\frac{735}{4r}=2.2$$
$$4r\left(\frac{105}{r}+\frac{735}{4r}\right)=4r(2.2)$$
$$420+735=8.8r$$
$$1155=8.8r$$
$$131.25=r$$
$$4r=(4)131.25=525$$
The rate of the jet was 525 mph.

61. Strategy
Rate the executive can walk: r
Rate the executive walks using the moving sidewalk: $r + 2$

	Distance	Rate	Time
Walking alone	360	r	$\frac{360}{r}$
Walking using moving sidewalk	480	$r + 2$	$\frac{480}{r+2}$

It takes the executive the same time to walk 480 ft using the moving sidewalk as it takes to walk 360 ft without the moving sidewalk.

$$\frac{360}{r} = \frac{480}{r+2}$$

Solution

$$\frac{360}{r} = \frac{480}{r+2}$$
$$r(r+2)\frac{360}{r} = r(r+2)\frac{480}{r+2}$$
$$(r+2)(360) = (r)(480)$$
$$360r + 720 = 480r$$
$$720 = 120r$$
$$6 = r$$

The executive walks at a rate of 6 ft/s.

62. Strategy
Rate of the jogger: r
Rate of the cyclist: $2r$

	Distance	Rate	Time
Jogger	18	r	$\frac{18}{r}$
Cyclist	18	$2r$	$\frac{18}{2r}$

The time for the jogger is 1.5 h more than the time for the cyclist.

$$\frac{18}{2r} + 1.5 = \frac{18}{r}$$

Solution

$$\frac{18}{2r} + 1.5 = \frac{18}{r}$$
$$2r\left(\frac{18}{2r} + 1.5\right) = 2r\left(\frac{18}{r}\right)$$
$$18 + 3r = 36$$
$$3r = 18$$
$$r = 6$$
$$2r = 2(6) = 12$$

The rate of the cyclist is 12 mph.

63. Strategy
Rate of the single-engine plane: r
Rate of the jet: $4r$

	Distance	Rate	Time
Single-engine plane	960	r	$\frac{960}{r}$
Jet	960	$4r$	$\frac{960}{4r}$

The time for the single-engine plane is 4 h more than the time for the jet.

$$\frac{960}{4r} + 4 = \frac{960}{r}$$

Solution

$$\frac{960}{4r} + 4 = \frac{960}{r}$$
$$4r\left(\frac{960}{4r} + 4\right) = 4r\left(\frac{960}{r}\right)$$
$$960 + 16r = 3840$$
$$16r = 2880$$
$$r = 180$$
$$4r = 4(180) = 720$$

The rate of the single-engine plane is 180 mph. The rate of the jet is 720 mph.

64. Strategy
Rate Marlys can swim: r
Rate Marlys can row: $r + 3$

	Distance	Rate	Time
Swimming	4	r	$\frac{4}{r}$
Rowing	10	$r + 3$	$\frac{10}{r+3}$

Marlys can row 10 mi in the same time it takes her to swim 4 mi.

$$\frac{4}{r} = \frac{10}{r+3}$$

Solution

$$\frac{4}{r} = \frac{10}{r+3}$$
$$r(r+3)\frac{4}{r} = r(r+3)\frac{10}{r+3}$$
$$(r+3)(4) = (r)(10)$$
$$4r + 12 = 10r$$
$$12 = 6r$$
$$2 = r$$

Marlys can swim at a rate of 2 mph.

65. Strategy

Rate of the Gulf Stream: r

Rate sailing with the Gulf Stream: $28 + r$

Rate sailing against the Gulf Stream: $28 - r$

	Distance	Rate	Time
With Gulf Stream	170	$28 + r$	$\frac{170}{28+r}$
Against Gulf Stream	110	$28 - r$	$\frac{110}{28-r}$

It takes the same time to sail 170 mi with the Gulf Stream as it takes to sail 110 mi against the Gulf Stream.

$$\frac{170}{28+r} = \frac{110}{28-r}$$

Solution

$$\frac{170}{28+r} = \frac{110}{28-r}$$
$$(28-r)(28+r)\frac{170}{28+r} = (28-r)(28+r)\frac{110}{28-r}$$
$$(28-r)(170) = (28+r)(110)$$
$$4760 - 170r = 3080 + 110r$$
$$1680 = 280r$$
$$6 = r$$

The rate of the Gulf Stream is 6 mph.

66. Strategy

Rate of the jet stream: r

Rate flying with jet stream: $500 + r$

Rate flying against jet stream: $500 - r$

	Distance	Rate	Time
With jet stream	2420	$500 + r$	$\frac{2420}{500+r}$
Against jet stream	1580	$500 - r$	$\frac{1580}{500-r}$

It takes the same amount of time to fly 2420 mi with the jet stream as it takes to fly 1580 mi against the jet stream.

$$\frac{2420}{500+r} = \frac{1580}{500-r}$$

Solution

$$\frac{2420}{500+r} = \frac{1580}{500-r}$$
$$(500-r)(500+r)\frac{2420}{500+r} = (500-r)(500+r)\frac{1580}{500-r}$$
$$(500-r)(2420) = (500+r)(1580)$$
$$1{,}210{,}000 - 2420r = 790{,}000 + 1580r$$
$$420{,}000 = 4000r$$
$$105 = r$$

The rate of the jet stream is 105 mph.

67. Strategy

Rate of the current: r

	Distance	Rate	Time
With current	20	$7 + r$	$\frac{20}{7+r}$
Against current	8	$7 - r$	$\frac{8}{7-r}$

The time traveling with the current equals the time traveling against the current.

$$\frac{20}{7+r} = \frac{8}{7-r}$$

Solution

$$\frac{20}{7+r} = \frac{8}{7-r}$$
$$(7+r)(7-r)\frac{20}{7+r} = (7+r)(7-r)\frac{8}{7-r}$$
$$(7-r)20 = (7+r)8$$
$$140 - 20r = 56 + 8r$$
$$140 = 56 + 28r$$
$$84 = 28r$$
$$3 = r$$

The rate of the current is 3 mph.

68. Strategy

Rate of the current: r

	Distance	Rate	Time
With current	15	$8 + r$	$\frac{15}{8+r}$
Against current	9	$8 - r$	$\frac{9}{8-r}$

The time traveling with the current equals the time traveling against the current.

$$\frac{15}{8+r} = \frac{9}{8-r}$$

Solution

$$\frac{15}{8+r} = \frac{9}{8-r}$$
$$(8+r)(8-r)\frac{15}{8+r} = (8+r)(8-r)\frac{9}{8-r}$$
$$(8-r)15 = (8+r)9$$
$$120 - 15r = 72 + 9r$$
$$120 = 72 + 24r$$
$$48 = 24r$$
$$2 = r$$

The rate of the current is 2 mph.

Applying Concepts 6.4

69. Strategy

Numerator: n

Denominator: $n + 4$

Numerator increased by 3: $n + 3$

Denominator increased by 3: $(n + 4) + 3 = n + 7$

If the numerator and denominator of the fraction are increased by 3, the new fraction is $\dfrac{5}{6}$.

Solution

$$\frac{n+3}{n+7} = \frac{5}{6}$$
$$6(n+7)\left(\frac{n+3}{n+7}\right) = 6(n+7)\left(\frac{5}{6}\right)$$
$$6(n+3) = (n+7)(5)$$
$$6n+18 = 5n+35$$
$$n+18 = 35$$
$$n = 17$$
$$n + 4 = 17 + 4 = 21$$

The original fraction is $\dfrac{17}{21}$.

70. Strategy

Time to fill the tank: t

	Rate	Time	Part
First pipe	$\frac{1}{3}$	t	$\frac{t}{3}$
Second pipe	$\frac{1}{4}$	t	$\frac{t}{4}$
Third pipe	$\frac{1}{6}$	t	$\frac{t}{6}$

The sum of the parts of the task completed by each pipe is 1.

Solution

$$\frac{t}{3} + \frac{t}{4} + \frac{t}{6} = 1$$
$$12\left(\frac{t}{3} + \frac{t}{4} + \frac{t}{6}\right) = 12(1)$$
$$4t + 3t + 2t = 12$$
$$9t = 12$$
$$t = \frac{12}{9} = \frac{4}{3}$$

It will take $1\dfrac{1}{3}$ h to fill the tank with all three pipes operating.

71. Strategy

Time to complete the job: t

	Rate	Time	Part
First printer	$\frac{1}{24}$	t	$\frac{t}{24}$
Second printer	$\frac{1}{16}$	t	$\frac{t}{16}$
Third printer	$\frac{1}{12}$	t	$\frac{t}{12}$

The sum of the parts of the task completed by each printer is 1.

Solution

$$\frac{t}{24} + \frac{t}{16} + \frac{t}{12} = 1$$
$$48\left(\frac{t}{24} + \frac{t}{16} + \frac{t}{12}\right) = 48(1)$$
$$2t + 3t + 4t = 48$$
$$9t = 48$$
$$t = \frac{48}{9} = \frac{16}{3}$$

It would take $5\dfrac{1}{3}$ min to print the checks.

72. Strategy

Usual rate: r

Increased rate: $r + 10$

	Distance	Rate	Time
Usual rate	200	r	$\frac{200}{r}$
Increased rate	200	$r + 10$	$\frac{200}{r+10}$

At the increased speed, the drive takes 40 min less time than usual. $\left(\text{Note: } 40 \text{ min} = \dfrac{2}{3}\text{h.}\right)$

Solution

$$\frac{200}{r} - \frac{2}{3} = \frac{200}{r+10}$$
$$3r(r+10)\left(\frac{200}{r} - \frac{2}{3}\right) = 3r(r+10)\left(\frac{200}{r+10}\right)$$
$$3(r+10)(200) - r(r+10)(2) = 3r(200)$$
$$600(r+10) - 2r(r+10) = 600r$$
$$600r + 6000 - 2r^2 - 20r = 600r$$
$$0 = 2r^2 + 20r - 6000$$
$$0 = 2(r^2 + 10r - 3000)$$
$$0 = r^2 + 10r - 3000$$
$$0 = (r+60)(r-50)$$

$$r + 60 = 0 \qquad r - 50 = 0$$
$$r = -60 \qquad r = 50$$

Because the rate cannot be negative, −60 is not a solution. The usual rate is 50 mph.

73. Strategy

Usual speed: r

Reduced speed: $r - 5$

	Distance	Rate	Time
Usual rate	165	r	$\frac{165}{r}$
Reduced speed	165	$r - 5$	$\frac{165}{r-5}$

At the decreased speed, the drive takes 15 min more than usual. $\left(\textit{Note:}\ 15\ \text{min} = \frac{1}{4}\ \text{h}\right)$

Solution

$$\frac{165}{r} = \frac{165}{r-5} - \frac{1}{4}$$

$$4r(r-5)\left(\frac{165}{r}\right) = 4r(r-5)\left(\frac{165}{r-5} - \frac{1}{4}\right)$$

$$4(r-5)(165) = 4r(165) - r(r-5)$$

$$660(r-5) = 660r - r^2 + 5r$$

$$660r - 3300 = 665r - r^2$$

$$r^2 - 5r - 3300 = 0$$

$$(r-60)(r+55) = 0$$

$$r - 60 = 0 \qquad r + 55 = 0$$

$$r = 60 \qquad r = -55$$

Because the rate cannot be negative, –55 is not a solution. The bus usually travels at 60 mph.

74. Strategy

Time it takes both pumps working together to fill the pool: t

	Rate	Time	Part
1st pump	$\frac{1}{A}$	t	$\frac{t}{A}$
2nd pump	$\frac{1}{B}$	t	$\frac{t}{B}$

The sum of the parts of the task completed by each pump must equal 1.

$$\frac{t}{A} + \frac{t}{B} = 1$$

Solution

$$\frac{t}{A} + \frac{t}{B} = 1$$

$$AB\left(\frac{t}{A} + \frac{t}{B}\right) = AB(1)$$

$$tB + tA = AB$$

$$t(B+A) = AB$$

$$t = \frac{AB}{B+A}$$

The time required to fill the pool is $\frac{AB}{B+A}$ hours.

75. Strategy

The rate running from front of parade to back of parade is the sum of the runner's rate and the rate of the parade (5 mph + 3 mph).

The rate running from back of parade to front of parade is the difference between the runner's rate and the rate of the parade (5 mph – 3 mph).

	Distance	Rate	Time
Back to front	1	2	$\frac{1}{2}$
Front to back	1	8	$\frac{1}{8}$

The sum of the time running from front to back and the time running from back to front is the total time t that the runner runs.

$$\frac{1}{2} + \frac{1}{8} = t$$

Solution

$$\frac{1}{2} + \frac{1}{8} = t$$

$$\frac{5}{8} = t$$

The total time is $\frac{5}{8}$ h.

76. The Rhind papyrus is named after the original owner, Henry Rhind from Scotland. He willed the papyrus to the British Museum. The actual author of the papyrus is an Egyptian scribe whose name was Ahmes. Consequently, the papyrus is also called the Ahmes papyrus. The papyrus dates from 1650 B.C. Ahmes, in turn, claims the papyrus is a transcription of a work that was completed around 1849 B.C. The translation of the document was aided by the discovery of the Rosetta Stone during Napoleon's expedition to Egypt. The Rhind papyrus contains 85 problems through which the nature of early Egyptian mathematics has been inferred. It was really a handbook (or textbook) of how to perform basic operations such as multiplication and division.

77. A unit fraction is a fraction in which the numerator is 1. In Egyptian mathematics, all fractions $\left(\text{except } \frac{2}{3}\right)$ had to be decomposed into unit fractions. The Rhind papyrus gave a table that showed the decomposition of fractions with numerator 2 and an odd-number denominator.

Section 6.5

Concept Review 6.5

1. Never true

If x varies inversely as y, then when x is doubled, y is halved.

2. Always true

3. Never true

If a varies jointly as b and c, then $a = kbc$.

4. Always true

5. Never true

If the area of a triangle is held constant, then the length varies inversely as the width.

6. Always true

Objective 6.5.1 Exercises

1. A ratio is the quotient of two quantities that have the same units. A rate is the quotient of two quantities that have different units.

2. A proportion is an equation that states that two ratios or rates are equal.

3.
$$\frac{x+1}{10} = \frac{2}{5}$$
$$50 \cdot \frac{x+1}{10} = 50 \cdot \frac{2}{5}$$
$$5(x+1) = 10(2)$$
$$5x+5 = 20$$
$$5x = 15$$
$$x = 3$$

4.
$$\frac{4}{x+2} = \frac{3}{4}$$
$$4(x+2)\frac{4}{x+2} = 4(x+2)\frac{3}{4}$$
$$4(4) = (x+2)3$$
$$16 = 3x+6$$
$$10 = 3x$$
$$\frac{10}{3} = x$$

5.
$$\frac{x}{4} = \frac{x-2}{8}$$
$$8 \cdot \frac{x}{4} = 8 \cdot \frac{x-2}{8}$$
$$2x = x-2$$
$$x = -2$$

6.
$$\frac{8}{x-5} = \frac{3}{x}$$
$$x(x-5)\frac{8}{x-5} = x(x-5)\frac{3}{x}$$
$$8x = (x-5)3$$
$$8x = 3x-15$$
$$5x = -15$$
$$x = -3$$

7.
$$\frac{8}{x-2} = \frac{4}{x+1}$$
$$(x+1)(x-2)\frac{8}{x-2} = (x+1)(x-2)\frac{4}{x+1}$$
$$(x+1)8 = (x-2)4$$
$$8x+8 = 4x-8$$
$$4x = -16$$
$$x = -4$$

8.
$$\frac{4}{x-4} = \frac{2}{x-2}$$
$$(x-2)(x-4)\frac{4}{x-4} = (x-2)(x-4)\frac{2}{x-2}$$
$$(x-2)4 = (x-4)2$$
$$4x-8 = 2x-8$$
$$2x = 0$$
$$x = 0$$

9.
$$\frac{8}{3x-2} = \frac{2}{2x+1}$$
$$(3x-2)(2x+1)\frac{8}{3x-2} = (3x-2)(2x+1)\frac{2}{2x+1}$$
$$(2x+1)8 = (3x-2)2$$
$$16x+8 = 6x-4$$
$$10x = -12$$
$$x = -\frac{6}{5}$$

10.
$$\frac{x-2}{x-5} = \frac{2x}{2x+5}$$
$$(2x+5)(x-5)\frac{x-2}{x-5} = (2x+5)(x-5)\frac{2x}{2x+5}$$
$$(2x+5)(x-2) = (x-5)2x$$
$$2x^2 + x - 10 = 2x^2 - 10x$$
$$11x = 10$$
$$x = \frac{10}{11}$$

11. Strategy

To find the number of ducks in the preserve, write and solve a proportion using x to represent the number of ducks in the preserve.

Solution
$$\frac{60}{x} = \frac{3}{200}$$
$$200x \cdot \frac{60}{x} = \frac{3}{200} \cdot 200x$$
$$12,000 = 3x$$
$$4000 = x$$

There are 4000 ducks in the preserve.

12. Strategy

To find the number of people expected to vote, write and solve a proportion using x to represent the number of people expected to vote.

Solution
$$\frac{7}{12} = \frac{x}{210,000}$$
$$\frac{7}{12} \cdot 210,000 = \frac{x}{210,000} \cdot 210,000$$
$$7 \cdot 17,500 = x$$
$$122,500 = x$$

122,500 people are expected to vote.

13. Strategy

To find the amount of additional fruit punch, write and solve a proportion using x to represent the additional amount of fruit punch. Then $x + 2$ is the total amount of fruit punch.

Solution

$$\frac{2}{30} = \frac{x+2}{75}$$

$$\frac{2}{30} \cdot 150 = \frac{x+2}{75} \cdot 150$$

$$2 \cdot 5 = (x+2)2$$

$$10 = 2x + 4$$

$$6 = 2x$$

$$3 = x$$

To serve 75 people, 3 additional gallons of fruit punch are necessary.

14. Strategy

To find the number of grams of protein, write and solve a proportion using x to represent the protein in the box.

Solution

$$\frac{7}{56} = \frac{x}{454}$$

$$454 \cdot 56 \cdot \frac{7}{56} = 454 \cdot 56 \cdot \frac{x}{454}$$

$$454 \cdot 7 = 56x$$

$$3178 = 56x$$

$$56.75 = x$$

There are 56.75 grams of protein in the box.

15. Strategy

To find the dimensions of the room, write and solve two proportions using L to represent the length of the room and W to represent the width of the room.

Solution

$$\frac{\frac{1}{4}}{1} = \frac{4\frac{1}{4}}{W} \qquad \frac{\frac{1}{4}}{1} = \frac{5\frac{1}{2}}{L}1$$

$$\frac{1}{4} \cdot W = \frac{4\frac{1}{4}}{W} \cdot W \qquad \frac{1}{4} \cdot L = \frac{5\frac{1}{2}}{L} \cdot L$$

$$\frac{1}{4}W = 4\frac{1}{4} \qquad \frac{1}{4}L = 5\frac{1}{2}$$

$$W = 17 \qquad L = 22$$

The dimensions of the room are 17 ft by 22 ft.

16. Strategy

To find the amount of window space, write and solve a proportion using x to represent the amount of window space allowed.

Solution

$$\frac{15}{160} = \frac{x}{3200}$$

$$\frac{15}{160} \cdot 3200 = \frac{x}{3200} \cdot 3200$$

$$15 \cdot 20 = x$$

$$300 = x$$

300 ft^2 of window space would be allowed.

17. Strategy

To find the number of miles to walk, write and solve a proportion using x to represent the number of miles.

Solution

$$\frac{4}{650} = \frac{x}{3500}$$

$$(3500)(650)\frac{4}{650} = (3500)(650)\frac{x}{3500}$$

$$4(3500) = 650x$$

$$14,000 = 650x$$

$$21.54 \approx x$$

A person would have to walk about 21.54 mi to lose one pound.

18. Strategy

To find the number of tiles, write and solve a proportion using x to represent the number of tiles.

Solution

$$\frac{120}{24} = \frac{x}{300}$$

$$5 = \frac{x}{300}$$

$$5 \cdot 300 = \frac{x}{300} \cdot 300$$

$$5 \cdot 300 = x$$

$$1500 = x$$

To tile 300 ft^2, 1500 tiles are required.

19. Strategy

To find the additional amount of medicine, write and solve a proportion using x to represent the additional amount of medicine. Then $x + 0.75$ is the total amount of medicine.

Solution

$$\frac{0.75}{120} = \frac{x+0.75}{200}$$

$$\frac{0.75}{120} \cdot 600 = \frac{x+0.75}{200} \cdot 600$$

$$0.75(5) = (x+0.75)3$$

$$3.75 = 3x + 2.25$$

$$1.5 = 3x$$

$$0.5 = x$$

An additional 0.5 oz of medicine is required.

20. Strategy

To find the weight on Venus, write and solve a proportion using x to represent the weight on Venus.

Solution
$$\frac{90.5}{100} = \frac{x}{150}$$
$$\frac{90.5}{100}(150)(100) = \frac{x}{150}(150)(100)$$
$$90.5(150) = 100x$$
$$13,575 = 100x$$
$$135.75 = x$$

The object weighs 135.75 lb on Venus.

21. Strategy

To find the additional amount of insecticide, write and solve a proportion using x to represent the additional amount of insecticide. Then $x + 6$ is the total amount of insecticide.

Solution
$$\frac{6}{15} = \frac{x+6}{100}$$
$$\frac{6}{15} \cdot 300 = \frac{x+6}{100} \cdot 300$$
$$6 \cdot 20 = (x+6)3$$
$$120 = 3x + 18$$
$$102 = 3x$$
$$34 = x$$

An additional 34 oz of insecticide are required.

22. Strategy

To find the number of Siberian tigers in the region, write and solve a proportion using x to represent the number of Siberian tigers in the region.

Solution
$$\frac{30}{150} = \frac{50}{x}$$
$$\frac{30}{150}(150)x = \frac{50}{x}(150)x$$
$$30x = 50(150)$$
$$30x = 7500$$
$$x = 250$$

There are 250 Siberian tigers in the region.

23. Strategy

Let x represent the number of pieces of mail delivered in one week.

Solution
$$\frac{200}{300} = \frac{x}{6}$$
$$6(300)\frac{200}{300} = 6(300)\frac{x}{6}$$
$$6(200) = 300x$$
$$1200 = 300x$$
$$4 = x$$

The U.S.P.S delivers 4 billion pieces of mail in one week.

24. Strategy

To find the number of additional cubic feet of cement, write and solve a proportion using x to represent the number of additional cubic feet of cement. Then $x + 30$ is the total number of cubic feet.

Solution
$$\frac{30}{90} = \frac{x+30}{120}$$
$$\frac{1}{3} = \frac{x+30}{120}$$
$$\frac{1}{3} \cdot 120 = \frac{x+30}{120} \cdot 120$$
$$40 = x + 30$$
$$10 = x$$

To make a 120 ft^2 concrete floor, 10 additional cubic feet of cement are required.

25. Strategy

To find the actual length of the whale, write and solve a proportion using x to represent the actual length of the whale. The length of the whale in the picture is 2 in.

Solution
$$\frac{1}{48} = \frac{2}{x}$$
$$\frac{1}{48}(48)x = \frac{2}{x}(48)x$$
$$x = 96$$

The whale is 96 ft long.

26. Strategy

To find the actual height of the elephant, write and solve a proportion using x to represent the actual height of the elephant. The height of the elephant in the picture is $\frac{3}{4}$ in.

Solution
$$\frac{1}{12} = \frac{\frac{3}{4}}{x}$$
$$\frac{1}{12}(12)x = \frac{\frac{3}{4}}{x}(12)x$$
$$x = \frac{3}{4}(12)$$
$$x = 9$$

The height of the elephant is 9 ft.

Objective 6.5.2 Exercises

27. A direct variation is a function that can be expressed as the equation $y = kx$, where k is a constant.

28. An inverse variation is a function that can be expressed as the equation $y = \frac{k}{x}$, where k is a constant.

29. Strategy
To find the pressure:
Write the basic direct variation equation, replace the variables by the given values, and solve for k.

Write the direct variation equation, replacing k by its value. Substitute 30 for d and solve for p.

Solution
$$p = kd$$
$$3.6 = k(8)$$
$$0.45 = k$$
$$p = 0.45d = 0.45(30) = 13.5$$
The pressure is 13.5 pounds per square inch.

30. Strategy
To find the force:
Write the basic direct variation equation, replace the variables by the given values, and solve for k.

Write the direct variation equation, replacing k by its value. Substitute 5 for d and solve for f.

Solution
$$d = kf$$
$$2 = k(5)$$
$$\frac{2}{5} = k$$
$$d = \frac{2}{5}f$$
$$5 = \frac{2}{5}f$$
$$12.5 = f$$
The required force is 12.5 lb.

31. Strategy
To find the profit:
Write the basic direct variation equation, replace the variables by the given values, and solve for k.

Write the direct variation equation, replacing k by its value. Substitute 300 for s and solve for P.

Solution
$$P = ks$$
$$2500 = k(20)$$
$$125 = k$$
$$P = 125s = 125(300) = 37,500$$
When the company sells 300 products, the profit is $37,500.

32. Strategy
To find the yield:
Write the basic direct variation equation, replace the variables by the given values, and solve for k.

Write the direct variation equation, replacing k by its value. Substitute 220 for A and solve for b.

Solution
$$b = kA$$
$$1125 = k(25)$$
$$45 = k$$
$$b = 45A = 45(220) = 9900$$
The yield of a 220-acre farm is 9900 bushels.

33. Strategy
To find the length of the person's face:
Write the basic direct variation equation, replace the variables by the given values, and solve for k.

Write the direct variation equation, replacing k by its value. Substitute 1.7 for x and solve for y.

Solution
$$y = kx \qquad\qquad y = 6x$$
$$9 = k(1.5) \qquad y = 6(1.7)$$
$$6 = k \qquad\qquad y = 10.2$$
The person's face is 10.2 in. long.

34. Strategy
To find the person's height:
Write the basic direct variation equation, replace the variables by the given values, and solve for k.

Write the direct variation equation, replacing k by its value. Substitute 16 for x and solve for y.

Solution
$$y = kx \qquad\qquad y = 4x$$
$$70 = k(17.5) \qquad y = 4(16)$$
$$4 = k \qquad\qquad y = 64$$
The person is 64 in. tall.

35. Strategy
To find the distance:
Write the basic direct variation equation, replace the variables by the given values, and solve for k.

Write the direct variation equation, replacing k by its value. Substitute 800 for H and solve for d.

Solution
$$d = k\sqrt{H}$$
$$19 = k\sqrt{500}$$
$$19 = k(22.36)$$
$$0.85 = k$$
$$d = 0.85\sqrt{H} = 0.85\sqrt{800} = 0.85(28.28) = 24.04$$
The horizon is 24.04 mi away from a point that is 800 ft high.

36. Strategy
    To find the period:
    Write the basic direct variation equation, replace the variables by the given values, and solve for k.

    Write the direct variation equation, replacing k by its value. Substitute 4.5 for L and solve for p.

    Solution
    $$p = k\sqrt{L}$$
    $$1.5 = k\sqrt{2}$$
    $$1.5 = k(1.414)$$
    $$1.06 = k$$

    $p = 1.06\sqrt{L} = 1.06\sqrt{4.5} = 1.06(2.121) = 2.25$
    The period of the pendulum is 2.25 s when the length is 4.5 ft.

37. Strategy
    To find the distance:
    Write the basic direct variation equation, replace the variables by the given values, and solve for k.

    Write the direct variation equation, replacing k by its value. Substitute 4 for t and solve for s.

    Solution
    $$s = kt^2$$
    $$5 = k(1)^2$$
    $$5 = k$$
    $$s = 5t^2 = 5(4)^2 = 5(16) = 80$$
    In 4 s, the ball will roll 80 ft.

38. Strategy
    To find the stopping distance:
    Write the basic direct variation equation, replace the variables by the given values, and solve for k.

    Write the direct variation equation replacing k by its value. Substitute 55 for v and solve for s.

    Solution
    $$s = kv^2$$
    $$60 = k(30)^2$$
    $$60 = k(900)$$
    $$0.0667 = k$$
    $$s = 0.0667v^2$$
    $$= 0.0667(55)^2$$
    $$= 0.0667(3025)$$
    $$= 201.8$$
    The stopping distance for a car traveling at 55 mph is 201.8 ft.

39. Strategy
    To find the pressure:
    Write the basic inverse variation equation, replace the variables by the given values, and solve for k.

    Write the inverse variation equation, replacing k by its value. Substitute 150 for V and solve for P.

    Solution
    $$P = \frac{k}{V}$$
    $$25 = \frac{k}{400}$$
    $$10,000 = k$$
    $$P = \frac{10,000}{V} = \frac{10,000}{150} = 66\frac{2}{3}$$
    When the volume is 150 ft^3, the pressure is $66\frac{2}{3}$ pounds per square inch.

40. Strategy
    To find the speed:
    Write the basic inverse variation equation, replace the variables by the given values, and solve for k.

    Write the inverse variation equation, replacing k by its value. Substitute 30 for t and solve for v.

    Solution
    $$v = \frac{k}{t}$$
    $$20 = \frac{k}{48}$$
    $$960 = k$$
    $$v = \frac{960}{t} = \frac{960}{30} = 32$$
    The gear that has 30 teeth will make 32 revolutions per minute.

41. Strategy
    To find the pressure:
    Write the basic combined variation equation, replace the variables by the given values, and solve for k.

    Write the combined variation equation, replacing k by its value. Substitute 60 for d and 1.2 for D, and solve for p.

    Solution
    $$p = kdD$$
    $$37.5 = k(100)(1.2)$$
    $$37.5 = 120k$$
    $$0.3125 = k$$
    $p = 0.3125dD = 0.3125(60)(1.2) = 22.5$
    The pressure is 22.5 pounds per square inch.

42. Strategy

To find the current:
Write the basic combined variation equation, replace the variables by the given values, and solve for k.

Write the combined variation equation, replacing k by its value. Substitute 195 for v and 12 for r, and solve for I.

Solution

$$I = \frac{kv}{r}$$
$$27.5 = \frac{k(110)}{4}$$
$$110 = 110k$$
$$1 = k$$
$$I = \frac{v}{r} = \frac{195}{12} = 16.25$$

The current is 16.25 amps.

43. Strategy

To find the repulsive force:
Write the basic inverse variation equation, replace the variables by the given values, and solve for k.

Write the inverse variation equation, replacing k by its value. Substitute 1.2 for d and solve for f.

Solution

$$f = \frac{k}{d^2}$$
$$18 = \frac{k}{3^2}$$
$$18 = \frac{k}{9}$$
$$162 = k$$
$$f = \frac{162}{d^2} = \frac{162}{1.2^2} = \frac{162}{1.44} = 112.5$$

The repulsive force is 112.5 lb when the distance is 1.2 in.

44. Strategy

To find the intensity:
Write the basic inverse variation equation, replace the variables by the given values, and solve for k.

Write the inverse variation equation, replacing k by its value. Substitute 4 for d and solve for l.

Solution

$$L = \frac{k}{d^2}$$
$$8 = \frac{k}{6^2}$$
$$8 = \frac{k}{36}$$
$$288 = k$$
$$L = \frac{288}{d^2} = \frac{288}{4^2} = \frac{288}{16} = 18$$

The intensity is 18 lumens when the distance is 4 ft.

45. Strategy

To find the resistance:
Write the basic combined variation equation, replace the variables by the given values, and solve for k.

Write the combined variation equation, replacing k by its value. Substitute 50 for L and 0.02 for d, and solve for R.

Solution

$$R = \frac{kL}{d^2}$$
$$9 = \frac{k(50)}{(0.05)^2}$$
$$9 = \frac{50k}{0.0025}$$
$$0.0225 = 50k$$
$$0.00045 = k$$
$$R = \frac{0.00045L}{d^2}$$
$$= \frac{0.00045(50)}{(0.02)^2}$$
$$= \frac{0.00045(50)}{0.0004}$$
$$= 56.25$$

The resistance is 56.25 ohms.

46. Strategy
To find the frequency:
Write the basic combined variation equation, replace the variables by the given values, and solve for k.

Write the combined variation equation, replacing k by its value. Substitute 36 for T and 4 for L, and solve for f.

Solution
$$f = \frac{k\sqrt{T}}{L}$$
$$40 = \frac{k\sqrt{25}}{3}$$
$$120 = 5k$$
$$24 = k$$
$$f = \frac{24\sqrt{T}}{L}$$
$$= \frac{24\sqrt{36}}{4}$$
$$= \frac{24(6)}{4}$$
$$= 36$$
The frequency is 36 vibrations per second.

47. Strategy
To find the wind force:
Write the basic combined variation equation, replace the variables by the given values, and solve for k.

Write the combined variation equation, replacing k by its value. Substitute 10 for A and 60 for v, and solve for w.

Solution
$$w = kAv^2$$
$$45 = k(10)(30)^2$$
$$45 = k(10)(900)$$
$$45 = 9000k$$
$$0.005 = k$$
$$w = 0.005Av^2$$
$$= 0.005(10)(60)^2$$
$$= 0.005(10)(3600)$$
$$= 180$$
The wind force is 180 lb.

48. Strategy
To find the power:
Write the basic combined variation equation, replace the variables by the given values, and solve for k.

Write the combined variation equation, replacing k by its value. Substitute 2 for I and 10 for R, and solve for P.

Solution
$$P = kIR^2$$
$$100 = k(4)(5)^2$$
$$100 = k(4)(25)$$
$$100 = 100k$$
$$1 = k$$
$$P = IR^2 = 2(10)^2 = 2(100) = 200$$
The power is 200 watts.

Applying Concepts 6.5

49. a.

b. The graph represents a linear function.

50. a.

b. The graph represents a linear function.

51. a.

b. The graph is the graph of a function.

52. a.

b. The graph is the graph of a function.

53. If y doubles, x is halved.

54. If x doubles, y doubles.

55. If a varies directly as b and inversely as c, then c varies *directly* as b and *inversely* as a.

56. If a varies *inversely* as b and c, then abc is constant.

57. If the width of a rectangle is held constant, the area of the rectangle varies *directly* as the length.

58. If the area of a rectangle is held constant, the length of the rectangle varies *inversely* as the width.

59. a. The average of a and b is $\dfrac{1}{h} = \dfrac{\frac{1}{a} + \frac{1}{b}}{2}$.

Solving for h,

$$\frac{1}{h} = \frac{\frac{1}{a} + \frac{1}{b}}{2}$$

$$2h\frac{1}{h} = 2h\frac{\frac{1}{a} + \frac{1}{b}}{2}$$

$$2 = h\left(\frac{1}{a} + \frac{1}{b}\right)$$

$$2ab = abh\left(\frac{1}{a} + \frac{1}{b}\right)$$

$$2ab = bh + ah$$

$$2ab = h(b + a)$$

$$\frac{2ab}{a+b} = h$$

b. Using the expression, $\dfrac{2ab}{a+b}$

$$\frac{2(10)(15)}{10+15} = \frac{300}{25} = 12$$

60. Probably the most familiar financial ratio is the *price/earnings ratio*. This is the ratio of the price of a stock to the earnings per share of the stock. Another financial ratio is the *current ratio*, which is the ratio of the current assets to current liabilities. A current ratio of 2.14 means that there is $2.14 available now to pay each current $1 in liabilities. The *quick ratio* is the ratio of current assets minus inventories to current liabilities. Other examples of financial ratios include the ratio of stockholders' equity to liabilities and the ratio of plant and equipment to long-term liabilities.

Section 6.6

Concept Review 6.6

1. Always true

2. Sometimes true

$A = \dfrac{1}{2} bh$ contains three variables.

3. Never true

$R_2 = \dfrac{R_1 R}{R_1 - R}$

4. Sometimes true
The rectangle with a width of 2 ft and a length of 4 ft has the same perimeter as a rectangle with a width of 1 ft and a length of 5 ft.

Objective 6.6.1 Exercises

1.
$$P = 2L + 2W$$
$$P - 2L = 2W$$
$$\frac{P - 2L}{2} = W$$

2.
$$F = \frac{9}{5}C + 32$$
$$F - 32 = \frac{9}{5}C$$
$$\frac{5}{9}(F - 32) = \frac{5}{9}\left(\frac{9}{5}C\right)$$
$$\frac{5}{9}(F - 32) = C$$

3.
$$S = C - rC$$
$$S = C(1 - r)$$
$$\frac{S}{1 - r} = C$$

4.
$$A = P + Prt$$
$$A - P = Prt$$
$$\frac{A - P}{Pr} = t$$

5.
$$PV = nRT$$
$$\frac{PV}{nT} = R$$

6.
$$A = \frac{1}{2}bh$$
$$2A = bh$$
$$\frac{2A}{b} = h$$

7.
$$F = \frac{Gm_1 m_2}{r^2}$$
$$Fr^2 = Gm_1 m_2$$
$$\frac{Fr^2}{Gm_1} = m_2$$

8.
$$\frac{P_1 V_1}{T_1} = \frac{P_2 V_2}{T_2}$$
$$\frac{P_1 V_1 T_2}{T_1} = P_2 V_2$$
$$\frac{P_1 V_1 T_2}{T_1 V_2} = P_2$$

9.
$$I = \frac{E}{R + r}$$
$$I(R + r) = E$$
$$IR + Ir = E$$
$$IR = E - Ir$$
$$R = \frac{E - Ir}{I}$$

10.
$$S = V_0 t - 16t^2$$
$$S + 16t^2 = V_0 t$$
$$\frac{S + 16t^2}{t} = V_0$$

11.
$$A = \frac{1}{2}h(b_1 + b_2)$$
$$2A = h(b_1 + b_2)$$
$$2A = hb_1 + hb_2$$
$$2A - hb_1 = hb_2$$
$$\frac{2A - hb_1}{h} = b_2$$

12.
$$V = \frac{1}{3}\pi r^2 h$$
$$3V = \pi r^2 h$$
$$\frac{3V}{\pi r^2} = h$$

13.
$$\frac{1}{R} = \frac{1}{R_1} + \frac{1}{R_2}$$
$$RR_1R_2\left(\frac{1}{R}\right) = RR_1R_2\left(\frac{1}{R_1} + \frac{1}{R_2}\right)$$
$$R_1R_2 = RR_1R_2\left(\frac{1}{R_1}\right) + RR_1R_2\left(\frac{1}{R_2}\right)$$
$$R_1R_2 = RR_2 + RR_1$$
$$R_1R_2 - RR_2 = RR_1$$
$$R_2(R_1 - R) = RR_1$$
$$R_2 = \frac{RR_1}{R_1 - R}$$

14.
$$\frac{1}{f} = \frac{1}{a} + \frac{1}{b}$$
$$abf\left(\frac{1}{f}\right) = abf\left(\frac{1}{a} + \frac{1}{b}\right)$$
$$ab = abf\left(\frac{1}{a}\right) + abf\left(\frac{1}{b}\right)$$
$$ab = bf + af$$
$$ab - bf = af$$
$$b(a - f) = af$$
$$b = \frac{af}{a - f}$$

15.
$$a_n = a_1 + (n-1)d$$
$$a_n - a_1 = (n-1)d$$
$$\frac{a_n - a_1}{n - 1} = d$$

16.
$$P = \frac{R - C}{n}$$
$$Pn = R - C$$
$$Pn + C = R$$

17.
$$S = 2WH + 2WL + 2LH$$
$$S - 2WL = 2WH + 2LH$$
$$S - 2WL = H(2W + 2L)$$
$$\frac{S - 2WL}{2W + 2L} = H$$

18.
$$S = 2\pi r^2 + 2\pi rH$$
$$S - 2\pi r^2 = 2\pi rH$$
$$\frac{S - 2\pi r^2}{2\pi r} = H$$

19.
$$ax + by + c = 0$$
$$ax + by = -c$$
$$ax = -by - c$$
$$x = \frac{-by - c}{a}$$

20.
$$x = ax + b$$
$$x - ax = b$$
$$x(1 - a) = b$$
$$x = \frac{b}{1 - a}$$

21.
$$ax + b = cx + d$$
$$ax + b - cx = d$$
$$ax - cx = d - b$$
$$x(a - c) = d - b$$
$$x = \frac{d - b}{a - c}$$

22.
$$y - y_1 = m(x - x_1)$$
$$\frac{y - y_1}{m} = x - x_1$$
$$\frac{y - y_1}{m} + x_1 = x$$
$$\frac{y - y_1}{m} + \frac{mx_1}{m} = x$$
$$\frac{y - y_1 + mx_1}{m} = x$$

23.
$$\frac{a}{x} = \frac{b}{c}$$
$$xc \cdot \frac{a}{x} = xc \cdot \frac{b}{c}$$
$$ac = xb$$
$$\frac{ac}{b} = x$$

24.
$$\frac{1}{x} + \frac{1}{a} = b$$
$$ax\left(\frac{1}{x} + \frac{1}{a}\right) = axb$$
$$a + x = axb$$
$$a = axb - x$$
$$a = x(ab - 1)$$
$$\frac{a}{ab - 1} = x$$

25.
$$\frac{1}{a} + \frac{1}{b} = \frac{1}{x}$$
$$abx\left(\frac{1}{a} + \frac{1}{b}\right) = abx\left(\frac{1}{x}\right)$$
$$bx + ax = ab$$
$$x(a + b) = ab$$
$$x = \frac{ab}{a + b}$$

26.
$$a(a-x) = b(b-x)$$
$$a^2 - ax = b^2 - bx$$
$$a^2 - ax + bx = b^2$$
$$-ax + bx = b^2 - a^2$$
$$x(-a+b) = b^2 - a^2$$
$$x = \frac{b^2 - a^2}{-a+b}$$
$$x = \frac{(b+a)(b-a)}{b-a}$$
$$x = b + a = a + b$$

Applying Concepts 6.6

27.
$$\frac{x-y}{y} = \frac{x+5}{2y}$$
$$2y\left(\frac{x-y}{y}\right) = 2y\left(\frac{x+5}{2y}\right)$$
$$2(x-y) = x+5$$
$$2x - 2y = x + 5$$
$$x - 2y = 5$$
$$x = 2y + 5$$
The solution is $2y + 5$.

28.
$$\frac{x-2}{y} = \frac{x+2}{5y}$$
$$5y\left(\frac{x-2}{y}\right) = 5y\left(\frac{x+2}{5y}\right)$$
$$5(x-2) = x+2$$
$$5x - 10 = x + 2$$
$$4x - 10 = 2$$
$$4x = 12$$
$$x = 3$$
The solution is 3.

29.
$$\frac{x}{x+y} = \frac{2x}{4y}$$
$$(4y)(x+y)\left(\frac{x}{x+y}\right) = (4y)(x+y)\left(\frac{2x}{4y}\right)$$
$$(4y)(x) = (x+y)(2x)$$
$$4xy = 2x^2 + 2xy$$
$$2xy = 2x^2$$
$$0 = 2x^2 - 2xy$$
$$0 = 2x(x-y)$$
$$2x = 0 \qquad x - y = 0$$
$$x = 0 \qquad x = y$$
The solutions are 0 and y.

30.
$$\frac{2x}{x-2y} = \frac{x}{2y}$$
$$(2y)(x-2y)\left(\frac{2x}{x-2y}\right) = (2y)(x-2y)\left(\frac{x}{2y}\right)$$
$$(2y)(2x) = (x-2y)(x)$$
$$4xy = x^2 - 2xy$$
$$6xy = x^2$$
$$0 = x^2 - 6xy$$
$$0 = x(x - 6y)$$
$$x = 0 \qquad x - 6y = 0$$
$$\qquad\qquad x = 6y$$
The solutions are 0 and $6y$.

31.
$$\frac{x-y}{2x} = \frac{x-3y}{5y}$$
$$(2x)(5y)\left(\frac{x-y}{2x}\right) = (2x)(5y)\left(\frac{x-3y}{5y}\right)$$
$$(5y)(x-y) = (2x)(x-3y)$$
$$5xy - 5y^2 = 2x^2 - 6xy$$
$$-5y^2 = 2x^2 - 11xy$$
$$0 = 2x^2 - 11xy + 5y^2$$
$$0 = (2x-y)(x-5y)$$
$$2x - y = 0 \qquad x - 5y = 0$$
$$2x = y \qquad x = 5y$$
$$x = \frac{y}{2}$$
The solutions are $\frac{y}{2}$ and $5y$.

32.
$$\frac{x-y}{x} = \frac{2x}{9y}$$
$$9xy\left(\frac{x-y}{x}\right) = 9xy\left(\frac{2x}{9y}\right)$$
$$9y(x-y) = x(2x)$$
$$9xy - 9y^2 = 2x^2$$
$$-9y^2 = 2x^2 - 9xy$$
$$0 = 2x^2 - 9xy + 9y^2$$
$$0 = (x-3y)(2x-3y)$$
$$x - 3y = 0 \qquad 2x - 3y = 0$$
$$x = 3y \qquad 2x = 3y$$
$$\qquad\qquad x = \frac{3y}{2}$$
The solutions are $3y$ and $\frac{3y}{2}$.

33.
$$\frac{w_1}{w_2} = \frac{f_2 - f}{f - f_1}$$
$$w_2(f - f_1)\left(\frac{w_1}{w_2}\right) = \left(\frac{f_2 - f}{f - f_1}\right)w_2(f - f_1)$$
$$(f - f_1)w_1 = (f_2 - f)w_2$$
$$fw_1 - f_1 w_1 = f_2 w_2 - f w_2$$
$$fw_1 + fw_2 = f_2 w_2 + f_1 w_1$$
$$f(w_1 + w_2) = f_2 w_2 + f_1 w_1$$
$$f = \frac{f_2 w_2 + f_1 w_1}{w_1 + w_2}$$

34.
$$v = \frac{v_1 + v_2}{1 + \frac{v_1 v_2}{c^2}}$$

$$\left(1 + \frac{v_1 v_2}{c^2}\right)v = \frac{v_1 + v_2}{1 + \frac{v_1 v_2}{c^2}}\left(1 + \frac{v_1 v_2}{c^2}\right)$$

$$v + \frac{v_1 v_2 v}{c^2} = v_1 + v_2$$

$$c^2\left(v + \frac{v v_1 v_2}{c^2}\right) = (v_1 + v_2)c^2$$

$$c^2 v + v v_1 v_2 = c^2 v_1 + c^2 v_2$$

$$c^2 v - c^2 v_2 = c^2 v_1 - v v_1 v_2$$

$$c^2 v - c^2 v_2 = v_1(c^2 - v v_2)$$

$$\frac{c^2 v - c^2 v_2}{c^2 - v v_2} = v_1$$

Focus on Problem Solving

1. Statement: If I live in Chicago, then I live in Illinois.
   Contrapositive: If I do not live in Illinois, then I do not live in Chicago.
   Converse: If I live in Illinois, then I live in Chicago.
   The converse is not true.

2. Statement: If today is June 1, then yesterday was May 31.
   Contrapositive: If yesterday was not May 31, then today is not June 1.
   Converse: If yesterday was May 31, then today is June 1.
   The converse is true. Today is June 1 if and only if yesterday was May 31.

3. Statement: If today is not Thursday, then tomorrow is not Friday.
   Contrapositive: If tomorrow is Friday, then today is Thursday.
   Converse: If tomorrow is not Friday, then today is not Thursday.
   The converse is true. Today is not Thursday if and only if tomorrow is not Friday.

4. Statement: If a number is divisible by 8, then it is divisible by 4.
   Contrapositive: If a number is not divisible by 4, then it is not divisible by 8.
   Converse: If a number is divisible by 4, then it is divisible by 8.
   The converse is not true.

5. Statement: If a number is an even number, then it is divisible by 4..
   Contrapositive: If a number is not divisible by 2, then it is not an even number.
   Converse: If a number is divisible by 2, then it is an even number..
   The converse is true. A number is an even number if and only if it is divisible by 2.

6. Statement: If a number is a multiple of 6, then it is a multiple of 3.
   Contrapositive: If a number is not a multiple of 3, then it is not a multiple of 6.
   Converse: If a number is a multiple of 3, then it is a multiple of 6.
   The converse is not true.

7. Statement: If $4z = 20$, then $z = 5$.
   Contrapositive: If $z \neq 5$, then $4z \neq 20$.
   Converse: If $z = 5$, then $4z = 20$.
   The converse is true. $4z = 20$ if and only if $z = 5$.

8. Statement: If an angle measures 90°, then it is a right angle.
   Contrapositive: If an angle is not a right angle, then it does not measure 90°.
   Converse: If an angle is a right angle, then it measures 90°.
   The converse is true. An angle measures 90° if and only if it is a right angle.

9. Statement: If p is a prime number greater than 2, then p is an odd number.
   Contrapositive: If p is not an odd number then it is not a prime number greater than 2.
   Converse: If p is an odd number, then it is a prime number greater than 2.
   The converse is not true.

10. Statement: If the equation of a graph is $y = mx + b$, then the graph of the equation is a straight line.
    Contrapositive: If the graph of an equation is not a straight line, then the equation of the graph is not $y = mx + b$.
    Converse: If the graph of an equation is a straight line, then the equation of the graph is $y = mx + b$.
    The converse is true. The equation of a graph is $y = mx + b$ if and only if the graph of the equation is a straight line.

11. Statement: If $a = 0$ or $b = 0$, then $ab = 0$.
    Contrapositive: If $ab \neq 0$, then $a \neq 0$ and $b \neq 0$.
    Converse: If $ab = 0$, then $a = 0$ or $b = 0$.
    The converse is true. $a = 0$ or $b = 0$ if and only if $ab = 0$.

12. Statement: If the coordinates of a point are (5, 0), then the point is on the x-axis.
    Contrapositive: If a point is not on the x-axis, then the coordinates of the point are not (5, 0).
    Converse: If a point is on the x-axis, then the coordinates of the point are (5, 0).
    The converse is not true.

13. Statement: If a quadrilateral is a square, then the quadrilateral has four sides of equal length.
    Contrapositive: If a quadrilateral does not have four sides of equal length, then the quadrilateral is not a square.
    Converse: If a quadrilateral has four sides of equal length, then the quadrilateral is a square.
    The converse is not true.

14. Statement: If $x = y$, then $x^2 = y^2$.
Contrapositive: If $x^2 \neq y^2$, then $x \neq y$.
Converse: If $x^2 = y^2$, then $x = y$.
The converse is not true.

Projects and Group Activities

Continued Fractions

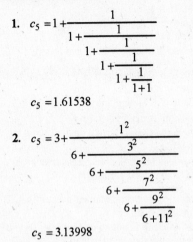

1. $c_5 = 1 + \cfrac{1}{1 + \cfrac{1}{1 + \cfrac{1}{1 + \cfrac{1}{1 + \cfrac{1}{1+1}}}}}$

$c_5 = 1.61538$

2. $c_5 = 3 + \cfrac{1^2}{6 + \cfrac{3^2}{6 + \cfrac{5^2}{6 + \cfrac{7^2}{6 + \cfrac{9^2}{6 + 11^2}}}}}$

$c_5 = 3.13998$

Transformers

1. $2000 = \dfrac{1000 I_2}{40}$
$80,000 = 1000 I_2$
$80 = I_2$
The current is 80 amperes.

2. $180 = \dfrac{9 I_2}{15}$
$2700 = 9 I_2$
$300 = I_2$
The current is 300 amperes.

3. $120 = \dfrac{9 I_2}{12}$
$1440 = 9 I_2$
$160 = I_2$
The current is 160 amperes.

4. $120 = \dfrac{40 V_2}{12}$
$1440 = 40 V_2$
$36 = V_2$
The voltage is 36 volts

5. $12 = \dfrac{60 V_2}{4.5}$
$54 = 60 V_2$
$0.9 = V_2$
The voltage is 0.9 volt.

6. $8 = \dfrac{400 V_2}{500}$
$4000 = 400 V_2$
$10 = V_2$
The voltage is 10 volts.

Chapter Review Exercises

1. $P(x) = \dfrac{x}{x-3}$
$P(4) = \dfrac{4}{4-3} = \dfrac{4}{1}$
$P(4) = 4$

2. $P(x) = \dfrac{x^2 - 2}{3x^2 - 2x + 5}$
$P(-2) = \dfrac{(-2)^2 - 2}{3(-2)^2 - 2(-2) + 5} = \dfrac{4-2}{12 + 4 + 5} = \dfrac{2}{21}$
$P(-2) = \dfrac{2}{21}$

3. $g(x) = \dfrac{2x}{x-3}$
$x - 3 = 0$
$x = 3$
The domain is $\{x | x \neq 3\}$

4. $f(x) = \dfrac{2x - 7}{3x^2 + 3x - 18}$
$3x^2 + 3x - 18 = 0$
$3(x^2 + x - 6) = 0$
$3(x + 3)(x - 2) = 0$
$x + 3 = 0 \qquad x - 2 = 0$
$\quad x = -3 \qquad\quad x = 2$
The domain is $\{x | x \neq -3, x \neq 2\}$.

5. The domain must exclude values of x for which $3x^2 + 4 = 0$. This is not possible, because $3x^2 \geq 0$, and a positive number added to a number equal to or greater than zero cannot equal zero. Therefore, there are no real numbers that must be excluded from the domain of F.
The domain of $F(x)$ is $\{x | x$ is a real number$\}$

6. $\dfrac{6a^{5n} + 4a^{4n} - 2a^{3n}}{2a^{3n}} = 3a^{2n} + 2a^n - 1$

7. $\dfrac{16 - x^2}{x^3 - 2x^2 - 8x} = \dfrac{(4+x)(4-x)}{x(x^2 - 2x - 8)}$
$= \dfrac{(4+x)(4-x)}{x(x-4)(x+2)}$
$= \dfrac{(4+x)(-1)}{x(1)(x+2)}$
$= -\dfrac{x+4}{x(x+2)}$

8. $\dfrac{x^3 - 27}{x^2 - 9} = \dfrac{(x-3)(x^2 + 3x + 9)}{(x+3)(x-3)} = \dfrac{x^2 + 3x + 9}{x+3}$

9. $\dfrac{a^6b^4 + a^4b^6}{a^5b^4 - a^4b^4} \cdot \dfrac{a^2 - b^2}{a^4 - b^4}$

$= \dfrac{a^4b^4(a^2 + b^2)}{a^4b^4(a-1)} \cdot \dfrac{(a+b)(a-b)}{(a^2+b^2)(a+b)(a-b)}$

$= \dfrac{a^4b^4(a^2+b^2)(a+b)(a-b)}{a^4b^4(a-1)(a^2+b^2)(a+b)(a-b)}$

$= \dfrac{1}{a-1}$

10. $\dfrac{x^3 - 8}{x^3 + 2x^2 + 4x} \cdot \dfrac{x^3 + 2x^2}{x^2 - 4}$

$= \dfrac{(x-2)(x^2+2x+4)}{x(x^2+2x+4)} \cdot \dfrac{x^2(x+2)}{(x+2)(x-2)}$

$= \dfrac{(x-2)(x^2+2x+4) \cdot x^2(x+2)}{x(x^2+2x+4)(x+2)(x-2)}$

$= x$

11. $\dfrac{16 - x^2}{6x - 6} \cdot \dfrac{x^2 + 5x + 6}{x^2 - 8x + 16}$

$= \dfrac{(4+x)(4-x)}{6(x-1)} \cdot \dfrac{(x+3)(x+2)}{(x-4)(x-4)}$

$= \dfrac{(4+x)(4-x)(x+3)(x+2)}{6(x-1)(x-4)(x-4)}$

$= -\dfrac{(x+4)(x+3)(x+2)}{6(x-1)(x-4)}$

12. $\dfrac{x^{2n} - 5x^n + 4}{x^{2n} - 2x^n - 8} \div \dfrac{x^{2n} - 4x^n + 3}{x^{2n} + 8x^n + 12}$

$= \dfrac{x^{2n} - 5x^n + 4}{x^{2n} - 2x^n - 8} \cdot \dfrac{x^{2n} + 8x^n + 12}{x^{2n} - 4x^n + 3}$

$= \dfrac{(x^n - 4)(x^n - 1)}{(x^n - 4)(x^n + 2)} \cdot \dfrac{(x^n + 6)(x^n + 2)}{(x^n - 3)(x^n - 1)}$

$= \dfrac{(x^n - 4)(x^n - 1)(x^n + 6)(x^n + 2)}{(x^n - 4)(x^n + 2)(x^n - 3)(x^n - 1)}$

$= \dfrac{x^n + 6}{x^n - 3}$

13. $\dfrac{27x^3 - 8}{9x^3 + 6x^2 + 4x} \div \dfrac{9x^2 - 12x + 4}{9x^2 - 4}$

$= \dfrac{27x^3 - 8}{9x^3 + 6x^2 + 4x} \cdot \dfrac{9x^2 - 4}{9x^2 - 12x + 4}$

$= \dfrac{(3x-2)(9x^2+6x+4)}{x(9x^2+6x+4)} \cdot \dfrac{(3x+2)(3x-2)}{(3x-2)(3x-2)}$

$= \dfrac{(3x-2)(9x^2+6x+4)(3x+2)(3x-2)}{x(9x^2+6x+4)(3x-2)(3x-2)}$

$= \dfrac{3x+2}{x}$

14. $\dfrac{3-x}{x^2 + 3x + 9} \div \dfrac{x^2 - 9}{x^3 - 27}$

$= \dfrac{3-x}{x^2 + 3x + 9} \cdot \dfrac{x^3 - 27}{x^2 - 9}$

$= \dfrac{3-x}{x^2 + 3x + 9} \cdot \dfrac{(x-3)(x^2 + 3x + 9)}{(x+3)(x-3)}$

$= \dfrac{(3-x)(x-3)(x^2 + 3x + 9)}{(x^2 + 3x + 9)(x+3)(x-3)}$

$= \dfrac{3-x}{x+3}$

$= \dfrac{(-1)(x-3)}{x+3}$

$= -\dfrac{x-3}{x+3}$

15. The LCM is $24a^2b^4$.

$\dfrac{5}{3a^2b^3} + \dfrac{7}{8ab^4} = \dfrac{5}{3a^2b^3} \cdot \dfrac{8b}{8b} + \dfrac{7}{8ab^4} \cdot \dfrac{3a}{3a}$

$= \dfrac{40b + 21a}{24a^2b^4}$

16. $\dfrac{3x^2 + 2}{x^2 - 4} - \dfrac{9x - x^2}{x^2 - 4} = \dfrac{3x^2 + 2 - (9x - x^2)}{x^2 - 4}$

$= \dfrac{3x^2 + 2 - 9x + x^2}{x^2 - 4}$

$= \dfrac{4x^2 - 9x + 2}{x^2 - 4}$

$= \dfrac{(4x-1)(x-2)}{(x+2)(x-2)}$

$= \dfrac{4x-1}{x+2}$

17. The LCM is $(3x + 2)(3x - 2)$.

$$\frac{8}{9x^2 - 4} + \frac{5}{3x - 2} - \frac{4}{3x + 2} = \frac{8}{(3x + 2)(3x - 2)} + \frac{5}{3x - 2} - \frac{4}{3x + 2}$$

$$= \frac{8}{(3x + 2)(3x - 2)} + \frac{5}{3x - 2} \cdot \frac{3x + 2}{3x + 2} - \frac{4}{3x + 2} \cdot \frac{3x - 2}{3x - 2}$$

$$= \frac{8 + 5(3x + 2) - 4(3x - 2)}{(3x + 2)(3x - 2)}$$

$$= \frac{8 + 15x + 10 - 12x + 8}{(3x + 2)(3x - 2)}$$

$$= \frac{3x + 26}{(3x + 2)(3x - 2)}$$

18. $3x^2 - 7x + 2 = (3x - 1)(x - 2)$

The LCM is $(3x - 1)(x - 2)$.

$$\frac{6x}{3x^2 - 7x + 2} - \frac{2}{3x - 1} + \frac{3x}{x - 2} = \frac{6x}{(3x - 1)(x - 2)} - \frac{2}{3x - 1} \cdot \frac{x - 2}{x - 2} + \frac{3x}{x - 2} \cdot \frac{3x - 1}{3x - 1}$$

$$= \frac{6x - 2(x - 2) + 3x(3x - 1)}{(3x - 1)(x - 2)}$$

$$= \frac{6x - 2x + 4 + 9x^2 - 3x}{(3x - 1)(x - 2)}$$

$$= \frac{9x^2 + x + 4}{(3x - 1)(x - 2)}$$

19. The LCM is $(x - 3)(x + 2)$.

$$= \frac{x}{x - 3} \cdot \frac{x + 2}{x + 2} - 4 \cdot \frac{(x - 3)(x + 2)}{(x - 3)(x + 2)} - \frac{2x - 5}{x + 2} \cdot \frac{x - 3}{x - 3}$$

$$\frac{x}{x - 3} - 4 - \frac{2x - 5}{x + 2} = \frac{x^2 + 2x - 4(x^2 - x - 6) - (2x^2 - 11x + 15)}{(x - 3)(x + 2)}$$

$$= \frac{x^2 + 2x - 4x^2 + 4x + 24 - 2x^2 + 11x - 15}{(x - 3)(x + 2)}$$

$$= \frac{-5x^2 + 17x + 9}{(x - 3)(x + 2)}$$

$$= \frac{-(5x^2 - 17x - 9)}{(x - 3)(x + 2)}$$

$$= -\frac{5x^2 - 17x - 9}{(x - 3)(x + 2)}$$

20. The LCM is $x - 1$.

$$\frac{x - 6 + \frac{6}{x - 1}}{x + 3 - \frac{12}{x - 1}} = \frac{x - 6 + \frac{6}{x - 1}}{x + 3 - \frac{12}{x - 1}} \cdot \frac{x - 1}{x - 1}$$

$$= \frac{(x - 6)(x - 1) + 6}{(x + 3)(x - 1) - 12}$$

$$= \frac{x^2 - 7x + 6 + 6}{x^2 + 2x - 3 - 12}$$

$$= \frac{x^2 - 7x + 12}{x^2 + 2x - 15}$$

$$= \frac{(x - 3)(x - 4)}{(x + 5)(x - 3)}$$

$$= \frac{x - 4}{x + 5}$$

21. The LCM is $x-4$.

$$\frac{x+\frac{3}{x-4}}{3+\frac{x}{x-4}}=\frac{x+\frac{3}{x-4}}{3+\frac{x}{x-4}}\cdot\frac{x-4}{x-4}$$

$$=\frac{x(x-4)+3}{3(x-4)+x}$$

$$=\frac{x^2-4x+3}{3x-12+x}$$

$$=\frac{(x-3)(x-1)}{4x-12}$$

$$=\frac{(x-3)(x-1)}{4(x-3)}$$

$$=\frac{x-1}{4}$$

22.

$$\frac{5x}{2x-3}+4=\frac{3}{2x-3}$$

$$(2x-3)\left(\frac{5x}{2x-3}+4\right)=\frac{3}{2x-3}(2x-3)$$

$$5x+4(2x-3)=3$$

$$5x+8x-12=3$$

$$13x-12=3$$

$$13x=15$$

$$x=\frac{15}{13}$$

The solution is $\frac{15}{13}$.

23.

$$\frac{x}{x-3}=\frac{2x+5}{x+1}$$

$$(x-3)(x+1)\left(\frac{x}{x-3}\right)=\left(\frac{2x+5}{x+1}\right)(x-3)(x+1)$$

$$(x+1)x=(2x+5)(x-3)$$

$$x^2+x=2x^2-x-15$$

$$0=x^2-2x-15$$

$$0=(x-5)(x+3)$$

$$x-5=0 \qquad x+3=0$$

$$x=5 \qquad x=-3$$

The solutions are 5 and −3.

24.

$$\frac{6}{x-3}-\frac{1}{x+3}=\frac{51}{x^2-9}$$

$$\frac{6}{x-3}-\frac{1}{x+3}=\frac{51}{(x+3)(x-3)}$$

$$(x+3)(x-3)\left(\frac{6}{x-3}-\frac{1}{x+3}\right)=\frac{51}{(x+3)(x-3)}\cdot(x+3)(x-3)$$

$$6(x+3)-1(x-3)=51$$

$$6x+18-x+3=51$$

$$5x+21=51$$

$$5x=30$$

$$x=6$$

The solution is 6.

25.

$$\frac{30}{x^2+5x+4}+\frac{10}{x+4}=\frac{4}{x+1}$$

$$\frac{30}{(x+4)(x+1)}+\frac{10}{x+4}=\frac{4}{x+1}$$

$$(x+4)(x+1)\left(\frac{30}{(x+4)(x+1)}+\frac{10}{x+4}\right)=\frac{4}{x+1}\cdot(x+4)(x+1)$$

$$30+10(x+1)=4(x+4)$$

$$30+10x+10=4x+16$$

$$10x+40=4x+16$$

$$6x+40=16$$

$$6x=-24$$

$$x=-4$$

-4 does not check as a solution. The equation has no solution.

26.

$$I=\frac{1}{R}V$$

$$R\cdot I=R\cdot\frac{1}{R}V$$

$$RI=V$$

$$\frac{RI}{I}=\frac{V}{I}$$

$$R=\frac{V}{I}$$

27.

$$Q=\frac{N-S}{N}$$

$$Q\cdot N=\frac{N-S}{N}\cdot N$$

$$QN=N-S$$

$$QN-N=-S$$

$$N(Q-1)=-S$$

$$N=\frac{-S}{Q-1}$$

$$N=\frac{S}{1-Q}$$

28.

$$S=\frac{a}{1-r}$$

$$S(1-r)=\frac{a}{1-r}(1-r)$$

$$S-Sr=a$$

$$-Sr=a-S$$

$$r=\frac{a-S}{-S}$$

$$r=\frac{S-a}{S}$$

29. Strategy

To find the number of tanks of fuel, write and solve a proportion using x to represent the number of tanks of fuel.

Solution

$$\frac{4}{1800}=\frac{x}{3000}$$

$$9000\cdot\frac{4}{1800}=\frac{x}{3000}\cdot9000$$

$$5\cdot4=3x$$

$$20=3x$$

$$x=\frac{20}{3}=6\frac{2}{3}$$

The number of tanks of fuel is $6\frac{2}{3}$.

30. Strategy

To find the number of miles represented, write and solve a proportion using x to represent the number of miles.

Solution

$$\frac{2.5}{10}=\frac{12}{x}$$

$$\frac{2.5}{10}\cdot10x=\frac{12}{x}\cdot10x$$

$$2.5x=120$$

$$x=48$$

The number of miles is 48.

31. Strategy

Unknown time for apprentice, working alone, to install fan: t

	Rate	Time	Part
Electrician	$\frac{1}{65}$	40	$\frac{40}{65}$
Apprentice	$\frac{1}{t}$	40	$\frac{40}{t}$

The sum of the part of the task completed by the electrician and the part of the task completed by the apprentice is 1.

$$\frac{40}{65} + \frac{40}{t} = 1$$

Solution

$$\frac{40}{65} + \frac{40}{t} = 1$$
$$65t\left(\frac{40}{65} + \frac{40}{t}\right) = 1 \cdot 65t$$
$$40t + 2600 = 65t$$
$$2600 = 25t$$
$$104 = t$$

The apprentice would take 104 min to complete the job alone.

32. Strategy

Unknown time to empty a full tub when both pipes are open: t

	Rate	Time	Part
Inlet pipe	$\frac{1}{24}$	t	$\frac{t}{24}$
Drain pipe	$\frac{1}{15}$	t	$\frac{t}{15}$

The difference between the part of the job done by the drain and the part of the job done by the inlet pipe is 1.

Solution

$$\frac{t}{15} - \frac{t}{24} = 1$$
$$120\left(\frac{t}{15} - \frac{t}{24}\right) = 1(120)$$
$$8t - 5t = 120$$
$$3t = 120$$
$$t = 40$$

It takes 40 min to empty the tub.

33. Strategy

Unknown time for 3 students to paint dormitory room working together: t

	Rate	Time	Part
1st painter	$\frac{1}{8}$	t	$\frac{t}{8}$
2nd painter	$\frac{1}{16}$	t	$\frac{t}{16}$
3rd painter	$\frac{1}{16}$	t	$\frac{t}{16}$

The sum of the parts of the task completed by 3 painters is 1.

Solution

$$\frac{t}{8} + \frac{t}{16} + \frac{t}{16} = 1$$
$$16\left(\frac{t}{8} + \frac{t}{16} + \frac{t}{16}\right) = 1(16)$$
$$2t + t + t = 16$$
$$4t = 16$$
$$t = 4$$

It takes 4 h for the 3 painters to paint the dormitory room.

34. Strategy

Rate of the current: c

	Distance	Rate	Time
With the current	60	$10 + c$	$\frac{60}{10+c}$
Against the current	40	$10 - c$	$\frac{40}{10-c}$

The time traveling with the current is equal to the time traveling against the current.

$$\frac{60}{10+c} = \frac{40}{10-c}$$

Solution

$$\frac{60}{10+c} = \frac{40}{10-c}$$
$$(10+c)(10-c)\frac{60}{10+c} = (10+c)(10-c)\frac{40}{10-c}$$
$$(10-c)60 = 40(10+c)$$
$$600 - 60c = 400 + 40c$$
$$200 = 100c$$
$$2 = c$$

The rate of the current is 2 mph.

35. Strategy

Rate of cyclist: r

Rate of bus: $3r$

	Distance	Rate	Time
Bus	90	$3r$	$\frac{90}{3r}$
Cyclist	90	r	$\frac{90}{r}$

The cyclist arrives 4 h after the bus.

$$\frac{90}{3r} + 4 = \frac{90}{r}$$

Solution

$$\frac{90}{3r} + 4 = \frac{90}{r}$$

$$3r\left(\frac{90}{3r} + 4\right) = \frac{90}{r} \cdot 3r$$

$$90 + 12r = 270$$

$$12r = 180$$

$$r = 15$$

$$3r = 3(15) = 45$$

The rate of the bus is 45 mph.

36. Strategy

Rate of the car: r

Rate of the tractor: $r - 15$

	Distance	Rate	Time
Car	15	r	$\frac{15}{r}$
Tractor	10	$r - 15$	$\frac{10}{r-15}$

The time that the car travels equals the time that the tractor travels.

$$\frac{15}{r} = \frac{10}{r-15}$$

Solution

$$\frac{15}{r} = \frac{10}{r-15}$$

$$r(r-15)\left(\frac{15}{r}\right) = \left(\frac{10}{r-15}\right)r(r-15)$$

$$15(r-15) = 10r$$

$$15r - 225 = 10r$$

$$-225 = -5r$$

$$45 = r$$

$$r - 15 = 45 - 15 = 30$$

The rate of the tractor is 30 mph.

37. Strategy

To find the pressure:

Write the basic joint variation equation, replace the variables with the given values, and solve for k.

Write the joint variation equation, replacing k with its value. Substitute 22 ft^2 for A and 20 mph for v.

Solution

$$P = kAv^2$$

$$10 = k \cdot 22 \cdot 10^2$$

$$\frac{1}{220} = k$$

$$P = \frac{1}{220} Av^2$$

$$P = \frac{1}{220} \cdot 22(20^2) = 40$$

The pressure is 40 lb.

38. Strategy

To find the illumination:

Write the basic inverse variation equation, replace the variables with the given values, and solve for k.

Write the inverse variation equation, replacing k with its value. Substitute d for 2 and solve for T.

Solution

$$I = \frac{k}{d^2}$$

$$12 = \frac{k}{(10)^2}$$

$$1200 = k$$

$$I = \frac{1200}{d^2} = \frac{1200}{(2)^2} = 300$$

The illumination is 300 lumens.

39. Strategy
To find the resistance:
Write the basic combined variation equation, replace the variables with the given values, and solve for k.

Write the combined variation equation, replacing k with its value. Substitute 8000 for l and $\frac{1}{2}$ for d, and solve for r.

Solution
$$r = \frac{kl}{d^2}$$
$$3.2 = \frac{k \cdot 16,000}{\left(\frac{1}{4}\right)^2}$$
$$0.0000125 = k$$
$$r = \frac{0.0000125l}{d^2} = \frac{0.0000125(8000)}{\left(\frac{1}{2}\right)^2} = 0.4$$

The resistance is 0.4 ohm.

Chapter Test

1. $\dfrac{v^3 - 4v}{2v^2 - 5v + 2} = \dfrac{v(v^2 - 4)}{(2v - 1)(v - 2)}$
$$= \frac{v(v + 2)(v - 2)}{(2v - 1)(v - 2)}$$
$$= \frac{v(v + 2)}{2v - 1}$$

2. $\dfrac{2a^2 - 8a + 8}{4 + 4a - 3a^2} = \dfrac{2(a^2 - 4a + 4)}{(2 - a)(2 + 3a)}$
$$= \frac{2(a - 2)(a - 2)}{(2 - a)(2 + 3a)}$$
$$= -\frac{2(a - 2)}{3a + 2}$$

3. $\dfrac{3x^2 - 12}{5x - 15} \cdot \dfrac{2x^2 - 18}{x^2 + 5x + 6}$
$$= \frac{3(x + 2)(x - 2)}{5(x - 3)} \cdot \frac{2(x + 3)(x - 3)}{(x + 3)(x + 2)}$$
$$= \frac{3(x + 2)(x - 2)2(x + 3)(x - 3)}{5(x - 3)(x + 3)(x + 2)}$$
$$= \frac{6(x - 2)}{5}$$

4. $P(x) = \dfrac{3 - x^2}{x^3 - 2x^2 + 4}$
$$P(-1) = \frac{3 - (-1)^2}{(-1)^3 - 2(-1)^2 + 4} = \frac{3 - 1}{-1 - 2 + 4} = \frac{2}{1}$$
$$P(-1) = 2$$

5. $\dfrac{2x^2 - x - 3}{2x^2 - 5x + 3} \div \dfrac{3x^2 - x - 4}{x^2 - 1}$
$$= \frac{2x^2 - x - 3}{2x^2 - 5x + 3} \cdot \frac{x^2 - 1}{3x^2 - x - 4}$$
$$= \frac{(2x - 3)(x + 1)}{(2x - 3)(x - 1)} \cdot \frac{(x + 1)(x - 1)}{(3x - 4)(x + 1)}$$
$$= \frac{(2x - 3)(x + 1)(x + 1)(x - 1)}{(2x - 3)(x - 1)(3x - 4)(x + 1)}$$
$$= \frac{x + 1}{3x - 4}$$

6. $\dfrac{x^{2n} - x^n - 2}{x^{2n} + x^n} \cdot \dfrac{x^{2n} - x^n}{x^{2n} - 4}$
$$= \frac{(x^n - 2)(x^n + 1)}{x^n(x^n + 1)} \cdot \frac{x^n(x^n - 1)}{(x^n + 2)(x^n - 2)}$$
$$= \frac{(x^n - 2)(x^n + 1)x^n(x^n - 1)}{x^n(x^n + 1)(x^n + 2)(x^n - 2)}$$
$$= \frac{x^n - 1}{x^n + 2}$$

7. The LCM is $2x^2y^2$.
$$\frac{2}{x^2} + \frac{3}{y^2} - \frac{5}{2xy}$$
$$= \frac{2}{x^2} \cdot \frac{2y^2}{2y^2} + \frac{3}{y^2} \cdot \frac{2x^2}{2x^2} - \frac{5}{2xy} \cdot \frac{xy}{xy}$$
$$= \frac{4y^2}{2x^2y^2} + \frac{6x^2}{2x^2y^2} - \frac{5xy}{x^2y^2}$$
$$= \frac{4y^2 + 6x^2 - 5xy}{2x^2y^2}$$

8. The LCM is $(x-2)(x+2)$.

$$\frac{3x}{x-2} - 3 + \frac{4}{x+2} = \frac{3x}{x-2} \cdot \frac{x+2}{x+2} - 3\frac{(x-2)(x+2)}{(x-2)(x+2)} + \frac{4}{x+2} \cdot \frac{x-2}{x-2}$$

$$= \frac{3x(x+2) - 3(x-2)(x+2) + 4(x-2)}{(x+2)(x-2)}$$

$$= \frac{3x^2 + 6x - 3(x^2-4) + 4x - 8}{(x+2)(x-2)}$$

$$= \frac{3x^2 + 6x - 3x^2 + 12 + 4x - 8}{(x+2)(x-2)}$$

$$= \frac{10x + 4}{(x+2)(x-2)}$$

$$= \frac{2(5x+2)}{(x+2)(x-2)}$$

9. $f(x) = \dfrac{3x^2 - x + 1}{x^2 - 9}$

$x^2 - 9 = 0$

$(x+3)(x-3) = 0$

$x + 3 = 0 \qquad\qquad x - 3 = 0$

$\quad x = -3 \qquad\qquad\quad x = 3$

The domain is $\left\{ x \mid x \neq -3, 3 \right\}$

10. $x^2 + 3x - 4 = (x+4)(x-1)$

$x^2 - 1 = (x+1)(x-1)$

The LCM is $(x+4)(x-1)(x+1)$.

$$\frac{x+2}{x^2+3x-4} - \frac{2x}{x^2-1} = \frac{x+2}{(x+4)(x-1)} \cdot \frac{x+1}{x+1} - \frac{2x}{(x+1)(x-1)} \cdot \frac{x+4}{x+4}$$

$$= \frac{(x+2)(x+1) - 2x(x+4)}{(x+4)(x-1)(x+1)}$$

$$= \frac{x^2 + 3x + 2 - 2x^2 - 8x}{(x+4)(x-1)(x+1)}$$

$$= \frac{-x^2 - 5x + 2}{(x+1)(x+4)(x-1)}$$

$$= -\frac{x^2 + 5x - 2}{(x+1)(x+4)(x-1)}$$

11.
$$\frac{1 - \frac{1}{x} - \frac{12}{x^2}}{1 + \frac{6}{x} + \frac{9}{x^2}} = \frac{1 - \frac{1}{x} - \frac{12}{x^2}}{1 + \frac{6}{x} + \frac{9}{x^2}} \cdot \frac{x^2}{x^2}$$

$$= \frac{x^2 - x - 12}{x^2 + 6x + 9}$$

$$= \frac{(x-4)(x+3)}{(x+3)(x+3)}$$

$$= \frac{x-4}{x+3}$$

12.
$$\frac{1 - \frac{1}{x+2}}{1 - \frac{3}{x+4}} = \frac{1 - \frac{1}{x+2}}{1 - \frac{3}{x+4}} \cdot \frac{(x+2)(x+4)}{(x+2)(x+4)}$$

$$= \frac{(x+2)(x+4) - (x+4)}{(x+2)(x+4) - 3(x+2)}$$

$$= \frac{x^2 + 6x + 8 - x - 4}{x^2 + 6x + 8 - 3x - 6}$$

$$= \frac{x^2 + 5x + 4}{x^2 + 3x + 2}$$

$$= \frac{(x+4)(x+1)}{(x+2)(x+1)}$$

$$= \frac{x+4}{x+2}$$

13.
$$\frac{3}{x+1}=\frac{2}{x}$$
$$\frac{3}{x+1}\cdot x(x+1)=\frac{2}{x}\cdot x(x+1)$$
$$3x=2(x+1)$$
$$3x=2x+2$$
$$x=2$$
The solution is 2.

14.
$$\frac{4x}{2x-1}=2-\frac{1}{2x-1}$$
$$(2x-1)\frac{4x}{2x-1}=\left(2-\frac{1}{2x-1}\right)(2x-1)$$
$$4x=2(2x-1)-1$$
$$4x=4x-2-1$$
$$4x=4x-3$$
$$0=-3$$
There is no solution.

15.
$$ax=bx+c$$
$$ax-bx=c$$
$$x(a-b)=c$$
$$x=\frac{c}{a-b}$$

16. Strategy
Unknown time to empty the tank with both pipes open: t

	Rate	Time	Part
Inlet pipe	$\frac{1}{48}$	t	$\frac{t}{48}$
Outlet pipe	$\frac{1}{30}$	t	$\frac{t}{30}$

The difference between the part of the task completed by the outlet pipe and the part of the task completed by the inlet pipe is 1.
$$\frac{t}{30}-\frac{t}{48}=1$$

Solution
$$\frac{t}{30}-\frac{t}{48}=1$$
$$240\left(\frac{t}{30}-\frac{t}{48}\right)=240(1)$$
$$8t-5t=240$$
$$3t=240$$
$$t=80$$
It will take 80 min to empty the full tank with both pipes open.

17. Strategy
To find the number of rolls of wallpaper, write and solve a proportion using x to represent the number of rolls.

Solution
$$\frac{2}{45}=\frac{x}{315}$$
$$\left(\frac{2}{45}\right)315=\left(\frac{x}{315}\right)315$$
$$14=x$$
The office requires 14 rolls of wallpaper.

18. Strategy
Unknown time for both landscapers working together: t

	Rate	Time	Part
First landscaper	$\frac{1}{30}$	t	$\frac{t}{30}$
Second landscaper	$\frac{1}{15}$	t	$\frac{t}{15}$

The sum of the part of the task completed by the first landscaper and the part of the task completed by the second landscaper is 1.
$$\frac{t}{30}+\frac{t}{15}=1$$

Solution
$$\frac{t}{30}+\frac{t}{15}=1$$
$$30\left(\frac{t}{30}+\frac{t}{15}\right)=1(30)$$
$$t+2t=30$$
$$3t=30$$
$$t=10$$
Working together, the landscapers can complete the task in 10 min.

19. Strategy

Rate of hiker: r

Rate of cyclist: $r + 7$

	Distance	Rate	Time
Hiker	6	r	$\frac{6}{r}$
Cyclist	20	$r + 7$	$\frac{20}{r+7}$

The time the hiker hikes equals the time the cyclist cycles.

$$\frac{6}{r} = \frac{20}{r+7}$$

Solution

$$\frac{6}{r} = \frac{20}{r+7}$$
$$\frac{6}{r}[r(r+7)] = \frac{20}{r+7}[r(r+7)]$$
$$6(r+7) = 20r$$
$$6r + 42 = 20r$$
$$42 = 14r$$
$$3 = r$$
$$r + 7 = 3 + 7 = 10$$

The rate of the cyclist is 10 mph.

20. Strategy

To find the stopping distance:
Write the general direct variation equation, replace the variables by the given values, and solve for k.

Write the direct variation equation, replacing k by its value. Substitute 30 for v and solve for s.

Solution

$$s = kv^2$$
$$170 = k(50)^2$$
$$170 = k(2500)$$
$$0.068 = k$$

$$s = kv^2$$
$$= 0.068v^2$$
$$= 0.068(30)^2$$
$$= 0.068(900)$$
$$= 61.2$$

The stopping distance for a car traveling at 30 mph is 61.2 ft.

Cumulative Review Exercises

1. $8 - 4[-3 - (-2)]^2 \div 5$

$$= 8 - 4[-3 + 2]^2 \div 5$$
$$= 8 - 4[-1]^2 \div 5$$
$$= 8 - 4(1) \div 5$$
$$= 8 - 4 \div 5$$
$$= 8 - \frac{4}{5}$$
$$= \frac{36}{5}$$

2.
$$\frac{2x-3}{6} - \frac{x}{9} = \frac{x-4}{3}$$
$$18\left(\frac{2x-3}{6} - \frac{x}{9}\right) = \left(\frac{x-4}{3}\right)18$$
$$3(2x-3) - 2x = 6(x-4)$$
$$6x - 9 - 2x = 6x - 24$$
$$4x - 9 = 6x - 24$$
$$-2x = -15$$
$$x = \frac{15}{2}$$

3. $5 - |x - 4| = 2$
$$-|x-4| = -3$$
$$|x-4| = 3$$

$x - 4 = 3 \qquad x - 4 = -3$
$\quad x = 7 \qquad\qquad x = 1$

The solutions are 7 and 1.

4. $\dfrac{x}{x-3}$
$$x - 3 = 0$$
$$x = 3$$

The domain is $\{x | x \neq 3\}$

5. $P(x) = \dfrac{x-1}{2x-3}$
$$P(-2) = \frac{-2-1}{2(-2)-3} = \frac{-3}{-4-3} = \frac{-3}{-7}$$
$$P(-2) = \frac{3}{7}$$

6. $0.000000035 = 3.5 \times 10^{-8}$

7.
$$\frac{x}{x+1} = 1$$
$$(x+1)\frac{x}{x+1} = 1(x+1)$$
$$x = x + 1$$
$$0 \neq 1$$

There is no solution.

8. $(9x - 1)(x - 4) = 0$
$9x - 1 = 0 \qquad x - 4 = 0$
$\quad 9x = 1 \qquad\qquad x = 4$
$\quad x = \dfrac{1}{9}$

The solutions are $\dfrac{1}{9}$ and 4.

9. $\dfrac{(2a^{-2}b^3)}{(4a)^{-1}} = 2a^{-2}b^3 \, 4a$
$$= \frac{2b^3 \, 4a}{a^2}$$
$$= \frac{8b^3 a}{a^2}$$
$$= \frac{8b^3}{a}$$

10. $x - 3(1 - 2x) \geq 1 - 4(2 - 2x)$
$x - 3 + 6x \geq 1 - 8 + 8x$
$7x - 3 \geq 8x - 7$
$-x - 3 \geq -7$
$-x \geq -4$
$(-1)(-x) \leq (-1)(-4)$
$x \leq 4$
$\{x | x \leq 4\}$

11. $(2a^2 - 3a + 1)(-2a^2) = -4a^4 + 6a^3 - 2a^2$

12. Let $x^n = u$.
$2x^{2n} + 3x^n - 2 = 2u^2 + 3u - 2$
$= (2u - 1)(u + 2)$
$= (2x^n - 1)(x^n + 2)$

13. $x^3 y^3 - 27 = (xy)^3 - (3)^3$
$= (xy - 3)(x^2 y^2 + 3xy + 9)$

14. $\dfrac{x^4 + x^3 y - 6x^2 y^2}{x^3 - 2x^2 y} = \dfrac{x^2(x^2 + xy - 6y^2)}{x^2(x - 2y)}$
$= \dfrac{x^2(x + 3y)(x - 2y)}{x^2(x - 2y)}$
$= x + 3y$

15. $3x - 2y = 6$
$-2y = -3x + 6$
$y = \dfrac{3}{2}x - 3$
$m = \dfrac{3}{2}$
$y - y_1 = m(x - x_1)$
$y - (-1) = \dfrac{3}{2}[x - (-2)]$
$y + 1 = \dfrac{3}{2}(x + 2)$
$y + 1 = \dfrac{3}{2}x + 3$
$y = \dfrac{3}{2}x + 2$

The equation of the line is $y = \dfrac{3}{2}x + 2$.

16. $(x - x^{-1})^{-1} = \dfrac{1}{x - x^{-1}}$
$= \dfrac{1}{x - \dfrac{1}{x}}$
$= \dfrac{1}{x - \dfrac{1}{x}} \cdot \dfrac{x}{x}$
$= \dfrac{x}{x^2 - 1}$

17. $-3x + 5y = -15$
x-intercept: $(5, 0)$
y-intercept: $(0, -3)$

18. $x + y \leq 3$ $-2x + y > 4$
$y \leq 3 - x$ $y > 4 + 2x$

19. $\dfrac{4x^3 + 2x^2 - 10x + 1}{x - 2}$

$$
\begin{array}{r|rrrr}
2 & 4 & 2 & -10 & 1 \\
  &   & 8 & 20 & 20 \\
\hline
  & 4 & 10 & 10 & 21
\end{array}
$$

The simplified form is $4x^2 + 10x + 10 + \dfrac{21}{x - 2}$.

20. $\dfrac{16x^2 - 9y^2}{16x^2 y - 12xy^2} \div \dfrac{4x^2 - xy - 3y^2}{12x^2 y^2}$
$= \dfrac{16x^2 - 9y^2}{16x^2 y - 12xy^2} \cdot \dfrac{12x^2 y^2}{4x^2 - xy - 3y^2}$
$= \dfrac{(4x - 3y)(4x + 3y)}{4xy(4x - 3y)} \cdot \dfrac{12x^2 y^2}{(4x + 3y)(x - y)}$
$= \dfrac{(4x - 3y)(4x + 3y) \cdot 12x^2 y^2}{4xy(4x - 3y)(4x + 3y)(x - y)}$
$= \dfrac{3xy}{x - y}$

21. The domain must exclude values of x for which $3x^2 + 5 = 0$. This is not possible, because $3x^2 \geq 0$, and a positive number added to a number equal to or greater than zero cannot equal zero. Therefore, there are no real numbers that must be excluded from the domain of f.
The domain of $f(x)$ is $\{x | x \text{ is a real number}\}$.

22. $3x^2 - x - 2 = (3x+2)(x-1)$

$x^2 - 1 = (x+1)(x-1)$

The LCM is $(3x+2)(x+1)(x-1)$.

$$\frac{5x}{3x^2-x-2} - \frac{2x}{x^2-1}$$

$$= \frac{5x}{(3x+2)(x-1)} \cdot \frac{x+1}{x+1} - \frac{2x}{(x+1)(x-1)} \cdot \frac{3x+2}{3x+2}$$

$$= \frac{5x(x+1) - 2x(x+2)}{(3x+2)(x-1)(x+1)}$$

$$= \frac{5x^2 + 5x - 6x^2 - 4x}{(3x+2)(x-1)(x+1)}$$

$$= \frac{-x^2 + x}{(3x+2)(x-1)(x+1)}$$

$$= \frac{-x(x-1)}{(3x+2)(x-1)(x+1)}$$

$$= -\frac{x}{(3x+2)(x+1)}$$

23. $\begin{vmatrix} 6 & 5 \\ 2 & -3 \end{vmatrix} = 6(-3) - 5 \cdot 2 = -18 - 10 = -28$

24. $\dfrac{x-4+\frac{5}{x+2}}{x+2-\frac{1}{x+2}} = \dfrac{x-4+\frac{5}{x+2}}{x+2-\frac{1}{x+2}} \cdot \dfrac{x+2}{x+2}$

$$= \frac{(x-4)(x+2)+5}{(x+2)^2 - 1}$$

$$= \frac{x^2 - 2x - 8 + 5}{x^2 + 4x + 4 - 1}$$

$$= \frac{x^2 - 2x - 3}{x^2 + 4x + 3}$$

$$= \frac{(x-3)(x+1)}{(x+3)(x+1)}$$

$$= \frac{x-3}{x+3}$$

25.
$$x + y + z = 3$$
$$-2x + y + 3z = 2$$
$$2x - 4y + z = -1$$

$$D = \begin{vmatrix} 1 & 1 & 1 \\ -2 & 1 & 3 \\ 2 & -4 & 1 \end{vmatrix} = 27$$

$$D_x = \begin{vmatrix} 3 & 1 & 1 \\ 2 & 1 & 3 \\ -1 & -4 & 1 \end{vmatrix} = 27$$

$$D_y = \begin{vmatrix} 1 & 3 & 1 \\ -2 & 2 & 3 \\ 2 & -1 & 1 \end{vmatrix} = 27$$

$$D_z = \begin{vmatrix} 1 & 1 & 3 \\ -2 & 1 & 2 \\ 2 & -4 & -1 \end{vmatrix} = 27$$

$$x = \frac{D_x}{D} = \frac{27}{27} = 1$$

$$y = \frac{D_y}{D} = \frac{27}{27} = 1$$

$$z = \frac{D_z}{D} = \frac{27}{27} = 1$$

The solution is $(1, 1, 1)$.

26. $f(x) = x^2 - 3x + 3$

$f(c) = c^2 - 3c + 3$

$1 = c^2 - 3c + 3$

$c^2 - 3c + 2 = 0$

$(c-2)(c-1) = 0$

$c - 2 = 0 \qquad c - 1 = 0$

$\quad c = 2 \qquad \quad c = 1$

The solutions are 1 and 2.

27.
$$\frac{2}{x-3} = \frac{5}{2x-3}$$

$$\left(\frac{2}{x-3}\right)(x-3)(2x-3) = \left(\frac{5}{2x-3}\right)(x-3)(2x-3)$$

$$2(2x-3) = 5(x-3)$$

$$4x - 6 = 5x - 15$$

$$-x - 6 = -15$$

$$-x = -9$$

$$x = 9$$

The solution is 9.

28.
$$\frac{3}{x^2 - 36} = \frac{2}{x-6} - \frac{5}{x+6}$$

$$\frac{3}{(x+6)(x-6)} = \frac{2}{x-6} - \frac{5}{x+6}$$

$$(x+6)(x-6)\left(\frac{3}{(x+6)(x-6)}\right) = \left(\frac{2}{x-6} - \frac{5}{x+6}\right)(x+6)(x-6)$$

$$3 = 2(x+6) - 5(x-6)$$

$$3 = 2x + 12 - 5x + 30$$

$$3 = -3x + 42$$

$$-39 = -3x$$

$$13 = x$$

The solution is 13.

29. $(a+5)(a^3-3a+4) = a(a^3-3a+4)+5(a^3-3a+4)$
$$= a^4-3a^2+4a+5a^3-15a+20$$
$$= a^4+5a^3-3a^2-11a+20$$

30. $$I = \frac{E}{R+r}$$
$$I(R+r) = \frac{E}{R+r}(R+r)$$
$$IR+Ir = E$$
$$Ir = E-IR$$
$$r = \frac{E-IR}{I}$$

31. $4x+3y = 12$ $\qquad$ $3x+4y = 16$
$\quad 3y = -4x+12$ $\qquad$ $4y = -3x+16$
$\quad y = -\dfrac{4}{3}x+4$ $\qquad$ $y = -\dfrac{3}{4}x+4$

The lines are not perpendicular, since the slopes are not negative reciprocals of each other.

32.

33. Strategy
Smaller integer: x
Larger integer: $15-x$

Five times the smaller is five more than twice the larger.
$5x = 5+2(15-x)$

Solution
$5x = 5+2(15-x)$
$5x = 5+30-2x$
$7x = 35$
$x = 5$
$15-x = 10$
The smaller integer is 5 and larger integer is 10.

34. Strategy
The unknown number of pounds of almonds: x

	Amount	Cost	Total
Almonds	x	5.40	$5.40x$
Peanuts	50	2.60	$50(2.60)$
Mixture	$x+50$	4.00	$4(x+50)$

The sum of the values before mixing equals the value after mixing.
$5.40x + 50(2.60) = 4(x+50)$

Solution
$5.40x+50(2.60) = 4(x+50)$
$\quad 5.4x+130 = 4x+200$
$\quad 1.4x+130 = 200$
$\quad\quad\ 1.4x = 70$
$\quad\quad\quad x = 50$
The number of pounds of almonds is 50.

35. Strategy
To find the number of people expected to vote, write and solve a proportion using x to represent the number of people expected to vote.

Solution
$$\frac{3}{5} = \frac{x}{125,000}$$
$$\frac{3}{5}\cdot 125,000 = \frac{x}{125,000}\cdot 125,000$$
$$75,000 = x$$
The number of people expected to vote is 75,000.

36. Strategy
Time it takes older computer: $6r$
Time it takes new computer: r

	Rate	Time	Part
Older computer	$\frac{1}{6r}$	12	$\frac{12}{6r}$
New computer	$\frac{1}{r}$	12	$\frac{12}{r}$

The sum of the parts of the task completed by the older computer and the part of the task completed by the new computer is 1.
$$\frac{12}{6r}+\frac{12}{r} = 1$$

Solution
$$\frac{12}{6r}+\frac{12}{r} = 1$$
$$6r\left(\frac{12}{6r}+\frac{12}{r}\right) = (1)6r$$
$$12+72 = 6r$$
$$84 = 6r$$
$$14 = r$$
It takes the new computer 14 minutes to do the job working alone.

37. Strategy
Unknown rate of the wind: r

	Distance	Rate	Time
With the wind	900	$300 + r$	$\frac{900}{300+r}$
Against the wind	600	$300 - r$	$\frac{600}{300-r}$

The time traveled with the wind equals the time traveled against the wind.
$$\frac{900}{300+r} = \frac{600}{300-r}$$

Solution
$$\frac{900}{300+r} = \frac{600}{300-r}$$
$$(300+r)(300-r)\left(\frac{900}{300+r}\right) = \left(\frac{600}{300-r}\right)(300+r)(300-r)$$
$$(300-r)(900) = 600(300+r)$$
$$270,000 - 900r = 180,000 + 600r$$
$$-1500r = -90,000$$
$$r = 60$$

The rate of the wind is 60 mph.

38. Strategy
To find the frequency:
Write the basic inverse variation equation, replace the variables by the given values, and solve for k.

Write the inverse variation equation, replacing k by its value. Substitute 1.5 for L and solve for f.

Solution
$$f = \frac{k}{L}$$
$$60 = \frac{k}{2}$$
$$120 = k$$
$$f = \frac{120}{L} = \frac{120}{1.5} = 80$$

The frequency is 80 vibrations per minute.

Chapter 7: Rational Exponents and Radicals

Prep Test

1. $48 \div 3 = 16$ [1.2.1]
   $48 = 16 \cdot 3$

2. $2^5 = 2 \cdot 2 \cdot 2 \cdot 2 \cdot 2 = 32$ [1.3.2]

3. $6\left(\dfrac{3}{2}\right) = 9$ [1.2.2]

4. $\dfrac{1}{2} - \dfrac{2}{3} + \dfrac{1}{4} = \dfrac{6}{12} - \dfrac{8}{12} + \dfrac{3}{12} = \dfrac{1}{12}$ [1.2.2]

5. $(3 - 7x) - (4 - 2x)$ [1.3.3]
   $= 3 - 7x - 4 + 2x$
   $= -5x - 1$

6. $\dfrac{3x^5 y^6}{12x^4 y} = \dfrac{xy^5}{4}$ [5.1.2]

7. $(3x - 2)^2$ [5.3.3]
   $= (3x - 2)(3x - 2)$
   $= 9x^2 - 12x + 4$

8. $(2 + 4x)(5 - 3x)$ [5.3.2]
   $= 10 + 14x - 12x^2$
   $= -12x^2 + 14x + 10$

9. $(6x - 1)(6x + 1) = 36x^2 - 1$ [5.3.3]

10. $x^2 - 14x - 5 = 10$ [5.7.1
    $x^2 - 14x - 15 = 0$
    $(x - 15)(x + 1) = 0$
    $x - 15 = 0 \quad x + 1 = 0$
    $x = 15 \quad\quad x = -1$
    The solutions are -1, 15.

Go Figure

There are less than 10 tables. If you seat 5 people at each table, and there are two people at the last table, you may have as many as 47 guests or as few as 7 guests. However, since we also know that if we seat 3 people at each table and have 9 people with nowhere to sit, we know that neither 47 nor 7 is the solution.

The number of guests can be written as the expression $5x + 2$ from the first sentence and $3y + 9$, from the second sentence, where x and y represent the number of tables and are integers less than 10. We want to find the value of the expressions when they are equal.

One way to approach the solution is to use trial and error and try all values of tables until a solution is determined:

$5(9) + 2 = 47$	$3(9) + 9 = 36$
$5(8) + 2 = 42$	$3(8) + 9 = 33$
$5(7) + 2 = 37$	$3(7) + 9 = 30$
$5(6) + 2 = 32$	$3(6) + 9 = 27$
$5(5) + 2 = 27$	

There are 27 guests.

Section 7.1

Concept Review 7.1

1. Sometimes true
   $\sqrt{x^2} = x$ is true for positive numbers, false for negative numbers.

2. Never true
   $\sqrt{(-2)^2} = \sqrt{4} = 2$

3. Always true

4. Always true

5. Always true

6. Sometimes true
   An odd root of a negative number is negative. An even root of a negative number is not a real number.

Objective 7.1.1 Exercises

1. The nth root of a number a is equal to $a^{\frac{1}{n}}$, or $\sqrt[n]{a}$. It is a number that, when multiplied by itself n times, is equal to a.

2. Students may write that $a^{\frac{m}{n}}$ can be viewed as $\left(a^m\right)^{\frac{1}{n}}$, the nth root of a raised to the m power.

3. $8^{1/3} = (2^3)^{1/3} = 2$

4. $16^{1/2} = (2^4)^{1/2} = 2^2 = 4$

5. $9^{3/2} = (3^2)^{3/2} = 3^3 = 27$

6. $25^{3/2} = (5^2)^{3/2} = 5^3 = 125$

7. $27^{-2/3} = (3^3)^{-2/3} = 3^{-2} = \dfrac{1}{3^2} = \dfrac{1}{9}$

8. $64^{-1/3} = (2^6)^{-1/3} = 2^{-2} = \dfrac{1}{2^2} = \dfrac{1}{4}$

9. $32^{2/5} = (2^5)^{2/5} = 2^2 = 4$

10. $16^{3/4} = (2^4)^{3/4} = 2^3 = 8$

11. $(-25)^{5/2}$
    The base of the exponential expression is a negative number, while the denominator of the exponent is a positive even number.
    Therefore, $(-25)^{5/2}$ is not a real number.

12. $(-36)^{1/4}$
The base of the exponential expression is a negative number, while the denominator of the exponent is a positive even number.
Therefore, $(-36)^{1/4}$ is not a real number.

13. $\left(\dfrac{25}{49}\right)^{-3/2} = \left(\dfrac{5^2}{7^2}\right)^{-3/2} = \left[\left(\dfrac{5}{7}\right)^2\right]^{-3/2}$
$= \left(\dfrac{5}{7}\right)^{-3} = \dfrac{5^{-3}}{7^{-3}} = \dfrac{7^3}{5^3} = \dfrac{343}{125}$

14. $\left(\dfrac{8}{27}\right)^{-2/3} = \left(\dfrac{2^3}{3^3}\right)^{-2/3} = \left[\left(\dfrac{2}{3}\right)^3\right]^{-2/3}$
$= \left(\dfrac{2}{3}\right)^{-2} = \dfrac{2^{-2}}{3^{-2}} = \dfrac{3^2}{2^2} = \dfrac{9}{4}$

15. $x^{1/2}x^{1/2} = x$

16. $a^{1/3}a^{5/3} = a^2$

17. $y^{-1/4}y^{3/4} = y^{1/2}$

18. $x^{2/5} \cdot x^{-4/5} = x^{-2/5} = \dfrac{1}{x^{2/5}}$

19. $x^{-2/3} \cdot x^{3/4} = x^{1/12}$

20. $x \cdot x^{-1/2} = x^{1/2}$

21. $a^{1/3} \cdot a^{3/4} \cdot a^{-1/2} = a^{7/12}$

22. $y^{-1/6} \cdot y^{2/3} \cdot y^{1/2} = y$

23. $\dfrac{a^{1/2}}{a^{3/2}} = a^{-1} = \dfrac{1}{a}$

24. $\dfrac{b^{1/3}}{b^{4/3}} = b^{-1} = \dfrac{1}{b}$

25. $\dfrac{y^{-3/4}}{y^{1/4}} = y^{-1} = \dfrac{1}{y}$

26. $\dfrac{x^{-3/5}}{x^{1/5}} = x^{-4/5} = \dfrac{1}{x^{4/5}}$

27. $\dfrac{y^{2/3}}{y^{-5/6}} = y^{9/6} = y^{3/2}$

28. $\dfrac{b^{3/4}}{b^{-3/2}} = b^{9/4}$

29. $(x^2)^{-1/2} = x^{-1} = \dfrac{1}{x}$

30. $(a^8)^{-3/4} = a^{-6} = \dfrac{1}{a^6}$

31. $(x^{-2/3})^6 = x^{-4} = \dfrac{1}{x^4}$

32. $(y^{-5/6})^{12} = y^{-10} = \dfrac{1}{y^{10}}$

33. $(a^{-1/2})^{-2} = a$

34. $(b^{-2/3})^{-6} = b^4$

35. $(x^{-3/8})^{-4/5} = x^{3/10}$

36. $(y^{-3/2})^{-2/9} = y^{1/3}$

37. $(a^{1/2} \cdot a)^2 = (a^{3/2})^2 = a^3$

38. $(b^{2/3} \cdot b^{1/6})^6 = (b^{5/6})^6 = b^5$

39. $(x^{-1/2}x^{3/4})^{-2} = (x^{1/4})^{-2}$
$= x^{-1/2}$
$= \dfrac{1}{x^{1/2}}$

40. $(a^{1/2}a^{-2})^3 = (a^{-3/2})^3 = a^{-9/2} = \dfrac{1}{a^{9/2}}$

41. $(y^{-1/2}y^{3/2})^{2/3} = y^{2/3}$

42. $(b^{-2/3} \cdot b^{1/4})^{-4/3} = (b^{-5/12})^{-4/3} = b^{5/9}$

43. $(x^8y^2)^{1/2} = x^4y$

44. $(a^3b^9)^{2/3} = a^2b^6$

45. $(x^4y^2z^6)^{3/2} = x^6y^3z^9$

46. $(a^8b^4c^4)^{3/4} = a^6b^3c^3$

47. $(x^{-3}y^6)^{-1/3} = xy^{-2} = \dfrac{x}{y^2}$

48. $(a^2b^{-6})^{-1/2} = a^{-1}b^3 = \dfrac{b^3}{a}$

49. $(x^{-2}y^{1/3})^{-3/4} = x^{3/2}y^{-1/4} = \dfrac{x^{3/2}}{y^{1/4}}$

50. $(a^{-2/3}b^{2/3})^{3/2} = a^{-1}b = \dfrac{b}{a}$

51. $\left(\dfrac{x^{1/2}}{y^{-2}}\right)^4 = \dfrac{x^2}{y^{-8}} = x^2y^8$

52. $\left(\dfrac{b^{-3/4}}{a^{-1/2}}\right)^8 = \dfrac{b^{-6}}{a^{-4}} = \dfrac{a^4}{b^6}$

53. $\dfrac{x^{1/4} \cdot x^{-1/2}}{x^{2/3}} = \dfrac{x^{-1/4}}{x^{2/3}} = x^{-11/12} = \dfrac{1}{x^{11/12}}$

54. $\dfrac{b^{1/2} \cdot b^{-3/4}}{b^{1/4}} = \dfrac{b^{-1/4}}{b^{1/4}} = b^{-1/2} = \dfrac{1}{b^{1/2}}$

55. $\left(\dfrac{y^{2/3} \cdot y^{-5/6}}{y^{1/9}}\right)^9 = \left(\dfrac{y^{-1/6}}{y^{1/9}}\right)^9$

$\qquad = (y^{-5/18})^9$

$\qquad = y^{-5/2}$

$\qquad = \dfrac{1}{y^{5/2}}$

56. $\left(\dfrac{a^{1/3} \cdot a^{-2/3}}{a^{1/2}}\right) = \left(\dfrac{a^{-1/3}}{a^{1/2}}\right)^4$

$\qquad = (a^{-5/6})^4$

$\qquad = a^{-10/3}$

$\qquad = \dfrac{1}{a^{10/3}}$

57. $\left(\dfrac{b^2 \cdot b^{-3/4}}{b^{-1/2}}\right)^{-1/2} = \left(\dfrac{b^{5/4}}{b^{-1/2}}\right)^{-1/2}$

$\qquad = (b^{7/4})^{-1/2}$

$\qquad = b^{-7/8}$

$\qquad = \dfrac{1}{b^{7/8}}$

58. $\dfrac{(x^{-5/6} \cdot x^3)^{-2/3}}{x^{4/3}} = \dfrac{(x^{13/6})^{-2/3}}{x^{4/3}}$

$\qquad = \dfrac{x^{-13/9}}{x^{4/3}}$

$\qquad = x^{-25/9}$

$\qquad = \dfrac{1}{x^{25/9}}$

59. $(a^{2/3}b^2)^6(a^3b^3)^{1/3} = (a^4b^{12})(ab) = a^5b^{13}$

60. $(x^3y^{-1/2})^{-2}(x^{-3}y^2)^{1/6} = (x^{-6}y)(x^{-1/2}y^{1/3})$

$\qquad = x^{-13/2}y^{4/3}$

$\qquad = \dfrac{y^{4/3}}{x^{13/2}}$

61. $(16m^{-2}n^4)^{-1/2}(mn^{1/2}) = (2^4)^{-1/2}mn^{-2} \cdot mn^{1/2}$

$\qquad = 2^{-2}m^2n^{-3/2}$

$\qquad = \dfrac{m^2}{2^2 n^{3/2}}$

$\qquad = \dfrac{m^2}{4n^{3/2}}$

62. $(27m^3n^{-6})^{1/3}(m^{-1/3}n^{5/6})^6$

$\qquad = (3^3)^{1/3}mn^{-2} \cdot m^{-2}n^5$

$\qquad = 3m^{-1}n^3$

$\qquad = \dfrac{3n^3}{m}$

63. $\left(\dfrac{x^{1/2}y^{-3/4}}{y^{2/3}}\right)^{-6} = (x^{1/2}y^{-17/12})^{-6}$

$\qquad = x^{-3}y^{17/2}$

$\qquad = \dfrac{y^{17/2}}{x^3}$

64. $\left(\dfrac{x^{1/2}y^{-5/4}}{y^{-3/4}}\right)^{-4} = (x^{1/2}y^{-1/2})^{-4}$

$\qquad = x^{-2}y^2$

$\qquad = \dfrac{y^2}{x^2}$

65. $\left(\dfrac{2^{-6}b^{-3}}{a^{-1/2}}\right)^{-2/3} = \dfrac{2^4b^2}{a^{1/3}} = \dfrac{16b^2}{a^{1/3}}$

66. $\left(\dfrac{49c^{5/3}}{a^{-1/4}b^{5/6}}\right)^{-3/2} = \dfrac{(7^2)^{-3/2}c^{-5/2}}{a^{3/8}b^{-5/4}}$

$\qquad = \dfrac{7^{-3}c^{-5/2}}{a^{3/8}b^{-5/4}}$

$\qquad = \dfrac{b^{5/4}}{7^3 a^{3/8}c^{5/2}}$

$\qquad = \dfrac{b^{5/4}}{343a^{3/8}c^{5/2}}$

67. $\dfrac{(x^{-2}y^4)^{1/2}}{(x^{1/2})^4} = \dfrac{x^{-1}y^2}{x^2} = \dfrac{y^2}{x^3}$

68. $\dfrac{(x^{-3})^{1/3}}{(x^9y^6)^{1/6}} = \dfrac{x^{-1}}{x^{3/2}y} = \dfrac{1}{x^{5/2}y}$

69. $a^{-1/4}(a^{5/4} - a^{9/4}) = a^1 - a^2 = a - a^2$

70. $x^{4/3}(x^{2/3} + x^{-1/3}) = x^2 + x^1 = x^2 + x$

71. $y^{2/3}(y^{1/3} + y^{-2/3}) = y^1 + y^0 = y + 1$

72. $b^{-2/5}(b^{-3/5} - b^{7/5}) = b^{-1} - b^1 = \dfrac{1}{b} - b$

73. $a^{1/6}(a^{5/6} - a^{-7/6}) = a^1 - a^{-1} = a - \dfrac{1}{a}$

74. $(x^{n/3})^{3n} = x^{n^2}$

75. $(a^{2/n})^{-5n} = a^{-10} = \dfrac{1}{a^{10}}$

76. $x^n \cdot x^{n/2} = x^{3n/2}$

77. $a^{n/2} \cdot a^{-n/3} = a^{n/6}$

78. $\dfrac{y^{n/2}}{y^{-n}} = y^{3n/2}$

79. $\dfrac{b^{m/3}}{b^m} = b^{-2m/3} = \dfrac{1}{b^{2m/3}}$

80. $(x^{2/n})^n = x^2$

81. $(x^{5n})^{2n} = x^{10n^2}$

82. $(x^{n/4}y^{n/8})^8 = x^{2n}y^n$

83. $(x^{n/2}y^{n/3})^6 = x^{3n}y^{2n}$

Objective 7.1.2 Exercises

84. $3^{1/4} = \sqrt[4]{3}$

85. $5^{1/2} = \sqrt{5}$

86. $a^{3/2} = (a^3)^{1/2} = \sqrt{a^3}$

87. $b^{4/3} = (b^4)^{1/3} = \sqrt[3]{b^4}$

88. $(2t)^{5/2} = \sqrt{(2t)^5} = \sqrt{32t^5}$

89. $(3x)^{2/3} = \sqrt[3]{(3x)^2} = \sqrt[3]{9x^2}$

90. $-2x^{2/3} = -2(x^2)^{1/3} = -2\sqrt[3]{x^2}$

91. $-3a^{2/5} = -3(a^2)^{1/5} = -3\sqrt[5]{a^2}$

92. $(a^2b)^{2/3} = \sqrt[3]{(a^2b)^2} = \sqrt[3]{a^4b^2}$

93. $(x^2y^3)^{3/4} = \sqrt[4]{(x^2y^3)^3} = \sqrt[4]{x^6y^9}$

94. $(a^2b^4)^{3/5} = \sqrt[5]{(a^2b^4)^3} = \sqrt[5]{a^6b^{12}}$

95. $(a^3b^7)^{3/2} = \sqrt{(a^3b^7)^3}$
$= \sqrt{a^9b^{21}}$

96. $(4x+3)^{3/4} = \sqrt[4]{(4x+3)^3}$

97. $(3x-2)^{1/3} = \sqrt[3]{3x-2}$

98. $x^{-2/3} = \dfrac{1}{x^{2/3}} = \dfrac{1}{\sqrt[3]{x^2}}$

99. $\sqrt{14} = 14^{1/2}$

100. $\sqrt{7} = 7^{1/2}$

101. $\sqrt[3]{x} = x^{1/3}$

102. $\sqrt[4]{y} = y^{1/4}$

103. $\sqrt[3]{x^4} = x^{4/3}$

104. $\sqrt[4]{a^3} = a^{3/4}$

105. $\sqrt[5]{b^3} = b^{3/5}$

106. $\sqrt[4]{b^5} = b^{5/4}$

107. $\sqrt[3]{2x^2} = (2x^2)^{1/3}$

108. $\sqrt[5]{4y^7} = (4y^7)^{1/5}$

109. $-\sqrt{3x^5} = -(3x^5)^{1/2}$

110. $-\sqrt[4]{4x^5} = -(4x^5)^{1/4}$

111. $3x\sqrt[3]{y^2} = 3xy^{2/3}$

112. $2y\sqrt{x^3} = 2yx^{3/2}$

113. $\sqrt{a^2+2} = (a^2+2)^{1/2}$

Objective 7.1.3 Exercises

114. $\sqrt{x^{16}} = x^8$

115. $\sqrt{y^{14}} = y^7$

116. $-\sqrt{x^8} = -x^4$

117. $-\sqrt{a^6} = -a^3$

118. $\sqrt{x^2y^{10}} = xy^5$

119. $\sqrt{a^{14}b^6} = a^7b^3$

120. $\sqrt{25x^6} = 5x^3$

121. $\sqrt{121y^{12}} = 11y^6$

122. $\sqrt[3]{x^3y^9} = xy^3$

123. $\sqrt[3]{a^6b^{12}} = a^2b^4$

124. $-\sqrt[3]{x^{15}y^3} = -x^5y$

125. $-\sqrt[3]{a^9b^9} = -a^3b^3$

126. $\sqrt[3]{27a^9} = \sqrt[3]{3^3a^9} = 3a^3$

127. $\sqrt[3]{125b^{15}} = \sqrt[3]{5^3b^{15}} = 5b^5$

128. $\sqrt[3]{-8x^3} = \sqrt[3]{(-2)^3x^3} = -2x$

129. $\sqrt[3]{-a^6b^9} = -a^2b^3$

130. $\sqrt{16a^4b^{12}} = \sqrt{2^4a^4b^{12}} = 2^2a^2b^6 = 4a^2b^6$

131. $\sqrt{25x^8y^2} = \sqrt{5^2x^8y^2} = 5x^4y$

132. $\sqrt{-16x^4y^2}$

The square root of a negative number is not a real number, since the square of a real number must be positive. Therefore, $\sqrt{-16x^4y^2}$ is not a real number.

133. $\sqrt{-9a^6b^8}$

The square root of a negative number is not a real number, since the square of a real number must be positive. Therefore, $\sqrt{-9a^6b^8}$ is not a real number.

134. $\sqrt[3]{27x^9} = \sqrt[3]{3^3x^9} = 3x^3$

135. $\sqrt[3]{8a^{21}b^6} = \sqrt[3]{2^3a^{21}b^6} = 2a^7b^2$

136. $\sqrt[3]{-64x^9y^{12}} = \sqrt[3]{(-4)^3x^9y^{12}} = -4x^3y^4$

137. $\sqrt[3]{-27a^3b^{15}} = \sqrt[3]{(-3)^3a^3b^{15}} = -3ab^5$

138. $\sqrt[4]{x^{16}} = x^4$

139. $\sqrt[4]{y^{12}} = y^3$

140. $\sqrt[4]{16x^{12}} = \sqrt[4]{2^4x^{12}} = 2x^3$

141. $\sqrt[4]{81a^{20}} = \sqrt[4]{3^4a^{20}} = 3a^5$

142. $-\sqrt[4]{x^8y^{12}} = -x^2y^3$

143. $-\sqrt[4]{a^{16}b^4} = -a^4b$

144. $\sqrt[5]{x^{20}y^{10}} = x^4y^2$

145. $\sqrt[5]{a^5b^{25}} = ab^5$

146. $\sqrt[4]{81x^4y^{20}} = \sqrt[4]{3^4x^4y^{20}} = 3xy^5$

147. $\sqrt[4]{16a^8b^{20}} = \sqrt[4]{2^4a^8b^{20}} = 2a^2b^5$

148. $\sqrt[5]{32a^5b^{10}} = \sqrt[5]{2^5a^5b^{10}} = 2ab^2$

149. $\sqrt[5]{-32x^{15}y^{20}} = \sqrt[5]{(-2)^5x^{15}y^{20}} = -2x^3y^4$

150. $\sqrt[5]{243x^{10}y^{40}} = \sqrt[5]{3^5x^{10}y^{40}} = 3x^2y^8$

151. $\sqrt{\dfrac{16x^2}{y^{14}}} = \sqrt{\dfrac{2^4x^2}{y^{14}}} = \dfrac{2^2x}{y^7} = \dfrac{4x}{y^7}$

152. $\sqrt{\dfrac{49a^4}{b^{24}}} = \sqrt{\dfrac{7^2a^4}{b^{24}}} = \dfrac{7a^2}{b^{12}}$

153. $\sqrt[3]{\dfrac{27b^3}{a^9}} = \sqrt[3]{\dfrac{3^3b^3}{a^9}} = \dfrac{3b}{a^3}$

154. $\sqrt[3]{\dfrac{64x^{15}}{y^6}} = \sqrt[3]{\dfrac{4^3x^{15}}{y^6}} = \dfrac{4x^5}{y^2}$

155. $\sqrt{(2x+3)^2} = 2x+3$

156. $\sqrt{(4x+1)^2} = 4x+1$

157. $\sqrt{x^2+2x+1} = \sqrt{(x+1)^2} = x+1$

158. $\sqrt{x^2+4x+4} = \sqrt{(x+2)^2} = x+2$

Applying Concepts 7.1

159. $\sqrt[3]{\sqrt{x^6}} = \sqrt[3]{x^3} = x$

160. $\sqrt{\sqrt[3]{y^6}} = \sqrt{y^2} = y$

161. $\sqrt[5]{\sqrt[3]{b^{15}}} = \sqrt[5]{b^5} = b$

162. $\sqrt{\sqrt{16x^{12}}} = \sqrt{\sqrt{2^4x^{12}}} = \sqrt{2^2x^6} = 2x^3$

163. $\sqrt[5]{\sqrt{a^{10}b^{20}}} = \sqrt[5]{a^5b^{10}} = ab^2$

164. $\sqrt[3]{\sqrt{64x^{36}y^{30}}} = \sqrt[3]{\sqrt{2^6x^{36}y^{30}}}$
$= \sqrt[3]{2^3x^{18}y^{15}}$
$= 2x^6y^5$

165. $y^py^{2/5} = y$
$y^p = \dfrac{y^1}{y^{2/5}}$
$y^p = y^{3/5}$
$p = \dfrac{3}{5}$

When the value of p is $\frac{3}{5}$, the equation is true.

166. $\dfrac{y^p}{y^{3/4}} = y^{1/2}$
$y^{p-(3/4)} = y^{1/2}$
$p - \dfrac{3}{4} = \dfrac{1}{2}$
$p = \dfrac{5}{4}$

When the value of p is $\frac{5}{4}$, the equation is true.

167. $x^px^{-1/2} = x^{1/4}$
$x^{p-(1/2)} = x^{1/4}$
$p - \dfrac{1}{2} = \dfrac{1}{4}$
$p = \dfrac{3}{4}$

When the value of p is $\frac{3}{4}$, the equation is true.

Section 7.2

Concept Review 7.2

1. Sometimes true
   If a is a positive number, $\sqrt{a}$ is a real number. If a is negative, $\sqrt{a}$ is not a real number.

2. Always true

3. Never true
   The index of each radical must be the same in order to multiply radical expressions.

4. Never true
   The conjugate of $\sqrt{a} + \sqrt{b}$ is found by replacing $\sqrt{b}$ with its opposite.

5. Always true

6. Always true

Objective 7.2.1 Exercises

1. The radical expression $\sqrt{8}$ is not in simplest form because the radicand contains a perfect square factor of 4.

2. The radical expression $\sqrt[3]{16}$ is not in simplest form because the radicand contains a perfect cube factor of 8.

3. $\sqrt{18} = \sqrt{3^2 \cdot 2}$
   $= \sqrt{3^2}\sqrt{2}$
   $= 3\sqrt{2}$

4. $\sqrt{40} = \sqrt{2^2 \cdot 10}$
   $= \sqrt{2^2}\sqrt{10}$
   $= 2\sqrt{10}$

5. $\sqrt{98} = \sqrt{7^2 \cdot 2}$
   $= \sqrt{7^2}\sqrt{2}$
   $= 7\sqrt{2}$

6. $\sqrt{128} = \sqrt{2^7} = \sqrt{2^6 \cdot 2}$
   $= \sqrt{2^6}\sqrt{2}$
   $= 2^3\sqrt{2}$
   $= 8\sqrt{2}$

7. $\sqrt[3]{72} = \sqrt[3]{2^3 \cdot 3^2}$
   $= \sqrt[3]{2^3}\sqrt[3]{3^2}$
   $= 2\sqrt[3]{9}$

8. $\sqrt[3]{54} = \sqrt[3]{3^3 \cdot 2}$
   $= \sqrt[3]{3^3}\sqrt[3]{2}$
   $= 3\sqrt[3]{2}$

9. $\sqrt[3]{16} = \sqrt[3]{2^3 \cdot 2}$
   $= \sqrt[3]{2^3}\sqrt[3]{2}$
   $= 2\sqrt[3]{2}$

10. $\sqrt[3]{128} = \sqrt[3]{2^7}$
    $= \sqrt[3]{2^6 \cdot 2}$
    $= \sqrt[3]{2^6}\sqrt[3]{2}$
    $= 2^{2}\sqrt[3]{2}$
    $= 4\sqrt[3]{2}$

11. $\sqrt{x^4 y^3 z^5} = \sqrt{x^4 y^2 z^4 (yz)}$
    $= \sqrt{x^4 y^2 z^4}\sqrt{yz}$
    $= x^2 y z^2 \sqrt{yz}$

12. $\sqrt{x^3 y^6 z^9} = \sqrt{x^2 y^6 z^8 (xz)}$
    $= \sqrt{x^2 y^6 z^8}\sqrt{xz}$
    $= x y^3 z^4 \sqrt{xz}$

13. $\sqrt{8 a^3 b^8} = \sqrt{2^3 a^3 b^8}$
    $= \sqrt{2^2 a^2 b^8 (2a)}$
    $= \sqrt{2^2 a^2 b^8}\sqrt{2a}$
    $= 2 a b^4 \sqrt{2a}$

14. $\sqrt{24 a^9 b^6} = \sqrt{2^3 \cdot 3 a^9 b^6}$
    $= \sqrt{2^2 a^8 b^6 (2 \cdot 3a)}$
    $= \sqrt{2^2 a^8 b^6}\sqrt{6a}$
    $= 2 a^4 b^3 \sqrt{6a}$

15. $\sqrt{45 x^2 y^3 z^5} = \sqrt{3^2 \cdot 5 x^2 y^3 z^5}$
    $= \sqrt{3^2 x^2 y^2 z^4 (5yz)}$
    $= \sqrt{3^2 x^2 y^2 z^4}\sqrt{5yz}$
    $= 3 x y z^2 \sqrt{5yz}$

16. $\sqrt{60 x y^7 z^{12}} = \sqrt{2^2 \cdot 3 \cdot 5 x y^7 z^{12}}$
    $= \sqrt{2^2 y^6 z^{12} (3 \cdot 5 xy)}$
    $= \sqrt{2^2 y^6 z^{12}}\sqrt{15xy}$
    $= 2 y^3 z^6 \sqrt{15xy}$

17. $\sqrt[3]{-125 x^2 y^4} = \sqrt[3]{(-5)^3 x^2 y^4}$
    $= \sqrt[3]{(-5)^3 y^3 (x^2 y)}$
    $= \sqrt[3]{(-5)^3 y^3}\sqrt[3]{x^2 y}$
    $= -5 y \sqrt[3]{x^2 y}$

18. $\sqrt[4]{16x^9y^5} = \sqrt[4]{2^4x^9y^5}$
$= \sqrt[4]{2^4x^8y^4(xy)}$
$= \sqrt[4]{2^4x^8y^4}\sqrt[4]{xy}$
$= 2x^2y\sqrt[4]{xy}$

19. $\sqrt[3]{-216x^5y^9} = \sqrt[3]{(-6)^3x^5y^9}$
$= \sqrt[3]{(-6)^3x^3y^9(x^2)}$
$= \sqrt[3]{(-6)^3x^3y^9}\sqrt[3]{x^2}$
$= -6xy^3\sqrt[3]{x^2}$

20. $\sqrt[3]{a^8b^{11}c^{15}} = \sqrt[3]{a^6b^9c^{15}(a^2b^2)}$
$= \sqrt[3]{a^6b^9c^{15}}\sqrt[3]{a^2b^2}$
$= a^2b^3c^5\sqrt[3]{a^2b^2}$

21. $\sqrt[3]{a^5b^8} = \sqrt[3]{a^3b^6(a^2b^2)}$
$= \sqrt[3]{a^3b^6}\sqrt[3]{a^2b^2}$
$= ab^2\sqrt[3]{a^2b^2}$

22. $\sqrt[4]{64x^8y^{10}} = \sqrt[4]{2^6x^8y^{10}}$
$= \sqrt[4]{2^4x^8y^8(2^2y^2)}$
$= \sqrt[4]{2^4x^8y^8}\sqrt[4]{4y^2}$
$= 2x^2y^2\sqrt[4]{4y^2}$

Objective 7.2.2 Exercises

23. $\sqrt{2} + \sqrt{2} = 2\sqrt{2}$

24. $\sqrt{5} - \sqrt{5} = 0$

25. $4\sqrt[3]{7} - \sqrt[3]{7} = 3\sqrt[3]{7}$

26. $3\sqrt[3]{11} - 8\sqrt[3]{11} = -5\sqrt[3]{11}$

27. $2\sqrt{x} - 8\sqrt{x} = -6\sqrt{x}$

28. $3\sqrt{y} + 12\sqrt{y} = 15\sqrt{y}$

29. $\sqrt{8} - \sqrt{32} = \sqrt{2^3} - \sqrt{2^5}$
$= \sqrt{2^2}\sqrt{2} - \sqrt{2^4}\sqrt{2}$
$= 2\sqrt{2} - 2^2\sqrt{2}$
$= 2\sqrt{2} - 4\sqrt{2}$
$= -2\sqrt{2}$

30. $\sqrt{27} - \sqrt{75} = \sqrt{3^3} - \sqrt{3 \cdot 5^2}$
$= \sqrt{3^2}\sqrt{3} - \sqrt{5^2}\sqrt{3}$
$= 3\sqrt{3} - 5\sqrt{3}$
$= -2\sqrt{3}$

31. $\sqrt{128x} - \sqrt{98x} = \sqrt{2^7x} - \sqrt{2 \cdot 7^2x}$
$= \sqrt{2^6}\sqrt{2x} - \sqrt{7^2}\sqrt{2x}$
$= 2^3\sqrt{2x} - 7\sqrt{2x}$
$= 8\sqrt{2x} - 7\sqrt{2x}$
$= \sqrt{2x}$

32. $\sqrt{48x} + \sqrt{147x} = \sqrt{2^4 \cdot 3x} + \sqrt{3 \cdot 7^2x}$
$= \sqrt{2^4}\sqrt{3x} + \sqrt{7^2}\sqrt{3x}$
$= 2^2\sqrt{3x} + 7\sqrt{3x}$
$= 4\sqrt{3x} + 7\sqrt{3x}$
$= 11\sqrt{3x}$

33. $\sqrt{27a} - \sqrt{8a} = \sqrt{3^3a} - \sqrt{2^3a}$
$= \sqrt{3^2}\sqrt{3a} - \sqrt{2^2}\sqrt{2a}$
$= 3\sqrt{3a} - 2\sqrt{2a}$

34. $\sqrt{18b} + \sqrt{75b} = \sqrt{2 \cdot 3^2b} + \sqrt{3 \cdot 5^2b}$
$= \sqrt{3^2}\sqrt{2b} + \sqrt{5^2}\sqrt{3b}$
$= 3\sqrt{2b} + 5\sqrt{3b}$

35. $2\sqrt{2x^3} + 4x\sqrt{8x} = 2\sqrt{2x^3} + 4x\sqrt{2^3x}$
$= 2\sqrt{x^2}\sqrt{2x} + 4x\sqrt{2^2}\sqrt{2x}$
$= 2x\sqrt{2x} + 2 \cdot 4x\sqrt{2x}$
$= 2x\sqrt{2x} + 8x\sqrt{2x}$
$= 10x\sqrt{2x}$

36. $5y\sqrt{8y} + 2\sqrt{50y^3} = 5y\sqrt{2^3y} + 2\sqrt{2 \cdot 5^2y^3}$
$= 5y\sqrt{2^2}\sqrt{2y} + 2\sqrt{5^2y^2}\sqrt{2y}$
$= 2 \cdot 5y\sqrt{2y} + 2 \cdot 5y\sqrt{2y}$
$= 10y\sqrt{2y} + 10y\sqrt{2y}$
$= 20y\sqrt{2y}$

37. $x\sqrt{75xy} - \sqrt{27x^3y} = x\sqrt{3 \cdot 5^2xy} - \sqrt{3^3x^3y}$
$= x\sqrt{5^2}\sqrt{3xy} - \sqrt{3^2x^2}\sqrt{3xy}$
$= 5x\sqrt{3xy} - 3x\sqrt{3xy}$
$= 2x\sqrt{3xy}$

38. $3\sqrt{8x^2y^3} - 2x\sqrt{32y^3}$
$= 3\sqrt{2^3x^2y^3} - 2x\sqrt{2^5y^3}$
$= 3\sqrt{2^2x^2y^2}\sqrt{2y} - 2x\sqrt{2^4y^2}\sqrt{2y}$
$= 3 \cdot 2xy\sqrt{2y} - 2x \cdot 2^2y\sqrt{2y}$
$= 6xy\sqrt{2y} - 8xy\sqrt{2y}$
$= -2xy\sqrt{2y}$

39. $2\sqrt{32x^2y^3} - xy\sqrt{98y}$

$\quad = 2\sqrt{2^5x^2y^3} - xy\sqrt{2\cdot 7^2 y}$

$\quad = 2\sqrt{2^4x^2y^2}\sqrt{2y} - xy\sqrt{7^2}\sqrt{2y}$

$\quad = 2\cdot 2^2 xy\sqrt{2y} - 7xy\sqrt{2y}$

$\quad = 8xy\sqrt{2y} - 7xy\sqrt{2y}$

$\quad = xy\sqrt{2y}$

40. $6y\sqrt{x^3y} - 2\sqrt{x^3y^3} = 6y\sqrt{x^2}\sqrt{xy} - 2\sqrt{x^2y^2}\sqrt{xy}$

$\quad\quad\quad\quad\quad\quad\quad = 6xy\sqrt{xy} - 2xy\sqrt{xy}$

$\quad\quad\quad\quad\quad\quad\quad = 4xy\sqrt{xy}$

41. $7b\sqrt{a^5b^3} - 2ab\sqrt{a^3b^3}$

$\quad = 7b\sqrt{a^4b^2}\sqrt{ab} - 2ab\sqrt{a^2b^2}\sqrt{ab}$

$\quad = 7b\cdot a^2b\sqrt{ab} - 2ab\cdot ab\sqrt{ab}$

$\quad = 7a^2b^2\sqrt{ab} - 2a^2b^2\sqrt{ab}$

$\quad = 5a^2b^2\sqrt{ab}$

42. $2a\sqrt{27ab^5} + 3b\sqrt{3a^3b}$

$\quad = 2a\sqrt{3^3ab^5} + 3b\sqrt{3a^3b}$

$\quad = 2a\sqrt{3^2b^4}\sqrt{3ab} + 3b\sqrt{a^2}\sqrt{3ab}$

$\quad = 2a\cdot 3b^2\sqrt{3ab} + 3ab\sqrt{3ab}$

$\quad = 6ab^2\sqrt{3ab} + 3ab\sqrt{3ab}$

43. $\sqrt[3]{128} + \sqrt[3]{250} = \sqrt[3]{2^7} + \sqrt[3]{2\cdot 5^3}$

$\quad\quad\quad\quad\quad\quad = \sqrt[3]{2^6}\sqrt[3]{2} + \sqrt[3]{5^3}\sqrt[3]{2}$

$\quad\quad\quad\quad\quad\quad = 2^2\sqrt[3]{2} + 5\sqrt[3]{2}$

$\quad\quad\quad\quad\quad\quad = 4\sqrt[3]{2} + 5\sqrt[3]{2}$

$\quad\quad\quad\quad\quad\quad = 9\sqrt[3]{2}$

44. $\sqrt[3]{16} - \sqrt[3]{54} = \sqrt[3]{2^4} - \sqrt[3]{2\cdot 3^3}$

$\quad\quad\quad\quad\quad\quad = \sqrt[3]{2^3}\sqrt[3]{2} - \sqrt[3]{3^3}\sqrt[3]{2}$

$\quad\quad\quad\quad\quad\quad = 2\sqrt[3]{2} - 3\sqrt[3]{2}$

$\quad\quad\quad\quad\quad\quad = -\sqrt[3]{2}$

45. $2\sqrt[3]{3a^4} - 3a\sqrt[3]{81a} = 2\sqrt[3]{3a^4} - 3a\sqrt[3]{3^4a}$

$\quad\quad\quad\quad\quad\quad\quad\quad = 2\sqrt[3]{a^3}\sqrt[3]{3a} - 3a\sqrt[3]{3^3}\sqrt[3]{3a}$

$\quad\quad\quad\quad\quad\quad\quad\quad = 2a\sqrt[3]{3a} - 3a\cdot 3\sqrt[3]{3a}$

$\quad\quad\quad\quad\quad\quad\quad\quad = 2a\sqrt[3]{3a} - 9a\sqrt[3]{3a}$

$\quad\quad\quad\quad\quad\quad\quad\quad = -7a\sqrt[3]{3a}$

46. $2b\sqrt[3]{16b^2} + \sqrt[3]{128b^5}$

$\quad = 2b\sqrt[3]{2^4b^2} + \sqrt[3]{2^7b^5}$

$\quad = 2b\sqrt[3]{2^3}\sqrt[3]{2b^2} + \sqrt[3]{2^6b^3}\sqrt[3]{2b^2}$

$\quad = 2b\cdot 2\sqrt[3]{2b^2} + 2^2b\sqrt[3]{2b^2}$

$\quad = 4b\sqrt[3]{2b^2} + 4b\sqrt[3]{2b^2}$

$\quad = 8b\sqrt[3]{2b^2}$

47. $3\sqrt[3]{x^5y^7} - 8xy\sqrt[3]{x^2y^4}$

$\quad = 3\sqrt[3]{x^3y^6}\sqrt[3]{x^2y} - 8xy\sqrt[3]{y^3}\sqrt[3]{x^2y}$

$\quad = 3xy^2\sqrt[3]{x^2y} - 8xy\cdot y\sqrt[3]{x^2y}$

$\quad = 3xy^2\sqrt[3]{x^2y} - 8xy^2\sqrt[3]{x^2y}$

$\quad = -5xy^2\sqrt[3]{x^2y}$

48. $3\sqrt[4]{32a^5} - a\sqrt[4]{162a} = 3\sqrt[4]{2^5a^5} - a\sqrt[4]{2\cdot 3^4 a}$

$\quad\quad\quad\quad\quad\quad\quad\quad = 3\sqrt[4]{2^4a^4}\sqrt[4]{2a} - a\sqrt[4]{3^4}\sqrt[4]{2a}$

$\quad\quad\quad\quad\quad\quad\quad\quad = 3\cdot 2a\sqrt[4]{2a} - 3a\sqrt[4]{2a}$

$\quad\quad\quad\quad\quad\quad\quad\quad = 6a\sqrt[4]{2a} - 3a\sqrt[4]{2a}$

$\quad\quad\quad\quad\quad\quad\quad\quad = 3a\sqrt[4]{2a}$

49. $2a\sqrt[4]{16ab^5} + 3b\sqrt[4]{256a^5b}$

$\quad = 2a\sqrt[4]{2^4ab^5} + 3b\sqrt[4]{2^8a^5b}$

$\quad = 2a\sqrt[4]{2^4b^4}\sqrt[4]{ab} + 3b\sqrt[4]{2^8a^4}\sqrt[4]{ab}$

$\quad = 2a\cdot 2b\sqrt[4]{ab} + 3b\cdot 2^2a\sqrt[4]{ab}$

$\quad = 4ab\sqrt[4]{ab} + 12ab\sqrt[4]{ab}$

$\quad = 16ab\sqrt[4]{ab}$

50. $2\sqrt{50} - 3\sqrt{125} + \sqrt{98}$

$\quad = 2\sqrt{2\cdot 5^2} - 3\sqrt{5^3} + \sqrt{2\cdot 7^2}$

$\quad = 2\sqrt{5^2}\sqrt{2} - 3\sqrt{5^2}\sqrt{5} + \sqrt{7^2}\sqrt{2}$

$\quad = 2\cdot 5\sqrt{2} - 3\cdot 5\sqrt{5} + 7\sqrt{2}$

$\quad = 10\sqrt{2} - 15\sqrt{5} + 7\sqrt{2}$

$\quad = 17\sqrt{2} - 15\sqrt{5}$

51. $3\sqrt{108} - 2\sqrt{18} - 3\sqrt{48}$

$\quad = 3\sqrt{2^2\cdot 3^3} - 2\sqrt{2\cdot 3^2} - 3\sqrt{2^4\cdot 3}$

$\quad = 3\sqrt{2^2\cdot 3^2}\sqrt{3} - 2\sqrt{3^2}\sqrt{2} - 3\sqrt{2^4}\sqrt{3}$

$\quad = 3\cdot 2\cdot 3\sqrt{3} - 2\cdot 3\sqrt{2} - 3\cdot 2^2\sqrt{3}$

$\quad = 18\sqrt{3} - 6\sqrt{2} - 12\sqrt{3}$

$\quad = 6\sqrt{3} - 6\sqrt{2}$

52. $\sqrt{9b^3} - \sqrt{25b^3} + \sqrt{49b^3}$

$\quad = \sqrt{3^2b^3} - \sqrt{5^2b^3} + \sqrt{7^2b^3}$

$\quad = \sqrt{3^2b^2}\sqrt{b} - \sqrt{5^2b^2}\sqrt{b} + \sqrt{7^2b^2}\sqrt{b}$

$\quad = 3b\sqrt{b} - 5b\sqrt{b} + 7b\sqrt{b}$

$\quad = 5b\sqrt{b}$

53. $\sqrt{4x^7y^5} + 9x^2\sqrt{x^3y^5} - 5xy\sqrt{x^5y^3} = \sqrt{2^2x^7y^5} + 9x^2\sqrt{x^3y^5} - 5xy\sqrt{x^5y^3}$

$= \sqrt{2^2x^6y^4}\sqrt{xy} + 9x^2\sqrt{x^2y^4}\sqrt{xy} - 5xy\sqrt{x^4y^2}\sqrt{xy}$

$= 2x^3y^2\sqrt{xy} + 9x^2 \cdot xy^2\sqrt{xy} - 5xy \cdot x^2y\sqrt{xy}$

$= 2x^3y^2\sqrt{xy} + 9x^3y^2\sqrt{xy} - 5x^3y^2\sqrt{xy}$

$= 6x^3y^2\sqrt{xy}$

54. $2x\sqrt{8xy^2} - 3y\sqrt{32x^3} + \sqrt{8x^3y^2} = 2x\sqrt{2^3xy^2} - 3y\sqrt{2^5x^3} + \sqrt{2^3x^3y^2}$

$= 2x\sqrt{2^2y^2}\sqrt{2x} - 3y\sqrt{2^4x^2}\sqrt{2x} + \sqrt{2^2x^2y^2}\sqrt{2x}$

$= 2x \cdot 2y\sqrt{2x} - 3y \cdot 2^2x\sqrt{2x} + 2xy\sqrt{2x}$

$= 4xy\sqrt{2x} - 12xy\sqrt{2x} + 2xy\sqrt{2x}$

$= -6xy\sqrt{2x}$

55. $5a\sqrt{3a^3b} + 2a^2\sqrt{27ab} - 4\sqrt{75a^5b} = 5a\sqrt{3a^3b} + 2a^2\sqrt{3^3ab} - 4\sqrt{3 \cdot 5^2a^5b}$

$= 5a\sqrt{a^2}\sqrt{3ab} + 2a^2\sqrt{3^2}\sqrt{3ab} - 4\sqrt{5^2a^4}\sqrt{3ab}$

$= 5a \cdot a\sqrt{3ab} + 2a^2 \cdot 3\sqrt{3ab} - 4 \cdot 5a^2\sqrt{3ab}$

$= 5a^2\sqrt{3ab} + 6a^2\sqrt{3ab} - 20a^2\sqrt{3ab}$

$= -9a^2\sqrt{3ab}$

56. $\sqrt[3]{54xy^3} - 5\sqrt[3]{2xy^3} + \sqrt[3]{128xy^3} = \sqrt[3]{2 \cdot 3^3xy^3} - 5\sqrt[3]{2xy^3} + \sqrt[3]{2^7xy^3}$

$= \sqrt[3]{3^3y^3}\sqrt[3]{2x} - 5\sqrt[3]{y^3}\sqrt[3]{2x} + \sqrt[3]{2^6y^3}\sqrt[3]{2x}$

$= 3y^3\sqrt[3]{2x} - 5y\sqrt[3]{2x} + 2^2y\sqrt[3]{2x}$

$= 3y\sqrt[3]{2x} - 5y\sqrt[3]{2x} + 4y\sqrt[3]{2x}$

$= 2y\sqrt[3]{2x}$

Objective 7.2.3 Exercises

57. $\sqrt{8}\sqrt{32} = \sqrt{256} = \sqrt{2^8} = 2^4 = 16$

58. $\sqrt{14}\sqrt{35} = \sqrt{490} = \sqrt{2 \cdot 5 \cdot 7^2} = \sqrt{7^2}\sqrt{2 \cdot 5} = 7\sqrt{10}$

59. $\sqrt[3]{4}\sqrt[3]{8} = \sqrt[3]{32} = \sqrt[3]{2^5} = \sqrt[3]{2^3}\sqrt[3]{2^2} = 2\sqrt[3]{4}$

60. $\sqrt[3]{6}\sqrt[3]{36} = \sqrt[3]{216} = \sqrt[3]{2^3 \cdot 3^3} = 2 \cdot 3 = 6$

61. $\sqrt{x^2y^5}\sqrt{xy} = \sqrt{x^3y^6} = \sqrt{x^2y^6}\sqrt{x} = xy^3\sqrt{x}$

62. $\sqrt{a^3b}\sqrt{ab^4} = \sqrt{a^4b^5} = \sqrt{a^4b^4}\sqrt{b} = a^2b^2\sqrt{b}$

63. $\sqrt{2x^2y}\sqrt{32xy} = \sqrt{64x^3y^2} = \sqrt{2^6x^3y^2} = \sqrt{2^6x^2y^2}\sqrt{x} = 2^3xy\sqrt{x} = 8xy\sqrt{x}$

64. $\sqrt{5x^3y}\sqrt{10x^3y^4} = \sqrt{50x^6y^5} = \sqrt{2 \cdot 5^2x^6y^5} = \sqrt{5^2x^6y^4}\sqrt{2y} = 5x^3y^2\sqrt{2y}$

65. $\sqrt[3]{x^2y}\sqrt[3]{16x^4y^2} = \sqrt[3]{16x^6y^3} = \sqrt[3]{2^4x^6y^3} = \sqrt[3]{2^3x^6y^3}\sqrt[3]{2} = 2x^2y\sqrt[3]{2}$

66. $\sqrt[3]{4a^2b^3}\sqrt[3]{8ab^5} = \sqrt[3]{32a^3b^8} = \sqrt[3]{2^5a^3b^8} = \sqrt[3]{2^3a^3b^6}\sqrt[3]{2^2b^2} = 2ab^2\sqrt[3]{4b^2}$

67. $\sqrt[4]{12ab^3}\sqrt[4]{4a^5b^2} = \sqrt[4]{48a^6b^5} = \sqrt[4]{2^4 \cdot 3a^6b^5} = \sqrt[4]{2^4a^4b^4}\sqrt[4]{3a^2b} = 2ab\sqrt[4]{3a^2b}$

68. $\sqrt[4]{36a^2b^4}\sqrt[4]{12a^5b^3} = \sqrt[4]{432a^7b^7} = \sqrt[4]{2^4 \cdot 3^3a^7b^7} = \sqrt[4]{2^4a^4b^4}\sqrt[4]{3^3a^3b^3} = 2ab\sqrt[4]{27a^3b^3}$

69. $\sqrt{3}(\sqrt{27}-\sqrt{3})=\sqrt{81}-\sqrt{9}$
$=\sqrt{3^4}-\sqrt{3^2}$
$=3^2-3$
$=9-3$
$=6$

70. $\sqrt{10}(\sqrt{10}-\sqrt{5})=\sqrt{100}-\sqrt{50}$
$=\sqrt{2^2\cdot5^2}-\sqrt{2\cdot5^2}$
$=2\cdot5-\sqrt{5^2}\sqrt{2}$
$=10-5\sqrt{2}$

71. $\sqrt{x}(\sqrt{x}-\sqrt{2})=\sqrt{x^2}-\sqrt{2x}=x-\sqrt{2x}$

72. $\sqrt{y}(\sqrt{y}-\sqrt{5})=\sqrt{y^2}-\sqrt{5y}=y-\sqrt{5y}$

73. $\sqrt{2x}(\sqrt{8x}-\sqrt{32})=\sqrt{16x^2}-\sqrt{64x}$
$=\sqrt{2^4x^2}-\sqrt{2^6x}$
$=2^2x-2^3\sqrt{x}$
$=4x-8\sqrt{x}$

74. $\sqrt{3a}(\sqrt{27a^2}-\sqrt{a})=\sqrt{81a^3}-\sqrt{3a^2}$
$=\sqrt{3^4a^3}-\sqrt{3a^2}$
$=\sqrt{3^4a^2}\sqrt{a}-\sqrt{a^2}\sqrt{3}$
$=9a\sqrt{a}-a\sqrt{3}$

75. $(\sqrt{x}-3)^2=(\sqrt{x})^2-3\sqrt{x}-3\sqrt{x}+9$
$=x-6\sqrt{x}+9$

76. $(\sqrt{2x}+4)^2=(\sqrt{2x})^2+4\sqrt{2x}+4\sqrt{2x}+16$
$=2x+8\sqrt{2x}+16$

77. $(4\sqrt{5}+2)^2=(4\sqrt{5})^2+8\sqrt{5}+8\sqrt{5}+4$
$=16\cdot5+16\sqrt{5}+4$
$=80+16\sqrt{5}+4$
$=84+16\sqrt{5}$

78. $2\sqrt{3x^2}\cdot3\sqrt{12xy^3}\cdot\sqrt{6x^3y}=6\sqrt{216x^6y^4}$
$=6\sqrt{2^3\cdot3^3x^6y^4}$
$=6\sqrt{2^2\cdot3^2x^6y^4}\sqrt{2\cdot3}$
$=6\cdot2\cdot3x^3y^2\sqrt{6}$
$=36x^3y^2\sqrt{6}$

79. $2\sqrt{14xy}\cdot4\sqrt{7x^2y}\cdot3\sqrt{8xy^2}=24\sqrt{784x^4y^4}$
$=24\sqrt{2^4\cdot7^2x^4y^4}$
$=24\cdot2^2\cdot7x^2y^2$
$=672x^2y^2$

80. $\sqrt[3]{8ab}\sqrt[3]{4a^2b^3}\sqrt[3]{9ab^4}=\sqrt[3]{288a^4b^8}$
$=\sqrt[3]{2^5\cdot3^2a^4b^8}$
$=\sqrt[3]{2^3\cdot a^3b^6}\sqrt[3]{2^2\cdot3^2ab^2}$
$=2ab^2\sqrt[3]{36ab^2}$

81. $\sqrt[3]{2a^2b}\sqrt[3]{4a^3b^2}\sqrt[3]{8a^5b^6}=\sqrt[3]{64a^{10}b^9}$
$=\sqrt[3]{2^6a^{10}b^9}$
$=\sqrt[3]{2^6a^9b^9}\sqrt[3]{a}$
$=2^2a^3b^3\sqrt[3]{a}$
$=4a^3b^3\sqrt[3]{a}$

82. $(\sqrt{2}-3)(\sqrt{2}+4)=\sqrt{2^2}+4\sqrt{2}-3\sqrt{2}-12$
$=2+\sqrt{2}-12$
$=-10+\sqrt{2}$

83. $(\sqrt{5}-5)(2\sqrt{5}+2)=2\sqrt{5^2}+2\sqrt{5}-10\sqrt{5}-10$
$=2\cdot5-8\sqrt{5}-10$
$=10-8\sqrt{5}-10$
$=-8\sqrt{5}$

84. $(\sqrt{y}-2)(\sqrt{y}+2)=\sqrt{y^2}-4=y-4$

85. $(\sqrt{x}-y)(\sqrt{x}+y)=\sqrt{x^2}-y^2=x-y^2$

86. $(\sqrt{2x}-3\sqrt{y})(\sqrt{2x}+3\sqrt{y})=\sqrt{2^2x^2}-9\sqrt{y^2}$
$=2x-9y$

87. $(2\sqrt{3x}-\sqrt{y})(2\sqrt{3x}+\sqrt{y})=4\sqrt{3^2x^2}-\sqrt{y^2}$
$=4\cdot3x-y$
$=12x-y$

88. $(\sqrt{a}-2)(\sqrt{a}-3)=\sqrt{a^2}-3\sqrt{a}-2\sqrt{a}+6$
$=a-5\sqrt{a}+6$

89. $(\sqrt{x}+4)(\sqrt{x}-7)=\sqrt{x^2}-7\sqrt{x}+4\sqrt{x}-28$
$=x-3\sqrt{x}-28$

90. $(\sqrt[3]{a}+2)(\sqrt[3]{a}+3)=\sqrt[3]{a^2}+3\sqrt[3]{a}+2\sqrt[3]{a}+6$
$=\sqrt[3]{a^2}+5\sqrt[3]{a}+6$

91. $(\sqrt[3]{x}-4)(\sqrt[3]{x}+5)=\sqrt[3]{x^2}+5\sqrt[3]{x}-4\sqrt[3]{x}-20$
$=\sqrt[3]{x^2}+\sqrt[3]{x}-20$

92. $(2\sqrt{x}-\sqrt{y})(3\sqrt{x}+\sqrt{y})$
$=6\sqrt{x^2}+2\sqrt{xy}-3\sqrt{xy}-\sqrt{y^2}$
$=6x-\sqrt{xy}-y$

Objective 7.2.4 Exercises

93. A radical expression is in simplest form when :
(1) The radicand contains no factor greater than 1 that is perfect power of the index.
(2) There is no fraction under the radical sign.
(3) There is no radical in the denominator of a radical expression.

94. To rationalize the denominator of a radical expression means to rewrite the expression with no radicals in the denominator. It is accomplished by multiplying both the numerator and the denominator by the same expression, one that removes the radical(s) from the denominator of the original expression.

95.
$$\frac{\sqrt{32x^2}}{\sqrt{2x}} = \sqrt{\frac{32x^2}{2x}} = \sqrt{16x} = \sqrt{2^4 x} = \sqrt{2^4}\sqrt{x} = 2^2\sqrt{x} = 4\sqrt{x}$$

96.
$$\frac{\sqrt{60y^4}}{\sqrt{12y}} = \sqrt{\frac{60y^4}{12y}} = \sqrt{5y^3} = \sqrt{y^2}\sqrt{5y} = y\sqrt{5y}$$

97.
$$\frac{\sqrt{42a^3b^5}}{\sqrt{14a^2b}} = \sqrt{\frac{42a^3b^5}{14a^2b}} = \sqrt{3ab^4} = \sqrt{b^4}\sqrt{3a} = b^2\sqrt{3a}$$

98.
$$\frac{\sqrt{65ab^4}}{\sqrt{5ab}} = \sqrt{\frac{65ab^4}{5ab}} = \sqrt{13b^3} = \sqrt{b^2}\sqrt{13b} = b\sqrt{13b}$$

99.
$$\frac{1}{\sqrt{5}} = \frac{1}{\sqrt{5}}\cdot\frac{\sqrt{5}}{\sqrt{5}} = \frac{\sqrt{5}}{\sqrt{5^2}} = \frac{\sqrt{5}}{5}$$

100.
$$\frac{1}{\sqrt{2}} = \frac{1}{\sqrt{2}}\cdot\frac{\sqrt{2}}{\sqrt{2}} = \frac{\sqrt{2}}{\sqrt{2^2}} = \frac{\sqrt{2}}{2}$$

101.
$$\frac{1}{\sqrt{2x}} = \frac{1}{\sqrt{2x}}\cdot\frac{\sqrt{2x}}{\sqrt{2x}} = \frac{\sqrt{2x}}{\sqrt{2^2x^2}} = \frac{\sqrt{2x}}{2x}$$

102.
$$\frac{2}{\sqrt{3y}} = \frac{2}{\sqrt{3y}}\cdot\frac{\sqrt{3y}}{\sqrt{3y}} = \frac{2\sqrt{3y}}{\sqrt{3^2y^2}} = \frac{2\sqrt{3y}}{3y}$$

103.
$$\frac{5}{\sqrt{5x}} = \frac{5}{\sqrt{5x}}\cdot\frac{\sqrt{5x}}{\sqrt{5x}} = \frac{5\sqrt{5x}}{\sqrt{5^2x^2}} = \frac{5\sqrt{5x}}{5x} = \frac{\sqrt{5x}}{x}$$

104.
$$\frac{9}{\sqrt{3a}} = \frac{9}{\sqrt{3a}}\cdot\frac{\sqrt{3a}}{\sqrt{3a}} = \frac{9\sqrt{3a}}{\sqrt{3^2a^2}} = \frac{9\sqrt{3a}}{3a} = \frac{3\sqrt{3a}}{a}$$

105.
$$\sqrt{\frac{x}{5}} = \frac{\sqrt{x}}{\sqrt{5}} = \frac{\sqrt{x}}{\sqrt{5}}\cdot\frac{\sqrt{5}}{\sqrt{5}} = \frac{\sqrt{5x}}{\sqrt{5^2}} = \frac{\sqrt{5x}}{5}$$

106.
$$\sqrt{\frac{y}{2}} = \frac{\sqrt{y}}{\sqrt{2}} = \frac{\sqrt{y}}{\sqrt{2}}\cdot\frac{\sqrt{2}}{\sqrt{2}} = \frac{\sqrt{2y}}{\sqrt{2^2}} = \frac{\sqrt{2y}}{2}$$

107.
$$\frac{3}{\sqrt[3]{2}} = \frac{3}{\sqrt[3]{2}}\cdot\frac{\sqrt[3]{2^2}}{\sqrt[3]{2^2}} = \frac{3\sqrt[3]{2^2}}{\sqrt[3]{2^3}} = \frac{3\sqrt[3]{4}}{2}$$

108.
$$\frac{5}{\sqrt[3]{9}} = \frac{5}{\sqrt[3]{3^2}}\cdot\frac{\sqrt[3]{3}}{\sqrt[3]{3}} = \frac{5\sqrt[3]{3}}{\sqrt[3]{3^3}} = \frac{5\sqrt[3]{3}}{3}$$

109.
$$\frac{3}{\sqrt[3]{4x^2}} = \frac{3}{\sqrt[3]{2^2x^2}}\cdot\frac{\sqrt[3]{2x}}{\sqrt[3]{2x}} = \frac{3\sqrt[3]{2x}}{\sqrt[3]{2^3x^3}} = \frac{3\sqrt[3]{2x}}{2x}$$

110.
$$\frac{5}{\sqrt[3]{3y}} = \frac{5}{\sqrt[3]{3y}}\cdot\frac{\sqrt[3]{3^2y^2}}{\sqrt[3]{3^2y^2}} = \frac{5\sqrt[3]{3^2y^2}}{\sqrt[3]{3^3y^3}} = \frac{5\sqrt[3]{9y^2}}{3y}$$

111.
$$\frac{\sqrt{40x^3y^2}}{\sqrt{80x^2y^3}} = \sqrt{\frac{40x^3y^2}{80x^2y^3}}$$
$$= \sqrt{\frac{x}{2y}}$$
$$= \frac{\sqrt{x}}{\sqrt{2y}}\cdot\frac{\sqrt{2y}}{\sqrt{2y}}$$
$$= \frac{\sqrt{2xy}}{\sqrt{2^2y^2}}$$
$$= \frac{\sqrt{2xy}}{2y}$$

112.
$$\frac{\sqrt{15a^2b^5}}{\sqrt{30a^5b^3}} = \sqrt{\frac{15a^2b^5}{30a^5b^3}}$$
$$= \sqrt{\frac{b^2}{2a^3}}$$
$$= \frac{\sqrt{b^2}}{\sqrt{a^2}\sqrt{2a}}$$
$$= \frac{b}{a\sqrt{2a}}\cdot\frac{\sqrt{2a}}{\sqrt{2a}}$$
$$= \frac{b\sqrt{2a}}{a\sqrt{2^2a^2}}$$
$$= \frac{b\sqrt{2a}}{a\cdot2a}$$
$$= \frac{b\sqrt{2a}}{2a^2}$$

113. $\dfrac{\sqrt{24a^2b}}{\sqrt{18ab^4}} = \sqrt{\dfrac{24a^2b}{18ab^4}}$

$= \sqrt{\dfrac{4a}{3b^3}}$

$= \dfrac{\sqrt{4a}}{\sqrt{3b^3}}$

$= \dfrac{\sqrt{2^2}\sqrt{a}}{\sqrt{b^2}\sqrt{3b}}$

$= \dfrac{2\sqrt{a}}{b\sqrt{3b}} \cdot \dfrac{\sqrt{3b}}{\sqrt{3b}}$

$= \dfrac{2\sqrt{3ab}}{b\sqrt{3^2b^2}}$

$= \dfrac{2\sqrt{3ab}}{b \cdot 3b}$

$= \dfrac{2\sqrt{3ab}}{3b^2}$

114. $\dfrac{\sqrt{12x^3y}}{\sqrt{20x^4y}} = \sqrt{\dfrac{12x^3y}{20x^4y}}$

$= \sqrt{\dfrac{3}{5x}}$

$= \dfrac{\sqrt{3}}{\sqrt{5x}} \cdot \dfrac{\sqrt{5x}}{\sqrt{5x}}$

$= \dfrac{\sqrt{15x}}{\sqrt{5^2x^2}}$

$= \dfrac{\sqrt{15x}}{5x}$

115. $\dfrac{2}{\sqrt{5}+2} = \dfrac{2}{\sqrt{5}+2} \cdot \dfrac{\sqrt{5}-2}{\sqrt{5}-2}$

$= \dfrac{2\sqrt{5}-4}{(\sqrt{5})^2 - 2^2}$

$= \dfrac{2\sqrt{5}-4}{5-4}$

$= \dfrac{2\sqrt{5}-4}{1}$

$= 2\sqrt{5}-4$

116. $\dfrac{5}{2-\sqrt{7}} = \dfrac{5}{2-\sqrt{7}} \cdot \dfrac{2+\sqrt{7}}{2+\sqrt{7}}$

$= \dfrac{10+5\sqrt{7}}{2^2-(\sqrt{7})^2}$

$= \dfrac{10+5\sqrt{7}}{4-7}$

$= \dfrac{10+5\sqrt{7}}{-3}$

$= -\dfrac{10+5\sqrt{7}}{3}$

117. $\dfrac{3}{\sqrt{y}-2} = \dfrac{3}{\sqrt{y}-2} \cdot \dfrac{\sqrt{y}+2}{\sqrt{y}+2}$

$= \dfrac{3\sqrt{y}+6}{(\sqrt{y})^2 - 2^2}$

$= \dfrac{3\sqrt{y}+6}{y-4}$

118. $\dfrac{-7}{\sqrt{x}-3} = -\dfrac{7}{\sqrt{x}-3} \cdot \dfrac{\sqrt{x}+3}{\sqrt{x}+3}$

$= -\dfrac{7\sqrt{x}+21}{(\sqrt{x})^2 - 3^2}$

$= -\dfrac{7\sqrt{x}+21}{x-9}$

119. $\dfrac{\sqrt{2}-\sqrt{3}}{\sqrt{2}+\sqrt{3}} = \dfrac{\sqrt{2}-\sqrt{3}}{\sqrt{2}+\sqrt{3}} \cdot \dfrac{\sqrt{2}-\sqrt{3}}{\sqrt{2}-\sqrt{3}}$

$= \dfrac{(\sqrt{2})^2 - \sqrt{6}-\sqrt{6}+(\sqrt{3})^2}{(\sqrt{2})^2-(\sqrt{3})^2}$

$= \dfrac{2-2\sqrt{6}+3}{2-3}$

$= \dfrac{5-2\sqrt{6}}{-1}$

$= -5+2\sqrt{6}$

120. $\dfrac{\sqrt{3}+\sqrt{4}}{\sqrt{2}+\sqrt{3}} = \dfrac{\sqrt{3}+\sqrt{2^2}}{\sqrt{2}+\sqrt{3}} = \dfrac{\sqrt{3}+2}{\sqrt{2}+\sqrt{3}} \cdot \dfrac{\sqrt{2}-\sqrt{3}}{\sqrt{2}-\sqrt{3}}$

$= \dfrac{\sqrt{6}-\sqrt{3^2}+2\sqrt{2}-2\sqrt{3}}{(\sqrt{2})^2-(\sqrt{3})^2}$

$= \dfrac{\sqrt{6}-3+2\sqrt{2}-2\sqrt{3}}{2-3}$

$= \dfrac{\sqrt{6}-3+2\sqrt{2}-2\sqrt{3}}{-1}$

$= -\sqrt{6}+3-2\sqrt{2}+2\sqrt{3}$

121. $\dfrac{4-\sqrt{2}}{2-\sqrt{3}} = \dfrac{4-\sqrt{2}}{2-\sqrt{3}} \cdot \dfrac{2+\sqrt{3}}{2+\sqrt{3}}$

$= \dfrac{8+4\sqrt{3}-2\sqrt{2}-\sqrt{6}}{(2)^2-(\sqrt{3})^2}$

$= \dfrac{8+4\sqrt{3}-2\sqrt{2}-\sqrt{6}}{4-3}$

$= \dfrac{8+4\sqrt{3}-2\sqrt{2}-\sqrt{6}}{1}$

$= 8+4\sqrt{3}-2\sqrt{2}-\sqrt{6}$

122. $\dfrac{3-\sqrt{x}}{3+\sqrt{x}} = \dfrac{3-\sqrt{x}}{3+\sqrt{x}} \cdot \dfrac{3-\sqrt{x}}{3-\sqrt{x}}$

$= \dfrac{9-3\sqrt{x}-3\sqrt{x}+\sqrt{x^2}}{3^2-(\sqrt{x})^2}$

$= \dfrac{9-6\sqrt{x}+x}{9-x}$

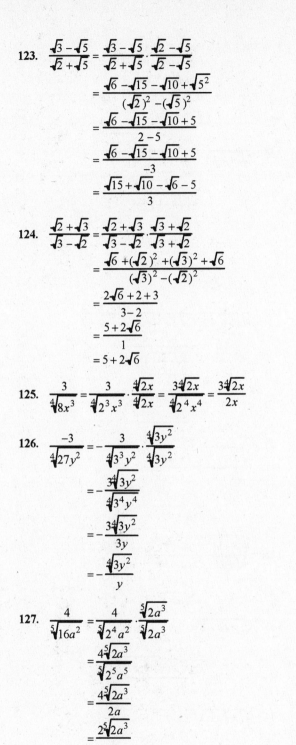

123. $\dfrac{\sqrt{3}-\sqrt{5}}{\sqrt{2}+\sqrt{5}} = \dfrac{\sqrt{3}-\sqrt{5}}{\sqrt{2}+\sqrt{5}} \cdot \dfrac{\sqrt{2}-\sqrt{5}}{\sqrt{2}-\sqrt{5}}$

$= \dfrac{\sqrt{6}-\sqrt{15}-\sqrt{10}+\sqrt{5^2}}{(\sqrt{2})^2-(\sqrt{5})^2}$

$= \dfrac{\sqrt{6}-\sqrt{15}-\sqrt{10}+5}{2-5}$

$= \dfrac{\sqrt{6}-\sqrt{15}-\sqrt{10}+5}{-3}$

$= \dfrac{\sqrt{15}+\sqrt{10}-\sqrt{6}-5}{3}$

124. $\dfrac{\sqrt{2}+\sqrt{3}}{\sqrt{3}-\sqrt{2}} = \dfrac{\sqrt{2}+\sqrt{3}}{\sqrt{3}-\sqrt{2}} \cdot \dfrac{\sqrt{3}+\sqrt{2}}{\sqrt{3}+\sqrt{2}}$

$= \dfrac{\sqrt{6}+(\sqrt{2})^2+(\sqrt{3})^2+\sqrt{6}}{(\sqrt{3})^2-(\sqrt{2})^2}$

$= \dfrac{2\sqrt{6}+2+3}{3-2}$

$= \dfrac{5+2\sqrt{6}}{1}$

$= 5+2\sqrt{6}$

125. $\dfrac{3}{\sqrt[4]{8x^3}} = \dfrac{3}{\sqrt[4]{2^3 x^3}} \cdot \dfrac{\sqrt[4]{2x}}{\sqrt[4]{2x}} = \dfrac{3\sqrt[4]{2x}}{\sqrt[4]{2^4 x^4}} = \dfrac{3\sqrt[4]{2x}}{2x}$

126. $\dfrac{-3}{\sqrt[4]{27y^2}} = -\dfrac{3}{\sqrt[4]{3^3 y^2}} \cdot \dfrac{\sqrt[4]{3y^2}}{\sqrt[4]{3y^2}}$

$= -\dfrac{3\sqrt[4]{3y^2}}{\sqrt[4]{3^4 y^4}}$

$= -\dfrac{3\sqrt[4]{3y^2}}{3y}$

$= -\dfrac{\sqrt[4]{3y^2}}{y}$

127. $\dfrac{4}{\sqrt[5]{16a^2}} = \dfrac{4}{\sqrt[5]{2^4 a^2}} \cdot \dfrac{\sqrt[5]{2a^3}}{\sqrt[5]{2a^3}}$

$= \dfrac{4\sqrt[5]{2a^3}}{\sqrt[5]{2^5 a^5}}$

$= \dfrac{4\sqrt[5]{2a^3}}{2a}$

$= \dfrac{2\sqrt[5]{2a^3}}{a}$

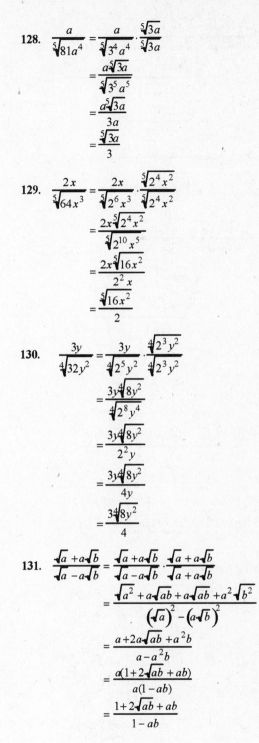

128. $\dfrac{a}{\sqrt[5]{81a^4}} = \dfrac{a}{\sqrt[5]{3^4 a^4}} \cdot \dfrac{\sqrt[5]{3a}}{\sqrt[5]{3a}}$

$= \dfrac{a\sqrt[5]{3a}}{\sqrt[5]{3^5 a^5}}$

$= \dfrac{a\sqrt[5]{3a}}{3a}$

$= \dfrac{\sqrt[5]{3a}}{3}$

129. $\dfrac{2x}{\sqrt[5]{64x^3}} = \dfrac{2x}{\sqrt[5]{2^6 x^3}} \cdot \dfrac{\sqrt[5]{2^4 x^2}}{\sqrt[5]{2^4 x^2}}$

$= \dfrac{2x\sqrt[5]{2^4 x^2}}{\sqrt[5]{2^{10} x^5}}$

$= \dfrac{2x\sqrt[5]{16x^2}}{2^2 x}$

$= \dfrac{\sqrt[5]{16x^2}}{2}$

130. $\dfrac{3y}{\sqrt[4]{32y^2}} = \dfrac{3y}{\sqrt[4]{2^5 y^2}} \cdot \dfrac{\sqrt[4]{2^3 y^2}}{\sqrt[4]{2^3 y^2}}$

$= \dfrac{3y\sqrt[4]{8y^2}}{\sqrt[4]{2^8 y^4}}$

$= \dfrac{3y\sqrt[4]{8y^2}}{2^2 y}$

$= \dfrac{3y\sqrt[4]{8y^2}}{4y}$

$= \dfrac{3\sqrt[4]{8y^2}}{4}$

131. $\dfrac{\sqrt{a}+a\sqrt{b}}{\sqrt{a}-a\sqrt{b}} = \dfrac{\sqrt{a}+a\sqrt{b}}{\sqrt{a}-a\sqrt{b}} \cdot \dfrac{\sqrt{a}+a\sqrt{b}}{\sqrt{a}+a\sqrt{b}}$

$= \dfrac{\sqrt{a^2}+a\sqrt{ab}+a\sqrt{ab}+a^2\sqrt{b^2}}{(\sqrt{a})^2-(a\sqrt{b})^2}$

$= \dfrac{a+2a\sqrt{ab}+a^2 b}{a-a^2 b}$

$= \dfrac{a(1+2\sqrt{ab}+ab)}{a(1-ab)}$

$= \dfrac{1+2\sqrt{ab}+ab}{1-ab}$

132. $\dfrac{\sqrt{3}-3\sqrt{y}}{\sqrt{3}+3\sqrt{y}} = \dfrac{\sqrt{3}-3\sqrt{y}}{\sqrt{3}+3\sqrt{y}} \cdot \dfrac{\sqrt{3}-3\sqrt{y}}{\sqrt{3}-3\sqrt{y}}$

$\qquad = \dfrac{\sqrt{3^2}-3\sqrt{3y}-3\sqrt{3y}+9\sqrt{y^2}}{\left(\sqrt{3}\right)^2-\left(3\sqrt{y}\right)^2}$

$\qquad = \dfrac{3-6\sqrt{3y}+9y}{3-9y}$

$\qquad = \dfrac{3(1-2\sqrt{3y}+3y)}{3(1-3y)}$

$\qquad = \dfrac{1-2\sqrt{3y}+3y}{1-3y}$

133. $\dfrac{3\sqrt{xy}+2\sqrt{xy}}{\sqrt{x}-\sqrt{y}} = \dfrac{5\sqrt{xy}}{\sqrt{x}-\sqrt{y}}$

$\qquad = \dfrac{5\sqrt{xy}}{\sqrt{x}-\sqrt{y}} \cdot \dfrac{\sqrt{x}+\sqrt{y}}{\sqrt{x}+\sqrt{y}}$

$\qquad = \dfrac{5\sqrt{x^2 y}+5\sqrt{xy^2}}{\left(\sqrt{x}\right)^2-\left(\sqrt{y}\right)^2}$

$\qquad = \dfrac{5\sqrt{x^2}\sqrt{y}+5\sqrt{y^2}\sqrt{x}}{x-y}$

$\qquad = \dfrac{5x\sqrt{y}+5y\sqrt{x}}{x-y}$

134. $\dfrac{2\sqrt{x}+3\sqrt{y}}{\sqrt{x}-4\sqrt{y}} = \dfrac{2\sqrt{x}+3\sqrt{y}}{\sqrt{x}-4\sqrt{y}} \cdot \dfrac{\sqrt{x}+4\sqrt{y}}{\sqrt{x}+4\sqrt{y}}$

$\qquad = \dfrac{2\sqrt{x^2}+8\sqrt{xy}+3\sqrt{xy}+12\sqrt{y^2}}{\left(\sqrt{x}\right)^2-\left(4\sqrt{y}\right)^2}$

$\qquad = \dfrac{2x+11\sqrt{xy}+12y}{x-16y}$

Applying Concepts 7.2

135. $(\sqrt{8}-\sqrt{2})^3 = (\sqrt{2^3}-\sqrt{2})^3 = (2\sqrt{2}-\sqrt{2})^3$

$\qquad = (\sqrt{2})^3 = \sqrt{2}\cdot\sqrt{2}\cdot\sqrt{2}$

$\qquad = 2\sqrt{2}$

136. $(\sqrt{27}-\sqrt{3})^3 = (\sqrt{3^3}-\sqrt{3})^3 = (3\sqrt{3}-\sqrt{3})^3$

$\qquad = (2\sqrt{3})^3 = 2\sqrt{3}\cdot 2\sqrt{3}\cdot 2\sqrt{3}$

$\qquad = 8\sqrt{3^3} = 24\sqrt{3}$

137. $(\sqrt{2}-3)^3 = (\sqrt{2}-3)(\sqrt{2}-3)(\sqrt{2}-3)$

$\qquad = (2-6\sqrt{2}+9)(\sqrt{2}-3)$

$\qquad = (-6\sqrt{2}+11)(\sqrt{2}-3)$

$\qquad = -12+18\sqrt{2}+11\sqrt{2}-33$

$\qquad = 29\sqrt{2}-45$

138. $(\sqrt{5}+2)^3 = (\sqrt{5}+2)(\sqrt{5}+2)(\sqrt{5}+2)$

$\qquad = (5+4\sqrt{5}+4)(\sqrt{5}+2)$

$\qquad = (4\sqrt{5}+9)(\sqrt{5}+2)$

$\qquad = 20+8\sqrt{5}+9\sqrt{5}+18$

$\qquad = 38+17\sqrt{5}$

139. $\dfrac{3}{\sqrt{y+1}+1} = \dfrac{3}{\sqrt{y+1}+1} \cdot \dfrac{\sqrt{y+1}-1}{\sqrt{y+1}-1}$

$\qquad = \dfrac{3\sqrt{y+1}-3}{\left(\sqrt{y+1}\right)^2-1^2}$

$\qquad = \dfrac{3\sqrt{y+1}-3}{y+1-1}$

$\qquad = \dfrac{3\sqrt{y+1}-3}{y}$

140. $\dfrac{2}{\sqrt{x+4}+2} = \dfrac{2}{\sqrt{x+4}+2} \cdot \dfrac{\sqrt{x+4}-2}{\sqrt{x+4}-2}$

$\qquad = \dfrac{2\sqrt{x+4}-4}{\left(\sqrt{x+4}\right)^2-2^2}$

$\qquad = \dfrac{2\sqrt{x+4}-4}{x+4-4}$

$\qquad = \dfrac{2\sqrt{x+4}-4}{x}$

141. $\dfrac{\sqrt[3]{(x+y)^2}}{\sqrt{x+y}} = \dfrac{(x+y)^{2/3}}{(x+y)^{1/2}}$

$\qquad = (x+y)^{1/6}$

$\qquad = \sqrt[6]{x+y}$

142. $\dfrac{\sqrt[4]{(a+b)^3}}{\sqrt{a+b}} = \dfrac{(a+b)^{3/4}}{(a+b)^{1/2}}$

$\qquad = (a+b)^{1/4}$

$\qquad = \sqrt[4]{a+b}$

143. $\sqrt[4]{2y}\sqrt{x+3} = (2y)^{1/4}(x+3)^{1/2}$

$\qquad = (2y)^{1/4}(x+3)^{2/4}$

$\qquad = \sqrt[4]{2y}\sqrt[4]{(x+3)^2}$

$\qquad = \sqrt[4]{2y(x+3)^2}$

144. $\sqrt[4]{2x}\sqrt{y-2} = (2x)^{1/4}(y-2)^{1/2}$

$\qquad = (2x)^{1/4}(y-2)^{2/4}$

$\qquad = \sqrt[4]{2x}\sqrt[4]{(y-2)^2}$

$\qquad = \sqrt[4]{2x(y-2)^2}$

145. $\sqrt{a}\sqrt[3]{a+3} = a^{1/2}(a+3)^{1/3}$

$\qquad = a^{3/6}(a+3)^{2/6}$

$\qquad = \sqrt[6]{a^3}\sqrt[6]{(a+3)^2}$

$\qquad = \sqrt[6]{a^3(a+3)^2}$

146. $\sqrt{b}\sqrt[3]{b-1} = b^{1/2}(b-1)^{1/3}$
$= b^{3/6}(b-1)^{2/6}$
$= \sqrt[6]{b^3}\sqrt[6]{(b-1)^2}$
$= \sqrt[6]{b^3(b-1)^2}$

147. $\sqrt{16^{1/2}} = (16^{1/2})^{1/2} = 16^{1/4} = 2$

148. $\sqrt[3]{4^{3/2}} = (4^{3/2})^{1/3} = 4^{1/2} = 2$

149. $\sqrt[4]{32^{-4/5}} = (32^{-4/5})^{1/4}$
$= 32^{-1/5}$
$= (2^5)^{-1/5}$
$= 2^{-1}$
$= \dfrac{1}{2}$

150. $\sqrt{243^{-4/5}} = (243^{-4/5})^{1/2}$
$= 243^{-2/5}$
$= (3^5)^{-2/5}$
$= 3^{-2}$
$= \dfrac{1}{9}$

151. a.
$D(x) = 3.50x^{0.2}$
$D(x) = 3.50x^{2/10}$
$D(x) = 3.50\sqrt[10]{x^2}$

b. For the year 1995, $x = 5$.
$D(5) = 3.50\sqrt[10]{5^2}$
$D(5) \approx 4.83$
The model predicted a debt of $4.83 trillion by 1995.

c. For the year 2010, $x = 20$.
$D(20) = 3.50\sqrt[10]{20^2}$
$D(20) \approx 6.37$
The model predicts a debt of $6.37 trillion by the year 2010.

152. A number, n, must be multiplied by 4 to double its square root. This follows from $\sqrt{4n} = 2\sqrt{n}$. To triple its square root, the number must be multiplied by 9. $\left(\sqrt{9n} = 3\sqrt{n}\right)$ To double the cube root of a number, multiply by 8. $\left(\sqrt[3]{8} = 2\sqrt[3]{n}\right)$ To triple the cube root of a number, multiply by 27. $\left(\sqrt[3]{27n} = 3\sqrt[3]{n}\right)$

Section 7.3

Concept Review 7.3

1. Always true

2. Always true

3. Never true
   The domain is $\{x | x \text{ is a real number}\}$.

4. Never true
   The expression $\sqrt{-x^2}$ does not represent a real number.

Objective 7.3.1 Exercises

1. A radical function is one that contains a variable underneath a radical sign or contains a fractional exponent.

2. Polynomial functions contain neither a variable underneath a radical sign nor a fractional exponent. All exponents on variables in a polynomial function are natural numbers. Polynomial functions can contain a radical expression, but the radicand must be a number, not a variable expression.

3. The domain of $f(x) = 2x^{1/3}$ is $\{x | x \text{ is a real number}\}$.

4. The domain of $r(x) = -3\sqrt[5]{2x}$ is $\{x | x \text{ is a real number}\}$.

5. $x + 1 \geq 0$
   $x \geq -1$
   The domain of $g(x) = -2\sqrt{x+1}$ is $\{x | x \geq -1\}$.

6. $x^{1/4} = \sqrt[4]{x}$
   $x \geq 0$
   The domain of $h(x) = 3x^{1/4} - 2$ is $\{x | x \geq 0\}$.

7. $x \geq 0$
   The domain of $f(x) = 2x\sqrt{x} - 3$ is $\{x | x \geq 0\}$.

8. The domain of $y(x) = -3\sqrt[3]{1+x}$ is $\{x | x \text{ is a real number}\}$.

9. $x^{3/4} = \sqrt[4]{x^3}$
   $x^3 \geq 0$
   $x \geq 0$
   The domain of $C(x) = -3x^{3/4} + 1$ is $\{x | x \geq 0\}$.

10. The domain of $G(x) = 6x^{2/5} + 5$ is $\{x | x \text{ is a real number}\}$.

11. $(3x - 6)^{1/2} = \sqrt{3x - 6}$
    $3x - 6 \geq 0$
    $3x \geq 6$
    $x \geq 2$
    The domain of $F(x) = 4(3x - 6)^{1/2}$ is $\{x | x \geq 2\}$.

12. $(4x - 12)^{1/2} = \sqrt{4x - 12}$
    $4x - 12 \geq 0$
    $4x \geq 12$
    $x \geq 3$
    The domain of $f(x) = -2(4x - 12)^{1/2}$ is $[3, \infty)$.

13. The domain of $g(x) = 2(2x - 10)^{2/3}$ is $(-\infty, \infty)$.

14. The domain of $J(x) = 4 - (3x - 3)^{2/5}$ is $(-\infty, \infty)$.

15. $12 - 4x \geq 0$
$\qquad -4x \geq -12$
$\qquad\quad x \leq 3$
The domain of $V(x) = x - \sqrt{12 - 4x}$ is $(-\infty, 3]$.

16. $6 - x \geq 0$
$\qquad -x \geq -6$
$\qquad\ x \leq 6$
The domain of $Y(x) = -6 + \sqrt{6 - x}$ is $(-\infty, 6]$.

17. $(x - 2)^2 \geq 0$
$\qquad x - 2 \geq 0$
$\qquad\quad x \geq 2$
The domain of $h(x) = 3\sqrt[4]{(x - 2)^3}$ is $[2, \infty)$.

18. $(4 - x)^3 \geq 0$
$\qquad 4 - x \geq 0$
$\qquad\ -x \geq -4$
$\qquad\quad x \leq 4$
The domain of $g(x) = \dfrac{2}{3}\sqrt[4]{(4 - x)^3}$ is $(-\infty, 4]$.

19. $(4 - 6x)^{1/2} = \sqrt{4 - 6x}$
$\qquad 4 - 6x \geq 0$
$\qquad\ -6x \geq -4$
$\qquad\quad x \leq \dfrac{2}{3}$
The domain of $f(x) = x - (4 - 6x)^{1/2}$ is $\left(-\infty, \dfrac{2}{3}\right]$.

20. $(9 + 12x)^{1/2} = \sqrt{9 + 12x}$
$\qquad 9 + 12x \geq 0$
$\qquad\quad 12x \geq -9$
$\qquad\qquad x \geq -\dfrac{3}{4}$
The domain of
$F(x) = (9 + 12x)^{1/2} - 4$ is $\left[-\dfrac{3}{4}, \infty\right)$.

Objective 7.3.2 Exercises

21.

22.

23.
24.
25.
26.
27.
28.
29.
30.
31.
32.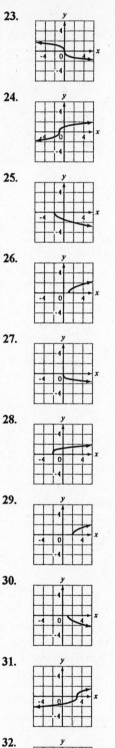

33.

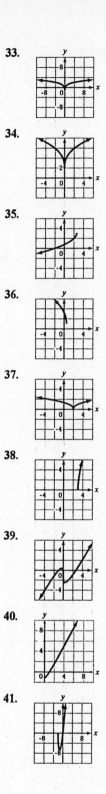

34.

35.

36.

37.

38.

39.

40.

41.

42. a.

b. The maximum value of this function for the given interval is approximately 400.

c. The point on the graph of f which $y = x$ is approximately (233, 233).

d.
$$a^2 + b^2 = c^2$$
$$233^2 + 233^2 = c^2$$
$$54,289 + 54,289 = c^2$$
$$108,578 = c^2$$
$$330 \approx c$$

The distance from home plate to the right field wall is approximately 330 ft.

43. a. In the context of the problem, the domain of the function is the numbers 1, 5, 10, 20, 50, 100. 0 is not in the domain because there is no $0 bill. Negative numbers are not in the domain because there are no bills whose denominators are negative.

b. The model predicts a life span of approximately 1.8 years for a $2 bill. This estimate is not reasonable. The $2 bill in not in circulation as much as the other denominations listed in the table. Therefore, its life span would not be accurately depicted by the mode.

44. The graphs of $f(x) = \left(x^2\right)^{\frac{1}{4}}$ and $g(x) = x^{\frac{1}{2}}$ follow.

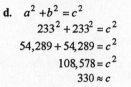

The expression $x^{\frac{2}{4}}$ and $x^{\frac{1}{2}}$ are not equal when $x < 0$. For example, if $x = -9$, then

$$x^{\frac{2}{4}} = (-9)^{\frac{2}{4}} = \left[(-9)^2\right]^{\frac{1}{4}} = (81)^{\frac{1}{4}} = 3 \text{ and}$$

$$x^{\frac{1}{2}} = (-9)^{\frac{1}{2}} = \pm 3i.$$ This exercise gives a graphical representation of the concept.

Section 7.4

Concept Review 7.4

1. Sometimes true
$(-2)^2 = 2^2$, but -2 does not equal 2.

2. Sometimes true
Squaring both sides of an equation may introduce an extraneous root.

3. Sometimes true
The Pythagorean Therorem is valid only for right triangles.

4. Always true

Objective 7.4.1 Exercises

1. The first step is to subtract 3 from both sides of the equation. This achieves the goal of getting the radical expression alone on one side of the equation.

2. When you raise both sides of an equation to an even power, the resulting equation may have a solution that is not a solution of the original equation.

3.
$$\sqrt{x} = 5$$
$$(\sqrt{x})^2 = 5^2$$
$$x = 25$$

Check:

$$\sqrt{x} = 5$$

$\sqrt{25}$	5

$$5 = 5$$

The solution is 25.

4.
$$\sqrt{y} = 2$$
$$(\sqrt{y})^2 = 2^2$$
$$y = 4$$

Check:

$$\sqrt{y} = 2$$

$\sqrt{4}$	2

$$2 = 2$$

The solution is 4.

5.
$$\sqrt[3]{a} = 3$$
$$(\sqrt[3]{a})^3 = 3$$
$$a = 27$$

Check:

$$\sqrt[3]{a} = 3$$

$\sqrt[3]{27}$	3

$$3 = 3$$

The solution is 27.

6.
$$\sqrt[3]{y} = 5$$
$$(\sqrt[3]{y})^3 = 5^3$$
$$y = 125$$

Check:

$$\sqrt[3]{y} = 5$$

$\sqrt[3]{125}$	5

$$5 = 5$$

The solution is 125.

7.
$$\sqrt{3x} = 12$$
$$(\sqrt{3x})^2 = 12^2$$
$$3x = 144$$
$$x = 48$$

Check:

$$\sqrt{3x} = 12$$

$\sqrt{3(48)}$	12
$\sqrt{144}$	12

$$12 = 12$$

The solution is 48.

8.
$$\sqrt{5x} = 10$$
$$(\sqrt{5x})^2 = 10^2$$
$$5x = 100$$
$$x = 20$$

Check:

$$\sqrt{5x} = 10$$

$\sqrt{5(20)}$	10
$\sqrt{100}$	10

$$10 = 10$$

The solution is 20.

9.
$$\sqrt[3]{4x} = -2$$
$$(\sqrt[3]{4x})^3 = (-2)^3$$
$$4x = -8$$
$$x = -2$$

Check:

$$\sqrt[3]{4x} = -2$$

$\sqrt[3]{4(-2)}$	-2
$\sqrt[3]{-8}$	-2
$-2 = -2$	

The solution is -2.

10.
$$\sqrt[3]{6x} = -3$$
$$(\sqrt[3]{6x})^3 = (-3)^3$$
$$6x = -27$$
$$x = -\frac{9}{2}$$

Check:

$$\sqrt[3]{6x} = -3$$

$\sqrt[3]{6\left(-\frac{9}{2}\right)}$	-3
$\sqrt[3]{-27}$	-3
$-3 = -3$	

The solution is $-\frac{9}{2}$.

11.
$$\sqrt{2x} = -4$$
$$(\sqrt{2x})^2 = (-4)^2$$
$$2x = 16$$
$$x = 8$$

Check:

$$\sqrt{2x} = -4$$

$\sqrt{2(8)}$	-4
$\sqrt{16}$	-4
$4 \neq -4$	

8 does not check as a solution.
The equation has no solution.

12.
$$\sqrt{5x} = -5$$
$$(\sqrt{5x})^2 = (-5)^2$$
$$5x = 25$$
$$x = 5$$

Check:

$$\sqrt{5x} = -5$$

$\sqrt{5(5)}$	-5
$\sqrt{25}$	-5
$5 \neq -5$	

5 does not check as a solution.
The equation has no solution.

13.
$$\sqrt{3x-2} = 5$$
$$(\sqrt{3x-2})^2 = 5^2$$
$$3x-2 = 25$$
$$3x = 27$$
$$x = 9$$

Check:

$$\sqrt{3x-2} = 5$$

$\sqrt{3(9)-2}$	5
$\sqrt{27-2}$	5
$\sqrt{25}$	5
$5 = 5$	

The solution is 9.

14.
$$\sqrt{5x-4} = 9$$
$$(\sqrt{5x-4})^2 = 9^2$$
$$5x-4 = 81$$
$$5x = 85$$
$$x = 17$$

Check:

$$\sqrt{5x-4} = 9$$

$\sqrt{5(17)-4}$	9
$\sqrt{85-4}$	9
$\sqrt{81}$	9
$9 = 9$	

The solution is 17.

15.
$$\sqrt{3-2x} = 7$$
$$(\sqrt{3-2x})^2 = 7^2$$
$$3 - 2x = 49$$
$$-2x = 46$$
$$x = -23$$

Check:

$\sqrt{3-2x} = 7$	
$\sqrt{3-2(-23)}$	7
$\sqrt{3+46}$	7
$\sqrt{49}$	7
$7 = 7$	

The solution is -23.

16.
$$\sqrt{9-4x} = 4$$
$$(\sqrt{9-4x})^2 = 4^2$$
$$9 - 4x = 16$$
$$-4x = 7$$
$$x = -\frac{7}{4}$$

Check:

$\sqrt{9-4x} = 4$	
$\sqrt{9-4\left(-\frac{7}{4}\right)}$	4
$\sqrt{9+7}$	4
$\sqrt{16}$	4
$4 = 4$	

The solution is $-\frac{7}{4}$.

17.
$$7 = \sqrt{1-3x}$$
$$(7)^2 = (\sqrt{1-3x})^2$$
$$49 = 1 - 3x$$
$$48 = -3x$$
$$-16 = x$$

Check:

$7 = \sqrt{1-3x}$	
7	$\sqrt{1-3(-16)}$
7	$\sqrt{1+48}$
7	$\sqrt{49}$
$7 = 7$	

The solution is -16.

18.
$$6 = \sqrt{8-7x}$$
$$(6)^2 = (\sqrt{8-7x})^2$$
$$36 = 8 - 7x$$
$$28 = -7x$$
$$-4 = x$$

Check:

$6 = \sqrt{8-7x}$	
6	$\sqrt{8-7(-4)}$
6	$\sqrt{36}$
$7 = 7$	

The solution is -4.

19.
$$\sqrt[3]{4x-1} = 2$$
$$(\sqrt[3]{4x-1})^3 = 2^3$$
$$4x - 1 = 8$$
$$4x = 9$$
$$4x = \frac{9}{4}$$

Check:

$\sqrt[3]{4x-1} = 2$	
$\sqrt[3]{4\left(\frac{9}{4}\right)-1}$	2
$\sqrt[3]{9-1}$	2
$\sqrt[3]{8}$	2
$2 = 2$	

The solution is $\frac{9}{4}$.

20.
$$\sqrt[3]{5x+2} = 3$$
$$(\sqrt[3]{5x+2})^3 = 3^3$$
$$5x + 2 = 27$$
$$5x = 25$$
$$x = 5$$

Check:

$\sqrt[3]{5x+2} = 3$	
$\sqrt[3]{5(5)+2}$	3
$\sqrt[3]{27}$	3
$3 = 3$	

The solution is 5.

21. $\sqrt[3]{1-2x} = -3$
$(\sqrt[3]{1-2x})^3 = (-3)^3$
$1-2x = -27$
$-2x = -28$
$x = 14$

Check:

$\sqrt[3]{1-2x} = -3$	
$\sqrt[3]{1-2(14)}$	-3
$\sqrt[3]{1-28}$	-3
$\sqrt[3]{-27}$	-3
	$-3 = -3$

The solution is 14.

22. $\sqrt[3]{3-2x} = -2$
$(\sqrt[3]{3-2x})^3 = (-2)^3$
$3-2x = -8$
$-2x = -11$
$x = \dfrac{11}{2}$

Check:

$\sqrt[3]{3-2x} = -2$	
$\sqrt[3]{3-2\left(\dfrac{11}{2}\right)}$	-2
$\sqrt[3]{3-11}$	-2
$\sqrt[3]{-8}$	-2
	$-2 = -2$

The solution is $\dfrac{11}{2}$.

23. $\sqrt[3]{9x+1} = 4$
$(\sqrt[3]{9x+1})^3 = 4^3$
$9x+1 = 64$
$9x = 63$
$x = 7$

Check:

$\sqrt[3]{9x+1} = 4$	
$\sqrt[3]{9(7)+1}$	4
$\sqrt[3]{63+1}$	4
$\sqrt[3]{64}$	4
	$4 = 4$

The solution is 7.

24. $\sqrt{3x+9} - 12 = 0$
$\sqrt{3x+9} = 12$
$(\sqrt{3x+9})^2 = 12^2$
$3x+9 = 144$
$3x = 135$
$x = 45$

Check:

$\sqrt{3x+9} - 12 = 0$	
$\sqrt{3(45)+9} - 12$	0
$\sqrt{135+9} - 12$	0
$\sqrt{144} - 12$	0
$12 - 12$	0
	$0 = 0$

The solution is 45.

25. $\sqrt{4x-3} - 5 = 0$
$\sqrt{4x-3} = 5$
$(\sqrt{4x-3})^2 = 5^2$
$4x-3 = 25$
$4x = 28$
$x = 7$

Check:

$\sqrt{4x-3} - 5 = 0$	
$\sqrt{4(7)-3} - 5$	0
$\sqrt{28-3} - 5$	0
$\sqrt{25} - 5$	0
$5 - 5$	0
	$0 = 0$

The solution is 7.

26. $\sqrt{x-2} = 4$
$(\sqrt{x-2})^2 = 4^2$
$x-2 = 16$
$x = 18$

Check:

$\sqrt{x-2} = 4$	
$\sqrt{18-2}$	4
$\sqrt{16}$	4
	$4 = 4$

The solution is 18.

27.
$$\sqrt[3]{x-3}+5=0$$
$$\sqrt[3]{x-3}=-5$$
$$(\sqrt[3]{x-3})^3=(-5)^3$$
$$x-3=-125$$
$$x=-122$$

Check:

$$\sqrt[3]{x-3}+5=0$$

$\sqrt[3]{-122-3}+5$	0
$\sqrt[3]{-125}+5$	0
$-5+5$	0
	$0=0$

The solution is -122.

28.
$$\sqrt[3]{x-2}=3$$
$$(\sqrt[3]{x-2})^3=3^3$$
$$x-2=27$$
$$x=29$$

Check:

$$\sqrt[3]{x-2}=3$$

$\sqrt[3]{29-2}$	3
$\sqrt[3]{27}$	3
	$3=3$

The solution is 29.

29.
$$\sqrt[3]{2x-6}=4$$
$$(\sqrt[3]{2x-6})^3=4^3$$
$$2x-6=64$$
$$2x=70$$
$$x=35$$

Check:

$$\sqrt[3]{2x-6}=4$$

$\sqrt[3]{2(35)-6}$	4
$\sqrt[3]{70-6}$	4
$\sqrt[3]{64}$	4
	$4=4$

The solution is 35.

30.
$$\sqrt[4]{4x+1}=2$$
$$(\sqrt[4]{4x+1})^4=2^4$$
$$4x+1=16$$
$$4x=15$$
$$x=\frac{15}{4}$$

Check:

$$\sqrt[4]{4x+1}=2$$

$\sqrt[4]{4\left(\dfrac{15}{4}\right)+1}$	2
$\sqrt[4]{15+1}$	2
$\sqrt[4]{16}$	2
	$2=2$

The solution is $\dfrac{15}{4}$.

31.
$$\sqrt[4]{2x-9}=3$$
$$(\sqrt[4]{2x-9})=3^4$$
$$2x-9=81$$
$$2x=90$$
$$x=45$$

Check:

$$\sqrt[4]{2x-9}=3$$

$\sqrt[4]{2(45)-9}$	3
$\sqrt[4]{90-9}$	3
$\sqrt[4]{81}$	3
	$3=3$

The solution is 45.

32.
$$\sqrt{2x-3}-2=1$$
$$\sqrt{2x-3}=3$$
$$(\sqrt{2x-3})^2=3^2$$
$$2x-3=9$$
$$2x=12$$
$$x=6$$

Check:

$$\sqrt{2x-3}-2=1$$

$\sqrt{2(6)-3}-2$	1
$\sqrt{12-3}-2$	1
$\sqrt{9}-2$	1
$3-2$	1
	$1=1$

The solution is 6.

33. $\sqrt{3x-5} - 5 = 3$
$\sqrt{3x-5} = 8$
$(\sqrt{3x-5})^2 = 8^2$
$3x - 5 = 64$
$3x = 69$
$x = 23$

Check:

$\sqrt{3x-5} - 5 = 3$	
$\sqrt{3(23)-5} - 5$	3
$\sqrt{69-5} - 5$	3
$\sqrt{64} - 5$	3
$8 - 5$	3
$3 = 3$	

The solution is 23.

34. $\sqrt[3]{2x-3} + 5 = 2$
$\sqrt[3]{2x-3} = -3$
$(\sqrt[3]{2x-3})^3 = (-3)^3$
$2x - 3 = -27$
$2x = -24$
$x = -12$

Check:

$\sqrt[3]{2x-3} + 5 = 2$	
$\sqrt[3]{2(-12)-3} + 5$	2
$\sqrt[3]{-24-3} + 5$	2
$\sqrt[3]{-27} + 5$	2
$-3 + 5$	2
$2 = 2$	

The solution is -12.

35. $\sqrt[3]{x-4} + 7 = 5$
$\sqrt[3]{x-4} = -2$
$(\sqrt[3]{x-4})^3 = (-2)^3$
$x - 4 = -8$
$x = -4$

Check:

$\sqrt[3]{x-4} + 7 = 5$	
$\sqrt[3]{-4-4} + 7$	5
$\sqrt[3]{-8} + 7$	5
$-2 + 7$	5
$5 = 5$	

The solution is -4.

36. $\sqrt{5x-16} + 1 = 4$
$(\sqrt{5x-16})^2 = (3)^2$
$5x - 16 = 9$
$5x = 25$
$x = 5$

Check:

$\sqrt{5x-16} + 1 = 4$	
$\sqrt{5(5)-16} + 1$	4
$\sqrt{25-16} + 1$	4
$\sqrt{9} + 1$	4
$3 + 1$	4
$4 = 4$	

The solution is 5.

37. $\sqrt{3x-5} - 2 = 3$
$(\sqrt{3x-5})^2 = (5)^2$
$3x - 5 = 25$
$3x = 30$
$x = 10$

Check:

$\sqrt{3x-5} - 2 = 3$	
$\sqrt{3(10)-5} - 2$	3
$\sqrt{30-5} - 2$	3
$\sqrt{25} - 2$	3
$5 - 2$	3
$3 = 3$	

The solution is 10.

38. $\sqrt{2x-1} - 8 = -5$
$(\sqrt{2x-1})^2 = (3)^2$
$2x - 1 = 9$
$2x = 10$
$x = 5$

Check:

$\sqrt{2x-1} - 8 = -5$	
$\sqrt{2(5)-1} - 8$	-5
$\sqrt{10-1} - 8$	-5
$\sqrt{9} - 8$	-5
$3 - 8$	-5
$-5 = -5$	

The solution is 5.

39.
$$\sqrt{7x+2} - 10 = -7$$
$$(\sqrt{7x+2})^2 = (3)^2$$
$$7x + 2 = 9$$
$$7x = 7$$
$$x = 1$$

Check:

$\sqrt{7x+2} - 10 = -7$	
$\sqrt{7(1)+2} - 10$	-7
$\sqrt{7+2} - 10$	-7
$\sqrt{9} - 10$	-7
$3 - 10$	-7
	$-7 = -7$

The solution is 1.

40.
$$\sqrt[3]{4x-3} - 2 = 3$$
$$(\sqrt[3]{4x-3})^3 = (5)^3$$
$$4x - 3 = 125$$
$$4x = 128$$
$$x = 32$$

Check:

$\sqrt[3]{4x-3} - 2 = 3$	
$\sqrt[3]{4(32)-3} - 2$	3
$\sqrt[3]{128-3} - 2$	3
$\sqrt[3]{125} - 2$	3
$5 - 2$	3
	$3 = 3$

The solution is 32.

41.
$$\sqrt[3]{1-3x} + 5 = 3$$
$$(\sqrt[3]{1-3x})^3 = (-2)^3$$
$$1 - 3x = -8$$
$$-3x = -9$$
$$x = 3$$

Check:

$\sqrt[3]{1-3x} + 5 = 3$	
$\sqrt[3]{1-3(3)} + 5$	3
$\sqrt[3]{1-9} + 5$	3
$\sqrt[3]{-8} + 5$	3
$-2 + 5$	3
	$3 = 3$

The solution is 3.

42.
$$1 - \sqrt{4x+3} = -5$$
$$(-\sqrt{4x+3})^2 = (-6)^2$$
$$4x + 3 = 36$$
$$4x = 33$$
$$x = \frac{33}{4}$$

Check:

$1 - \sqrt{4x+3} = -5$	
$1 - \sqrt{4\left(\dfrac{33}{4}\right)+3}$	-5
$1 - \sqrt{33+3}$	-5
$1 - \sqrt{36}$	-5
$1 - 6$	-5
	$-5 = -5$

The solution is $\dfrac{33}{4}$.

43.
$$7 - \sqrt{3x+1} = -1$$
$$(-\sqrt{3x+1})^2 = (-8)^2$$
$$3x + 1 = 64$$
$$3x = 63$$
$$x = 21$$

Check:

$7 - \sqrt{3x+1} = -1$	
$7 - \sqrt{3(21)+1}$	-1
$7 - \sqrt{63+1}$	-1
$7 - \sqrt{64}$	-1
$7 - 8$	-1
	$-1 = -1$

The solution is 21.

44.
$$\sqrt{x+1} = 2 - \sqrt{x}$$
$$(\sqrt{x+1})^2 = (2 - \sqrt{x})^2$$
$$x+1 = 4 - 4\sqrt{x} + x$$
$$-3 = -4\sqrt{x}$$
$$(-3)^2 = (-4\sqrt{x})^2$$
$$9 = 16x$$
$$\frac{9}{16} = x$$

Check:

$$\sqrt{x+1} = 2 - \sqrt{x}$$

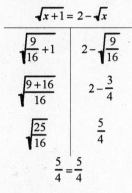

$$\sqrt{\frac{9}{16}+1} \quad \bigg| \quad 2 - \sqrt{\frac{9}{16}}$$

$$\sqrt{\frac{9+16}{16}} \quad \bigg| \quad 2 - \frac{3}{4}$$

$$\sqrt{\frac{25}{16}} \quad \bigg| \quad \frac{5}{4}$$

$$\frac{5}{4} = \frac{5}{4}$$

The solution is $\frac{9}{16}$.

45.
$$\sqrt{2x+4} = 3 - \sqrt{2x}$$
$$(\sqrt{2x+4})^2 = (3 - \sqrt{2x})^2$$
$$2x+4 = 9 - 6\sqrt{2x} + 2x$$
$$6\sqrt{2x} = 5$$
$$(6\sqrt{2x})^2 = (5)^2$$
$$36(2x) = 25$$
$$72x = 25$$
$$x = \frac{25}{72}$$

Check:

$$\sqrt{2x+4} = 3 - \sqrt{2x}$$

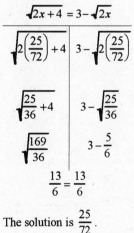

$$\sqrt{2\left(\frac{25}{72}\right)+4} \quad \bigg| \quad 3 - \sqrt{2\left(\frac{25}{72}\right)}$$

$$\sqrt{\frac{25}{36}+4} \quad \bigg| \quad 3 - \sqrt{\frac{25}{36}}$$

$$\sqrt{\frac{169}{36}} \quad \bigg| \quad 3 - \frac{5}{6}$$

$$\frac{13}{6} = \frac{13}{6}$$

The solution is $\frac{25}{72}$.

46.
$$\sqrt{x^2+3x-2} - x = 1$$
$$\sqrt{x^2+3x-2} = x+1$$
$$(\sqrt{x^2+3x-2})^2 = (x+1)^2$$
$$x^2+3x-2 = x^2+2x+1$$
$$x-2 = 1$$
$$x = 3$$

Check:

$$\sqrt{x^2+3x-2} - x = 1$$

$\sqrt{3^2+3(3)-2} - 3$	1
$\sqrt{9+9-2} - 3$	1
$\sqrt{16} - 3$	1
$4 - 3$	1
	$1 = 1$

The solution is 3.

47.
$$\sqrt{x^2-4x-1} + 3 = x$$
$$\sqrt{x^2-4x-1} = x-3$$
$$(\sqrt{x^2-4x-1})^2 = (x-3)^2$$
$$x^2-4x-1 = x^2-6x+9$$
$$2x = 10$$
$$x = 5$$

Check:

$$\sqrt{x^2-4x-1} + 3 = x$$

$\sqrt{5^2-4(5)-1} + 3$	5
$\sqrt{25-20-1} + 3$	5
$\sqrt{4} + 3$	5
	$2 + 3 = 5$

The solution is 5.

48.
$$\sqrt{x^2 - 3x - 1} = 3$$
$$(\sqrt{x^2 - 3x - 1})^2 = 3^2$$
$$x^2 - 3x - 1 = 9$$
$$x^2 - 3x - 10 = 0$$
$$(x - 5)(x + 2) = 0$$
$$x - 5 = 0 \quad x + 2 = 0$$
$$x = 5 \qquad x = -2$$

Check:

$\sqrt{x^2 - 3x - 1} = 3$		$\sqrt{x^2 - 3x - 1} = 3$	
$\sqrt{5^2 - 3(5) - 1}$	3	$\sqrt{(-2)^2 - 3(-2) - 1}$	3
$\sqrt{25 - 15 - 1}$	3	$\sqrt{4 + 6 - 1}$	3
$\sqrt{9}$	3	$\sqrt{9}$	3
	$3 = 3$		$3 = 3$

The solutions are 5 and –2.

49.
$$\sqrt{x^2 - 2x + 1} = 3$$
$$(\sqrt{x^2 - 2x + 1})^2 = 3^2$$
$$x^2 - 2x + 1 = 9$$
$$x^2 - 2x - 8 = 0$$
$$(x - 4)(x + 2) = 0$$
$$x - 4 = 0 \quad x + 2 = 0$$
$$x = 4 \qquad x = -2$$

Check:

$\sqrt{x^2 - 2x + 1} = 3$		$\sqrt{x^2 - 2x + 1} = 3$	
$\sqrt{4^2 - 2(4) + 1}$	3	$\sqrt{(-2)^2 - 2(-2) + 1}$	3
$\sqrt{16 - 8 + 1}$	3	$\sqrt{4 + 4 + 1}$	3
$\sqrt{9}$	3	$\sqrt{9}$	3
	$3 = 3$		$3 = 3$

The solutions are 4 and –2.

50. $\sqrt{2x+5} - \sqrt{3x-2} = 1$

$$(\sqrt{2x+5})^2 = (1+\sqrt{3x-2})^2$$
$$2x+5 = 1+2\sqrt{3x-2}+3x-2$$
$$2x+5 = 3x-1+2\sqrt{3x-2}$$
$$(-x+6)^2 = (2\sqrt{3x-2})^2$$
$$x^2-12x+36 = 4(3x-2)$$
$$x^2-12x+36 = 12x-8$$
$$x^2-24x+44 = 0$$
$$(x-2)(x-22) = 0$$
$$x-2 = 0 \quad x-22 = 0$$
$$x = 2 \qquad x = 22$$

Check:

$\sqrt{2x+5} - \sqrt{3x-2} = 1$		$\sqrt{2x+5} - \sqrt{3x-2} = 1$	
$\sqrt{2(2)+5} - \sqrt{3(2)-2}$	1	$\sqrt{2(22)+5} - \sqrt{3(22)-2}$	1
$\sqrt{4+5} - \sqrt{6-2}$	1	$\sqrt{44+5} - \sqrt{66-2}$	1
$\sqrt{9} - \sqrt{4}$	1	$\sqrt{49} - \sqrt{64}$	1
$3-2$	1	$7-8$	1
	$1 = 1$		$-1 \ne 1$

The solution is 2.

51. $\sqrt{4x+1} - \sqrt{2x+4} = 1$

$$(\sqrt{4x+1})^2 = (1+\sqrt{2x+4})^2$$
$$4x+1 = 1+2\sqrt{2x+4}+2x+4$$
$$4x+1 = 5+2x+2\sqrt{2x+4}$$
$$(2x-4)^2 = (2\sqrt{2x+4})^2$$
$$4x^2-16x+16 = 4(2x+4)$$
$$4x^2-16x+16 = 8x+16$$
$$4x^2-24x = 0$$
$$4x(x-6) = 0$$
$$x = 0 \quad x-6 = 0$$
$$\qquad x = 6$$

Check:

$\sqrt{4x+1} - \sqrt{2x+4} = 1$		$\sqrt{4x+1} - \sqrt{2x+4} = 1$	
$\sqrt{4(0)+1} - \sqrt{2(0)+4}$	1	$\sqrt{4(6)+1} - \sqrt{2(6)+4}$	1
$\sqrt{1} - \sqrt{4}$	1	$\sqrt{24+1} - \sqrt{12+4}$	1
$1-2$	1	$\sqrt{25} - \sqrt{16}$	1
	$-1 \ne 1$	$5-4$	1
			$1 = 1$

The solution is 6.

52. $\sqrt{5x-1} - \sqrt{3x-2} = 1$

$$(\sqrt{5x-1})^2 = (1+\sqrt{3x-2})^2$$
$$5x-1 = 1+2\sqrt{3x-2}+3x-2$$
$$5x-1 = 3x-1+2\sqrt{3x-2}$$
$$(2x)^2 = (2\sqrt{3x-2})^2$$
$$4x^2 = 4(3x-2)$$
$$4x^2 = 12x-8$$
$$4x^2-12x+8 = 0$$
$$4(x^2-3x+2) = 0$$
$$4(x-2)(x-1) = 0$$
$$x-2 = 0 \quad x-1 = 0$$
$$x = 2 \qquad x = 1$$

Check:

$\sqrt{5x-1} - \sqrt{3x-2} = 1$	
$\sqrt{5(2)-1} - \sqrt{3(2)-2}$	1
$\sqrt{10-1} - \sqrt{6-2}$	1
$\sqrt{9} - \sqrt{4}$	1
$3-2$	1
	$1 = 1$

$\sqrt{5x-1} - \sqrt{3x-2} = 1$	
$\sqrt{5(1)-1} - \sqrt{3(1)-2}$	1
$\sqrt{5-1} - \sqrt{3-2}$	1
$\sqrt{4} - \sqrt{1}$	1
$2-1$	1
	$1 = 1$

The solutions are 2 and 1.

53. $\sqrt{5x+4} - \sqrt{3x+1} = 1$

$$(\sqrt{5x+4})^2 = (1+\sqrt{3x+1})^2$$
$$5x+4 = 1+2\sqrt{3x+1}+3x+1$$
$$5x+4 = 2+3x+2\sqrt{3x+1}$$
$$(2x+2)^2 = (2\sqrt{3x+1})^2$$
$$4x^2+8x+4 = 4(3x+1)$$
$$4x^2+8x+4 = 12x+4$$
$$4x^2-4x = 0$$
$$4x(x-1) = 0$$
$$x = 0 \quad x-1 = 0$$
$$\qquad x = 1$$

Check:

$\sqrt{5x+4} - \sqrt{3x+1} = 1$	
$\sqrt{5(0)+4} - \sqrt{3(0)+1}$	1
$\sqrt{4} - \sqrt{1}$	1
$2-1$	1
	$1 = 1$

$\sqrt{5x+4} - \sqrt{3x+1} = 1$	
$\sqrt{5(1)+4} - \sqrt{3(1)+1}$	1
$\sqrt{5+4} - \sqrt{3+1}$	1
$\sqrt{9} - \sqrt{4}$	1
$3-2$	1
	$1 = 1$

The solutions are 0 and 1.

54. $\sqrt[4]{x^2+2x+8}-2=0$

$\qquad \sqrt[4]{x^2+2x+8}=2$

$\qquad (\sqrt[4]{x^2+2x+8})^4=2^4$

$\qquad x^2+2x+8=16$

$\qquad x^2+2x-8=0$

$\qquad (x+4)(x-2)=0$

$x+4=0 \qquad x-2=0$

$\qquad x=-4 \qquad x=2$

Check:

$\sqrt[4]{x^2+2x+8}-2=0$	
$\sqrt[4]{(-4)^2+2(-4)+8}-2$	0
$\sqrt[4]{16-8+8}-2$	0
$\sqrt[4]{16}-2$	0
$2-2$	0
	$0=0$

$\sqrt[4]{x^2+2x+8}-2=0$	
$\sqrt[4]{2^2+2(2)+8}-2$	0
$\sqrt[4]{4+4+8}-2$	0
$\sqrt[4]{16}-2$	0
$2-2$	0
	$0=0$

The solutions are –4 and 2.

55. $\sqrt[4]{x^2+x-1}-1=0$

$\qquad \sqrt[4]{x^2+x-1}=1$

$\qquad (\sqrt[4]{x^2+x-1})^4=1^4$

$\qquad x^2+x-1=1$

$\qquad x^2+x-2=0$

$\qquad (x+2)(x-1)=0$

$x+2=0 \qquad x-1=0$

$\qquad x=-2 \qquad x=1$

Check:

$\sqrt[4]{x^2+x-1}-1=0$	
$\sqrt[4]{(-2)^2+(-2)-1}-1$	0
$\sqrt[4]{4-2-1}-1$	0
$\sqrt[4]{1}-1$	0
$1-1$	0
	$0=0$

$\sqrt[4]{x^2+x-1}-1=0$	
$\sqrt[4]{1^2+1-1}-1$	0
$\sqrt[4]{1+1-1}-1$	0
$\sqrt[4]{1}-1$	0
$1-1$	0
	$0=0$

The solutions are –2 and 1.

56. $4\sqrt{x+1} - x = 1$

$4\sqrt{x+1} = x+1$

$(4\sqrt{x+1})^2 = (x+1)^2$

$16(x+1) = x^2 + 2x + 1$

$16x + 16 = x^2 + 2x + 1$

$0 = x^2 - 14x - 15$

$0 = (x-15)(x+1)$

$x - 15 = 0 \quad x + 1 = 0$

$\quad x = 15 \qquad x = -1$

Check:

$4\sqrt{x+1} - x = 1$	
$4\sqrt{15+1} - 15$	1
$4\sqrt{16} - 15$	1
$4(4) - 15$	1
$16 - 15$	1
$1 = 1$	

$4\sqrt{x+1} - x = 1$	
$4\sqrt{-1+1} - (-1)$	1
$4\sqrt{0} + 1$	1
$0 + 1$	1
$1 = 1$	

The solutions are 15 and -1.

57. $3\sqrt{x-2} + 2 = x$

$3\sqrt{x-2} = x - 2$

$(3\sqrt{x-2})^2 = (x-2)^2$

$9(x-2) = x^2 - 4x + 4$

$9x - 18 = x^2 - 4x + 4$

$0 = x^2 - 13x + 22$

$0 = (x-2)(x-11)$

$x - 2 = 0 \quad x - 11 = 0$

$\quad x = 2 \qquad x = 11$

Check:

$3\sqrt{x-2} + 2 = x$	
$3\sqrt{2-2} + 2$	2
$3\sqrt{0} + 2$	2
$3(0) + 2$	2
$0 + 2$	2
$2 = 2$	

$3\sqrt{x-2} + 2 = x$	
$3\sqrt{11-2} + 2$	11
$3\sqrt{9} + 2$	11
$3(3) + 2$	11
$9 + 2$	11
$11 = 11$	

The solutions are 2 and 11.

58. $x + 3\sqrt{x-2} = 12$

$\ 3\sqrt{x-2} = 12 - x$

$\ (3\sqrt{x-2})^2 = (12-x)^2$

$\ 9(x-2) = 144 - 24x + x^2$

$\ 9x - 18 = 144 - 24x + x^2$

$\ 0 = 162 - 33x + x^2$

$\ 0 = (27-x)(6-x)$

$27 - x = 0 \quad 6 - x = 0$

$27 = x \qquad 6 = x$

Check:

$x + 3\sqrt{x-2} = 12$	
$27 + 3\sqrt{27-2}$	12
$27 + 3\sqrt{25}$	12
$27 + 3(5)$	12
$27 + 15$	12
	$42 \neq 12$

$x + 3\sqrt{x-2} = 12$	
$6 + 3\sqrt{6-2}$	12
$6 + 3\sqrt{4}$	12
$6 + 3(2)$	12
$6 + 6$	12
	$12 = 12$

The solution is 6.

59. $x + 2\sqrt{x+1} = 7$

$\ 2\sqrt{x+1} = 7 - x$

$\ (2\sqrt{x+1})^2 = (7-x)^2$

$\ 4(x+1) = 49 - 14x + x^2$

$\ 4x + 4 = 49 - 14x + x^2$

$\ 0 = x^2 - 18x + 45$

$\ 0 = (x-3)(x-15)$

$x - 3 = 0 \quad x - 15 = 0$

$x = 3 \qquad x = 15$

Check:

$x + 2\sqrt{x+1} = 7$	
$3 + 2\sqrt{3+1}$	7
$3 + 2\sqrt{4}$	7
$3 + 2(2)$	7
$3 + 4$	7
	$7 = 7$

$x + 2\sqrt{x+1} = 7$	
$15 + 2\sqrt{15+1}$	7
$15 + 2\sqrt{16}$	7
$15 + 2(4)$	7
$15 + 8$	7
	$23 \neq 7$

The solution is 3.

Objective 7.4.2 Exercises

60. Strategy
To find the number of rowers, replace s in the equation by 20 and solve for n.

Solution
$$s = 16.97\sqrt[9]{n}$$
$$20 = 16.97\sqrt[9]{n}$$
$$\frac{20}{16.97} = \sqrt[9]{n}$$
$$\left(\frac{20}{16.97}\right)^9 = \left(\sqrt[9]{n}\right)^9$$
$$4 = n$$
4 rowers are needed to travel 20 ft/s. If 8 rowers are rowing, then the maximum speed of the scull is $16.97\sqrt[9]{8} = 21.38$, which is not twice as fast as with 4 rowers.

61. Strategy
To find the air pressure, replace v in the equation by 64 and solve for p.

Solution
$$v = 6.3\sqrt{1013 - p}$$
$$64 = 6.3\sqrt{1013 - p}$$
$$\frac{64}{6.3} = \sqrt{1013 - p}$$
$$\left(\frac{64}{5.3}\right)^2 = 1013 - p$$
$$p = 1013 - \left(\frac{64}{6.3}\right)^2$$
$$p = 909.8$$
The air pressure is 909.8 mb.
As air pressure decreases, the wind speed increases.

62. Strategy
To find the mean distance of Venus from the sun, replace T in the equation by 226 and solve for d.

Solution
$$T = 0.407\sqrt{d^3}$$
$$226 = 0.407\sqrt{d^3}$$
$$\frac{226}{0.407} = d^{3/2}$$
$$\left(\frac{226}{0.407}\right)^{2/3} = d$$
$$68 = d$$
The mean distance of Venus from the sun is 68 million mi.

63. Strategy
To find the mean distance of Tethys from Saturn, replace T in the equation by 1.89 and solve for d.

Solution
$$T = 0.373\sqrt{d^3}$$
$$1.89 = 0.373\sqrt{d^3}$$
$$\frac{1.89}{0.373} = d^{3/2}$$
$$\left(\frac{1.89}{0.373}\right)^{2/3} = d$$
$$2.95 = d$$
Tethys is 295,000 km from Saturn.

64. Strategy
To find the height, replace v in the equation by 114, and solve for h.

Solution
$$v = 8\sqrt{h}$$
$$114 = 8\sqrt{h}$$
$$\frac{114}{8} = \sqrt{h}$$
$$\left(\frac{114}{8}\right)^2 = h$$
$$203 = h$$
The highest hill is 203 ft tall.

65. Strategy
To find the weight, replace M in the equation by 60,000 and solve for W.

Solution
$$M = 126.4\sqrt[4]{W^3}$$
$$60,000 = 126.4\sqrt[4]{W^3}$$
$$\frac{60,000}{126.4} = W^{3/4}$$
$$\left(\frac{60,000}{126.4}\right)^{4/3} = W$$
$$3700 = W$$
The elephant weighs 3700 lb.

66. Strategy

To find the distance, use the Pythagorean Therem. The hypotenuse is the length of the ladder. One leg is the distance from the bottom of the ladder to the base of the building. The distance along the building from the ground to the top of the ladder is the unknown leg.

Solution

$$c^2 = a^2 + b^2$$
$$12^2 = 4^2 + b^2$$
$$144 = 16 + b^2$$
$$128 = b^2$$
$$\sqrt{128} = \sqrt{b^2}$$
$$\sqrt{128} = b$$
$$11.3 = b$$

The distance is 11.3 ft.

67. Strategy

To find the distance, use the Pythagorean Theorem. The hypotenuse is the length of the ladder. The distance along the ground from the building to the ladder is the unknown leg.

Solution

$$c^2 = a^2 + b^2$$
$$26^2 = 24^2 + b^2$$
$$676 = 576 + b^2$$
$$100 = b^2$$
$$\sqrt{100} = \sqrt{b^2}$$
$$10 = b$$

The distance is 10 ft.

68. Strategy

To find the distance, use the Pythagorean Theorem. The distance from the starting point to the first jogger (8 ft/s for 60 sec = 480 ft) is the first leg. The distance from the starting point to the second jogger (9 ft/s for 60 sec = 540 ft) is the other leg. The hypotenuse, the distance between the joggers, is unknown.

Solution

$$c^2 = a^2 + b^2$$
$$c^2 = 480^2 + 540^2$$
$$c^2 = 230,400 + 291,600$$
$$c^2 = 522,000$$
$$\sqrt{c^2} = \sqrt{522,000}$$
$$c \approx 722.5$$

The distance is 722.5 ft.

69. Strategy

To find the distance, use the Pythagorean Theorem. The distance from the starting point to the jogger traveling east (3 m/s for 180 sec = 540 m) is the first leg. The distance from the starting point to the jogger traveling south (3.5 m/s for 180 sec = 630 ft) is the other leg. The hypotenuse, the distance between the joggers, is unknown.

Solution

$$c^2 = a^2 + b^2$$
$$c^2 = 540^2 + 630^2$$
$$c^2 = 291,600 + 396,900$$
$$c^2 = 688,500$$
$$\sqrt{c^2} = \sqrt{688,500}$$
$$c \approx 829.76$$

The distance is 829.76 m.

70. Strategy

To find the distance, use the Pythagorean Theorem. The distance from vertex to the corner is the first leg. The distance from the corner to the opposite vertex is the other leg. The hypotenuse, the length of the diagonal, is unknown.

Solution

$$c^2 = a^2 + b^2$$
$$c^2 = 3^2 + 9^2$$
$$c^2 = 9 + 81$$
$$c^2 = 90$$
$$\sqrt{c^2} = \sqrt{90}$$
$$c \approx 9.5$$

The length is 9.5 m.

71. Strategy

To find the distance, use the Pythagorean Theorem. The distance from vertex to the corner is the first leg. The distance from the vertex to the opposite corner is the other leg. The hypotenuse, the length of the diagonal, is unknown.

Solution

$$c^2 = a^2 + b^2$$
$$c^2 = 2.5^2 + 8.5^2$$
$$c^2 = 6.25 + 72.25$$
$$c^2 = 78.5$$
$$\sqrt{c^2} = \sqrt{78.5}$$
$$c \approx 8.9$$

The length is 8.9 cm.

72. Strategy
To find the distance above the water, replace d in the equation by the given value and solve for h.

Solution
$$d = \sqrt{1.5h}$$
$$3.2 = \sqrt{1.5h}$$
$$(3.2)^2 = (\sqrt{1.5h})^2$$
$$(3.2)^2 = 1.5h$$
$$\frac{(3.2)^2}{1.5} = h$$
$$6.83 = h$$
The periscope must be 6.83 ft above the water.

73. Strategy
To find the distance above the water, replace d in the equation by the given value and solve for h.

Solution
$$d = \sqrt{1.5h}$$
$$3.5 = \sqrt{1.5h}$$
$$(3.5)^2 = (\sqrt{1.5h})^2$$
$$(3.5)^2 = 1.5h$$
$$\frac{(3.5)^2}{1.5} = h$$
$$8.17 = h$$
The periscope must be 8.17 ft above the water.

74. Strategy
To find the distance, replace the variable v in the equation by 80 and solve for d.

Solution
$$v = 8\sqrt{d}$$
$$80 = 8\sqrt{d}$$
$$\frac{80}{8} = \sqrt{d}$$
$$10 = \sqrt{d}$$
$$10^2 = (\sqrt{d})^2$$
$$100 = d$$
The distance is 100 ft.

75. Strategy
To find the distance, replace the variable v in the equation by 120 and solve for d.

Solution
$$v = 8\sqrt{d}$$
$$120 = 8\sqrt{d}$$
$$\frac{120}{8} = \sqrt{d}$$
$$\left(\frac{120}{8}\right)^2 = (\sqrt{d})^2$$
$$225 = d$$
The distance is 225 ft.

76. Strategy
To find the distance, replace the variables v and a in the equation by their given values and solve for s.

Solution
$$v = \sqrt{2as}$$
$$60 = \sqrt{20s}$$
$$60^2 = (\sqrt{20s})^2$$
$$3600 = 20s$$
$$180 = s$$
The distance is 180 m.

77. Strategy
To find the distance, replace the variables v and a in the equation by their given values and solve for s.

Solution
$$v = \sqrt{2as}$$
$$48 = \sqrt{24s}$$
$$(48)^2 = (\sqrt{24s})^2$$
$$2304 = 24s$$
$$96 = s$$
The distance is 96 ft.

78. Strategy
To find the length of the pendulum, replace T in the equation by the given value and solve for L.

Solution
$$T = 2\pi\sqrt{\frac{L}{32}}$$
$$3 = 2(3.14)\sqrt{\frac{L}{32}}$$
$$\frac{3}{2(3.14)} = \sqrt{\frac{L}{32}}$$
$$\left(\frac{3}{2(3.14)}\right)^2 = \left(\sqrt{\frac{L}{32}}\right)^2$$
$$\left(\frac{3}{6.28}\right)^2 = \frac{L}{32}$$
$$7.30 = L$$
The length of the pendulum is 7.30 ft.

79. Strategy

To find the length of the pendulum, replace T in the equation by the given value and solve for L.

Solution

$$T = 2\pi\sqrt{\frac{L}{32}}$$

$$2.4 = 2(3.14)\sqrt{\frac{L}{32}}$$

$$\frac{2.4}{2(3.14)} = \sqrt{\frac{L}{32}}$$

$$\left(\frac{2.4}{2(3.14)}\right)^2 = \left(\sqrt{\frac{L}{32}}\right)^2$$

$$\left(\frac{2.4}{6.28}\right)^2 = \frac{L}{32}$$

$$4.67 = L$$

The length of the pendulum is 4.67 ft.

Applying Concepts 7.4

80.
$$x^{3/4} = 8$$
$$(x^{3/4})^{4/3} = 8^{4/3}$$
$$x = (\sqrt[3]{8})^4$$
$$x = 2^4$$
$$x = 16$$

81.
$$x^{2/3} = 9$$
$$(x^{2/3})^{3/2} = 9^{3/2}$$
$$x = (\sqrt{9})^3$$
$$x = 3^3$$
$$x = 27$$

82.
$$x^{5/4} = 32$$
$$(x^{5/4})^{4/5} = 32^{4/5}$$
$$x = (\sqrt[5]{32})^4$$
$$x = 2^4$$
$$x = 16$$

83.
$$v = \sqrt{64d}$$
$$v^2 = (\sqrt{64d})^2$$
$$v^2 = 64d$$
$$\frac{v^2}{64} = d$$

84.
$$a^2 + b^2 = c^2$$
$$a^2 = c^2 - b^2$$
$$\sqrt{a^2} = \sqrt{c^2 - b^2}$$
$$a = \sqrt{c^2 - b^2}$$

85.
$$V = \pi r^2 h$$
$$\frac{V}{\pi h} = r^2$$
$$\sqrt{\frac{V}{\pi h}} = \sqrt{r^2}$$
$$\sqrt{\frac{V}{\pi h}} = r$$
$$r = \frac{\sqrt{V}}{\sqrt{\pi h}} \cdot \frac{\sqrt{\pi h}}{\sqrt{\pi h}} = \frac{\sqrt{V\pi h}}{\pi h}$$

86.
$$V = \frac{4}{3}\pi r^3$$
$$\frac{3V}{4} = \pi r^3$$
$$\frac{3V}{4\pi} = r^3$$
$$\sqrt[3]{\frac{3V}{4\pi}} = \sqrt[3]{r^3}$$
$$\sqrt[3]{\frac{3V}{4\pi}} = r$$
$$r = \frac{\sqrt[3]{3V}}{\sqrt[3]{4\pi}} \cdot \frac{\sqrt[3]{2\pi^2}}{\sqrt[3]{2\pi^2}} = \frac{\sqrt[3]{6V\pi^2}}{\sqrt[3]{2^3\pi^3}} = \frac{\sqrt[3]{6V\pi^2}}{2\pi}$$

87.
$$\sqrt{3x-2} = \sqrt{2x-3} + \sqrt{x-1}$$
$$(\sqrt{3x-2})^2 = (\sqrt{2x-3} + \sqrt{x-1})^2$$
$$3x-2 = 2x-3 + 2\sqrt{2x-3}\sqrt{x-1} + x-1$$
$$2 = 2\sqrt{2x-3}\sqrt{x-1}$$
$$1 = \sqrt{2x-3}\sqrt{x-1}$$
$$1^2 = (\sqrt{2x-3}\sqrt{x-1})^2$$
$$1 = (2x-3)(x-1)$$
$$1 = 2x^2 - 5x + 3$$
$$0 = 2x^2 - 5x + 2$$
$$0 = (2x-1)(x-2)$$
$$2x-1=0 \quad x-2=0$$
$$2x=1 \quad\quad x=2$$
$$x = \frac{1}{2}$$

Check:

$$\sqrt{3x-2} = \sqrt{2x-3} + \sqrt{x-1}$$

$$\sqrt{3\left(\frac{1}{2}\right)-2} \quad \bigg| \quad \sqrt{2\left(\frac{1}{2}\right)-3} + \sqrt{\frac{1}{2}-1}$$

$$\sqrt{-\frac{1}{2}} \neq \sqrt{-2} + \sqrt{-\frac{1}{2}}$$

$$\sqrt{3x-2} = \sqrt{2x-3} + \sqrt{x-1}$$

$$\sqrt{3(2)-2} \quad \bigg| \quad \sqrt{2(2)-3} + \sqrt{2-1}$$

$$\sqrt{4} \quad \bigg| \quad \sqrt{1} + \sqrt{1}$$

$$2 \quad \bigg| \quad 1+1$$

$$2 = 2$$

The solution is 2.

88.

$$\sqrt{2x+3} + \sqrt{x+2} = \sqrt{x+5}$$
$$\left(\sqrt{2x+3} + \sqrt{x+2}\right)^2 = \left(\sqrt{x+5}\right)^2$$
$$2x+3+2\sqrt{2x+3}\sqrt{x+2} + x+2 = x+5$$
$$2\sqrt{2x+3}\sqrt{x+2} = -2x$$
$$\sqrt{2x+3}\sqrt{x+2} = -x$$
$$\left(\sqrt{2x+3}\sqrt{x+2}\right)^2 = (-x)^2$$
$$(2x+3)(x+2) = (-x)^2$$
$$2x^2 + 7x + 6 = x^2$$
$$x^2 + 7x + 6 = 0$$
$$(x+1)(x+6) = 0$$
$$x+1 = 0 \qquad x+6 = 0$$
$$x = -1 \qquad x = -6$$

Check:

$$\sqrt{2x+3} + \sqrt{x+2} = \sqrt{x+5}$$

$\sqrt{2(-6)+3} + \sqrt{-6+2}$	$\sqrt{-6+5}$
$\sqrt{-9} + \sqrt{-4}$	$\sqrt{-1}$
$3i + 2i$	i

$$5i \neq 2i$$

$$\sqrt{2x+3} + \sqrt{x+2} = \sqrt{x+5}$$

$\sqrt{2(-1)+3} + \sqrt{-1+2}$	$\sqrt{-1+5}$
$\sqrt{1} + \sqrt{1}$	$\sqrt{4}$
$1 + 1$	2

$$2 = 2$$

The solution is -1.

89. Strategy

The greatest distance between the two corners is the hypotenuse of the triangle whose legs are the diagonal of the base of the box (d) and the height of the box (3 in.). The diagonal of the base (d) is the hypotenuse of the triangle whose lengths are the sides of the base (4 in. by 6 in.)
To find the greatest distance
(1) use the Pythagorean Theorem with $c = d$ (diagonal of the base) and $a = 4$, $b = 6$.
(2) use the Pythagorean Theorem with $c =$ greatest distance, $a = d$, and $b = 3$.

Solution
$$d^2 = 4^2 + 6^2$$
$$d^2 = 16 + 36$$
$$d^2 = 52$$
$$d = \sqrt{52}$$
$$c^2 = a^2 + b^2$$
$$c^2 = d^2 + 3^2$$
$$c^2 = \left(\sqrt{52}\right)^2 + 9$$
$$c^2 = 52 + 9$$
$$c = \sqrt{61} \approx 7.81$$
The greatest distance is
$\sqrt{61}$ in. ≈ 7.81 in.

90. Impossible; at least one of the integers must be even.

91. Strategy
Find the hypotenuses of the triangles in order, letting each become a leg of the next triangle.
Triangle 1: $a^2 = b^2 + c^2$
$$a^2 = 1^2 + 1^2$$
$$a^2 = 2$$
$$a = \sqrt{2}$$

Triangle 2: Let a become b. Then the new a is
$$a^2 = (\sqrt{2})^2 + 1^2$$
$$a^2 = 2 + 1$$
$$a^2 = 3$$
$$a = \sqrt{3}$$

Triangle 3: Let a become b. Then the new a is
$$a^2 = (\sqrt{3})^2 + 1^2$$
$$a^2 = 3 + 1$$
$$a^2 = 4$$
$$a = 2$$

Triangle 4: Let a become b. Then the new a is
$$a^2 = (2)^2 + (1)^2$$
$$a^2 = 4 + 1$$
$$a^2 = 5$$
$$a = \sqrt{5}$$

For the last triangle, let a become b. Then x is
$$x^2 = (\sqrt{5})^2 + 1^2$$
$$x^2 = 5 + 1$$
$$x^2 = 6$$
$$x = \sqrt{6}$$

92. The equation $\sqrt{a^2 + b^2} = a + b$, where both a and b are nonnegative, is true when both a and b are zero and when either a or b is zero. In all other cases, the equation is false.

93. If a and b are both positive and $a > b$, then the relationship between a^b and b^a depends on the values of a and b. For instance if $a = 4$, and $b = 2$, then $a^b = b^a$; if $a = 5$ and $b = 2$, then $a^b < b^a$; if $a = \frac{1}{2}$ and $b = \frac{1}{4}$, then $a^b > b^a$.

Section 7.5

Concept Review 7.5

1. Always true

2. Sometimes true
   The sum $2i + 4i$ is $6i$, a complex number.

3. Always true

4. Sometimes true
   The product $2i(4 + i)$ is $-2 + 8i$, a complex number.

Objective 7.5.1 Exercises

1. An imaginary number is a number whose square is a negative number. Imaginary numbers are defined in terms of i, the number whose square is -1.
   A complex number is of the form $a + bi$, where a and b are real numbers and $i = \sqrt{-1}$.

2. All real numbers are complex numbers; they are complex numbers of the form $a + bi$ where $b = 0$. Not all complex numbers are real numbers; any complex number of the form $a + bi$, $b \neq 0$, is not a real number.

3. $\sqrt{-4} = i\sqrt{4} = i\sqrt{2^2} = 2i$

4. $\sqrt{-64} = i\sqrt{64} = i\sqrt{2^6} = 2^3 i = 8i$

5. $\sqrt{-98} = i\sqrt{98} = i\sqrt{2 \cdot 7^2} = 7i\sqrt{2}$

6. $\sqrt{-72} = i\sqrt{72} = i\sqrt{2^2 \cdot 2 \cdot 3^2} = 6i\sqrt{2}$

7. $\sqrt{-27} = i\sqrt{27} = i\sqrt{3^2 \cdot 3} = 3i\sqrt{3}$

8. $\sqrt{-75} = i\sqrt{75} = i\sqrt{5^2 \cdot 3} = 5i\sqrt{3}$

9. $\sqrt{16} + \sqrt{-4} = \sqrt{16} + i\sqrt{4} = \sqrt{2^4} + i\sqrt{2^2} = 4 + 2i$

10. $\sqrt{25} + \sqrt{-9} = \sqrt{25} + i\sqrt{9} = \sqrt{5^2} + i\sqrt{3^2} = 5 + 3i$

11. $\sqrt{12} - \sqrt{-18} = \sqrt{12} - i\sqrt{18}$
    $$= \sqrt{2^2 \cdot 3} - i\sqrt{3^2 \cdot 2}$$
    $$= 2\sqrt{3} - 3i\sqrt{2}$$

12. $\sqrt{60} - \sqrt{-48} = \sqrt{60} - i\sqrt{48}$
    $$= \sqrt{2^2 \cdot 3 \cdot 5} - i\sqrt{2^4 \cdot 3}$$
    $$= 2\sqrt{15} - 4i\sqrt{3}$$

13. $\sqrt{160} - \sqrt{-147} = \sqrt{160} - i\sqrt{147}$
    $$= \sqrt{2^4 \cdot 2 \cdot 5} - i\sqrt{7^2 \cdot 3}$$
    $$= 4\sqrt{10} - 7i\sqrt{3}$$

14. $\sqrt{96} - \sqrt{-125} = \sqrt{96} - i\sqrt{125}$
    $$= \sqrt{2^4 \cdot 2 \cdot 3} - i\sqrt{5^2 \cdot 5}$$
    $$= 4\sqrt{6} - 5i\sqrt{5}$$

15. $\sqrt{-4a^2} = i\sqrt{4a^2} = i\sqrt{2^2 a^2} = 2ai$

16. $\sqrt{-16b^6} = i\sqrt{16b^6} = i\sqrt{2^4 b^6} = 2^2 ib^3 = 4b^3 i$

17. $\sqrt{-49x^{12}} = i\sqrt{49x^{12}} = i\sqrt{7^2 x^{12}} = 7x^6 i$

18. $\sqrt{-32x^3 y^2} = i\sqrt{2^5 x^3 y^2}$
    $$= 2^2 ixy\sqrt{2x}$$
    $$= 4xyi\sqrt{2x}$$

19. $\sqrt{-144a^3b^5} = i\sqrt{2^4 \cdot 3^2 a^3 b^5}$
$\qquad = 2^2 \cdot 3iab^2\sqrt{ab}$
$\qquad = 12ab^2 i\sqrt{ab}$

20. $\sqrt{-18a^{10}b^9} = i\sqrt{3^2 \cdot 2a^{10}b^9}$
$\qquad = 3ab^5b^4 i\sqrt{2b}$

21. $\sqrt{4a} + \sqrt{-12a^2} = \sqrt{2^2 a} + i\sqrt{2^2 \cdot 3a^2}$
$\qquad = 2\sqrt{a} + 2ai\sqrt{3}$

22. $\sqrt{25b} - \sqrt{-48b^2} = \sqrt{5^2 b} - i\sqrt{2^4 \cdot 3b^2}$
$\qquad = 5\sqrt{b} - 2^2 ib\sqrt{3}$
$\qquad = 5\sqrt{b} - 4bi\sqrt{3}$

23. $\sqrt{18b^5} - \sqrt{-27b^3} = \sqrt{2 \cdot 3^2 b^5} - i\sqrt{3 \cdot 3^2 b^3}$
$\qquad = 3b^2\sqrt{2b} - 3bi\sqrt{3b}$

24. $\sqrt{a^5 b^2} - \sqrt{-a^5 b^2} = a^2 b\sqrt{a} - a^2 bi\sqrt{a}$

25. $\sqrt{-50x^3 y^3} + x\sqrt{25x^4 y^3}$
$\qquad = i\sqrt{5^2 \cdot 2x^3 y^3} + x\sqrt{5^2 x^4 y^3}$
$\qquad = 5ixy\sqrt{2xy} + 5x^3 y\sqrt{y}$
$\qquad = 5x^3 y\sqrt{y} + 5xyi\sqrt{2xy}$

26. $\sqrt{-121xy} + \sqrt{60x^2 y^2}$
$\qquad = i\sqrt{11^2 xy} + \sqrt{2^2 \cdot 3 \cdot 5x^2 y^2}$
$\qquad = 11i\sqrt{xy} + 2xy\sqrt{15}$
$\qquad = 2xy\sqrt{15} + 11i\sqrt{xy}$

27. $\sqrt{-49a^5 b^2} - ab\sqrt{-25a^3}$
$\qquad = i\sqrt{7^2 a^5 b^2} - iab\sqrt{5^2 a^3}$
$\qquad = 7ia^2 b\sqrt{a} - 5ia^2 b\sqrt{a}$
$\qquad = 2a^2 bi\sqrt{a}$

28. $\sqrt{-16x^2 y} - x\sqrt{-49y}$
$\qquad = i\sqrt{2^4 x^2 y} - ix\sqrt{7^2 y}$
$\qquad = 2^2 ix\sqrt{y} - 7ix\sqrt{y}$
$\qquad = 4ix\sqrt{y} - 7ix\sqrt{y}$
$\qquad = -3xi\sqrt{y}$

29. $\sqrt{12a^3} + \sqrt{-27b^3}$
$\qquad = \sqrt{2^2 \cdot 3a^3} + i\sqrt{3^2 \cdot 3b^3}$
$\qquad = 2a\sqrt{3a} + 3bi\sqrt{3b}$

Objective 7.5.2 Exercises

30. $(2 + 4i) + (6 - 5i) = 8 - i$

31. $(6 - 9i) + (4 + 2i) = 10 - 7i$

32. $(-2 - 4i) - (6 - 8i) = -8 + 4i$

33. $(3 - 5i) + (8 - 2i) = 11 - 7i$

34. $(8 - \sqrt{-4}) - (2 + \sqrt{-16}) = (8 - i\sqrt{4}) - (2 + i\sqrt{16})$
$\qquad = (8 - i\sqrt{2^2}) - (2 + i\sqrt{2^4})$
$\qquad = (8 - 2i) - (2 + 4i)$
$\qquad = 6 - 6i$

35. $(5 - \sqrt{-25}) - (11 - \sqrt{-36})$
$\qquad = (5 - i\sqrt{25}) - (11 - i\sqrt{36})$
$\qquad = (5 - i\sqrt{5^2}) - (11 - i\sqrt{2^2 \cdot 3^2})$
$\qquad = (5 - 5i) - (11 - 6i)$
$\qquad = -6 + i$

36. $(12 - \sqrt{-50}) + (7 - \sqrt{-8})$
$\qquad = (12 - i\sqrt{50}) + (7 - i\sqrt{8})$
$\qquad = (12 - i\sqrt{5^2 \cdot 2}) + (7 - i\sqrt{2^2 \cdot 2})$
$\qquad = (12 - 5i\sqrt{2}) + (7 - 2i\sqrt{2})$
$\qquad = 19 - 7i\sqrt{2}$

37. $(5 - \sqrt{-12}) - (9 + \sqrt{-108})$
$\qquad = (5 - i\sqrt{12}) - (9 + i\sqrt{108})$
$\qquad = (5 - i\sqrt{2^2 \cdot 3}) - (9 + i\sqrt{2^2 \cdot 3^2 \cdot 3})$
$\qquad = (5 - 2i\sqrt{3}) - (9 + 6i\sqrt{3})$
$\qquad = -4 - 8i\sqrt{3}$

38. $(\sqrt{8} + \sqrt{-18}) + (\sqrt{32} - \sqrt{-72})$
$\qquad = (\sqrt{8} + i\sqrt{18}) + (\sqrt{32} - i\sqrt{72})$
$\qquad = (\sqrt{2^2 \cdot 2} + i\sqrt{3^2 \cdot 2}) + (\sqrt{2^4 \cdot 2} - i\sqrt{2^2 \cdot 3^2 \cdot 2})$
$\qquad = (2\sqrt{2} + 3i\sqrt{2}) + (4\sqrt{2} - 6i\sqrt{2})$
$\qquad = 6\sqrt{2} - 3i\sqrt{2}$

39. $(\sqrt{40} - \sqrt{-98}) - (\sqrt{90} + \sqrt{-32})$
$\qquad = (\sqrt{40} - i\sqrt{98}) - (\sqrt{90} + i\sqrt{32})$
$\qquad = (\sqrt{2^2 \cdot 2 \cdot 5} - i\sqrt{7^2 \cdot 2}) - (\sqrt{3^2 \cdot 2 \cdot 5} + i\sqrt{2^4 \cdot 2})$
$\qquad = (2\sqrt{10} - 7i\sqrt{2}) - (3\sqrt{10} + 4i\sqrt{2})$
$\qquad = -\sqrt{10} - 11i\sqrt{2}$

40. $(5 - 3i) + 2i = 5 - i$

41. $(6 - 8i) + 4i = 6 - 4i$

42. $(7 + 2i) + (-7 - 2i) = 0$

43. $(8 - 3i) + (-8 + 3i) = 0$

44. $(9 + 4i) + 6 = (9 + 4i) + (6 + 0i) = 15 + 4i$

45. $(4 + 6i) + 7 = (4 + 6i) + (7 + 0i) = 11 + 6i$

Objective 7.5.3 Exercises

46. $(7i)(-9i) = -63i^2 = -63(-1) = 63$

47. $(-6i)(-4i) = 24i^2 = 24(-1) = -24$

48. $\sqrt{-2}\sqrt{-8} = i\sqrt{2} \cdot i\sqrt{8} = i^2\sqrt{16} = -\sqrt{2^4} = -4$

49. $\sqrt{-5}\sqrt{-45} = i\sqrt{5} \cdot i\sqrt{45}$
$= i^2\sqrt{225}$
$= -\sqrt{3^2 \cdot 5^2}$
$= -15$

50. $\sqrt{-3}\sqrt{-6} = i\sqrt{3} \cdot i\sqrt{6} = i^2\sqrt{18}$
$= -\sqrt{3^2 \cdot 2} = -3\sqrt{2}$

51. $\sqrt{-5}\sqrt{-10} = i\sqrt{5} \cdot i\sqrt{10} = i^2\sqrt{50}$
$= -\sqrt{5^2 \cdot 2} = -5\sqrt{2}$

52. $2i(6 + 2i) = 12i + 4i^2$
$= 12i + 4(-1)$
$= -4 + 12i$

53. $-3i(4 - 5i) = -12i + 15i^2$
$= -12i + 15(-1)$
$= -15 - 12i$

54. $\sqrt{-2}(\sqrt{8} + \sqrt{-2}) = i\sqrt{2}(\sqrt{8} + i\sqrt{2})$
$= i\sqrt{16} + i^2\sqrt{2^2}$
$= i\sqrt{2^4} - \sqrt{2^2}$
$= 4i - 2$
$= -2 + 4i$

55. $\sqrt{-3}(\sqrt{12} - \sqrt{-6}) = i\sqrt{3}(\sqrt{12} - i\sqrt{6})$
$= i\sqrt{36} - i^2\sqrt{18}$
$= i\sqrt{2^2 \cdot 3^2} + \sqrt{3^2 \cdot 2}$
$= 6i + 3\sqrt{2}$
$= 3\sqrt{2} + 6i$

56. $(5 - 2i)(3 + i) = 15 + 5i - 6i - 2i^2$
$= 15 - i - 2i^2$
$= 15 - i - 2(-1)$
$= 17 - i$

57. $(2 - 4i)(2 - i) = 4 - 2i - 8i + 4i^2$
$= 4 - 10i + 4i^2$
$= 4 - 10i + 4(-1)$
$= -10i$

58. $(6 + 5i)(3 + 2i) = 18 + 12i + 15i + 10i^2$
$= 18 + 27i + 10i^2$
$= 18 + 27i + 10(-1)$
$= 8 + 27i$

59. $(4 - 7i)(2 + 3i) = 8 + 12i - 14i - 21i^2$
$= 8 - 2i - 21i^2$
$= 8 - 2i - 21(-1)$
$= 29 - 2i$

60. $(1 - i)\left(\dfrac{1}{2} + \dfrac{1}{2}i\right) = \dfrac{1}{2} + \dfrac{1}{2}i - \dfrac{1}{2}i - \dfrac{1}{2}i^2$
$= \dfrac{1}{2} - \dfrac{1}{2}i^2$
$= \dfrac{1}{2} - \dfrac{1}{2}(-1)$
$= \dfrac{1}{2} + \dfrac{1}{2}$
$= 1$

61. $\left(\dfrac{4}{5} - \dfrac{2}{5}i\right)\left(1 + \dfrac{1}{2}i\right) = \dfrac{4}{5} + \dfrac{2}{5}i - \dfrac{2}{5}i - \dfrac{1}{5}i^2$
$= \dfrac{4}{5} - \dfrac{1}{5}i^2$
$= \dfrac{4}{5} - \dfrac{1}{5}(-1)$
$= \dfrac{4}{5} + \dfrac{1}{5}$
$= 1$

62. $\left(\dfrac{6}{5} + \dfrac{3}{5}i\right)\left(\dfrac{2}{3} - \dfrac{1}{3}i\right) = \dfrac{4}{5} - \dfrac{2}{5}i + \dfrac{2}{5}i - \dfrac{1}{5}i^2$
$= \dfrac{4}{5} - \dfrac{1}{5}i^2$
$= \dfrac{4}{5} - \dfrac{1}{5}(-1)$
$= \dfrac{4}{5} + \dfrac{1}{5}$
$= 1$

63. $(2 - i)\left(\dfrac{2}{5} + \dfrac{1}{5}i\right) = \dfrac{4}{5} + \dfrac{2}{5}i - \dfrac{2}{5}i - \dfrac{1}{5}i^2$
$= \dfrac{4}{5} - \dfrac{1}{5}i^2$
$= \dfrac{4}{5} - \dfrac{1}{5}(-1)$
$= \dfrac{4}{5} + \dfrac{1}{5}$
$= 1$

64. $(4 - 3i)(4 + 3i) = 4^2 + 3^2 = 16 + 9 = 25$

65. $(8 - 5i)(8 + 5i) = 8^2 + 5^2 = 64 + 25 = 89$

66. $(3 - i)(3 + i) = 3^2 + 1^2 = 9 + 1 = 10$

67. $(7 - i)(7 + i) = 7^2 + 1^2 = 49 + 1 = 50$

68. $(6 + i)^2 = (6 + i)(6 + i)$
$= 36 + 12i + i^2$
$= 36 + 12i - 1$
$= 35 + 12i$

69. $(4 - 3i)^2 = (4 - 3i)(4 - 3i)$
$= 16 - 24i + 9i^2$
$= 16 - 24i - 9$
$= 7 - 24i$

70. $(5 - 2i)^2 = (5 - 2i)(5 - 2i)$
$= 25 - 20i + 4i^2$
$= 25 - 20i - 4$
$= 21 - 20i$

71. $(-1+i)^2 = (-1+i)(-1+i)$
$$= 1 - 2i + i^2$$
$$= 1 - 2i - 1$$
$$= -2i$$

Objective 7.5.4 Exercises

72. $\dfrac{3}{i} = \dfrac{3}{i} \cdot \dfrac{i}{i} = \dfrac{3i}{i^2} = \dfrac{3i}{-1} = -3i$

73. $\dfrac{4}{5i} = \dfrac{4}{5i} \cdot \dfrac{i}{i} = \dfrac{4i}{5i^2} = \dfrac{4i}{5(-1)} = \dfrac{4i}{-5} = -\dfrac{4}{5}i$

74. $\dfrac{2-3i}{-4i} = \dfrac{2-3i}{-4i} \cdot \dfrac{i}{i}$
$$= \dfrac{2i - 3i^2}{-4i^2}$$
$$= \dfrac{2i - 3(-1)}{-4(-1)}$$
$$= \dfrac{3 + 2i}{4}$$
$$= \dfrac{3}{4} + \dfrac{1}{2}i$$

75. $\dfrac{16+5i}{-3i} = \dfrac{16+5i}{-3i} \cdot \dfrac{i}{i}$
$$= \dfrac{16i + 5i^2}{-3i^2}$$
$$= \dfrac{16i + 5(-1)}{-3(-1)}$$
$$= \dfrac{-5 + 16i}{3}$$
$$= -\dfrac{5}{3} + \dfrac{16}{3}i$$

76. $\dfrac{4}{5+i} = \dfrac{4}{5+i} \cdot \dfrac{5-i}{5-i}$
$$= \dfrac{20 - 4i}{25 + 1}$$
$$= \dfrac{20 - 4i}{26}$$
$$= \dfrac{10 - 2i}{13}$$
$$= \dfrac{10}{13} - \dfrac{2}{13}i$$

77. $\dfrac{6}{5+2i} = \dfrac{6}{5+2i} \cdot \dfrac{5-2i}{5-2i}$
$$= \dfrac{30 - 12i}{25 + 4}$$
$$= \dfrac{30 - 12i}{29}$$
$$= \dfrac{30}{29} - \dfrac{12}{29}i$$

78. $\dfrac{2}{2-i} = \dfrac{2}{2-i} \cdot \dfrac{2+i}{2+i}$
$$= \dfrac{4 + 2i}{4 + 1}$$
$$= \dfrac{4 + 2i}{5}$$
$$= \dfrac{4}{5} + \dfrac{2}{5}i$$

79. $\dfrac{5}{4-i} = \dfrac{5}{4-i} \cdot \dfrac{4+i}{4+i}$
$$= \dfrac{20 + 5i}{16 + 1}$$
$$= \dfrac{20 + 5i}{17}$$
$$= \dfrac{20}{17} + \dfrac{5}{17}i$$

80. $\dfrac{1-3i}{3+i} = \dfrac{1-3i}{3+i} \cdot \dfrac{3-i}{3-i}$
$$= \dfrac{3 - i - 9i + 3i^2}{9 + 1}$$
$$= \dfrac{3 - 10i + 3i^2}{10}$$
$$= \dfrac{3 - 10i + 3(-1)}{10}$$
$$= \dfrac{-10i}{10} = -i$$

81. $\dfrac{2+12i}{5+i} = \dfrac{2+12i}{5+i} \cdot \dfrac{5-i}{5-i}$
$$= \dfrac{10 - 2i + 60i - 12i^2}{25 + 1}$$
$$= \dfrac{10 + 58i - 12(-1)}{26}$$
$$= \dfrac{22 + 58i}{26}$$
$$= \dfrac{11 + 29i}{13}$$
$$= \dfrac{11}{13} + \dfrac{29}{13}i$$

82.

$$\frac{\sqrt{-10}}{\sqrt{8}-\sqrt{-2}}$$

$$=\frac{i\sqrt{10}}{\sqrt{8}-i\sqrt{2}}$$

$$=\frac{i\sqrt{10}}{\sqrt{2^2\cdot 2}-i\sqrt{2}}$$

$$=\frac{i\sqrt{10}}{2\sqrt{2}-i\sqrt{2}}\cdot\frac{2\sqrt{2}+i\sqrt{2}}{2\sqrt{2}+i\sqrt{2}}=\frac{2i\sqrt{20}+i^2\sqrt{20}}{(2\sqrt{2})^2+(\sqrt{2})^2}$$

$$=\frac{2i\sqrt{2^2\cdot 5}-\sqrt{2^2\cdot 5}}{8+2}$$

$$=\frac{2i\cdot 2\sqrt{5}-2\sqrt{5}}{10}$$

$$=\frac{-2\sqrt{5}+4i\sqrt{5}}{10}$$

$$=\frac{-\sqrt{5}+2i\sqrt{5}}{5}$$

$$=-\frac{\sqrt{5}}{5}+\frac{2\sqrt{5}}{5}i$$

83.

$$\frac{\sqrt{-2}}{\sqrt{12}-\sqrt{-8}}=\frac{i\sqrt{2}}{\sqrt{12}-i\sqrt{8}}$$

$$=\frac{i\sqrt{2}}{\sqrt{2^2\cdot 3}-i\sqrt{2^2\cdot 2}}$$

$$=\frac{i\sqrt{2}}{2\sqrt{3}-2i\sqrt{2}}\cdot\frac{2\sqrt{3}+2i\sqrt{2}}{2\sqrt{3}+2i\sqrt{2}}$$

$$=\frac{2i^2\sqrt{6}+2i^2\sqrt{2^2}}{(2\sqrt{3})^2+(2\sqrt{2})^2}$$

$$=\frac{2i\sqrt{6}-2\cdot 2}{12+8}$$

$$=\frac{-4+2i\sqrt{6}}{20}$$

$$=\frac{-2+i\sqrt{6}}{10}$$

$$=-\frac{1}{5}+\frac{\sqrt{6}}{10}i$$

84.

$$\frac{2-3i}{3+i}=\frac{2-3i}{3+i}\cdot\frac{3-i}{3-i}$$

$$=\frac{6-2i-9i+3i^2}{9+1}$$

$$=\frac{6-11i+3i^2}{10}$$

$$=\frac{6-11i+3(-1)}{10}$$

$$=\frac{3-11i}{10}$$

$$=\frac{3}{10}-\frac{11}{10}i$$

85.

$$\frac{3+5i}{1-i}=\frac{3+5i}{1-i}\cdot\frac{1+i}{1+i}$$

$$=\frac{3+3i+5i+5i^2}{1+1}$$

$$=\frac{3+8i+5i^2}{2}$$

$$=\frac{3+8i+5(-1)}{2}$$

$$=\frac{-2+8i}{2}$$

$$=-1+4i$$

Applying Concepts 7.3

86. When the exponent on i is a multiple of 4, the power equals 1.

87. $i^6=i^4\cdot i^2=1(-1)=-1$

88. $i^9=i^8\cdot i=1\cdot i=i$

89. $i^{57}=i^{56}\cdot i=1\cdot i=i$

90. $i^{65}=i^{64}\cdot i=1\cdot i=i$

91. $i^{-6}=\frac{1}{i^6}=\frac{1}{i^4\cdot i^2}=\frac{1}{1\cdot-1}=\frac{1}{-1}=-1$

92. $i^{-34}=\frac{1}{i^{34}}=\frac{1}{i^{32}\cdot i^2}=\frac{1}{1(-1)}=\frac{1}{-1}=-1$

93. $i^{-58}=\frac{1}{i^{58}}=\frac{1}{i^{56}\cdot i^2}=\frac{1}{1(-1)}=\frac{1}{-1}=-1$

94. 180 is divisble by 4.

$$i^{-180}=\frac{1}{i^{180}}=\frac{1}{1}=1$$

95. **a.**

$2x^2+18=0$	
$2(3i)^2+18$	0
$2(9i^2)+18$	0
$18i^2+18$	0
$-18+18$	0
	$0=0$

Yes, $3i$ is a solution of $2x^2+18=0$.

b.

$2x^2+18=0$	
$2(-3i)^2+18$	0
$2(9i^2)+18$	0
$18i^2+18$	0
$-18+18$	0
	$0=0$

Yes, $-3i$ is a solution of $2x^2+18=0$.

96. a.

$$x^2 - 2x - 10 = 0$$

$(1+3i)^2 - 2(1+3i) - 10$	0
$1 + 6i + 9i^2 - 2 - 6i - 10$	0
$9i^2 - 11$	0
$-9 - 11$	0
$-20 \neq 0$	

No, $1 + 3i$ is not a solution of $x^2 - 2x - 10 = 0$.

b.

$$x^2 - 2x - 10 = 0$$

$(1-3i)^2 - 2(1-3i) - 10$	0
$1 - 6i + 9i^2 - 2 + 6i - 10$	0
$9i^2 - 11$	0
$-9 - 11$	0
$-20 \neq 0$	

No, $1 - 3i$ is not a solution of $x^2 - 2x - 10 = 0$.

97. a. $x^2 + 3 = 7$
$$x^2 = 4$$
$$x = \pm 2$$

x is an integer, a rational number, and a real number.

b. $x^2 + 1 = 0$
$$x^2 = -1$$
$$x = \pm i$$

x is an imaginary number.

c. $\dfrac{5}{8}x = \dfrac{2}{3}$
$$\dfrac{8}{5} \cdot \dfrac{5}{8}x = \dfrac{8}{5} \cdot \dfrac{2}{3}$$
$$x = \dfrac{16}{15}$$

x is a rational number and a real number.

d. $x^2 + 1 = 9$
$$x^2 = 8$$
$$x = \pm 2\sqrt{2}$$

x is a irrational number and a real number.

e. $x^{3/4} = 8$
$$\left(x^{3/4}\right)^{4/3} = (8)^{4/3}$$
$$x = \left(\sqrt[3]{8}\right)^4 = 2^4 = 16$$

x is an integer, a rational number, and a real number.

f. $\sqrt[3]{x} = -27$
$$\left(\sqrt[3]{x}\right)^3 = (-27)^3$$
$$x = -19,683$$

x is an integer, a rational number, and a real number.

Focus on Problem Solving

Here are two other examples of "words" for which the product of the numerical values of the letters equals 1,000,000: PAYJAJY, DETTEY.

Projects and Group Activities

Graphing Complex Numbers

1. $m_1 = \dfrac{4-0}{3-0} = \dfrac{4}{3}$

2. $m_2 = \dfrac{3-0}{-4-0} = -\dfrac{3}{4}$

3. $m_1 m_2 = \dfrac{4}{3}\left(-\dfrac{3}{4}\right) = -1$

The product of the slopes of the two lines is -1. This means that the lines are perpendicular.

4. $d_1 = \sqrt{(-4-0)^2 + (3-0)^2} = \sqrt{16+9} = 5$

$d_2 = \sqrt{(3-0)^2 + (4-0)^2} = \sqrt{9+16} = 5$

The point $(3, 4)$ is 5 units from the origin. The point $(-4, 3)$ is 5 units from the origin.

Solving Radical Equations with a Graphing Calculator

1. $\sqrt{x+0.3} = 1.3$

$y = \sqrt{x+0.3} - 1.3$

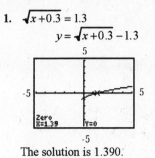

The solution is 1.390.

2. $\sqrt[3]{x+1.2} = -1.1$

$y = \sqrt[3]{x+1.2} + 1.1$

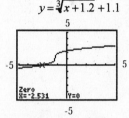

The solution is -2.531.

3. $\sqrt[4]{3x-1.5} = 1.4$

$y = \sqrt[4]{3x-1.5} - 1.4$

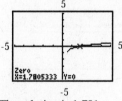

The solution is 1.781.

The Golden Rectangle

1.

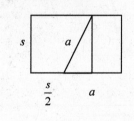

2. Solving for a,

$a^2 = s^2 + \left(\dfrac{s}{2}\right)^2$

$= s^2 + \dfrac{s^2}{4}$

$= \dfrac{5s^2}{4}$

$\sqrt{a^2} = \sqrt{\dfrac{5s^2}{4}}$

$a = \dfrac{s\sqrt{5}}{2}$

Area is length times width.

$A = \left(\dfrac{s}{2} + a\right)s$

$= \left(\dfrac{s}{2} + \dfrac{s\sqrt{5}}{2}\right)s$

$= \dfrac{s^2 + s^2\sqrt{5}}{2}$

The area of the golden rectangle is

$A = \dfrac{s^2 + s^2\sqrt{5}}{2}$.

3. The ratio of length to width:

$\dfrac{\text{length}}{\text{width}} = \dfrac{\dfrac{s}{2} + a}{s}$

$= \dfrac{\dfrac{s}{2} + \dfrac{s\sqrt{5}}{2}}{s}$

$= \dfrac{\dfrac{s + s\sqrt{5}}{2}}{s}$

$= \dfrac{\dfrac{s(1+\sqrt{5})}{2}}{s}$

$= \dfrac{s(1+\sqrt{5})}{2} \cdot \dfrac{1}{s}$

$= \dfrac{1+\sqrt{5}}{2}$

4. Answers will vary. Here are a few examples. LeCorbusier's United Nations building in New York City incorporates the golden rectangle. The building is L-shaped; it is the upright part that is a golden rectangle.

Many artists have painted on canvases that have the dimensions of the golden rectangle. Albrecht Dürer, Georges Seurut, Paul Signac, and Piet Mondrian are among them. But perhaps the most famous is Leonardo DaVinci, who painted the Mona Lisa on a canvas with the shape of a golden rectangle.

Other instances of the golden rectangle in DaVinci's Mona Lisa include Mona Lisa's face; the upper portion of her face, bounded by the eyes; the region from the neck to just below the hands; and the region from the neckline on the dress to just below the arms.

Chapter Review Exercises

1. $81^{-1/4} = (3^4)^{-1/4} = 3^{-1} = \dfrac{1}{3}$

2. $\dfrac{x^{-3/2}}{x^{7/2}} = x^{-10/2} = x^{-5} = \dfrac{1}{x^5}$

3. $(a^{16})^{-5/8} = a^{-10} = \dfrac{1}{a^{10}}$

4. $(16x^{-4}y^{12})(100x^6 y^{-2})^{1/2}$
$= 16x^{-4}y^{12} \cdot (10^2)^{1/2} x^3 y^{-1}$
$= 160x^{-1}y^{11}$
$= \dfrac{160y^{11}}{x}$

5. $3x^{3/4} = 3\sqrt[4]{x^3}$

6. $7y\sqrt[3]{x^2} = 7x^{2/3}y$

7. $\sqrt[4]{81a^8 b^{12}} = \sqrt[4]{3^4 a^8 b^{12}} = 3a^2 b^3$

8. $-\sqrt{49x^6 y^{16}} = -\sqrt{7^2 x^6 y^{16}} = -7x^3 y^8$

9. $\sqrt[3]{-8a^6 b^{12}} = \sqrt[3]{(-2)^3 a^6 b^{12}} = -2a^2 b^4$

10. $\sqrt{18a^3 b^6} = \sqrt{3^2 a^2 b^6 (2a)} = 3ab^3\sqrt{2a}$

11. $\sqrt[5]{-64a^8 b^{12}} = \sqrt[5]{(-2)^5 a^5 b^{10}(2a^3 b^2)}$
$= -2ab^2\sqrt[5]{2a^3 b^2}$

12.
$\sqrt[4]{x^6 y^8 z^{10}} = \sqrt[4]{x^4 y^8 z^8 \cdot x^2 z^2}$
$= xy^2 z^2 \sqrt[4]{x^2 z^2}$

13. $\sqrt{54} + \sqrt{24} = \sqrt{3^2 \cdot 6} + \sqrt{2^2 \cdot 6}$
$= 3\sqrt{6} + 2\sqrt{6}$
$= 5\sqrt{6}$

14. $\sqrt{48x^5 y} - x\sqrt{80x^3 y}$
$= \sqrt{4^2 x^4 (3xy)} - x\sqrt{4^2 x^2 (5xy)}$
$= 4x^2\sqrt{3xy} - 4x^2\sqrt{5xy}$

15. $\sqrt{50a^4 b^3} - ab\sqrt{18a^2 b}$
$= \sqrt{5^2 a^4 b^2 (2b)} - ab\sqrt{3^2 a^2 (2b)}$
$= 5a^2 b\sqrt{2b} - 3a^2 b\sqrt{2b}$
$= 2a^2 b\sqrt{2b}$

16. $4x\sqrt{12x^2 y} + \sqrt{3x^4 y} - x^2\sqrt{27y}$
$= 4x\sqrt{2^2 x^2 (3y)} + \sqrt{x^4 (3y)} - x^2\sqrt{3^2 (3y)}$
$= 8x^2\sqrt{3y} + x^2\sqrt{3y} - 3x^2\sqrt{3y}$
$= 6x^2\sqrt{3y}$

17. $\sqrt{32}\sqrt{50} = \sqrt{1600} = \sqrt{40^2} = 40$

18. $\sqrt[3]{16x^4 y^3}\sqrt[3]{4xy^5} = \sqrt[3]{64x^5 y^6}$
$= \sqrt[3]{4^3 x^3 y^6 (x^2)}$
$= 4xy^2\sqrt[3]{x^2}$

19. $\sqrt{3x}(3 + \sqrt{3x}) = 3\sqrt{3x} + (\sqrt{3x})^2$
$= 3\sqrt{3x} + 3x$
$= 3x + 3\sqrt{3x}$

20. $(5 - \sqrt{6})^2 = 25 - 10\sqrt{6} + \sqrt{6}^2$
$= 25 - 10\sqrt{6} + 6$
$= 31 - 10\sqrt{6}$

21. $(\sqrt{3} + 8)(\sqrt{3} - 2) = \sqrt{3^2} + 6\sqrt{3} - 16$
$= 3 + 6\sqrt{3} - 16$
$= -13 + 6\sqrt{3}$

22. $\dfrac{\sqrt{125x^6}}{\sqrt{5x^3}} = \sqrt{\dfrac{125x^6}{5x^3}}$
$= \sqrt{25x^3}$
$= \sqrt{5^2 x^2 (x)}$
$= 5x\sqrt{x}$

23. $\dfrac{8}{\sqrt{3y}} = \dfrac{8}{\sqrt{3y}} \cdot \dfrac{\sqrt{3y}}{\sqrt{3y}} = \dfrac{8\sqrt{3y}}{\sqrt{3^2 y^2}} = \dfrac{8\sqrt{3y}}{3y}$

24. $\dfrac{x+2}{\sqrt{x}+\sqrt{2}} = \dfrac{x+2}{\sqrt{x}+\sqrt{2}} \cdot \dfrac{\sqrt{x}-\sqrt{2}}{\sqrt{x}-\sqrt{2}}$
$= \dfrac{x\sqrt{x} - x\sqrt{2} + 2\sqrt{x} - 2\sqrt{2}}{\sqrt{x^2} - \sqrt{2^2}}$
$= \dfrac{x\sqrt{x} - x\sqrt{2} + 2\sqrt{x} - 2\sqrt{2}}{x - 2}$

25. $\dfrac{\sqrt{x}+\sqrt{y}}{\sqrt{x}-\sqrt{y}} = \dfrac{\sqrt{x}+\sqrt{y}}{\sqrt{x}-\sqrt{y}} \cdot \dfrac{\sqrt{x}+\sqrt{y}}{\sqrt{x}+\sqrt{y}}$
$= \dfrac{\sqrt{x^2} + \sqrt{xy} + \sqrt{xy} + \sqrt{y^2}}{\sqrt{x^2} - \sqrt{y^2}}$
$= \dfrac{x + 2\sqrt{xy} + y}{x - y}$

26. $\sqrt{-36} = \sqrt{-1}\sqrt{36} = i\sqrt{6^2} = 6i$

27. $\sqrt{-50} = i\sqrt{50} = i\sqrt{5^2 \cdot 2} = 5i\sqrt{2}$

28. $\sqrt{49} - \sqrt{-16} = \sqrt{7^2} - \sqrt{-1}\sqrt{16}$
$= 7 - i\sqrt{4^2}$
$= 7 - 4i$

29. $\sqrt{200} + \sqrt{-12} = \sqrt{10^2 \cdot 2} + \sqrt{-1}\sqrt{2^2}\sqrt{3}$
$= 10\sqrt{2} + 2i\sqrt{3}$

30. $(5 + 2i) + (4 - 3i) = (5 + 4) + (2 + (-3))i$
$= 9 - i$

31. $(-8 + 3i) - (4 - 7i)$
$= (-8 + 3i) + (-4 + 7i)$
$= (-8 + (-4)) + (3 + 7)i$
$= -12 + 10i$

32. $(9 - \sqrt{-16}) + (5 + \sqrt{-36})$
$= (9 - 4i) + (5 + 6i)$
$= (9 + 5) + (-4 + 6)i$
$= 14 + 2i$

33. $(\sqrt{50} + \sqrt{-72}) - (\sqrt{162} - \sqrt{-8})$
$= (\sqrt{5^2 \cdot 2} + i\sqrt{6^2 \cdot 2}) - (\sqrt{9^2 \cdot 2} - i\sqrt{2^2 \cdot 2})$
$= (5\sqrt{2} + 6i\sqrt{2}) - (9\sqrt{2} - 2i\sqrt{2})$
$= -4\sqrt{2} + 8i\sqrt{2}$

34. $(3 - 9i) + 7 = 10 - 9i$

35. $(8i)(2i) = 16i^2 = 16(-1) = -16$

36. $i(3 - 7i) = 3i - 7i^2 = 3i - 7(-1) = 7 + 3i$

37. $\sqrt{-12}\sqrt{-6} = i\sqrt{12} \cdot i\sqrt{6}$
$= i^2\sqrt{72}$
$= (-1)\sqrt{6^2 \cdot 2}$
$= -6\sqrt{2}$

38. $(6 - 5i)(4 + 3i) = 24 + 18i - 20i - 15i^2$
$= 24 - 2i - 15(-1)$
$= 24 + 15 - 2i$
$= 39 - 2i$

39. $\dfrac{-6}{i} = -\dfrac{6}{i} \cdot \dfrac{i}{i} = \dfrac{-6i}{i^2} = \dfrac{-6i}{-1} = 6i$

40. $\dfrac{5 + 2i}{3i} = \dfrac{5 + 2i}{3i} \cdot \dfrac{-3i}{-3i}$
$= \dfrac{-15i - 6i^2}{-9i^2}$
$= \dfrac{-15i - 6(-1)}{-9(-1)}$
$= \dfrac{-15i + 6}{9}$
$= \dfrac{6}{9} - \dfrac{15}{9}i$
$= \dfrac{2}{3} - \dfrac{5}{3}i$

41. $\dfrac{7}{2 - i} = \dfrac{7}{2 - i} \cdot \dfrac{2 + i}{2 + i}$
$= \dfrac{14 + 7i}{2^2 + 1}$
$= \dfrac{14 + 7i}{4 + 1}$
$= \dfrac{14 + 7i}{5}$
$= \dfrac{14}{5} + \dfrac{7}{5}i$

42. $\dfrac{\sqrt{16}}{\sqrt{4} - \sqrt{-4}} = \dfrac{4}{2 - 2i}$
$= \dfrac{4}{2 - 2i} \cdot \dfrac{2 + 2i}{2 + 2i}$
$= \dfrac{8 + 8i}{4 - 4i^2}$
$= \dfrac{8 + 8i}{8}$
$= 1 + i$

43. $\dfrac{5 + 9i}{1 - i} = \dfrac{5 + 9i}{1 - i} \cdot \dfrac{1 + i}{1 + i}$
$= \dfrac{5 + 5i + 9i + 9i^2}{1 + 1}$
$= \dfrac{5 + 14i + 9(-1)}{2}$
$= \dfrac{5 - 9 + 14i}{2}$
$= \dfrac{-4 + 14i}{2}$
$= -2 + 7i$

44. $\sqrt[3]{9x} = -6$
$(\sqrt[3]{9x})^3 = (-6)^3$
$9x = -216$
$x = -24$

Check:

$\sqrt[3]{9x} = -6$	
$\sqrt[3]{9(-24)}$	-6
$\sqrt[3]{-216}$	-6
$-6 = -6$	

The solution is -24.

45. The function f contains an even root. The radicand must be greater than or equal to zero.
$3x - 2 \geq 0$
$3x \geq 2$
$x \geq \dfrac{2}{3}$

The domain is $\left\{ x \middle| x \geq \dfrac{2}{3} \right\}$.

46. The function f contains an odd root. The radicand may be positive or negative.

    The domain is $\{x | x$ is a real number$\}$.

47.

48.

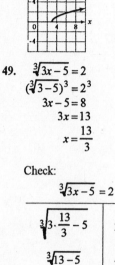

49. $\sqrt[3]{3x-5}=2$

    $(\sqrt[3]{3-5})^3=2^3$

    $3x-5=8$

    $3x=13$

    $x=\dfrac{13}{3}$

    Check:

    $$\sqrt[3]{3x-5}=2$$

$\sqrt[3]{3\cdot\dfrac{13}{3}-5}$	2
$\sqrt[3]{13-5}$	2
$\sqrt[3]{8}$	2
	$2=2$

    The solution is $\dfrac{13}{3}$.

50. $\sqrt{4x+9}+10=11$

    $\sqrt{4x+9}=1$

    $(\sqrt{4x+9})^2=1^2$

    $4x+9=1$

    $4x=-8$

    $x=-2$

    Check:

    $$\sqrt{4x+9}+10=11$$

$\sqrt{4(-2)+9}+10$	11
$\sqrt{1}+10$	11
$1+10$	11
	$11=11$

    The solution is –2.

51. **Strategy**
    To find the width of the rectangle, use the Pythagorean Theorem. The unknown width is one leg, the length is the other leg, and the diagonal is the hypotenuse.

    Solution
    $a^2+b^2=c^2$
    $a^2+(12)^2=(13)^2$
    $a^2+144=169$
    $a^2=25$
    $a=5$
    The width is 5 in.

52. **Strategy**
    To find the amount of power, replace v in the equation with the given value and solve for p.

    Solution
    $v=4.05\sqrt[3]{P}$
    $20=4.05\sqrt[3]{P}$
    $\dfrac{20}{4.05}\approx\sqrt[3]{P}$
    $\left(\dfrac{20}{4.05}\right)^3=(\sqrt[3]{P})^3$
    $120\approx P$
    The amount of power is 120 watts.

53. **Strategy**
    To find the distance required, replace v and a in the equation with the given values and solve for s.

    Solution
    $v=\sqrt{2as}$
    $88=\sqrt{2\cdot16s}$
    $7744=32s$
    $242=s$
    The distance required is 242 feet.

54. **Strategy**
    To find the distance, use the Pythagorean Theorem. The hypotenuse is the length of the ladder (12 ft). One leg is the height on the building that the ladder reaches (10 ft). The distance from the bottom of the ladder to the building is the other leg.

    Solution
    $c^2=a^2+b^2$
    $12^2=10^2+b^2$
    $144=100+b^2$
    $44=b^2$
    $44^{1/2}=(b^2)^{1/2}$
    $\sqrt{44}=b$
    $6.63=b$

    The distance is 6.63 feet.

Chapter Test

1. $\dfrac{r^{2/3}r^{-1}}{r^{-1/2}} = \dfrac{r^{-1/3}}{r^{-1/2}} = r^{1/6}$

2. $\dfrac{(2x^{1/3}y^{-2/3})^6}{(x^{-4}y^8)^{1/4}} = \dfrac{2^6 x^2 y^{-4}}{x^{-1}y^2} = 2^6 x^3 y^{-6} = \dfrac{64x^3}{y^6}$

3. $\left(\dfrac{4a^4}{b^2}\right)^{-3/2} = \dfrac{4^{-3/2}a^{-6}}{b^{-3}}$

   $= (2^2)^{-3/2}a^{-6}b^3$

   $= 2^{-3}a^{-6}b^3$

   $= \dfrac{b^3}{8a^6}$

4. $3y^{2/5} = 3\sqrt[5]{y^2}$

5. $\dfrac{1}{2}\sqrt[4]{x^3} = \dfrac{1}{2}x^{3/4}$

6. The function f contains an even root. The radicand must be greater than or equal to zero.

   $4 - x \geq 0$

   $-x \geq -4$

   $x \leq 4$

   The domain is $\{x \mid x \leq 4\}$.

7. The function f contains an odd root. The radicand may be positive or negative.

   The domain is $(-\infty, \infty)$.

8. $\sqrt[3]{27a^4b^3c^7} = \sqrt[3]{3^3 a^3 b^3 c^6 (ac)} = 3abc^2\sqrt[3]{ac}$

9. $\sqrt{18a^3} + a\sqrt{50a} = \sqrt{3^2 a^2 (2a)} + a\sqrt{5^2(2a)}$

   $= 3a\sqrt{2a} + 5a\sqrt{2a}$

   $= 8a\sqrt{2a}$

10. $\sqrt[3]{54x^7y^3} - x\sqrt[3]{128x^4y^3} - x^2\sqrt[3]{2xy^3}$

    $= \sqrt[3]{3^3 x^6 y^3 (2x)} - x\sqrt[3]{4^3 x^3 y^3 (2x)} - x^2\sqrt[3]{y^3(2x)}$

    $= 3x^2 y\sqrt[3]{2x} - 4x^2 y\sqrt[3]{2x} - x^2 y\sqrt[3]{2x}$

    $= -2x^2 y\sqrt[3]{2x}$

11. $\sqrt{3x}(\sqrt{x} - \sqrt{25x}) = \sqrt{3x^2} - \sqrt{75x^2}$

    $= \sqrt{x^2(3)} - \sqrt{5^2 x^2(3)}$

    $= x\sqrt{3} - 5x\sqrt{3}$

    $= -4x\sqrt{3}$

12. $(2\sqrt{3} + 4)(3\sqrt{3} - 1) = 6\sqrt{3^2} - 2\sqrt{3} + 12\sqrt{3} - 4$

    $= 18 + 10\sqrt{3} - 4$

    $= 14 + 10\sqrt{3}$

13. $(\sqrt{a} - 3\sqrt{b})(2\sqrt{a} + 5\sqrt{b})$

    $= 2\sqrt{a^2} + 5\sqrt{ab} - 6\sqrt{ab} - 15\sqrt{b^2}$

    $= 2a - \sqrt{ab} - 15b$

14. $(2\sqrt{x} + \sqrt{y})^2 = 4\sqrt{x^2} + 4\sqrt{xy} + \sqrt{y^2}$

    $= 4x + 4\sqrt{xy} + y$

15. $\dfrac{\sqrt{32x^5 y}}{\sqrt{2xy^3}} = \sqrt{\dfrac{32x^5 y}{2xy^3}} = \sqrt{\dfrac{16x^4}{y^2}} = \sqrt{\dfrac{4^2 x^4}{y^2}} = \dfrac{4x^2}{y}$

16. $\dfrac{4 - 2\sqrt{5}}{2 - \sqrt{5}} = \dfrac{4 - 2\sqrt{5}}{2 - \sqrt{5}} \cdot \dfrac{2 + \sqrt{5}}{2 + \sqrt{5}}$

    $= \dfrac{8 + 4\sqrt{5} - 4\sqrt{5} - 2\sqrt{5^2}}{2^2 - \sqrt{5^2}}$

    $= \dfrac{8 - 2 \cdot 5}{4 - 5}$

    $= \dfrac{8 - 10}{-1}$

    $= \dfrac{-2}{-1}$

    $= 2$

17. $\dfrac{\sqrt{x}}{\sqrt{x} - \sqrt{y}} = \dfrac{\sqrt{x}}{\sqrt{x} - \sqrt{y}} \cdot \dfrac{\sqrt{x} + \sqrt{y}}{\sqrt{x} + \sqrt{y}}$

    $= \dfrac{\sqrt{x^2} + \sqrt{xy}}{\sqrt{x^2} - \sqrt{y^2}}$

    $= \dfrac{x + \sqrt{xy}}{x - y}$

18. $(\sqrt{-8})(\sqrt{-2}) = i\sqrt{8} \cdot i\sqrt{2} = i^2\sqrt{16} = -1 \cdot 4 = -4$

19. $(5 - 2i) - (8 - 4i) = -3 + 2i$

20. $(2 + 5i)(4 - 2i) = 8 - 4i + 20i - 10i^2$

    $= 8 + 16i - 10(-1)$

    $= 8 + 16i + 10$

    $= 18 + 16i$

21. $\dfrac{2 + 3i}{1 - 2i} = \dfrac{2 + 3i}{1 - 2i} \cdot \dfrac{1 + 2i}{1 + 2i}$

    $= \dfrac{2 + 4i + 3i + 6i^2}{1 + 4}$

    $= \dfrac{2 + 7i + 6(-1)}{5}$

    $= \dfrac{2 - 6 + 7i}{5} = \dfrac{-4 + 7i}{5}$

    $= -\dfrac{4}{5} + \dfrac{7}{5}i$

22. $(2 + i) + (2 - i) = 4$

23. $\sqrt{x+12} - \sqrt{x} = 2$

$\sqrt{x+12} = 2 + \sqrt{x}$

$(\sqrt{x+12})^2 = (2 + \sqrt{x})^2$

$x + 12 = 4 + 4\sqrt{x} + x$

$12 = 4 + 4\sqrt{x}$

$8 = 4\sqrt{x}$

$2 = \sqrt{x}$

$2^2 = (\sqrt{x})^2$

$4 = x$

Check:

$$\sqrt{x+12} - \sqrt{x} = 2$$

$\sqrt{4+12} - \sqrt{4}$	2
$\sqrt{16} - \sqrt{4}$	2
$4 - 2$	2
	$2 = 2$

The solution is 4.

24. $\sqrt[3]{2x-2} + 4 = 2$

$\sqrt[3]{2x-2} = -2$

$(\sqrt[3]{2x-2})^3 = (-2)^3$

$2x - 2 = -8$

$2x = -6$

$x = -3$

Check:

$$\sqrt[3]{2x-2} + 4 = 2$$

$\sqrt[3]{2(-3)-2} + 4$	2
$\sqrt[3]{-8} + 4$	2
$-2 + 4$	2
	$2 = 2$

The solution is -3.

25. Strategy
To find the distance, use the Pythagorean Theorem. The hypotenuse is the length of the guy wire. The distance along the ground from the pole to the wire (6 ft) is one leg.

Solution

$c^2 = a^2 + b^2$

$c^2 = 6^2 + 30^2$

$c^2 = 36 + 900$

$c^2 = 936$

$\sqrt{c^2} = \sqrt{936}$

$c \approx 30.6$

The length of the wire is 30.6 ft.

Cumulative Review Exercises

1. The Distributive Property

2. $2x - 3[x - 2(x - 4) + 2x]$

$= 2x - 3[x - 2x + 8 + 2x]$

$= 2x - 3[x + 8]$

$= 2x - 3x - 24$

$= -x - 24$

3. $A \cap B = \varnothing$

4. $\sqrt[3]{2x-5} + 3 = 6$

$\sqrt[3]{2x-5} = 3$

$(\sqrt[3]{2x-5})^3 = 3^3$

$2x - 5 = 27$

$2x = 32$

$x = 16$

Check:

$$\sqrt[3]{2x-5} + 3 = 6$$

$\sqrt[3]{2(16)-5} + 3$	6
$\sqrt[3]{32-5} + 3$	6
$\sqrt[3]{27} + 3$	6
	$6 = 6$

The solution is 16.

5. $5 - \dfrac{2}{3}x = 4$

$5 - \dfrac{2}{3}x - 5 = 4 - 5$

$-\dfrac{2}{3}x = -1$

$\left(-\dfrac{3}{2}\right)\left(-\dfrac{2}{3}\right)x = -1\left(-\dfrac{3}{2}\right)$

$x = \dfrac{3}{2}$

The solution is $\dfrac{3}{2}$.

6. $2[4 - 2(3 - 2x)] = 4(1 - x)$

$2[4 - 6 + 4x] = 4 - 4x$

$2[-2 + 4x] = 4 - 4x$

$-4 + 8x = 4 - 4x$

$-4 + 8x + 4x = 4 - 4x + 4x$

$12x - 4 = 4$

$12x - 4 + 4 = 4 + 4$

$12x = 8$

$\left(\dfrac{1}{12}\right)12x = \dfrac{1}{12}(8)$

$x = \dfrac{2}{3}$

The solution is $\dfrac{2}{3}$.

7. $3x - 4 \le 8x + 1$

$-5x - 4 \le 1$

$-5x \le 5$

$x \ge -1$

$\{x | x \ge -1\}$

8.
$$5 < 2x - 3 < 7$$
$$5 + 3 < 2x - 3 + 3 < 7 + 3$$
$$8 < 2x < 10$$
$$\frac{1}{2} \cdot 8 < \frac{1}{2} \cdot 2x < \frac{1}{2} \cdot 10$$
$$4 < x < 5$$
$$\{x | 4 < x < 5\}$$

9.
$$|7 - 3x| > 1$$
$$7 - 3x < -1 \quad \text{or} \quad 7 - 3x > 1$$
$$-3x < -8 \qquad\qquad -3x > -6$$
$$x > \frac{8}{3} \qquad\qquad x < 2$$
$$\left\{x \middle| x > \frac{8}{3}\right\} \qquad \{x | x < 2\}$$
$$\left\{x \middle| x > \frac{8}{3}\right\} \cup \{x | x < 2\} = \left\{x \middle| x < 2 \text{ or } x > \frac{8}{3}\right\}$$

10. $64a^2 - b^2 = (8a)^2 - b^2 = (8a + b)(8a - b)$

11.
$$x^5 + 2x^3 - 3x = x(x^4 + 2x^2 - 3)$$
$$= x(x^2 + 3)(x^2 - 1)$$
$$= x(x^2 + 3)(x + 1)(x - 1)$$

12.
$$3x^2 + 13x - 10 = 0$$
$$(3x - 2)(x + 5) = 0$$
$$3x - 2 = 0 \quad x + 5 = 0$$
$$3x = 2 \qquad x = -5$$
$$x = \frac{2}{3}$$

The solutions are $\frac{2}{3}$ and -5.

13.

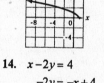

14.
$$x - 2y = 4 \qquad\qquad 2x + y = 4$$
$$-2y = -x + 4 \qquad\quad y = -2x + 4$$
$$y = \frac{1}{2}x - 2$$
$$m_1 m_2 = \frac{1}{2}(-2) = -1$$
Yes, the lines are perpendicular.

15.
$$(3^{-1}x^3y^{-5})(3^{-1}y^{-2})^{-2} = (3^{-1}x^3y^{-5})(3^2y^4)$$
$$= \frac{x^3}{3y^5}(3^2y^4)$$
$$= \frac{3x^3}{y}$$

16.
$$\left(\frac{x^{-1/2}y^{3/4}}{y^{-5/4}}\right)^4 = \left(\frac{y^2}{x^{1/2}}\right)^4 = \frac{y^8}{x^2}$$

17.
$$\sqrt{20x^3} - x\sqrt{45x} = \sqrt{2^2 x^2 \cdot 5x} - x\sqrt{3^2 \cdot 5x}$$
$$= \sqrt{2^2 x^2}\sqrt{5x} - x\sqrt{3^2}\sqrt{5x}$$
$$= 2x\sqrt{5x} - 3x\sqrt{5x}$$
$$= -x\sqrt{5x}$$

18.
$$(\sqrt{5} - 3)(\sqrt{5} - 2) = 5 - 2\sqrt{5} - 3\sqrt{5} + 6$$
$$= 11 - 5\sqrt{5}$$

19.
$$\frac{\sqrt[3]{4x^5y^4}}{\sqrt[3]{8x^2y^5}} = \sqrt[3]{\frac{4x^5y^4}{8x^2y^5}}$$
$$= \sqrt[3]{\frac{x^3}{2y}}$$
$$= \frac{\sqrt[3]{x^3}}{\sqrt[3]{2y}}$$
$$= \frac{x}{\sqrt[3]{2y}} \cdot \frac{\sqrt[3]{4y^2}}{\sqrt[3]{4y^2}}$$
$$= \frac{x\sqrt[3]{4y^2}}{\sqrt[3]{2^3y^3}}$$
$$= \frac{x\sqrt[3]{4y^2}}{2y}$$

20.
$$\frac{3i}{2 - i} = \frac{3i}{2 - i} \cdot \frac{2 + i}{2 + i}$$
$$= \frac{6i + 3i^2}{2^2 - i^2}$$
$$= \frac{6i + 3(-1)}{4 - (-1)}$$
$$= \frac{-3 + 6i}{5}$$
$$= -\frac{3}{5} + \frac{6}{5}i$$

21.
```
  -5 -4 -3 -2 -1  0  1  2  3  4  5
```

22. The function g contains an odd root. The radicand may be positive or negative. The domain is $\{x | x$ is a real number$\}$.

23.
$$f(x) = 3x^2 - 2x + 1$$
$$f(-3) = 3(-3)^2 - 2(-3) + 1$$
$$f(-3) = 27 + 6 + 1$$
$$f(-3) = 34$$
The value of $f(-3)$ is 34.

24. First find the slope of the line.

$$m = \frac{y_2 - y_1}{x_2 - x_1} = \frac{2-3}{-1-2} = \frac{-1}{-3} = \frac{1}{3}$$

Use the point-slope form to find an equation of the line.

$$y - y_1 = m(x - x_1)$$

$$y - 3 = \frac{1}{3}(x - 2)$$

$$y - 3 = \frac{1}{3}x - \frac{2}{3}$$

$$y = \frac{1}{3}x + \frac{7}{3}$$

An equation of the line is $y = \frac{1}{3}x + \frac{7}{3}$.

25.
$$\begin{vmatrix} 1 & 2 & -3 \\ 0 & -1 & 2 \\ 3 & 1 & -2 \end{vmatrix} = 1 \cdot \begin{vmatrix} -1 & 2 \\ 1 & -2 \end{vmatrix} - 2 \begin{vmatrix} 0 & 2 \\ 3 & -2 \end{vmatrix} - 3 \begin{vmatrix} 0 & -1 \\ 3 & 1 \end{vmatrix}$$

$$= 1 \cdot 0 - 2(-6) - 3 \cdot 3$$
$$= 3$$

26.
$$2x - y = 4$$
$$-2x + 3y = 5$$

$$D = \begin{vmatrix} 2 & -1 \\ -2 & 3 \end{vmatrix} = 4$$

$$D_x = \begin{vmatrix} 4 & -1 \\ 5 & 3 \end{vmatrix} = 17$$

$$D_y = \begin{vmatrix} 2 & 4 \\ -2 & 5 \end{vmatrix} = 18$$

$$x = \frac{D_x}{D} = \frac{17}{4}$$

$$y = \frac{D_y}{D} = \frac{18}{4} = \frac{9}{2}$$

The solution is $\left(\frac{17}{4}, \frac{9}{2} \right)$.

27. Find the y-intercept at $x = 0$.

$$3(0) - 2y = -6$$
$$y = 3 \quad \text{The } y\text{-intercept is } (0, 3).$$

To find the slope, find the x-intercept and use it to get the slope

$$3x - 2(0) = -6$$
$$x = -2 \quad \text{The } x\text{-intercept is } (-2, 0).$$

$$m = \frac{y_2 - y_1}{x_2 - x_1}$$

$$m = \frac{3 - 0}{0 - (-2)} = \frac{3}{2}$$

The slope is $\frac{3}{2}$, and the y-intercept is $(0, 3)$.

28.
$$3x + 2y \le 4$$
$$2y \le -3x + 4$$
$$y \le -\frac{3}{2}x + 2$$

Sketch the solid line $y = -\frac{3}{2}x + 2$. Shade below the solid line.

29. Strategy

Number of 18¢ stamps: x

Number of 13¢ stamps: $30 - x$

Stamps	Number	Value	Total Value
18¢	x	18	$18x$
13¢	$30 - x$	13	$13(30 - x)$

The sum of the total values of each type of stamp equals the total value of the stamps (485¢).

$$18x + 13(30 - x) = 485$$

Solution

$$18x + 13(30 - x) = 485$$
$$18x + 390 - 13x = 485$$
$$5x + 390 = 485$$
$$5x = 95$$
$$x = 19$$

There are nineteen 18¢ stamps.

30. Strategy

Amount invested at 8.4%: x

	Principal	Rate	Interest
Amount invested at 7.2%	2500	0.072	0.072(2500)
Amount invested at 8.4%	x	0.084	$0.084x$

The total amount of interest earned is $516.

$$0.072(2500) + 0.084x = 516$$

Solution

$$0.072(2500) + 0.084x = 516$$
$$180 + 0.084x = 516$$
$$0.084x = 336$$
$$x = 4000$$

The additional investment must be $4000.

31. Strategy

Length of the rectangle: x

Width of the rectangle: $x - 6$

Use the equation for the area of a rectangle, $A = L \cdot W$.

Solution

$A = L \cdot W$

$72 = x(x - 6)$

$72 = x^2 - 6x$

$0 = x^2 - 6x - 72$

$0 = (x - 12)(x + 6)$

$x - 12 = 0 \quad x + 6 = 0$

$\quad x = 12 \quad\quad x = -6$

The length cannot be negative, so –6 is not a solution.

$x - 6 = 12 - 6 = 6$

The length is 12 ft and the width is 6 ft.

32. Strategy

Unknown rate of the car: x

Unknown rate of the plane: $5x$

	Distance	Rate	Time
Car	25	x	$\dfrac{25}{x}$
Plane	625	$5x$	$\dfrac{625}{5x}$

The total time of the trip was 3 h.

$\dfrac{25}{x} + \dfrac{625}{5x} = 3$

Solution

$5x\left(\dfrac{25}{x} + \dfrac{625}{5x}\right) = 3(5x)$

$125 + 625 = 15x$

$750 = 15x$

$50 = x$

$250 = 5x$

The rate of the plane is 250 mph.

33. Strategy

To find the time it takes light to travel from the earth to the moon, use the formula $RT = D$, substituting for R and D and solving for T.

Solution

$RT = D$

$1.86 \times 10^5 \cdot T = 232{,}500$

$1.86 \times 10^5 \cdot T = 2.325 \times 10^5$

$T = 1.25 \times 10^0$

$T = 1.25$

The time is 1.25 seconds.

34. Strategy

To find the height of the periscope, replace d in the equation by the given value and solve for h.

Solution

$d = \sqrt{1.5h}$

$7 = \sqrt{1.5h}$

$7^2 = 1.5h$

$\dfrac{7^2}{1.5} = h$

$32.7 = h$

The height of the periscope is 32.7 ft.

35. Slope $m = \dfrac{y_2 - y_1}{x_2 - x_1} = \dfrac{400 - 0}{5000 - 0} = \dfrac{400}{5000} = 0.08$

The slope represents the simple interest on the investment. The interest rate is 8%.

Chapter 8: Quadratic Equations and Inequalities

Prep Test

1. $\sqrt{18} = \sqrt{2 \cdot 9} = 3\sqrt{2}$ [7.2.1]

2. $\sqrt{-9} = 3i$ [7.2.1]

3. $\dfrac{3x-2}{x-1} - 1 = \dfrac{3x-2}{x-1} - \dfrac{x-1}{x-1}$ [6.2.2]

   $\qquad\qquad = \dfrac{3x-2-x+1}{x-1}$

   $\qquad\qquad = \dfrac{2x-1}{x-1}$

4. $b^2 - 4ac$ [1.3.2]

   $(-4)^2 - 4(2)(1) = 16 - 8 = 8$

5. $4x^2 + 28x + 49 = (2x+7)^2$ [5.6.1]

   Yes

6. $4x^2 - 4x + 1 = (2x-1)^2$ [5.6.1]

7. $9x^2 - 4 = (3x+2)(3x-2)$ [5.6.1]

8. $\{x \,|\, x < -1\} \cap \{x \,|\, x < 4\}$ [1.1.2]

9. $\quad x(x-1) = x + 15$ [5.7.1]

   $\qquad x^2 - x = x + 15$

   $\quad x^2 - 2x - 15 = 0$

   $\quad (x-5)(x+3) = 0$

   $x - 5 = 0 \quad x + 3 = 0$

   $\quad x = 5 \qquad x = -3$

   The solutions are −3, 5.

10. $\qquad \dfrac{4}{x-3} = \dfrac{16}{x}$ [6.4.1]

    $x(x-3)\dfrac{4}{x-3} = x(x-3)\dfrac{16}{x}$

    $\qquad 4x = 16x - 48$

    $\qquad -12x = -48$

    $\qquad\quad x = 4$

    The solution is 4.

Go Figure

The repeating decimal 0.999... has digits 9. The repeating decimal 0.999... is equivalent to 9/9 which equals 1, and $\sqrt{1} = 1$. Therefore the value of A is 9.

Section 8.1

Concept Review 8.1

1. Sometimes true
   A quadratic equation may have two real roots, one real root, or two imaginary roots.

2. Always true

3. Never true
   The Principle of Zero Products states that at least one of the factors must be zero if the product is zero. In this case the product is 8.

4. Sometimes true
   A quadratic equation may have two roots.

Objective 8.1.1 Exercises

1. If $a = 0$ in $ax^2 + bx + c = 0$, then there is no second-degree term in the equation and it is, therefore, not a quadratic equation.

2. If the product of two factors is zero, then at least one of the factors must be zero. It is used to solve a quadratic equation of the form $ax^2 + bx + c = 0$ in which $ax^2 + bx + c$ is factorable and can, therefore, be written as a product of factors.

3. $2x^2 - 4x - 5 = 0$

   $a = 2, b = -4, c = -5$

4. $x^2 - 3x - 1 = 0$

   $a = 1, b = -3, c = -1$

5. $4x^2 - 5x - 6 = 0$

   $a = 4, b = -5, c = -6$

6. $3x^2 - 7 = 0$

   $a = 3, b = 0, c = -7$

7. $x^2 - 4x = 0$

   $x(x-4) = 0$

   $x = 0 \qquad x - 4 = 0$

   $\qquad\qquad\quad x = 4$

   The solutions are 0 and 4.

8. $y^2 + 6y = 0$

   $y(y+6) = 0$

   $y = 0 \qquad y + 6 = 0$

   $\qquad\qquad\quad y = -6$

   The solutions are 0 and −6.

9. $t^2 - 25 = 0$

   $(t-5)(t+5) = 0$

   $t - 5 = 0 \qquad t + 5 = 0$

   $\quad t = 5 \qquad\quad t = -5$

   The solutions are 5 and −5.

10. $p^2 - 81 = 0$

    $(p-9)(p+9) = 0$

    $p - 9 = 0 \qquad p + 9 = 0$

    $\quad p = 9 \qquad\quad p = -9$

    The solutions are 9 and −9.

11. $s^2 - s - 6 = 0$

    $(s-3)(s+2) = 0$

    $s - 3 = 0 \qquad s + 2 = 0$

    $\quad s = 3 \qquad\quad s = -2$

    The solutions are 3 and −2.

12. $v^2 + 4v - 5 = 0$
$(v-1)(v+5) = 0$
$v - 1 = 0 \qquad v + 5 = 0$
$v = 1 \qquad\quad v = -5$
The solutions are 1 and –5.

13. $y^2 - 6y + 9 = 0$
$(y-3)(y-3) = 0$
$y - 3 = 0 \qquad y - 3 = 0$
$y = 3 \qquad\quad y = 3$
The solution is 3.

14. $x^2 + 10x + 25 = 0$
$(x+5)(x+5) = 0$
$x + 5 = 0 \qquad x + 5 = 0$
$x = -5 \qquad\quad x = -5$
The solution is –5.

15. $9z^2 - 18z = 0$
$9z(z-2) = 0$
$9z = 0 \qquad z - 2 = 0$
$z = 0 \qquad\quad z = 2$
The solutions are 0 and 2.

16. $4y^2 + 20y = 0$
$4y(y+5) = 0$
$4y = 0 \qquad y + 5 = 0$
$y = 0 \qquad\quad y = -5$
The solutions are 0 and –5.

17. $r^2 - 3r = 10$
$r^2 - 3r - 10 = 0$
$(r-5)(r+2) = 0$
$r - 5 = 0 \qquad r + 2 = 0$
$r = 5 \qquad\quad r = -2$
The solutions are 5 and –2.

18. $p^2 + 5p = 6$
$p^2 + 5p - 6 = 0$
$(p-1)(p+6) = 0$
$p - 1 = 0 \qquad p + 6 = 0$
$p = 1 \qquad\quad p = -6$
The solutions are 1 and –6.

19. $v^2 + 10 = 7v$
$v^2 - 7v + 10 = 0$
$(v-2)(v-5) = 0$
$v - 2 = 0 \qquad v - 5 = 0$
$v = 2 \qquad\quad v = 5$
The solutions are 2 and 5.

20. $t^2 - 16 = 15t$
$t^2 - 15t - 16 = 0$
$(t-16)(t+1) = 0$
$t - 16 = 0 \qquad t + 1 = 0$
$t = 16 \qquad\quad t = -1$
The solutions are 16 and –1.

21. $2x^2 - 9x - 18 = 0$
$(x-6)(2x+3) = 0$
$x - 6 = 0 \qquad 2x + 3 = 0$
$x = 6 \qquad\quad 2x = -3$
$$x = -\frac{3}{2}$$
The solutions are 6 and $-\dfrac{3}{2}$.

22. $3y^2 - 4y - 4 = 0$
$(3y+2)(y-2) = 0$
$3y + 2 = 0 \qquad y - 2 = 0$
$3y = -2 \qquad\quad y = 2$
$$y = -\frac{2}{3}$$
The solutions are $-\dfrac{2}{3}$ and 2.

23. $4z^2 - 9z + 2 = 0$
$(z-2)(4z-1) = 0$
$z - 2 = 0 \qquad 4z - 1 = 0$
$z = 2 \qquad\quad 4z = 1$
$$z = \frac{1}{4}$$
The solutions are 2 and $\dfrac{1}{4}$.

24. $2s^2 - 9s + 9 = 0$
$(2s-3)(s-3) = 0$
$2s - 3 = 0 \qquad s - 3 = 0$
$2s = 3 \qquad\quad s = 3$
$$s = \frac{3}{2}$$
The solutions are $\dfrac{3}{2}$ and 3.

25. $3w^2 + 11w = 4$
$3w^2 + 11w - 4 = 0$
$(3w-1)(w+4) = 0$
$3w - 1 = 0 \qquad w + 4 = 0$
$3w = 1 \qquad\quad w = -4$
$$w = \frac{1}{3}$$
The solutions are $\dfrac{1}{3}$ and –4.

26. $2r^2 + r = 6$
$2r^2 + r - 6 = 0$
$(2r-3)(r+2) = 0$
$2r - 3 = 0 \qquad r + 2 = 0$
$2r = 3 \qquad\quad r = -2$
$$r = \frac{3}{2}$$
The solutions are $\dfrac{3}{2}$ and –2.

27.
$$6x^2 = 23x + 18$$
$$6x^2 - 23x - 18 = 0$$
$$(2x - 9)(3x + 2) = 0$$
$$2x - 9 = 0 \qquad 3x + 2 = 0$$
$$2x = 9 \qquad 3x = -2$$
$$x = \frac{9}{2} \qquad x = -\frac{2}{3}$$
The solutions are $\frac{9}{2}$ and $-\frac{2}{3}$.

28.
$$6x^2 = 7x - 2$$
$$6x^2 - 7x + 2 = 0$$
$$(3x - 2)(2x - 1) = 0$$
$$3x - 2 = 0 \qquad 2x - 1 = 0$$
$$3x = 2 \qquad 2x = 1$$
$$x = \frac{2}{3} \qquad x = \frac{1}{2}$$
The solutions are $\frac{2}{3}$ and $\frac{1}{2}$.

29.
$$4 - 15u - 4u^2 = 0$$
$$(1 - 4u)(4 + u) = 0$$
$$1 - 4u = 0 \qquad 4 + u = 0$$
$$-4u = -1 \qquad u = -4$$
$$u = \frac{1}{4}$$
The solutions are $\frac{1}{4}$ and -4.

30.
$$3 - 2y - 8y^2 = 0$$
$$(1 - 2y)(3 + 4y) = 0$$
$$1 - 2y = 0 \qquad 3 + 4y = 0$$
$$-2y = -1 \qquad 4y = -3$$
$$y = \frac{1}{2} \qquad y = -\frac{3}{4}$$
The solutions are $\frac{1}{2}$ and $-\frac{3}{4}$.

31.
$$x + 18 = x(x - 6)$$
$$x + 18 = x^2 - 6x$$
$$0 = x^2 - 7x - 18$$
$$0 = (x - 9)(x + 2)$$
$$x - 9 = 0 \qquad x + 2 = 0$$
$$x = 9 \qquad x = -2$$
The solutions are 9 and -2.

32.
$$t + 24 = t(t + 6)$$
$$t + 24 = t^2 + 6t$$
$$0 = t^2 + 5t - 24$$
$$0 = (t - 3)(t + 8)$$
$$t - 3 = 0 \qquad t + 8 = 0$$
$$t = 3 \qquad t = -8$$
The solutions are 3 and -8.

33.
$$4s(s + 3) = s - 6$$
$$4s^2 + 12s = s - 6$$
$$4s^2 + 11s + 6 = 0$$
$$(s + 2)(4s + 3) = 0$$
$$s + 2 = 0 \qquad 4s + 3 = 0$$
$$s = -2 \qquad 4s = -3$$
$$s = -\frac{3}{4}$$
The solutions are -2 and $-\frac{3}{4}$.

34.
$$3v(v - 2) = 11v + 6$$
$$3v^2 - 6v = 11v + 6$$
$$3v^2 - 17v - 6 = 0$$
$$(3v + 1)(v - 6) = 0$$
$$3v + 1 = 0 \qquad v - 6 = 0$$
$$3v = -1 \qquad v = 6$$
$$v = -\frac{1}{3}$$
The solutions are $-\frac{1}{3}$ and 6.

35.
$$u^2 - 2u + 4 = (2u - 3)(u + 2)$$
$$u^2 - 2u + 4 = 2u^2 + u - 6$$
$$0 = u^2 + 3u - 10$$
$$0 = (u - 2)(u + 5)$$
$$u - 2 = 0 \qquad u + 5 = 0$$
$$u = 2 \qquad u = -5$$
The solutions are 2 and -5.

36.
$$(3v - 2)(2v + 1) = 3v^2 - 11v - 10$$
$$6v^2 - v - 2 = 3v^2 - 11v - 10$$
$$3v^2 + 10v + 8 = 0$$
$$(v + 2)(3v + 4) = 0$$
$$v + 2 = 0 \qquad 3v + 4 = 0$$
$$v = -2 \qquad 3v = -4$$
$$v = -\frac{4}{3}$$
The solutions are -2 and $-\frac{4}{3}$.

37.
$$(3x - 4)(x + 4) = x^2 - 3x - 28$$
$$3x^2 + 8x - 16 = x^2 - 3x - 28$$
$$2x^2 + 11x + 12 = 0$$
$$(x + 4)(2x + 3) = 0$$
$$x + 4 = 0 \qquad 2x + 3 = 0$$
$$x = -4 \qquad 2x = -3$$
$$x = -\frac{3}{2}$$
The solutions are -4 and $-\frac{3}{2}$.

38.
$$x^2 + 14ax + 48a^2 = 0$$
$$(x + 6a)(x + 8a) = 0$$
$$x + 6a = 0 \qquad x + 8a = 0$$
$$x = -6a \qquad x = -8a$$
The solutions are $-6a$ and $-8a$.

39. $x^2 - 9bx + 14b^2 = 0$
$(x - 2b)(x - 7b) = 0$
$x - 2b = 0 \qquad x - 7b = 0$
$x = 2b \qquad x = 7b$
The solutions are $2b$ and $7b$.

40. $x^2 + 9xy - 36y^2 = 0$
$(x + 12y)(x - 3y) = 0$
$x + 12y = 0 \qquad x - 3y = 0$
$x = -12y \qquad x = 3y$
The solutions are $-12y$ and $3y$.

41. $x^2 - 6cx - 7c^2 = 0$
$(x - 7c)(x + c) = 0$
$x - 7c = 0 \qquad x + c = 0$
$x = 7c \qquad x = -c$
The solutions are $7c$ and $-c$.

42. $x^2 - ax - 20a^2 = 0$
$(x + 4a)(x - 5a) = 0$
$x + 4a = 0 \qquad x - 5a = 0$
$x = -4a \qquad x = 5a$
The solutions are $-4a$ and $5a$.

43. $2x^2 + 3bx + b^2 = 0$
$(2x + b)(x + b) = 0$
$2x + b = 0 \qquad x + b = 0$
$2x = -b \qquad x = -b$
$x = -\dfrac{b}{2}$
The solutions are $-\dfrac{b}{2}$ and $-b$.

44. $3x^2 - 4cx + c^2 = 0$
$(3x - c)(x - c) = 0$
$3x - c = 0 \qquad x - c = 0$
$3x = c \qquad x = c$
$x = \dfrac{c}{3}$
The solutions are $\dfrac{c}{3}$ and c.

45. $3x^2 - 14ax + 8a^2 = 0$
$(x - 4a)(3x - 2a) = 0$
$x - 4a = 0 \qquad 3x - 2a = 0$
$x = 4a \qquad 3x = 2a$
$x = \dfrac{2a}{3}$
The solutions are $4a$ and $\dfrac{2a}{3}$.

46. $3x^2 - 11xy + 6y^2 = 0$
$(3x - 2y)(x - 3y) = 0$
$3x - 2y = 0 \qquad x - 3y = 0$
$3x = 2y \qquad x = 3y$
$x = \dfrac{2y}{3}$
The solutions are $\dfrac{2y}{3}$ and $3y$.

Objective 8.1.2 Exercises

47. $(x - r_1)(x - r_2) = 0$
$(x - 2)(x - 5) = 0$
$x^2 - 7x + 10 = 0$

48. $(x - r_1)(x - r_2) = 0$
$(x - 3)(x - 1) = 0$
$x^2 - 4x + 3 = 0$

49. $(x - r_1)(x - r_2) = 0$
$[x - (-2)][x - (-4)] = 0$
$(x + 2)(x + 4) = 0$
$x^2 + 6x + 8 = 0$

50. $(x - r_1)(x - r_2) = 0$
$[x - (-1)][x - (-3)] = 0$
$(x + 1)(x + 3) = 0$
$x^2 + 4x + 3 = 0$

51. $(x - r_1)(x - r_2) = 0$
$(x - 6)[x - (-1)] = 0$
$(x - 6)(x + 1) = 0$
$x^2 - 5x - 6 = 0$

52. $(x - r_1)(x - r_2) = 0$
$[x - (-2)](x - 5) = 0$
$(x + 2)(x - 5) = 0$
$x^2 - 3x - 10 = 0$

53. $(x - r_1)(x - r_2) = 0$
$(x - 3)[x - (-3)] = 0$
$(x - 3)(x + 3) = 0$
$x^2 - 9 = 0$

54. $(x - r_1)(x - r_2) = 0$
$(x - 5)[x - (-5)] = 0$
$(x - 5)(x + 5) = 0$
$x^2 - 25 = 0$

55. $(x - r_1)(x - r_2) = 0$
$(x - 4)(x - 4) = 0$
$x^2 - 8x + 16 = 0$

56. $(x - r_1)(x - r_2) = 0$
$(x - 2)(x - 2) = 0$
$x^2 - 4x + 4 = 0$

57. $(x - r_1)(x - r_2) = 0$
$(x - 0)(x - 5) = 0$
$x(x - 5) = 0$
$x^2 - 5x = 0$

58. $(x - r_1)(x - r_2) = 0$
$(x - 0)[x - (-2)] = 0$
$x(x + 2) = 0$
$x^2 + 2x = 0$

59. $(x - r_1)(x - r_2) = 0$
$(x - 0)(x - 3) = 0$
$x(x - 3) = 0$
$x^2 - 3x = 0$

60.
$$(x - r_1)(x - r_2) = 0$$
$$(x - 0)[x - (-1)] = 0$$
$$x(x + 1) = 0$$
$$x^2 + x = 0$$

61.
$$(x - r_1)(x - r_2) = 0$$
$$(x - 3)\left(x - \frac{1}{2}\right) = 0$$
$$x^2 - \frac{7}{2}x + \frac{3}{2} = 0$$
$$2\left(x^2 - \frac{7}{2}x + \frac{3}{2}\right) = 2 \cdot 0$$
$$2x^2 - 7x + 3 = 0$$

62.
$$(x - r_1)(x - r_2) = 0$$
$$(x - 2)\left(x - \frac{2}{3}\right) = 0$$
$$x^2 - \frac{8}{3}x + \frac{4}{3} = 0$$
$$3\left(x^2 - \frac{8}{3}x + \frac{4}{3}\right) = 3 \cdot 0$$
$$3x^2 - 8x + 4 = 0$$

63.
$$(x - r_1)(x - r_2) = 0$$
$$\left[x - \left(-\frac{3}{4}\right)\right](x - 2) = 0$$
$$\left(x + \frac{3}{4}\right)(x - 2) = 0$$
$$x^2 - \frac{5}{4}x - \frac{3}{2} = 0$$
$$4\left(x^2 - \frac{5}{4}x - \frac{3}{2}\right) = 4 \cdot 0$$
$$4x^2 - 5x - 6 = 0$$

64.
$$(x - r_1)(x - r_2) = 0$$
$$\left[x - \left(-\frac{1}{2}\right)\right](x - 5) = 0$$
$$\left(x + \frac{1}{2}\right)(x - 5) = 0$$
$$x^2 - \frac{9}{2}x - \frac{5}{2} = 0$$
$$2\left(x^2 - \frac{9}{2}x - \frac{5}{2}\right) = 2 \cdot 0$$
$$2x^2 - 9x - 5 = 0$$

65.
$$(x - r_1)(x - r_2) = 0$$
$$\left[x - \left(-\frac{5}{3}\right)\right][x - (-2)] = 0$$
$$\left(x + \frac{5}{3}\right)(x + 2) = 0$$
$$x^2 + \frac{11}{3}x + \frac{10}{3} = 0$$
$$3\left(x^2 + \frac{11}{3}x + \frac{10}{3}\right) = 3 \cdot 0$$
$$3x^2 + 11x + 10 = 0$$

66.
$$(x - r_1)(x - r_2) = 0$$
$$\left[x - \left(-\frac{3}{2}\right)\right][x - (-1)] = 0$$
$$\left(x + \frac{3}{2}\right)(x + 1) = 0$$
$$x^2 + \frac{5}{2}x + \frac{3}{2} = 0$$
$$2\left(x^2 + \frac{5}{2}x + \frac{3}{2}\right) = 2 \cdot 0$$
$$2x^2 + 5x + 3 = 0$$

67.
$$(x - r_1)(x - r_2) = 0$$
$$\left[x - \left(-\frac{2}{3}\right)\right]\left(x - \frac{2}{3}\right) = 0$$
$$\left(x + \frac{2}{3}\right)\left(x - \frac{2}{3}\right) = 0$$
$$x^2 - \frac{4}{9} = 0$$
$$9\left(x^2 - \frac{4}{9}\right) = 9 \cdot 0$$
$$9x^2 - 4 = 0$$

68.
$$(x - r_1)(x - r_2) = 0$$
$$\left[x - \left(-\frac{1}{2}\right)\right]\left(x - \frac{1}{2}\right) = 0$$
$$\left(x + \frac{1}{2}\right)\left(x - \frac{1}{2}\right) = 0$$
$$x^2 - \frac{1}{4} = 0$$
$$4\left(x^2 - \frac{1}{4}\right) = 4 \cdot 0$$
$$4x^2 - 1 = 0$$

69.
$$(x - r_1)(x - r_2) = 0$$
$$\left(x - \frac{1}{2}\right)\left(x - \frac{1}{3}\right) = 0$$
$$x^2 - \frac{5}{6}x + \frac{1}{6} = 0$$
$$6\left(x^2 - \frac{5}{6}x + \frac{1}{6}\right) = 6 \cdot 0$$
$$6x^2 - 5x + 1 = 0$$

70.
$$(x - r_1)(x - r_2) = 0$$
$$\left(x - \frac{3}{4}\right)\left(x - \frac{2}{3}\right) = 0$$
$$x^2 - \frac{17}{12}x + \frac{1}{2} = 0$$
$$12\left(x^2 - \frac{17}{12}x + \frac{1}{2}\right) = 12 \cdot 0$$
$$12x^2 - 17x + 6 = 0$$

71.
$$(x - r_1)(x - r_2) = 0$$
$$\left(x - \frac{6}{5}\right)\left[x - \left(-\frac{1}{2}\right)\right] = 0$$
$$\left(x - \frac{6}{5}\right)\left(x + \frac{1}{2}\right) = 0$$
$$x^2 - \frac{7}{10}x - \frac{3}{5} = 0$$
$$10\left(x^2 - \frac{7}{10}x - \frac{3}{5}\right) = 10 \cdot 0$$
$$10x^2 - 7x - 6 = 0$$

72.
$$(x - r_1)(x - r_2) = 0$$
$$\left(x - \frac{3}{4}\right)\left[x - \left(-\frac{3}{2}\right)\right] = 0$$
$$\left(x - \frac{3}{4}\right)\left(x + \frac{3}{2}\right) = 0$$
$$x^2 + \frac{3}{4}x - \frac{9}{8} = 0$$
$$8\left(x^2 + \frac{3}{4}x - \frac{9}{8}\right) = 8 \cdot 0$$
$$8x^2 + 6x - 9 = 0$$

73.
$$(x - r_1)(x - r_2) = 0$$
$$\left[x - \left(-\frac{1}{4}\right)\right]\left[x - \left(-\frac{1}{2}\right)\right] = 0$$
$$\left(x + \frac{1}{4}\right)\left(x + \frac{1}{2}\right) = 0$$
$$x^2 + \frac{3}{4}x + \frac{1}{8} = 0$$
$$8\left(x^2 + \frac{3}{4}x + \frac{1}{8}\right) = 8 \cdot 0$$
$$8x^2 + 6x + 1 = 0$$

74.
$$(x - r_1)(x - r_2) = 0$$
$$\left[x - \left(-\frac{5}{6}\right)\right]\left[x - \left(-\frac{2}{3}\right)\right] = 0$$
$$\left(x + \frac{5}{6}\right)\left(x + \frac{2}{3}\right) = 0$$
$$x^2 + \frac{9}{6}x + \frac{5}{9} = 0$$
$$18\left(x^2 + \frac{9}{6}x + \frac{5}{9}\right) = 18 \cdot 0$$
$$18x^2 + 27x + 10 = 0$$

75.
$$(x - r_1)(x - r_2) = 0$$
$$\left(x - \frac{3}{5}\right)\left[x - \left(-\frac{1}{10}\right)\right] = 0$$
$$\left(x - \frac{3}{5}\right)\left(x + \frac{1}{10}\right) = 0$$
$$x^2 - \frac{1}{2}x - \frac{3}{50} = 0$$
$$50\left(x^2 - \frac{1}{2}x - \frac{3}{50}\right) = 50 \cdot 0$$
$$50x^2 - 25x - 3 = 0$$

76.
$$(x - r_1)(x - r_2) = 0$$
$$\left(x - \frac{7}{2}\right)\left[x - \left(-\frac{1}{4}\right)\right] = 0$$
$$\left(x - \frac{7}{2}\right)\left(x + \frac{1}{4}\right) = 0$$
$$x^2 - \frac{13}{4}x - \frac{7}{8} = 0$$
$$8\left(x^2 - \frac{13}{4}x - \frac{7}{8}\right) = 8 \cdot 0$$
$$8x^2 - 26x - 7 = 0$$

Objective 8.1.3 Exercises

77.
$$y^2 = 49$$
$$\sqrt{y^2} = \sqrt{49}$$
$$y = \pm\sqrt{49} = \pm 7$$
The solutions are 7 and −7.

78.
$$x^2 = 64$$
$$\sqrt{x^2} = \sqrt{64}$$
$$x = \pm\sqrt{64} = \pm 8$$
The solutions are 8 and −8.

79.
$$z^2 = -4$$
$$\sqrt{z^2} = \sqrt{-4}$$
$$z = \pm\sqrt{-4} = \pm 2i$$
The solutions are $2i$ and $-2i$.

80.
$$v^2 = -16$$
$$\sqrt{v^2} = \sqrt{-16}$$
$$v = \pm\sqrt{-16} = \pm 4i$$
The solutions are $4i$ and $-4i$.

81.
$$s^2 - 4 = 0$$
$$s^2 = 4$$
$$\sqrt{s^2} = \sqrt{4}$$
$$s = \pm\sqrt{4} = \pm 2$$
The solutions are 2 and −2.

82.
$$r^2 - 36 = 0$$
$$r^2 = 36$$
$$\sqrt{r^2} = \sqrt{36}$$
$$r = \pm\sqrt{36} = \pm 6$$
The solutions are 6 and −6.

83. $4x^2 - 81 = 0$

$4x^2 = 81$

$x^2 = \dfrac{81}{4}$

$\sqrt{x^2} = \sqrt{\dfrac{81}{4}}$

$x = \pm\sqrt{\dfrac{81}{4}} = \pm\dfrac{9}{2}$

The solutions are $\dfrac{9}{2}$ and $-\dfrac{9}{2}$.

84. $9x^2 - 16 = 0$

$9x^2 = 16$

$x^2 = \dfrac{16}{9}$

$\sqrt{x^2} = \sqrt{\dfrac{16}{9}}$

$x = \pm\sqrt{\dfrac{16}{9}} = \pm\dfrac{4}{3}$

The solutions are $\dfrac{4}{3}$ and $-\dfrac{4}{3}$.

85. $y^2 + 49 = 0$

$y^2 = -49$

$\sqrt{y^2} = \sqrt{-49}$

$y = \pm\sqrt{-49} = \pm 7i$

The solutions are $7i$ and $-7i$.

86. $z^2 + 16 = 0$

$z^2 = -16$

$\sqrt{z^2} = \sqrt{-16}$

$z = \pm\sqrt{-16} = \pm 4i$

The solutions are $4i$ and $-4i$.

87. $v^2 - 48 = 0$

$v^2 = 48$

$\sqrt{v^2} = \sqrt{48}$

$v = \pm\sqrt{48} = \pm 4\sqrt{3}$

The solutions are $4\sqrt{3}$ and $-4\sqrt{3}$.

88. $s^2 - 32 = 0$

$s^2 = 32$

$\sqrt{s^2} = \sqrt{32}$

$s = \pm\sqrt{32} = \pm 4\sqrt{2}$

The solutions are $4\sqrt{2}$ and $-4\sqrt{2}$.

89. $r^2 - 75 = 0$

$r^2 = 75$

$\sqrt{r^2} = \sqrt{75}$

$r = \pm\sqrt{75} = \pm 5\sqrt{3}$

The solutions are $5\sqrt{3}$ and $-5\sqrt{3}$.

90. $u^2 - 54 = 0$

$u^2 = 54$

$\sqrt{u^2} = \sqrt{54}$

$u = \pm\sqrt{54} = \pm 3\sqrt{6}$

The solutions are $3\sqrt{6}$ and $-3\sqrt{6}$.

91. $z^2 + 18 = 0$

$z^2 = -18$

$\sqrt{z^2} = \sqrt{-18}$

$z = \pm\sqrt{-18} = \pm 3i\sqrt{2}$

The solutions are $3i\sqrt{2}$ and $-3i\sqrt{2}$.

92. $t^2 + 27 = 0$

$t^2 = -27$

$\sqrt{t^2} = \sqrt{-27}$

$t = \pm\sqrt{-27} = \pm 3i\sqrt{3}$

The solutions are $3i\sqrt{3}$ and $-3i\sqrt{3}$.

93. $(x-1)^2 = 36$

$\sqrt{(x-1)^2} = \sqrt{36}$

$x - 1 = \pm\sqrt{36} = \pm 6$

$x - 1 = 6 \qquad x - 1 = -6$

$x = 7 \qquad\quad x = -5$

The solutions are 7 and –5.

94. $(x+2)^2 = 25$

$\sqrt{(x+2)^2} = \sqrt{25}$

$x + 2 = \pm\sqrt{25} = \pm 5$

$x + 2 = 5 \qquad x + 2 = -5$

$x = 3 \qquad\quad x = -7$

The solutions are 3 and –7.

95. $3(y+3)^2 = 27$

$(y+3)^2 = 9$

$\sqrt{(y+3)^2} = \sqrt{9}$

$y + 3 = \pm\sqrt{9} = \pm 3$

$y + 3 = 3 \qquad y + 3 = -3$

$y = 0 \qquad\quad y = -6$

The solutions are 0 and –6.

96. $4(s-2)^2 = 36$

$(s-2)^2 = 9$

$\sqrt{(s-2)^2} = \sqrt{9}$

$s - 2 = \pm\sqrt{9} = \pm 3$

$s - 2 = 3 \qquad s - 2 = -3$

$s = 5 \qquad\quad s = -1$

The solutions are 5 and –1.

97. $5(z+2)^2 = 125$

$\qquad (z+2)^2 = 25$

$\qquad \sqrt{(z+2)^2} = \sqrt{25}$

$\qquad z+2 = \pm\sqrt{25} = \pm 5$

$\qquad z+2 = 5 \qquad z+2 = -5$

$\qquad z = 3 \qquad\quad z = -7$

The solutions are 3 and –7.

98. $(x-2)^2 = -4$

$\qquad \sqrt{(x-2)^2} = \sqrt{-4}$

$\qquad x-2 = \pm\sqrt{-4} = \pm 2i$

$\qquad x-2 = 2i \qquad x-2 = -2i$

$\qquad x = 2+2i \qquad x = 2-2i$

The solutions are $2 + 2i$ and $2 – 2i$.

99. $(x+5)^2 = -25$

$\qquad \sqrt{(x+5)^2} = \sqrt{-25}$

$\qquad x+5 = \pm\sqrt{-25} = \pm 5i$

$\qquad x+5 = 5i \qquad x+5 = -5i$

$\qquad x = -5+5i \qquad x = -5-5i$

The solutions are $-5 + 5i$ and $-5 – 5i$.

100. $(x-8)^2 = -64$

$\qquad \sqrt{(x-8)^2} = \sqrt{-64}$

$\qquad x-8 = \pm\sqrt{-64} = \pm 8i$

$\qquad x-8 = 8i \qquad x-8 = -8i$

$\qquad x = 8+8i \qquad x = 8-8i$

The solutions are $8 + 8i$ and $8 – 8i$.

101. $3(x-4)^2 = -12$

$\qquad (x-4)^2 = -4$

$\qquad \sqrt{(x-4)^2} = \sqrt{-4}$

$\qquad x-4 = \pm\sqrt{-4} = \pm 2i$

$\qquad x-4 = 2i \qquad x-4 = -2i$

$\qquad x = 4+2i \qquad x = 4-2i$

The solutions are $4 + 2i$ and $4 – 2i$.

102. $5(x+2)^2 = -125$

$\qquad (x+2)^2 = -25$

$\qquad \sqrt{(x+2)^2} = \sqrt{-25}$

$\qquad x+2 = \pm\sqrt{-25} = \pm 5i$

$\qquad x+2 = 5i \qquad x+2 = -5i$

$\qquad x = -2+5i \qquad x = -2-5i$

The solutions are $-2 + 5i$ and $-2 – 5i$.

103. $3(x-9)^2 = -27$

$\qquad (x-9)^2 = -9$

$\qquad \sqrt{(x-9)^2} = \sqrt{-9}$

$\qquad x-9 = \pm\sqrt{-9} = \pm 3i$

$\qquad x-9 = 3i \qquad x-9 = -3i$

$\qquad x = 9+3i \qquad x = 9-3i$

The solutions are $9 + 3i$ and $9 – 3i$.

104. $2(y-3)^2 = 18$

$\qquad (y-3)^2 = 9$

$\qquad \sqrt{(y-3)^2} = \sqrt{9}$

$\qquad y-3 = \pm\sqrt{9} = \pm 3$

$\qquad y-3 = 3 \qquad y-3 = -3$

$\qquad y = 6 \qquad\quad y = 0$

The solutions are 6 and 0.

105. $\left(v-\dfrac{1}{2}\right)^2 = \dfrac{1}{4}$

$\qquad \sqrt{\left(v-\dfrac{1}{2}\right)^2} = \sqrt{\dfrac{1}{4}}$

$\qquad v-\dfrac{1}{2} = \pm\sqrt{\dfrac{1}{4}} = \pm\dfrac{1}{2}$

$\qquad v-\dfrac{1}{2} = \dfrac{1}{2} \qquad v-\dfrac{1}{2} = -\dfrac{1}{2}$

$\qquad v = 1 \qquad\qquad v = 0$

The solutions are 1 and 0.

106. $\left(r+\dfrac{2}{3}\right)^2 = \dfrac{1}{9}$

$\qquad \sqrt{\left(r+\dfrac{2}{3}\right)^2} = \sqrt{\dfrac{1}{9}}$

$\qquad r+\dfrac{2}{3} = \pm\sqrt{\dfrac{1}{9}} = \pm\dfrac{1}{3}$

$\qquad r+\dfrac{2}{3} = \dfrac{1}{3} \qquad r+\dfrac{2}{3} = -\dfrac{1}{3}$

$\qquad r = -\dfrac{1}{3} \qquad\qquad r = -1$

The solutions are $-\dfrac{1}{3}$ and –1.

107. $\left(x-\dfrac{2}{5}\right)^2 = \dfrac{9}{25}$

$\qquad \sqrt{\left(x-\dfrac{2}{5}\right)^2} = \sqrt{\dfrac{9}{25}}$

$\qquad x-\dfrac{2}{5} = \pm\sqrt{\dfrac{9}{25}} = \pm\dfrac{3}{5}$

$\qquad x-\dfrac{2}{5} = \dfrac{3}{5} \qquad\qquad x-\dfrac{2}{5} = -\dfrac{3}{5}$

$\qquad x = \dfrac{2}{5}+\dfrac{3}{5} = \dfrac{5}{5} \qquad x = \dfrac{2}{5}-\dfrac{3}{5}$

$\qquad x = 1 \qquad\qquad\qquad\quad x = -\dfrac{1}{5}$

The solutions are 1 and $-\dfrac{1}{5}$.

108. $\left(y+\dfrac{1}{3}\right)^2 = \dfrac{4}{9}$

$\sqrt{\left(y+\dfrac{1}{3}\right)^2} = \sqrt{\dfrac{4}{9}}$

$y+\dfrac{1}{3} = \pm\sqrt{\dfrac{4}{9}} = \pm\dfrac{2}{3}$

$y+\dfrac{1}{3} = \dfrac{2}{3}$ $y+\dfrac{1}{3} = -\dfrac{2}{3}$

$y = \dfrac{2}{3}-\dfrac{1}{3}$ $y = -\dfrac{1}{3}-\dfrac{2}{3} = -\dfrac{3}{3}$

$y = \dfrac{1}{3}$ $y = -1$

The solutions are $\dfrac{1}{3}$ and -1.

109. $\left(a+\dfrac{3}{4}\right)^2 = \dfrac{9}{16}$

$\sqrt{\left(a+\dfrac{3}{4}\right)^2} = \sqrt{\dfrac{9}{16}}$

$a+\dfrac{3}{4} = \pm\sqrt{\dfrac{9}{16}} = \pm\dfrac{3}{4}$

$a+\dfrac{3}{4} = \dfrac{3}{4}$ $a+\dfrac{3}{4} = -\dfrac{3}{4}$

$a = \dfrac{3}{4}-\dfrac{3}{4}$ $a = -\dfrac{3}{4}-\dfrac{3}{4} = -\dfrac{6}{4}$

$a = 0$ $a = -\dfrac{3}{2}$

The solutions are 0 and $-\dfrac{3}{2}$.

110. $4\left(x-\dfrac{1}{2}\right)^2 = 1$

$\left(x-\dfrac{1}{2}\right)^2 = \dfrac{1}{4}$

$\sqrt{\left(x-\dfrac{1}{2}\right)^2} = \sqrt{\dfrac{1}{4}}$

$x-\dfrac{1}{2} = \pm\sqrt{\dfrac{1}{4}} = \pm\dfrac{1}{2}$

$x-\dfrac{1}{2} = \dfrac{1}{2}$ $x-\dfrac{1}{2} = -\dfrac{1}{2}$

$x = \dfrac{1}{2}+\dfrac{1}{2} = \dfrac{2}{2}$ $x = \dfrac{1}{2}-\dfrac{1}{2}$

$x = 1$ $x = 0$

The solutions are 1 and 0.

111. $3\left(x-\dfrac{5}{3}\right)^2 = \dfrac{4}{3}$

$\left(x-\dfrac{5}{3}\right)^2 = \dfrac{4}{9}$

$\sqrt{\left(x-\dfrac{5}{3}\right)^2} = \sqrt{\dfrac{4}{9}}$

$x-\dfrac{5}{3} = \pm\sqrt{\dfrac{4}{9}} = \pm\dfrac{2}{3}$

$x-\dfrac{5}{3} = \dfrac{2}{3}$ $x-\dfrac{5}{3} = -\dfrac{2}{3}$

$x = \dfrac{5}{3}+\dfrac{2}{3}$ $x = \dfrac{5}{3}-\dfrac{2}{3} = \dfrac{3}{3}$

$x = \dfrac{7}{3}$ $x = 1$

The solutions are $\dfrac{7}{3}$ and 1.

112. $2\left(x+\dfrac{3}{5}\right)^2 = \dfrac{8}{25}$

$\left(x+\dfrac{3}{5}\right)^2 = \dfrac{4}{25}$

$\sqrt{\left(x+\dfrac{3}{5}\right)^2} = \sqrt{\dfrac{4}{25}}$

$x+\dfrac{3}{5} = \pm\sqrt{\dfrac{4}{25}} = \pm\dfrac{2}{5}$

$x+\dfrac{3}{5} = \dfrac{2}{5}$ $x+\dfrac{3}{5} = -\dfrac{2}{5}$

$x = -\dfrac{3}{5}+\dfrac{2}{5}$ $x = -\dfrac{3}{5}-\dfrac{2}{5} = -\dfrac{5}{5}$

$x = -\dfrac{1}{5}$ $x = -1$

The solutions are $-\dfrac{1}{5}$ and -1.

113. $(x+5)^2 - 6 = 0$

$(x+5)^2 = 6$

$\sqrt{(x+5)^2} = \sqrt{6}$

$x+5 = \pm\sqrt{6}$

$x+5 = \sqrt{6}$ $x+5 = -\sqrt{6}$

$x = -5+\sqrt{6}$ $x = -5-\sqrt{6}$

The solutions are $-5+\sqrt{6}$ and $-5-\sqrt{6}$.

114. $(t-1)^2 - 15 = 0$

$(t-1)^2 = 15$

$\sqrt{(t-1)^2} = \sqrt{15}$

$t-1 = \pm\sqrt{15}$

$t-1 = \sqrt{15}$ $t-1 = -\sqrt{15}$

$t = 1+\sqrt{15}$ $t = 1-\sqrt{15}$

The solutions are $1+\sqrt{15}$ and $1-\sqrt{15}$.

115. $(s-2)^2 - 24 = 0$
$$(s-2)^2 = 24$$
$$\sqrt{(s-2)^2} = \sqrt{24}$$
$$s-2 = \pm\sqrt{24} = \pm 2\sqrt{6}$$
$$s-2 = 2\sqrt{6} \qquad s-2 = -2\sqrt{6}$$
$$s = 2+2\sqrt{6} \qquad s = 2-2\sqrt{6}$$
The solutions are $2+2\sqrt{6}$ and $2-2\sqrt{6}$.

116. $(y+3)^2 - 18 = 0$
$$(y+3)^2 = 18$$
$$\sqrt{(y+3)^2} = \sqrt{18}$$
$$y+3 = \pm\sqrt{18} = \pm 3\sqrt{2}$$
$$y+3 = 3\sqrt{2} \qquad y+3 = -3\sqrt{2}$$
$$y = -3+3\sqrt{2} \qquad y = -3-3\sqrt{2}$$
The solutions are $-3+3\sqrt{2}$ and $-3-3\sqrt{2}$.

117. $(z+1)^2 + 12 = 0$
$$(z+1)^2 = -12$$
$$\sqrt{(z+1)^2} = \sqrt{-12}$$
$$z+1 = \pm\sqrt{-12} = \pm 2i\sqrt{3}$$
$$z+1 = 2i\sqrt{3} \qquad z+1 = -2i\sqrt{3}$$
$$z = -1+2i\sqrt{3} \qquad z = -1-2i\sqrt{3}$$
The solutions are $-1+2i\sqrt{3}$ and $-1-2i\sqrt{3}$.

118. $(r-2)^2 + 28 = 0$
$$(r-2)^2 = -28$$
$$\sqrt{(r-2)^2} = \sqrt{-28}$$
$$r-2 = \pm\sqrt{-28} = \pm 2i\sqrt{7}$$
$$r-2 = 2i\sqrt{7} \qquad r-2 = -2i\sqrt{7}$$
$$r = 2+2i\sqrt{7} \qquad r = 2-2i\sqrt{7}$$
The solutions are $2+2i\sqrt{7}$ and $2-2i\sqrt{7}$.

119. $(v-3)^2 + 45 = 0$
$$(v-3)^2 = -45$$
$$\sqrt{(v-3)^2} = \sqrt{-45}$$
$$v-3 = \pm\sqrt{-45} = \pm 3i\sqrt{5}$$
$$v-3 = 3i\sqrt{5} \qquad v-3 = -3i\sqrt{5}$$
$$v = 3+3i\sqrt{5} \qquad v = 3-3i\sqrt{5}$$
The solutions are $3+3i\sqrt{5}$ and $3-3i\sqrt{5}$.

120. $(x+5)^2 + 32 = 0$
$$(x+5)^2 = -32$$
$$\sqrt{(x+5)^2} = \sqrt{-32}$$
$$x+5 = \pm\sqrt{-32} = \pm 4i\sqrt{2}$$
$$x+5 = 4i\sqrt{2} \qquad x+5 = -4i\sqrt{2}$$
$$x = -5+4i\sqrt{2} \qquad x = -5-4i\sqrt{2}$$
The solutions are $-5+4i\sqrt{2}$ and $-5-4i\sqrt{2}$.

121. $\left(u+\dfrac{2}{3}\right)^2 - 18 = 0$
$$\left(u+\frac{2}{3}\right)^2 = 18$$
$$\sqrt{\left(u+\frac{2}{3}\right)^2} = \sqrt{18}$$
$$u+\frac{2}{3} = \pm\sqrt{18} = \pm 3\sqrt{2}$$
$$u+\frac{2}{3} = 3\sqrt{2} \qquad u+\frac{2}{3} = -3\sqrt{2}$$
$$u = -\frac{2}{3}+3\sqrt{2} \qquad u = -\frac{2}{3}-3\sqrt{2}$$
$$u = \frac{-2+9\sqrt{2}}{3} \qquad u = \frac{-2-9\sqrt{2}}{3}$$
The solutions are $\dfrac{-2+9\sqrt{2}}{3}$ and $\dfrac{-2-9\sqrt{2}}{3}$.

122. $\left(z-\dfrac{1}{2}\right)^2 - 20 = 0$
$$\left(z-\frac{1}{2}\right)^2 = 20$$
$$\sqrt{\left(z-\frac{1}{2}\right)^2} = \sqrt{20}$$
$$z-\frac{1}{2} = \pm\sqrt{20} = \pm 2\sqrt{5}$$
$$z-\frac{1}{2} = 2\sqrt{5} \qquad z-\frac{1}{2} = -2\sqrt{5}$$
$$z = \frac{1}{2}+2\sqrt{5} \qquad z = \frac{1}{2}-2\sqrt{5}$$
$$z = \frac{1+4\sqrt{5}}{2} \qquad z = \frac{1-4\sqrt{5}}{2}$$
The solutions are $\dfrac{1+4\sqrt{5}}{2}$ and $\dfrac{1-4\sqrt{5}}{2}$.

123. $\left(x+\dfrac{1}{2}\right)^2 + 40 = 0$
$$\left(x+\frac{1}{2}\right)^2 = -40$$
$$\sqrt{\left(x+\frac{1}{2}\right)^2} = \sqrt{-40}$$
$$x+\frac{1}{2} = \pm\sqrt{-40} = \pm 2i\sqrt{10}$$
$$x+\frac{1}{2} = 2i\sqrt{10}$$
$$x = -\frac{1}{2}+2i\sqrt{10}$$
$$x+\frac{1}{2} = -2i\sqrt{10}$$
$$x = -\frac{1}{2}-2i\sqrt{10}$$
The solutions are
$$-\frac{1}{2}+2i\sqrt{10} \text{ and } -\frac{1}{2}-2i\sqrt{10}.$$

124.
$$\left(r - \frac{3}{2}\right)^2 + 48 = 0$$
$$\left(r - \frac{3}{2}\right)^2 = -48$$
$$\sqrt{\left(r - \frac{3}{2}\right)^2} = \sqrt{-48}$$
$$r - \frac{3}{2} = \pm\sqrt{-48} = \pm 4i\sqrt{3}$$
$$r - \frac{3}{2} = 4i\sqrt{3} \qquad r - \frac{3}{2} = -4i\sqrt{3}$$
$$r = \frac{3}{2} + 4i\sqrt{3} \qquad r = \frac{3}{2} - 4i\sqrt{3}$$

The solutions are $\frac{3}{2} + 4i\sqrt{3}$ and $\frac{3}{2} - 4i\sqrt{3}$.

Applying Concepts 8.1

125.
$$(x - r_1)(x - r_2) = 0$$
$$(x - \sqrt{2})[x - (-\sqrt{2})] = 0$$
$$(x - \sqrt{2})(x + \sqrt{2}) = 0$$
$$x^2 - 2 = 0$$

126.
$$(x - r_1)(x - r_2) = 0$$
$$(x - \sqrt{5})[x - (-\sqrt{5})] = 0$$
$$(x - \sqrt{5})(x + \sqrt{5}) = 0$$
$$x^2 - 5 = 0$$

127.
$$(x - r_1)(x - r_2) = 0$$
$$(x - i)[x - (-i)] = 0$$
$$(x - i)(x + i) = 0$$
$$x^2 - i^2 = 0$$
$$x^2 + 1 = 0$$

128.
$$(x - r_1)(x - r_2) = 0$$
$$(x - 2i)[x - (-2i)] = 0$$
$$(x - 2i)(x + 2i) = 0$$
$$x^2 - 4i^2 = 0$$
$$x^2 + 4 = 0$$

129.
$$(x - r_1)(x - r_2) = 0$$
$$(x - 2\sqrt{2})[x - (-2\sqrt{2})] = 0$$
$$(x - 2\sqrt{2})(x + 2\sqrt{2}) = 0$$
$$x^2 - 4(2) = 0$$
$$x^2 - 8 = 0$$

130.
$$(x - r_1)(x - r_2) = 0$$
$$(x - 3\sqrt{2})[x - (-3\sqrt{2})] = 0$$
$$(x - 3\sqrt{2})(x + 3\sqrt{2}) = 0$$
$$x^2 - 9(2) = 0$$
$$x^2 - 18 = 0$$

131.
$$(x - r_1)(x - r_2) = 0$$
$$(x - 2\sqrt{3})[x - (-2\sqrt{3})] = 0$$
$$(x - 2\sqrt{3})(x + 2\sqrt{3}) = 0$$
$$x^2 - 4(3) = 0$$
$$x^2 - 12 = 0$$

132.
$$(x - r_1)(x - r_2) = 0$$
$$(x - i\sqrt{2})[x - (-i\sqrt{2})] = 0$$
$$(x - i\sqrt{2})(x + i\sqrt{2}) = 0$$
$$x^2 - i^2(2) = 0$$
$$x^2 - 2i^2 = 0$$
$$x^2 + 2 = 0$$

133.
$$(x - r_1)(x - r_2) = 0$$
$$(x - 2i\sqrt{3})[x - (-2i\sqrt{3})] = 0$$
$$(x - 2i\sqrt{3})(x + 2i\sqrt{3}) = 0$$
$$x^2 - 4i^2(3) = 0$$
$$x^2 - 12i^2 = 0$$
$$x^2 + 12 = 0$$

134.
$$2a^2x^2 = 32b^2$$
$$a^2x^2 = 16b^2$$
$$a^2x^2 - 16b^2 = 0$$
$$(ax + 4b)(ax - 4b) = 0$$
$$ax + 4b = 0 \qquad ax - 4b = 0$$
$$ax = -4b \qquad ax = 4b$$
$$x = -\frac{4b}{a} \qquad x = \frac{4b}{a}$$

The solutions are $-\frac{4b}{a}$ and $\frac{4b}{a}$.

135.
$$5y^2x^2 = 125z^2$$
$$y^2x^2 = 25z^2$$
$$y^2x^2 - 25z^2 = 0$$
$$(xy + 5z)(xy - 5z) = 0$$
$$xy + 5z = 0 \qquad xy - 5z = 0$$
$$xy = -5z \qquad xy = 5z$$
$$x = -\frac{5z}{y} \qquad x = \frac{5z}{y}$$

The solutions are $-\frac{5z}{y}$ and $\frac{5z}{y}$.

136.
$$(x + a)^2 - 4 = 0$$
$$(x + a)^2 = 4$$
$$\sqrt{(x + a)^2} = \sqrt{4}$$
$$x + a = \pm 2$$
$$x = -a \pm 2$$

The solutions are $-a + 2$ and $-a - 2$.

137.
$$2(x - y)^2 - 8 = 0$$
$$(x - y)^2 - 4 = 0$$
$$(x - y)^2 = 4$$
$$\sqrt{(x - y)^2} = \sqrt{4}$$
$$x - y = \pm 2$$
$$x = y \pm 2$$

The solutions are $y + 2$ and $y - 2$.

138.
$$(2x-1)^2 = (2x+3)^2$$
$$4x^2 - 4x + 1 = 4x^2 + 12x + 9$$
$$4x^2 - 4x^2 - 4x + 1 = 4x^2 - 4x^2 + 12x + 9$$
$$-4x + 1 = 12x + 9$$
$$-16x + 1 = 9$$
$$-16x = 8$$
$$x = -\frac{1}{2}$$

The solution is $-\frac{1}{2}$.

139.
$$(x-4)^2 = (x+2)^2$$
$$x^2 - 8x + 16 = x^2 + 4x + 4$$
$$x^2 - x^2 - 8x + 16 = x^2 - x^2 + 4x + 4$$
$$-8x + 16 = 4x + 4$$
$$-12x + 16 = 4$$
$$-12x = -12$$
$$x = 1$$

The solution is 1.

140.
$$ax^2 + bx = 0$$
$$x(ax + b) = 0$$
$$x = 0 \qquad ax + b = 0$$
$$ax = -b$$
$$x = -\frac{b}{a}$$

The solutions are 0 and $-\frac{b}{a}$.

141.
$$ax^2 + c = 0$$
$$ax^2 = -c$$
$$x^2 = -\frac{c}{a}$$
$$x = \pm\sqrt{-\frac{c}{a}}$$
$$= \pm\sqrt{\frac{c}{a}}\,i$$
$$= \pm\frac{\sqrt{c}}{\sqrt{a}}\,i$$
$$= \pm\frac{\sqrt{c}}{\sqrt{a}}\,i \cdot \frac{\sqrt{a}}{\sqrt{a}}$$
$$= \pm\frac{\sqrt{ac}}{\sqrt{a^2}}\,i$$
$$= \pm\frac{\sqrt{ac}}{a}\,i$$

The solutions are $\frac{\sqrt{ac}}{a}i$ and $-\frac{\sqrt{ac}}{a}i$.

142.
$$0.58 = \frac{x^2}{(0.02 - x)^2}$$
$$0.58(0.02 - x)^2 = x^2$$
$$\sqrt{0.58(0.02 - x)^2} = \sqrt{x^2}$$
$$0.7615773(0.02 - x) \approx x$$
$$0.0152315 - 0.7615773x \approx x$$
$$0.0152315 \approx 1.7615773x$$
$$0.0086465124 \approx x$$
$$x \approx 0.0086$$

143. There are a couple of methods to prove this result. Here is one that does not depend on properties of conjugates. Because $z = z_1 + z_2 i$ is a solution of $ax^2 + bx + c = 0$ $a \neq 0$ and all coefficients are real numbers, $a(z_1 + z_2 i)^2 + b(z_1 + z_2 i) + c = 0$. Multiplying this out and collecting the real and imaginary parts, we have
$$\left[a(z_1^2 - z_2^2) + bz_1 + c\right] + (2az_1z_2 + bz_2)i = 0.$$ This implies $a(z_1^2 - z_2^2) + bz_1 + c = 0$ and $2az_1z_2 + bz_2 = 0$. Now consider the complex conjugate.
$$a(z_1 - z_2 i)^2 + b(z_1 - z_2 i) + c$$
$$= \left[a(z_1^2 - z_2^2) + bz_1 + c\right] - (2az_1z_2 + bz_2)i$$
$$= 0 - 0i$$
$$= 0$$
Thus the complex conjugate is also a solution.

144. Here are some highlights. For more information see *The History of Mathematics: An Introduction* (1985) by David Burton or *A History of Mathematics: An Introduction* (1993) by Victor Katz.
The Babylonians had a method for solving (for positive values) a quadratic equation as early as 2000 B.C. Although their formulas were given in word form rather than in symbols, the essence of the formula was $x = \sqrt{\left[\frac{a}{2}\right]^2 + b} - \frac{a}{2}$ for solving an equation of the form $x^2 + ax = b$.
The Indian mathematician Brahmagupta (circa A.D. 600) essentially knew the quadratic formula we use today. He stated the formula in words, a translation of which gives $x = \dfrac{\sqrt{4ac + b^2} - b}{2a}$.
Euclid presents a geometric method of solving a special quadratic equation in the *Elements*.
The Arabic mathematician al-Khowarizmi (circa A.D. 780) divided the solution of quadratic equations into different forms. The forms were $x^2 + ax = b$, $x^2 + b = ax$, and $x^2 = ax + b$. Although, in the modern sense, these equations are equivalent, Arabic mathematicians did not yet admit negative numbers. His solutions of these equations are essentially those of the Babylonians.

Section 8.2

Concept Review 8.2

1. Always true

2. Always true

3. Never true

   If $b^2 > 4ac$, then $b^2 - 4ac > 0$ and the quadratic equation has two real roots.

4. Always true

5. Never true

   $\left[\left(\dfrac{1}{2}\right)5\right]^2 = \dfrac{25}{4}$, so the last term is not correct.

6. Never true

   For us to complete the square, the coefficient of x^2 must be 1.

Objective 8.2.1 Exercises

1. The next step is to add, to each side of the equation, the constant term that completes the square on $x^2 + 6x$. $\left[\dfrac{1}{2}(6)\right]^2 = 9$

2. No. Any quadratic equation can be solved by completing the square.

3. $x^2 - 4x - 5 = 0$
   $x^2 - 4x = 5$
   Complete the square.
   $x^2 - 4x + 4 = 5 + 4$
   $(x-2)^2 = 9$
   $\sqrt{(x-2)^2} = \sqrt{9}$
   $x - 2 = \pm\sqrt{9} = \pm 3$
   $x - 2 = 3 \qquad x - 2 = -3$
   $x = 5 \qquad\quad x = -1$
   The solutions are 5 and −1.

4. $y^2 + 6y + 5 = 0$
   $y^2 + 6y = -5$
   Complete the square.
   $y^2 + 6y + 9 = -5 + 9$
   $(y+3)^2 = 4$
   $\sqrt{(y+3)^2} = \sqrt{4}$
   $y + 3 = \pm\sqrt{4} = \pm 2$
   $y + 3 = 2 \qquad y + 3 = -2$
   $y = -1 \qquad\quad y = -5$
   The solutions are −1 and −5.

5. $v^2 + 8v - 9 = 0$
   $v^2 + 8v = 9$
   Complete the square.
   $v^2 + 8v + 16 = 9 + 16$
   $(v+4)^2 = 25$
   $\sqrt{(v+4)^2} = \sqrt{25}$
   $v + 4 = \pm\sqrt{25} = \pm 5$
   $v + 4 = 5 \qquad v + 4 = -5$
   $v = 1 \qquad\quad v = -9$
   The solutions are 1 and −9.

6. $w^2 - 2w - 24 = 0$
   $w^2 - 2w = 24$
   Complete the square.
   $w^2 - 2w + 1 = 24 + 1$
   $(w-1)^2 = 25$
   $\sqrt{(w-1)^2} = \sqrt{25}$
   $w - 1 = \pm\sqrt{25} = \pm 5$
   $w - 1 = 5 \qquad w - 1 = -5$
   $w = 6 \qquad\quad w = -4$
   The solutions are 6 and −4.

7. $z^2 - 6z + 9 = 0$
   $z^2 - 6z = -9$
   Complete the square.
   $z^2 - 6z + 9 = -9 + 9$
   $(z-3)^2 = 0$
   $\sqrt{(z-3)^2} = \sqrt{0}$
   $z - 3 = 0$
   $z = 3$
   The solution is 3.

8. $u^2 + 10u + 25 = 0$
   $u^2 + 10u = -25$
   Complete the square.
   $u^2 + 10u + 25 = -25 + 25$
   $(u+5)^2 = 0$
   $\sqrt{(u+5)^2} = \sqrt{0}$
   $u + 5 = 0$
   $u = -5$
   The solution is −5.

9. $r^2 + 4r - 7 = 0$
   $r^2 + 4r = 7$
   Complete the square.
   $r^2 + 4r + 4 = 7 + 4$
   $(r+2)^2 = 11$
   $\sqrt{(r+2)^2} = \sqrt{11}$
   $r + 2 = \pm\sqrt{11}$
   $r + 2 = \sqrt{11} \qquad\qquad r + 2 = -\sqrt{11}$
   $r = -2 + \sqrt{11} \qquad\quad r = -2 - \sqrt{11}$
   The solutions are $-2 + \sqrt{11}$ and $-2 - \sqrt{11}$.

10. $s^2 + 6s - 1 = 0$

$s^2 + 6s = 1$

Complete the square.

$s^2 + 6s + 9 = 1 + 9$

$(s+3)^2 = 10$

$\sqrt{(s+3)^2} = \sqrt{10}$

$s + 3 = \pm\sqrt{10}$

$s + 3 = \sqrt{10}$ $\qquad$ $s + 3 = -\sqrt{10}$

$s = -3 + \sqrt{10}$ $\qquad$ $s = -3 - \sqrt{10}$

The solutions are $-3 + \sqrt{10}$ and $-3 - \sqrt{10}$.

11. $x^2 - 6x + 7 = 0$

$x^2 - 6x = -7$

Complete the square.

$x^2 - 6x + 9 = -7 + 9$

$(x-3)^2 = 2$

$\sqrt{(x-3)^2} = \sqrt{2}$

$x - 3 = \pm\sqrt{2}$

$x - 3 = \sqrt{2}$ $\qquad$ $x - 3 = -\sqrt{2}$

$x = 3 + \sqrt{2}$ $\qquad$ $x = 3 - \sqrt{2}$

The solutions are $3 + \sqrt{2}$ and $3 - \sqrt{2}$.

12. $y^2 + 8y + 13 = 0$

$y^2 + 8y = -13$

Complete the square.

$y^2 + 8y + 16 = -13 + 16$

$(y+4)^2 = 3$

$\sqrt{(y+4)^2} = \sqrt{3}$

$y + 4 = \pm\sqrt{3}$

$y + 4 = \sqrt{3}$ $\qquad$ $y + 4 = -\sqrt{3}$

$y = -4 + \sqrt{3}$ $\qquad$ $y = -4 - \sqrt{3}$

The solutions are $-4 + \sqrt{3}$ and $-4 - \sqrt{3}$.

13. $z^2 - 2z + 2 = 0$

$z^2 - 2z = -2$

Complete the square.

$z^2 - 2z + 1 = -2 + 1$

$(z-1)^2 = -1$

$\sqrt{(z-1)^2} = \sqrt{-1}$

$z - 1 = \pm i$

$z - 1 = i$ $\qquad$ $z - 1 = -i$

$z = 1 + i$ $\qquad$ $z = 1 - i$

The solutions are $1 + i$ and $1 - i$.

14. $t^2 - 4t + 8 = 0$

$t^2 - 4t = -8$

Complete the square.

$t^2 - 4t + 4 = -8 + 4$

$(t-2)^2 = -4$

$\sqrt{(t-2)^2} = \sqrt{-4}$

$t - 2 = \pm 2i$

$t - 2 = 2i$ $\qquad$ $t - 2 = -2i$

$t = 2 + 2i$ $\qquad$ $t = 2 - 2i$

The solutions are $2 + 2i$ and $2 - 2i$.

15. $t^2 - t - 1 = 0$

$t^2 - t = 1$

Complete the square.

$t^2 - t + \dfrac{1}{4} = 1 + \dfrac{1}{4}$

$\left(t - \dfrac{1}{2}\right)^2 = \dfrac{5}{4}$

$\sqrt{\left(t - \dfrac{1}{2}\right)^2} = \sqrt{\dfrac{5}{4}}$

$t - \dfrac{1}{2} = \pm\dfrac{\sqrt{5}}{2}$

$t - \dfrac{1}{2} = \dfrac{\sqrt{5}}{2}$ $\qquad$ $t - \dfrac{1}{2} = -\dfrac{\sqrt{5}}{2}$

$t = \dfrac{1}{2} + \dfrac{\sqrt{5}}{2}$ $\qquad$ $t = \dfrac{1}{2} - \dfrac{\sqrt{5}}{2}$

The solutions are $\dfrac{1+\sqrt{5}}{2}$ and $\dfrac{1-\sqrt{5}}{2}$.

16. $u^2 - u - 7 = 0$

$u^2 - u = 7$

Complete the square.

$u^2 - u + \dfrac{1}{4} = 7 + \dfrac{1}{4}$

$\left(u - \dfrac{1}{2}\right)^2 = \dfrac{29}{4}$

$\sqrt{\left(u - \dfrac{1}{2}\right)^2} = \sqrt{\dfrac{29}{4}}$

$u - \dfrac{1}{2} = \pm\dfrac{\sqrt{29}}{2}$

$u - \dfrac{1}{2} = \dfrac{\sqrt{29}}{2}$ $\qquad$ $u - \dfrac{1}{2} = -\dfrac{\sqrt{29}}{2}$

$u = \dfrac{1}{2} + \dfrac{\sqrt{29}}{2}$ $\qquad$ $u = \dfrac{1}{2} - \dfrac{\sqrt{29}}{2}$

The solutions are $\dfrac{1+\sqrt{29}}{2}$ and $\dfrac{1-\sqrt{29}}{2}$.

17. $y^2 - 6y = 4$
Complete the square.
$$y^2 - 6y + 9 = 4 + 9$$
$$(y - 3)^2 = 13$$
$$\sqrt{(y - 3)^2} = \sqrt{13}$$
$$y - 3 = \pm\sqrt{13}$$

$y - 3 = \sqrt{13}$	$y - 3 = -\sqrt{13}$
$y = 3 + \sqrt{13}$	$y = 3 - \sqrt{13}$

The solutions are $3 + \sqrt{13}$ and $3 - \sqrt{13}$.

18. $w^2 + 4w = 2$
Complete the square.
$$w^2 + 4w + 4 = 2 + 4$$
$$(w + 2)^2 = 6$$
$$\sqrt{(w + 2)^2} = \sqrt{6}$$
$$w + 2 = \pm\sqrt{6}$$

$w + 2 = \sqrt{6}$	$w + 2 = -\sqrt{6}$
$w = -2 + \sqrt{6}$	$w = -2 - \sqrt{6}$

The solutions are $-2 + \sqrt{6}$ and $-2 - \sqrt{6}$.

19. $x^2 = 8x - 15$
$$x^2 - 8x = -15$$
Complete the square.
$$x^2 - 8x + 16 = -15 + 16$$
$$(x - 4)^2 = 1$$
$$\sqrt{(x - 4)^2} = \sqrt{1}$$
$$x - 4 = \pm 1$$

$x - 4 = 1$	$x - 4 = -1$
$x = 5$	$x = 3$

The solutions are 5 and 3.

20. $z^2 = 4z - 3$
$$z^2 - 4z = -3$$
Complete the square.
$$z^2 - 4z + 4 = -3 + 4$$
$$(z - 2)^2 = 1$$
$$\sqrt{(z - 2)^2} = \sqrt{1}$$
$$z - 2 = \pm 1$$

$z - 2 = 1$	$z - 2 = -1$
$z = 3$	$z = 1$

The solutions are 3 and 1.

21. $v^2 = 4v - 13$
$$v^2 - 4v = -13$$
Complete the square.
$$v^2 - 4v + 4 = -13 + 4$$
$$(v - 2)^2 = -9$$
$$\sqrt{(v - 2)^2} = \sqrt{-9}$$
$$v - 2 = \pm 3i$$

$v - 2 = 3i$	$v - 2 = -3i$
$v = 2 + 3i$	$v = 2 - 3i$

The solutions are $2 + 3i$ and $2 - 3i$.

22. $x^2 = 2x - 17$
$$x^2 - 2x = -17$$
Complete the square.
$$x^2 - 2x + 1 = -17 + 1$$
$$(x - 1)^2 = -16$$
$$\sqrt{(x - 1)^2} = \sqrt{-16}$$
$$x - 1 = \pm 4i$$

$x - 1 = 4i$	$x - 1 = -4i$
$x = 1 + 4i$	$x = 1 - 4i$

The solutions are $1 + 4i$ and $1 - 4i$.

23. $p^2 + 6p = -13$
Complete the square.
$$p^2 + 6p + 9 = -13 + 9$$
$$(p + 3)^2 = -4$$
$$\sqrt{(p + 3)^2} = \sqrt{-4}$$
$$p + 3 = \pm 2i$$

$p + 3 = 2i$	$p + 3 = -2i$
$p = -3 + 2i$	$p = -3 - 2i$

The solutions are $-3 + 2i$ and $-3 - 2i$.

24. $x^2 + 4x = -20$
Complete the square.
$$x^2 + 4x + 4 = -20 + 4$$
$$(x + 2)^2 = -16$$
$$\sqrt{(x + 2)^2} = \sqrt{-16}$$
$$x + 2 = \pm 4i$$

$x + 2 = 4i$	$x + 2 = -4i$
$x = -2 + 4i$	$x = -2 - 4i$

The solutions are $-2 + 4i$ and $-2 - 4i$.

25. $y^2 - 2y = 17$
Complete the square.
$$y^2 - 2y + 1 = 17 + 1$$
$$(y - 1)^2 = 18$$
$$\sqrt{(y - 1)^2} = \sqrt{18}$$
$$y - 1 = \pm 3\sqrt{2}$$

$y - 1 = 3\sqrt{2}$	$y - 1 = -3\sqrt{2}$
$y = 1 + 3\sqrt{2}$	$y = 1 - 3\sqrt{2}$

The solutions are $1 + 3\sqrt{2}$ and $1 - 3\sqrt{2}$.

26. $x^2 + 10x = 7$
Complete the square.
$$x^2 + 10x + 25 = 7 + 25$$
$$(x + 5)^2 = 32$$
$$\sqrt{(x + 5)^2} = \sqrt{32}$$
$$x + 5 = \pm 4\sqrt{2}$$

$x + 5 = 4\sqrt{2}$	$x + 5 = -4\sqrt{2}$
$x = -5 + 4\sqrt{2}$	$x = -5 - 4\sqrt{2}$

The solutions are $-5 + 4\sqrt{2}$ and $-5 - 4\sqrt{2}$.

27. $z^2 = z + 4$

$z^2 - z = 4$

Complete the square.

$z^2 - z + \dfrac{1}{4} = 4 + \dfrac{1}{4}$

$\left(z - \dfrac{1}{2}\right)^2 = \dfrac{17}{4}$

$\sqrt{\left(z - \dfrac{1}{2}\right)^2} = \sqrt{\dfrac{17}{4}}$

$z - \dfrac{1}{2} = \pm\dfrac{\sqrt{17}}{2}$

$z - \dfrac{1}{2} = \dfrac{\sqrt{17}}{2}$ $z - \dfrac{1}{2} = -\dfrac{\sqrt{17}}{2}$

$z = \dfrac{1}{2} + \dfrac{\sqrt{17}}{2}$ $z = \dfrac{1}{2} - \dfrac{\sqrt{17}}{2}$

The solutions are $\dfrac{1 + \sqrt{17}}{2}$ and $\dfrac{1 - \sqrt{17}}{2}$.

28. $r^2 = 3r - 1$

$r^2 - 3r = -1$

Complete the square.

$r^2 - 3r + \dfrac{9}{4} = -1 + \dfrac{9}{4}$

$\left(r - \dfrac{3}{2}\right)^2 = \dfrac{5}{4}$

$\sqrt{\left(r - \dfrac{3}{2}\right)^2} = \sqrt{\dfrac{5}{4}}$

$r - \dfrac{3}{2} = \pm\dfrac{\sqrt{5}}{2}$

$r - \dfrac{3}{2} = \dfrac{\sqrt{5}}{2}$ $r - \dfrac{3}{2} = -\dfrac{\sqrt{5}}{2}$

$r = \dfrac{3}{2} + \dfrac{\sqrt{5}}{2}$ $r = \dfrac{3}{2} - \dfrac{\sqrt{5}}{2}$

The solutions are $\dfrac{3 + \sqrt{5}}{2}$ and $\dfrac{3 - \sqrt{5}}{2}$.

29. $x^2 + 13 = 2x$

$x^2 - 2x = -13$

Complete the square.

$x^2 - 2x + 1 = -13 + 1$

$(x - 1)^2 = -12$

$\sqrt{(x - 1)^2} = \sqrt{-12}$

$x - 1 = \pm 2i\sqrt{3}$

$x - 1 = 2i\sqrt{3}$ $x - 1 = -2i\sqrt{3}$

$x = 1 + 2i\sqrt{3}$ $x = 1 - 2i\sqrt{3}$

The solutions are $1 + 2i\sqrt{3}$ and $1 - 2i\sqrt{3}$.

30. $x^2 + 27 = 6x$

$x^2 - 6x = -27$

Complete the square.

$x^2 - 6x + 9 = -27 + 9$

$(x - 3)^2 = -18$

$\sqrt{(x - 3)^2} = \sqrt{-18}$

$x - 3 = \pm 3i\sqrt{2}$

$x - 3 = 3i\sqrt{2}$ $x - 3 = -3i\sqrt{2}$

$x = 3 + 3i\sqrt{2}$ $x = 3 - 3\sqrt{2}$

The solutions are $3 + 3i\sqrt{2}$ and $3 - 3i\sqrt{2}$.

31. $2y^2 + 3y + 1 = 0$

$2y^2 + 3y = -1$

$\dfrac{1}{2}(2y^2 + 3y) = \dfrac{1}{2}(-1)$

$y^2 + \dfrac{3}{2}y = -\dfrac{1}{2}$

Complete the square.

$y^2 + \dfrac{3}{2}y + \dfrac{9}{16} = -\dfrac{1}{2} + \dfrac{9}{16}$

$\left(y + \dfrac{3}{4}\right)^2 = \dfrac{1}{16}$

$\sqrt{\left(y + \dfrac{3}{4}\right)^2} = \sqrt{\dfrac{1}{16}}$

$y + \dfrac{3}{4} = \pm\dfrac{1}{4}$

$y + \dfrac{3}{4} = \dfrac{1}{4}$ $y + \dfrac{3}{4} = -\dfrac{1}{4}$

$y = -\dfrac{2}{4} = -\dfrac{1}{2}$ $y = -\dfrac{4}{4} = -1$

The solutions are $-\dfrac{1}{2}$ and -1.

32. $2t^2 + 5t - 3 = 0$

$2t^2 + 5t = 3$

$\dfrac{1}{2}(2t^2 + 5t) = \dfrac{1}{2}(3)$

$t^2 + \dfrac{5}{2}t = \dfrac{3}{2}$

Complete the square.

$t^2 + \dfrac{5}{2}t + \dfrac{25}{16} = \dfrac{3}{2} + \dfrac{25}{16}$

$\left(t + \dfrac{5}{4}\right)^2 = \dfrac{49}{16}$

$\sqrt{\left(t + \dfrac{5}{4}\right)^2} = \sqrt{\dfrac{49}{16}}$

$t + \dfrac{5}{4} = \pm\dfrac{7}{4}$

$t + \dfrac{5}{4} = \dfrac{7}{4}$ $t + \dfrac{5}{4} = -\dfrac{7}{4}$

$t = \dfrac{2}{4} = \dfrac{1}{2}$ $t = -\dfrac{12}{4} = -3$

The solutions are $\dfrac{1}{2}$ and -3.

33. $4r^2 - 8r = -3$

$\dfrac{1}{4}(4r^2 - 8r) = \dfrac{1}{4}(-3)$

$r^2 - 2r = -\dfrac{3}{4}$

Complete the square.

$r^2 - 2r + 1 = -\dfrac{3}{4} + 1$

$(r-1)^2 = \dfrac{1}{4}$

$\sqrt{(r-1)^2} = \sqrt{\dfrac{1}{4}}$

$r - 1 = \pm\dfrac{1}{2}$

$r - 1 = \dfrac{1}{2} \qquad r - 1 = -\dfrac{1}{2}$

$r = \dfrac{3}{2} \qquad\quad r = \dfrac{1}{2}$

The solutions are $\dfrac{3}{2}$ and $\dfrac{1}{2}$.

34. $4u^2 - 20u = -9$

$\dfrac{1}{4}(4u^2 - 20u) = \dfrac{1}{4}(-9)$

$u^2 - 5u = -\dfrac{9}{4}$

Complete the square.

$u^2 - 5u + \dfrac{25}{4} = -\dfrac{9}{4} + \dfrac{25}{4}$

$\left(u - \dfrac{5}{2}\right)^2 = 4$

$\sqrt{\left(u - \dfrac{5}{2}\right)^2} = \sqrt{4}$

$u - \dfrac{5}{2} = \pm 2$

$u - \dfrac{5}{2} = 2 \qquad\qquad u - \dfrac{5}{2} = -2$

$u = \dfrac{5}{2} + \dfrac{4}{2} = \dfrac{9}{2} \qquad u = \dfrac{5}{2} - \dfrac{4}{2} = \dfrac{1}{2}$

The solutions are $\dfrac{9}{2}$ and $\dfrac{1}{2}$.

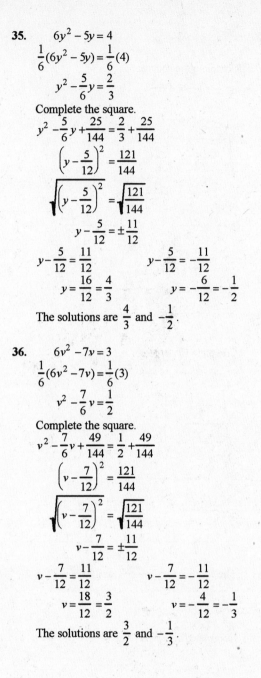

35. $6y^2 - 5y = 4$

$\dfrac{1}{6}(6y^2 - 5y) = \dfrac{1}{6}(4)$

$y^2 - \dfrac{5}{6}y = \dfrac{2}{3}$

Complete the square.

$y^2 - \dfrac{5}{6}y + \dfrac{25}{144} = \dfrac{2}{3} + \dfrac{25}{144}$

$\left(y - \dfrac{5}{12}\right)^2 = \dfrac{121}{144}$

$\sqrt{\left(y - \dfrac{5}{12}\right)^2} = \sqrt{\dfrac{121}{144}}$

$y - \dfrac{5}{12} = \pm\dfrac{11}{12}$

$y - \dfrac{5}{12} = \dfrac{11}{12} \qquad\quad y - \dfrac{5}{12} = -\dfrac{11}{12}$

$y = \dfrac{16}{12} = \dfrac{4}{3} \qquad y = -\dfrac{6}{12} = -\dfrac{1}{2}$

The solutions are $\dfrac{4}{3}$ and $-\dfrac{1}{2}$.

36. $6v^2 - 7v = 3$

$\dfrac{1}{6}(6v^2 - 7v) = \dfrac{1}{6}(3)$

$v^2 - \dfrac{7}{6}v = \dfrac{1}{2}$

Complete the square.

$v^2 - \dfrac{7}{6}v + \dfrac{49}{144} = \dfrac{1}{2} + \dfrac{49}{144}$

$\left(v - \dfrac{7}{12}\right)^2 = \dfrac{121}{144}$

$\sqrt{\left(v - \dfrac{7}{12}\right)^2} = \sqrt{\dfrac{121}{144}}$

$v - \dfrac{7}{12} = \pm\dfrac{11}{12}$

$v - \dfrac{7}{12} = \dfrac{11}{12} \qquad\quad v - \dfrac{7}{12} = -\dfrac{11}{12}$

$v = \dfrac{18}{12} = \dfrac{3}{2} \qquad v = -\dfrac{4}{12} = -\dfrac{1}{3}$

The solutions are $\dfrac{3}{2}$ and $-\dfrac{1}{3}$.

37. $4x^2 - 4x + 5 = 0$

$$4x^2 - 4x = -5$$

$$\frac{1}{4}(4x^2 - 4x) = \frac{1}{4}(-5)$$

$$x^2 - x = -\frac{5}{4}$$

Complete the square.

$$x^2 - x + \frac{1}{4} = -\frac{5}{4} + \frac{1}{4}$$

$$\left(x - \frac{1}{2}\right)^2 = -1$$

$$\sqrt{\left(x - \frac{1}{2}\right)^2} = \sqrt{-1}$$

$$x - \frac{1}{2} = \pm i$$

$$x - \frac{1}{2} = i \qquad\qquad x - \frac{1}{2} = -i$$

$$x = \frac{1}{2} + i \qquad\qquad x = \frac{1}{2} - i$$

The solutions are $\frac{1}{2} + i$ and $\frac{1}{2} - i$.

38. $4t^2 - 4t + 17 = 0$

$$4t^2 - 4t = -17$$

$$\frac{1}{4}(4t^2 - 4t) = \frac{1}{4}(-17)$$

$$t^2 - t = -\frac{17}{4}$$

Complete the square.

$$t^2 - t + \frac{1}{4} = -\frac{17}{4} + \frac{1}{4}$$

$$\left(t - \frac{1}{2}\right)^2 = -4$$

$$\sqrt{\left(t - \frac{1}{2}\right)^2} = \sqrt{-4}$$

$$t - \frac{1}{2} = \pm 2i$$

$$t - \frac{1}{2} = 2i \qquad\qquad t - \frac{1}{2} = -2i$$

$$t = \frac{1}{2} + 2i \qquad\qquad t = \frac{1}{2} - 2i$$

The solutions are $\frac{1}{2} + 2i$ and $\frac{1}{2} - 2i$.

39. $9x^2 - 6x + 2 = 0$

$$9x^2 - 6x = -2$$

$$\frac{1}{9}(9x^2 - 6x) = \frac{1}{9}(-2)$$

$$x^2 - \frac{2}{3}x = -\frac{2}{9}$$

Complete the square.

$$x^2 - \frac{2}{3}x + \frac{1}{9} = -\frac{2}{9} + \frac{1}{9}$$

$$\left(x - \frac{1}{3}\right)^2 = -\frac{1}{9}$$

$$\sqrt{\left(x - \frac{1}{3}\right)^2} = \sqrt{-\frac{1}{9}}$$

$$x - \frac{1}{3} = \pm \frac{1}{3}i$$

$$x - \frac{1}{3} = \frac{1}{3}i \qquad\qquad x - \frac{1}{3} = -\frac{1}{3}i$$

$$x = \frac{1}{3} + \frac{1}{3}i \qquad\qquad x = \frac{1}{3} - \frac{1}{3}i$$

The solutions are $\frac{1}{3} + \frac{1}{3}i$ and $\frac{1}{3} - \frac{1}{3}i$.

40. $9y^2 - 12y + 13 = 0$

$$9y^2 - 12y = -13$$

$$\frac{1}{9}(9y^2 - 12y) = \frac{1}{9}(-13)$$

$$y^2 - \frac{4}{3}y = -\frac{13}{9}$$

Complete the square.

$$y^2 - \frac{4}{3}y + \frac{4}{9} = -\frac{13}{9} + \frac{4}{9}$$

$$\left(y - \frac{2}{3}\right)^2 = -1$$

$$\sqrt{\left(y - \frac{2}{3}\right)^2} = \sqrt{-1}$$

$$y - \frac{2}{3} = \pm i$$

$$y - \frac{2}{3} = i \qquad\qquad y - \frac{2}{3} = -i$$

$$y = \frac{2}{3} + i \qquad\qquad y = \frac{2}{3} - i$$

The solutions are $\frac{2}{3} + i$ and $\frac{2}{3} - i$.

41.
$$2s^2 = 4s + 5$$
$$2s^2 - 4s = 5$$
$$\frac{1}{2}(2s^2 - 4s) = \frac{1}{2}(5)$$
$$s^2 - 2s = \frac{5}{2}$$
Complete the square.
$$s^2 - 2s + 1 = \frac{5}{2} + 1$$
$$(s-1)^2 = \frac{7}{2}$$
$$\sqrt{(s-1)^2} = \sqrt{\frac{7}{2}}$$
$$s - 1 = \pm\sqrt{\frac{7}{2}} = \pm\frac{\sqrt{14}}{2}$$

$$s - 1 = \frac{\sqrt{14}}{2} \qquad s - 1 = -\frac{\sqrt{14}}{2}$$
$$s = \frac{2}{2} + \frac{\sqrt{14}}{2} \qquad x = \frac{2}{2} - \frac{\sqrt{14}}{2}$$

The solutions are $\dfrac{2+\sqrt{14}}{2}$ and $\dfrac{2-\sqrt{14}}{2}$.

42.
$$3u^2 = 6u + 1$$
$$3u^2 - 6u = 1$$
$$\frac{1}{3}(3u^2 - 6u) = \frac{1}{3}(1)$$
$$u^2 - 2u = \frac{1}{3}$$
Complete the square.
$$u^2 - 2u + 1 = \frac{1}{3} + 1$$
$$(u-1)^2 = \frac{4}{3}$$
$$\sqrt{(u-1)^2} = \sqrt{\frac{4}{3}}$$
$$u - 1 = \pm\sqrt{\frac{4}{3}} = \pm\frac{2\sqrt{3}}{3}$$

$$u - 1 = \frac{2\sqrt{3}}{3} \qquad u - 1 = -\frac{2\sqrt{3}}{3}$$
$$u = \frac{3}{3} + \frac{2\sqrt{3}}{3} \qquad u = \frac{3}{3} - \frac{2\sqrt{3}}{3}$$

The solutions are $\dfrac{3+2\sqrt{3}}{3}$ and $\dfrac{3-2\sqrt{3}}{3}$.

43.
$$2r^2 = 3 - r$$
$$2r^2 + r = 3$$
$$\frac{1}{2}(2r^2 + r) = \frac{1}{2}(3)$$
$$r^2 + \frac{1}{2}r = \frac{3}{2}$$
Complete the square.
$$r^2 + \frac{1}{2}r + \frac{1}{16} = \frac{3}{2} + \frac{1}{16}$$
$$\left(r + \frac{1}{4}\right)^2 = \frac{25}{16}$$
$$\sqrt{\left(r + \frac{1}{4}\right)^2} = \sqrt{\frac{25}{16}}$$
$$r + \frac{1}{4} = \pm\frac{5}{4}$$

$$r + \frac{1}{4} = \frac{5}{4} \qquad r + \frac{1}{4} = -\frac{5}{4}$$
$$r = \frac{4}{4} = 1 \qquad r = -\frac{6}{4} = -\frac{3}{2}$$

The solutions are 1 and $-\dfrac{3}{2}$.

44.
$$2x^2 = 12 - 5x$$
$$2x^2 + 5x = 12$$
$$\frac{1}{2}(2x^2 + 5x) = \frac{1}{2}(12)$$
$$x^2 + \frac{5}{2}x = 6$$
Complete the square.
$$x^2 + \frac{5}{2}x + \frac{25}{16} = 6 + \frac{25}{16}$$
$$\left(x + \frac{5}{4}\right)^2 = \frac{121}{16}$$
$$\sqrt{\left(x + \frac{5}{4}\right)^2} = \sqrt{\frac{121}{16}}$$
$$x + \frac{5}{4} = \pm\frac{11}{4}$$

$$x + \frac{5}{4} = \frac{11}{4} \qquad x + \frac{5}{4} = -\frac{11}{4}$$
$$x = \frac{6}{4} = \frac{3}{2} \qquad x = -\frac{16}{4} = -4$$

The solutions are $\dfrac{3}{2}$ and -4.

45.
$$y - 2 = (y - 3)(y + 2)$$
$$y - 2 = y^2 - y - 6$$
$$y^2 - 2y = 4$$
Complete the square.
$$y^2 - 2y + 1 = 4 + 1$$
$$(y-1)^2 = 5$$
$$\sqrt{(y-1)^2} = \sqrt{5}$$
$$y - 1 = \pm\sqrt{5}$$

$$y - 1 = \sqrt{5} \qquad y - 1 = -\sqrt{5}$$
$$y = 1 + \sqrt{5} \qquad y = 1 - \sqrt{5}$$

The solutions are $1 + \sqrt{5}$ and $1 - \sqrt{5}$.

46.
$$8s - 11 = (s - 4)(s - 2)$$
$$8s - 11 = s^2 - 6s + 8$$
$$s^2 - 14s = -19$$
Complete the square.
$$s^2 - 14s + 49 = -19 + 49$$
$$(s - 7)^2 = 30$$
$$\sqrt{(s - 7)^2} = \sqrt{30}$$
$$s - 7 = \pm\sqrt{30}$$

$$s - 7 = \sqrt{30} \qquad s - 7 = -\sqrt{30}$$
$$s = 7 + \sqrt{30} \qquad s = 7 - \sqrt{30}$$
The solutions are $7 + \sqrt{30}$ and $7 - \sqrt{30}$.

47.
$$6t - 2 = (2t - 3)(t - 1)$$
$$6t - 2 = 2t^2 - 5t + 3$$
$$2t^2 - 11t = -5$$
$$\frac{1}{2}(2t^2 - 11t) = \frac{1}{2}(-5)$$
$$t^2 - \frac{11}{2}t = -\frac{5}{2}$$
Complete the square.
$$t^2 - \frac{11}{2}t + \frac{121}{16} = -\frac{5}{2} + \frac{121}{16}$$
$$\left(t - \frac{11}{4}\right)^2 = \frac{81}{16}$$
$$\sqrt{\left(t - \frac{11}{4}\right)^2} = \sqrt{\frac{81}{16}}$$
$$t - \frac{11}{4} = \pm\frac{9}{4}$$

$$t - \frac{11}{4} = \frac{9}{4} \qquad t - \frac{11}{4} = -\frac{9}{4}$$
$$t = \frac{20}{4} = 5 \qquad t = \frac{2}{4} = \frac{1}{2}$$
The solutions are 5 and $\frac{1}{2}$.

48.
$$2z + 9 = (2z + 3)(z + 2)$$
$$2z + 9 = 2z^2 + 7z + 6$$
$$2z^2 + 5z = 3$$
$$\frac{1}{2}(2z^2 + 5z) = \frac{1}{2}(3)$$
$$z^2 + \frac{5}{2}z = \frac{3}{2}$$
Complete the square.
$$z^2 + \frac{5}{2}z + \frac{25}{16} = \frac{3}{2} + \frac{25}{16}$$
$$\left(z + \frac{5}{4}\right)^2 = \frac{49}{16}$$
$$\sqrt{\left(z + \frac{5}{4}\right)^2} = \sqrt{\frac{49}{16}}$$
$$z + \frac{5}{4} = \pm\frac{7}{4}$$

$$z + \frac{5}{4} = \frac{7}{4} \qquad z + \frac{5}{4} = -\frac{7}{4}$$
$$z = \frac{2}{4} = \frac{1}{2} \qquad z = -\frac{12}{4} = -3$$
The solutions are $\frac{1}{2}$ and -3.

49.
$$(x - 4)(x + 1) = x - 3$$
$$x^2 - 3x - 4 = x - 3$$
$$x^2 - 4x = 1$$
Complete the square.
$$x^2 - 4x + 4 = 1 + 4$$
$$(x - 2)^2 = 5$$
$$\sqrt{(x - 2)^2} = \sqrt{5}$$
$$x - 2 = \pm\sqrt{5}$$

$$x - 2 = \sqrt{5} \qquad x - 2 = -\sqrt{5}$$
$$x = 2 + \sqrt{5} \qquad x = 2 - \sqrt{5}$$
The solutions are $2 + \sqrt{5}$ and $2 - \sqrt{5}$.

50.
$$(y - 3)^2 = 2y + 10$$
$$y^2 - 6y + 9 = 2y + 10$$
$$y^2 - 8y = 1$$
Complete the square.
$$y^2 - 8y + 16 = 1 + 16$$
$$(y - 4)^2 = 17$$
$$\sqrt{(y - 4)^2} = \sqrt{17}$$
$$y - 4 = \pm\sqrt{17}$$

$$y - 4 = \sqrt{17} \qquad y - 4 = -\sqrt{17}$$
$$y = 4 + \sqrt{17} \qquad y = 4 - \sqrt{17}$$
The solutions are $4 + \sqrt{17}$ and $4 - \sqrt{17}$.

51. $z^2 + 2z = 4$

Complete the square.

$z^2 + 2z + 1 = 4 + 1$

$(z+1)^2 = 5$

$\sqrt{(z+1)^2} = \sqrt{5}$

$z + 1 = \pm 2.236$

$z + 1 \approx 2.236$	$z + 1 \approx -2.236$
$z \approx -1 + 2.236$	$z \approx -1 - 2.236$
$z \approx 1.236$	$z \approx -3.236$

The solutions are approximately 1.236 and -3.236.

52. $t^2 - 4t = 7$

Complete the square.

$t^2 - 4t + 4 = 7 + 4$

$(t-2)^2 = 11$

$\sqrt{(t-2)^2} = \sqrt{11}$

$t - 2 = \pm 3.317$

$t - 2 \approx 3.317$	$t - 2 \approx -3.317$
$t \approx 2 + 3.317$	$t \approx 2 - 3.317$
$t \approx 5.317$	$t \approx -1.317$

The solutions are approximately 5.317 and -1.317.

53. $2x^2 = 4x - 1$

$2x^2 - 4x = -1$

$\frac{1}{2}(2x^2 - 4x) = \frac{1}{2}(-1)$

$x^2 - 2x = -\frac{1}{2}$

Complete the square.

$x^2 - 2x + 1 = -\frac{1}{2} + 1$

$(x-1)^2 = \frac{1}{2}$

$\sqrt{(x-1)^2} = \sqrt{\frac{1}{2}}$

$x - 1 \approx \pm 0.707$

$x - 1 \approx 0.707$	$x - 1 \approx -0.707$
$x \approx 1 + 0.707$	$x \approx 1 - 0.707$
$x \approx 1.707$	$x \approx 0.293$

The solutions are approximately 1.707 and 0.293.

54. $3y^2 = 5y - 1$

$3y^2 - 5y = -1$

$\frac{1}{3}(3y^2 - 5y) = \frac{1}{3}(-1)$

$y^2 - \frac{5}{3}y = -\frac{1}{3}$

Complete the square.

$y^2 - \frac{5}{3}y + \frac{25}{36} = -\frac{1}{3} + \frac{25}{36}$

$\left(y - \frac{5}{6}\right)^2 = \frac{13}{36}$

$\sqrt{\left(y - \frac{5}{6}\right)^2} = \sqrt{\frac{13}{36}}$

$y - \frac{5}{6} \approx \pm 0.601$

$y - \frac{5}{6} \approx 0.601$	$y - \frac{5}{6} \approx -0.601$
$y \approx \frac{5}{6} + 0.601$	$y \approx \frac{5}{6} - 0.601$
$y \approx 1.434$	$y \approx 0.232$

The solutions are approximately 1.434 and 0.232.

55. $4z^2 + 2z - 1 = 0$

$4z^2 + 2z = 1$

$\frac{1}{4}(4z^2 + 2z) = \frac{1}{4}(1)$

$z^2 + \frac{1}{2}z = \frac{1}{4}$

Complete the square.

$z^2 + \frac{1}{2}z + \frac{1}{16} = \frac{1}{4} + \frac{1}{16}$

$\left(z + \frac{1}{4}\right)^2 = \frac{5}{16}$

$\sqrt{\left(z + \frac{1}{4}\right)^2} = \sqrt{\frac{5}{16}}$

$z + \frac{1}{4} \approx \pm 0.559$

$z + \frac{1}{4} \approx 0.559$	$z + \frac{1}{4} \approx -0.559$
$z \approx -\frac{1}{4} + 0.559$	$z \approx -\frac{1}{4} - 0.559$
$z \approx 0.309$	$z \approx -0.809$

The solutions are approximately 0.309 and -0.809.

56.
$$4w^2 - 8w = 3$$
$$\frac{1}{4}(4w^2 - 8w) = \frac{1}{4}(3)$$
$$w^2 - 2w = \frac{3}{4}$$

Complete the square.
$$w^2 - 2w + 1 = \frac{3}{4} + 1$$
$$(w-1)^2 = \frac{7}{4}$$
$$\sqrt{(w-1)^2} = \sqrt{\frac{7}{4}}$$
$$w - 1 \approx \pm 1.323$$

$w - 1 \approx 1.323 \qquad w - 1 \approx -1.323$
$w \approx 1 + 1.323 \qquad w \approx 1 - 1.323$
$w \approx 2.323 \qquad\quad w \approx -0.323$

The solutions are approximately 2.323 and –0.323.

Objective 8.2.2 Exercises

57. The quadratic formula is $x = \dfrac{-b \pm \sqrt{b^2 - 4ac}}{2a}$. In this formula, a is the coefficient of x^2, b is the coefficient of x, and c is the constant term in the quadratic equation.

58. The expression $b^2 - 4ac$ appears under the radical symbol in the quadratic formula. It is called the discriminant. It can be used to determine whether a quadratic equation has one real number solution, two unequal real numbers solutions, or two complex number solutions.

59. No, it does not matter which way you write the equation. There will be differences in the values of a, b, and c in the quadratic equation, but the solutions will be the same.

60. Answers will vary.

61.
$$x^2 - 3x - 10 = 0$$
$$a = 1, b = -3, c = -10$$
$$x = \frac{-b \pm \sqrt{b^2 - 4ac}}{2a}$$
$$= \frac{-(-3) \pm \sqrt{(-3)^2 - 4(1)(-10)}}{2(1)}$$
$$= \frac{3 \pm \sqrt{9 + 40}}{2}$$
$$= \frac{3 \pm \sqrt{49}}{2}$$
$$= \frac{3 \pm 7}{2}$$

$x = \dfrac{3+7}{2} \qquad x = \dfrac{3-7}{2}$
$= \dfrac{10}{2} \qquad\quad = \dfrac{-4}{2}$
$= 5 \qquad\qquad = -2$

The solutions are 5 and –2.

62.
$$z^2 - 4z - 8 = 0$$
$$a = 1, b = -4, c = -8$$
$$z = \frac{-b \pm \sqrt{b^2 - 4ac}}{2a}$$
$$= \frac{-(-4) \pm \sqrt{(-4)^2 - 4(1)(-8)}}{2(1)}$$
$$= \frac{4 \pm \sqrt{16 + 32}}{2}$$
$$= \frac{4 \pm \sqrt{48}}{2}$$
$$= \frac{4 \pm 4\sqrt{3}}{2}$$
$$= 2 \pm 2\sqrt{3}$$

The solutions are $2 + 2\sqrt{3}$ and $2 - 2\sqrt{3}$.

63.
$$y^2 + 5y - 36 = 0$$
$$a = 1, b = 5, c = -36$$
$$y = \frac{-b \pm \sqrt{b^2 - 4ac}}{2a}$$
$$= \frac{-5 \pm \sqrt{(5)^2 - 4(1)(-36)}}{2(1)}$$
$$= \frac{-5 \pm \sqrt{25 + 144}}{2}$$
$$= \frac{-5 \pm \sqrt{169}}{2}$$
$$= \frac{-5 \pm 13}{2}$$

$y = \dfrac{-5+13}{2} \qquad y = \dfrac{-5-13}{2}$
$= \dfrac{8}{2} \qquad\qquad = \dfrac{-18}{2}$
$= 4 \qquad\qquad\quad = -9$

The solutions are 4 and –9.

64.
$$z^2 - 3z - 40 = 0$$
$$a = 1, b = -3, c = -40$$
$$z = \frac{-b \pm \sqrt{b^2 - 4ac}}{2a}$$
$$= \frac{-(-3) \pm \sqrt{(-3)^2 - 4(1)(-40)}}{2(1)}$$
$$= \frac{3 \pm \sqrt{9 + 160}}{2}$$
$$= \frac{3 \pm \sqrt{169}}{2}$$
$$= \frac{3 \pm 13}{2}$$

$z = \dfrac{3+13}{2} \qquad z = \dfrac{3-13}{2}$
$= \dfrac{16}{2} \qquad\qquad = \dfrac{-10}{2}$
$= 8 \qquad\qquad\quad = -5$

The solutions are 8 and –5.

65.
$$w^2 = 8w + 72$$
$$w^2 - 8w - 72 = 0$$
$a = 1,\ b = -8,\ c = -72$
$$w = \frac{-b \pm \sqrt{b^2 - 4ac}}{2a}$$
$$= \frac{-(-8) \pm \sqrt{(-8)^2 - 4(1)(-72)}}{2(1)}$$
$$= \frac{8 \pm \sqrt{64 + 288}}{2}$$
$$= \frac{8 \pm \sqrt{352}}{2}$$
$$= \frac{8 \pm 4\sqrt{22}}{2}$$
$$= 4 \pm 2\sqrt{22}$$
The solutions are $4 + 2\sqrt{22}$ and $4 - 2\sqrt{22}$.

66.
$$t^2 = 2t + 35$$
$$t^2 - 2t - 35 = 0$$
$a = 1,\ b = -2,\ c = -35$
$$t = \frac{-b \pm \sqrt{b^2 - 4ac}}{2a}$$
$$= \frac{-(-2) \pm \sqrt{(-2)^2 - 4(1)(-35)}}{2(1)}$$
$$= \frac{2 \pm \sqrt{4 + 140}}{2}$$
$$= \frac{2 \pm \sqrt{144}}{2}$$
$$= \frac{2 \pm 12}{2}$$
$$t = \frac{2 + 12}{2} \qquad t = \frac{2 - 12}{2}$$
$$= \frac{14}{2} \qquad\quad = \frac{-10}{2}$$
$$= 7 \qquad\qquad = -5$$
The solutions are 7 and –5.

67.
$$v^2 = 24 - 5v$$
$$v^2 + 5v - 24 = 0$$
$a = 1,\ b = 5,\ c = -24$
$$v = \frac{-b \pm \sqrt{b^2 - 4ac}}{2a}$$
$$= \frac{-5 \pm \sqrt{(5)^2 - 4(1)(-24)}}{2(1)}$$
$$= \frac{-5 \pm \sqrt{25 + 96}}{2}$$
$$= \frac{-5 \pm \sqrt{121}}{2}$$
$$= \frac{-5 \pm 11}{2}$$
$$v = \frac{-5 + 11}{2} \qquad v = \frac{-5 - 11}{2}$$
$$= \frac{6}{2} \qquad\qquad = \frac{-16}{2}$$
$$= 3 \qquad\qquad = -8$$
The solutions are 3 and –8.

68.
$$x^2 = 18 - 7x$$
$$x^2 + 7x - 18 = 0$$
$a = 1,\ b = 7,\ c = -18$
$$x = \frac{-b \pm \sqrt{b^2 - 4ac}}{2a}$$
$$= \frac{-7 \pm \sqrt{(7)^2 - 4(1)(-18)}}{2(1)}$$
$$= \frac{-7 \pm \sqrt{49 + 72}}{2}$$
$$= \frac{-7 \pm \sqrt{121}}{2}$$
$$= \frac{-7 \pm 11}{2}$$
$$x = \frac{-7 + 11}{2} \qquad x = \frac{-7 - 11}{2}$$
$$= \frac{4}{2} \qquad\qquad = \frac{-18}{2}$$
$$= 2 \qquad\qquad = -9$$
The solutions are 2 and –9.

69.
$$2y^2 + 5y - 3 = 0$$
$a = 2,\ b = 5,\ c = -3$
$$y = \frac{-b \pm \sqrt{b^2 - 4ac}}{2a}$$
$$= \frac{-5 \pm \sqrt{(5)^2 - 4(2)(-3)}}{2(2)}$$
$$= \frac{-5 \pm \sqrt{25 + 24}}{4}$$
$$= \frac{-5 \pm \sqrt{49}}{4}$$
$$= \frac{-5 \pm 7}{4}$$
$$y = \frac{-5 + 7}{4} \qquad y = \frac{-5 - 7}{4}$$
$$= \frac{2}{4} \qquad\qquad = \frac{-12}{4}$$
$$= \frac{1}{2} \qquad\qquad = -3$$
The solutions are $\frac{1}{2}$ and –3.

70. $4p^2 - 7p + 3 = 0$
$a = 4, b = -7, c = 3$

$$p = \frac{-b \pm \sqrt{b^2 - 4ac}}{2a}$$

$$= \frac{-(-7) \pm \sqrt{(-7)^2 - 4(4)(3)}}{2(4)}$$

$$= \frac{7 \pm \sqrt{49 - 48}}{8}$$

$$= \frac{7 \pm \sqrt{1}}{8}$$

$$= \frac{7 \pm 1}{8}$$

$$p = \frac{7 + 1}{8} \qquad p = \frac{7 - 1}{8}$$

$$= \frac{8}{8} \qquad\qquad = \frac{6}{8}$$

$$= 1 \qquad\qquad = \frac{3}{4}$$

The solutions are 1 and $\frac{3}{4}$.

71. $8s^2 = 10s + 3$
$8s^2 - 10s - 3 = 0$
$a = 8, b = -10, c = -3$

$$s = \frac{-b \pm \sqrt{b^2 - 4ac}}{2a}$$

$$= \frac{-(-10) \pm \sqrt{(-10)^2 - 4(8)(-3)}}{2(8)}$$

$$= \frac{10 \pm \sqrt{100 + 96}}{16}$$

$$= \frac{10 \pm \sqrt{196}}{16}$$

$$= \frac{10 \pm 14}{16}$$

$$s = \frac{10 + 14}{16} \qquad s = \frac{10 - 14}{16}$$

$$= \frac{24}{16} \qquad\qquad = \frac{-4}{16}$$

$$= \frac{3}{2} \qquad\qquad = -\frac{1}{4}$$

The solutions are $\frac{3}{2}$ and $-\frac{1}{4}$.

72. $12t^2 = 5t + 2$
$12t^2 - 5t - 2 = 0$
$a = 12, b = -5, c = -2$

$$t = \frac{-b \pm \sqrt{b^2 - 4ac}}{2a}$$

$$= \frac{-(-5) \pm \sqrt{(-5)^2 - 4(12)(-2)}}{2(12)}$$

$$= \frac{5 \pm \sqrt{25 + 96}}{24}$$

$$= \frac{5 \pm \sqrt{121}}{24}$$

$$= \frac{5 \pm 11}{24}$$

$$t = \frac{5 + 11}{24} \qquad t = \frac{5 - 11}{24}$$

$$= \frac{16}{24} \qquad\qquad = \frac{-6}{24}$$

$$= \frac{2}{3} \qquad\qquad = -\frac{1}{4}$$

The solutions are $\frac{2}{3}$ and $-\frac{1}{4}$.

73. $v^2 - 2v - 7 = 0$
$a = 1, b = -2, c = -7$

$$v = \frac{-b \pm \sqrt{b^2 - 4ac}}{2a}$$

$$= \frac{-(-2) \pm \sqrt{(-2)^2 - 4(1)(-7)}}{2(1)}$$

$$= \frac{2 \pm \sqrt{4 + 28}}{2}$$

$$= \frac{2 \pm \sqrt{32}}{2}$$

$$= \frac{2 \pm 4\sqrt{2}}{2}$$

$$= 1 \pm 2\sqrt{2}$$

The solutions are $1 + 2\sqrt{2}$ and $1 - 2\sqrt{2}$.

74. $t^2 - 2t - 11 = 0$
$a = 1, b = -2, c = -11$

$$t = \frac{-b \pm \sqrt{b^2 - 4ac}}{2a}$$

$$= \frac{-(-2) \pm \sqrt{(-2)^2 - 4(1)(-11)}}{2(1)}$$

$$= \frac{2 \pm \sqrt{4 + 44}}{2}$$

$$= \frac{2 \pm \sqrt{48}}{2}$$

$$= \frac{2 \pm 4\sqrt{3}}{2}$$

$$= 1 \pm 2\sqrt{3}$$

The solutions are $1 + 2\sqrt{3}$ and $1 - 2\sqrt{3}$.

75. $y^2 - 8y - 20 = 0$

$a = 1, b = -8, c = -20$

$$y = \frac{-b \pm \sqrt{b^2 - 4ac}}{2a}$$

$$= \frac{-(-8) \pm \sqrt{(-8)^2 - 4(1)(-20)}}{2(1)}$$

$$= \frac{8 \pm \sqrt{64 + 80}}{2}$$

$$= \frac{8 \pm \sqrt{144}}{2}$$

$$= \frac{8 \pm 12}{2}$$

$$y = \frac{8 + 12}{2} \qquad y = \frac{8 - 12}{2}$$

$$= \frac{20}{2} \qquad\qquad = \frac{-4}{2}$$

$$= 10 \qquad\qquad = -2$$

The solutions are 10 and –2.

76. $x^2 = 14x - 24$

$x^2 - 14x + 24 = 0$

$a = 1, b = -14, c = 24$

$$x = \frac{-b \pm \sqrt{b^2 - 4ac}}{2a}$$

$$= \frac{-(-14) \pm \sqrt{(-14)^2 - 4(1)(24)}}{2(1)}$$

$$= \frac{14 \pm \sqrt{196 - 96}}{2}$$

$$= \frac{14 \pm \sqrt{100}}{2}$$

$$= \frac{14 \pm 10}{2}$$

$$x = \frac{14 + 10}{2} \qquad x = \frac{14 - 10}{2}$$

$$= \frac{24}{2} \qquad\qquad = \frac{4}{2}$$

$$= 12 \qquad\qquad = 2$$

The solutions are 12 and 2.

77. $v^2 = 12v - 24$

$v^2 - 12v + 24 = 0$

$a = 1, b = -12, c = 24$

$$v = \frac{-b \pm \sqrt{b^2 - 4ac}}{2a}$$

$$= \frac{-(-12) \pm \sqrt{(-12)^2 - 4(1)(24)}}{2(1)}$$

$$= \frac{12 \pm \sqrt{144 - 96}}{2}$$

$$= \frac{12 \pm \sqrt{48}}{2}$$

$$= \frac{12 \pm 4\sqrt{3}}{2}$$

$$= 6 \pm 2\sqrt{3}$$

The solutions are $6 + 2\sqrt{3}$ and $6 - 2\sqrt{3}$.

78. $2z^2 - 2z - 1 = 0$

$a = 2, b = -2, c = -1$

$$z = \frac{-b \pm \sqrt{b^2 - 4ac}}{2a}$$

$$= \frac{-(-2) \pm \sqrt{(-2)^2 - 4(2)(-1)}}{2(2)}$$

$$= \frac{2 \pm \sqrt{4 + 8}}{4}$$

$$= \frac{2 \pm \sqrt{12}}{4}$$

$$= \frac{2 \pm 2\sqrt{3}}{4}$$

$$= \frac{1 \pm \sqrt{3}}{2}$$

The solutions are $\dfrac{1 + \sqrt{3}}{2}$ and $\dfrac{1 - \sqrt{3}}{2}$.

79. $4x^2 - 4x - 7 = 0$

$a = 4, b = -4, c = -7$

$$x = \frac{-b \pm \sqrt{b^2 - 4ac}}{2a}$$

$$= \frac{-(-4) \pm \sqrt{(-4)^2 - 4(4)(-7)}}{2(4)}$$

$$= \frac{4 \pm \sqrt{16 + 112}}{8}$$

$$= \frac{4 \pm \sqrt{128}}{8}$$

$$= \frac{4 \pm 8\sqrt{2}}{8}$$

$$= \frac{1 \pm 2\sqrt{2}}{2}$$

The solutions are $\dfrac{1 + 2\sqrt{2}}{2}$ and $\dfrac{1 - 2\sqrt{2}}{2}$.

80. $2p^2 - 8p + 5 = 0$

$a = 2, b = -8, c = 5$

$$p = \frac{-b \pm \sqrt{b^2 - 4ac}}{2a}$$

$$= \frac{-(-8) \pm \sqrt{(-8)^2 - 4(2)(5)}}{2(2)}$$

$$= \frac{8 \pm \sqrt{64 - 40}}{4}$$

$$= \frac{8 \pm \sqrt{24}}{4}$$

$$= \frac{8 \pm 2\sqrt{6}}{4}$$

$$= \frac{4 \pm \sqrt{6}}{2}$$

The solutions are $\dfrac{4 + \sqrt{6}}{2}$ and $\dfrac{4 - \sqrt{6}}{2}$.

81. $2s^2 - 3s + 1 = 0$

$a = 2, b = -3, c = 1$

$s = \dfrac{-b \pm \sqrt{b^2 - 4ac}}{2a}$

$= \dfrac{-(-3) \pm \sqrt{(-3)^2 - 4(2)(1)}}{2(2)}$

$= \dfrac{3 \pm \sqrt{9 - 8}}{4}$

$= \dfrac{3 \pm \sqrt{1}}{4}$

$= \dfrac{3 \pm 1}{4}$

$s = \dfrac{3 + 1}{4} \qquad s = \dfrac{3 - 1}{4}$

$\quad = \dfrac{4}{4} \qquad\qquad = \dfrac{2}{4}$

$\quad = 1 \qquad\qquad\quad = \dfrac{1}{2}$

The solutions are 1 and $\dfrac{1}{2}$.

82. $4w^2 - 4w - 1 = 0$

$a = 4, b = -4, c = -1$

$w = \dfrac{-b \pm \sqrt{b^2 - 4ac}}{2a}$

$= \dfrac{-(-4) \pm \sqrt{(-4)^2 - 4(4)(-1)}}{2(4)}$

$= \dfrac{4 \pm \sqrt{16 + 16}}{8}$

$= \dfrac{4 \pm \sqrt{32}}{8}$

$= \dfrac{4 \pm 4\sqrt{2}}{8}$

$= \dfrac{1 \pm \sqrt{2}}{2}$

The solutions are $\dfrac{1 + \sqrt{2}}{2}$ and $\dfrac{1 - \sqrt{2}}{2}$.

83. $3x^2 + 10x + 6 = 0$

$a = 3, b = 10, c = 6$

$x = \dfrac{-b \pm \sqrt{b^2 - 4ac}}{2a}$

$= \dfrac{-10 \pm \sqrt{(10)^2 - 4(3)(6)}}{2(3)}$

$= \dfrac{-10 \pm \sqrt{100 - 72}}{6}$

$= \dfrac{-10 \pm \sqrt{28}}{6}$

$= \dfrac{-10 \pm 2\sqrt{7}}{6}$

$= \dfrac{-5 \pm \sqrt{7}}{3}$

The solutions are $\dfrac{-5 + \sqrt{7}}{3}$ and $\dfrac{-5 - \sqrt{7}}{3}$.

84. $3v^2 = 6v - 2$

$3v^2 - 6v + 2 = 0$

$a = 3, b = -6, c = 2$

$v = \dfrac{-b \pm \sqrt{b^2 - 4ac}}{2a}$

$= \dfrac{-(-6) \pm \sqrt{(-6)^2 - 4(3)(2)}}{2(3)}$

$= \dfrac{6 \pm \sqrt{36 - 24}}{6}$

$= \dfrac{6 \pm \sqrt{12}}{6}$

$= \dfrac{6 \pm 2\sqrt{3}}{6}$

$= \dfrac{3 \pm \sqrt{3}}{3}$

The solutions are $\dfrac{3 + \sqrt{3}}{3}$ and $\dfrac{3 - \sqrt{3}}{3}$.

85. $6w^2 = 19w - 10$

$6w^2 - 19w + 10 = 0$

$a = 6, b = -19, c = 10$

$w = \dfrac{-b \pm \sqrt{b^2 - 4ac}}{2a}$

$= \dfrac{-(-19) \pm \sqrt{(-19)^2 - 4(6)(10)}}{2(6)}$

$= \dfrac{19 \pm \sqrt{361 - 240}}{12}$

$= \dfrac{19 \pm \sqrt{121}}{12}$

$= \dfrac{19 \pm 11}{12}$

$w = \dfrac{19 + 11}{12} \qquad w = \dfrac{19 - 11}{12}$

$\quad = \dfrac{30}{12} \qquad\qquad = \dfrac{8}{12}$

$\quad = \dfrac{5}{2} \qquad\qquad\; = \dfrac{2}{3}$

The solutions are $\dfrac{5}{2}$ and $\dfrac{2}{3}$.

86. $z^2 + 2z + 2 = 0$

$a = 1, b = 2, c = 2$

$z = \dfrac{-b \pm \sqrt{b^2 - 4ac}}{2a}$

$= \dfrac{-2 \pm \sqrt{(2)^2 - 4(1)(2)}}{2(1)}$

$= \dfrac{-2 \pm \sqrt{4 - 8}}{2}$

$= \dfrac{-2 \pm \sqrt{-4}}{2}$

$= \dfrac{-2 \pm 2i}{2}$

$= -1 \pm i$

The solutions are $-1 + i$ and $-1 - i$.

87. $p^2 - 4p + 5 = 0$
$a = 1, b = -4, c = 5$

$$p = \frac{-b \pm \sqrt{b^2 - 4ac}}{2a}$$

$$= \frac{-(-4) \pm \sqrt{(-4)^2 - 4(1)(5)}}{2(1)}$$

$$= \frac{4 \pm \sqrt{16 - 20}}{2}$$

$$= \frac{4 \pm \sqrt{-4}}{2}$$

$$= \frac{4 \pm 2i}{2}$$

$$= 2 \pm i$$

The solutions are $2 + i$ and $2 - i$.

88. $y^2 - 2y + 5 = 0$
$a = 1, b = -2, c = 5$

$$y = \frac{-b \pm \sqrt{b^2 - 4ac}}{2a}$$

$$= \frac{-(-2) \pm \sqrt{(-2)^2 - 4(1)(5)}}{2(1)}$$

$$= \frac{2 \pm \sqrt{4 - 20}}{2}$$

$$= \frac{2 \pm \sqrt{-16}}{2}$$

$$= \frac{2 \pm 4i}{2}$$

$$= 1 \pm 2i$$

The solutions are $1 + 2i$ and $1 - 2i$.

89. $x^2 + 6x + 13 = 0$
$a = 1, b = 6, c = 13$

$$x = \frac{-b \pm \sqrt{b^2 - 4ac}}{2a}$$

$$= \frac{-6 \pm \sqrt{(6)^2 - 4(1)(13)}}{2(1)}$$

$$= \frac{-6 \pm \sqrt{36 - 52}}{2}$$

$$= \frac{-6 \pm \sqrt{-16}}{2}$$

$$= \frac{-6 \pm 4i}{2}$$

$$= -3 \pm 2i$$

The solutions are $-3 + 2i$ and $-3 - 2i$.

90. $s^2 - 4s + 13 = 0$
$a = 1, b = -4, c = 13$

$$s = \frac{-b \pm \sqrt{b^2 - 4ac}}{2a}$$

$$= \frac{-(-4) \pm \sqrt{(-4)^2 - 4(1)(13)}}{2(1)}$$

$$= \frac{4 \pm \sqrt{16 - 52}}{2}$$

$$= \frac{4 \pm \sqrt{-36}}{2}$$

$$= \frac{4 \pm 6i}{2}$$

$$= 2 \pm 3i$$

The solutions are $2 + 3i$ and $2 - 3i$.

91. $t^2 - 6t + 10 = 0$
$a = 1, b = -6, c = 10$

$$t = \frac{-b \pm \sqrt{b^2 - 4ac}}{2a}$$

$$= \frac{-(-6) \pm \sqrt{(-6)^2 - 4(1)(10)}}{2(1)}$$

$$= \frac{6 \pm \sqrt{36 - 40}}{2}$$

$$= \frac{6 \pm \sqrt{-4}}{2}$$

$$= \frac{6 \pm 2i}{2}$$

$$= 3 \pm i$$

The solutions are $3 + i$ and $3 - i$.

92. $2w^2 - 2w + 5 = 0$
$a = 2, b = -2, c = 5$

$$w = \frac{-b \pm \sqrt{b^2 - 4ac}}{2a}$$

$$= \frac{-(-2) \pm \sqrt{(-2)^2 - 4(2)(5)}}{2(2)}$$

$$= \frac{2 \pm \sqrt{4 - 40}}{4}$$

$$= \frac{2 \pm \sqrt{-36}}{4}$$

$$= \frac{2 \pm 6i}{4}$$

$$= \frac{1 \pm 3i}{2}$$

The solutions are $\frac{1}{2} + \frac{3}{2}i$ and $\frac{1}{2} - \frac{3}{2}i$.

93. $4v^2 + 8v + 3 = 0$

$a = 4, b = 8, c = 3$

$v = \dfrac{-b \pm \sqrt{b^2 - 4ac}}{2a}$

$= \dfrac{-8 \pm \sqrt{(8)^2 - 4(4)(3)}}{2(4)}$

$= \dfrac{-8 \pm \sqrt{64 - 48}}{8}$

$= \dfrac{-8 \pm \sqrt{16}}{8}$

$= \dfrac{-8 \pm 4}{8}$

$v = \dfrac{-8 + 4}{8} \qquad v = \dfrac{-8 - 4}{8}$

$= \dfrac{-4}{8} \qquad\qquad = \dfrac{-12}{8}$

$= -\dfrac{1}{2} \qquad\qquad = -\dfrac{3}{2}$

The solutions are $-\dfrac{1}{2}$ and $-\dfrac{3}{2}$.

94. $2x^2 + 6x + 5 = 0$

$a = 2, b = 6, c = 5$

$x = \dfrac{-b \pm \sqrt{b^2 - 4ac}}{2a}$

$= \dfrac{-6 \pm \sqrt{(6)^2 - 4(2)(5)}}{2(2)}$

$= \dfrac{-6 \pm \sqrt{36 - 40}}{4}$

$= \dfrac{-6 \pm \sqrt{-4}}{4}$

$= \dfrac{-6 \pm 2i}{4}$

$= \dfrac{-3 \pm i}{2}$

The solutions are $-\dfrac{3}{2} + \dfrac{1}{2}i$ and $-\dfrac{3}{2} - \dfrac{1}{2}i$.

95. $2y^2 + 2y + 13 = 0$

$a = 2, b = 2, c = 13$

$y = \dfrac{-b \pm \sqrt{b^2 - 4ac}}{2a}$

$= \dfrac{-2 \pm \sqrt{(2)^2 - 4(2)(13)}}{2(2)}$

$= \dfrac{-2 \pm \sqrt{4 - 104}}{4}$

$= \dfrac{-2 \pm \sqrt{-100}}{4}$

$= \dfrac{-2 \pm 10i}{4}$

$= \dfrac{-1 \pm 5i}{2}$

The solutions are $-\dfrac{1}{2} + \dfrac{5}{2}i$ and $-\dfrac{1}{2} - \dfrac{5}{2}i$.

96. $4t^2 - 6t + 9 = 0$

$a = 4, b = -6, c = 9$

$t = \dfrac{-b \pm \sqrt{b^2 - 4ac}}{2a}$

$= \dfrac{-(-6) \pm \sqrt{(-6)^2 - 4(4)(9)}}{2(4)}$

$= \dfrac{6 \pm \sqrt{36 - 144}}{8}$

$= \dfrac{6 \pm \sqrt{-108}}{8}$

$= \dfrac{6 \pm 6i\sqrt{3}}{8}$

$= \dfrac{3 \pm 3i\sqrt{3}}{4}$

The solutions are $\dfrac{3}{4} + \dfrac{3\sqrt{3}}{4}i$ and $\dfrac{3}{4} - \dfrac{3\sqrt{3}}{4}i$.

97. $3v^2 + 6v + 1 = 0$

$a = 3, b = 6, c = 1$

$x = \dfrac{-b \pm \sqrt{b^2 - 4ac}}{2a}$

$= \dfrac{-6 \pm \sqrt{(6)^2 - 4(3)(1)}}{2(3)}$

$= \dfrac{-6 \pm \sqrt{36 - 12}}{6}$

$= \dfrac{-6 \pm \sqrt{24}}{6}$

$= \dfrac{-6 \pm 2\sqrt{6}}{6}$

$= \dfrac{-3 \pm \sqrt{6}}{3}$

The solutions are $\dfrac{-3 + \sqrt{6}}{3}$ and $\dfrac{-3 - \sqrt{6}}{3}$.

98. $2r^2 = 4r - 11$

$2r^2 - 4r + 11 = 0$

$a = 2, b = -4, c = 11$

$r = \dfrac{-b \pm \sqrt{b^2 - 4ac}}{2a}$

$= \dfrac{-(-4) \pm \sqrt{(-4)^2 - 4(2)(11)}}{2(2)}$

$= \dfrac{4 \pm \sqrt{16 - 88}}{4}$

$= \dfrac{4 \pm \sqrt{-72}}{4}$

$= \dfrac{4 \pm 6i\sqrt{2}}{4}$

$= \dfrac{2 \pm 3i\sqrt{2}}{2}$

The solutions are $1 + \dfrac{3\sqrt{2}}{2}i$ and $1 - \dfrac{3\sqrt{2}}{2}i$.

99.
$$3y^2 = 6y - 5$$
$$3y^2 - 6y + 5 = 0$$
$$a = 3, b = -6, c = 5$$
$$y = \frac{-b \pm \sqrt{b^2 - 4ac}}{2a}$$
$$= \frac{-(-6) \pm \sqrt{(-6)^2 - 4(3)(5)}}{2(3)}$$
$$= \frac{6 \pm \sqrt{36 - 60}}{6}$$
$$= \frac{6 \pm \sqrt{-24}}{6}$$
$$= \frac{6 \pm 2i\sqrt{6}}{6}$$
$$= \frac{3 \pm i\sqrt{6}}{3}$$

The solutions are $1 + \frac{\sqrt{6}}{3}i$ and $1 - \frac{\sqrt{6}}{3}i$.

100.
$$2x(x - 2) = x + 12$$
$$2x^2 - 4x = x + 12$$
$$2x^2 - 5x - 12 = 0$$
$$a = 2, b = -5, c = -12$$
$$x = \frac{-b \pm \sqrt{b^2 - 4ac}}{2a}$$
$$= \frac{-(-5) \pm \sqrt{(-5)^2 - 4(2)(-12)}}{2(2)}$$
$$= \frac{5 \pm \sqrt{25 + 96}}{4}$$
$$= \frac{5 \pm \sqrt{121}}{4}$$
$$= \frac{5 \pm 11}{4}$$

$$x = \frac{5 + 11}{4} \qquad x = \frac{5 - 11}{4}$$
$$= \frac{16}{4} \qquad = \frac{-6}{4}$$
$$= 4 \qquad = -\frac{3}{2}$$

The solutions are 4 and $-\frac{3}{2}$.

101.
$$10y(y + 4) = 15y - 15$$
$$10y^2 + 40y = 15y - 15$$
$$10y^2 + 25y + 15 = 0$$
$$5(2y^2 + 5y + 3) = 0$$
$$2y^2 + 5y + 3 = 0$$
$$a = 2, b = 5, c = 3$$
$$y = \frac{-b \pm \sqrt{b^2 - 4ac}}{2a}$$
$$= \frac{-5 \pm \sqrt{(5)^2 - 4(2)(3)}}{2(2)}$$
$$= \frac{-5 \pm \sqrt{25 - 24}}{4}$$
$$= \frac{-5 \pm \sqrt{1}}{4}$$
$$= \frac{-5 \pm 1}{4}$$

$$y = \frac{-5 + 1}{4} \qquad y = \frac{-5 - 1}{4}$$
$$= \frac{-4}{4} \qquad = \frac{-6}{4}$$
$$= -1 \qquad = -\frac{3}{2}$$

The solutions are -1 and $-\frac{3}{2}$.

102.
$$(3s - 2)(s + 1) = 2$$
$$3s^2 + s - 2 = 2$$
$$3s^2 + s - 4 = 0$$
$$a = 3, b = 1, c = -4$$
$$s = \frac{-b \pm \sqrt{b^2 - 4ac}}{2a}$$
$$= \frac{-1 \pm \sqrt{(1)^2 - 4(3)(-4)}}{2(3)}$$
$$= \frac{-1 \pm \sqrt{1 + 48}}{6}$$
$$= \frac{-1 \pm \sqrt{49}}{6}$$
$$= \frac{-1 \pm 7}{6}$$

$$s = \frac{-1 + 7}{6} \qquad s = \frac{-1 - 7}{6}$$
$$= \frac{6}{6} \qquad = \frac{-8}{6}$$
$$= 1 \qquad = -\frac{4}{3}$$

The solutions are 1 and $-\frac{4}{3}$.

103. $(2t+1)(t-3)=9$

$2t^2-5t-3=9$

$2t^2-5t-12=0$

$a=2, b=-5, c=-12$

$t=\dfrac{-b\pm\sqrt{b^2-4ac}}{2a}$

$=\dfrac{-(-5)\pm\sqrt{(-5)^2-4(2)(-12)}}{2(2)}$

$=\dfrac{5\pm\sqrt{25+96}}{4}$

$=\dfrac{5\pm\sqrt{121}}{4}$

$=\dfrac{5\pm11}{4}$

$t=\dfrac{5+11}{4}\qquad t=\dfrac{5-11}{4}$

$=\dfrac{16}{4}\qquad\quad =\dfrac{-6}{4}$

$=4\qquad\qquad =-\dfrac{3}{2}$

The solutions are 4 and $-\dfrac{3}{2}$.

104. $x^2-6x-6=0$

$a=1, b=-6, c=-6$

$x=\dfrac{-b\pm\sqrt{b^2-4ac}}{2a}$

$=\dfrac{6\pm\sqrt{(-6)^2-4(1)(-6)}}{2(1)}$

$=\dfrac{6\pm\sqrt{36+24}}{2}$

$=\dfrac{6\pm\sqrt{60}}{2}$

$=\dfrac{6\pm2\sqrt{15}}{2}$

$=3\pm\sqrt{15}$

$\approx3\pm3.873$

$x\approx3+3.873\qquad x\approx3-3.873$

$\approx6.873\qquad\qquad \approx-0.873$

The solutions are approximately 6.873 and –0.873.

105. $p^2-8p+3=0$

$a=1, b=-8, c=3$

$p=\dfrac{-b\pm\sqrt{b^2-4ac}}{2a}$

$=\dfrac{-(-8)\pm\sqrt{(-8)^2-4(1)(3)}}{2(1)}$

$=\dfrac{8\pm\sqrt{64-12}}{2}$

$=\dfrac{8\pm\sqrt{52}}{2}$

$=\dfrac{8\pm2\sqrt{13}}{2}$

$=4\pm\sqrt{13}$

$\approx4\pm3.606$

$p\approx4+3.606\qquad p\approx4-3.606$

$\approx7.606\qquad\qquad \approx0.394$

The solutions are approximately 7.606 and 0.394.

106. $r^2-2r-4=0$

$a=1, b=-2, c=-4$

$r=\dfrac{-b\pm\sqrt{b^2-4ac}}{2a}$

$=\dfrac{-(-2)\pm\sqrt{(-2)^2-4(1)(-4)}}{2(1)}$

$=\dfrac{2\pm\sqrt{4+16}}{2}$

$=\dfrac{2\pm\sqrt{20}}{2}$

$=\dfrac{2\pm2\sqrt{5}}{2}$

$=1\pm\sqrt{5}$

$\approx1\pm2.236$

$r\approx1+2.236\qquad r\approx1-2.236$

$\approx3.236\qquad\qquad \approx-1.236$

The solutions are approximately 3.236 and –1.236.

107. $w^2+4w-1=0$

$a=1, b=4, c=-1$

$w=\dfrac{-b\pm\sqrt{b^2-4ac}}{2a}$

$=\dfrac{-4\pm\sqrt{(4)^2-4(1)(-1)}}{2(1)}$

$=\dfrac{-4\pm\sqrt{16+4}}{2}$

$=\dfrac{-4\pm\sqrt{20}}{2}$

$=\dfrac{-4\pm2\sqrt{5}}{2}$

$=-2\pm\sqrt{5}$

$\approx-2\pm2.236$

$w\approx-2+2.236\qquad w\approx-2-2.236$

$\approx0.236\qquad\qquad \approx-4.236$

The solutions are approximately 0.236 and –4.236.

108.

$$3t^2 = 7t + 1$$
$$3t^2 - 7t - 1 = 0$$
$$a = 3, b = -7, c = -1$$
$$t = \frac{-b \pm \sqrt{b^2 - 4ac}}{2a}$$
$$= \frac{-(-7) \pm \sqrt{(-7)^2 - 4(3)(-1)}}{2(3)}$$
$$= \frac{7 \pm \sqrt{49 + 12}}{6}$$
$$= \frac{7 \pm \sqrt{61}}{6}$$
$$\approx \frac{7 \pm 7.810}{6}$$

$$t \approx \frac{7 + 7.810}{6} \qquad t \approx \frac{7 - 7.810}{6}$$
$$\approx \frac{14.810}{6} \qquad\qquad \approx \frac{-0.810}{6}$$
$$\approx 2.468 \qquad\qquad \approx -0.135$$

The solutions are approximately 2.468 and
−0.135.

109.

$$2y^2 = y + 5$$
$$2y^2 - y - 5 = 0$$
$$a = 2, b = -1, c = -5$$
$$y = \frac{-b \pm \sqrt{b^2 - 4ac}}{2a}$$
$$= \frac{-(-1) \pm \sqrt{(-1)^2 - 4(2)(-5)}}{2(2)}$$
$$= \frac{1 \pm \sqrt{1 + 40}}{4}$$
$$= \frac{1 \pm \sqrt{41}}{4}$$
$$\approx \frac{1 \pm 6.403}{4}$$

$$y \approx \frac{1 + 6.403}{4} \qquad y \approx \frac{1 - 6.403}{4}$$
$$\approx \frac{7.403}{4} \qquad\qquad \approx \frac{-5.403}{4}$$
$$\approx 1.851 \qquad\qquad \approx -1.351$$

The solutions are approximately 1.851 and
−1.351.

110. $2z^2 - z + 5 = 0$
$$a = 2, b = -1, c = 5$$
$$b^2 - 4ac$$
$$(-1)^2 - 4(2)(5) = 1 - 40 = -39$$
$$-39 < 0$$
Since the discriminant is less than zero, the
equation has two complex number solutions.

111. $3y^2 + y + 1 = 0$
$$a = 3, b = 1, c = 1$$
$$b^2 - 4ac$$
$$1^2 - 4(3)(1) = 1 - 12 = -11$$
$$-11 < 0$$
Since the discriminant is less than zero, the
equation has two complex number solutions.

112. $9x^2 - 12x + 4 = 0$
$$a = 9, b = -12, c = 4$$
$$b^2 - 4ac$$
$$(-12)^2 - 4(9)(4) = 144 - 144 = 0$$
Since the discriminant is equal to zero, the
equation has one real number solution, a double
root.

113. $4x^2 + 20x + 25 = 0$
$$a = 4, b = 20, c = 25$$
$$b^2 - 4ac$$
$$20^2 - 4(4)(25) = 400 - 400 = 0$$
Since the discriminant is equal to zero, the
equation has one real number solution, a double
root.

114. $2v^2 - 3v - 1 = 0$
$$a = 2, b = -3, c = -1$$
$$b^2 - 4ac$$
$$(-3)^2 - 4(2)(-1) = 9 + 8 = 17$$
$$17 > 0$$
Since the discriminant is greater than zero, the
equation has two real number solutions that are
not equal.

115. $3w^2 + 3w - 2 = 0$
$$a = 3, b = 3, c = -2$$
$$b^2 - 4ac$$
$$3^2 - 4(3)(-2) = 9 + 24 = 33$$
$$33 > 0$$
Since the discriminant is greater than zero, the
equation has two real number solutions that are
not equal.

116. $2p^2 + 5p + 1 = 0$
$$a = 2, b = 5, c = 1$$
$$b^2 - 4ac$$
$$5^2 - 4(2)(1) = 25 - 8 = 17$$
$$17 > 0$$
Since the discriminant is greater than zero, the
equation has two real number solutions that are
not equal.

117. $2t^2 + 9t + 3 = 0$
$$a = 2, b = 9, c = 3$$
$$b^2 - 4ac$$
$$9^2 - 4(2)(3) = 81 - 24 = 57$$
$$57 > 0$$
Since the discriminant is greater than zero, the
equation has two real number solutions that are
not equal.

118. $5z^2 + 2 = 0$
$$a = 5, b = 0, c = 2$$
$$b^2 - 4ac$$
$$0^2 - 4(5)(2) = -40$$
$$-40 < 0$$
Since the discriminant is less than zero, the
equation has two complex number solutions.

119. $2x^2 + 3x = 1$
quadratic

120. $2x = 3x - 1$
linear

121. $4x - 2 = 5$
linear

122. $4x^2 - 2x = 5$
quadratic

123. $6x(x - 2) = 7$
$6x^2 - 12x = 7$
quadratic

124. $6x - 2 = 7$
linear

Applying Concepts 8.2

125. $\sqrt{2}y^2 + 3y - 2\sqrt{2} = 0$
$a = \sqrt{2}, \quad b = 3, \quad c = -2\sqrt{2}$
$$y = \frac{-b \pm \sqrt{b^2 - 4ac}}{2a}$$
$$= \frac{-3 \pm \sqrt{(3)^2 - 4(\sqrt{2})(-2\sqrt{2})}}{2(\sqrt{2})}$$
$$= \frac{-3 \pm \sqrt{9 + 16}}{2\sqrt{2}}$$
$$= \frac{-3 \pm \sqrt{25}}{2\sqrt{2}} = \frac{-3 \pm 5}{2\sqrt{2}}$$
$$y = \frac{-3 + 5}{2\sqrt{2}}$$
$$= \frac{2}{2\sqrt{2}} \cdot \frac{\sqrt{2}}{\sqrt{2}}$$
$$= \frac{2\sqrt{2}}{4}$$
$$= \frac{\sqrt{2}}{2}$$
$$= \frac{-3 - 5}{2\sqrt{2}}$$
$$= \frac{-8}{2\sqrt{2}}$$
$$= -\frac{4}{\sqrt{2}}$$
$$= -\frac{4}{\sqrt{2}} \cdot \frac{\sqrt{2}}{\sqrt{2}}$$
$$= -\frac{4\sqrt{2}}{2}$$
$$= -2\sqrt{2}$$
The solutions are $\dfrac{\sqrt{2}}{2}$ and $-2\sqrt{2}$.

126. $\sqrt{3}z^2 + 10z - 3\sqrt{3} = 0$
$a = \sqrt{3}, \quad b = 10, \quad c = -3\sqrt{3}$
$$z = \frac{-b \pm \sqrt{b^2 - 4ac}}{2a}$$
$$= \frac{-10 \pm \sqrt{(10)^2 - 4(\sqrt{3})(-3\sqrt{3})}}{2(\sqrt{3})}$$
$$= \frac{-10 \pm \sqrt{100 + 36}}{2\sqrt{3}}$$
$$= \frac{-10 \pm \sqrt{136}}{2\sqrt{3}}$$
$$= \frac{-10 \pm 2\sqrt{34}}{2\sqrt{3}}$$
$$z = \frac{-10 + 2\sqrt{34}}{2\sqrt{3}} = \frac{-5 + \sqrt{34}}{\sqrt{3}}$$
$$= \frac{-5 + \sqrt{34}}{\sqrt{3}} \cdot \frac{\sqrt{3}}{\sqrt{3}}$$
$$= \frac{-5\sqrt{3} + \sqrt{102}}{3}$$
$$= \frac{-10 - 2\sqrt{34}}{2\sqrt{3}}$$
$$= \frac{-5 - \sqrt{34}}{\sqrt{3}}$$
$$= \frac{-5 - \sqrt{34}}{\sqrt{3}} \cdot \frac{\sqrt{3}}{\sqrt{3}}$$
$$= \frac{-5\sqrt{3} - \sqrt{102}}{3}$$
The solutions are
$\dfrac{-5\sqrt{3} + \sqrt{102}}{3}$ and $\dfrac{-5\sqrt{3} - \sqrt{102}}{3}$.

127. $\sqrt{2}x^2 + 5x - 3\sqrt{2} = 0$

$a = \sqrt{2},\ b = 5,\ c = -3\sqrt{2}$

$x = \dfrac{-b \pm \sqrt{b^2 - 4ac}}{2a}$

$= \dfrac{-5 \pm \sqrt{(5)^2 - 4(\sqrt{2})(-3\sqrt{2})}}{2(\sqrt{2})}$

$= \dfrac{-5 \pm \sqrt{25 + 24}}{2\sqrt{2}}$

$= \dfrac{-5 \pm \sqrt{49}}{2\sqrt{2}}$

$= \dfrac{-5 \pm 7}{2\sqrt{2}}$

$x = \dfrac{-5 + 7}{2\sqrt{2}}$

$= \dfrac{2}{2\sqrt{2}}$

$= \dfrac{1}{\sqrt{2}}$

$= \dfrac{1}{\sqrt{2}} \cdot \dfrac{\sqrt{2}}{\sqrt{2}}$

$= \dfrac{\sqrt{2}}{2}$

$= \dfrac{-5 - 7}{2\sqrt{2}}$

$= \dfrac{-12}{2\sqrt{2}}$

$= \dfrac{-6}{\sqrt{2}}$

$= -\dfrac{6}{\sqrt{2}} \cdot \dfrac{\sqrt{2}}{\sqrt{2}}$

$= -\dfrac{6\sqrt{2}}{2}$

$= -3\sqrt{2}$

The solutions are $\dfrac{\sqrt{2}}{2}$ and $-3\sqrt{2}$.

128. $\sqrt{3}w^2 + w - 2\sqrt{3} = 0$

$a = \sqrt{3},\ b = 1,\ c = -2\sqrt{3}$

$w = \dfrac{-b \pm \sqrt{b^2 - 4ac}}{2a}$

$= \dfrac{-1 \pm \sqrt{(1)^2 - 4(\sqrt{3})(-2\sqrt{3})}}{2(\sqrt{3})}$

$= \dfrac{-1 \pm \sqrt{1 + 24}}{2\sqrt{3}}$

$= \dfrac{-1 \pm \sqrt{25}}{2\sqrt{3}}$

$= \dfrac{-1 \pm 5}{2\sqrt{3}}$

$w = \dfrac{-1 + 5}{2\sqrt{3}}$

$= \dfrac{4}{2\sqrt{3}}$

$= \dfrac{2}{\sqrt{3}}$

$= \dfrac{2}{\sqrt{3}} \cdot \dfrac{\sqrt{3}}{\sqrt{3}}$

$= \dfrac{2\sqrt{3}}{3}$

$= \dfrac{-1 - 5}{2\sqrt{3}}$

$= \dfrac{-6}{2\sqrt{3}}$

$= -\dfrac{3}{\sqrt{3}} \cdot \dfrac{\sqrt{3}}{\sqrt{3}}$

$= -\dfrac{3\sqrt{3}}{3} = -\sqrt{3}$

The solutions are $\dfrac{2\sqrt{3}}{3}$ and $-\sqrt{3}$.

129. $t^2 - t\sqrt{3} + 1 = 0$

$a = 1,\ b = -\sqrt{3},\ c = 1$

$t = \dfrac{-b \pm \sqrt{b^2 - 4ac}}{2a}$

$= \dfrac{-(-\sqrt{3}) \pm \sqrt{(-\sqrt{3})^2 - 4(1)(1)}}{2(1)}$

$= \dfrac{\sqrt{3} \pm \sqrt{3 - 4}}{2}$

$= \dfrac{\sqrt{3} \pm \sqrt{-1}}{2}$

$= \dfrac{\sqrt{3} \pm i}{2}$

$= \dfrac{\sqrt{3}}{2} \pm \dfrac{1}{2}i$

The solutions are $\dfrac{\sqrt{3}}{2} + \dfrac{1}{2}i$ and $\dfrac{\sqrt{3}}{2} - \dfrac{1}{2}i$.

130. $y^2 + y\sqrt{7} + 2 = 0$

$a = 1, \ b = \sqrt{7}, \ c = 2$

$y = \dfrac{-b \pm \sqrt{b^2 - 4ac}}{2a}$

$= \dfrac{-\sqrt{7} \pm \sqrt{(\sqrt{7})^2 - 4(1)(2)}}{2(1)}$

$= \dfrac{-\sqrt{7} \pm \sqrt{7 - 8}}{2}$

$= \dfrac{-\sqrt{7} \pm \sqrt{-1}}{2}$

$= \dfrac{-\sqrt{7} \pm i}{2}$

$= -\dfrac{\sqrt{7}}{2} \pm \dfrac{1}{2}i$

The solutions are $-\dfrac{\sqrt{7}}{2} + \dfrac{1}{2}i$ and $-\dfrac{\sqrt{7}}{2} - \dfrac{1}{2}i$.

131. $x^2 - ax - 2a^2 = 0$

$(x - 2a)(x + a) = 0$

$x - 2a = 0 \qquad x + a = 0$

$\qquad x = 2a \qquad\qquad x = -a$

The solutions are $2a$ and $-a$.

132. $x^2 - ax - 6a^2 = 0$

$(x - 3a)(x + 2a) = 0$

$x - 3a = 0 \qquad x + 2a = 0$

$\qquad x = 3a \qquad\qquad x = -2a$

The solutions are $3a$ and $-2a$.

133. $2x^2 + 3ax - 2a^2 = 0$

$(2x - a)(x + 2a) = 0$

$2x - a = 0 \qquad x + 2a = 0$

$\qquad 2x = a \qquad\qquad x = -2a$

$\qquad x = \dfrac{a}{2}$

The solutions are $\dfrac{a}{2}$ and $-2a$.

134. $2x^2 - 7ax + 3a^2 = 0$

$(2x - a)(x - 3a) = 0$

$2x - a = 0 \qquad x - 3a = 0$

$\qquad 2x = a \qquad\qquad x = 3a$

$\qquad x = \dfrac{a}{2}$

The solutions are $\dfrac{a}{2}$ and $3a$.

135. $x^2 - 2x - y = 0$

$a = 1, \ b = -2, \ c = -y$

$x = \dfrac{-b \pm \sqrt{b^2 - 4ac}}{2a}$

$= \dfrac{-(-2) \pm \sqrt{(-2)^2 - 4(1)(-y)}}{2(1)}$

$= \dfrac{2 \pm \sqrt{4 + 4y}}{2}$

$= \dfrac{2 \pm 2\sqrt{1 + y}}{2}$

$= 1 \pm \sqrt{1 + y}$

The solutions are $1 + \sqrt{y + 1}$ and $1 - \sqrt{y + 1}$.

136. $x^2 - 4xy - 4 = 0$

$a = 1, \ b = -4y, \ c = -4$

$x = \dfrac{-b \pm \sqrt{b^2 - 4ac}}{2a}$

$= \dfrac{-(-4y) \pm \sqrt{(-4y)^2 - 4(1)(-4)}}{2(1)}$

$= \dfrac{4y \pm \sqrt{16y^2 + 16}}{2}$

$= \dfrac{4y \pm \sqrt{16(y^2 + 1)}}{2}$

$= \dfrac{4y \pm 4\sqrt{y^2 + 1}}{2}$

$= 2y \pm 2\sqrt{y^2 + 1}$

The solutions are

$2y + 2\sqrt{y^2 + 1}$ and $2y - 2\sqrt{y^2 + 1}$.

137. $x^2 - 6x + p = 0$

$a = 1, \ b = -6, \ c = p$

$\qquad b^2 - 4ac > 0$

$(-6)^2 - 4(1)(p) > 0$

$\qquad 36 - 4p > 0$

$\qquad\qquad -4p > -36$

$\qquad\qquad\quad p < 9$

$\{p | p < 9, \ p \in \text{real numbers}\}$

138. $x^2 + 10x + p = 0$

$a = 1, \ b = 10, \ c = p$

$\qquad b^2 - 4ac > 0$

$10^2 - 4(1)(p) > 0$

$\qquad 100 - 4p > 0$

$\qquad\qquad -4p > -100$

$\qquad\qquad\quad p < 25$

$\{p | p < 25, \ p \in \text{real numbers}\}$

139. $x^2 - 2x + p = 0$

$a = 1, b = -2, c = p$

$b^2 - 4ac < 0$

$(-2)^2 - 4(1)(p) < 0$

$4 - 4p < 0$

$-4p < -4$

$p > 1$

$\{p | p > 1, \ p \in \text{real numbers}\}$

140. $x^2 + 4x + p = 0$

$a = 1, b = 4, c = p$

$b^2 - 4ac < 0$

$4^2 - 4(1)(p) < 0$

$16 - 4p < 0$

$-4p < -16$

$p > 4$

$\{p | p > 4, \ p \in \text{real numbers}\}$

141. Using the quadratic formula with $a = 1$, $b = i$, and $c = 2$,

$$x = \frac{-i \pm \sqrt{i^2 - 4(1)(2)}}{2(1)}$$

$$= \frac{-i \pm \sqrt{-1 - 8}}{2}$$

$$= \frac{-i \pm \sqrt{-9}}{2}$$

$$= \frac{-i \pm 3i}{2}$$

$$x = \frac{-i + 3i}{2} \qquad x = \frac{-i - 3i}{2}$$

$$= \frac{2i}{2} \qquad\qquad = \frac{-4i}{2}$$

$$= i \qquad\qquad\quad = -2i$$

The values of x are $i, -2i$.

142. $2x^2 + bx - 2 = 0$

$b^2 - 4ac = b^2 - 4(2)(-2) = b^2 + 16$

Because b^2 is greater than zero regardless of the value of b, $b^2 + 16$ is greater than zero regardless of the value of b. Therefore, $2x^2 + bx - 2 = 0$ has real number solutions, regardless of the value of b.

143. Strategy

To find the time it takes for the ball to hit the ground, use the value for height ($h = 0$) and solve for t.

Solution

$$h = -16t^2 + 70t + 4$$

$$0 = -16t^2 + 70t + 4$$

$$-4 = -16t^2 + 70t$$

$$-\frac{1}{16}(-4) = -\frac{1}{16}(16t^2 + 70t)$$

$$\frac{1}{4} = t^2 - \frac{35}{8}t$$

Complete the square.

$$\frac{1}{4} + \frac{1225}{256} = t^2 - \frac{35}{8}t + \frac{1225}{256}$$

$$\frac{1289}{256} = \left(t - \frac{35}{16}\right)^2$$

$$\sqrt{\frac{1289}{256}} = \sqrt{\left(t - \frac{35}{16}\right)^2}$$

$$\pm\sqrt{\frac{1289}{256}} = t - \frac{35}{16}$$

$$t - \frac{35}{16} = \sqrt{\frac{1289}{256}} \qquad t - \frac{35}{16} = -\sqrt{\frac{1289}{256}}$$

$$t = \frac{35}{16} + \sqrt{\frac{1289}{256}} \qquad t = \frac{35}{16} - \sqrt{\frac{1289}{256}}$$

$$t \approx 4.431 \qquad\qquad t \approx -0.0564$$

The solution $t = -0.0564$ is not possible because it represents a time before the ball is thrown. The ball takes about 4.43 seconds to hit the ground.

144. Strategy
First find the time it takes for the ball to hit ground using $h = -16t^2 + 70t + 4$ (the answer is found in Exercise 143). Use this time to find the horizontal distance the ball travels.

Solution
$t = 4.431$ seconds, the length of time the ball is in the air.
$s = 44.5t$
$s = 44.5(4.431)$
$s = 197.2$ feet
The ball will not clear the fence.

145. **a.**
$$x^2 - s_a x - s_j s_s f = 0$$
$$x^2 - 0.97x - (0.34)(0.97)(0.24) = 0$$
$$x^2 - 0.97x - 0.079152 = 0$$
$$x = \frac{0.97 \pm \sqrt{(-0.97)^2 - 4(1)(-0.079152)}}{2(1)}$$
$x \approx 1.05$ and $x \approx -0.08$
The larger of the two roots is 1.05.
$1.05 > 1$
The model predicts that the population will increase.

b.
$$x^2 - s_a x - s_j s_s f = 0$$
$$x^2 - 0.94x - (0.11)(0.71)(0.24) = 0$$
$$x^2 - 0.94x - 0.018744 = 0$$
$$x = \frac{0.94 \pm \sqrt{(-0.94)^2 - 4(1)(-0.018744)}}{2(1)}$$
$x \approx 0.96$ and $x \approx -0.02$
The larger of the two roots is 0.96.
$0.96 < 1$
The model predicts that the population will decrease.

146. The year at which the amount received in taxes will equal the amount paid out in benefits is where the curves of $A(x)$ and $B(x)$ intersect. To find the year, set $A(x)$ equal to $B(x)$ and solve for x.
$$A(x) = B(x)$$
$$6.145x^2 - 73.954x + 422.744 = 10.287x^2 - 156.632x + 486.345$$
$$0 = 4.142x^2 - 82.678x + 63.601$$
Thus $a = 4.142$, $b = -82.678$, and $c = 63.601$.
$$x = \frac{-b \pm \sqrt{b^2 - 4ac}}{2a}$$
$$= \frac{-(-82.678) \pm \sqrt{(-82.678)^2 - 4(4.142)(63.601)}}{2(4.142)}$$
$$= \frac{82.678 \pm \sqrt{6835.651684 - 1053.741368}}{8.284}$$
$$= \frac{82.678 \pm \sqrt{5781.910316}}{8.284}$$
$$= \frac{82.678 \pm 76.03887372}{8.284}$$
$$= \frac{82.678 + 76.03887372}{8.284} = 19.15944$$
The amount paid out in benefits will exceed the amount received in taxes 19 years after 1994. This will be the year 2013.

147.
$$ax^2 + bx + c = 0$$
$$ax^2 + bx = -c$$
$$4a^2x^2 + 4abx = -4ac$$
$$4a^2x + 4abx + b^2 = b^2 - 4ac$$
$$(2ax + b)^2 = b^2 - 4ac$$
$$2ax + b = \pm\sqrt{b^2 - 4ac}$$
$$2ax = -b \pm \sqrt{b^2 - 4ac}$$
$$x = \frac{-b \pm \sqrt{b^2 - 4ac}}{2a}$$

148. $x^2 + bx$ Find the constant term. $\left(\frac{1}{2}b\right)^2 = \frac{1}{4}b^2$

Add the constant term to the binomial to complete the square.

$$x^2 + bx + \frac{1}{4}b^2$$

Write the resulting perfect-square trinomial as the square of a binomial.

$$x^2 + bx + \frac{1}{4}b^2 = \left(x + \frac{1}{2}b\right)^2$$

Section 8.3

Concept Review 8.3

1. Always true

2. Sometimes true
   Sometimes squaring both sides of a radical equation produces an extraneous root. That is why you should check the solution when squaring both sides of a radical equation.

3. Always true

4. Never true
   $\left(\sqrt{3x}\right)^2$ is $3x$ so the trinomial is not quadratic in form because the exponent on one variable is not one-half the exponent on the other term.

Objective 8.3.1 Exercises

1. An equation is quadratic in form if it can be written as $au^2 + bu + c = 0$.

2. Let $x^2 = u$. Replace x^2 by u in the equation.
$$x^4 - 2x^2 - 3 = 0$$
$$(x^2)^2 - 2x^2 - 3 = 0$$
$$u^2 - 2u - 3 = 0$$
The equation is quadratic in form.

3.
$$x^4 - 13x^2 + 36 = 0$$
$$(x^2)^2 - 13(x^2) + 36 = 0$$
$$u^2 - 13u + 36 = 0$$
$$(u - 4)(u - 9) = 0$$

$u - 4 = 0$	$u - 9 = 0$
$u = 4$	$u = 9$

Replace u by x^2.

$x^2 = 4$	$x^2 = 9$
$\sqrt{x^2} = \sqrt{4}$	$\sqrt{x^2} = \sqrt{9}$
$x = \pm 2$	$x = \pm 3$

The solutions are 2, −2, 3, and −3.

4.
$$y^4 - 5y^2 + 4 = 0$$
$$(y^2)^2 - 5(y^2) + 4 = 0$$
$$u^2 - 5u + 4 = 0$$
$$(u - 1)(u - 4) = 0$$

$u - 1 = 0$	$u - 4 = 0$
$u = 1$	$u = 4$

Replace u by y^2.

$y^2 = 1$	$y^2 = 4$
$\sqrt{y^2} = \sqrt{1}$	$\sqrt{y^2} = \sqrt{4}$
$y = \pm 1$	$y = \pm 2$

The solutions are 1, −1, 2, and −2.

5.
$$z^4 - 6z^2 + 8 = 0$$
$$(z^2)^2 - 6(z^2) + 8 = 0$$
$$u^2 - 6u + 8 = 0$$
$$(u - 4)(u - 2) = 0$$

$u - 4 = 0$	$u - 2 = 0$
$u = 4$	$u = 2$

Replace u by z^2.

$z^2 = 4$	$z^2 = 2$
$\sqrt{z^2} = \sqrt{4}$	$\sqrt{z^2} = \sqrt{2}$
$z = \pm 2$	$z = \pm\sqrt{2}$

The solutions are 2, −2, $\sqrt{2}$, and $-\sqrt{2}$.

6.
$$t^4 - 12t^2 + 27 = 0$$
$$(t^2)^2 - 12(t^2) + 27 = 0$$
$$u^2 - 12u + 27 = 0$$
$$(u - 9)(u - 3) = 0$$

$u - 9 = 0$	$u - 3 = 0$
$u = 9$	$u = 3$

Replace u by t^2.

$t^2 = 9$	$t^2 = 3$
$\sqrt{t^2} = \sqrt{9}$	$\sqrt{t^2} = \sqrt{3}$
$t = \pm 3$	$t = \pm\sqrt{3}$

The solutions are 3, −3, $\sqrt{3}$, and $-\sqrt{3}$.

7.
$$p - 3p^{1/2} + 2 = 0$$
$$(p^{1/2})^2 - 3(p^{1/2}) + 2 = 0$$
$$u^2 - 3u + 2 = 0$$
$$(u - 1)(u - 2) = 0$$

$u - 1 = 0 \qquad u - 2 = 0$
$u = 1 \qquad u = 2$

Replace u by $p^{1/2}$.

$p^{1/2} = 1 \qquad\qquad p^{1/2} = 2$
$(p^{1/2})^2 = 1^2 \qquad (p^{1/2})^2 = 2^2$
$p = 1 \qquad\qquad p = 4$

The solutions are 1 and 4.

8.
$$v - 7v^{1/2} + 12 = 0$$
$$(v^{1/2})^2 - 7(v^{1/2}) + 12 = 0$$
$$u^2 - 7u + 12 = 0$$
$$(u - 3)(u - 4) = 0$$

$u - 3 = 0 \qquad u - 4 = 0$
$u = 3 \qquad u = 4$

Replace u by $v^{1/2}$.

$v^{1/2} = 3 \qquad\qquad v^{1/2} = 4$
$(v^{1/2})^2 = 3^2 \qquad (v^{1/2})^2 = 4^2$
$v = 9 \qquad\qquad v = 16$

The solutions are 9 and 16.

9.
$$x - x^{1/2} - 12 = 0$$
$$(x^{1/2})^2 - (x^{1/2}) - 12 = 0$$
$$u^2 - u - 12 = 0$$
$$(u + 3)(u - 4) = 0$$

$u + 3 = 0 \qquad u - 4 = 0$
$u = -3 \qquad u = 4$

Replace u by $x^{1/2}$.

$x^{1/2} = -3 \qquad\qquad x^{1/2} = 4$
$(x^{1/2})^2 = (-3)^2 \qquad (x^{1/2})^2 = 4^2$
$x = 9 \qquad\qquad x = 16$

16 checks as a solution.
9 does not check as a solution.
The solution is 16.

10.
$$w - 2w^{1/2} - 15 = 0$$
$$(w^{1/2})^2 - 2(w^{1/2}) - 15 = 0$$
$$u^2 - 2u - 15 = 0$$
$$(u - 5)(u + 3) = 0$$

$u - 5 = 0 \qquad u + 3 = 0$
$u = 5 \qquad u = -3$

Replace u by $w^{1/2}$.

$w^{1/2} = 5 \qquad\qquad w^{1/2} = -3$
$(w^{1/2})^2 = 5^2 \qquad (w^{1/2})^2 = (-3)^2$
$w = 25 \qquad\qquad w = 9$

25 checks as a solution.
9 does not check as a solution.
The solution is 25.

11.
$$z^4 + 3z^2 - 4 = 0$$
$$(z^2)^2 + 3(z^2) - 4 = 0$$
$$u^2 + 3u - 4 = 0$$
$$(u + 4)(u - 1) = 0$$

$u + 4 = 0 \qquad u - 1 = 0$
$u = -4 \qquad u = 1$

Replace u by z^2.

$z^2 = -4 \qquad\qquad z^2 = 1$
$\sqrt{z^2} = \sqrt{-4} \qquad \sqrt{z^2} = \sqrt{1}$
$z = \pm 2i \qquad\qquad z = \pm 1$

The solutions are $2i$, $-2i$, 1, and -1.

12.
$$y^4 + 5y^2 - 36 = 0$$
$$(y^2)^2 + 5(y^2) - 36 = 0$$
$$u^2 + 5u - 36 = 0$$
$$(u - 4)(u + 9) = 0$$

$u - 4 = 0 \qquad u + 9 = 0$
$u = 4 \qquad u = -9$

Replace u by y^2.

$y^2 = 4 \qquad\qquad y^2 = -9$
$\sqrt{y^2} = \sqrt{4} \qquad \sqrt{y^2} = \sqrt{-9}$
$y = \pm 2 \qquad\qquad y = \pm 3i$

The solutions are 2, -2, $3i$, and $-3i$.

13.
$$x^4 + 12x^2 - 64 = 0$$
$$(x^2)^2 + 12(x^2) - 64 = 0$$
$$u^2 + 12u - 64 = 0$$
$$(u + 16)(u - 4) = 0$$

$u + 16 = 0 \qquad u - 4 = 0$
$u = -16 \qquad u = 4$

Replace u by x^2.

$x^2 = -16 \qquad\qquad x^2 = 4$
$\sqrt{x^2} = \sqrt{-16} \qquad \sqrt{x^2} = \sqrt{4}$
$x = \pm 4i \qquad\qquad x = \pm 2$

The solutions are $4i$, $-4i$, 2, and -2.

14.
$$x^4 - 81 = 0$$
$$(x^2)^2 - 81 = 0$$
$$u^2 - 81 = 0$$
$$(u + 9)(u - 9) = 0$$

$u + 9 = 0 \qquad u - 9 = 0$
$u = -9 \qquad u = 9$

Replace u by x^2.

$x^2 = -9 \qquad\qquad x^2 = 9$
$\sqrt{x^2} = \sqrt{-9} \qquad \sqrt{x^2} = \sqrt{9}$
$x = \pm 3i \qquad\qquad x = \pm 3$

The solutions are $3i$, $-3i$, 3, and -3.

15.
$$p + 2p^{1/2} - 24 = 0$$
$$(p^{1/2})^2 + 2(p^{1/2}) - 24 = 0$$
$$u^2 + 2u - 24 = 0$$
$$(u+6)(u-4) = 0$$
$$u + 6 = 0 \qquad u - 4 = 0$$
$$u = -6 \qquad u = 4$$
Replace u by $p^{1/2}$.
$$p^{1/2} = -6 \qquad p^{1/2} = 4$$
$$(p^{1/2})^2 = (-6)^2 \qquad (p^{1/2})^2 = 4^2$$
$$p = 36 \qquad p = 16$$
16 checks as a solution.
36 does not check as a solution.
The solution is 16.

16.
$$v + 3v^{1/2} - 4 = 0$$
$$(v^{1/2})^2 + 3(v^{1/2}) - 4 = 0$$
$$u^2 + 3u - 4 = 0$$
$$(u+4)(u-1) = 0$$
$$u + 4 = 0 \qquad u - 1 = 0$$
$$u = -4 \qquad u = 1$$
Replace u by $v^{1/2}$.
$$v^{1/2} = -4 \qquad v^{1/2} = 1$$
$$(v^{1/2})^2 = (-4)^2 \qquad (v^{1/2})^2 = 1^2$$
$$v = 16 \qquad v = 1$$
1 checks as a solution.
16 does not check as a solution.
The solution is 1.

17.
$$y^{2/3} - 9y^{1/3} + 8 = 0$$
$$(y^{1/3})^2 - 9(y^{1/3}) + 8 = 0$$
$$u^2 - 9u + 8 = 0$$
$$(u-1)(u-8) = 0$$
$$u - 1 = 0 \qquad u - 8 = 0$$
$$u = 1 \qquad u = 8$$
Replace u by $y^{1/3}$.
$$y^{1/3} = 1 \qquad y^{1/3} = 8$$
$$(y^{1/3})^3 = 1^3 \qquad (y^{1/3})^3 = 8^3$$
$$y = 1 \qquad y = 512$$
The solutions are 1 and 512.

18.
$$z^{2/3} - z^{1/3} - 6 = 0$$
$$(z^{1/3})^2 - (z^{1/3}) - 6 = 0$$
$$u^2 - u - 6 = 0$$
$$(u+2)(u-3) = 0$$
$$u + 2 = 0 \qquad u - 3 = 0$$
$$u = -2 \qquad u = 3$$
Replace u by $z^{1/3}$.
$$z^{1/3} = -2 \qquad z^{1/3} = 3$$
$$(z^{1/3})^3 = (-2)^3 \qquad (z^{1/3})^3 = 3^3$$
$$z = -8 \qquad z = 27$$
The solutions are -8 and 27.

19.
$$x^6 - 9x^3 + 8 = 0$$
$$(x^3)^2 - 9(x^3) + 8 = 0$$
$$u^2 - 9u + 8 = 0$$
$$(u-8)(u-1) = 0$$
$$u - 8 = 0 \qquad u - 1 = 0$$
Replace u by x^3.
$$x^3 - 8 = 0 \qquad\qquad x^3 - 1 = 0$$
$$(x-2)(x^2 + 2x + 4) = 0 \qquad (x-1)(x^2 + x + 1) = 0$$

$$x - 2 = 0 \qquad x^2 + 2x + 4 = 0 \qquad\qquad x - 1 = 0 \qquad x^2 + x + 1 = 0$$
$$x = 2 \qquad x = \dfrac{-2 \pm \sqrt{2^2 - 4(1)(4)}}{2(1)} \qquad\qquad x = 1 \qquad x = \dfrac{-1 \pm \sqrt{1^2 - 4(1)(1)}}{2(1)}$$
$$= \dfrac{-2 \pm \sqrt{-12}}{2} \qquad\qquad\qquad\qquad = \dfrac{-1 \pm \sqrt{-3}}{2}$$
$$= \dfrac{-2 \pm 2i\sqrt{3}}{2} \qquad\qquad\qquad\qquad = \dfrac{-1 \pm i\sqrt{3}}{2}$$
$$= -1 \pm i\sqrt{3}$$

The solutions are 2, 1, $-1 + i\sqrt{3}$, $-1 - i\sqrt{3}$, $-\dfrac{1}{2} + \dfrac{\sqrt{3}}{2}i$, and $-\dfrac{1}{2} - \dfrac{\sqrt{3}}{2}i$.

20.
$$y^6 + 9y^3 + 8 = 0$$
$$(y^3)^2 + 9(y^3) + 8 = 0$$
$$u^2 - 9u + 8 = 0$$
$$(u + 8)(u + 1) = 0$$
$$u + 8 = 0 \qquad u + 1 = 0$$

Replace u by y^3.

$$y^3 + 8 = 0 \qquad\qquad y^3 + 1 = 0$$
$$(y + 2)(y^2 - 2y + 4) = 0 \quad (y + 1)(y^2 - y + 1) = 0$$

$$y + 2 = 0 \qquad y^2 - 2y + 4 = 0 \qquad\qquad y + 1 = 0 \qquad y^2 - y + 1 = 0$$
$$y = -2 \qquad\qquad y = \dfrac{2 \pm \sqrt{(-2)^2 - 4(1)(4)}}{2(1)} \qquad\quad y = -1 \qquad\qquad y = \dfrac{1 \pm \sqrt{(-1)^2 - 4(1)(1)}}{2(1)}$$
$$= \dfrac{2 \pm \sqrt{-12}}{2} \qquad\qquad\qquad\qquad\qquad\quad = \dfrac{1 \pm \sqrt{-3}}{2}$$
$$= \dfrac{2 \pm 2i\sqrt{3}}{2} \qquad\qquad\qquad\qquad\qquad\quad = \dfrac{1 \pm i\sqrt{3}}{2}$$
$$= 1 \pm i\sqrt{3}$$

The solutions are -2, -1, $1 + i\sqrt{3}$, $1 - i\sqrt{3}$, $\dfrac{1}{2} + \dfrac{\sqrt{3}}{2}i$, and $\dfrac{1}{2} - \dfrac{\sqrt{3}}{2}i$.

21.
$$z^8 - 17z^4 + 16 = 0$$
$$(z^4)^2 - 17(z^4) + 16 = 0$$
$$u^2 - 17u + 16 = 0$$
$$(u - 16)(u - 1) = 0$$
$$u - 16 = 0 \qquad u - 1 = 0$$

Replace u by z^4.

$$z^4 - 16 = 0 \qquad z^4 - 1 = 0$$
$$(z^2)^2 - 16 = 0 \quad (z^2)^2 - 1 = 0$$
$$v^2 - 16 = 0 \qquad v^2 - 1 = 0$$

$$(v + 4)(v - 4) = 0 \quad (v + 1)(v - 1) = 0$$
$$v + 4 = 0 \qquad v - 4 = 0 \qquad v + 1 = 0 \qquad v - 1 = 0$$
$$v = -4 \qquad v = 4 \qquad v = -1 \qquad v = 1$$

Replace v by z^2.

$$z^2 = -4 \qquad z^2 = 4 \qquad z^2 = -1 \qquad z^2 = 1$$
$$\sqrt{z^2} = \sqrt{-4} \qquad \sqrt{z^2} = \sqrt{4} \qquad \sqrt{z^2} = \sqrt{-1} \qquad \sqrt{z^2} = \sqrt{1}$$
$$z = \pm 2i \qquad\quad z = \pm 2 \qquad\quad z = \pm i \qquad\quad z = \pm 1$$

The solutions are -2, 2, $2i$, $-2i$, -1, 1, i, and $-i$.

22.
$$v^4 - 15v^2 - 16 = 0$$
$$(v^2)^2 - 15(v^2) - 16 = 0$$
$$u^2 - 15u - 16 = 0$$
$$(u - 16)(u + 1) = 0$$
$$u - 16 = 0 \qquad u + 1 = 0$$
$$u = 16 \qquad\quad u = -1$$

Replace u by v^2.

$$v^2 = 16 \qquad\qquad v^2 = -1$$
$$\sqrt{v^2} = \sqrt{16} \qquad \sqrt{v^2} = \sqrt{-1}$$
$$v = \pm 4 \qquad\qquad v = \pm i$$

The solutions are 4, -4, i, and $-i$.

23.
$$p^{2/3} + 2p^{1/3} - 8 = 0$$
$$(p^{1/3})^2 + 2(p^{1/3}) - 8 = 0$$
$$u^2 + 2u - 8 = 0$$
$$(u + 4)(u - 2) = 0$$
$$u + 4 = 0 \qquad u - 2 = 0$$
$$u = -4 \qquad\quad u = 2$$

Replace u by $p^{1/3}$.

$$p^{1/3} = -4 \qquad\qquad p^{1/3} = 2$$
$$(p^{1/3})^3 = (-4)^3 \qquad (p^{1/3})^3 = 2^3$$
$$p = -64 \qquad\qquad p = 8$$

The solutions are -64 and 8.

24.
$$w^{2/3} + 3w^{1/3} - 10 = 0$$
$$(w^{1/3})^2 + 3(w^{1/3}) - 10 = 0$$
$$u^2 + 3u - 10 = 0$$
$$(u + 5)(u - 2) = 0$$

$$u + 5 = 0 \qquad u - 2 = 0$$
$$u = -5 \qquad u = 2$$

Replace u by $w^{1/3}$.

$$w^{1/3} = -5 \qquad w^{1/3} = 2$$
$$(w^{1/3})^3 = (-5)^3 \qquad (w^{1/3})^3 = (2)^3$$
$$w = -125 \qquad w = 8$$

The solutions are −125 and 8.

25.
$$2x - 3x^{1/2} + 1 = 0$$
$$2(x^{1/2})^2 - 3(x^{1/2}) + 1 = 0$$
$$2u^2 - 3u + 1 = 0$$
$$(2u - 1)(u - 1) = 0$$

$$2u - 1 = 0 \qquad u - 1 = 0$$
$$2u = 1 \qquad u = 1$$
$$u = \frac{1}{2}$$

Replace u by $x^{1/2}$.

$$x^{1/2} = \frac{1}{2} \qquad x^{1/2} = 1$$
$$(x^{1/2})^2 = \left(\frac{1}{2}\right)^2 \qquad (x^{1/2})^2 = 1^2$$
$$\qquad\qquad\qquad x = 1$$
$$x = \frac{1}{4}$$

The solutions are $\frac{1}{4}$ and 1.

26.
$$3y - 5y^{1/2} - 2 = 0$$
$$3(y^{1/2})^2 - 5(y^{1/2}) - 2 = 0$$
$$3u^2 - 5u - 2 = 0$$
$$(3u + 1)(u - 2) = 0$$

$$3u + 1 = 0 \qquad u - 2 = 0$$
$$3u = -1 \qquad u = 2$$
$$u = -\frac{1}{3}$$

Replace u by $y^{1/2}$.

$$y^{1/2} = -\frac{1}{3} \qquad y^{1/2} = 2$$
$$(y^{1/2})^2 = \left(-\frac{1}{3}\right)^2 \qquad (y^{1/2})^2 = 2^2$$
$$\qquad\qquad\qquad y = 4$$
$$y = \frac{1}{9}$$

$\frac{1}{9}$ does not check as a solution.

4 checks as a solution.
The solution is 4.

Objective 8.3.2 Exercises

27.
$$\sqrt{x + 1} + x = 5$$
$$\sqrt{x + 1} = 5 - x$$
$$(\sqrt{x + 1})^2 = (5 - x)^2$$
$$x + 1 = 25 - 10x + x^2$$
$$0 = 24 - 11x + x^2$$
$$0 = (3 - x)(8 - x)$$

$$3 - x = 0 \qquad 8 - x = 0$$
$$3 = x \qquad 8 = x$$

3 checks as a solution.
8 does not check as a solution.
The solution is 3.

28.
$$\sqrt{x - 4} + x = 6$$
$$\sqrt{x - 4} = 6 - x$$
$$(\sqrt{x - 4})^2 = (6 - x)^2$$
$$x - 4 = 36 - 12x + x^2$$
$$0 = 40 - 13x + x^2$$
$$0 = (5 - x)(8 - x)$$

$$5 - x = 0 \qquad 8 - x = 0$$
$$5 = x \qquad 8 = x$$

5 checks as a solution.
8 does not check as a solution.
The solution is 5.

29.
$$x = \sqrt{x} + 6$$
$$x - 6 = \sqrt{x}$$
$$(x-6)^2 = (\sqrt{x})^2$$
$$x^2 - 12x + 36 = x$$
$$x^2 - 13x + 36 = 0$$
$$(x-4)(x-9) = 0$$
$$x - 4 = 0 \qquad x - 9 = 0$$
$$x = 4 \qquad x = 9$$
9 checks as a solution.
4 does not check as a solution.
The solution is 9.

30.
$$\sqrt{2y-1} = y - 2$$
$$(\sqrt{2y-1})^2 = (y-2)^2$$
$$2y - 1 = y^2 - 4y + 4$$
$$0 = y^2 - 6y + 5$$
$$0 = (y-5)(y-1)$$
$$y - 5 = 0 \qquad y - 1 = 0$$
$$y = 5 \qquad y = 1$$
5 checks as a solution.
1 does not check as a solution.
The solution is 5.

31.
$$\sqrt{3w+3} = w + 1$$
$$(\sqrt{3w+3})^2 = (w+1)^2$$
$$3w + 3 = w^2 + 2w + 1$$
$$0 = w^2 - w - 2$$
$$0 = (w-2)(w+1)$$
$$w - 2 = 0 \qquad w + 1 = 0$$
$$w = 2 \qquad w = -1$$
2 and −1 check as solutions.
The solutions are 2 and −1.

32.
$$\sqrt{2s+1} = s - 1$$
$$(\sqrt{2s+1})^2 = (s-1)^2$$
$$2s + 1 = s^2 - 2s + 1$$
$$0 = s^2 - 4s$$
$$0 = s(s-4)$$
$$s = 0 \qquad s - 4 = 0$$
$$\qquad s = 4$$
4 checks as a solution.
0 does not check as a solution.
The solution is 4.

33.
$$\sqrt{4y+1} - y = 1$$
$$\sqrt{4y+1} = y + 1$$
$$(\sqrt{4y+1})^2 = (y+1)^2$$
$$4y + 1 = y^2 + 2y + 1$$
$$0 = y^2 - 2y$$
$$0 = y(y-2)$$
$$y = 0 \qquad y - 2 = 0$$
$$\qquad y = 2$$
0 and 2 check as solutions.
The solutions are 0 and 2.

34.
$$\sqrt{3s+4} + 2s = 12$$
$$\sqrt{3s+4} = 12 - 2s$$
$$(\sqrt{3s+4})^2 = (12-2s)^2$$
$$3s + 4 = 144 - 48s + 4s^2$$
$$0 = 140 - 51s + 4s^2$$
$$0 = (35-4s)(4-s)$$
$$35 - 4s = 0 \qquad 4 - s = 0$$
$$35 = 4s \qquad 4 = s$$
$$\frac{35}{4} = s$$
4 checks as a solution.
$\frac{35}{4}$ does not check as a solution.
The solution is 4.

35.
$$\sqrt{10x+5} - 2x = 1$$
$$\sqrt{10x+5} = 2x + 1$$
$$(\sqrt{10x+5})^2 = (2x+1)^2$$
$$10x + 5 = 4x^2 + 4x + 1$$
$$0 = 4x^2 - 6x - 4$$
$$0 = 2(2x^2 - 3x - 2)$$
$$0 = 2(2x+1)(x-2)$$
$$2x + 1 = 0 \qquad x - 2 = 0$$
$$2x = -1 \qquad x = 2$$
$$x = -\frac{1}{2}$$
$-\frac{1}{2}$ and 2 check as solutions.
The solutions are $-\frac{1}{2}$ and 2.

36.
$$\sqrt{t+8} = 2t + 1$$
$$(\sqrt{t+8})^2 = (2t+1)^2$$
$$t + 8 = 4t^2 + 4t + 1$$
$$0 = 4t^2 + 3t - 7$$
$$0 = (4t+7)(t-1)$$
$$4t + 7 = 0 \qquad t - 1 = 0$$
$$4t = -7 \qquad t = 1$$
$$t = -\frac{7}{4}$$
1 checks as a solution.
$-\frac{7}{4}$ does not check as a solution.
The solution is 1.

37.
$$\sqrt{p+11} = 1 - p$$
$$(\sqrt{p+11})^2 = (1-p)^2$$
$$p + 11 = 1 - 2p + p^2$$
$$0 = -10 - 3p + p^2$$
$$0 = p^2 - 3p - 10$$
$$0 = (p-5)(p+2)$$
$$p - 5 = 0 \qquad p + 2 = 0$$
$$p = 5 \qquad\quad p = -2$$
−2 checks as a solution.
5 does not check as a solution.
The solution is −2.

38.
$$x - 7 = \sqrt{x-5}$$
$$(x-7)^2 = (\sqrt{x-5})^2$$
$$x^2 - 14x + 49 = x - 5$$
$$x^2 - 15x + 54 = 0$$
$$(x-6)(x-9) = 0$$
$$x - 6 = 0 \qquad x - 9 = 0$$
$$x = 6 \qquad\quad x = 9$$
9 checks as a solution.
6 does not check as a solution.
The solution is 9.

39.
$$\sqrt{x-1} - \sqrt{x} = -1$$
$$\sqrt{x-1} = \sqrt{x} - 1$$
$$(\sqrt{x-1})^2 = (\sqrt{x}-1)^2$$
$$x - 1 = x - 2\sqrt{x} + 1$$
$$2\sqrt{x} = 2$$
$$\sqrt{x} = 1$$
$$(\sqrt{x})^2 = 1^2$$
$$x = 1$$
1 checks as a solution.
The solution is 1.

40.
$$\sqrt{y} + 1 = \sqrt{y+5}$$
$$(\sqrt{y}+1)^2 = (\sqrt{y+5})^2$$
$$y + 2\sqrt{y} + 1 = y + 5$$
$$2\sqrt{y} = 4$$
$$\sqrt{y} = 2$$
$$(\sqrt{y})^2 = 2^2$$
$$y = 4$$
4 checks as a solution.
The solution is 4.

41.
$$\sqrt{2x-1} = 1 - \sqrt{x-1}$$
$$(\sqrt{2x-1})^2 = (1-\sqrt{x-1})^2$$
$$2x - 1 = 1 - 2\sqrt{x-1} + x - 1$$
$$2\sqrt{x-1} = -x + 1$$
$$(2\sqrt{x-1})^2 = (-x+1)^2$$
$$4(x-1) = x^2 - 2x + 1$$
$$4x - 4 = x^2 - 2x + 1$$
$$0 = x^2 - 6x + 5$$
$$0 = (x-5)(x-1)$$
$$x - 5 = 0 \qquad x - 1 = 0$$
$$x = 5 \qquad\quad x = 1$$
1 checks as a solution.
5 does not check as a solution.
The solution is 1.

42.
$$\sqrt{x+6} + \sqrt{x+2} = 2$$
$$\sqrt{x+6} = 2 - \sqrt{x+2}$$
$$(\sqrt{x+6})^2 = (2-\sqrt{x+2})^2$$
$$x + 6 = 4 - 4\sqrt{x+2} + x + 2$$
$$4\sqrt{x+2} = 0$$
$$\sqrt{x+2} = 0$$
$$(\sqrt{x+2})^2 = 0^2$$
$$x + 2 = 0$$
$$x = -2$$
−2 checks as a solution.
The solution is −2.

43.
$$\sqrt{t+3} + \sqrt{2t+7} = 1$$
$$\sqrt{2t+7} = 1 - \sqrt{t+3}$$
$$(\sqrt{2t+7})^2 = (1-\sqrt{t+3})^2$$
$$2t + 7 = 1 - 2\sqrt{t+3} + t + 3$$
$$t + 3 = -2\sqrt{t+3}$$
$$(t+3)^2 = (-2\sqrt{t+3})^2$$
$$t^2 + 6t + 9 = 4(t+3)$$
$$t^2 + 6t + 9 = 4t + 12$$
$$t^2 + 2t - 3 = 0$$
$$(t+3)(t-1) = 0$$
$$t + 3 = 0 \qquad t - 1 = 0$$
$$t = -3 \qquad\quad t = 1$$
−3 checks as a solution.
1 does not check as a solution.
The solution is −3.

44.
$$\sqrt{5-2x} = \sqrt{2-x} + 1$$
$$(\sqrt{5-2x})^2 = (\sqrt{2-x}+1)^2$$
$$5 - 2x = 2 - x + 2\sqrt{2-x} + 1$$
$$-x + 2 = 2\sqrt{2-x}$$
$$(-x+2)^2 = (2\sqrt{2-x})^2$$
$$x^2 - 4x + 4 = 4(2-x)$$
$$x^2 - 4x + 4 = 8 - 4x$$
$$x^2 - 4 = 0$$
$$(x-2)(x+2) = 0$$
$$x - 2 = 0 \qquad x + 2 = 0$$
$$x = 2 \qquad x = -2$$
2 and −2 check as solutions.
The solutions are 2 and −2.

Objective 8.3.3 Exercises

45.
$$x = \frac{10}{x-9}$$
$$(x-9)x = (x-9)\frac{10}{x-9}$$
$$x^2 - 9x = 10$$
$$x^2 - 9x - 10 = 0$$
$$(x-10)(x+1) = 0$$
$$x - 10 = 0 \qquad x + 1 = 0$$
$$x = 10 \qquad x = -1$$
The solutions are 10 and −1.

46.
$$z = \frac{5}{z-4}$$
$$(z-4)z = (z-4)\frac{5}{z-4}$$
$$z^2 - 4z = 5$$
$$z^2 - 4z - 5 = 0$$
$$(z-5)(z+1) = 0$$
$$z - 5 = 0 \qquad z + 1 = 0$$
$$z = 5 \qquad z = -1$$
The solutions are 5 and −1.

47.
$$\frac{t}{t+1} = \frac{-2}{t-1}$$
$$(t-1)(t+1)\frac{t}{t+1} = (t-1)(t+1)\frac{-2}{t-1}$$
$$(t-1)t = (t+1)(-2)$$
$$t^2 - t = -2t - 2$$
$$t^2 + t + 2 = 0$$
$$t = \frac{-b \pm \sqrt{b^2 - 4ac}}{2a}$$
$$= \frac{-1 \pm \sqrt{1^2 - 4(1)(2)}}{2(1)}$$
$$= \frac{-1 \pm \sqrt{1-8}}{2} = \frac{-1 \pm \sqrt{-7}}{2} = \frac{-1 \pm i\sqrt{7}}{2}$$
The solutions are $-\frac{1}{2} + \frac{\sqrt{7}}{2}i$ and
$-\frac{1}{2} - \frac{\sqrt{7}}{2}i$.

48.
$$\frac{2v}{v-1} = \frac{5}{v+2}$$
$$(v-1)(v+2)\left(\frac{2v}{v-1}\right) = (v-1)(v+2)\frac{5}{v+2}$$
$$(v+2)2v = (v-1)5$$
$$2v^2 + 4v = 5v - 5$$
$$2v^2 - v + 5 = 0$$
$$v = \frac{-b \pm \sqrt{b^2 - 4ac}}{2a}$$
$$= \frac{-(-1) \pm \sqrt{(-1)^2 - 4(2)(5)}}{2(2)}$$
$$= \frac{1 \pm \sqrt{1-40}}{4} = \frac{1 \pm \sqrt{-39}}{4} = \frac{1 \pm i\sqrt{39}}{4}$$
The solutions are $\frac{1}{4} + \frac{\sqrt{39}}{4}i$ and $\frac{1}{4} - \frac{\sqrt{39}}{4}i$.

49.
$$\frac{y-1}{y+2} + y = 1$$
$$(y+2)\left(\frac{y-1}{y+2} + y\right) = (y+2)1$$
$$(y+2)\frac{y-1}{y+2} + (y+2)y = y+2$$
$$y - 1 + y^2 + 2y = y + 2$$
$$y^2 + 3y - 1 = y + 2$$
$$y^2 + 2y - 3 = 0$$
$$(y+3)(y-1) = 0$$
$$y + 3 = 0 \qquad y - 1 = 0$$
$$y = -3 \qquad y = 1$$
The solutions are −3 and 1.

50.
$$\frac{2p-1}{p-2} + p = 8$$
$$(p-2)\left(\frac{2p-1}{p-2} + p\right) = (p-2)8$$
$$(p-2)\frac{2p-1}{p-2} + (p-2)p = 8p - 16$$
$$2p - 1 + p^2 - 2p = 8p - 16$$
$$p^2 - 1 = 8p - 16$$
$$p^2 - 8p + 15 = 0$$
$$(p-5)(p-3) = 0$$
$$p - 5 = 0 \qquad p - 3 = 0$$
$$p = 5 \qquad p = 3$$
The solutions are 5 and 3.

51.
$$\frac{3r+2}{r+2} - 2r = 1$$
$$(r+2)\left(\frac{3r+2}{r+2} - 2r\right) = (r+2)1$$
$$(r+2)\frac{3r+2}{r+2} - (r+2)2r = r+2$$
$$3r+2-2r^2-4r = r+2$$
$$-2r^2-r+2 = r+2$$
$$-2r^2-2r = 0$$
$$-2r(r+1) = 0$$
$$-2r = 0 \qquad r+1 = 0$$
$$r = 0 \qquad r = -1$$
The solutions are 0 and -1.

52.
$$\frac{2v+3}{v+4} + 3v = 4$$
$$(v+4)\left(\frac{2v+3}{v+4} + 3v\right) = (v+4)4$$
$$(v+4)\frac{2v+3}{v+4} + (v+4)3v = 4v+16$$
$$2v+3+3v^2+12v = 4v+16$$
$$3v^2+14v+3 = 4v+16$$
$$3v^2+10v-13 = 0$$
$$(3v+13)(v-1) = 0$$
$$3v+13 = 0 \qquad v-1 = 0$$
$$3v = -13 \qquad v = 1$$
$$v = -\frac{13}{3}$$
The solutions are $-\dfrac{13}{3}$ and 1.

53.
$$\frac{2}{2x+1} + \frac{1}{x} = 3$$
$$x(2x+1)\left(\frac{2}{2x+1} + \frac{1}{x}\right) = x(2x+1)3$$
$$x(2x+1)\frac{2}{2x+1} + x(2x+1)\frac{1}{x} = 3x(2x+1)$$
$$2x+2x+1 = 6x^2+3x$$
$$4x+1 = 6x^2+3x$$
$$0 = 6x^2-x-1$$
$$0 = (2x-1)(3x+1)$$
$$2x-1 = 0 \qquad 3x+1 = 0$$
$$2x = 1 \qquad 3x = -1$$
$$x = \frac{1}{2} \qquad x = -\frac{1}{3}$$
The solutions are $\dfrac{1}{2}$ and $-\dfrac{1}{3}$.

54.
$$\frac{3}{s} - \frac{2}{2s-1} = 1$$
$$s(2s-1)\left(\frac{3}{s} - \frac{2}{2s-1}\right) = s(2s-1)1$$
$$s(2s-1)\frac{3}{s} - s(2s-1)\frac{2}{2s-1} = 2s^2-s$$
$$(2s-1)3 - s(2) = 2s^2-s$$
$$6s-3-2s = 2s^2-s$$
$$0 = 2s^2-5s+3$$
$$0 = (2s-3)(s-1)$$
$$2s-3 = 0 \qquad s-1 = 0$$
$$2s = 3 \qquad s = 1$$
$$s = \frac{3}{2}$$
The solutions are $\dfrac{3}{2}$ and 1.

55.
$$\frac{16}{z-2}+\frac{16}{z+2}=6$$
$$(z-2)(z+2)\left(\frac{16}{z-2}+\frac{16}{z+2}\right)=(z-2)(z+2)6$$
$$(z-2)(z+2)\frac{16}{z-2}+(z-2)(z+2)\frac{16}{z+2}=(z^2-4)6$$
$$(z+2)16+(z-2)16=6z^2-24$$
$$16z+32+16z-32=6z^2-24$$
$$32z=6z^2-24$$
$$0=6z^2-32z-24$$
$$0=2(3z^2-16z-12)$$
$$0=2(3z+2)(z-6)$$

$$3z+2=0 \qquad z-6=0$$
$$3z=-2 \qquad \ \ z=6$$
$$z=-\frac{2}{3}$$

The solutions are $-\frac{2}{3}$ and 6.

56.
$$\frac{2}{y+1}+\frac{1}{y-1}=1$$
$$(y+1)(y-1)\left(\frac{2}{y+1}+\frac{1}{y-1}\right)=(y+1)(y-1)1$$
$$(y+1)(y-1)\frac{2}{y+1}+(y+1)(y-1)\frac{1}{y-1}=y^2-1$$
$$(y-1)2+(y+1)1=y^2-1$$
$$2y-2+y+1=y^2-1$$
$$3y-1=y^2-1$$
$$0=y^2-3y$$
$$0=y(y-3)$$

$$y=0 \qquad y-3=0$$
$$\qquad \qquad \ y=3$$

The solutions are 0 and 3.

57.
$$\frac{t}{t-2}+\frac{2}{t-1}=4$$
$$(t-2)(t-1)\left(\frac{t}{t-2}+\frac{2}{t-1}\right)=(t-2)(t-1)4$$
$$(t-2)(t-1)\frac{t}{t-2}+(t-2)(t-1)\frac{2}{t-1}=(t^2-3t+2)4$$
$$(t-1)t+(t-2)2=4t^2-12t+8$$
$$t^2-t+2t-4=4t^2-12t+8$$
$$t^2+t-4=4t^2-12t+8$$
$$0=3t^2-13t+12$$
$$0=(3t-4)(t-3)$$

$$3t-4=0 \qquad t-3=0$$
$$3t=4 \qquad \ \ t=3$$
$$t=\frac{4}{3}$$

The solutions are $\frac{4}{3}$ and 3.

58.

$$\frac{4t+1}{t+4}+\frac{3t-1}{t+1}=2$$

$$(t+4)(t+1)\left(\frac{4t+1}{t+4}+\frac{3t-1}{t+1}\right)=(t+4)(t+1)2$$

$$(t+4)(t+1)\frac{4t+1}{t+4}+(t+4)(t+1)\frac{3t-1}{t+1}=(t^2+5t+4)2$$

$$(t+1)(4t+1)+(t+4)(3t-1)=2t^2+10t+8$$

$$4t^2+5t+1+3t^2+11t-4=2t^2+10t+8$$

$$7t^2+16t-3=2t^2+10t+8$$

$$5t^2+6t-11=0$$

$$(5t+11)(t-1)=0$$

$$\begin{array}{ll} 5t+11=0 & t-1=0 \\ 5t=-11 & t=1 \\ t=-\dfrac{11}{5} & \end{array}$$

The solutions are $-\dfrac{11}{5}$ and 1.

59.

$$\frac{5}{2p-1}+\frac{4}{p+1}=2$$

$$(2p-1)(p+1)\left(\frac{5}{2p-1}+\frac{4}{p+1}\right)=2(p-1)(p+1)2$$

$$(2p-1)(p+1)\frac{5}{2p-1}+(2p-1)(p+1)\frac{4}{p+1}=(2p^2+p-1)2$$

$$(p+1)5+(2p-1)4=4p^2+2p-2$$

$$5p+5+8p-4=4p^2+2p-2$$

$$13p+1=4p^2+2p-2$$

$$0=4p^2-11p-3$$

$$0=(4p+1)(p-3)$$

$$\begin{array}{ll} 4p+1=0 & p-3=0 \\ 4p=-1 & p=3 \\ p=-\dfrac{1}{4} & \end{array}$$

The solutions are $-\dfrac{1}{4}$ and 3.

60.

$$\frac{3w}{2w+3}+\frac{2}{w+2}=1$$

$$(2w+3)(w+2)\left(\frac{3w}{2w+3}+\frac{2}{w+2}\right)=(2w+3)(w+2)1$$

$$(2w+3)(w+2)\frac{3w}{2w+3}+(2w+3)(w+2)\frac{2}{w+2}=2w^2+7w+6$$

$$(w+2)3w+(2w+3)2=2w^2+7w+6$$

$$3w^2+6w+4w+6=2w^2+7w+6$$

$$3w^2+10w+6=2w^2+7w+6$$

$$w^2+3w=0$$

$$w(w+3)=0$$

$$\begin{array}{ll} w=0 & w+3=0 \\ & w=-3 \end{array}$$

The solutions are 0 and -3.

61.
$$\frac{2v}{v+2} + \frac{3}{v+4} = 1$$

$$(v+2)(v+4)\left(\frac{2v}{v+2} + \frac{3}{v+4}\right) = (v+2)(v+4)1$$

$$(v+2)(v+4)\frac{2v}{v+2} + (v+2)(v+4)\frac{3}{v+4} = v^2 + 6v + 8$$

$$(v+4)2v + (v+2)3 = v^2 + 6v + 8$$

$$2v^2 + 8v + 3v + 6 = v^2 + 6v + 8$$

$$2v^2 + 11v + 6 = v^2 + 6v + 8$$

$$v^2 + 5v - 2 = 0$$

$$v = \frac{-b \pm \sqrt{b^2 - 4ac}}{2a} = \frac{-5 \pm \sqrt{5^2 - 4(1)(-2)}}{2(1)} = \frac{-5 \pm \sqrt{25 + 8}}{2} = \frac{-5 \pm \sqrt{33}}{2}$$

The solutions are $\dfrac{-5 + \sqrt{33}}{2}$ and $\dfrac{-5 - \sqrt{33}}{2}$.

62.
$$\frac{x+3}{x+1} - \frac{x-2}{x+3} = 5$$

$$(x+1)(x+3)\left(\frac{x+3}{x+1} - \frac{x-2}{x+3}\right) = (x+1)(x+3)5$$

$$(x+1)(x+3)\frac{x+3}{x+1} - (x+1)(x+3)\frac{x-2}{x+3} = (x^2 + 4x + 3)5$$

$$(x+3)(x+3) - (x+1)(x-2) = 5x^2 + 20x + 15$$

$$x^2 + 6x + 9 - (x^2 - x - 2) = 5x^2 + 20x + 15$$

$$x^2 + 6x + 9 - x^2 + x + 2 = 5x^2 + 20x + 15$$

$$7x + 11 = 5x^2 + 20x + 15$$

$$0 = 5x^2 + 13x + 4$$

$$x = \frac{-b \pm \sqrt{b^2 - 4ac}}{2a} = \frac{-13 \pm \sqrt{13^2 - 4(5)(4)}}{2(5)} = \frac{-13 \pm \sqrt{169 - 80}}{10} = \frac{-13 \pm \sqrt{89}}{10}$$

The solutions are $\dfrac{-13 + \sqrt{89}}{10}$ and $\dfrac{-13 - \sqrt{89}}{10}$.

Applying Concepts 8.3

63.
$$\frac{x^2}{4}+\frac{x}{2}=6$$

$$4\left(\frac{x^2}{4}+\frac{x}{2}\right)=4(6)$$

$$x^2+2x=24$$

$$x^2+2x-24=0$$

$$(x+6)(x-4)=0$$

$$x+6=0 \qquad x-4=0$$

$$x=-6 \qquad\quad x=4$$

The solutions are –6 and 4.

64.
$$3\left(\frac{x+1}{2}\right)^2=54$$

$$3\left(\frac{x^2+2x+1}{4}\right)=54$$

$$\frac{x^2+2x+1}{4}=18$$

$$4\left(\frac{x^2+2x+1}{4}\right)=4(18)$$

$$x^2+2x+1=72$$

$$x^2+2x-71=0$$

$$x=\frac{-b\pm\sqrt{b^2-4ac}}{2a}$$

$$=\frac{-2\pm\sqrt{2^2-4(1)(-71)}}{2(1)}$$

$$=\frac{-2\pm\sqrt{4+284}}{2}$$

$$=\frac{-2\pm\sqrt{288}}{2}$$

$$=\frac{-2\pm12\sqrt{2}}{2}$$

$$=-1\pm6\sqrt{2}$$

The solutions are $-1+6\sqrt{2}$ and $-1-6\sqrt{2}$.

65.
$$\frac{x+2}{3}+\frac{2}{x-2}=3$$

$$3(x-2)\left(\frac{x+2}{3}+\frac{2}{x-2}\right)=3(x-2)3$$

$$(x-2)(x+2)+3\cdot2=9(x-2)$$

$$x^2-4+6=9x-18$$

$$x^2+2=9x-18$$

$$x^2-9x+20=0$$

$$(x-4)(x-5)=0$$

$$x-4=0 \qquad x-5=0$$

$$x=4 \qquad\quad x=5$$

The solutions are 4 and 5.

66.
$$\frac{x^4}{4}+1=\frac{5x^2}{4}$$

$$4\left(\frac{x^4}{4}+1\right)=4\left(\frac{5x^2}{4}\right)$$

$$x^4+4=5x^2$$

$$x^4-5x^2+4=0$$

$$(x^2)^2-5(x^2)+4=0$$

$$u^2-5u+4=0$$

$$(u-1)(u-4)=0$$

$$u-1=0 \qquad u-4=0$$

$$u=1 \qquad\quad u=4$$

Replace u by x^2.

$$x^2=1 \qquad\qquad x^2=4$$

$$\sqrt{x^2}=\sqrt{1} \qquad \sqrt{x^2}=\sqrt{4}$$

$$x=\pm1 \qquad\qquad x=\pm2$$

The solutions are 1, –1, 2, and –2.

67.
$$\frac{x^4}{3}-\frac{8x^2}{3}=3$$

$$3\left(\frac{x^4}{3}-\frac{8x^2}{3}\right)=3(3)$$

$$x^4-8x^2=9$$

$$x^4-8x^2-9=0$$

$$(x^2)^2-8(x^2)-9=0$$

$$u^2-8u-9=0$$

$$(u-9)(u+1)=0$$

$$u-9=0 \qquad u+1=0$$

$$u=9 \qquad\quad u=-1$$

Replace u by x^2.

$$x^2=9 \qquad\qquad x^2=-1$$

$$\sqrt{x^2}=\sqrt{9} \qquad \sqrt{x^2}=\sqrt{-1}$$

$$x=\pm3 \qquad\qquad x=\pm i$$

The solutions are 3, –3, i, and $-i$.

68.
$$\frac{x^2}{4} + \frac{x}{2} + \frac{1}{8} = 0$$

$$8\left(\frac{x^2}{4} + \frac{x}{2} + \frac{1}{8}\right) = 8(0)$$

$$2x^2 + 4x + 1 = 0$$

$$x = \frac{-b \pm \sqrt{b^2 - 4ac}}{2a}$$

$$= \frac{-4 \pm \sqrt{4^2 - 4(2)(1)}}{2(2)}$$

$$= \frac{-4 \pm \sqrt{16 - 8}}{4}$$

$$= \frac{-4 \pm \sqrt{8}}{4}$$

$$= \frac{-4 \pm 2\sqrt{2}}{4}$$

$$= \frac{-2 \pm \sqrt{2}}{2}$$

The solutions are $\dfrac{-2 + \sqrt{2}}{2}$ and $\dfrac{-2 - \sqrt{2}}{2}$.

69.
$$\frac{x^4}{8} + \frac{x^2}{4} = 3$$

$$8\left(\frac{x^4}{8} + \frac{x^2}{4}\right) = 8(3)$$

$$x^4 + 2x^2 = 24$$

$$x^4 + 2x^2 - 24 = 0$$

$$(x^2)^2 + 2(x^2) - 24 = 0$$

$$u^2 + 2u - 24 = 0$$

$$(u + 6)(u - 4) = 0$$

$$u + 6 = 0 \qquad u - 4 = 0$$

$$u = -6 \qquad u = 4$$

Replace u by x^2.

$$x^2 = -6 \qquad\qquad x^2 = 4$$

$$\sqrt{x^2} = \sqrt{-6} \qquad \sqrt{x^2} = \sqrt{4}$$

$$x = \pm i\sqrt{6} \qquad\qquad x = \pm 2$$

The solutions are $2, -2, i\sqrt{6}$, and $-i\sqrt{6}$.

70.
$$\sqrt{x^4 - 2} = x$$

$$(\sqrt{x^4 - 2})^2 = x^2$$

$$x^4 - 2 = x^2$$

$$x^4 - x^2 - 2 = 0$$

$$(x^2)^2 - x^2 - 2 = 0$$

$$u^2 - u - 2 = 0$$

$$(u - 2)(u + 1) = 0$$

$$u - 2 = 0 \quad u + 1 = 0$$

$$u = 2 \qquad u = -1$$

Replace u by x^2.

$$x^2 = 2 \qquad\qquad x^2 = -1$$

$$\sqrt{x^2} = \sqrt{2} \qquad \sqrt{x^2} = \sqrt{-1}$$

$$x = \pm\sqrt{2} \qquad\qquad x = \pm i$$

$-\sqrt{2}$ and $-i$ do not check as solutions.

$\sqrt{2}$ and i check as solutions.

The solutions are $\sqrt{2}$ and i.

71.
$$\sqrt{x^4 + 4} = 2x$$

$$(\sqrt{x^4 + 4})^2 = (2x)^2$$

$$x^4 + 4 = 4x^2$$

$$x^4 - 4x^2 + 4 = 0$$

$$(x^2)^2 - 4(x^2) + 4 = 0$$

$$u^2 - 4u + 4 = 0$$

$$(u - 2)(u - 2) = 0$$

$$u - 2 = 0 \quad u - 2 = 0$$

$$u = 2 \qquad u = 2$$

Replace u by x^2.

$$x^2 = 2$$

$$\sqrt{x^2} = \sqrt{2}$$

$$x = \pm\sqrt{2}$$

$\sqrt{2}$ checks as a solution.

$-\sqrt{2}$ does not check as a solution.

The solution is $\sqrt{2}$.

72.
$$(\sqrt{x} - 2)^2 - 5\sqrt{x} + 14 = 0$$

$$(\sqrt{x} - 2)^2 - 5\sqrt{x} + 10 + 4 = 0$$

$$(\sqrt{x} - 2)^2 - 5(\sqrt{x} - 2) + 4 = 0$$

Let $u = \sqrt{x} - 2$.

$$u^2 - 5u + 4 = 0$$

$$(u - 4)(u - 1) = 0$$

$$u - 4 = 0 \qquad u - 1 = 0$$

$$u = 4 \qquad\qquad u = 1$$

Replace u by $\sqrt{x} - 2$.

$$\sqrt{x} - 2 = 4 \qquad\qquad \sqrt{x} - 2 = 1$$

$$\sqrt{x} = 6 \qquad\qquad \sqrt{x} = 3$$

$$(\sqrt{x})^2 = 6^2 \qquad (\sqrt{x})^2 = 3^2$$

$$x = 36 \qquad\qquad x = 9$$

The solutions are 36 and 9.

73.
$$(\sqrt{x}+3)^2 - 4\sqrt{x} - 17 = 0$$
$$(\sqrt{x}+3)^2 - 4\sqrt{x} - 12 - 5 = 0$$
$$(\sqrt{x}+3)^2 - 4(\sqrt{x}+3) - 5 = 0$$
Let $u = \sqrt{x}+3$.
$$u^2 - 4u - 5 = 0$$
$$(u-5)(u+1) = 0$$

$u - 5 = 0$ $u + 1 = 0$
$u = 5$ $u = -1$

Replace u by $\sqrt{x}+3$.

$\sqrt{x}+3 = 5$	$\sqrt{x}+3 = -1$
$\sqrt{x} = 2$	$\sqrt{x} = -4$
$(\sqrt{x})^2 = 2^2$	$(\sqrt{x})^2 = (-4)^2$
$x = 4$	$x = 16$

16 does not check in the original equation.
The solution is 4.

74. a.
$$1 - \frac{x^2}{29.7366} \ge 0$$
$$\frac{29.7366 - x^2}{29.7366} \ge 0$$
$$29.7366 - x^2 \ge 0$$
$$29.7366 \ge x^2$$
The domain of the equation is
$$\left\{ x \mid -\sqrt{29.7366} \le x \le \sqrt{29.7366} \right\}.$$

b.

The $\pm$ symbol occurs in the equation so that the graph represents the entire shape of the football.

c.
$$y = 3.3041\sqrt{1 - \frac{x^2}{29.7366}}$$
$$y = 3.3041\sqrt{1 - \frac{3^2}{29.7366}} \approx 2.7592$$
The radius of the football is approximately 2.7592 in.

Section 8.4

Concept Review 8.4

1. Sometimes true
If $x = 2$,
$x^2 = 2^2$ and $(x+2)^2 = 4^2$.
These are the squares of two consecutive even integers.

2. Always true

3. Always true

4. Always true

Objective 8.4.1 Exercises

1. Strategy
This is a geometry problem.
The width of the rectangle: x
The length of the rectangle: $2x + 8$
The area of the rectangle is 640 ft^2. Use the equation for the area of a rectangle
$(A = L \cdot W)$.

Solution
$$A = L \cdot W$$
$$640 = (2x+8)x$$
$$640 = 2x^2 + 8x$$
$$0 = 2x^2 + 8x - 640$$
$$0 = 2(x^2 + 4x - 320)$$
$$0 = 2(x+20)(x-16)$$

$x + 20 = 0$ $x - 16 = 0$
$x = -20$ $x = 16$

Since the width of the rectangle cannot be negative, –20 cannot be a solution.
$2x + 8 = 2(16) + 8 = 32 + 8 = 40$
The width of the rectangle is 16 ft.
The length of the rectangle is 40 ft.

2. Strategy
This is a geometry problem.
The surface area of the cone is 11.25π in^2 and the slant height is 6 in. Use the formula for the surface area and solve for r $(A = \pi r^2 + \pi rs)$.

Solution
$$A = \pi r^2 + \pi rs$$
$$11.25\pi = \pi r^2 + \pi r(6)$$
$$11.25\pi = \pi r^2 + 6\pi r$$
$$0 = \pi r^2 + 6\pi r - 11.25\pi$$
$$0 = \pi(r^2 + 6r - 11.25)$$
$$0 = \pi(r - 1.5)(r + 7.5)$$

$r - 1.5 = 0$ $r + 7.5 = 0$
$r = 1.5$ $r = -7.5$

Since the radius of the cone cannot be negative, –7.5 cannot be a solution. The radius of the cone is 1.5 in.

3. Strategy
This is a geometry problem.
The width of the rectangle: x
The length of the rectangle: $3x - 2$
The area of the rectangle is 65 ft^2. Use the equation for the area of a rectangle ($A = L \cdot W$).

Solution
$$A = L \cdot W$$
$$65 = (3x - 2)x$$
$$65 = 3x^2 - 2x$$
$$0 = 3x^2 - 2x - 65$$
$$0 = (3x + 13)(x - 5)$$
$$3x + 13 = 0 \qquad x - 5 = 0$$
$$x = -\frac{13}{3} \qquad\quad x = 5$$

Since the width cannot be negative, $-\dfrac{13}{3}$ cannot be a solution.
$3x + 2 = 3(5) - 2 = 15 - 2 = 13$
The length is of the rectangle is 13 ft.
The width of the rectangle is 5 ft.

4. Strategy
This is a geometry problem.
The width of the rectangle: x
The length of the rectangle: $2x - 2$
The area of the rectangle is 180 cm^2.
Use the equation for the area of a rectangle ($A = L \cdot W$).

Solution
$$A = L \cdot W$$
$$180 = (2x - 2)x$$
$$180 = 2x^2 - 2x$$
$$0 = 2x^2 - 2x - 180$$
$$0 = 2(x^2 - x - 90)$$
$$0 = 2(x - 10)(x + 9)$$
$$x - 10 = 0 \qquad x + 9 = 0$$
$$x = 10 \qquad\quad x = -9$$

Since the width of the rectangle cannot be negative, -9 cannot be a solution.
$2x - 2 = 2(10) - 2 = 20 - 2 = 18$
The width of the rectangle is 10 cm.
The length of the rectangle is 18 cm.

5. Strategy
This is a geometry problem.
The side of the square: x
The length of the side of the square that is folded up: $x - 20$
The height of the box : 10
The volume of the box is 49,000 cm^3. Use the equation for the volume ($A = L \cdot W \cdot H$).

Solution
$$A = L \cdot W \cdot H$$
$$49{,}000 = (x - 20)(x - 20)10$$
$$4900 = x^2 - 40x + 400$$
$$0 = x^2 - 40x - 4500$$
$$0 = (x - 90)(x + 50)$$
$$x - 90 = 0 \qquad x + 50 = 0$$
$$x = 90 \qquad\quad x = -50$$

Since the width cannot be negative, -50 cannot be a solution.
The cardboard needs to be 90 cm by 90 cm.

6. Strategy

This is a geometry problem.

The width of Colorado: x

The length of Colorado: $x + 111$

The area of Colorado is 104,000 mi². Use the equation for the area of a rectangle ($A = L \cdot W$).

Solution

$$A = L \cdot W$$
$$104{,}000 = (x + 111)x$$
$$104{,}000 = x^2 + 111x$$
$$0 = x^2 + 111x - 104{,}000$$
$$x = \frac{-111 \pm \sqrt{(111)^2 - 4(1)(-104{,}000)}}{2(1)}$$
$$= \frac{-111 \pm \sqrt{428{,}321}}{2}$$

$x = 272$ or -383

Since the dimensions cannot be negative, -383 cannot be a solution.

$x + 111 = 272 + 111 = 383$

Colorado is 272 mi by 383 mi.

7. Strategy

This is a uniform motion problem.

Rate of truck on return trip: r

	Distance	Rate	Time
With load	550	$r - 5$	$\dfrac{550}{r-5}$
Without load	550	r	$\dfrac{550}{r}$

The total time of the trip was 21 h.

Solution

$$\frac{550}{r-5} + \frac{550}{r} = 21$$
$$r(r-5)\left(\frac{550}{r-5} + \frac{550}{r}\right) = r(r-5)21$$
$$550r + 550(r-5) = (r^2 - 5r)21$$
$$550r + 550r - 2750 = 21r^2 - 105r$$
$$1100r - 2750 = 21r^2 - 105r$$
$$0 = 21r^2 - 1205 + 2750$$
$$0 = (21r - 50)(r - 55)$$

$21r - 50 = 0 \qquad r - 55 = 0$

$21r = 0 \qquad\qquad r = 55$

$r = \dfrac{50}{21}$

$r - 5 = \dfrac{50}{21} = \dfrac{50 - 105}{21} = -\dfrac{55}{21}$ or

$r - 5 = 55 - 5 = 50$

$\dfrac{50}{21}$ cannot be a solution because then the rate of the trip with the load would be negative. The rate of the truck on the return trip was 55 mph.

8. Strategy

Rate of the second cyclist: r

Rate of the first cyclist: $r + 10$

	Distance	Rate	Time
First cyclist	210	$r + 10$	$\dfrac{210}{r+10}$
Second cyclist	210	r	$\dfrac{210}{r}$

The first cyclist covers the distance in 2.4 h less time than the second cyclist.

$$\frac{210}{r} = \frac{210}{r+10} + 2.4$$

Solution

$$\frac{210}{r} = \frac{210}{r+10} + 2.4$$
$$r(r+10)\left(\frac{210}{r}\right) = r(r+10)\left(\frac{210}{r+10} + 2.4\right)$$
$$(r+10)(210) = 210r + 24r(r+10)$$
$$210r + 2100 = 210r + 2.4r^2 + 24r$$
$$0 = 2.4r^2 + 24r - 2100$$
$$0 = 2.4(r^2 + 10r - 875)$$
$$0 = 2.4(r + 35)(r - 25)$$

$r + 35 = 0 \qquad r - 25 = 0$

$r = -35 \qquad\qquad r = 25$

The rate cannot be negative, so -35 is not a solution.

$r + 10 = 25 + 10 = 35$

The first cyclist traveled 35 mph.

9. Strategy

To find the time for a projectile to return to Earth, substitute the values for height ($s = 0$) and initial velocity ($v_0 = 200$ ft/s) and solve for t.

Solution

$s = v_0 t - 16t^2$

$0 = 200t - 16t^2$

$0 = 8t(25 - 2t)$

$8t = 0 \qquad 25 - 2t = 0$

$t = 0 \qquad\qquad -2t = -25$

$\qquad\qquad\qquad t = 12.5$

The solution $t = 0$ is not appropriate because the projectile has not yet left Earth. The rocket takes 12.5 s to return to Earth.

10. Strategy

To find the time for a projectile to reach a height of 64 ft, substitute for height ($s = 64$) and initial velocity ($v_0 = 128$ ft/s) and solve for t.

Solution

$$s = v_0 t - 16t^2$$
$$64 = 128t - 16t^2$$
$$16t^2 - 128t + 64 = 0$$
$$16(t^2 - 8t + 4) = 0$$
$$t^2 - 8t + 4 = 0$$

$$t = \frac{-b \pm \sqrt{b^2 - 4ac}}{2a}$$
$$= \frac{8 \pm \sqrt{64 - 4(1)(4)}}{2(1)}$$
$$= \frac{8 \pm \sqrt{48}}{2}$$
$$\approx 7.46 \text{ or } 0.54$$

The projectile first reaches the height of 64 ft at 0.54 s after it is fired and then again at 7.46 s after it is fired.

11. Strategy

To find the maximum speed, substitute for distance ($d = 150$) and solve for v.

Solution

$$d = 0.019v^2 + 0.69v$$
$$150 = 0.019v^2 + 0.69v$$
$$0 = 0.019v^2 + 0.69v - 150$$
$$v = \frac{-b \pm \sqrt{b^2 - 4ac}}{2a}$$
$$= \frac{-0.69 \pm \sqrt{(0.69)^2 - 4(0.019)(-150)}}{2(0.019)}$$
$$= \frac{-0.69 \pm \sqrt{11.8761}}{0.038}$$
$$= 72.5 \text{ or } -108.85$$

Since the speed cannot be negative, -108.85 cannot be a solution.

The maximum speed a driver can be going and still be able to stop within 150 m is 72.5 km/h.

12. Strategy

To determine whether the ball lands in the net, substitute for distance from the goal ($x = 36$) and solve for h.

Solution

$$h = -0.002x^2 + 0.35x$$

$$h = -0.002(36)^2 + 0.35(36)$$
$$h = 10.008$$

Since the ball's height is 10.008 ft and the soccer goal is only 8 ft high, the ball will not land in the net.

13. Strategy

To find when the rocket will be 300 ft above the ground, substitute for height ($h = 300$) and solve for t.

Solution

$$h = -16t^2 + 200t$$
$$300 = -16t^2 + 200t$$
$$0 = -16t^2 + 200t - 300$$
$$t = \frac{-b \pm \sqrt{b^2 - 4ac}}{2a}$$
$$t = \frac{-200 \pm \sqrt{(200)^2 - 4(-16)(-300)}}{2(-16)}$$
$$t = \frac{-200 \pm \sqrt{20,800}}{-32}$$
$$t = 1.74 \text{ or } 10.76$$

The rocket will be 300 ft above the ground 1.74 s and 10.76 s after the launch.

14. Strategy

To find when the diver will enter the water, substitute for height ($h = 0$) and solve for t.

Solution

$$h = -4.9t^2 + 3.2t + 10.5$$
$$0 = -4.9t^2 + 3.2t + 10.5$$
$$t = \frac{-b \pm \sqrt{b^2 - 4ac}}{2a}$$
$$t = \frac{-3.2 \pm \sqrt{(3.2)^2 - 4(-4.9)(10.5)}}{2(-4.9)}$$
$$t = \frac{-3.2 \pm \sqrt{216.04}}{-9.8}$$
$$t \approx -1.17 \text{ or } 1.83$$

Since the time cannot be negative, -1.17 cannot be a solution.

The diver will enter the water 1.83 s after the beginning of the dive.

15. Strategy
This is a work problem.
Time for the smaller pipe to fill the tank: t
Time for the larger pipe to fill the tank: $t - 6$

	Rate	Time	Part
Smaller pipe	$\dfrac{1}{t}$	4	$\dfrac{4}{t}$
Larger pipe	$\dfrac{1}{t-6}$	4	$\dfrac{4}{t-6}$

The sum of the parts of the task completed must equal 1.
$$\frac{4}{t} + \frac{4}{t-6} = 1$$

Solution
$$\frac{4}{t} + \frac{4}{t-6} = 1$$
$$t(t-6)\left(\frac{4}{t} + \frac{4}{t-6}\right) = t(t-6)1$$
$$(t-6)4 + 4t = t^2 - 6t$$
$$4t - 24 + 4t = t^2 - 6t$$
$$8t - 24 = t^2 - 6t$$
$$0 = t^2 - 14t + 24$$
$$0 = (t-12)(t-2)$$

$t - 12 = 0 \qquad t - 2 = 0$
$\quad t = 12 \qquad\qquad t = 2$
$t - 6 = 12 - 6 = 6 \qquad t - 6 = 2 - 6 = -4$

The solution -4 is not possible, since time cannot be a negative number.
It would take the larger pipe 6 min to fill the tank.
It would take the smaller pipe 12 min to fill the tank.

16. Strategy
This is a work problem.
Time for the larger heating unit to melt the iron: t
Time for the smaller heating unit to melt the iron: $t + 8$

	Rate	Time	Part
Larger unit	$\dfrac{1}{t}$	3	$\dfrac{3}{t}$
Smaller unit	$\dfrac{1}{t+8}$	3	$\dfrac{3}{t+8}$

The sum of the parts of the task completed must equal 1.
$$\frac{3}{t} + \frac{3}{t+8} = 1$$

Solution
$$\frac{3}{t} + \frac{3}{t+8} = 1$$
$$t(t+8)\left(\frac{3}{t} + \frac{3}{t+8}\right) = t(t+8)1$$
$$(t+8)3 + 3t = t^2 + 8t$$
$$3t + 24 + 3t = t^2 + 8t$$
$$6t + 24 = t^2 + 8t$$
$$0 = t^2 + 2t - 24$$
$$0 = (t-4)(t+6)$$

$t - 4 = 0 \qquad t + 6 = 0$
$\quad t = 4 \qquad\qquad t = -6$

The solution -6 is not possible, since time cannot be a negative number.
$t + 8 = 4 + 8 = 12$
It would take the larger heating unit 4 h to melt the iron. It would take the smaller heating unit 12 h to melt the iron.

17. Strategy
This is a distance-rate problem.
Rate of the cruise ship for the first 40 mi: r
Rate of the cruise ship for the next 60 mi: $r + 5$

	Distance	Rate	Time
First 40 mi	40	r	$\dfrac{40}{r}$
Next 60 mi	60	$r + 5$	$\dfrac{60}{r+5}$

The total time of travel was 8 h.
$$\frac{40}{r} + \frac{60}{r+5} = 8$$

Solution
$$\frac{40}{r} + \frac{60}{r+5} = 8$$
$$r(r+5)\left(\frac{40}{r} + \frac{60}{r+5}\right) = r(r+5)8$$
$$(r+5)40 + 60r = 8r(r+5)$$
$$40r + 200 + 60r = 8r^2 + 40r$$
$$100r + 200 = 8r^2 + 40r$$
$$0 = 8r^2 - 60r - 200$$
$$0 = 4(2r^2 - 15r - 50)$$
$$0 = 4(2r + 5)(r - 10)$$

$$2r + 5 = 0 \qquad\qquad r - 10 = 0$$
$$2r = -5 \qquad\qquad\quad r = 10$$
$$r = -\frac{5}{2}$$

The solution $-\dfrac{5}{2}$ is not possible, since rate

cannot be a negative number. The rate of the cruise ship for the first 40 mi was 10 mph.

18. Strategy
This is a distance-rate problem.
Rate for the first 60 mi: r
Rate for the next 40 mi: $r - 2$

	Distance	Rate	Time
First 60 mi	60	r	$\dfrac{60}{r}$
Next 40 mi	40	$r - 2$	$\dfrac{40}{r-2}$

The total time for the trip was 9 h.
$$\frac{60}{r} + \frac{40}{r-2} = 9$$

Solution
$$\frac{60}{r} + \frac{40}{r-2} = 9$$
$$r(r-2)\left(\frac{60}{r} + \frac{40}{r-2}\right) = r(r-2)9$$
$$60(r-2) + 40r = 9r(r-2)$$
$$60r - 120 + 40r = 9r^2 - 18r$$
$$100r - 120 = 9r^2 - 18r$$
$$0 = 9r^2 - 118r + 120$$
$$0 = (9r - 10)(r - 12)$$

$$9r - 10 = 0 \qquad\qquad r - 12 = 0$$
$$9r = 10 \qquad\qquad\quad r = 12$$
$$r = \frac{10}{9}$$

$$r - 2 = \frac{10}{9} - 2 \qquad r - 2 = 12 - 2$$
$$= -\frac{8}{9} \qquad\qquad\qquad = 10$$

The solution $-\dfrac{8}{9}$ is not possible, since rate cannot be a negative number. The rate of the cyclist during the first

60 mi was 12 mph.

19. Strategy

This is a distance-rate problem.

Rate of the wind: w

	Distance	Rate	Time
With wind	240	$100 + w$	$\dfrac{240}{100+w}$
Against wind	240	$100 - w$	$\dfrac{240}{100-w}$

The time with the wind is 1 h less than the time against the wind.

$$\frac{240}{100+w} = \frac{240}{100-w} - 1$$

Solution

$$\frac{240}{100+w} = \frac{240}{100-w} - 1$$

$$(100+w)(100-w)\left(\frac{240}{100+w}\right) = (100+w)(100-w)\left(\frac{240}{100-w} - 1\right)$$

$$240(100-w) = 240(100+w) - (100+w)(100-w)$$

$$24,000 - 240w = 24,000 + 240w - 10,000 + w^2$$

$$0 = w^2 + 480w - 10,000$$

$$0 = (w + 500)(w - 20)$$

$$w + 500 = 0 \qquad w - 20 = 0$$

$$w = -500 \qquad w = 20$$

The solution –500 is not possible, since rate cannot be a negative number.

The rate of the wind is 20 mph.

20. Strategy

This is a distance-rate problem.

Rate of the first car: r

Rate of the second car: $r + 10$

	Distance	Rate	Time
1st car	120	r	$\dfrac{120}{r}$
2nd car	120	$r + 10$	$\dfrac{120}{r+10}$

The second car makes the trip in 1 h less time.

$$\frac{120}{r} = \frac{120}{r+10} + 1$$

Solution

$$\frac{120}{r} = \frac{120}{r+10} + 1$$

$$r(r+10)\frac{120}{r} = r(r+10)\left(\frac{120}{r+10} + 1\right)$$

$$120(r+10) = 120r + r^2 + 10r$$

$$120r + 1200 = r^2 + 130r$$

$$0 = r^2 + 10r - 1200$$

$$0 = (r+40)(r-30)$$

$$r + 40 = 0 \qquad r - 30 = 0$$

$$r = -40 \qquad r = 30$$

The solution –40 is not possible, since rate cannot be a negative number.

$r + 10 = 30 + 10 = 40$

The speed of the first car is 30 mph. The speed of the second car is 40 mph.

21. Strategy
This is a distance-rate problem.
Rate of crew in calm water: x

	Distance	Rate	Time
With current	16	$x+2$	$\dfrac{16}{x+2}$
Against current	16	$x-2$	$\dfrac{16}{x-2}$

The total trip took 6 h.
$$\frac{16}{x+2}+\frac{16}{x-2}=6$$

Solution
$$\frac{16}{x+2}+\frac{16}{x-2}=6$$
$$(x+2)(x-2)\left(\frac{16}{x+2}+\frac{16}{x-2}\right)=(x+2)(x-2)6$$
$$16(x-2)+16(x+2)=6(x^2-4)$$
$$16x-32+16x+32=6x^2-24$$
$$32x=6x^2-24$$
$$0=6x^2-32x-24$$
$$0=2(3x^2-16x-12)$$
$$0=2(3x+2)(x-6)$$

$$3x+2=0 \qquad x-6=0$$
$$x=-\frac{2}{3} \qquad x=6$$

The solution $x=-\dfrac{2}{3}$ is not possible, since rate

cannot be a negative number.
The rate of the crew in calm water is 6 mph.

22. Strategy
This is a distance-rate problem.
Rate of the boat in still water: r

	Distance	Rate	Time
With current	30	$r+4$	$\dfrac{30}{r+4}$
Against current	30	$r-4$	$\dfrac{30}{r-4}$

The total time of the trip was 4 h.
$$\frac{30}{r+4}+\frac{30}{r-4}=4$$

Solution
$$\frac{30}{r+4}+\frac{30}{r-4}=4$$
$$(r+4)(r-4)\left(\frac{30}{r+4}+\frac{30}{r-4}\right)=(r+4)(r-4)4$$
$$(r-4)30+(r+4)30=(r^2-16)4$$
$$30r-120+30r+120=4r^2-64$$
$$60r=4r^2-64$$
$$0=4r^2-60r-64$$
$$0=4(r^2-15r-16)$$
$$0=4(r-16)(r+1)$$

$$r-16=0 \qquad r+1=0$$
$$r=16 \qquad r=-1$$

The solution −1 is not possible, since rate cannot
be a negative number. The rate of the boat in still
water is 16 mph.

Applying Concepts 8.4

23. Strategy

The numerator of the fraction: n

The denominator of the fraction: $n + 3$

The fraction: $\dfrac{n}{n+3}$

Four times the reciprocal of the fraction:

$4 \cdot \dfrac{n+3}{n} = \dfrac{4(n+3)}{n}$

The sum of the fraction and four times its

reciprocal is $\dfrac{17}{2}$.

Solution

$$\frac{n}{n+3} + \frac{4(n+3)}{n} = \frac{17}{2}$$

$$\frac{n}{n+3} + \frac{4n+12}{n} = \frac{17}{2}$$

$$2n(n+3)\left(\frac{n}{n+3} + \frac{4n+12}{n}\right) = 2n(n+3)\left(\frac{17}{2}\right)$$

$$2n^2 + 2(n+3)(4n+12) = n(n+3)(17)$$

$$2n^2 + 2(4n^2 + 24n + 36) = 17n(n+3)$$

$$2n^2 + 8n^2 + 48n + 72 = 17n^2 + 51n$$

$$10n^2 + 48n + 72 = 17n^2 + 51n$$

$$-7n^2 - 3n + 72 = 0$$

$$7n^2 + 3n - 72 = 0$$

$$(7n + 24)(n - 3) = 0$$

$$7n + 24 = 0 \qquad n - 3 = 0$$

$$7n = -24 \qquad\quad n = 3$$

$$n = -\frac{24}{7}$$

The numerator cannot be a fraction, so $-\dfrac{24}{7}$

cannot be a solution.

$$\frac{n}{n+3} = \frac{3}{3+3} = \frac{3}{6}$$

The fraction is $\dfrac{3}{6}$.

24. Strategy

This is an integer problem.

The first integer: n

Next consecutive even integer: $n + 2$

The difference between the cubes is 488.

Solution

$$(n+2)^3 - n^3 = 488$$

$$(n+2)(n+2)(n+2) - n^3 = 488$$

$$(n^2 + 4n + 4)(n+2) - n^3 = 488$$

$$(n^3 + 2n^2 + 4n^2 + 8n + 4n + 8) - n^3 = 488$$

$$n^3 + 6n^2 + 12n + 8 - n^3 = 488$$

$$6n^2 + 12n + 8 = 488$$

$$6n^2 + 12n - 480 = 0$$

$$6(n^2 + 2n - 80) = 0$$

$$n^2 + 2n - 80 = 0$$

$$(n - 8)(n + 10) = 0$$

$$n - 8 = 0 \qquad n + 10 = 0$$

$$n = 8 \qquad\quad n = -10$$

For $n = 8$, $n + 2 = 8 + 2 = 10$.

For $n = -10$, $n + 2 = -10 + 2 = -8$.

The integers are 8 and 10, or −10 and −8.

25. Strategy

This is a geometry problem.

Width of rectangular piece of cardboard: w

Length of rectangular piece of cardboard: $w + 8$

Width of open box: $w - 2(2) = w - 4$

Length of open box: $w + 8 - 2(2) = w + 4$

Height of open box: 2

Use the equation $V = lwh$.

Solution

$$V = lwh$$

$$256 = (w + 4)(w - 4)(2)$$

$$256 = (w^2 - 16)(2)$$

$$256 = 2w^2 - 32$$

$$0 = 2w^2 - 288$$

$$0 = 2(w^2 - 144)$$

$$0 = (w + 12)(w - 12)$$

$$w + 12 = 0 \qquad w - 12 = 0$$

$$w = -12 \qquad\quad w = 12$$

The width cannot be negative, so −12 is not a

solution.

$w - 4 = 12 - 4 = 8$

$w + 4 = 12 + 4 = 16$

The width is 8 cm.

The length is 16 cm.

The height is 2 cm.

26. a. Strategy

The maximum height occurs in the middle of the arch, when $x = 0$.

Solution

$$h(x) = -\frac{3}{64}x^2 + 27$$

$$h(0) = -\frac{3}{64}(0)^2 + 27$$

$$= 27$$

The maximum height of the arch is 27 ft.

b. Strategy

Let $x = 8$ in the height equation.

Solution

$$h(x) = -\frac{3}{64}x^2 + 27$$

$$h(8) = -\frac{3}{64}8^2 + 27 = 24$$

The arch is 24 ft high, 8 ft to the right of center.

c. Strategy

Let $h(x) = 8$ in the height equation. Solve for x.

Solution

$$h(x) = -\frac{3}{64}x^2 + 27$$

$$8 = -\frac{3}{64}x^2 + 27$$

$$-19 = -\frac{3}{64}x^2$$

$$\frac{1216}{3} = x^2$$

$$\pm 20.13 \approx x$$

The solution –20.13 is not possible, since distance cannot be a negative number.
The arch is 8 ft high, 20.13 ft from the center.

27. To find when the depth will be 10 cm, substitute 10 for d and solve for t.

$$d = 0.0034t^2 - 0.52518t + 20$$

$$10 = 0.0034t^2 - 0.52518t + 20$$

$$0 = 0.0034t^2 - 0.52518t + 10$$

$$t = \frac{-b \pm \sqrt{b^2 - 4ac}}{2a}$$

$$t = \frac{-(-0.52518) \pm \sqrt{(0.0034)^2 - 4(0.0034)(10)}}{2(0.0034)}$$

$$t = \frac{0.52518 \pm \sqrt{0.139814}}{0.0068}$$

$$t \approx 132.2 \text{ or } t \approx 22.2$$

The depth will first reach 10 cm in 22.2 s.

28. Strategy

This is a geometry problem.
Radius of the larger sphere: r_1
Radius of the smaller sphere: $r_2 = r_1 - 3$

Use the equation $V = \frac{4}{3}\pi r^3$.

The volumes of the spheres differ by 372π cm^3.

Solution

$$\frac{4}{3}\pi(r_1)^3 - \frac{4}{3}\pi(r_2)^3 = 372\pi$$

$$\frac{4}{3}\pi r_1^3 - \frac{4}{3}\pi(r_1 - 3)^3 = 372\pi$$

$$\frac{3}{4\pi}\left(\frac{4}{3}\pi r_1^3 - \frac{4}{3}\pi(r_1 - 3)^3\right) = \frac{3}{4\pi}(372\pi)$$

$$r_1^3 - (r_1 - 3)^3 = 279$$

$$r_1^3 - (r_1 - 3)(r_1 - 3)(r_1 - 3) = 279$$

$$r_1^3 - (r_1^2 - 6r_1 + 9)(r_1 - 3) = 279$$

$$r_1^3 - (r_1^3 - 3r_1^2 - 6r_1^2 + 18r_1 + 9r_1 - 27) = 279$$

$$r_1^3 - (r_1^3 - 9r_1^2 + 27r_1 - 27) = 279$$

$$r_1^3 - r_1^3 + 9r_1^2 - 27r_1 + 27 = 279$$

$$9r_1^2 - 27r_1 + 27 = 279$$

$$9r_1^2 - 27r_1 - 252 = 0$$

$$9(r_1^2 - 3r_1 - 28) = 0$$

$$r_1^2 - 3r_1 - 28 = 0$$

$$(r_1 - 7)(r_1 + 4) = 0$$

$$r_1 - 7 = 0 \qquad r_1 + 4 = 0$$

$$r_1 = 7 \qquad r_1 = -4$$

The radius cannot be negative, so –4 is not a solution.
The radius of the larger sphere is 7 cm.

29. Strategy
This is a geometry problem.
Use the Pythagorean formula $(a^2 + b^2 = c^2)$,
with the legs being $a = 1.5$, $b = 3.5$, and the
hypotenuse being
$c = x + 1.5$.

Solution
$$a^2 + b^2 = c^2$$
$$(1.5)^2 + (3.5)^2 = (x+1.5)^2$$
$$14.5 = (x+1.5)^2$$
$$\pm 3.8 \approx x + 1.5$$
$$3.8 = x + 1.5 \qquad -3.8 = x + 1.5$$
$$2.3 = x \qquad\qquad -5.3 = x$$
The solution $x = -5.3$ is not possible since
distance cannot be negative.
The bottom of the scoop of ice cream is 2.3 in.
from the bottom of the cone.

Section 8.5

Concept Review 8.5

1. Sometimes true
   The end points of $x^2 - 4 \le 0$ are included in the solution set.

2. Never true
   The solution set is $\{x \mid -2 < x < 2\} \cup \{x \mid x > 3\}$.

3. Sometimes true
   The solution set of $x^2 \le 0$ is $\{0\}$.

4. Always true

Objective 8.5.1 Exercises

1. It must be true either that $x - 3 > 0$ and $x - 5 > 0$
   or that $x - 3 < 0$ and $x - 5 < 0$. In other words,
   either both factors are positive or both factors are
   negative.

2. 3 is not possible element of the solution set
   because the value 3 makes the denominator 0.

3. $(x-4)(x+2) > 0$

   $\{x \mid x < -2 \text{ or } x > 4\}$

4. $(x+1)(x-3) > 0$

   $\{x \mid x < -1 \text{ or } x > 3\}$

5. $x^2 - 3x + 2 \ge 0$
   $(x-1)(x-2) \ge 0$

   $\{x \mid x \le 1 \text{ or } x \ge 2\}$

6. $x^2 + 5x + 6 > 0$
   $(x+2)(x+3) > 0$

   $\{x \mid x < -3 \text{ or } x > -2\}$

7. $x^2 - x - 12 < 0$
   $(x+3)(x-4) < 0$

   $\{x \mid -3 < x < 4\}$

8. $x^2 + x - 20 < 0$
   $(x+5)(x-4) < 0$

   $\{x \mid -5 < x < 4\}$

9. $(x-1)(x+2)(x-3) < 0$

   $\{x \mid x < -2 \text{ or } 1 < x < 3\}$

10. $(x+4)(x-2)(x-1) \ge 0$

    $\{x \mid -4 \le x \le 1 \text{ or } x \ge 2\}$

11. $\dfrac{x-4}{x+2} > 0$

    $\{x \mid x < -2 \text{ or } x > 4\}$

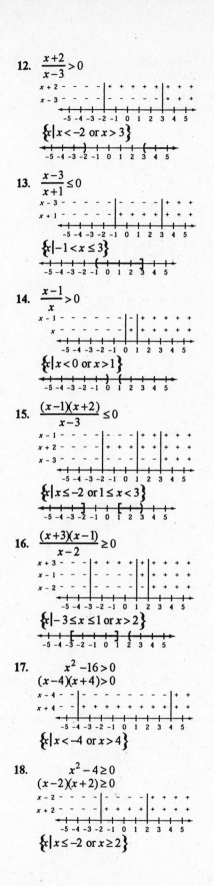

12. $\dfrac{x+2}{x-3} > 0$

$x+2$ — — — | + + + + + | + + +
$x-3$ — — — — — — — | + + +
-5 -4 -3 -2 -1 0 1 2 3 4 5

$\{x \mid x < -2 \text{ or } x > 3\}$
-5 -4 -3 -2 -1 0 1 2 3 4 5

13. $\dfrac{x-3}{x+1} \le 0$

$x-3$ — — — — — — — | + +
$x+1$ — — — — | + + + + + +
-5 -4 -3 -2 -1 0 1 2 3 4 5

$\{x \mid -1 < x \le 3\}$
-5 -4 -3 -2 -1 0 1 2 3 4 5

14. $\dfrac{x-1}{x} > 0$

$x-1$ — — — — — | + + + +
x — — — — | + + + + + +
-5 -4 -3 -2 -1 0 1 2 3 4 5

$\{x \mid x < 0 \text{ or } x > 1\}$
-5 -4 -3 -2 -1 0 1 2 3 4 5

15. $\dfrac{(x-1)(x+2)}{x-3} \le 0$

$x-1$ — — — | — — | + + + + +
$x+2$ — — | + + + + + + + +
$x-3$ — — — — — — — | + +
-5 -4 -3 -2 -1 0 1 2 3 4 5

$\{x \mid x \le -2 \text{ or } 1 \le x < 3\}$
-5 -4 -3 -2 -1 0 1 2 3 4 5

16. $\dfrac{(x+3)(x-1)}{x-2} \ge 0$

$x+3$ — — | + + + + | + + + +
$x-1$ — — — — — | + + + + +
$x-2$ — — — — — — | + + + +
-5 -4 -3 -2 -1 0 1 2 3 4 5

$\{x \mid -3 \le x \le 1 \text{ or } x > 2\}$
-5 -4 -3 -2 -1 0 1 2 3 4 5

17. $x^2 - 16 > 0$
$(x-4)(x+4) > 0$

$x-4$ — — — — — — — | + +
$x+4$ — | + + + + + + + + +
-5 -4 -3 -2 -1 0 1 2 3 4 5

$\{x \mid x < -4 \text{ or } x > 4\}$

18. $x^2 - 4 \ge 0$
$(x-2)(x+2) \ge 0$

$x-2$ — — — — | — — | + + +
$x+2$ — — — | + + + + + + +
-5 -4 -3 -2 -1 0 1 2 3 4 5

$\{x \mid x \le -2 \text{ or } x \ge 2\}$

19. $x^2 - 4x + 4 > 0$
$(x-2)(x-2) > 0$

$x-2$ — — — — — | + + +
$x-2$ — — — — — | + + +
-5 -4 -3 -2 -1 0 1 2 3 4 5

$\{x \mid x < 2 \text{ or } x > 2\}$

20. $x^2 + 6x + 9 > 0$
$(x+3)(x+3) > 0$

$x+3$ — — | + + + + + + + +
$x+3$ — — | + + + + + + + +
-5 -4 -3 -2 -1 0 1 2 3 4 5

$\{x \mid x < -3 \text{ or } x > -3\}$

21. $x^2 - 9x \le 36$
$x^2 - 9x - 36 \le 0$
$(x+3)(x-12) \le 0$

$x+3$ — — — — | + + + + | +
$x-12$ — — — — — — — — | +
-15 -12 -9 -6 -3 0 3 6 9 12 15

$\{x \mid -3 \le x \le 12\}$

22. $x^2 + 4x > 21$
$x^2 + 4x - 21 > 0$
$(x-3)(x+7) > 0$

$x-3$ — — | — — — — | + + +
$x+7$ — | + + + + + | + + +
-10 -8 -6 -4 -2 0 2 4 6 8 10

$\{x \mid x < -7 \text{ or } x > 3\}$

23. $2x^2 - 5x + 2 \ge 0$
$(2x-1)(x-2) \ge 0$

$2x-1$ — — — — | + + | + + + +
$x-2$ — — — — — — | + + +
-5 -4 -3 -2 -1 0 1 2 3 4 5

$\left\{x \mid x \le \dfrac{1}{2} \text{ or } x \ge 2\right\}$

24. $4x^2 - 9x + 2 < 0$
$(4x-1)(x-2) < 0$

$4x-1$ — — — — — | + + | + + +
$x-2$ — — — — — — | + + +
-5 -4 -3 -2 -1 0 1 2 3 4 5

$\left\{x \mid \dfrac{1}{4} < x < 2\right\}$

25. $4x^2 - 8x + 3 < 0$
$(2x-1)(2x-3) < 0$

$2x-1$ — — — — — | + | + + + +
$2x-3$ — — — — — | + + + +
-5 -4 -3 -2 -1 0 1 2 3 4 5

$\left\{x \mid \dfrac{1}{2} < x < \dfrac{3}{2}\right\}$

26. $2x^2 + 11x + 12 \geq 0$
$(2x+3)(x+4) \geq 0$

$2x+3$ $\quad - - - | - - | + + + + + +$
$x+4$ $\quad - | + + | + + + + + + +$
$\qquad \overline{\,-5\;-4\;-3\;-2\;-1\;\;0\;\;1\;\;2\;\;3\;\;4\;\;5\,}$

$\left\{x \mid x \leq -4 \text{ or } x \geq -\dfrac{3}{2}\right\}$

27. $(x-6)(x+3)(x-2) \leq 0$

$x-6$ $\quad - - - - - - | + +$
$x+3$ $\quad - - | + + + + | + +$
$x-2$ $\quad - - - - | + + | + +$
$\qquad \overline{\,-10\;-8\;-6\;-4\;-2\;\;0\;\;2\;\;4\;\;6\;\;8\;\;10\,}$

$\left\{x \mid x \leq -3 \text{ or } 2 \leq x \leq 6\right\}$

28. $(x+5)(x-2)(x-3) > 0$

$x+5$ $\quad - | + + + + + + | + | + +$
$x-2$ $\quad - - - - - | + | + +$
$x-3$ $\quad - - - - - - | + +$
$\qquad \overline{\,-5\;-4\;-3\;-2\;-1\;\;0\;\;1\;\;2\;\;3\;\;4\;\;5\,}$

$\left\{x \mid -5 < x < 2 \text{ or } x > 3\right\}$

29. $(2x-1)(x-4)(2x+3) > 0$

$2x-1$ $\quad - - - - | + + + | + +$
$x-4$ $\quad - - - - | - - - | + +$
$2x+3$ $\quad - - - | + + + + | + +$
$\qquad \overline{\,-5\;-4\;-3\;-2\;-1\;\;0\;\;1\;\;2\;\;3\;\;4\;\;5\,}$

$\left\{x \mid -\dfrac{3}{2} < x < \dfrac{1}{2} \text{ or } x > 4\right\}$

30. $(x-2)(3x-1)(x+2) \leq 0$

$x-2$ $\quad - - - - | - - | + +$
$3x-1$ $\quad - - - - | + | + + +$
$x+2$ $\quad - - | + + + | + + +$
$\qquad \overline{\,-5\;-4\;-3\;-2\;-1\;\;0\;\;1\;\;2\;\;3\;\;4\;\;5\,}$

$\left\{x \mid x \leq -2 \text{ or } \dfrac{1}{3} \leq x \leq 2\right\}$

31. $x^3 + 3x^2 - x - 3 \leq 0$
$x^2(x+3) - 1(x+3) \leq 0$
$(x+3)(x^2-1) \leq 0$
$(x+3)(x+1)(x-1) \leq 0$

$x+3$ $\quad - - | + | + | + + + +$
$x+1$ $\quad - - | - | + | + + + +$
$x-1$ $\quad - - - - | + + + +$
$\qquad \overline{\,-5\;-4\;-3\;-2\;-1\;\;0\;\;1\;\;2\;\;3\;\;4\;\;5\,}$

$\left\{x \mid x \leq -3 \text{ or } -1 \leq x \leq 1\right\}$

32. $x^3 + x^2 - 9x - 9 < 0$
$x^2(x+1) - 9(x+1) < 0$
$(x+1)(x^2-9) < 0$
$(x+1)(x+3)(x-3) < 0$

$x+1$ $\quad - - - | - - | + + +$
$x+3$ $\quad - - | + + + + | + +$
$x-3$ $\quad - - - - - - | + +$
$\qquad \overline{\,-5\;-4\;-3\;-2\;-1\;\;0\;\;1\;\;2\;\;3\;\;4\;\;5\,}$

$\left\{x \mid x < -3 \text{ or } -1 < x < 3\right\}$

33. $x^3 - x^2 - 4x + 4 \geq 0$
$x^2(x-1) - 4(x-1) \geq 0$
$(x-1)(x^2-4) \geq 0$
$(x-1)(x+2)(x-2) \geq 0$

$x-1$ $\quad - - - - - | + | + + +$
$x+2$ $\quad - - | + + + | + | + +$
$x-2$ $\quad - - - - - | - | + +$
$\qquad \overline{\,-5\;-4\;-3\;-2\;-1\;\;0\;\;1\;\;2\;\;3\;\;4\;\;5\,}$

$\left\{x \mid -2 \leq x \leq 1 \text{ or } x \geq 2\right\}$

34. $2x^3 + 3x^2 - 8x - 12 \geq 0$
$x^2(2x+3) - 4(2x+3) \geq 0$
$(2x+3)(x^2-4) \geq 0$
$(2x+3)(x+2)(x-2) \geq 0$

$2x+3$ $\quad - - | - | + + + | + + +$
$x+2$ $\quad - - | + | + + + | + +$
$x-2$ $\quad - - - - - - | + +$
$\qquad \overline{\,-5\;-4\;-3\;-2\;-1\;\;0\;\;1\;\;2\;\;3\;\;4\;\;5\,}$

$\left\{x \mid -2 \leq x \leq -\dfrac{3}{2} \text{ or } x \geq 2\right\}$

35. $\dfrac{3x}{x-2} > 1$
$\dfrac{3x}{x-2} - 1 > 0$
$\dfrac{3x}{x-2} - \dfrac{x-2}{x-2} > 0$
$\dfrac{2x+2}{x-2} > 0$

$2x+2$ $\quad - - - - | + + + | + + +$
$x-2$ $\quad - - - - - - | + + +$
$\qquad \overline{\,-5\;-4\;-3\;-2\;-1\;\;0\;\;1\;\;2\;\;3\;\;4\;\;5\,}$

$\left\{x \mid x < -1 \text{ or } x > 2\right\}$

36. $\dfrac{2x}{x+1} < 1$
$\dfrac{2x}{x+1} - 1 < 0$
$\dfrac{2x}{x+1} - \dfrac{x+1}{x+1} < 0$
$\dfrac{x-1}{x+1} < 0$

$x-1$ $\quad - - - - - | - | + + + +$
$x+1$ $\quad - - - - - | + | + + + +$
$\qquad \overline{\,-5\;-4\;-3\;-2\;-1\;\;0\;\;1\;\;2\;\;3\;\;4\;\;5\,}$

$\left\{x \mid -1 < x < 1\right\}$

37.

$$\frac{2}{x+1} \geq 2$$

$$\frac{2}{x+1} - 2 \geq 0$$

$$\frac{2}{x+1} - \frac{2x+2}{x+1} \geq 0$$

$$\frac{-2x}{x+1} \geq 0$$

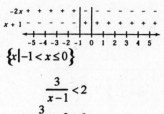

$$\{x \mid -1 < x \leq 0\}$$

38.

$$\frac{3}{x-1} < 2$$

$$\frac{3}{x-1} - 2 < 0$$

$$\frac{3}{x-1} - \frac{2x-2}{x-1} < 0$$

$$\frac{-2x+5}{x-1} < 0$$

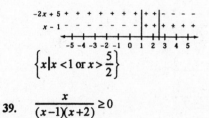

$$\left\{x \mid x < 1 \text{ or } x > \frac{5}{2}\right\}$$

39. $\dfrac{x}{(x-1)(x+2)} \geq 0$

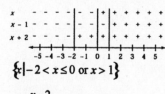

$$\{x \mid -2 < x \leq 0 \text{ or } x > 1\}$$

40. $\dfrac{x-2}{(x+1)(x-1)} \leq 0$

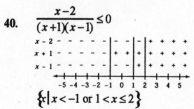

$$\{x \mid x < -1 \text{ or } 1 < x \leq 2\}$$

41.

$$\frac{1}{x} < 2$$

$$\frac{1}{x} - 2 < 0$$

$$\frac{1}{x} - \frac{2x}{x} < 0$$

$$\frac{1-2x}{x} < 0$$

$$\left\{x \mid x < 0 \text{ or } x > \frac{1}{2}\right\}$$

42.

$$\frac{x}{2x-1} \geq 1$$

$$\frac{x}{2x-1} - 1 \geq 0$$

$$\frac{x}{2x-1} - \frac{2x-1}{2x-1} \geq 0$$

$$\frac{-x+1}{2x-1} \geq 0$$

$$\left\{x \mid \frac{1}{2} < x \leq 1\right\}$$

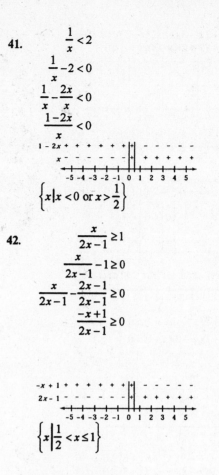

Applying Concepts 8.5

43. $(x+2)(x-3)(x+1)(x+4) > 0$

$$\{x \mid x < -4 \text{ or } -2 < x < -1 \text{ or } x > 3\}$$

44. $(x-1)(x+3)(x-2)(x-4) \geq 0$

$$\{x \mid x \leq -3 \text{ or } 1 \leq x \leq 2 \text{ or } x \geq 4\}$$

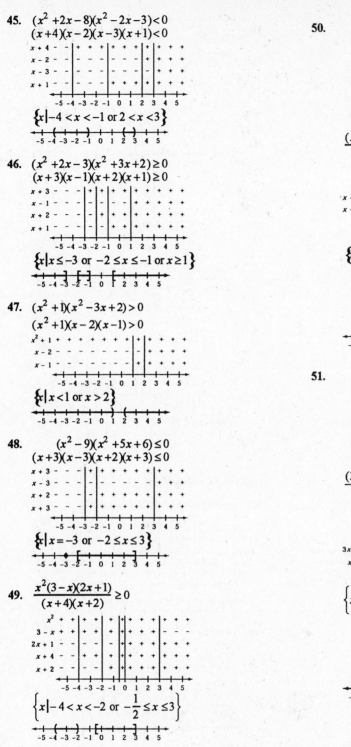

45. $(x^2 +2x-8)(x^2 -2x-3)<0$
$(x+4)(x-2)(x-3)(x+1)<0$

$\{x| -4<x<-1 \text{ or } 2<x<3\}$

46. $(x^2 +2x-3)(x^2 +3x+2)\ge 0$
$(x+3)(x-1)(x+2)(x+1)\ge 0$

$\{x| x\le -3 \text{ or } -2\le x \le -1 \text{ or } x\ge 1\}$

47. $(x^2 +1)(x^2 -3x+2)>0$
$(x^2 +1)(x-2)(x-1)>0$

$\{x| x<1 \text{ or } x>2\}$

48. $(x^2 -9)(x^2 +5x+6)\le 0$
$(x+3)(x-3)(x+2)(x+3)\le 0$

$\{x| x=-3 \text{ or } -2\le x \le 3\}$

49. $\dfrac{x^2(3-x)(2x+1)}{(x+4)(x+2)}\ge 0$

$\left\{x\middle| -4<x<-2 \text{ or } -\dfrac{1}{2}\le x \le 3\right\}$

50.
$\dfrac{1}{x}+x>2$

$\dfrac{1}{x}+x-2>0$

$\dfrac{1+x^2-2x}{x}>0$

$\dfrac{x^2-2x+1}{x}>0$

$\dfrac{(x-1)(x-1)}{x}>0$

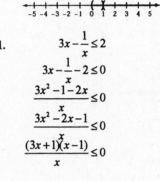

$\{x| 0<x<1 \text{ or } x>1\}$

51.
$3x-\dfrac{1}{x}\le 2$

$3x-\dfrac{1}{x}-2\le 0$

$\dfrac{3x^2-1-2x}{x}\le 0$

$\dfrac{3x^2-2x-1}{x}\le 0$

$\dfrac{(3x+1)(x-1)}{x}\le 0$

$\left\{x\middle| x\le -\dfrac{1}{3} \text{ or } 0<x\le 1\right\}$

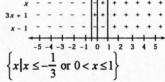

52.
$$x^2 - x < \frac{1-x}{x}$$

$$x^2 - x - \frac{1-x}{x} < 0$$

$$\frac{x^3 - x^2 - (1-x)}{x} < 0$$

$$\frac{x^3 - x^2 + x - 1}{x} < 0$$

$$\frac{x^2(x-1) + 1(x-1)}{x} < 0$$

$$\frac{(x-1)(x^2+1)}{x} < 0$$

```
x - 1   - - - - - | - | + + + + +
x² + 1  + + + + + | + | + + + + +
x       - - - - - | + | + + + + +
      +--+--+--+--+--+--+--+--+--+--+
     -5 -4 -3 -2 -1  0  1  2  3  4  5
```

$$\{x \mid 0 < x < 1\}$$

```
  +--+--+--+--+--(--)--+--+--+--+
 -5 -4 -3 -2 -1  0  1  2  3  4  5
```

Section 8.6

Concept Review 8.6

1. Sometimes true
   If the vertex is on an axis, the axis of symmetry will intersect the origin.

2. Sometimes true
   If a is negative, the vertex will be the highest point on the graph.

3. Sometimes true
   A parabola may have one, two or no x-intercepts.

4. Always true

5. Always true

6. Always true

Objective 8.6.1 Exercises

1. A quadratic function is a function of the form
   $f(x) = ax^2 + bx + c$, $a \neq 0$.

2. The vertex of a parabola is the point with the smallest y-coordinate or the largest y-coordinate. When $a > 0$, the parabola opens up and the vertex of the parabola is the point with the smallest y-coordinate. When $a < 0$, the parabola opens down and the vertex is the point with the largest y-coordinate.
   The axis of symmetry of the graph of a parabola is the vertical line that passes through the vertex of the parabola and is parallel to the y-axis.

3. The x-coordinate of the vertex is -5.

4. The x-coordinate of the vertex is 8.

5. The axis of symmetry is $x = 7$.

6. The axis of symmetry is $x = -4$.

7. $a = 1, b = 0$
   $-\dfrac{b}{2a} = -\dfrac{0}{2(1)} = 0$
   $y = 0^2 = 0$
   Vertex: $(0, 0)$
   Axis of symmetry: $x = 0$

8. $a = -1, b = 0$
   $-\dfrac{b}{2a} = -\dfrac{0}{2(-1)} = 0$
   $y = -0^2 = 0$
   Vertex: $(0, 0)$
   Axis of symmetry: $x = 0$

9. $a = 1, b = 0$
   $-\dfrac{b}{2a} = -\dfrac{0}{2(1)} = 0$
   $y = 0^2 - 2 = -2$
   Vertex: $(0, -2)$
   Axis of symmetry: $x = 0$

10. $a = 1, b = 0$
    $-\dfrac{b}{2a} = -\dfrac{0}{2(1)} = 0$
    $y = 0^2 + 2 = 2$
    Vertex: $(0, 2)$
    Axis of symmetry: $x = 0$

11. $a = -1, b = 0$
    $-\dfrac{b}{2a} = -\dfrac{0}{2(-1)} = 0$
    $y = -0^2 + 3 = 3$
    Vertex: $(0, 3)$
    Axis of symmetry: $x = 0$

12. $a = -1, b = 0$
    $-\dfrac{b}{2a} = -\dfrac{0}{2(-1)} = 0$
    $y = -0^2 - 1 = -1$
    Vertex: $(0, -1)$
    Axis of symmetry: $x = 0$

13. $a = \dfrac{1}{2}, b = 0$
    $-\dfrac{b}{2a} = -\dfrac{0}{2\left(\frac{1}{2}\right)} = 0$
    $y = \dfrac{1}{2}(0)^2 = 0$
    Vertex: $(0, 0)$
    Axis of symmetry: $x = 0$

14. $a = 2, b = 0$

$-\dfrac{b}{2a} = -\dfrac{0}{2(2)} = 0$

$y = 2(0)^2 = 0$

Vertex: $(0, 0)$

Axis of symmetry: $x = 0$

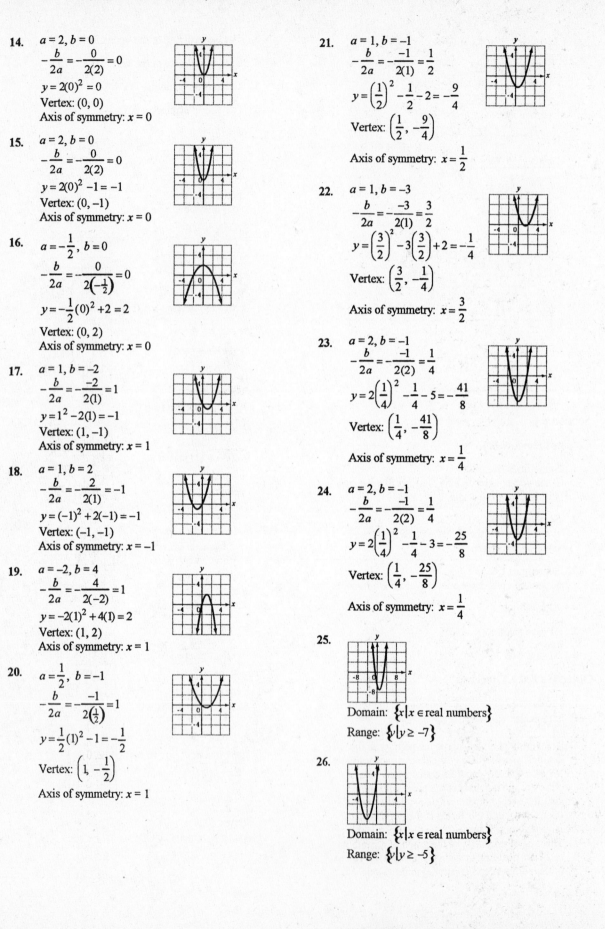

15. $a = 2, b = 0$

$-\dfrac{b}{2a} = -\dfrac{0}{2(2)} = 0$

$y = 2(0)^2 - 1 = -1$

Vertex: $(0, -1)$

Axis of symmetry: $x = 0$

16. $a = -\dfrac{1}{2}, b = 0$

$-\dfrac{b}{2a} = -\dfrac{0}{2\left(-\frac{1}{2}\right)} = 0$

$y = -\dfrac{1}{2}(0)^2 + 2 = 2$

Vertex: $(0, 2)$

Axis of symmetry: $x = 0$

17. $a = 1, b = -2$

$-\dfrac{b}{2a} = -\dfrac{-2}{2(1)} = 1$

$y = 1^2 - 2(1) = -1$

Vertex: $(1, -1)$

Axis of symmetry: $x = 1$

18. $a = 1, b = 2$

$-\dfrac{b}{2a} = -\dfrac{2}{2(1)} = -1$

$y = (-1)^2 + 2(-1) = -1$

Vertex: $(-1, -1)$

Axis of symmetry: $x = -1$

19. $a = -2, b = 4$

$-\dfrac{b}{2a} = -\dfrac{4}{2(-2)} = 1$

$y = -2(1)^2 + 4(1) = 2$

Vertex: $(1, 2)$

Axis of symmetry: $x = 1$

20. $a = \dfrac{1}{2}, b = -1$

$-\dfrac{b}{2a} = -\dfrac{-1}{2\left(\frac{1}{2}\right)} = 1$

$y = \dfrac{1}{2}(1)^2 - 1 = -\dfrac{1}{2}$

Vertex: $\left(1, -\dfrac{1}{2}\right)$

Axis of symmetry: $x = 1$

21. $a = 1, b = -1$

$-\dfrac{b}{2a} = -\dfrac{-1}{2(1)} = \dfrac{1}{2}$

$y = \left(\dfrac{1}{2}\right)^2 - \dfrac{1}{2} - 2 = -\dfrac{9}{4}$

Vertex: $\left(\dfrac{1}{2}, -\dfrac{9}{4}\right)$

Axis of symmetry: $x = \dfrac{1}{2}$

22. $a = 1, b = -3$

$-\dfrac{b}{2a} = -\dfrac{-3}{2(1)} = \dfrac{3}{2}$

$y = \left(\dfrac{3}{2}\right)^2 - 3\left(\dfrac{3}{2}\right) + 2 = -\dfrac{1}{4}$

Vertex: $\left(\dfrac{3}{2}, -\dfrac{1}{4}\right)$

Axis of symmetry: $x = \dfrac{3}{2}$

23. $a = 2, b = -1$

$-\dfrac{b}{2a} = -\dfrac{-1}{2(2)} = \dfrac{1}{4}$

$y = 2\left(\dfrac{1}{4}\right)^2 - \dfrac{1}{4} - 5 = -\dfrac{41}{8}$

Vertex: $\left(\dfrac{1}{4}, -\dfrac{41}{8}\right)$

Axis of symmetry: $x = \dfrac{1}{4}$

24. $a = 2, b = -1$

$-\dfrac{b}{2a} = -\dfrac{-1}{2(2)} = \dfrac{1}{4}$

$y = 2\left(\dfrac{1}{4}\right)^2 - \dfrac{1}{4} - 3 = -\dfrac{25}{8}$

Vertex: $\left(\dfrac{1}{4}, -\dfrac{25}{8}\right)$

Axis of symmetry: $x = \dfrac{1}{4}$

25.

Domain: $\{x \,|\, x \in \text{real numbers}\}$

Range: $\{y \,|\, y \geq -7\}$

26.

Domain: $\{x \,|\, x \in \text{real numbers}\}$

Range: $\{y \,|\, y \geq -5\}$

27.

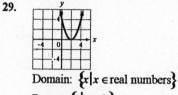

Domain: $\{x \mid x \in \text{real numbers}\}$

Range: $\left\{y \mid y \le \dfrac{25}{8}\right\}$

28.

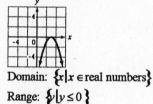

Domain: $\{x \mid x \in \text{real numbers}\}$

Range: $\left\{y \mid y \ge -\dfrac{25}{8}\right\}$

29.

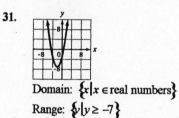

Domain: $\{x \mid x \in \text{real numbers}\}$

Range: $\{y \mid y \ge 0\}$

30.

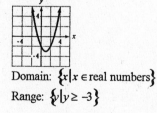

Domain: $\{x \mid x \in \text{real numbers}\}$

Range: $\{y \mid y \le 0\}$

31.

Domain: $\{x \mid x \in \text{real numbers}\}$

Range: $\{y \mid y \ge -7\}$

32.

Domain: $\{x \mid x \in \text{real numbers}\}$

Range: $\{y \mid y \ge -3\}$

33.

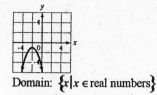

Domain: $\{x \mid x \in \text{real numbers}\}$

Range: $\{y \mid y \le -1\}$

34.

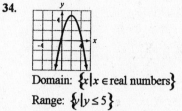

Domain: $\{x \mid x \in \text{real numbers}\}$

Range: $\{y \mid y \le 5\}$

Objective 8.6.2 Exercises

35. To find the x-intercepts for the graph of the quadratic function $f(x) = ax^2 + bx + c$, solve the equation $0 = ax^2 + bx + c$ for x.

36. Let $f(x) = ax^2 + bx + c$ be a quadratic function. Then the discriminant is $b^2 - 4ac$. If $b^2 - 4ac = 0$, the graph of $f(x)$ has one x-intercept. If $b^2 - 4ac > 0$, the graph of $f(x)$ has two x-intercepts. If $b^2 - 4ac < 0$, the graph of $f(x)$ has no x-intercepts.

37. $y = x^2 - 4$

$0 = x^2 - 4$

$0 = (x - 2)(x + 2)$

$\begin{array}{ll} x - 2 = 0 & x + 2 = 0 \\ x = 2 & x = -2 \end{array}$

The x-intercepts are $(2, 0)$ and $(-2, 0)$.

38. $y = x^2 - 9$

$0 = x^2 - 9$

$0 = (x - 3)(x + 3)$

$\begin{array}{ll} x - 3 = 0 & x + 3 = 0 \\ x = 3 & x = -3 \end{array}$

The x-intercepts are $(3, 0)$ and $(-3, 0)$.

39. $y = 2x^2 - 4x$

$0 = 2x^2 - 4x$

$0 = 2x(x - 2)$

$\begin{array}{ll} 2x = 0 & x - 2 = 0 \\ x = 0 & x = 2 \end{array}$

The x-intercepts are $(0, 0)$ and $(2, 0)$.

40. $y = 3x^2 + 6x$

$0 = 3x^2 + 6x$

$0 = 3x(x + 2)$

$\begin{array}{ll} 3x = 0 & x + 2 = 0 \\ x = 0 & x = -2 \end{array}$

The x-intercepts are $(0, 0)$ and $(-2, 0)$.

41. $y = x^2 - x - 2$
$0 = x^2 - x - 2$
$0 = (x-2)(x+1)$
$x - 2 = 0 \qquad x + 1 = 0$
$\quad x = 2 \qquad\quad x = -1$
The x-intercepts are $(2, 0)$ and $(-1, 0)$.

42. $y = x^2 - 2x - 8$
$0 = x^2 - 2x - 8$
$0 = (x-4)(x+2)$
$x - 4 = 0 \qquad x + 2 = 0$
$\quad x = 4 \qquad\quad x = -2$
The x-intercepts are $(4, 0)$ and $(-2, 0)$.

43. $y = 2x^2 - 5x - 3$
$0 = 2x^2 - 5x - 3$
$0 = (2x+1)(x-3)$
$2x + 1 = 0 \qquad x - 3 = 0$
$\quad 2x = -1 \qquad\quad x = 3$
$\quad x = -\dfrac{1}{2}$
The x-intercepts are $\left(-\dfrac{1}{2}, 0\right)$ and $(3, 0)$.

44. $y = 4x^2 + 11x + 6$
$0 = 4x^2 + 11x + 6$
$0 = (4x+3)(x+2)$
$4x + 3 = 0 \qquad x + 2 = 0$
$\quad 4x = -3 \qquad\quad x = -2$
$\quad x = -\dfrac{3}{4}$
The x-intercepts are $\left(-\dfrac{3}{4}, 0\right)$ and $(-2, 0)$.

45. $y = 3x^2 - 19x - 14$
$0 = 3x^2 - 19x - 14$
$0 = (3x+2)(x-7)$
$3x + 2 = 0 \qquad x - 7 = 0$
$\quad 3x = -2 \qquad\quad x = 7$
$\quad x = -\dfrac{2}{3}$
The x-intercepts are $\left(-\dfrac{2}{3}, 0\right)$ and $(7, 0)$.

46. $y = 6x^2 + 7x + 2$
$0 = 6x^2 + 7x + 2$
$0 = (2x+1)(3x+2)$
$2x + 1 = 0 \qquad 3x + 2 = 0$
$\quad 2x = -1 \qquad\quad 3x = -2$
$\quad x = -\dfrac{1}{2} \qquad\quad x = -\dfrac{2}{3}$
The x-intercepts are $\left(-\dfrac{1}{2}, 0\right)$ and $\left(-\dfrac{2}{3}, 0\right)$.

47. $y = 3x^2 - 19x + 20$
$0 = 3x^2 - 19x + 20$
$0 = (3x-4)(x-5)$
$3x - 4 = 0 \qquad x - 5 = 0$
$\quad 3x = 4 \qquad\quad x = 5$
$\quad x = \dfrac{4}{3}$
The x-intercepts are $\left(\dfrac{4}{3}, 0\right)$ and $(5, 0)$.

48. $y = 3x^2 + 19x + 28$
$0 = 3x^2 + 19x + 28$
$0 = (3x+7)(x+4)$
$3x + 7 = 0 \qquad x + 4 = 0$
$\quad 3x = -7 \qquad\quad x = -4$
$\quad x = -\dfrac{7}{3}$
The x-intercepts are $\left(-\dfrac{7}{3}, 0\right)$ and $(-4, 0)$.

49. $y = 9x^2 - 12x + 4$
$0 = 9x^2 - 12x + 4$
$0 = (3x-2)(3x-2)$
$3x - 2 = 0 \qquad 3x - 2 = 0$
$\quad 3x = 2 \qquad\quad 3x = 2$
$\quad x = \dfrac{2}{3} \qquad\quad x = \dfrac{2}{3}$
The x-intercept is $\left(\dfrac{2}{3}, 0\right)$.

50. $y = x^2 - 2$
$0 = x^2 - 2$
$2 = x^2$
$\sqrt{2} = \sqrt{x^2}$
$\pm\sqrt{2} = x$
The x-intercepts are $(\sqrt{2}, 0)$ and $(-\sqrt{2}, 0)$.

51. $y = 9x^2 - 2$
$0 = 9x^2 - 2$
$2 = 9x^2$
$\dfrac{2}{9} = x^2$
$\sqrt{\dfrac{2}{9}} = \sqrt{x^2}$
$\pm\dfrac{\sqrt{2}}{3} = x$
The x-intercepts are
$\left(\dfrac{\sqrt{2}}{3}, 0\right)$ and $\left(-\dfrac{\sqrt{2}}{3}, 0\right)$.

52. $y = 2x^2 - x - 1$

$0 = 2x^2 - x - 1$

$0 = (2x+1)(x-1)$

$2x+1 = 0 \qquad x-1 = 0$

$2x = -1 \qquad x = 1$

$x = -\dfrac{1}{2}$

The x-intercepts are $\left(-\dfrac{1}{2},\ 0\right)$ and $(1, 0)$.

53. $y = 4x^2 - 4x - 15$

$0 = 4x^2 - 4x - 15$

$0 = (2x+3)(2x-5)$

$2x+3 = 0 \qquad (2x-5) = 0$

$2x = -3 \qquad 2x = 5$

$x = -\dfrac{3}{2} \qquad x = \dfrac{5}{2}$

The x-intercepts are $\left(-\dfrac{3}{2},\ 0\right)$ and $\left(\dfrac{5}{2}, 0\right)$

54. $y = x^2 + 2x - 1$

$0 = x^2 + 2x - 1$

$a = 1, b = 2, c = -1$

$x = \dfrac{-b \pm \sqrt{b^2 - 4ac}}{2a}$

$= \dfrac{-2 \pm \sqrt{2^2 - 4(1)(-1)}}{2(1)}$

$= \dfrac{-2 \pm \sqrt{4+4}}{2}$

$= \dfrac{-2 \pm \sqrt{8}}{2}$

$= \dfrac{-2 \pm 2\sqrt{2}}{2}$

$= -1 \pm \sqrt{2}$

The x-intercepts are $(-1+\sqrt{2},\ 0)$ and $(-1-\sqrt{2},\ 0)$.

55. $y = x^2 + 4x - 3$

$0 = x^2 + 4x - 3$

$a = 1, b = 4, c = -3$

$x = \dfrac{-b \pm \sqrt{b^2 - 4ac}}{2a}$

$= \dfrac{-4 \pm \sqrt{4^2 - 4(1)(-3)}}{2(1)}$

$= \dfrac{-4 \pm \sqrt{16+12}}{2}$

$= \dfrac{-4 \pm \sqrt{28}}{2}$

$= \dfrac{-4 \pm 2\sqrt{7}}{2}$

$= -2 \pm \sqrt{7}$

The x-intercepts are $(-2+\sqrt{7},\ 0)$ and $(-2-\sqrt{7},\ 0)$.

56. $y = x^2 + 6x + 10$

$0 = x^2 + 6x + 10$

$a = 1, b = 6, c = 10$

$x = \dfrac{-b \pm \sqrt{b^2 - 4ac}}{2a}$

$= \dfrac{-6 \pm \sqrt{6^2 - 4(1)(10)}}{2(1)}$

$= \dfrac{-6 \pm \sqrt{36-40}}{2}$

$= \dfrac{-6 \pm \sqrt{-4}}{2}$

$= \dfrac{-6 \pm 2i}{2}$

$= -3 \pm i$

The equation has no real solutions.
The parabola has no x-intercepts.

57. $y = -x^2 - 4x - 5$

$0 = -x^2 - 4x - 5$

$a = -1, b = -4, c = -5$

$x = \dfrac{-b \pm \sqrt{b^2 - 4ac}}{2a}$

$= \dfrac{-(-4) \pm \sqrt{(-4)^2 - 4(-1)(-5)}}{2(-1)}$

$= \dfrac{4 \pm \sqrt{16-20}}{-2}$

$= \dfrac{4 \pm \sqrt{-4}}{-2}$

$= \dfrac{4 \pm 2i}{-2}$

$= -2 \pm i$

The equation has no real solutions.
The parabola has no x-intercepts.

58. $y = x^2 - 2x - 2$

$0 = x^2 - 2x - 2$

$a = 1, b = -2, c = -2$

$x = \dfrac{-b \pm \sqrt{b^2 - 4ac}}{2a}$

$= \dfrac{-(-2) \pm \sqrt{(-2)^2 - 4(1)(-2)}}{2(1)}$

$= \dfrac{2 \pm \sqrt{4+8}}{2}$

$= \dfrac{2 \pm \sqrt{12}}{2}$

$= \dfrac{2 \pm 2\sqrt{3}}{2}$

$= 1 \pm \sqrt{3}$

The x-intercepts are $(1+\sqrt{3},\ 0)$ and $(1-\sqrt{3},\ 0)$.

59. $y = -x^2 - 2x + 1$

$0 = -x^2 - 2x + 1$

$0 = x^2 + 2x - 1$

$a = 1, b = 2, c = -1$

$x = \dfrac{-b \pm \sqrt{b^2 - 4ac}}{2a}$

$\quad = \dfrac{-2 \pm \sqrt{2^2 - 4(1)(-1)}}{2(1)}$

$\quad = \dfrac{-2 \pm \sqrt{4 + 4}}{2}$

$\quad = \dfrac{-2 \pm \sqrt{8}}{2}$

$\quad = \dfrac{-2 \pm 2\sqrt{2}}{2}$

$\quad = -1 \pm \sqrt{2}$

The x-intercepts are $(-1 + \sqrt{2}, \ 0)$ and $(-1 - \sqrt{2}, \ 0)$.

60. $y = -x^2 + 4x + 1$

$0 = -x^2 + 4x + 1$

$0 = x^2 - 4x - 1$

$a = 1, b = -4, c = -1$

$x = \dfrac{-b \pm \sqrt{b^2 - 4ac}}{2a}$

$\quad = \dfrac{-(-4) \pm \sqrt{(-4)^2 - 4(1)(-1)}}{2(1)}$

$\quad = \dfrac{4 \pm \sqrt{16 + 4}}{2}$

$\quad = \dfrac{4 \pm \sqrt{20}}{2}$

$\quad = \dfrac{4 \pm 2\sqrt{5}}{2}$

$\quad = 2 \pm \sqrt{5}$

The x-intercepts are $(2 + \sqrt{5}, \ 0)$ and $(2 - \sqrt{5}, \ 0)$.

61. $f(x) = x^2 + 3x + 2$

$0 = x^2 + 3x + 2$

$0 = (x + 2)(x + 1)$

$x + 2 = 0 \qquad x + 1 = 0$

$x = -2 \qquad\quad x = -1$

The zeros are $-2, -1$.

62. $f(x) = x^2 - 6x + 9$

$0 = x^2 - 6x + 9$

$0 = (x - 3)(x - 3)$

$x - 3 = 0 \qquad x - 3 = 0$

$x = 3 \qquad\quad x = 3$

The zero is 3.

63. $f(x) = -x^2 + 4x - 5$

$0 = -x^2 + 4x - 5$

$a = -1, b = 4, c = -5$

$x = \dfrac{-b \pm \sqrt{b^2 - 4ac}}{2a}$

$\quad = \dfrac{-4 \pm \sqrt{(4)^2 - 4(-1)(-5)}}{2(-1)}$

$\quad = \dfrac{-4 \pm \sqrt{16 - 20}}{-2}$

$\quad = \dfrac{-4 \pm \sqrt{-4}}{-2}$

$\quad = \dfrac{-4 \pm 2i}{-2}$

$\quad = 2 \pm i$

The zeros are $2 + i, \ 2 - i$.

64. $f(x) = -x^2 + 3x + 8$

$0 = -x^2 + 3x + 8$

$a = -1, b = 3, c = 8$

$x = \dfrac{-b \pm \sqrt{b^2 - 4ac}}{2a}$

$\quad = \dfrac{-3 \pm \sqrt{3^2 - 4(-1)(8)}}{2(-1)}$

$\quad = \dfrac{-3 \pm \sqrt{9 + 32}}{-2}$

$\quad = \dfrac{-3 \pm \sqrt{41}}{-2}$

$\quad = \dfrac{3 \pm \sqrt{41}}{2}$

The zeros are $\dfrac{3 + \sqrt{41}}{2}$ and $\dfrac{3 - \sqrt{41}}{2}$.

65. $f(x) = 2x^2 - 3x$

$0 = 2x^2 - 3x$

$0 = x(2x - 3)$

$x = 0 \qquad 2x - 3 = 0$

$\qquad\qquad\quad 2x = 3$

$\qquad\qquad\quad x = \dfrac{3}{2}$

The zeros are 0 and $\dfrac{3}{2}$.

66. $f(x) = -3x^2 + 4x$

$0 = -3x^2 + 4x$

$0 = x(-3x + 4)$

$x = 0 \qquad -3x + 4 = 0$

$\qquad\qquad\quad -3x = -4$

$\qquad\qquad\quad x = \dfrac{4}{3}$

The zeros are 0 and $\dfrac{4}{3}$.

67. $f(x) = 2x^2 - 4$
$0 = 2x^2 - 4$
$4 = 2x^2$
$2 = x^2$
$\sqrt{2} = \sqrt{x^2}$
$\pm\sqrt{2} = x$

The zeros are $\sqrt{2}$ and $-\sqrt{2}$.

68. $f(x) = 3x^2 + 6$
$0 = 3x^2 + 6$
$-6 = 3x^2$
$-2 = x^2$
$\sqrt{-2} = \sqrt{x^2}$
$\pm i\sqrt{2} = x$

The zeros are $i\sqrt{2}$ and $-i\sqrt{2}$.

69. $f(x) = 2x^2 + 3x + 2$
$0 = 2x^2 + 3x + 2$
$a = 2, b = 3, c = 2$
$x = \dfrac{-b \pm \sqrt{b^2 - 4ac}}{2a}$
$= \dfrac{-3 \pm \sqrt{3^2 - 4(2)(2)}}{2(2)}$
$= \dfrac{-3 \pm \sqrt{9 - 16}}{4}$
$= \dfrac{-3 \pm \sqrt{-7}}{4}$
$= \dfrac{-3 \pm i\sqrt{7}}{4}$

The zeros are $-\dfrac{3}{4} + \dfrac{\sqrt{7}}{4}i$ and $-\dfrac{3}{4} - \dfrac{\sqrt{7}}{4}i$.

70. $f(x) = 3x^2 - x + 4$
$0 = 3x^2 - x + 4$
$a = 3, b = -1, c = 4$
$x = \dfrac{-b \pm \sqrt{b^2 - 4ac}}{2a}$
$= \dfrac{-(-1) \pm \sqrt{(-1)^2 - 4(3)(4)}}{2(3)}$
$= \dfrac{1 \pm \sqrt{1 - 48}}{6}$
$= \dfrac{1 \pm \sqrt{-47}}{6}$
$= \dfrac{1 \pm i\sqrt{47}}{6}$

The zeros are $\dfrac{1}{6} + \dfrac{\sqrt{47}}{6}i$ and $\dfrac{1}{6} - \dfrac{\sqrt{47}}{6}i$.

71. $f(x) = -3x^2 + 4x - 1$
$0 = -3x^2 + 4x - 1$
$0 = (-3x + 1)(x - 1)$

$-3x + 1 = 0 \qquad x - 1 = 0$
$\quad -3x = -1 \qquad\quad x = 1$
$\quad\ \ x = \dfrac{1}{3}$

The zeros are $\dfrac{1}{3}$ and 1.

72. $f(x) = -2x^2 + x + 5$
$0 = -2x^2 + x + 5$
$a = -2, b = 1, c = 5$
$x = \dfrac{-b \pm \sqrt{b^2 - 4ac}}{2a}$
$= \dfrac{-1 \pm \sqrt{1^2 - 4(-2)(5)}}{2(-2)}$
$= \dfrac{-1 \pm \sqrt{1 + 40}}{-4}$
$= \dfrac{-1 \pm \sqrt{41}}{-4}$
$= \dfrac{1 \pm \sqrt{41}}{4}$

The zeros are $\dfrac{1 + \sqrt{41}}{4}$ and $\dfrac{1 - \sqrt{41}}{4}$.

73.

To the nearest tenth, the zeros of
$f(x) = x^2 + 3x - 1$ are -3.3 and 0.3.

74.

To the nearest tenth, the zeros of
$f(x) = x^2 - 2x - 4$ are -1.2 and 3.2.

75.

To the nearest tenth, the zeros of
$f(x) = 2x^2 - 3x - 7$ are -1.3 and 2.8.

76.

To the nearest tenth, the zeros of
$f(x) = -2x^2 - x + 2$ are -1.3 and 0.8.

77.

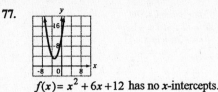

$f(x) = x^2 + 6x + 12$ has no x-intercepts.

78.

$f(x) = x^2 - 3x + 9$ has no x-intercepts.

79. $y = 2x^2 + x + 1$
$a = 2, b = 1, c = 1$
$b^2 - 4ac$
$1^2 - 4(2)(1) = 1 - 8 = -7$
$-7 < 0$
Since the discriminant is less than zero, the parabola has no x-intercepts.

80. $y = 2x^2 + 2x - 1$
$a = 2, b = 2, c = -1$
$b^2 - 4ac$
$2^2 - 4(2)(-1) = 4 + 8 = 12$
$12 > 0$
Since the discriminant is greater than zero, the parabola has two x-intercepts.

81. $y = -x^2 - x + 3$
$a = -1, b = -1, c = 3$
$b^2 - 4ac$
$(-1)^2 - 4(-1)(3) = 1 + 12 = 13$
$13 > 0$
Since the discriminant is greater than zero, the parabola has two x-intercepts.

82. $y = -2x^2 + x + 1$
$a = -2, b = 1, c = 1$
$b^2 - 4ac$
$1^2 - 4(-2)(1) = 1 + 8 = 9$
$9 > 0$
Since the discriminant is greater than zero, the parabola has two x-intercepts.

83. $y = x^2 - 8x + 16$
$a = 1, b = -8, c = 16$
$b^2 - 4ac$
$(-8)^2 - 4(1)(16) = 64 - 64 = 0$
Since the discriminant is equal to zero, the parabola has one x-intercept.

84. $y = x^2 - 10x + 25$
$a = 1, b = -10, c = 25$
$b^2 - 4ac$
$(-10)^2 - 4(1)(25) = 100 - 100 = 0$
Since the discriminant is equal to zero, the parabola has one x-intercept.

85. $y = -3x^2 - x - 2$
$a = -3, b = -1, c = -2$
$b^2 - 4ac$
$(-1)^2 - 4(-3)(-2) = 1 - 24 = -23$
$-23 < 0$
Since the discriminant is less than zero, the parabola has no x-intercepts.

86. $y = -2x^2 + x - 1$
$a = -2, b = 1, c = -1$
$b^2 - 4ac$
$1^2 - 4(-2)(-1) = 1 - 8 = -7$
$-7 < 0$
Since the discriminant is less than zero, the parabola has no x-intercepts.

87. $y = 4x^2 - x - 2$
$a = 4, b = -1, c = -2$
$b^2 - 4ac$
$(-1)^2 - 4(4)(-2) = 1 + 32 = 33$
$33 > 0$
Since the discriminant is greater than zero, the parabola has two x-intercepts.

88. $y = 2x^2 + x + 4$
$a = 2, b = 1, c = 4$
$b^2 - 4ac$
$1^2 - 4(2)(4) = 1 - 32 = -31$
$-31 < 0$
Since the discriminant is less than zero, the parabola has no x-intercepts.

89. $y = -2x^2 - x - 5$
$a = -2, b = -1, c = -5$
$b^2 - 4ac$
$(-1)^2 - 4(-2)(-5) = 1 - 40 = -39$
$-39 < 0$
Since the discriminant is less than zero, the parabola has no x-intercepts.

90. $y = -3x^2 + 4x - 5$
$a = -3, b = 4, c = -5$
$b^2 - 4ac$
$4^2 - 4(-3)(-5) = 16 - 60 = -44$
$-44 < 0$
Since the discriminant is less than zero, the parabola has no x-intercepts.

91. $y = x^2 + 8x + 16$
$a = 1, b = 8, c = 16$
$b^2 - 4ac$
$8^2 - 4(1)(16) = 64 - 64 = 0$
Since the discriminant is equal to zero, the parabola has one x-intercept.

92. $y = x^2 - 12x + 36$
$a = 1, b = -12, c = 36$
$b^2 - 4ac$
$(-12)^2 - 4(1)(36) = 144 - 144 = 0$
Since the discriminant is equal to zero, the parabola has one x-intercept.

93. $y = x^2 + x - 3$
$a = 1, b = 1, c = -3$
$b^2 - 4ac$
$1^2 - 4(1)(-3) = 1 + 12 = 13$
$13 > 0$
Since the discriminant is greater than zero, the parabola has two x-intercepts.

94. If the zeros of the function are -1 and 3, then the x-intercepts are $(-1, 0)$ and $(3, 0)$.

95. If the zeros of the function are -4 and 5, then the x-intercepts are $(-4, 0)$ and $(5, 0)$.

Applying Concepts 8.6

96. $y = x^2 - 3x + k$
$5 = 2^2 - 3(2) + k$
$5 = 4 - 6 + k$
$5 = -2 + k$
$7 = k$
The value of k is 7.

97. $y = x^2 + 2x + k$
$1 = (-3)^2 + 2(-3) + k$
$1 = 9 - 6 + k$
$1 = 3 + k$
$-2 = k$
The value of k is -2.

98. $y = 2x^2 + kx - 3$
$-3 = 2(4)^2 + k(4) - 3$
$-3 = 2(16) + 4k - 3$
$-3 = 32 + 4k - 3$
$-3 = 29 + 4k$
$-32 = 4k$
$-8 = k$
The value of k is -8.

99. $y = 3x^2 + kx - 6$
$4 = 3(-2)^2 + k(-2) - 6$
$4 = 3(4) - 2k - 6$
$4 = 12 - 2k - 6$
$4 = 6 - 2k$
$0 = 2 - 2k$
$2k = 2$
$k = 1$
The value of k is 1.

100. $2x^2 - 5x + k = 0$
$2(4)^2 - 5(4) + k = 0$
$32 - 20 + k = 0$
$12 + k = 0$
$k = -12$
$2x^2 - 5x - 12 = 0$
$(2x + 3)(x - 4) = 0$
$2x + 3 = 0 \qquad x - 4 = 0$
$2x = -3 \qquad\quad x = 4$
$x = -\dfrac{3}{2}$
The other solution is $-\dfrac{3}{2}$

101. If the vertex is on the x-axis, then the value of y is zero.
Find the value of the x-coordinate of the vertex:
$x = \dfrac{-b}{2a}$
$= \dfrac{-(-8)}{2(1)}$
$= 4$
$y = x^2 - 8x + k$
$0 = (4)^2 - 8(4) + k$
$0 = 16 - 32 + k$
$0 = -16 + k$
$16 = k$
The value of k is 16.

102. If the roots are -2 and 3, then
$0 = (x + 2)(x - 3)$
$0 = x^2 - x - 6$
$f(x) = x^2 - x - 6$
So $m = 1$ and $n = -1$.
$0 = -x^2 + x + 6$
$0 = (-x + 3)(x + 2)$
$-x + 3 = 0 \qquad x + 2 = 0$
$3 = x \qquad\quad x = -2$
The roots of $g(x)$ are -2 and 3.

103. Substitute 5 for y in the equation and solve for x.

$$5 = 3x^2 - 2x - 1$$
$$0 = 3x^2 - 2x - 6$$
$$a = 3, b = -2, c = -6$$
$$x = \frac{-b \pm \sqrt{b^2 - 4ac}}{2a}$$
$$= \frac{-(-2) \pm \sqrt{(-2)^2 - 4(3)(-6)}}{2(3)}$$
$$= \frac{2 \pm \sqrt{4 + 72}}{6}$$
$$= \frac{2 \pm \sqrt{76}}{6}$$
$$= \frac{2 \pm 2\sqrt{19}}{6}$$
$$= \frac{1 \pm \sqrt{19}}{3}$$

$\frac{1 - \sqrt{19}}{3}$ is not a possible solution because

$\left(\frac{1 - \sqrt{19}}{3}, 5 \right)$ is in quadrant II.

The solution is $\frac{1 + \sqrt{19}}{3}$.

104. Substitute 9 for y in the equation and solve for x.

$$9 = 2x^2 + 5x - 3$$
$$0 = 2x^2 + 5x - 12$$
$$0 = (2x - 3)(x + 4)$$
$$2x - 3 = 0 \qquad x + 4 = 0$$
$$2x = 3 \qquad\qquad x = -4$$
$$x = \frac{3}{2}$$

$\frac{3}{2}$ is not a possible solution because $\left(\frac{3}{2}, 9 \right)$ is

in quadrant I.
The solution is -4.

105. i. The function $f(x) = x^2$ has a minimum
vertex $(0, 0)$.
The graph is E.

ii. The function $f(x) = x^2 - 1$ has a minimum
vertex $(-1, 0)$.
The graph is F.

iii. The function $f(x) = -x^2$ has a maximum
vertex $(0, 0)$.
The graph is C.

iv. The function $f(x) = -x^2 + 3$ has a maximum
vertex $(3, 0)$.
The graph is A.

v. The function $f(x) = x^2 + 3x - 2$ has a
minimum vertex $(-1.5, -4.25)$.
The graph is B.

vi. The function $f(x) = -x^2 - 3x + 2$ has a
maximum vertex $(-1.5, 4.25)$.
The graph is D.

106. The vertex $(0, 0)$ means that at 0 mph, the force
is 0 lb.

107. $F(v) = 0.151v^2$
$F(15) = 0.151(15)^2$
$\qquad\quad = 33.975$
The drag force is 33.975 lb.

108.

109. $y = x^2 - 4x + 7$
$\quad = (x^2 - 4x) + 7$
$\quad = (x^2 - 4x + 4) - 4 + 7$
$\quad = (x - 2)^2 + 3$
$x - 2 = 0$
$\quad x = 2$
$y = (x - 2)^2 + 3$
$\quad = (2 - 2)^2 + 3$
$\quad = 3$
The vertex is $(2, 3)$.

110. $y = x^2 - 2x - 2$
$\quad = (x^2 - 2x) - 2$
$\quad = (x^2 - 2x + 1) - 1 - 2$
$\quad = (x - 1)^2 - 3$
$x - 1 = 0$
$\quad x = 1$
$y = (x - 1)^2 - 3$
$\quad = (1 - 1)^2 - 3$
$\quad = -3$
The vertex is $(1, -3)$.

111.
$$y = x^2 + x + 2$$
$$= (x^2 + x) + 2$$
$$= \left(x^2 + x + \frac{1}{4}\right) - \frac{1}{4} + 2$$
$$= \left(x + \frac{1}{2}\right)^2 + \frac{7}{4}$$
$$x + \frac{1}{2} = 0$$
$$x = -\frac{1}{2}$$
$$y = \left(x + \frac{1}{2}\right)^2 + \frac{7}{4}$$
$$= \left(-\frac{1}{2} + \frac{1}{2}\right)^2 + \frac{7}{4}$$
$$= \frac{7}{4}$$
The vertex is $\left(-\frac{1}{2}, \frac{7}{4}\right)$.

112.
$$y = x^2 - x - 3$$
$$= (x^2 - x) - 3$$
$$= \left(x^2 - x + \frac{1}{4}\right) - \frac{1}{4} - 3$$
$$= \left(x - \frac{1}{2}\right)^2 - \frac{13}{4}$$
$$x - \frac{1}{2} = 0$$
$$x = \frac{1}{2}$$
$$y = \left(x - \frac{1}{2}\right)^2 - \frac{13}{4}$$
$$= \left(\frac{1}{2} - \frac{1}{2}\right)^2 - \frac{13}{4}$$
$$= -\frac{13}{4}$$
The vertex is $\left(\frac{1}{2}, -\frac{13}{4}\right)$.

113.
$$y = a(x - h)^2 + k$$
Vertex $(1, 2)$: $h = 1, k = 2$
$P(2, 5)$: $x = 2, y = 5$
Substitute into the equation:
$$5 = a(2 - 1)^2 + 2$$
$$5 = a(1)^2 + 2$$
$$5 = a + 2$$
$$3 = a$$
$$y = 3(x - 1)^2 + 2$$
$$y = 3(x^2 - 2x + 1) + 2$$
$$y = 3x^2 - 6x + 3 + 2$$
$$y = 3x^2 - 6x + 5$$

114.
$$y = a(x - h)^2 + k$$
Vertex $(0, -3)$: $h = 0, k = -3$
$P(3, -2)$: $x = 3, y = -2$
Substitute into the equation:
$$-2 = a(3 - 0)^2 + (-3)$$
$$-2 = a(3)^2 - 3$$
$$-2 = 9a - 3$$
$$1 = 9a$$
$$\frac{1}{9} = a$$
$$y = \frac{1}{9}(x - 0)^2 - 3$$
$$y = \frac{1}{9}x^2 - 3$$

Section 8.7

Concept Review 8.7

1. Sometimes true
   If the parabola opens down, it has a maximum value. The range of the parabola would be from negative infinity to the maximum value. Thus, there would be no minimum value.

2. Sometimes true
   In some cases, the y-coordinate may be the maximum value of the function.

3. Always true

4. Always true

5. Sometimes true
   If a parabola opens down and the parabola is below the x-axis, the maximum value of the parabola is a negative number.

6. Always true

Objective 8.7.1 Exercises

1. The minimum value or the maximum value of a quadratic function is the value of the function at the vertex of the graph of the function; it is the y-coordinate of the vertex. A quadratic function has a minimum value when $a > 0$ in
   $f(x) = ax^2 + bx + c$. A quadratic function has a maximum value when $a < 0$ in
   $f(x) = ax^2 + bx + c$.

2. To find the minimum or maximum value of a quadratic function, find the x-coordinate of the vertex. Then evaluate the function at the value of the x-coordinate of the vertex.

3. a. The function $f(x) = -x^2 + 6x - 1$ has a maximum since $a = -1 < 0$.

b. The function $f(x) = 2x^2 - 4$ has a minimum since $a = 2 > 0$.

c. The function $f(x) = -5x^2 + x$ has a maximum since $a = -5 < 0$.

4. a. The function $f(x) = 3x^2 - 2x + 4$ has a minimum since $a = 3 > 0$.

b. The function $f(x) = -x^2 + 9$ has a maximum since $a = -1 < 0$.

c. The function $f(x) = 6x^2 - 3x$ has a minimum since $a = 6 > 0$.

5. $f(x) = x^2 - 2x + 3$

$$x = -\frac{b}{2a} = -\frac{-2}{2(1)} = 1$$

$f(x) = x^2 - 2x + 3$
$f(1) = (1)^2 - 2(1) + 3 = 2$

Since a is positive, the function has a minimum value. The minimum value of the function is 2.

6. $f(x) = 2x^2 + 4x$

$$x = -\frac{b}{2a} = -\frac{4}{2(2)} = -1$$

$f(x) = 2x^2 + 4x$
$f(-1) = 2(-1)^2 + 4(-1) = 2 - 4 = -2$

Since a is positive, the function has a minimum value. The minimum value of the function is –2.

7. $f(x) = -2x^2 + 4x - 3$

$$x = -\frac{b}{2a} = -\frac{4}{2(-2)} = 1$$

$f(x) = -2x^2 + 4x - 3$
$f(1) = -2(1)^2 + 4(1) - 3$
$\quad = -2 + 4 - 3 = -1$

Since a is negative, the function has a maximum value. The maximum value of the function is –1.

8. $f(x) = -2x^2 + 4x - 5$

$$x = -\frac{b}{2a} = -\frac{4}{2(-2)} = 1$$

$f(x) = -2x^2 + 4x - 5$
$f(1) = -2(1)^2 + 4(1) - 5 = -2 + 4 - 5 = -3$

Since a is negative, the function has a maximum value. The maximum value of the function is –3.

9. $f(x) = -2x^2 - 3x + 4$

$$x = -\frac{b}{2a} = -\frac{-3}{2(-2)} = -\frac{3}{4}$$

$f(x) = -2x^2 - 3x + 4$

$$f\left(-\frac{3}{4}\right) = -2\left(-\frac{3}{4}\right)^2 - 3\left(-\frac{3}{4}\right) + 4$$

$$= -\frac{9}{8} + \frac{9}{4} + 4 = \frac{41}{8}$$

Since a is negative, the function has a maximum value. The maximum value of the function is $\frac{41}{8}$.

10. $f(x) = -2x^2 - 3x$

$$x = -\frac{b}{2a} = -\frac{-3}{2(-2)} = -\frac{3}{4}$$

$f(x) = -2x^2 - 3x$

$$f\left(-\frac{3}{4}\right) = -2\left(-\frac{3}{4}\right)^2 - 3\left(-\frac{3}{4}\right) = -\frac{9}{8} + \frac{9}{4} = \frac{9}{8}$$

Since a is negative, the function has a maximum value. The maximum value of the function is $\frac{9}{8}$.

11. $f(x) = 2x^2 + 3x - 8$

$$x = -\frac{b}{2a} = -\frac{3}{2(2)} = -\frac{3}{4}$$

$f(x) = 2x^2 + 3x - 8$

$$f\left(-\frac{3}{4}\right) = 2\left(-\frac{3}{4}\right)^2 + 3\left(-\frac{3}{4}\right) - 8$$

$$= \frac{9}{8} - \frac{9}{4} - 8$$

$$= -\frac{73}{8}$$

Since a is positive, the function has a minimum value. The minimum value of the function is $-\frac{73}{8}$.

12. $f(x) = 3x^2 + 3x - 2$

$$x = -\frac{b}{2a} = -\frac{3}{2(3)} = -\frac{1}{2}$$

$f(x) = 3x^2 + 3x - 2$

$$f\left(-\frac{1}{2}\right) = 3\left(-\frac{1}{2}\right)^2 + 3\left(-\frac{1}{2}\right) - 2$$

$$= \frac{3}{4} - \frac{3}{2} - 2$$

$$= -\frac{11}{4}$$

Since a is positive, the function has a minimum value. The minimum value of the function is $-\frac{11}{4}$.

13. $f(x) = -3x^2 + x - 6$

$$x = -\frac{b}{2a} = -\frac{1}{2(-3)} = \frac{1}{6}$$

$$f(x) = -3x^2 + x - 6$$

$$f\left(\frac{1}{6}\right) = -3\left(\frac{1}{6}\right)^2 + \left(\frac{1}{6}\right) - 6 = -\frac{1}{12} + \frac{1}{6} - 6 = -\frac{71}{12}$$

Since a is negative, the function has a maximum value. The maximum value of the function is $-\frac{71}{12}$.

14. $f(x) = -x^2 - x + 2$

$$x = -\frac{b}{2a} = -\frac{-1}{2(-1)} = -\frac{1}{2}$$

$$f(x) = -x^2 - x + 2$$

$$f\left(-\frac{1}{2}\right) = -\left(-\frac{1}{2}\right)^2 - \left(-\frac{1}{2}\right) + 2$$

$$= -\frac{1}{4} + \frac{1}{2} + 2$$

$$= \frac{9}{4}$$

Since a is negative, the function has a maximum value. The maximum value of the function is $\frac{9}{4}$.

15. $f(x) = x^2 - 5x + 3$

$$x = -\frac{b}{2a} = -\frac{-5}{2(1)} = \frac{5}{2}$$

$$f(x) = x^2 - 5x + 3$$

$$f\left(\frac{5}{2}\right) = \left(\frac{5}{2}\right)^2 - 5\left(\frac{5}{2}\right) + 3$$

$$= \frac{25}{4} - \frac{25}{2} + 3$$

$$= -\frac{13}{4}$$

Since a is positive, the function has a minimum value. The minimum value of the function is $-\frac{13}{4}$.

16. $f(x) = 3x^2 + 5x + 2$

$$x = -\frac{b}{2a} = -\frac{5}{2(3)} = -\frac{5}{6}$$

$$f(x) = 3x^2 + 5x + 2$$

$$f\left(-\frac{5}{6}\right) = 3\left(-\frac{5}{6}\right)^2 + 5\left(-\frac{5}{6}\right) + 2$$

$$= \frac{25}{12} - \frac{25}{6} + 2$$

$$= -\frac{1}{12}$$

Since a is positive, the function has a minimum value. The minimum value of the function is $-\frac{1}{12}$.

17. Strategy

To find the highest minimum value, find the x-coordinate of the vertex for each parabola and evaluate the parabola at that point.

Solution

For a, $y = x^2 - 2x - 3$,

$$\frac{-b}{2a} = \frac{-(-2)}{2(1)} = \frac{2}{2} = 1$$

$$y = (1)^2 - 2(1) - 3 = -4$$

For b, $y = x^2 - 10x + 20$,

$$\frac{-b}{2a} = \frac{-(-10)}{2(1)} = \frac{10}{2} = 5$$

$$y = (5)^2 - 10(5) + 20 = -5$$

For c, $y = 3x^2 - 6$,

$$\frac{-b}{2a} = \frac{0}{2(3)} = 0$$

$$y = 3(0)^2 - 6 = -6$$

a has the highest minimum value.

18. Strategy

To find the highest maximum value, find the x-coordinate of the vertex for each parabola and evaluate the parabola at that point.

Solution

For a, $y = -2x^2 + 2x - 1$,

$$\frac{-b}{2a} = \frac{-2}{2(-2)} = \frac{-2}{-4} = \frac{1}{2}$$

$$y = -2\left(\frac{1}{2}\right)^2 + 2\left(\frac{1}{2}\right) - 1 = -\frac{1}{2}$$

For b, $y = -x^2 + 8x - 2$,

$$\frac{-b}{2a} = \frac{-8}{2(-1)} = \frac{-8}{-2} = 4$$

$$y = -(4)^2 + 8(4) - 2 = 14$$

For c, $y = -4x^2 + 3$,

$$\frac{-b}{2a} = \frac{0}{2(-4)} = 0$$

$$y = -4(0)^2 + 3 = 3$$

b has the highest minimum value.

19. Since the parabola open up, it has a minimum value. The minimum value of the function is 7.

20. Since the parabola open down, it has a maximum value. The maximum value of the function is –5.

21. Strategy

To find the time it takes the rock to reach its maximum height, find the t-coordinate of the vertex.

To find the maximum height, evaluate the function at the t-coordinate of the vertex.

Solution

$$t = -\frac{b}{2a} = -\frac{64}{2(-16)} = 2$$

The rock reaches its maximum height in 2 s.

$$s(t) = -16t^2 + 64t + 50$$
$$s(2) = -16(2)^2 + 64(2) + 50$$
$$= -64 + 128 + 50 = 114$$

The maximum height is 114 ft.

22. Strategy

To find the time it takes the diver to reach the maximum height, find the t-coordinate of the vertex.

To find the maximum height, evaluate the function at the t-coordinate of the vertex.

Solution

$$t = -\frac{b}{2a} = -\frac{7.8}{2(-4.9)} = 0.80$$

The diver reaches the maximum height in 0.8 s.

$$s(t) = -4.9t^2 + 7.8t + 10$$
$$s(0.8) = -4.9(0.8)^2 + 7.8(0.8) + 10$$
$$= -3.136 + 6.24 + 10$$
$$= 13.1$$

The maximum height is 13.1 m.

23. Strategy

To find the number of tickets that will give the maximum profit, find the x-coordinate of the vertex and evaluate the function at that point.

Solution

$$x = -\frac{b}{2a} = -\frac{40}{2(-0.25)} = 80$$

$$P(x) = 40x - 0.25x^2$$
$$P(80) = 40(80) - 0.25(80)^2$$
$$= 3200 - 1600$$
$$= 1600$$

The operator can expect a maximum profit of $1600.

24. Strategy

To find the price that will give the maximum revenue, find the P-coordinate of the vertex.

Solution

$$P = -\frac{b}{2a} = -\frac{125}{2\left(-\frac{1}{4}\right)} = 250$$

A price of $250 will give the maximum revenue.

25. Strategy

To find the number of days for the least amount of algae, find the t-coordinate of the vertex.

Solution

$$t = -\frac{b}{2a} = -\frac{-400}{2(40)} = 5$$

The pool will have the least amount of algae 5 days after treatment.

26. Strategy

To find the distance from one end of the bridge where the cable is at its minimum height, find the x-coordinate of the vertex.

To find the minimum height, evaluate the function at the x-coordinate of the vertex.

Solution

$$x = -\frac{b}{2a} = -\frac{-0.8}{2(0.25)} = 1.6$$

The cable is at its minimum height 1.6 ft from one end of the bridge.

$$h(x) = 0.25x^2 - 0.8x + 25$$
$$h(1.6) = 0.25(1.6)^2 - 0.8(1.6) + 25$$
$$= 0.64 - 1.28 + 25$$
$$= 24.36$$

The minimum height is 24.36 ft.

27. Strategy

To find the point where the thickness will be a minimum, find the x-coordinate of the vertex.

To find the minimum thickness, evaluate the function at the x-coordinate of the vertex.

Solution

$$h(x) = 0.000379x^2 - 0.0758x + 24$$

$$x = -\frac{b}{2a} = -\frac{-0.0758}{2(0.000379)} = 100$$

The thickness is a minimum 100 inches from the edge.

$$h(x) = 0.000379x^2 - 0.0758x + 24$$
$$h(100) = 0.000379(100)^2 - 0.0758(100) + 24$$
$$= 3.79 - 7.58 + 24$$
$$= 20.21$$

The minimum thickness is 20.21 in.

28. Strategy

To find the maximum height, find the t-coordinate of the vertex and evaluate the function at that value.

Solution

$$h(t) = -16t^2 + 90t + 15$$
$$t = -\frac{b}{2a} = -\frac{90}{2(-16)} = 2.8125$$

$$h(2.8125) = -16(2.8125)^2 + 90(2.8125) + 15$$
$$= 141.6$$

The maximum height of the waterspout is 141.6 ft.

29. Strategy
To find how far up the water will land, evaluate the function at 40 ft.

Solution

$$s(x) = -\frac{1}{30}x^2 + 2x + 5$$

$$s(40) = -\frac{1}{30}(40)^2 + 2(40) + 5 = 31\frac{2}{3}$$

The water will land $31\frac{2}{3}$ ft.

30. Strategy
To find the speed, substitute for distance ($s = 44$) and solve for v.

Solution

$$s(v) = 0.055v^2 + 1.1v$$

$$44 = 0.055v^2 + 1.1v$$

$$0 = 0.055v^2 + 1.1v - 44$$

$$v = \frac{-b \pm \sqrt{b^2 - 4ac}}{2a}$$

$$v = \frac{-1.1 \pm \sqrt{(1.1)^2 - 4(0.055)(-44)}}{2(0.055)}$$

$$v = \frac{-1.1 \pm 3.3}{0.11}$$

$$v = 20 \text{ or } -40$$

Since the speed cannot be negative, –40 cannot be a solution.
The car can be traveling 20 mph and still stop at a stop sign 44 ft away.

31. Strategy
The first number: x
The second number: $20 - x$
Find the number that will maximize the product of the two numbers.

Solution

$$x(20 - x) = 0$$

$$-x^2 + 20x = 0$$

$$x = -\frac{b}{2a} = -\frac{20}{2(-1)} = 10$$

$$20 - x = 20 - 10 = 10$$

The numbers are 10 and 10.

32. Strategy
The first number: x
The second number: $x + 14$
Find the number that will minimize the product of the two numbers.

Solution

$$x(x + 14) = 0$$

$$x^2 + 14x = 0$$

$$x = -\frac{b}{2a} = -\frac{14}{2(1)} = -7$$

$$x + 14 = -7 + 14 = 7$$

The numbers are 7 and –7.

33. Strategy
The length of fencing is 200 ft.
$$200 = 2W + L$$
$$200 - 2W = L$$
The area is $LW = (200 - 2W)W = 200W - 2W^2$
To find the width that will maximize the area, find the W-coordinate of the vertex.
To find the length, replace W in $200 - 2W$ by the W-coordinate of the vertex and evaluate.

Solution

$$A = 200W - 2W^2$$

$$W = -\frac{b}{2a} = -\frac{200}{2(-2)} = 50$$

$$L = 200 - 2(W)$$
$$= 200 - 2(50)$$
$$= 100$$

To maximize the area, the length is 100 ft and the width is 50 ft.

Applying Concepts 8.7

34. Strategy
Find the minimum value of the function.
Determine the average of 2, 5, 4, and 7.

Solution

$$S(x) = (2 - x)^2 + (5 - x)^2 + (4 - x)^2 + (7 - x)^2$$
$$= 4 - 4x + x^2 + 25 - 10x + x^2 + 16 - 8x + x^2 + 49 - 14x + x^2$$
$$= 4x^2 - 36x + 94$$

$$x = -\frac{b}{2a} = -\frac{-36}{2(4)} = 4.5$$

$$\frac{2 + 5 + 4 + 7}{4} = 4.5$$

The minimum value of S is 4.5; the average of 2, 5, 4, and 7 is 4.5.

35. The minimum value of the function
$f(x) = x^4 - 2x^2 + 4$ is 3.0.

36. The minimum value of the function
$f(x) = x^4 + 2x^3 + 1$ is -0.7.

37. The maximum value of the function
$f(x) = -x^6 + x^4 - x^3 + x$ is 0.5.

38. The maximum value of the function
$f(x) = -x^8 + x^6 - x^4 + 5x^2 + 7$ is 11.2.

39. When the highest power is an even exponent and the sign of the leading coefficient of a polynomial function is positive, the function will have a minimum value. When the highest power is an even exponent and the sign of the leading coefficient of a polynomial function is negative, the function will have a maximum value.

40. a.

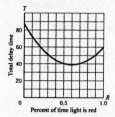

b. *R* is the percent of time that the light is red in the horizontal direction. Since 1 = 100%, and the percent of time the light is red in the horizontal direction cannot be more than 100%, *R* cannot be greater than 1. Since 0 = 0%, and the percent of time the light is red in the horizontal direction cannot be less than 0%, *R* cannot be less than 0. Therefore, the graph is drawn only for $0 \le R \le 1$.

c.
$$T = \left(\frac{100+150}{2}\right)R^2 + [(0.08(100)$$
$$- 1.08(150)]R + 0.58(150)$$
$$T = 125R^2 - 154R + 87$$
$$R = -\frac{b}{2a} = -\frac{-154}{2(125)} = 0.616$$

The traffic light should remain red in the horizontal direction approximately 62% of the time.

41. Here are some highlights. For more information see *The History of Mathematics: An Introduction* (1985) by David Burton or *A History of Mathematics: An Introduction* (1993) by Victor Katz.

The Babylonians had solved quadratic equations by 2000 B.C. The solution of cubic equations did not come until much later. Around 1100 A.D., Omar Khayyam gave the first complete *geometric* solutions of method relied heavily on Euclid's *Elements*.

Scipione del Ferro (1465-1526) was the first mathematician to give an algebraic solution of the cubic equation. He solved the special case $x^3 + cx = d$. Academic promotion during del Ferr's time was frequently based on public challenges in which mathematicians would challenge each other to solve certain problems. Having the secret of the solution of $x^3 + cx = d$ guaranteed del Ferro's continued success at winning these competitions and, consequently, retaining his professorship.

In the sixteenth century, Ludovico Ferrari solved a fourth-degree equation by reducing it to third-degree equation.

Paolo Ruffini (1765-1822) was the first to prove that the quintic equation could not be solved by explicit formulas similar to quadratic, cubic, and quartic equations. His proof was generally sound but contained some flaws. Neils Henrik Abel (1802-1829) gave a more rigorous proof in 1824. It was Evariste Galois (1812-1832) who first showed that no polynomial equation of degree greater than 4 could be solved by a general formula.

Focus on Problem Solving

1. The sum of the first *n* odd integers is n^2. If this conjecture is true, then the sum of $1+3+5+7+9+11+13+15 = 8^2 = 64$.

2. The next figure should be 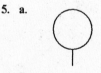.

3. All even numbers are divisible by 2. Because 14,386 is an even number, it is divisible by 2.

4. **a.** P 62 63

   b. Inductive reasoning

5. **a.**

   b. Inductive reasoning

6. **a.** If 5 ◊'s = 4 ∇'s, then 8 ∇'s = 10 ◊'s.

    b. Deductive reasoning

7. **a.** 2♠'s = 6 ♦'s and 3♦'s = 2 ♣'s, so
        6 ♦'s = 4 ♣'s, and 4 ♣'s = 1♥.
        If 2 ♠'s = 1 ♥, then 6 ♠'s = 3 ♥'s.

    b. Deductive reasoning

8. Inductive reasoning

9. Deductive reasoning

10. Deductive reasoning

11. Inductive reasoning

Projects and Group Activities

Completing the Square

Solve $x^2 + 4x = 12$ by completing the square.
  Begin with a line of unknown length, x, and form
  a square with x as a side.
  Draw a rectangle with width x and length 2 at the
  right of the square and another such rectangle
  below the square.
  Complete the square with sides $x + 2$.
  The area of the large square is $(x+2)^2$.
  From the diagram, we see that
  $$x^2 + 4x + 4 = (x+2)^2$$
  From the original equation, $x^2 + 4x = 12$. Thus
  $$12 + 4 = (x+2)^2$$
  $$16 = (x+2)^2$$
  $$4 = x + 2$$
  $$2 = x$$
  The positive solution is 2.

Using a Graphing Calculator to Solve a Quadratic Equation

1. For $x^2 + 6x + 1 = 0$,
    solution at $(-5.828427, -0.1715729)$

    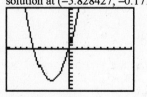

2. For $-x^2 + x + 3 = 0$,
    solution at $(-1.302776, 2.3027756)$

    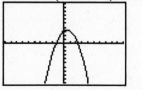

3. For $2x^2 + 4x - 1 = 0$,
    solution at $(-2.224745, 0.22474487)$

    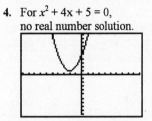

4. For $x^2 + 4x + 5 = 0$,
    no real number solution.

    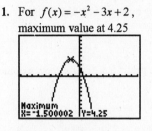

Finding the Maximum or Minimum of a Function Using a Graphing Calculator

1. For $f(x) = -x^2 - 3x + 2$,
    maximum value at 4.25

    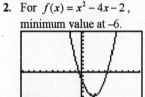

2. For $f(x) = x^2 - 4x - 2$,
    minimum value at –6.

    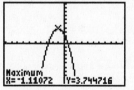

3. For $f(x) = -\sqrt{2}x^2 - \pi x + 2$,
    maximum value at 3.744716.

    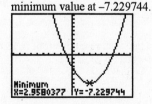

4. For $f(x) = \dfrac{x^2}{\sqrt{5}} - \sqrt{7}x - \sqrt{11}$,
    minimum value at –7.229744.

5. The minimum cost is with 100 lenses.

6. a. The physician's income will be maximum at age 48.

b. The maximum income is $148,000.

Business Applications of Maximum and Minimum Values of Quadratic Functions

1. a. Strategy
Use the equation $P = R - C$ to represent the profit. Determine the n-coordinate to find the number of DVDs to maximize profit.

Solution
$$P(n) = R(n) - C(n)$$
$$= 275n - 0.2n^2 - (25n + 4000)$$
$$= -0.2n^2 + 250n - 4000$$
$$n = -\frac{b}{2a} = -\frac{250}{2(-0.2)} = 625$$

The company must product 625 DVDs to maximize profit.

b. Strategy
Evaluate the profit function for the maximum value of n.

Solution
$$P(n) = -0.2n^2 + 250n - 4000$$
$$P(625) = -0.2(625)^2 + 250(625) - 4000$$
$$= 74,125$$

The maximum profit is $74,125.

2. Strategy
Use the equation $P = R - C$ to represent the profit. Determine the x-coordinate to find the number of packages to maximize profit

Solution
$$R(x) = x(24 - 0.02x)$$
$$C(x) = 1000 + 6x$$
$$P = R - C$$
$$= 24x - 0.02x^2 - (1000 + 6x)$$
$$= -0.02x^2 + 18x - 1000$$
$$x = -\frac{b}{2a} = -\frac{18}{2(-0.02)} = 450$$

$$P(x) = -0.02x^2 + 18x - 1000$$
$$P(450) = -0.02(450)^2 + 18(450) - 1000$$
$$= 3050$$
$$R(x) = 24 - 0.02x$$
$$R(450) = 24 - 0.02(450)$$
$$= 15$$

The company's maximum weekly profit is $3050. The price per package is $15.

Chapter Review Exercises

1. $2x^2 - 3x = 0$
$x(2x - 3) = 0$

$x = 0$ $2x - 3 = 0$
                     $2x = 3$
                     $x = \dfrac{3}{2}$

The solutions are 0 and $\dfrac{3}{2}$.

2. $6x^2 + 9xc = 6c^2$
$$6x^2 + 9xc - 6c^2 = 0$$
$$3\left(2x^2 + 3cx - 2c^2\right) = 0$$
$$3(2x - c)(x + 2c) = 0$$

$2x - c = 0$ $x + 2c = 0$
$2x = c$ $x = -2c$
$x = \dfrac{c}{2}$

The solutions are $\dfrac{c}{2}$ and $-2c$.

3. $x^2 = 48$
$$\sqrt{x^2} = \sqrt{48}$$
$$x = \pm\sqrt{48} = \pm4\sqrt{3}$$

The solutions are $4\sqrt{3}$ and $-4\sqrt{3}$.

4. $\left(x + \dfrac{1}{2}\right)^2 + 4 = 0$
$$\left(x + \dfrac{1}{2}\right)^2 = -4$$
$$\sqrt{\left(x + \dfrac{1}{2}\right)^2} = \sqrt{-4}$$
$$x + \frac{1}{2} = \pm\sqrt{-4} = \pm2i$$

$x + \dfrac{1}{2} = 2i$ $x + \dfrac{1}{2} = -2i$

$x = -\dfrac{1}{2} + 2i$ $x = -\dfrac{1}{2} - 2i$

The solutions are $-\dfrac{1}{2} + 2i$ and $-\dfrac{1}{2} - 2i$.

5. $-\dfrac{b}{2a} = -\dfrac{-7}{2(1)} = \dfrac{7}{2}$
$$f(x) = x^2 - 7x + 8$$
$$f\left(\frac{7}{2}\right) = \left(\frac{7}{2}\right)^2 - 7\left(\frac{7}{2}\right) + 8$$
$$= \frac{49}{4} - \frac{49}{2} + 8$$
$$= -\frac{17}{4}$$

The minimum value of the function is $-\dfrac{17}{4}$.

6. $-\dfrac{b}{2a} = -\dfrac{4}{2(-2)} = 1$

$f(x) = -2x^2 + 4x + 1$

$f(1) = -2(1)^2 + 4(1) + 1$

$\quad = -2 + 4 + 1$

$\quad = 3$

The maximum value of the function is 3.

7. $(x - r_1)(x - r_2) = 0$

$\left(x - \dfrac{1}{3}\right)[x - (-3)] = 0$

$\left(x - \dfrac{1}{3}\right)(x + 3) = 0$

$x^2 + \dfrac{8}{3}x - 1 = 0$

$3\left(x^2 + \dfrac{8}{3}x - 1\right) = 3 \cdot 0$

$3x^2 + 8x - 3 = 0$

8. $2x^2 + 9x = 5$

$2x^2 + 9x - 5 = 0$

$(2x - 1)(x + 5) = 0$

$2x - 1 = 0 \qquad\qquad x + 5 = 0$

$\quad 2x = 1 \qquad\qquad\quad x = -5$

$\quad x = \dfrac{1}{2}$

The solutions are $\dfrac{1}{2}$ and -5.

9. $2(x + 1)^2 - 36 = 0$

$2(x + 1)^2 = 36$

$(x + 1)^2 = 18$

$\sqrt{(x + 1)^2} = \sqrt{18}$

$x + 1 = \pm 3\sqrt{2}$

$x + 1 = 3\sqrt{2} \qquad\qquad x + 1 = -3\sqrt{2}$

$\quad x = -1 + 3\sqrt{2} \qquad\quad x = -1 - 3\sqrt{2}$

The solutions are $-1 + 3\sqrt{2}$ and $-1 - 3\sqrt{2}$.

10. $x^2 + 6x + 10 = 0$

$a = 1, b = 6, c = 10$

$x = \dfrac{-b \pm \sqrt{b^2 - 4ac}}{2a}$

$\quad = \dfrac{-6 \pm \sqrt{6^2 - 4(1)(10)}}{2(1)}$

$\quad = \dfrac{-6 \pm \sqrt{36 - 40}}{2}$

$\quad = \dfrac{-6 \pm \sqrt{-4}}{2}$

$\quad = \dfrac{-6 \pm 2i}{2}$

$\quad = -3 \pm i$

The solutions are $-3 + i$ and $-3 - i$.

11. $\dfrac{2}{x - 4} + 3 = \dfrac{x}{2x - 3}$

$(x - 4)(2x - 3)\left(\dfrac{2}{x - 4} + 3\right) = (x - 4)(2x - 3)\dfrac{x}{2x - 3}$

$(2x - 3)2 + 3(x - 4)(2x - 3) = (x - 4)x$

$4x - 6 + 3(2x^2 - 11x + 12) = x^2 - 4x$

$4x - 6 + 6x^2 - 33x + 36 = x^2 - 4x$

$6x^2 - 29x + 30 = x^2 - 4x$

$5x^2 - 25x + 30 = 0$

$5(x^2 - 5x + 6) = 0$

$5(x - 2)(x - 3) = 0$

$x - 2 = 0 \qquad\qquad x - 3 = 0$

$\quad x = 2 \qquad\qquad\quad x = 3$

The solutions are 2 and 3.

12. $x^4 - 6x^2 + 8 = 0$

$(x^2)^2 - 6(x^2) + 8 = 0$

$u^2 - 6u + 8 = 0$

$(u - 2)(u - 4) = 0$

$u - 2 = 0 \qquad\qquad u - 4 = 0$

$\quad u = 2 \qquad\qquad\quad u = 4$

Replace u by x^2.

$x^2 = 2 \qquad\qquad\qquad x^2 = 4$

$\sqrt{x^2} = \sqrt{2} \qquad\qquad \sqrt{x^2} = \sqrt{4}$

$\quad x = \pm\sqrt{2} \qquad\qquad\quad x = \pm 2$

The solutions are $\sqrt{2}$, $-\sqrt{2}$, 2, and -2

13. $\sqrt{2x - 1} + \sqrt{2x} = 3$

$\sqrt{2x - 1} = 3 - \sqrt{2x}$

$\left(\sqrt{2x - 1}\right)^2 = \left(3 - \sqrt{2x}\right)^2$

$2x - 1 = 9 - 6\sqrt{2x} + 2x$

$-10 = -6\sqrt{2x}$

$\dfrac{-10}{-6} = \dfrac{-6\sqrt{2x}}{-6}$

$\dfrac{5}{3} = \sqrt{2x}$

$\left(\dfrac{5}{3}\right)^2 = \left(\sqrt{2x}\right)^2$

$\dfrac{25}{9} = 2x$

$\dfrac{1}{2}\left(\dfrac{25}{9}\right) = \dfrac{1}{2}(2x)$

$\dfrac{25}{18} = x$

The solution is $\dfrac{25}{18}$.

14. $2x^{2/3} + 3x^{1/3} - 2 = 0$

$2\left(x^{1/3}\right)^2 + 3\left(x^{1/3}\right) - 2 = 0$

$2u^2 + 3u - 2 = 0$

$(2u - 1)(u + 2) = 0$

$2u - 1 = 0 \qquad u + 2 = 0$

$2u = 1 \qquad\qquad u = -2$

$u = \dfrac{1}{2}$

Replace u by $x^{1/3}$.

$x^{1/3} = \dfrac{1}{2} \qquad\qquad x^{1/3} = -2$

$\left(x^{1/3}\right)^3 = \left(\dfrac{1}{2}\right)^3 \qquad \left(x^{1/3}\right)^3 = (-2)^3$

$\qquad\qquad\qquad\qquad\qquad x = -8$

$x = \dfrac{1}{8}$

The solutions are $\dfrac{1}{8}$ and -8.

16. $x^2 - 6x - 2 = 0$

$a = 1, b = -6, c = -2$

$x = \dfrac{-b \pm \sqrt{b^2 - 4ac}}{2a}$

$\quad = \dfrac{6 \pm \sqrt{(-6)^2 - 4(1)(-2)}}{2(1)}$

$\quad = \dfrac{6 \pm \sqrt{36 + 8}}{2}$

$\quad = \dfrac{6 \pm \sqrt{44}}{2}$

$\quad = \dfrac{6 \pm 2\sqrt{11}}{2}$

$\quad = 3 \pm \sqrt{11}$

The solutions are $3 + \sqrt{11}$ and $3 - \sqrt{11}$.

17.
$$\dfrac{2x}{x-4} + \dfrac{6}{x+1} = 11$$

$(x-4)(x+1)\left(\dfrac{2x}{x-4} + \dfrac{6}{x+1}\right) = (x-4)(x+1)11$

$(x-4)(x+1)\dfrac{2x}{x-4} + (x-4)(x+1)\dfrac{6}{x+1} = 11(x-4)(x+1)$

$2x(x+1) + 6(x-4) = 11\left(x^2 - 3x - 4\right)$

$2x^2 + 2x + 6x - 24 = 11x^2 - 33x - 44$

$2x^2 + 8x - 24 = 11x^2 - 33x - 44$

$0 = 9x^2 - 41x - 20$

$0 = (9x + 4)(x - 5)$

$9x + 4 = 0 \qquad\qquad x - 5 = 0$

$9x = -4 \qquad\qquad\quad x = 5$

$x = -\dfrac{4}{9}$

The solutions are $-\dfrac{4}{9}$ and 5.

15. $\sqrt{3x - 2} + 4 = 3x$

$\sqrt{3x - 2} = 3x - 4$

$\left(\sqrt{3x - 2}\right)^2 = (3x - 4)^2$

$3x - 2 = 9x^2 - 24x + 16$

$0 = 9x^2 - 27x + 18$

$0 = 9\left(x^2 - 3x + 2\right)$

$0 = 9(x - 2)(x - 1)$

$x - 2 = 0 \qquad\qquad x - 1 = 0$

$x = 2 \qquad\qquad\quad x = 1$

1 does not check as a solution.
The solution is 2.

18. $2x^2 - 2x = 1$

$2x^2 - 2x - 1 = 0$

$a = 2, b = -2, c = -1$

$x = \dfrac{-b \pm \sqrt{b^2 - 4ac}}{2a}$

$= \dfrac{2 \pm \sqrt{(-2)^2 - 4(2)(-1)}}{2(2)}$

$= \dfrac{2 \pm \sqrt{4 + 8}}{4}$

$= \dfrac{2 \pm \sqrt{12}}{4}$

$= \dfrac{2 \pm 2\sqrt{3}}{4}$

$= \dfrac{1 \pm \sqrt{3}}{2}$

The solutions are $\dfrac{1 + \sqrt{3}}{2}$ and $\dfrac{1 - \sqrt{3}}{2}$.

19. $2x = 4 - 3\sqrt{x - 1}$

$2x - 4 = -3\sqrt{x - 1}$

$(2x - 4)^2 = \left(-3\sqrt{x - 1}\right)^2$

$4x^2 - 16x + 16 = 9(x - 1)$

$4x^2 - 16x + 16 = 9x - 9$

$4x^2 - 25x + 25 = 0$

$(4x - 5)(x - 5) = 0$

$4x - 5 = 0 \qquad\qquad x - 5 = 0$

$\quad 4x = 5 \qquad\qquad\qquad x = 5$

$\quad\ x = \dfrac{5}{4}$

5 does not check as a solution. The solution is $\dfrac{5}{4}$.

20. $3x = \dfrac{9}{x - 2}$

$3x(x - 2) = \dfrac{9}{x - 2}(x - 2)$

$3x^2 - 6x = 9$

$3x^2 - 6x - 9 = 0$

$3\left(x^2 - 2x - 3\right) = 0$

$3(x - 3)(x + 1) = 0$

$x - 3 = 0 \qquad\qquad x + 1 = 0$

$\quad x = 3 \qquad\qquad\qquad x = -1$

The solutions are 3 and -1.

21. $\dfrac{3x + 7}{x + 2} + x = 3$

$(x + 2)\left(\dfrac{3x + 7}{x + 2} + x\right) = (x + 2)3$

$3x + 7 + x(x + 2) = 3x + 6$

$3x + 7 + x^2 + 2x = 3x + 6$

$x^2 + 5x + 7 = 3x + 6$

$x^2 + 2x + 1 = 0$

$(x + 1)^2 = 0$

$\sqrt{(x + 1)^2} = \sqrt{0}$

$x + 1 = 0$

$x = -1$

The solution is -1.

22. $\dfrac{x - 2}{2x + 3} - \dfrac{x - 4}{x} = 2$

$x(2x + 3)\left(\dfrac{x - 2}{2x + 3} - \dfrac{x - 4}{x}\right) = x(2x + 3)2$

$x(x - 2) - (2x + 3)(x - 4) = 2x(2x + 3)$

$x^2 - 2x - \left(2x^2 - 5x - 12\right) = 4x^2 + 6x$

$x^2 - 2x - 2x^2 + 5x + 12 = 4x^2 + 6x$

$-x^2 + 3x + 12 = 4x^2 + 6x$

$0 = 5x^2 + 3x - 12$

$a = 5, \ b = 3, \ c = -12$

$x = \dfrac{-b \pm \sqrt{b^2 - 4ac}}{2a}$

$= \dfrac{-3 \pm \sqrt{3^2 - 4(5)(-12)}}{2(5)}$

$= \dfrac{-3 \pm \sqrt{9 + 240}}{10}$

$= \dfrac{-3 \pm \sqrt{249}}{10}$

The solutions are $\dfrac{-3 + \sqrt{249}}{10}$ and $\dfrac{-3 - \sqrt{249}}{10}$.

23.

$$1 - \frac{x+4}{2-x} = \frac{x-3}{x+2}$$

$$(x+2)(2-x)\left(1-\frac{x+4}{2-x}\right) = (x+2)(2-x)\frac{x-3}{x+2}$$

$$(x+2)(2-x) - (x+2)(x+4) = (2-x)(x-3)$$

$$4 - x^2 - \left(x^2 + 6x + 8\right) = -x^2 + 5x - 6$$

$$4 - x^2 - x^2 - 6x - 8 = -x^2 + 5x - 6$$

$$-2x^2 - 6x - 4 = -x^2 + 5x - 6$$

$$0 = x^2 + 11x - 2$$

$$a = 1, \ b = 11, \ c = -2$$

$$x = \frac{-b \pm \sqrt{b^2 - 4ac}}{2a}$$

$$= \frac{-11 \pm \sqrt{11^2 - 4(1)(-2)}}{2(1)}$$

$$= \frac{-11 \pm \sqrt{121 + 8}}{2}$$

$$= \frac{-11 \pm \sqrt{129}}{2}$$

The solutions are $\dfrac{-11 + \sqrt{129}}{2}$ and $\dfrac{-11 - \sqrt{129}}{2}$.

24. $y = -x^2 + 6x - 5$

The axis of symmetry is the line with equation

$x = -\dfrac{b}{2a}$.

$a = -1, \ b = 6$

$x = -\dfrac{6}{2(-1)} = -\dfrac{6}{-2} = 3$

The axis of symmetry is $x = 3$.

25. $y = -x^2 + 3x - 2$

The x-coordinate of the vertex is $-\dfrac{b}{2a}$.

$a = -1, \ b = 3$

$-\dfrac{b}{2a} = -\dfrac{3}{2(-1)} = -\dfrac{3}{-2} = \dfrac{3}{2}$

$y = -x^2 + 3x - 2$

$ = -\left(\dfrac{3}{2}\right)^2 + 3\left(\dfrac{3}{2}\right) - 2$

$ = \dfrac{1}{4}$

The vertex is $\left(\dfrac{3}{2}, \dfrac{1}{4}\right)$.

26. $y = -2x^2 + 2x - 3$

$a = -2, \ b = 2, \ c = -3$

$b^2 - 4ac$

$(2)^2 - 4(-2)(-3) = 4 - 24 = -20$

$-20 < 0$

Since the discriminant is less than zero, the parabola has no x-intercepts.

27. $y = 3x^2 - 2x - 4$

$a = 3, \ b = -2, \ c = -4$

$b^2 - 4ac$

$(-2)^2 - 4(3)(-4) = 4 + 48 = 52$

$50 > 0$

Since the discriminant is greater than zero, the parabola has two x-intercepts.

28. $y = 4x^2 + 12x + 4$

$0 = 4x^2 + 12x + 4$

$0 = 4\left(x^2 + 3x + 1\right)$

$a = 1, \ b = 3, \ c = 1$

$x = \dfrac{-b \pm \sqrt{b^2 - 4ac}}{2a}$

$ = \dfrac{-3 \pm \sqrt{3^2 - 4(1)(1)}}{2(1)}$

$ = \dfrac{-3 \pm \sqrt{9 - 4}}{2}$

$ = \dfrac{-3 \pm \sqrt{5}}{2}$

The x-intercepts are $\left(\dfrac{-3 + \sqrt{5}}{2}, 0\right)$ and

$\left(\dfrac{-3 - \sqrt{5}}{2}, 0\right)$.

29. $y = -2x^2 - 3x + 2$

$0 = -2x^2 - 3x + 2$

$0 = (-2x + 1)(x + 2)$

$-2x + 1 = 0 \qquad x + 2 = 0$

$-2x = -1 \qquad\quad x = -2$

$x = \dfrac{1}{2}$

The x-intercepts are $\left(\dfrac{1}{2},\, 0\right)$ and $(-2, 0)$.

30. $f(x) = 3x^2 + 2x + 2$

$0 = 3x^2 + 2x + 2$

$a = 3,\ b = 2,\ c = -2$

$x = \dfrac{-b \pm \sqrt{b^2 - 4ac}}{2a}$

$= \dfrac{-2 \pm \sqrt{2^2 - 4(3)(2)}}{2(3)}$

$= \dfrac{-2 \pm \sqrt{4 - 24}}{6}$

$= \dfrac{-2 \pm \sqrt{-20}}{6}$

$= \dfrac{-2 \pm 2i\sqrt{5}}{6}$

$= \dfrac{-1 \pm i\sqrt{5}}{3}$

The zeros are $-\dfrac{1}{3} + \dfrac{\sqrt{5}}{3}i$ and $-\dfrac{1}{3} - \dfrac{\sqrt{5}}{3}i$

31. $(x + 3)(2x - 5) < 0$

$\left\{x \mid -3 < x < \dfrac{5}{2}\right\}$

32. $(x - 2)(x + 4)(2x + 3) \le 0$

$\left\{x \mid x \le -4 \ \text{or} \ -\dfrac{3}{2} \le x \le 2\right\}$

33. $\dfrac{x - 2}{2x - 3} \ge 0$

$\left\{x \mid x < \dfrac{3}{2} \ \text{or} \ x \ge 2\right\}$

34. $\dfrac{(2x - 1)(x + 3)}{x - 4} \le 0$

$\left\{x \mid x \le -3 \ \text{or} \ \dfrac{1}{2} \le x < 4\right\}$

35. $-\dfrac{b}{2a} = -\dfrac{2}{2(1)} = -1$

$y = (-1)^2 + 2(-1) - 4 = -5$

The vertex is $(-1, -5)$.

The axis of symmetry is $x = -1$.

The domain is $\{x \mid x \in \text{real numbers}\}$

The range is $\{y \mid y \ge -5\}$.

36. $-\dfrac{b}{2a} = -\dfrac{-2}{2(1)} = 1$

$y = 1^2 - 2(1) + 3 = 2$

The vertex is $(1, 2)$.

The axis of symmetry is $x = 1$.

37. Strategy

This is an integer problem.

The first integer: x

The second consecutive even integer: $x + 2$

The third consecutive even integer: $x + 4$

The sum of the squares of the three consecutive integers is 56.

$x^2 + (x + 2)^2 + (x + 4)^2 = 56$

Solution

$x^2 + (x + 2)^2 + (x + 4)^2 = 56$

$x^2 + x^2 + 4x + 4 + x^2 + 8x + 16 = 56$

$3x^2 + 12x - 36 = 0$

$3\left(x^2 + 4 - 12\right) = 0$

$3(x + 6)(x - 2) = 0$

$x + 6 = 0 \qquad\qquad x - 2 = 0$

$x = -6 \qquad\qquad\ \ x = 2$

$x = 2,\ x + 2 = 4,\ x + 4 = 6$

$x = -6,\ x + 2 = -4,\ x + 4 = -2$

The integers are 2, 4, and 6 or -6, -4, and -2.

38. Strategy

This is a geometry problem.

The width of the rectangle: x

The length of the rectangle: $2x + 2$

The area of the rectangle is 60 cm^2.

Use the equation for the area of the rectangle $(A = L \cdot W)$.

Solution

$A = L \cdot W$

$60 = x(2x + 2)$

$60 = 2x^2 + 2x$

$0 = 2x^2 + 2x - 60$

$0 = 2\left(x^2 + x - 30\right)$

$0 = 2(x + 6)(x - 5)$

$x + 6 = 0 \qquad\qquad x - 5 = 0$

$\qquad x = -6 \qquad\qquad\qquad x = 5$

Since the width cannot be negative, –6 cannot be a solution.

$2x + 2 = 2(5) + 2 = 10 + 2 = 12$

The width of the rectangle is 5 cm.

The length of the rectangle is 12 cm.

39. Strategy

This is a work problem.

Time for new computer to print payroll: x

Time for older computer to print payroll: $x + 12$

	Rate	Time	Part
New computer	$\dfrac{1}{x}$	8	$\dfrac{8}{x}$
Older computer	$\dfrac{1}{x + 12}$	8	$\dfrac{8}{x + 12}$

The sum of the parts of the task completed must be 1.

$\dfrac{8}{x} + \dfrac{8}{x + 12} = 1$

Solution

$\dfrac{8}{x} + \dfrac{8}{x + 12} = 1$

$x(x + 12)\left(\dfrac{8}{x} + \dfrac{8}{x + 12}\right) = x(x + 12)(1)$

$8(x + 12) + 8x = x(x + 12)$

$8x + 96 + 8x = x^2 + 12x$

$16x + 96 = x^2 + 12x$

$0 = x^2 - 4x - 96$

$0 = (x - 12)(x + 8)$

$x - 12 = 0 \qquad\qquad x + 8 = 0$

$\qquad x = 12 \qquad\qquad\qquad x = -8$

The solution –8 is not possible, since time cannot be a negative number. Working alone, the new computer can print the payroll in 12 min.

40. Strategy

This is a distance-rate problem.

Rate of the first car: r

Rate of the second car: $r + 10$

	Distance	Rate	Time
First car	200	r	$\dfrac{200}{r}$
Second car	200	$r + 10$	$\dfrac{200}{r + 10}$

The second car's time is one hour less than the time of the first car.

$\dfrac{200}{r + 10} = \dfrac{200}{r} - 1$

Solution

$\dfrac{200}{r + 10} = \dfrac{200}{r} - 1$

$r(r + 10)\left(\dfrac{200}{r + 10}\right) = r(r + 10)\left(\dfrac{200}{r} - 1\right)$

$200r = 200(r + 10) - r(r + 10)$

$200r = 200r + 2000 - r^2 - 10r$

$r^2 + 10r - 2000 = 0$

$(r + 50)(r - 40) = 0$

$r + 50 = 0 \qquad\qquad r - 40 = 0$

$\qquad r = -50 \qquad\qquad\qquad r = 40$

The solution –50 is not possible, since rate cannot be a negative number.

$r + 10 = 40 + 10 = 50$

The rate of the first car is 40 mph.

The rate of the second car is 50 mph.

Chapter Test

1.
$2x^2 + x = 6$

$2x^2 + x - 6 = 0$

$(2x - 3)(x + 2) = 0$

$2x - 3 = 0 \qquad\qquad x + 2 = 0$

$2x = 3 \qquad\qquad\qquad x = -2$

$x = \dfrac{3}{2}$

The solutions are $\dfrac{3}{2}$ and –2.

2. $12x^2 + 7x - 12 = 0$

$(3x + 4)(4x - 3) = 0$

$3x + 4 = 0 \qquad\qquad 4x - 3 = 0$

$3x = -4 \qquad\qquad\qquad 4x = 3$

$x = -\dfrac{4}{3} \qquad\qquad\qquad x = \dfrac{3}{4}$

The solutions are $-\dfrac{4}{3}$ and $\dfrac{3}{4}$.

3. $f(x) = -x^2 + 8x - 7$

$x = -\dfrac{b}{2a} = -\dfrac{8}{2(-1)} = 4$

$f(4) = -4^2 + 8(4) - 7 = 9.$

The maximum value of the function is 9.

4. $(x - r_1)(x - r_2) = 0$

$\left[x - \left(-\dfrac{1}{3}\right)\right](x - 3) = 0$

$\left(x + \dfrac{1}{3}\right)(x - 3) = 0$

$x^2 - 3x + \dfrac{1}{3}x - 1 = 0$

$x^2 - \dfrac{8}{3}x - 1 = 0$

$3\left(x^2 - \dfrac{8}{3}x - 1\right) = 3 \cdot 0$

$3x^2 - 8x - 3 = 0$

5. $2(x + 3)^2 - 36 = 0$

$2(x + 3)^2 = 36$

$(x + 3)^2 = 18$

$\sqrt{(x + 3)^2} = \sqrt{18}$

$x + 3 = \pm 3\sqrt{2}$

$x = -3 \pm 3\sqrt{2}$

The solutions are $-3 + 3\sqrt{2}$ and $-3 - 3\sqrt{2}$.

6. $x^2 + 4x - 1 = 0$

$x^2 + 4x = 1$

Complete the square.

$x^2 + 4x + 4 = 1 + 4$

$(x + 2)^2 = 5$

$\sqrt{(x + 2)^2} = \sqrt{5}$

$x + 2 = \pm\sqrt{5}$

$x = -2 \pm \sqrt{5}$

The solutions are $-2 + \sqrt{5}$ and $-2 - \sqrt{5}$.

7. $g(x) = x^2 + 3x - 8$

$0 = x^2 + 3x - 8$

$a = 1, \ b = 3, \ c = -8$

$x = \dfrac{-b \pm \sqrt{b^2 - 4ac}}{2a}$

$= \dfrac{-3 \pm \sqrt{3^2 - 4(1)(-8)}}{2(1)}$

$= \dfrac{-3 \pm \sqrt{9 + 32}}{2}$

$= \dfrac{-3 \pm \sqrt{41}}{2}$

The zeros of $g(x)$ are $\dfrac{-3 + \sqrt{41}}{2}$ and $\dfrac{-3 - \sqrt{41}}{2}$.

8. $3x^2 - x + 8 = 0$

$a = 3, \ b = -1, \ c = 8$

$x = \dfrac{-b \pm \sqrt{b^2 - 4ac}}{2a}$

$= \dfrac{-(-1) \pm \sqrt{(-1)^2 - 4(3)(8)}}{2(3)}$

$= \dfrac{1 \pm \sqrt{1 - 96}}{6}$

$= \dfrac{1 \pm \sqrt{-95}}{6}$

$= \dfrac{1 \pm i\sqrt{95}}{6}$

The solutions are $= \dfrac{1}{6} + \dfrac{\sqrt{95}}{6}i$ and $= \dfrac{1}{6} - \dfrac{\sqrt{95}}{6}i$.

9. $\dfrac{2x}{x - 1} + \dfrac{3}{x + 2} = 1$

$(x - 1)(x + 2)\left(\dfrac{2x}{x - 1} + \dfrac{3}{x + 2}\right) = (x - 1)(x + 2)1$

$2x(x + 2) + 3(x - 1) = x^2 + x - 2$

$2x^2 + 4x + 3x - 3 = x^2 + x - 2$

$2x^2 + 7x - 3 = x^2 + x - 2$

$x^2 + 6x - 1 = 0$

$a = 1, \ b = 6, \ c = -1$

$x = \dfrac{-b \pm \sqrt{b^2 - 4ac}}{2a}$

$= \dfrac{-6 \pm \sqrt{6^2 - 4(1)(-1)}}{2(1)}$

$= \dfrac{-6 \pm \sqrt{36 + 4}}{2}$

$= \dfrac{-6 \pm \sqrt{40}}{2}$

$= \dfrac{-6 \pm 2\sqrt{10}}{2}$

$= -3 \pm \sqrt{10}$

The solutions are $-3 + \sqrt{10}$ and $-3 - \sqrt{10}$.

10.
$$2x + 7x^{1/2} - 4 = 0$$
$$2\left(x^{1/2}\right)^2 + 7x^{1/2} - 4 = 0$$
$$2u^2 + 7u - 4 = 0$$
$$(2u - 1)(u + 4) = 0$$

$2u - 1 = 0$	$u + 4 = 0$
$2u = 1$	$u = -4$
$u = \dfrac{1}{2}$	

Replace u by $x^{1/2}$.

$x^{1/2} = \dfrac{1}{2}$	$x^{1/2} = -4$
$\left(x^{1/2}\right)^2 = \left(\dfrac{1}{2}\right)^2$	$\left(x^{1/2}\right)^2 = (-4)^2$
	$x = 16$
$x = \dfrac{1}{4}$	

16 does not check as a solution.

$\dfrac{1}{4}$ does check as a solution.

The solution is $\dfrac{1}{4}$.

11.
$$x^4 - 11x^2 + 18 = 0$$
$$\left(x^2\right)^2 - 11x^2 + 18 = 0$$
$$u^2 - 11u + 18 = 0$$
$$(u - 9)(u - 2) = 0$$

$u - 9 = 0$	$u - 2 = 0$
$u = 9$	$u = 2$

Replace u by x^2.

$x^2 = 9$	$x^2 = 2$
$\sqrt{x^2} = \sqrt{9}$	$\sqrt{x^2} = \sqrt{2}$
$x = \pm 3$	$x = \pm\sqrt{2}$

The solutions are 3, –3, $\sqrt{2}$, $-\sqrt{2}$.

12.
$$\sqrt{2x+1} + 5 = 2x$$
$$\sqrt{2x+1} = 2x - 5$$
$$\left(\sqrt{2x+1}\right)^2 = (2x - 5)^2$$
$$2x + 1 = 4x^2 - 20x + 25$$
$$0 = 4x^2 - 22x + 24$$
$$0 = 2\left(2x^2 - 11x + 12\right)$$
$$0 = 2(2x - 3)(x - 4)$$

$2x - 3 = 0$	$x - 4 = 0$
$2x = 3$	$x = 4$
$x = \dfrac{3}{2}$	

$\dfrac{3}{2}$ does not check as a solution.

4 does check as a solution.

The solution is 4.

13.
$$\sqrt{x-2} = \sqrt{x} - 2$$
$$\left(\sqrt{x-2}\right)^2 = \left(\sqrt{x} - 2\right)^2$$
$$x - 2 = x - 4\sqrt{x} + 4$$
$$-6 = -4\sqrt{x}$$
$$-\frac{1}{4}(-6) = \left(-\frac{1}{4}\right)\left(-4\sqrt{x}\right)$$
$$\frac{3}{2} = \sqrt{x}$$
$$\frac{9}{4} = x$$

$\dfrac{9}{4}$ does not check as a solution.

The equation has no solution.

14. $b^2 - 4ac = 2^2 - 4(3)(-4)$
$$= 4 + 48$$
$$= 52$$
The discriminant is positive.
The parabola has two x-intercepts.

15. $y = 2x^2 + 5x - 12$
$$0 = 2x^2 + 5x - 12$$
$$0 = (2x - 3)(x + 4)$$

$2x - 3 = 0$	$x + 4 = 0$
$2x = 3$	$x = -4$
$x = \dfrac{3}{2}$	

The x-intercepts of the parabola are $\left(\dfrac{3}{2}, 0\right)$ and $(-4, 0)$.

16. $y = 2x^2 + 6x + 3$
The equation of the axis of symmetry is
$$x = -\frac{b}{2a}.$$
$a = 2, \ b = 6$
$$x = -\frac{b}{2a} = -\frac{6}{2(2)} = -\frac{6}{4} = -\frac{3}{2}$$
The axis of symmetry is $x = -\dfrac{3}{2}$.

17. $-\dfrac{b}{2a} = -\dfrac{1}{2\left(\frac{1}{2}\right)} = -1$
$$y = \frac{1}{2}(-1)^2 - 1 - 4 = -4.5$$
The vertex is $(-1, -4.5)$.
The axis of symmetry is $x = -1$.

The domain is $\{x \mid x \in \text{real numbers}\}$.
The range is $\{y \mid y \geq -4.5\}$.

18. $\dfrac{2x-3}{x+4}\le 0$

$$2x-3 \ \ -\ \ |\ -\ -\ -\ -\ -\ |\ +\ +\ +\ +$$
$$x+4 \ \ -\ \ |\ +\ +\ +\ +\ +\ |\ +\ +\ +\ +$$

$$\left\{x\mid -4 < x \le \dfrac{3}{2}\right\}$$

19. Strategy
This is a geometry problem.
The height of the triangle: x
The base of the triangle: $3x+3$
The area of the triangle is 30 ft^2. Use the
formula for the area of a triangle $\left(A=\dfrac{1}{2}bh\right)$.

Solution
$$A=\dfrac{1}{2}bh$$
$$30=\dfrac{1}{2}(3x+3)x$$
$$60=3x^2+3x$$
$$0=3x^2+3x-60$$
$$0=3\left(x^2+x-20\right)$$
$$0=3(x+5)(x-4)$$
$$x+5=0 \qquad\qquad x-4=0$$
$$x=-5 \qquad\qquad\ \ x=4$$
The solution −5 is not possible, since height
cannot be a negative number.
$$x=4,\ 3x+3=3(4)+3=15$$
The height of the triangle is 4 ft.
The base of the triangle is 15 ft.

20. Strategy
This is a distance-rate problem.
The rate of the canoe in calm water: x

	Distance	Rate	Time
With current	6	$x+2$	$\dfrac{6}{x+2}$
Against current	6	$x-2$	$\dfrac{6}{x-2}$

The total traveling time is 4 h.
$$\dfrac{6}{x+2}+\dfrac{6}{x-2}=4$$

Solution
$$\dfrac{6}{x+2}+\dfrac{6}{x-2}=4$$
$$(x+2)(x-2)\left(\dfrac{6}{x+2}+\dfrac{6}{x-2}\right)=(x+2)(x-2)4$$
$$6(x-2)+6(x+2)=4\left(x^2-4\right)$$
$$6x-12+6x+12=4x^2-16$$
$$12x=4x^2-16$$
$$0=4x^2-12x-16$$
$$0=4\left(x^2-3x-4\right)$$
$$0=4(x-4)(x+1)$$
$$x-4=0 \qquad\qquad x+1=0$$
$$x=4 \qquad\qquad\ \ x=-1$$
The solution −1 is not possible, since the rate
cannot be a negative number.
The rate of the canoe in calm water is 4 mph.

Cumulative Review Exercises

1. $2a^2-b^2\div c^2$
$$2(3)^2-(-4)^2\div(-2)^2$$
$$=2(9)-16\div4$$
$$=18-16\div4$$
$$=18-4$$
$$=14$$

2. $\dfrac{2x-3}{4}-\dfrac{x+4}{6}=\dfrac{3x-2}{8}$
$$24\left(\dfrac{2x-3}{4}-\dfrac{x+4}{6}\right)=24\left(\dfrac{3x-2}{8}\right)$$
$$6(2x-3)-4(x+4)=3(3x-2)$$
$$12x-18-4x-16=9x-6$$
$$8x-34=9x-6$$
$$-x-34=-6$$
$$-x=28$$
$$x=-28$$
The solution is −28.

3. $P_1(3,-4),\ P_2(-1,2)$
$$m=\dfrac{y_2-y_1}{x_2-x_1}=\dfrac{2-(-4)}{-1-3}=\dfrac{2+4}{-4}=\dfrac{6}{-4}=-\dfrac{3}{2}$$

4. $x - y = 1$
   $y = x - 1$
   $m = 1 \;\; (x_1, y_1) = (1, 2)$
   $y - y_1 = m(x - x_1)$
   $\;\; y - 2 = 1(x - 1)$
   $\;\; y - 2 = x - 1$
   $\;\;\;\;\; y = x + 1$

5. $-3x^3 y + 6x^2 y^2 - 9xy^3$
   $-3xy\left(x^2 - 2xy + 3y^2\right)$

6. $6x^2 - 7x - 20 = (2x - 5)(3x + 4)$

7. $a^n x + a^n y - 2x - 2y = a^n(x + y) - 2(x + y)$
   $\qquad\qquad\qquad\quad = (x + y)\left(a^n - 2\right)$

8.
$$\begin{array}{r}
x^2 - 3x - 4 \\
3x - 4 \overline{\smash{\big)}\,3x^3 - 13x^2 \qquad\quad +10} \\
\underline{3x^3 - 4x^2} \qquad\qquad\quad \\
-9x^2 \qquad\qquad\quad \\
\underline{-9x^2 + 12x} \qquad\quad \\
-12x + 10 \\
\underline{-12x + 16} \\
-6
\end{array}$$

$\left(3x^3 - 13x^2 + 10\right) \div (3x - 4) = x^2 - 3x - 4 - \dfrac{6}{3x - 4}$

9. $\dfrac{x^2 + 2x + 1}{8x^2 + 8x} \cdot \dfrac{4x^3 - 4x^2}{x^2 - 1}$
   $= \dfrac{(x+1)(x+1)}{8x(x+1)} \cdot \dfrac{4x^2(x-1)}{(x+1)(x-1)}$
   $= \dfrac{(x+1)(x+1)4x^2(x-1)}{8x(x+1)(x+1)(x-1)}$
   $= \dfrac{x}{2}$

10. Distance between points is
$$\sqrt{(x_2 - x_1)^2 + (y_2 - y_1)^2}$$
$\text{Distance} = \sqrt{[2 - (-2)]^2 + (5 - 3)^2}$
$\qquad\;\;\; = \sqrt{4^2 + 2^2}$
$\qquad\;\;\; = \sqrt{20}$
$\qquad\;\;\; = \sqrt{4 \cdot 5}$
$\qquad\;\;\; = 2\sqrt{5}$

The distance between the points is $2\sqrt{5}$

11. $\qquad S = \dfrac{n}{2}(a + b)$
    $\qquad 2S = 2\dfrac{n}{2}(a + b)$
    $\qquad 2S = n(a + b)$
    $\qquad 2S = an + bn$
    $2S - an = bn$
    $\dfrac{2S - an}{n} = b$

12. $-2i(7 - 4i) = -14i + 8i^2$
    $\qquad\qquad\;\; = -14i + 8(-1)$
    $\qquad\qquad\;\; = -8 - 14i$

13. $a^{-1/2}\left(a^{1/2} - a^{3/2}\right) = a^{-1/2 + 1/2} - a^{-1/2 + 3/2}$
    $\qquad\qquad\qquad\quad = a^0 - a^1$
    $\qquad\qquad\qquad\quad = 1 - a$

14. $\dfrac{\sqrt[3]{8x^4 y^5}}{\sqrt[3]{16xy^6}} = \sqrt[3]{\dfrac{8x^4 y^5}{16xy^6}}$
    $\qquad\quad = \sqrt[3]{\dfrac{x^3}{2y}}$
    $\qquad\quad = \sqrt[3]{\dfrac{x^3}{2y}}\sqrt[3]{\dfrac{4y^2}{4y^2}}$
    $\qquad\quad = \sqrt[3]{\dfrac{4y^2 x^3}{8y^3}}$
    $\qquad\quad = \sqrt[3]{\dfrac{x^3\left(4y^2\right)}{8y^3}}$
    $\qquad\quad = \dfrac{x\sqrt[3]{4y^2}}{2y}$

15.
$$\frac{x}{x+2} - \frac{4x}{x+3} = 1$$

$$(x+2)(x+3)\left(\frac{x}{x+2} - \frac{4x}{x+3}\right) = (x+2)(x+3)1$$

$$x(x+3) - 4x(x+2) = (x+2)(x+3)$$

$$x^2 + 3x - 4x^2 - 8x = x^2 + 5x + 6$$

$$-3x^2 - 5x = x^2 + 5x + 6$$

$$0 = 4x^2 + 10x + 6$$

$$0 = 2(2x^2 + 5x + 3)$$

$$0 = 2(2x+3)(x+1)$$

$$2x + 3 = 0 \qquad x + 1 = 0$$
$$2x = -3 \qquad x = -1$$
$$x = -\frac{3}{2}$$

The solutions are $-\frac{3}{2}$ and -1.

16.
$$\frac{x}{2x+3} - \frac{3}{4x^2 - 9} = \frac{x}{2x-3}$$

$$\frac{x}{2x+3} - \frac{3}{(2x+3)(2x-3)} = \frac{x}{2x-3}$$

$$(2x+3)(2x-3)\left[\frac{x}{2x+3} - \frac{3}{(2x+3)(2x-3)}\right] = (2x+3)(2x-3)\frac{x}{2x-3}$$

$$(2x-3)x - 3 = (2x+3)x$$

$$2x^2 - 3x - 3 = 2x^2 + 3x$$

$$-3 = 6x$$

$$-\frac{1}{2} = x$$

Check: $\dfrac{-\frac{1}{2}}{2\left(-\frac{1}{2}\right)+3} - \dfrac{3}{4\left(-\frac{1}{2}\right)^2 - 9} = \dfrac{-\frac{1}{2}}{2\left(-\frac{1}{2}\right) - 3}$

$$\frac{-\frac{1}{2}}{2} - \frac{3}{-8} = \frac{-\frac{1}{2}}{-4}$$

$$\frac{1}{8} = \frac{1}{8}$$

The solution is $x = -\frac{1}{2}$.

17.
$$x^4 - 6x^2 + 8 = 0$$
$$\left(x^2\right)^2 - 6x^2 + 8 = 0$$
$$u^2 - 6u + 8 = 0$$
$$(u-4)(u-2) = 0$$

$$u - 4 = 0 \qquad u - 2 = 0$$
$$u = 4 \qquad u = 2$$

Replace u by x^2

$$x^2 = 4 \qquad x^2 = 2$$
$$\sqrt{x^2} = \sqrt{4} \qquad \sqrt{x^2} = \sqrt{2}$$
$$x = \pm 2 \qquad x = \pm\sqrt{2}$$

The solutions are $2, -2, \sqrt{2}$, and $-\sqrt{2}$.

18.
$$\sqrt{3x+1} - 1 = x$$
$$\sqrt{3x+1} = x + 1$$
$$\left(\sqrt{3x+1}\right)^2 = (x+1)^2$$
$$3x + 1 = x^2 + 2x + 1$$
$$0 = x^2 - x$$
$$0 = x(x-1)$$

$$x = 0 \qquad x - 1 = 0$$
$$\qquad\qquad x = 1$$

0 and 1 both check as solutions. The solutions are 0 and 1.

19.
$$|3x-2|<8$$
$$-8<3x-2<8$$
$$-8+2<3x-2+2<8+2$$
$$-6<3x<10$$
$$\frac{1}{3}\cdot(-6)<\frac{1}{3}\cdot(3x)<\frac{1}{3}\cdot10$$
$$-2<x<\frac{10}{3}$$
$$\left\{x\mid-2<x<\frac{10}{3}\right\}$$

21. Solve each inequality.

$$\begin{array}{ll} x+y\le3 & 2x-y<4 \\ y\le3-x & -y<4-2x \\ & y>-4+2x \end{array}$$

20.
$$6x-5y=15$$
$$6x-5(0)=15$$
$$6x=15$$
$$x=\frac{15}{6}=\frac{5}{2}$$
The x-intercept is $\left(\frac{5}{2},0\right)$.

$$6x-5y=15$$
$$6(0)-5y=15$$
$$-5y=15$$
$$y=-3$$
The y-intercept is $(0,-3)$.

22.
$$x+y+z=2$$
$$-x+2y-3z=-9$$
$$x-2y-2z=-1$$

$$D=\begin{vmatrix}1&1&1\\-1&2&-3\\1&-2&-2\end{vmatrix}=\begin{vmatrix}2&-3\\-2&-2\end{vmatrix}-\begin{vmatrix}-1&-3\\1&-2\end{vmatrix}+\begin{vmatrix}-1&2\\1&-2\end{vmatrix}=(-4-6)-[2-(-3)]+(2-2)=-10-5+0=-15$$

$$D_x=\begin{vmatrix}2&1&1\\-9&2&-3\\-1&-2&-2\end{vmatrix}=2\begin{vmatrix}2&-3\\-2&-2\end{vmatrix}-\begin{vmatrix}-9&-3\\-1&-2\end{vmatrix}+\begin{vmatrix}-9&2\\-1&-2\end{vmatrix}=2(-4-6)-(18-3)+[18-(-2)]=-20-15+20=-15$$

$$D_y=\begin{vmatrix}1&2&1\\-1&-9&-3\\1&-1&-2\end{vmatrix}=\begin{vmatrix}-9&-3\\-1&-2\end{vmatrix}-2\begin{vmatrix}-1&-3\\1&-2\end{vmatrix}+\begin{vmatrix}-1&-9\\1&-1\end{vmatrix}=(18-3)-2[2-(-3)]+[1-(-9)]=15-10+10=15$$

$$D_z=\begin{vmatrix}1&1&2\\-1&2&-9\\1&-2&-1\end{vmatrix}=\begin{vmatrix}2&-9\\-2&-1\end{vmatrix}-\begin{vmatrix}-1&-9\\1&-1\end{vmatrix}+2\begin{vmatrix}-1&2\\1&-2\end{vmatrix}=(-2-18)-[1-(-9)]+2(2-2)=-20-10+0=-30$$

$$x=\frac{D_x}{D}=\frac{-15}{-15}=1$$
$$y=\frac{D_y}{D}=\frac{15}{-15}=-1$$
$$z=\frac{D_z}{D}=\frac{-30}{-15}=2$$
The solution is $(1,-1,2)$.

23.
$$f(x)=\frac{2x-3}{x^2-1}$$
$$f(-2)=\frac{2(-2)-3}{(-2)^2-1}=-\frac{7}{3}$$

24. $f(x) = \dfrac{x-2}{x^2 - 2x - 15}$

$f(x) = \dfrac{x-2}{(x-5)(x+3)}$

$0 = (x-5)(x+3)$

$x - 5 = 0 \qquad\qquad x + 3 = 0$

$\quad x = 5 \qquad\qquad\quad x = -3$

The domain of $f(x)$ is $\{x \mid x \neq 5 \text{ and } x \neq -3\}$

25. $x^3 + x^2 - 6x < 0$

$x(x^2 + x - 6) < 0$

$x(x+3)(x-2) < 0$

$$
\begin{array}{l}
x \quad - - - \mid - - - \mid + + \mid + + + + + \\
x+3 \quad - - - \mid + + + \mid + + \mid + + + + + \\
x-2 \quad - - - \mid - - - \mid - - \mid + + + + + \\
\hline
\quad -5\ -4\ -3\ -2\ -1\ \ 0\ \ 1\ \ 2\ \ 3\ \ 4\ \ 5
\end{array}
$$

$\{x \mid x < -3 \text{ or } 0 < x < 2\}$

$$
\begin{array}{c}
\longleftarrow\!\!\!+\!\!+\!\!+\!\!+\ \ +\!\!+\ )(\!\!-\!\!-\!\!)\ +\!\!+\!\!+\!\!\longrightarrow \\
-5\ -4\ -3\ -2\ -1\ \ 0\ \ 1\ \ 2\ \ 3\ \ 4\ \ 5
\end{array}
$$

26. $\dfrac{(x-1)(x-5)}{x+3} \geq 0$

$$
\begin{array}{l}
x-1 \quad - - - \mid - - - - \mid + + + + \mid + \\
x-5 \quad - - - \mid - - - - \mid - - - - \mid + \\
x+3 \quad - - - \mid + + + + \mid + + + + \mid + \\
\hline
\quad -5\ -4\ -3\ -2\ -1\ \ 0\ \ 1\ \ 2\ \ 3\ \ 4\ \ 5
\end{array}
$$

$\{x \mid -3 < x \leq 1 \text{ or } x \geq 5\}$

$$
\begin{array}{c}
\longleftarrow\!\!\!+\!\!+\ (\!\!-\!\!-\!\!-\!\!]\ +\!\!+\!\!+\!\![\!\!+\!\!\longrightarrow \\
-5\ -4\ -3\ -2\ -1\ \ 0\ \ 1\ \ 2\ \ 3\ \ 4\ \ 5
\end{array}
$$

27. For 2000 to 2004,

$\text{ave} = \dfrac{33 - 7}{2004 - 2000}$

$\quad = \dfrac{26}{4}$

$\quad = 6.5$

For 2002 to 2004,

$\text{ave} = \dfrac{33 - 19}{2004 - 2002}$

$\quad = \dfrac{14}{2}$

$\quad = 7$

The average annual rate of change for 2000 to 2004 is 6.5 million subscribers, which is not the same as the average annual rate of change from 2002 to 2004.

28. Strategy

Let p represent the length of the piston rod, T the tolerance, and m the given length.

Solve the absolute value inequality $|m - p| \leq T$ for m.

Solution

$|m - p| \leq T$

$\left| m - 9\dfrac{3}{8} \right| \leq \dfrac{1}{64}$

$-\dfrac{1}{64} \leq m - 9\dfrac{3}{8} \leq \dfrac{1}{64}$

$-\dfrac{1}{64} + 9\dfrac{3}{8} \leq m \leq \dfrac{1}{64} + 9\dfrac{3}{8}$

$9\dfrac{23}{64} \leq m \leq 9\dfrac{25}{64}$

The lower limit is $9\dfrac{23}{64}$ in.

The upper limit is $9\dfrac{25}{64}$ in.

29. $A = \dfrac{1}{2} b \cdot h$

$\quad = \dfrac{1}{2}(x+8)(2x-4)$

$\quad = \dfrac{1}{2}\left(2x^2 + 12x - 32\right)$

$\quad = \left(x^2 + 6x - 16\right) \text{ ft}^2$

30. $m = \dfrac{y_2 - y_1}{x_2 - x_1}$

$\quad = \dfrac{0 - 250{,}000}{30 - 0}$

$\quad = \dfrac{-250{,}000}{30}$

$\quad = -\dfrac{25{,}000}{3}$

The slope represents the amount in dollars that the building depreciates \$8333.33 each year.

Chapter 9: Functions and Relations

Prep Test

1. $-\dfrac{(-4)}{2(2)} = \dfrac{4}{4} = 1$ [1.3.2]

2. $y = (-2)^2 + 2(-2) + 1$ [1.3.2]
   $= -4 - 4 + 1$
   $= -7$

3. $f(4) = (-4)^2 - 3(-4) + 2$ [3.2.1]
   $= 16 + 12 + 2$
   $= 30$

4. $p(2 + h) = (2 + h)^2 - 5$ [3.2.1]
   $= 4 + 4h + h^2 - 5$
   $= h^2 + 4h - 1$

5. $0 = 3x^2 - 7x - 6$ [8.1.1]
   $0 = (3x + 2)(x - 3)$

   $3x + 2 = 0 \qquad x - 3 = 0$
   $3x = -2 \qquad\quad x = 3$
   $x = -\dfrac{2}{3}$

   The solutions are 3 and $-\dfrac{2}{3}$.

6. $\quad 0 = x^2 - 4x + 1$ [8.2.1, 8.2.2]
   $\quad -1 = x^2 - 4x$
   $-1 + 4 = x^2 - 4x + 4$
   $\quad 3 = (x - 2)^2$
   $\pm\sqrt{3} = x - 2$
   $2 \pm \sqrt{3} = x$

   The solutions are $2 + \sqrt{3}$ and $2 - \sqrt{3}$.

7. $x = 2y + 4$ [3.3.2]
   $2y = x - 4$
   $y = \dfrac{1}{2}x - 2$

8. D: {−2, 3, 4, 6}; R: {4, 5, 6}; Yes   [3.2.1]

9. 8   [3.2.1]

10.   [3.3.2]

Go Figure

It is important to recall that the hour hand of a standard, analog, 12-hour clock moves slowly forward from one hour to the next during the 60 minutes that the minute hand rotates around the clock. For example, at 5:30PM, when the minute hand has reached the 30-minute mark, the hour hand is half way between the 5 and 6. Starting from noon, the bell chimes at 12:32, 1:38, 2:43, 3:48, 4:54, and then 6:00, 7:05, 8:11, 9:16, 10:22, 11:27 for both A.M. and P.M. The bell chimes 22 times during the 24 hours.

Section 9.1

Concept Review 9.1

1. Sometimes true
   For the absolute value function $f(x) = |x| - 3$, the value of $f(1) = -2$.

2. Always true

3. Sometimes true
   The range of $f(x) = x^2$ is $\{y \mid y \geq 0\}$.

4. Sometimes true
   The relation $f(x) = x + 2$ is a function. The relation {(2, −3), (2, 4), (3, 6)} is not a function.

5. Always true

6. Always true

Objective 9.1.1 Exercises

1. The vertical line test is used to determine whether a graph is the graph of a function. A graph is the graph of a function if any vertical line intersects the graph at no more than one point.

2. A bracket next to a number indicates that the number is included in the interval. A parenthesis next to a number indicates that all numbers up to but not including the number are included in the interval.

3. A vertical line intersects the graph at most once. The graph is the graph of a function.

4. A vertical line intersects the graph at most once. The graph is the graph of a function.

5. A vertical line exists that intersects the graph more than once. The graph is not the graph of a function.

6. A vertical line intersects the graph at most once. The graph is the graph of a function.

7. A vertical line intersects the graph at most once. The graph is the graph of a function.

8. A vertical line exists that intersects the graph more than once. The graph is not the graph of a function.

9.

The domain is {x|x ∈ real numbers}.
The range is {y|y ∈ real numbers}.

10.
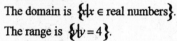

The domain is {x|x ∈ real numbers}.
The range is {y|y = 4}.

11.

The domain is {x|x ∈ real numbers}.
The range is {y|y ≥ −1}.

12.

The domain is {x|x ∈ real numbers}.
The range is {y|y ≥ −3}.

13.

The domain is {x|x ∈ real numbers}.
The range is {y|y ≥ 0}.

14.

The domain is {x|x ∈ real numbers}.
The range is {y|y ≥ 0}.

15.

The domain is {x|x ∈ real numbers}.
The range is {y|y ∈ real numbers}.

16.

The domain is {x|x ∈ real numbers}.
The range is {y|y ∈ real numbers}.

17.

The domain is {x|x ≥ −1}.
The range is {y|y ≥ 0}.

18.

The domain is {x|x ≤ 4}.
The range is {y|y ≥ 0}.

19.

The domain is {x|x ∈ real numbers}.
The range is {y|y ≥ 0}.

20.

The domain is {x|x ∈ real numbers}.
The range is {y|y ≥ 0}.

21.

The domain is $\{x \mid x \in \text{real numbers}\}$.

The range is $\{y \mid y \geq 1\}$.

22.

The domain is $\{x \mid x \in \text{real numbers}\}$.

The range is $\{y \mid y \geq -1\}$.

23.

The domain is $\{x \mid x \in \text{real numbers}\}$.

The range is $\{y \mid y \in \text{real numbers}\}$.

24.

The domain is $\{x \mid x \in \text{real numbers}\}$.

The range is $\{y \mid y \in \text{real numbers}\}$.

25.

The domain is $\{x \mid x \geq -2\}$.

The range is $\{y \mid y \leq 0\}$.

26.

The domain is $\{x \mid x \geq 3\}$.

The range is $\{y \mid y \leq 0\}$.

27.

The domain is $\{x \mid x \in \text{real numbers}\}$.

The range is $\{y \mid y \geq -5\}$.

28.

The domain is $\{x \mid x \in \text{real numbers}\}$.

The range is $\{y \mid y = -1\}$.

29.

The domain is $\{x \mid x \in \text{real numbers}\}$.

The range is $\{y \mid y \geq -1\}$.

30.

The domain is $\{x \mid x \in \text{real numbers}\}$.

The range is $\{y \mid y \geq 2\}$.

31.

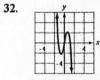

The domain is $\{x \mid x \in \text{real numbers}\}$.

The range is $\{y \mid y \in \text{real numbers}\}$.

32.

The domain is $\{x \mid x \in \text{real numbers}\}$.

The range is $\{y \mid y \in \text{real numbers}\}$.

33.

The domain is $\{x | x \in \text{real numbers}\}$.

The range is $\{y | y \in \text{real numbers}\}$.

34.

The domain is $\{x | x \in \text{real numbers}\}$.

The range is $\{y | y = -3\}$.

35.

The domain is $\{x | x \in \text{real numbers}\}$.

The range is $\{y | y \geq -5\}$.

36.

The domain is $\{x | x \in \text{real numbers}\}$.

The range is $\{y | y \leq 0\}$.

37.

The domain is $\{x | x \in \text{real numbers}\}$.

The range is $\{y | y \leq 0\}$.

38.

The domain is $\{x | x \in \text{real numbers}\}$.

The range is $\{y | y \leq 0\}$.

39.

The domain is $\{x | x \in \text{real numbers}\}$.

The range is $\{y | y \in \text{real numbers}\}$.

40.

The domain is $\{x | x \in \text{real numbers}\}$.

The range is $\{y | y \in \text{real numbers}\}$.

Applying Concepts 9.1

41. a. $f(x) = x$ is a function.

   b. $f(x) = \left|\dfrac{x}{2}\right|$ is a function.

   c. $\{(3, 1), (1, 3), (3, 0), (0, 3)\}$ is not a function because the number 3 in the domain is paired with different values in the range.

42. a. $f(x) = -x$ is a function.

   b. $f(x) = \dfrac{2}{\sqrt{x}}$ is a function (note that $\sqrt{x}$ represents the principal square root of x and there is thus only one value of $f(x)$ for each value of x.)

   c. $\{(1, 4), (4, 1), (1, -4), (-4, 1)\}$ is not a function because the number 1 in the domain is paired with different values in the range.

43. $f(x) = \sqrt{x - 2}$

$f(a) = 4 = \sqrt{a - 2}$

$4^2 = \left(\sqrt{a - 2}\right)^2$

$16 = a - 2$

$18 = a$

44. $f(x) = \sqrt{x + 5}$

$f(a) = 3 = \sqrt{a + 5}$

$3^2 = \left(\sqrt{a + 5}\right)^2$

$9 = a + 5$

$4 = a$

45. a and c are true.

$f(0) = -1$

46. $f(a, b) = a + b$

$g(a, b) = a \cdot b$

$f(2, 5) = 2 + 5 = 7$

$g(2, 5) = 2 \cdot 5 = 10$

$f(2, 5) + g(2, 5) = 7 + 10 = 17$

47. $f(14, 35)$: The greatest common divisor is 7.
$g(14, 35)$: The least common multiple is 70.
$f(14, 35) + g(14, 35) = 7 + 70 = 77$

48.

$x + 2$ - - - - | + + + | + + + +
$x - 2$ - - - - | - - - | + + + +

-5 -4 -3 -2 -1 0 1 2 3 4 5

$\{x | -2 < x < 2\}$

49.

$x + 1$ - - - - | + + | + + + + +
$x - 1$ - - - - | - - | + + + + +

-5 -4 -3 -2 -1 0 1 2 3 4 5

$\{x | -1 < x < 1\}$

50. $f(14) = 8$

51. $f(x) = -|x + 3|$
$f(x)$ is greatest when $x + 3 = 0$
$x = -3$

52. $f(x) = |2x - 2|$
$f(x)$ is smallest when $2x - 2 = 0$
$2x = 2$
$x = 1$

53. a. $x^3 = 0$
$\sqrt[3]{x} = \sqrt[3]{0}$
$x = 0$

b. The x-intercept of the graph of $f(x) = x^3$ is (0, 0).

54. a. $x^3 - 1 = 0$
$x^3 = 1$
$\sqrt[3]{x^3} = \sqrt[3]{1}$
$x = 1$

b. The x-intercept of the graph of $f(x) = x^3 - 1$ is (1, 0).

55.

The graph has one turning point.

56.

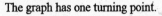

The graph has three turning points.

57. Students may conjecture that the graph of a fourth-degree polynomial has either one or three turning points. Any answer along these lines is acceptable. Students should not be expected at this point to state that a polynomial function of degree n has at most $n - 1$ turning points.

Section 9.2

Concept Review 9.2

1. Always true

2. Never true
   The graph of $f(x + c)$ is the graph of $f(x)$ translated c units to the left.

3. Always true

4. Never true
   The graph of $y = |x| + 2$ is the graph of $y = |x|$ shifted upward 2 units.

5. Never true
   If c_1 and c_2 are positive constants, the graph of $y = f(x + c_1) + c_2$ is the graph of $y = f(x)$ translated to the left c_1 units and shifted upward c_2 units.

6. Always true

Objective 9.2.1 Exercises

1. A vertical or horizontal translation of a graph is the graph with the same shape but shifted vertically or horizontally.

2. The graph of $y = f(x - 2) + 1$ has the same shape as the graph of $y = f(x)$ but it is shifted 2 units to the right and 1 unit up.

3.

4.

5.

6.

7.

8. **9.** **10.** **11.** **12.** **13.** **14.** **15.** **16.** **17.** **18.**

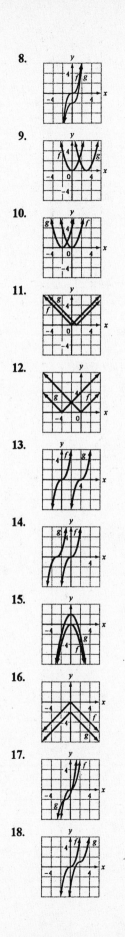

19. **20.** **21.** **22.** **23.** **24.** **25.** **26.** **27.** **28.**

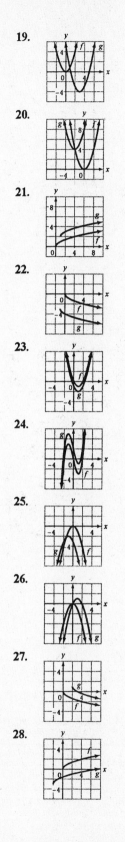

Applying Concepts 9.2

29.

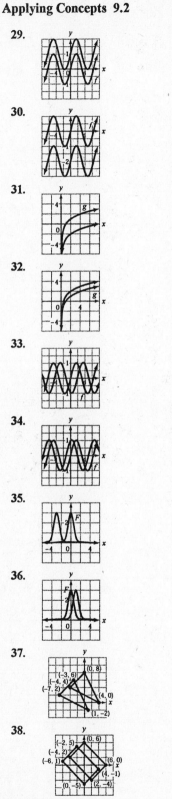

30.

31.

32.

33.

34.

35.

36.

37.

38.

2. Always true

3. Never true
$$(f \circ g)(x) = 2(x+4)+1$$

4. Never true
$$(f \circ g)(x) = [(x^3)]^2 - 4$$

Objective 9.3.1 Exercises

1. $(f-g)(2) = f(2) - g(2)$
$$= [2(2)^2 - 3] - [-2(2)+4]$$
$$= 5 - 0$$
$$= 5$$
$$(f-g)(2) = 5$$

2. $(f-g)(3) = f(3) - g(3)$
$$= [2(3^2) - 3] - [-2(3)+4]$$
$$= 15 - (-2)$$
$$= 17$$
$$(f-g)(3) = 17$$

3. $(f+g)(0) = f(0) + g(0)$
$$= [2(0)^2 - 3] + [-2(0)+4]$$
$$= -3 + 4$$
$$= 1$$
$$(f+g)(0) = 1$$

4. $(f+g)(1) = f(1) + g(1)$
$$= [2(1)^2 - 3] + [-2(1)+4]$$
$$= (-1) + 2$$
$$= 1$$
$$(f+g)(1) = 1$$

5. $(f \cdot g)(2) = f(2) \cdot g(2)$
$$= [2(2)^2 - 3] \cdot [-2(2)+4]$$
$$= 5 \cdot 0$$
$$= 0$$
$$(f \cdot g)(2) = 0$$

6. $(f \cdot g)(-1) = f(-1) \cdot g(-1)$
$$= [2(-1)^2 - 3] \cdot [-2(-1)+4]$$
$$= (-1) \cdot 6$$
$$= -6$$
$$(f \cdot g)(-1) = -6$$

7. $\left(\dfrac{f}{g}\right)(4) = \dfrac{f(4)}{g(4)}$
$$= \dfrac{2(4)^2 - 3}{-2(4)+4}$$
$$= -\dfrac{29}{4}$$
$$\dfrac{f}{g}(4) = -\dfrac{29}{4}$$

Section 9.3

Concept Review 9.3

1. Always true

8. $\left(\dfrac{f}{g}\right)(-1) = \dfrac{f(-1)}{g(-1)}$

$= \dfrac{2(-1)^2 - 3}{-2(-1) + 4}$

$= -\dfrac{1}{6}$

$\left(\dfrac{f}{g}\right)(-1) = -\dfrac{1}{6}$

9. $\left(\dfrac{g}{f}\right)(-3) = \dfrac{g(-3)}{f(-3)}$

$= \dfrac{-2(-3) + 4}{2(-3)^2 - 3}$

$= \dfrac{10}{15}$

$= \dfrac{2}{3}$

$\left(\dfrac{g}{f}\right)(-3) = \dfrac{2}{3}$

10. $(f + g)(-3) = f(-3) + g(-3)$

$= [2(-3)^2 + 3(-3) - 1] + [2(-3) - 4]$

$= 8 + (-10)$

$= -2$

$(f + g)(-3) = -2$

11. $(f + g)(1) = f(1) + g(1)$

$= [2(1)^2 + 3(1) - 1] + [2(1) - 4]$

$= [2 + 3 - 1] + [2 - 4]$

$= 4 - 2$

$= 2$

$(f + g)(1) = 2$

12. $(f + g)(-2) = f(-2) + g(-2)$

$= [2(-2)^2 + 3(-2) - 1] + [2(-2) - 4]$

$= [8 - 6 - 1] + [-4 - 4]$

$= 1 + (-8)$

$= -7$

$(f + g)(-2) = -7$

13. $(f - g)(4) = f(4) - g(4)$

$= [2(4)^2 + 3(4) - 1] - [2(4) - 4]$

$= [32 + 12 - 1] - [8 - 4]$

$= 43 - 4$

$= 39$

$(f - g)(4) = 39$

14. $(f \cdot g)(-2) = f(-2) \cdot g(-2)$

$= [2(-2)^2 + 3(-2) - 1] \cdot [2(-2) - 4]$

$= [8 - 6 - 1] \cdot [-4 - 4]$

$= 1(-8)$

$= -8$

$(f \cdot g)(-2) = -8$

15. $(f \cdot g)(1) = f(1) \cdot g(1)$

$= [2(1)^2 + 3(1) - 1] \cdot [2(1) - 4]$

$= [2 + 3 - 1] \cdot [2 - 4]$

$= 4(-2)$

$= -8$

$(f \cdot g)(1) = -8$

16. $\left(\dfrac{f}{g}\right)(2) = \dfrac{f(2)}{g(2)}$

$= \dfrac{2(2^2) + 3(2) - 1}{2(2) - 4}$

$= \dfrac{8 + 6 - 1}{4 - 4}$

$= \dfrac{13}{0}$

Division by zero is undefined.

17. $\left(\dfrac{f}{g}\right)(-3) = \dfrac{f(-3)}{g(-3)}$

$= \dfrac{2(-3)^2 + 3(-3) - 1}{2(-3) - 4}$

$= \dfrac{18 - 9 - 1}{-6 - 4}$

$= \dfrac{8}{-10}$

$= -\dfrac{4}{5}$

$\left(\dfrac{f}{g}\right)(-3) = -\dfrac{4}{5}$

18. $(f \cdot g)\left(\dfrac{1}{2}\right) = f\left(\dfrac{1}{2}\right) \cdot g\left(\dfrac{1}{2}\right)$

$= \left[2\left(\dfrac{1}{2}\right)^2 + 3\left(\dfrac{1}{2}\right) - 1\right]\left[2\left(\dfrac{1}{2}\right) - 4\right]$

$= \left[\dfrac{1}{2} + \dfrac{3}{2} - 1\right] \cdot [1 - 4]$

$= 1(-3)$

$= -3$

$(f \cdot g)\left(\dfrac{1}{2}\right) = -3$

19. $(f - g)(2) = f(2) - g(2)$

$= [2^2 + 3(2) - 5] - [2^3 - 2(2) + 3]$

$= [4 + 6 - 5] - [8 - 4 + 3]$

$= 5 - 7$

$= -2$

$(f - g)(-2) = -2$

20. $(f \cdot g)(-3) = f(-3) \cdot g(-3)$

$= [(-3)^2 + 3(-3) - 5] \cdot [(-3)^3 - 2(-3) + 3]$

$= [9 - 9 - 5] \cdot [-27 + 6 + 3]$

$= (-5) \cdot (-18)$

$= 90$

$(f \cdot g)(-3) = 90$

21. $\left(\dfrac{f}{g}\right)(-2) = \dfrac{f(-2)}{g(-2)}$

$= \dfrac{(-2)^2 + 3(-2) - 5}{(-2)^3 - 2(-2) + 3}$

$= \dfrac{4 - 6 - 5}{-8 + 4 + 3}$

$= \dfrac{-7}{-1} = 7$

$\left(\dfrac{f}{g}\right)(-2) = 7$

Objective 9.3.2 Exercises

22. The expression $f[g(2)]$ means to evaluate the function f at $g(2)$.

23. The expression $(f \circ g)(x)$ means to evaluate the function f at $g(x)$.

24. $g(x) = 4x - 1$
$g(0) = 4(0) - 1 = 0 - 1 = -1$
$f(x) = 2x - 3$
$f[g(0)] = f(-1) = 2(-1) - 3 = -2 - 3 = -5$
$f[g(0)] = -5$

25. $f(x) = 2x - 3$
$f(0) = 2(0) - 3 = 0 - 3 = -3$
$g(x) = 4x - 1$
$g[f(0)] = g(-3) = 4(-3) - 1 = -12 - 1 = -13$
$g[f(0)] = -13$

26. $g(x) = 4x - 1$
$g(2) = 4(2) - 1 = 8 - 1 = 7$
$f(x) = 2x - 3$
$f[g(2)] = f(7) = 2(7) - 3 = 14 - 3 = 11$
$f[g(2)] = 11$

27. $f(x) = 2x - 3$
$f(-2) = 2(-2) - 3 = -4 - 3 = -7$
$g(x) = 4x - 1$
$g[f(-2)] = g(-7) = 4(-7) - 1 = -28 - 1 = -29$
$g[f(-2)] = -29$

28. $g(x) = 4x - 1$
$f(x) = 2x - 3$
$f[g(x)] = f(4x - 1)$
$= 2(4x - 1) - 3$
$= 8x - 2 - 3$
$= 8x - 5$
$f[g(x)] = 8x - 5$

29. $f(x) = 2x - 3$
$g(x) = 4x - 1$
$g[f(x)] = g(2x - 3)$
$= 4(2x - 3) - 1$
$= 8x - 12 - 1$
$= 8x - 13$
$g[f(x)] = 8x - 13$

30. $h(x) = x - 2$
$h(0) = 0 - 2 = -2$
$g(x) = x^2 + 3$
$g[h(0)] = g(-2) = (-2)^2 + 3 = 4 + 3 = 7$
$g[h(0)] = 7$

31. $g(x) = x^2 + 3$
$g(0) = 0^2 + 3 = 3$
$h(x) = x - 2$
$h[g(0)] = h(3) = 3 - 2 = 1$
$h[g(0)] = 1$

32. $h(x) = x - 2$
$h(4) = 4 - 2 = 2$
$g(x) = x^2 + 3$
$g[h(4)] = g(2) = 2^2 + 3 = 4 + 3 = 7$
$g[h(4)] = 7$

33. $g(x) = x^2 + 3$
$g(-2) = (-2)^2 + 3 = 4 + 3 = 7$
$h(x) = x - 2$
$h[g(-2)] = h(7) = 7 - 2 = 5$
$h[g(-2)] = 5$

34. $h(x) = x - 2$
$g(x) = x^2 + 3$
$g[h(x)] = g(x - 2) = (x - 2)^2 + 3$
$= x^2 - 4x + 4 + 3$
$= x^2 - 4x + 7$
$g[h(x)] = x^2 - 4x + 7$

35. $g(x) = x^2 + 3$
$h(x) = x - 2$
$h[g(x)] = h(x^2 + 3) = x^2 + 3 - 2 = x^2 + 1$
$h[g(x)] = x^2 + 1$

36. $h(x) = 3x + 2$
$h(0) = 3(0) + 2 = 0 + 2 = 2$
$f(x) = x^2 + x + 1$
$f[h(0)] = f(2) = 2^2 + 2 + 1 = 4 + 2 + 1 = 7$
$f[h(0)] = 7$

37. $f(x) = x^2 + x + 1$
$f(0) = 0^2 + 0 + 1 = 0 + 0 + 1 = 1$
$h(x) = 3x + 2$
$h[f(0)] = h(1) = 3(1) + 2 = 3 + 2 = 5$
$h[f(0)] = 5$

38. $h(x) = 3x + 2$
$h(-1) = 3(-1) + 2 = -3 + 2 = -1$
$f(x) = x^2 + x + 1$
$f[h(-1)] = f(-1) = (-1)^2 - 1 + 1 = 1 - 1 + 1 = 1$
$f[h(-1)] = 1$

39. $f(x) = x^2 + x + 1$
$f(-2) = (-2)^2 - 2 + 1 = 4 - 2 + 1 = 3$
$h(x) = 3x + 2$
$h[f(-2)] = h(3) = 3(3) + 2 = 9 + 2 = 11$
$h[f(-2)] = 11$

40. $h(x) = 3x + 2$
$f(x) = x^2 + x + 1$
$f[h(x)] = f(3x + 2) = (3x + 2)^2 + (3x + 2) + 1$
$\quad = 9x^2 + 12x + 4 + 3x + 2 + 1$
$\quad = 9x^2 + 15x + 7$
$f[h(x)] = 9x^2 + 15x + 7$

41. $f(x) = x^2 + x + 1$
$h(x) = 3x + 2$
$h[f(x)] = h(x^2 + x + 1) = 3(x^2 + x + 1) + 2$
$\quad = 3x^2 + 3x + 3 + 2$
$\quad = 3x^2 + 3x + 5$
$h[f(x)] = 3x^2 + 3x + 5$

42. $g(x) = x^3$
$g(2) = 2^3 = 8$
$f(x) = x - 2$
$f[g(2)] = f(8) = 8 - 2 = 6$
$f[g(2)] = 6$

43. $g(x) = x^3$
$g(-1) = (-1)^3 = -1$
$f(x) = x - 2$
$f[g(-1)] = f(-1) = -1 - 2 = -3$
$f[g(-1)] = -3$

44. $f(x) = x - 2$
$f(2) = 2 - 2 = 0$
$g(x) = x^3$
$g[f(2)] = g(0) = 0^3 = 0$
$g[f(2)] = 0$

45. $f(x) = x - 2$
$f(-1) = -1 - 2 = -3$
$g(x) = x^3$
$g[f(-1)] = g(-3) = (-3)^3 = -27$
$g[f(-1)] = -27$

46. $g(x) = x^3$
$f(x) = x - 2$
$f[g(x)] = f(x^3) = x^3 - 2$
$f[g(x)] = x^3 - 2$

47. $f(x) = x - 2, \ g(x) = x^3$
$g[f(x)] = g(x - 2) = (x - 2)^3$
$g[f(x)] = x^3 - 6x^2 - 12x - 8$

Applying Concepts 9.3

48. $g(2 + h) = (2 + h)^2 - 1$
$\quad = 4 + 4h + h^2 - 1$
$g(2 + h) = h^2 + 4h + 3$

49. $g(3 + h) - g(3) = (3 + h)^2 - 1 - [(3)^2 - 1]$
$\quad = 9 + 6h + h^2 - 1 - 8$
$g(3 + h) - g(3) = h^2 + 6h$

50. $g(-1 + h) - g(-1) = (-1 + h)^2 - 1 - [(-1)^2 - 1]$
$\quad = 1 - 2h + h^2 - 1 - 0$
$g(-1 + h) - g(-1) = h^2 - 2h$

51. $\dfrac{g(1 + h) - g(1)}{h} = \dfrac{[(1 + h)^2 - 1] - [(1)^2 - 1]}{h}$
$\quad = \dfrac{1 + 2h + h^2 - 1 - 0}{h}$
$\quad = \dfrac{2h + h^2}{h}$
$\dfrac{g(1 - h) - g(1)}{h} = 2 + h$

52. $\dfrac{g(-2 + h) - g(-2)}{h} = \dfrac{[(-2 + h)^2 - 1] - [(-2)^2 - 1]}{h}$
$\quad = \dfrac{4 - 4h + h^2 - 1 - 3}{h}$
$\quad = \dfrac{-4h + h^2}{h}$
$\dfrac{g(-2 + h) - g(-2)}{h} = -4 + h$

53. $\dfrac{g(a + h) - g(a)}{h} = \dfrac{[(a + h)^2 - 1] - (a^2 - 1)}{h}$
$\quad = \dfrac{a^2 + 2ah + h^2 - 1 - a^2 + 1}{h}$
$\quad = \dfrac{2ah + h^2}{h}$
$\dfrac{g(a + h) - g(a)}{h} = 2a + h$

54. $h(x) = x - 2$
$h(2) = 2 - 2 = 0$
$g(x) = 3x - 1$
$g(0) = 3 \cdot 0 - 1 = -1$
$f(x) = 2x$
$f(-1) = 2(-1) = -2$
$f(g[h(2)]) = -2$

55. $f(x) = 2x$
$f(1) = 2 \cdot 1 = 2$
$h(x) = x - 2$
$h(2) = 2 - 2 = 0$
$g(x) = 3x - 1$
$g(0) = 3 \cdot 0 - 1 = -1$
$g(h[f(1)]) = -1$

56.
$$f(x) = 2x$$
$$f(-1) = 2(-1) = -2$$
$$g(x) = 3x - 1$$
$$g(-2) = 3(-2) - 1 = -7$$
$$h(x) = x - 2$$
$$h(-7) = -7 - 2 = -9$$
$$h(g[f(-1)]) = -9$$

57.
$$g(x) = 3x - 1$$
$$g(0) = 3 \cdot 0 - 1 = -1$$
$$h(x) = x - 2$$
$$h(-1) = -1 - 2 = -3$$
$$f(x) = 2x$$
$$f(-3) = 2(-3) = -6$$
$$f(h[g(0)]) = -6$$

58.
$$h(x) = x - 2$$
$$g(x - 2) = 3(x - 2) - 1 = 3x - 6 - 1 = 3x - 7$$
$$f(3x - 7) = 2(3x - 7) = 6x - 14$$
$$f(g[h(x)]) = 6x - 14$$

59.
$$h(x) = x - 2$$
$$f(x - 2) = 2(x - 2) = 2x - 4$$
$$g(2x - 4) = 3(2x - 4) - 1 = 6x - 12 - 1 = 6x - 13$$

60. $f(g(0)) = f(-2) = -3$

61. $f(g(2)) = f(0) = -2$

62. $f(g(4)) = f(6) = 1$

63. $f(g(-2)) = f(0) = -2$

64. $f(g(-4)) = f(6) = 1$

65. $g(f(0)) = g(-2) = 0$

66. $g(f(4)) = g(0) = -2$

67. $g(f(-4)) = g(-4) = 6$

Section 9.4

Concept Review 9.4

1. Always true

2. Always true

3. Never true
   The function {(2, 3), (4, 5), (6, 3)} is not a 1-1 function. The function does not have an inverse.

4. Always true

5. Sometimes true
   If a function is a 1-1 function, then the inverse is a function.

6. Never true
   A horizontal line will intersect the graph at more than one point, so the graph is not a 1-1 function. The inverse is not a function.

Objective 9.4.1 Exercises

1. A function is a set of ordered pairs in which no two ordered pairs that have the same first coordinate have different second coordinates. This means that given any x, there is only one y that can be paired with that x. A 1-1 function satisfies the additional condition that given any y, there is only one x that can be paired with the given y.

2. The horizontal line test is used to determine whether the graph of a function is the graph of a 1-1 function. The horizontal line test states that the graph of a function represents the graph of a 1-1 function if any horizontal line intersects the graph at no more than one point.

3. The graph represents a 1-1 function.

4. The graph represents a 1-1 function.

5. The graph is not a 1-1 function. It fails the horizontal-line test.

6. The graph is not a 1-1 function. It fails the horizontal-line test.

7. The graph is a 1-1 function.

8. The graph is a 1-1 function.

9. The graph is not a 1-1 function. It fails the horizontal- and vertical-line tests.

10. The graph is not a 1-1 function. It fails the vertical-line test.

11. The graph is not a 1-1 function. It fails the horizontal-line test.

12. The graph is a 1-1 function.

13. The graph is not a 1-1 function. It fails the horizontal-line test.

14. The graph is not a 1-1 function. It fails the vertical- and horizontal-line tests.

Objective 9.4.2 Exercises

15. The coordinates of each ordered pair of the inverse function are in the reverse order of the coordinates of the ordered pairs of the function. For example, if (-1, 5) is an ordered pair of the function, then (5, -1) is an ordered pair of the inverse function.

16. Not all functions have an inverse function because sometimes reversing the coordinates of the ordered pairs results in a set of ordered pairs that is not a function. For example, consider the constant function $f(x) = 5$. Some ordered pairs of this function are (0, 5), (−3, 5), and (2, 5). Reversing the coordinates of these ordered pairs gives (5, 0), (5, −3), and (5, 2). These ordered pairs do not satisfy the condition of a function because they are ordered pairs with the same first coordinate and different second coordinates.

17. The inverse of {(1, 0), (2, 3), (3, 8), (4, 15)} is {(0, 1), (3, 2), (8, 3), (15, 4)}.

18. {(1, 0), (2, 1), (−1, 0), (−2, 1)} has no inverse because the numbers 0 and 1 would be paired with more than one member of the range.

19. {(3, 5), (−3, −5), (2, 5), (−2, −5)} has no inverse because the numbers 5 and −5 would be paired with more than one member of the range.

20. The inverse of {(−5, −5), (−3, −1), (−1, 3), (1, 7)} is {(−5, −5), (−1, −3), (3, −1), (7, 1)}.

21.
$$f(x) = 4x - 8$$
$$y = 4x - 8$$
$$x = 4y - 8$$
$$x + 8 = 4y$$
$$\frac{1}{4}x + 2 = y$$

The inverse function is $f^{-1}(x) = \frac{1}{4}x + 2$.

22.
$$f(x) = 3x + 6$$
$$y = 3x + 6$$
$$x = 3y + 6$$
$$x - 6 = 3y$$
$$\frac{1}{3}x - 2 = y$$

The inverse function is $f^{-1}(x) = \frac{1}{3}x - 2$.

23. $f(x) = x^2 - 1$ is not a 1-1 function. Therefore, it has no inverse.

24.
$$f(x) = 2x + 4$$
$$y = 2x + 4$$
$$x = 2y + 4$$
$$x - 4 = 2y$$
$$\frac{1}{2}x - 2 = y$$

The inverse function is $f^{-1}(x) = \frac{1}{2}x - 2$.

25.
$$f(x) = x - 5$$
$$y = x - 5$$
$$x = y - 5$$
$$x + 5 = y$$

The inverse function is $f^{-1}(x) = x + 5$.

26.
$$f(x) = \frac{1}{2}x - 1$$
$$y = \frac{1}{2}x - 1$$
$$x = \frac{1}{2}y - 1$$
$$x + 1 = \frac{1}{2}y$$
$$2x + 2 = y$$

The inverse function is $f^{-1}(x) = 2x + 2$.

27.
$$f(x) = \frac{1}{3}x + 2$$
$$y = \frac{1}{3}x + 2$$
$$x = \frac{1}{3}y + 2$$
$$x - 2 = \frac{1}{3}y$$
$$3x - 6 = y$$

The inverse function is $f^{-1}(x) = 3x - 6$.

28.
$$f(x) = -2x + 2$$
$$y = -2x + 2$$
$$x = -2y + 2$$
$$2y = -x + 2$$
$$y = -\frac{1}{2}x + 1$$

The inverse function is $f^{-1}(x) = -\frac{1}{2}x + 1$.

29.
$$f(x) = -3x - 9$$
$$y = -3x - 9$$
$$x = -3y - 9$$
$$3y = -x - 9$$
$$y = -\frac{1}{3}x - 3$$

The inverse function is $f^{-1}(x) = -\frac{1}{3}x - 3$.

30. $f(x) = 2x^2 + 2$ is not a 1-1 function. Therefore, it has no inverse.

31.
$$f(x) = \frac{2}{3}x + 4$$
$$y = \frac{2}{3}x + 4$$
$$x = \frac{2}{3}y + 4$$
$$x - 4 = \frac{2}{3}y$$
$$\frac{3}{2}(x - 4) = y$$
$$\frac{3}{2}x - 6 = y$$

The inverse function is $f^{-1}(x) = \frac{3}{2}x - 6$.

32.
$$f(x) = \frac{3}{4}x - 4$$
$$y = \frac{3}{4}x - 4$$
$$x = \frac{3}{4}y - 4$$
$$x + 4 = \frac{3}{4}y$$
$$\frac{4}{3}(x + 4) = y$$
$$\frac{4}{3}x + \frac{16}{3} = y$$

The inverse function is $f^{-1}(x) = \frac{4}{3}x + \frac{16}{3}$.

33.
$$f(x) = -\frac{1}{3}x + 1$$
$$y = -\frac{1}{3}x + 1$$
$$x = -\frac{1}{3}y + 1$$
$$x - 1 = -\frac{1}{3}y$$
$$-3(x - 1) = y$$
$$-3x + 3 = y$$

The inverse function is $f^{-1}(x) = -3x + 3$.

34.
$$f(x) = -\frac{1}{2}x + 2$$
$$y = -\frac{1}{2}x + 2$$
$$x = -\frac{1}{2}y + 2$$
$$x - 2 = -\frac{1}{2}y$$
$$-2(x - 2) = y$$
$$-2x + 4 = y$$

The inverse function is $f^{-1}(x) = -2x + 4$.

35.
$$f(x) = 2x - 5$$
$$y = 2x - 5$$
$$x = 2y - 5$$
$$x + 5 = 2y$$
$$\frac{1}{2}x + \frac{5}{2} = y$$

The inverse function is $f^{-1}(x) = \frac{1}{2}x + \frac{5}{2}$.

36.
$$f(x) = 3x + 4$$
$$y = 3x + 4$$
$$x = 3y + 4$$
$$x - 4 = 3y$$
$$\frac{1}{3}x - \frac{4}{3} = y$$

The inverse function is $f^{-1}(x) = \frac{1}{3}x - \frac{4}{3}$.

37. $f(x) = x^2 + 3$ is not a 1-1 function. Therefore, it has no inverse.

38.
$$f(x) = 5x - 2$$
$$y = 5x - 2$$
$$x = 5y - 2$$
$$x + 2 = 5y$$
$$\frac{1}{5}x + \frac{2}{5} = y$$

The inverse function is $f^{-1}(x) = \frac{1}{5}x + \frac{2}{5}$.

39.
$$f(x) = 3x - 5$$
$$y = 3x - 5$$
$$x = 3y - 5$$
$$x + 5 = 3y$$
$$\frac{1}{3}x + \frac{5}{3} = y$$
$$f^{-1}(x) = \frac{1}{3}x + \frac{5}{3}$$
$$f^{-1}(0) = \frac{1}{3}(0) + \frac{5}{3}$$
$$f^{-1}(0) = 0 + \frac{5}{3}$$
$$f^{-1}(0) = \frac{5}{3}$$

40. $f(x) = 3x - 5$
From exercise 54,
$$f^{-1}(x) = \frac{1}{3}x + \frac{5}{3}$$
$$f^{-1}(2) = \frac{1}{3}(2) + \frac{5}{3}$$
$$f^{-1}(2) = \frac{2}{3} + \frac{5}{3}$$
$$f^{-1}(2) = \frac{7}{3}$$

41. $f(x) = 3x - 5$
From exercise 54,
$$f^{-1}(x) = \frac{1}{3}x + \frac{5}{3}$$
$$f^{-1}(4) = \frac{1}{3}(4) + \frac{5}{3}$$
$$f^{-1}(4) = \frac{4}{3} + \frac{5}{3}$$
$$f^{-1}(4) = 3$$

42. The graph passes the vertical line test. So the graph is a function. The graph does not pass the horizontal line test. The graph does not have an inverse.

43. The graph passes the vertical line test. So the graph is a function. The graph passes the horizontal line test. The graph has an inverse.

44. The graph passes the vertical line test. So the graph is a function. The graph passes the horizontal line test. The graph has an inverse.

45. $f(g(x)) = f\left(\dfrac{x}{4}\right)$

    $= 4\left(\dfrac{x}{4}\right)$

    $= x$

    $g(f(x)) = g(4x)$

    $= \dfrac{4x}{4}$

    $= x$

    The functions are inverses of each other.

46. $g(h(x)) = g(x - 5)$

    $= x - 5 + 5$

    $= x$

    $h(g(x)) = h(x + 5)$

    $= x + 5 - 5$

    $= x$

    The functions are inverses of each other.

47. $f(h(x)) = f\left(\dfrac{1}{3x}\right)$

    $= 3\left(\dfrac{1}{3x}\right)$

    $= \dfrac{1}{x}$

    $h(f(x)) = h(3x)$

    $= \dfrac{1}{3 \cdot 3x}$

    $= \dfrac{1}{9x}$

    The functions are not inverses of each other.

48. $h(g(x)) = h(2 - x)$

    $= 2 - x + 2$

    $= 4 - x$

    $g(h(x)) = g(x + 2)$

    $= 2 - (x + 2)$

    $= 2 - x - 2$

    $= -x$

    The functions are not inverses of each other.

49. $g(f(x)) = g\left(\dfrac{1}{3}x - \dfrac{2}{3}\right)$

    $= 3\left(\dfrac{1}{3}x - \dfrac{2}{3}\right) + 2$

    $= x - 2 + 2$

    $= x$

    $f(g(x)) = f(3x + 2)$

    $= \dfrac{1}{3}(3x + 2) - \dfrac{2}{3}$

    $= x + \dfrac{2}{3} - \dfrac{2}{3}$

    $= x$

    The functions are inverses of each other.

50. $h(f(x)) = h\left(\dfrac{1}{4}x + \dfrac{1}{4}\right)$

    $= 4\left(\dfrac{1}{4}x + \dfrac{1}{4}\right) - 1$

    $= x + 1 - 1$

    $= x$

    $f(h(x)) = f(4x - 1)$

    $= \dfrac{1}{4}(4x - 1) + \dfrac{1}{4}$

    $= x - \dfrac{1}{4} + \dfrac{1}{4}$

    $= x$

    The functions are inverses of each other.

51. $f(g(x)) = f(2x + 3)$

    $= \dfrac{1}{2}(2x + 3) - \dfrac{3}{2}$

    $= x + \dfrac{3}{2} - \dfrac{3}{2}$

    $= x$

    $g(f(x)) = g\left(\dfrac{1}{2}x - \dfrac{3}{2}\right)$

    $= 2\left(\dfrac{1}{2}x - \dfrac{3}{2}\right) + 3$

    $= x - 3 + 3$

    $= x$

    The functions are inverses of each other.

52. $g(h(x)) = g(-2x + 1)$

    $= -\dfrac{1}{2}(-2x + 1) - \dfrac{1}{2}$

    $= x - \dfrac{1}{2} - \dfrac{1}{2}$

    $= x - 1$

    $h(g(x)) = h\left(-\dfrac{1}{2}x - \dfrac{1}{2}\right)$

    $= -2\left(-\dfrac{1}{2}x - \dfrac{1}{2}\right) + 1$

    $= x + 1 + 1$

    $= x + 2$

    The functions are not inverses of each other.

53. The domain of the inverse of f^{-1} is the range of f.

54. The range of the inverse function f^{-1} is the domain of f.

55. For any linear function f and its inverse f^{-1},,

    $f[f^{-1}(3)] = 3$.

56. For any linear function f and its inverse f^{-1},

    $f^{-1}[f(-4)] = -4$.

57. If f is a 1-1 function and $f(0) = 5$, then

    $f^{-1}(5) = 0$.

58. If f is a 1-1 function and $f(3) = 11$, then

    $f^{-1}(11) = 3$.

59. If f is a 1-1 function and $f(2) = 9$ then
$f^{-1}(9) = 2$.

60. If f is a 1-1 function and $f(1) = 7$, then
$f^{-1}(7) = 1$.

Applying Concepts 9.4

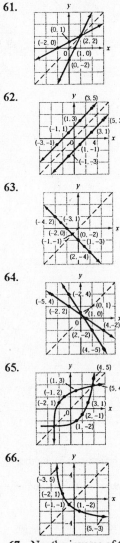

61.

62.

63.

64.

65.

66.

67. No, the inverse of the grading scale is not a function because each grade is paired with more than one score.

68. No, the inverse of the first-class postage is not a function because each cost is paired with more than one weight.

69. A constant function is defined as $y = b$. The inverse function would be $x = a$, which is not a function. (See also the answer to exercise 16.)

70. Yes, all functions given by $f(x) = mx + b$, $m \neq 0$, are 1-1 functions. These are linear functions, and all linear functions of this form pass the horizontal line test.

Projects and Group Activities

Applications of the Composition of Functions

1. a. $(S \circ M)(x) = 1.45\left(\dfrac{60x + 34,000}{x}\right)$

$= 1.45(60) + 1.45\left(\dfrac{34,000}{x}\right)$

$= 87 + \dfrac{49,300}{x}$

b. $(S \circ M)(24,650) = 87 + \dfrac{49,300}{24,650} = 89$

$89 is the selling price per computer monitor if 24,650 computer monitors are manufactured.

2. a. $b(h) = 40h$
$b(5) = 40(5) = 200$
The factory can produce 200 bookcases per day when it operates for 5 hours.

b. $c(b) = 0.1b^2 + 90b + 800$
$c(5) = 0.1(5)^2 + 90(5) + 800 = 1252.5$
The daily cost to manufacture 5 bookcases is $1252.50.

c. $(c \circ b)(h) = 0.1(40h)^2 + 90(40h) + 800$
$= 160h^2 + 3600h + 800$
This is the cost to manufacture bookcases for h hours per day.

d. $(c \circ b)(h) = 160h^2 + 3600h + 800$
$(c \circ b)(10) = 160(10)^2 + 3600(10) + 800$
$= 52,800$
The cost to manufacture bookcases for 10 hours per day is $52,800.

3. a. $d[r(p)] = 0.90(p - 1500)$
$= 0.90p - 1350$

b. $r[d(p)] = 0.90p - 1500$

c. $r[d(p)]$ The cost is less.

4. a. $A(r) = \pi r^2$

b. $C = 2\pi r$
$r = \dfrac{C}{2\pi}$

c. $A(C) = \pi\left(\dfrac{C}{2\pi}\right)^2$
$= \dfrac{C^2}{4\pi}$

Chapter Review Exercises

1. Yes, the graph is that of a function. It passes the vertical-line test.

2. $f(x) = |x| - 3$
   Domain: $\{x | x \in \text{real numbers}\}$.
   Range: $\{y | y \geq -3\}$

3. $f(x) = 3x^3 - 2$
   Domain: $\{x | x \in \text{real numbers}\}$
   Range: $\{y | y \in \text{real numbers}\}$

4. $f(x) = \sqrt{x + 4}$
   Domain: $[-4, \infty)$
   Range: $[0, \infty)$

5.

6.

7.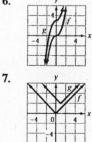

8.

9. $(f + g)(2) = f(2) + g(2)$
   $= [2^2 + 2(2) - 3] + [2^2 - 2]$
   $= [4 + 4 - 3] + [4 - 2]$
   $= 5 + 2$
   $= 7$
   $(f + g)(2) = 7$

10. $(f - g)(-4) = f(-4) - g(-4)$
    $= [(-4)^2 + 2(-4) - 3] - [(-4)^2 - 2]$
    $= [16 - 8 - 3] - [16 - 2]$
    $= 5 - 14$
    $= -9$
    $(f - g)(-4) = -9$

11. $(f \cdot g)(-4) = f(-4) \cdot g(-4)$
    $= [(-4)^2 + 2(-4) - 3] \cdot [(-4)^2 - 2]$
    $= [16 - 8 - 3] \cdot [16 - 2]$
    $= 5 \cdot 14$
    $= 70$
    $(f \cdot g)(-4) = 70$

12. $\left(\dfrac{f}{g}\right)(3) = \dfrac{f(3)}{g(3)}$
    $= \dfrac{3^2 + 2(3) - 3}{3^2 - 2}$
    $= \dfrac{9 + 6 - 3}{9 - 2}$
    $= \dfrac{12}{7}$
    $\left(\dfrac{f}{g}\right)(3) = \dfrac{12}{7}$

13. $f(x) = 3x^2 - 4, \ g(x) = 2x + 1$
    $f[g(x)] = f(2x + 1)$
    $= 3(2x + 1)^2 - 4$
    $= 3(4x^2 + 4x + 1) - 4$
    $= 12x^2 + 12x + 3 - 4$
    $f[g(x)] = 12x^2 + 12x - 1$

14. $f(x) = x^2 + 4, \ g(x) = 4x - 1$
    $g(0) = 4(0) - 1 = 0 - 1 = -1$
    $f(-1) = (-1)^2 + 4 = 1 + 4 = 5$
    $f[g(0)] = 5$

15. $f(x) = 6x + 8, \ g(x) = 4x + 2$
    $f(-1) = 6(-1) + 8 = -6 + 8 = 2$
    $g(2) = 4(2) + 2 = 8 + 2 = 10$
    $g[f(-1)] = 10$

16. $f(x) = 2x^2 + x - 5, \ g(x) = 3x - 1$
    $g[f(x)] = g(2x^2 + x - 5)$
    $= 3(2x^2 + x - 5) - 1$
    $= 6x^2 + 3x - 15 - 1$
    $g[f(x)] = 6x^2 + 3x - 16$

17. No

18. The inverse of $\{(-2, 1), (2, 3), (5, -4), (7, 9)\}$ is
$\{(1, -2), (3, 2), (-4, 5), (9, 7)\}$

19. A vertical line will intersect the graph at no more than one point. The graph is the graph of a function. A horizontal line will intersect the graph at more than one point. The graph is not the graph of a 1-1 function.

20. A vertical line will intersect the graph at no more than one point. The graph is the graph of a function. A horizontal line will intersect the graph at no more than one point. The graph is the graph of a 1-1 function.

21.
$$f(x) = \frac{1}{2}x + 8$$
$$y = \frac{1}{2}x + 8$$
$$x = \frac{1}{2}y + 8$$
$$x - 8 = \frac{1}{2}y$$
$$2(x - 8) = 2 \cdot \frac{1}{2}y$$
$$2x - 16 = y$$

The inverse function is $f^{-1}(x) = 2x - 16$.

22.
$$f(x) = -6x + 4$$
$$y = -6x + 4$$
$$x = -6y + 4$$
$$x - 4 = -6y$$
$$-\frac{1}{6}x + \frac{2}{3} = y$$

The inverse function is $f^{-1}(x) = -\frac{1}{6}x + \frac{2}{3}$.

23.
$$f(x) = \frac{2}{3}x - 12$$
$$y = \frac{2}{3}x - 12$$
$$x = \frac{2}{3}y - 12$$
$$x + 12 = \frac{2}{3}y$$
$$\frac{3}{2}(x + 12) = y$$
$$\frac{3}{2}x + 18 = y$$

The inverse function is $f^{-1}(x) = \frac{3}{2}x + 18$.

24. $f(g(x)) = f(-4x + 5) = -\frac{1}{4}(-4x + 5) + \frac{5}{4}$
$$= x - \frac{5}{4} + \frac{5}{4} = x$$
$g(f(x)) = g\left(-\frac{1}{4}x + \frac{5}{4}\right) = -4\left(-\frac{1}{4}x + \frac{5}{4}\right) + 5$
$$= x - 5 + 5 = x$$
The functions are inverses of each other.

Chapter Test

1. A vertical line intersects the graph at more than one point. The graph is not a function.

2. $(f - g)(2) = f(2) - g(2)$
$$= [2^2 + 2(2) - 3] - [2^3 - 1]$$
$$= [4 + 4 - 3] - [8 - 1]$$
$$= 5 - 7$$
$$= -2$$
$(f - g)(2) = -2$

3. $(f \cdot g)(-3) = f(-3) \cdot g(-3)$
$$= [(-3)^3 + 1][2(-3) - 3]$$
$$= [-27 + 1][-9]$$
$$= 234$$
$(f \cdot g)(-3) = 234$

4. $\left(\frac{f}{g}\right)(-2) = \frac{f(-2)}{g(-2)}$
$$= \frac{4(-2) - 5}{(-2)^2 + 3(-2) + 4}$$
$$= \frac{-8 - 5}{4 - 6 + 4}$$
$$= -\frac{13}{2}$$
$\frac{f}{g}(-2) = \frac{-13}{2} = -\frac{13}{2}$

5. $(f - g)(-4) = f(-4) - g(-4)$
$$= [(-4)^2 + 4] - [2(-4)^2 + 2(-4) + 1]$$
$$= [16 + 4] - [32 - 8 + 1]$$
$$= 20 - 25$$
$$= -5$$
$(f - g)(-4) = -5$

6. $g(x) = \frac{x}{x + 1}$
$$g(3) = \frac{3}{3 + 1} = \frac{3}{4}$$
$$f(x) = 4x + 2$$
$$f\left(\frac{3}{4}\right) = 4\left(\frac{3}{4}\right) + 2$$
$$f[g(3)] = 3 + 2 = 5$$

7.

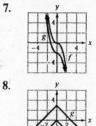

8.

9. $f(x) = -\sqrt{3-x}$

The domain is $(-\infty, 3]$

The range is $(-\infty, 0]$

10. $f(x) = \left|\frac{1}{2}x\right| - 2$

The domain is $\{x | x \in \text{real numbers}\}$.

The range is $\{y | y \geq -2\}$.

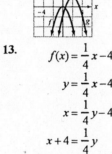

11.

12.

13.
$$f(x) = \frac{1}{4}x - 4$$
$$y = \frac{1}{4}x - 4$$
$$x = \frac{1}{4}y - 4$$
$$x + 4 = \frac{1}{4}y$$
$$4x + 16 = y$$

The inverse of the function is $f^{-1}(x) = 4x + 16$.

14. The inverse of the function of $\{(2, 6), (3, 5), (4, 4), (5, 3)\}$ is $\{(6, 2), (5, 3), (4, 4), (3, 5)\}$.

15.
$$f[g(x)] = \frac{1}{2}(2x - 4) + 2$$
$$= x - 2 + 2$$
$$= x$$
$$g[f(x)] = 2\left(\frac{1}{2}x + 2\right) - 4$$
$$= x + 4 - 4$$
$$= x$$
The functions are inverses of each other.

16.
$$f[g(x)] = f(x - 1)$$
$$f[g(x)] = 2(x - 1)^2 - 7$$
$$= 2(x^2 - 2x + 1) - 7$$
$$= 2x^2 - 4x + 2 - 7$$
$$= 2x^2 - 4x - 5$$

17.
$$f(x) = \frac{1}{2}x - 3$$
$$y = \frac{1}{2}x - 3$$
$$x = \frac{1}{2}y - 3$$
$$2x = y - 6$$
$$y = 2x + 6$$
$$f^{-1}(x) = 2x + 6$$

18.
$$f[g(x)] = f\left(\frac{3}{2}x - 3\right)$$
$$= \frac{2}{3}\left(\frac{3}{2}x - 3\right) + 3$$
$$= x - 2 + 3$$
$$= x + 1$$
$$g[f(x)] = g\left(\frac{2}{3}x + 3\right)$$
$$= \frac{3}{2}\left(\frac{2}{3}x + 3\right) - 3$$
$$= x + \frac{9}{2} - 3$$
$$= x + \frac{3}{2}$$
The functions are not inverses of each other.

19. $f(x) = x^3 - 3x + 2$

The domain is $\{x | x \in \text{real numbers}\}$.

The range is $\{y | y \in \text{real numbers}\}$.

20. The graph does not represent a 1-1 function. It fails the horizontal- and vertical-line tests.

516 **Chapter 9:** *Functions and Relations*

Cumulative Review Exercises

1. $-3a+\left|\dfrac{3b-ab}{3b-c}\right|=-3(2)+\left|\dfrac{3(2)-2(2)}{3(2)-(-2)}\right|$

$=-6+\left|\dfrac{6-4}{6+2}\right|$

$=-6+\left|\dfrac{2}{8}\right|$

$=-6+\left|\dfrac{1}{4}\right|$

$=-6+\dfrac{1}{4}=-\dfrac{23}{4}$

2.

3. $\dfrac{3x-1}{6}-\dfrac{5-x}{4}=\dfrac{5}{6}$

$12\left(\dfrac{3x-1}{6}-\dfrac{5-x}{4}\right)=12\left(\dfrac{5}{6}\right)$

$2(3x-1)-3(5-x)=2(5)$

$6x-2-15+3x=10$

$9x-17=10$

$9x=27$

$x=3$

4. $4x-2<-10$ or $3x-1>8$

$\quad 4x<-8 \qquad\qquad 3x>9$

$\quad x<-2 \qquad\qquad\ x>3$

$\{x|x<-2\}$ $\qquad\qquad \{x|x>3\}$

$\{x|x<-2\}\cup\{x|x>3\}=\{x|x<-2\text{ or }x>3\}$

5. Vertex: $(0, 0)$
Axis of symmetry: $x=0$

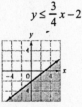

6. $3x-4y\geq 8$

$\quad -4y\geq -3x+8$

$\quad\quad y\leq\dfrac{3}{4}x-2$

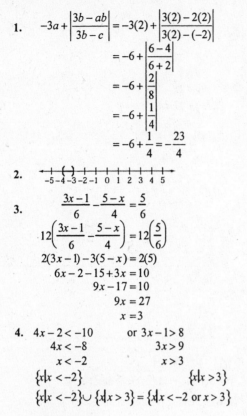

7. $|8-2x|\geq 0$

$8-2x\leq 0$ or $8-2x\geq 0$

$\quad 8\leq 2x \qquad\qquad 8\geq 2x$

$\quad 4\leq x \qquad\qquad 4\geq x$

$\{x|x\geq 4\}$ $\qquad\quad \{x|x\leq 4\}$

$\{x|x\geq 4\}\cup\{x|x\leq 4\}=\{x|x\in\text{real numbers}\}$

8. $\left(\dfrac{3a^3b}{2a}\right)^2\left(\dfrac{a^2}{-3b^2}\right)^3=\left(\dfrac{3a^2b}{2}\right)^2\left(\dfrac{a^2}{-3b^2}\right)^3$

$=\left(\dfrac{3^2a^4b^2}{2^2}\right)\left(\dfrac{a^6}{(-3)^3b^6}\right)$

$=\left(\dfrac{9a^4b^2}{4}\right)\left(\dfrac{a^6}{-27b^6}\right)$

$=\dfrac{9a^4b^2a^6}{4(-27)b^6}$

$=\dfrac{9a^{10}b^2}{-108b^6}$

$=-\dfrac{a^{10}}{12b^4}$

9. $\quad 2x^2+4x-1$

$\qquad\qquad\quad x-4$

$\overline{\qquad -8x^2-16x+4}$

$\quad 2x^3+4x^2-\ x$

$\overline{\ 2x^3-4x^2-17x+4}$

10. $a^4-2a^2-8=(a^2)^2-2(a^2)-8$

$=(a^2-4)(a^2+2)$

$=(a+2)(a-2)(a^2+2)$

11. $x^3y+x^2y^2-6xy^3=xy(x^2+xy-6y^2)$

$=xy(x+3y)(x-2y)$

12. $(b+2)(b-5)=2b+14$

$b^2-3b-10=2b+14$

$b^2-5b-24=0$

$(b-8)(b+3)=0$

$b-8=0\quad b+3=0$

$b=8\qquad b=-3$

The solutions are 8 and –3.

13. $\quad x^2-2x>15$

$x^2-2x-15>0$

$(x-5)(x+3)>0$

$\{x|x<-3\text{ or }x>5\}$

14. $\dfrac{x^2+4x-5}{2x^2-3x+1}-\dfrac{x}{2x-1}=\dfrac{(x+5)(x-1)}{(2x-1)(x-1)}-\dfrac{x}{2x-1}$

$$=\dfrac{x+5}{2x-1}-\dfrac{x}{2x-1}$$

$$=\dfrac{x+5-x}{2x-1}$$

$$=\dfrac{5}{2x-1}$$

15.
$$\dfrac{5}{x^2+7x+12}=\dfrac{9}{x+4}-\dfrac{2}{x+3}$$

$$(x+4)(x+3)\dfrac{5}{(x+4)(x+3)}=(x+4)(x+3)\left[\dfrac{9}{x+4}-\dfrac{2}{x+3}\right]$$

$$5=(x+3)9-(x+4)2$$

$$5=9x+27-2x-8$$

$$5=7x+19$$

$$-14=7x$$

$$-2=x$$

The solution is –2.

16. $\dfrac{4-6i}{2i}=\dfrac{4-6i}{2i}\cdot\dfrac{i}{i}$

$$=\dfrac{4i-6i^2}{2i^2}$$

$$=\dfrac{4i+6}{-2}$$

$$=-3-2i$$

17. $m=\dfrac{y_2-y_1}{x_2-x_1}=\dfrac{-6-4}{2-(-3)}=\dfrac{-10}{5}=-2$

$$y-y_1=m(x-x_1)$$

$$y-4=-2[x-(-3)]$$

$$y-4=-2(x+3)$$

$$y-4=-2x-6$$

$$y=-2x-2$$

18. The product of the slopes of perpendicular lines is –1.

$$2x-3y=6 \qquad m_1\cdot m_2=-1$$

$$-3y=-2x+6 \qquad \dfrac{2}{3}\cdot m_2=-1$$

$$y=\dfrac{2}{3}x-2 \qquad m_2=-\dfrac{3}{2}$$

$$y-y_1=m(x-x_1)$$

$$y-1=-\dfrac{3}{2}[x-(-3)]$$

$$y-1=-\dfrac{3}{2}(x+3)$$

$$y-1=-\dfrac{3}{2}x-\dfrac{9}{2}$$

$$y=-\dfrac{3}{2}x-\dfrac{7}{2}$$

19.
$$3x^2=3x-1$$

$$3x^2-3x+1=0$$

$$a=3,\,b=-3,\,c=1$$

$$x=\dfrac{-b\pm\sqrt{b^2-4ac}}{2a}$$

$$=\dfrac{-(-3)\pm\sqrt{(-3)^2-4(3)(1)}}{2(3)}$$

$$=\dfrac{3\pm\sqrt{9-12}}{6}$$

$$=\dfrac{3\pm\sqrt{-3}}{6}$$

$$=\dfrac{3\pm i\sqrt{3}}{6}$$

$$=\dfrac{1}{2}\pm\dfrac{\sqrt{3}}{6}i$$

The solutions are $\dfrac{1}{2}+\dfrac{\sqrt{3}}{6}i$ and $\dfrac{1}{2}-\dfrac{\sqrt{3}}{6}i$.

20. $\sqrt{8x+1} = 2x-1$

$\left(\sqrt{8x+1}\right)^2 = (2x-1)^2$

$8x+1 = 4x^2 - 4x + 1$

$0 = 4x^2 - 12x$

$0 = 4x(x-3)$

$4x = 0 \quad x-3 = 0$

$x = 0 \qquad x = 3$

Check:

$\sqrt{8x+1}$	$= 2x-1$
$\sqrt{8(0)+1}$	$2(0)-1$
$\sqrt{1}$	-1
1	$\neq -1$

$\sqrt{8x+1}$	$= 2x-1$
$\sqrt{8(3)+1}$	$2(3)-1$
$\sqrt{24+1}$	$6-1$
$\sqrt{25}$	5
5	$= 5$

The solution is 3.

21. $f(x) = 2x^2 - 3$

$a = 2, b = 0, c = -3$

$x = -\dfrac{b}{2a} = \dfrac{-0}{2 \cdot 2} = 0$

$f(0) = 2(0)^2 - 3 = -3$

The minimum value of the function is –3.

22. $f(x) = |3x - 4|$;

domain = {0, 1, 2, 3}

$f(x) = |3x - 4|$

$f(0) = |3(0) - 4| = |0 - 4| = |-4| = 4$

$f(1) = |3(1) - 4| = |3 - 4| = |-1| = 1$

$f(2) = |3(2) - 4| = |6 - 4| = |2| = 2$

$f(3) = |3(3) - 4| = |9 - 4| = |5| = 5$

The range is {1, 2, 4, 5}.

23. {(–3, 0), (–2, 0), (–1, 1), (0, 1)}

Each member of the domain is paired with only one member of the range. The set of ordered pairs is a function.

24. $\sqrt[3]{5x-2} = 2$

$\left(\sqrt[3]{5x-2}\right)^3 = 2^3$

$5x - 2 = 8$

$5x = 10$

$x = 2$

The solution is 2.

25. $h(x) = \dfrac{1}{2}x + 4$

$h(2) = \dfrac{1}{2}(2) + 4 = 1 + 4 = 5$

$g(x) = 3x - 5$

$g(5) = 3(5) - 5 = 15 - 5 = 10$

$g(h(2)) = 10$

26. $f(x) = -3x + 9$

$y = -3x + 9$

$x = -3y + 9$

$3y = -x + 9$

$y = -\dfrac{1}{3}x + 3$

The inverse function is $f^{-1}(x) = -\dfrac{1}{3}x + 3$.

27. Strategy

Cost per pounds of the mixture: x

	Amount	Cost	Value
$4.50 tea	30	4.50	4.50(30)
$3.60 tea	45	3.60	3.60(45)
Mixture	75	x	75x

The sum of the values before mixing equals the value after mixing.

Solution

$4.50(30) + 3.60(45) = 75x$

$135 + 162 = 75x$

$297 = 75x$

$3.96 = x$

The cost per pound of the mixture is $3.96.

28. Strategy

Pounds of 80% copper alloy: x

	Amount	Percent	Quantity
80%	x	0.80	0.80x
20%	50	0.20	0.20(50)
40%	50 + x	0.40	0.40(50 + x)

The sum of the quantities before mixing is equal to the quantity after mixing.

Solution

$0.80x + 0.20(50) = 0.40(50 + x)$

$0.80x + 10 = 20 + 0.40x$

$0.40x + 10 = 20$

$0.40x = 10$

$x = 25$

25 lb of the 80% copper alloy must be used.

29. Strategy

To find the additional amount of insecticide, write and solve a proportion, using x to represent the additional amount of insecticide. Then, $x + 6$ is the total amount of insecticide.

Solution

$$\frac{6}{16} = \frac{x+6}{28}$$

$$\frac{3}{8} = \frac{x+6}{28}$$

$$\frac{3}{8} \cdot 56 = \frac{x+6}{28} \cdot 56$$

$$21 = (x+6)2$$

$$21 = 2x + 12$$

$$9 = 2x$$

$$4.5 = x$$

An additional 4.5 oz of insecticide are required.

30. Strategy

This is a work problem.

Time for the smaller pipe to fill the tank: t

Time for the larger pipe to fill the tank: $t - 8$

	Rate	Time	Part
Smaller pipe	$\frac{1}{t}$	3	$\frac{3}{t}$
Larger pipe	$\frac{1}{t-8}$	3	$\frac{3}{t-8}$

The sum of the parts of the task completed must equal 1.

Solution

$$\frac{3}{t} + \frac{3}{t-8} = 1$$

$$t(t-8)\left(\frac{3}{t} + \frac{3}{t-8}\right) = t(t-8)$$

$$(t-8)3 + 3t = t^2 - 8t$$

$$3t - 24 + 3t = t^2 - 8t$$

$$6t - 24 = t^2 - 8t$$

$$0 = t^2 - 14t + 24$$

$$= (t-2)(t-12)$$

$$t - 2 = 0 \quad t - 12 = 0$$

$$t = 2 \qquad t = 12$$

The solution 2 is not possible since the time for the larger pipe would then be a negative number.

$t - 8 = 12 - 8 = 4$

It would take the larger pipe 4 minutes to fill the tank.

31. Strategy

To find the distance:

Write the basic direct variation equation, replace the variables by the given values, and solve for k. Write the direct variation equation, replacing k by its value. Substitute 40 for f and solve for d.

Solution

$$d = kf \qquad\qquad d = \frac{3}{5}f$$

$$30 = k(50) \qquad\qquad = \frac{3}{5}(40)$$

$$\frac{3}{5} = k \qquad\qquad = 24$$

A force of 40 lb will stretch the string 24 in.

32. Strategy

To find which average annual rate of change is greater:

Find the average annual rate of change for 2000 to 2004.

Find the average annual rate of change for 2000 to 2002.

Solution

For 2000 to 2004,

$$\frac{68-11}{2004-2000} = \frac{57}{4} = 14.25$$

For 2000 to 2002,

$$\frac{36-11}{2002-2000} = \frac{25}{2} = 12.5$$

The average annual rate of change for 2000 to 2004 is 14.25 million subscribers per year. The average annual rate of change for 2000 to 2004 is greater than that of 2000 to 2002.

33. Strategy

To find the frequency:

Write the basic inverse variation equation, replace the variables by the given values, and solve for k.

Write the inverse variation equation, replacing k by its value. Substitute 1.5 for L and solve for f.

Solution

$$f = \frac{k}{L} \qquad\qquad f = \frac{120}{L}$$

$$60 = \frac{k}{2} \qquad\qquad = \frac{120}{1.5}$$

$$120 = k \qquad\qquad = 80$$

The frequency is 80 vibrations per minute.

Chapter 10: Exponential and Logarithmic Functions

Prep Test

1. $3^{-2} = \dfrac{1}{9}$ [5.1.2]

2. $\left(\dfrac{1}{2}\right)^{-4} = 2^4 = 16$ [5.1.2]

3. $\dfrac{1}{8} = 2^{-3}$ [5.1.2]

4. $f(-1) = (-1)^4 + (-1)^3$ [3.2.1]
   $= 1 - 1$
   $= 0$
   $f(3) = (3)^4 + (3)^3$
   $= 81 + 27$
   $= 108$

5. $3x + 7 = x - 5$ [2.1.1]
   $2x = -12$
   $x = -6$

6. $16 = x^2 - 6x$ [8.1.1]
   $0 = x^2 - 6x - 16$
   $0 = (x-8)(x+2)$

   $x - 8 = 0 \qquad x + 2 = 0$
   $x = 8 \qquad\quad x = -2$
   The solutions are –2 and 8.

7. $5000(1+0.04)^6 = 5000(1.04)^6$ [1.3.2]
   $= 5000(1.265319)$
   $= 6326.60$

8. $f(x) = x^2 - 1$ [9.1.1]

Go Figure

Rewrite the expression as
$9^0 + 9^1 + 9^2 + 9^3 + ... + 9^{2000} + 9^{2001}$.
If we pair and add the first two terms,
$9^0 + 9^1 = 1 + 9 = 10$, the ones digit is 0. If we pair and add the second two terms,
$9^2 + 9^3 = 81 + 729 = 810$, the ones digit is 0. If we pair and add each of the pairs in the middle, the ones digit is 0. Finally, if we pair and add the last two terms, $9^{2000} + 9^{2001}$, the sum of the ones digit, $1 + 9 = 10$, is 0. The sum of all the zeros is 0.

Section 10.1

Concept Review 10.1

1. Never true
   The domain is $\{x \mid x \text{ is a real number}\}$

2. Always true

3. Never true
   The graph of $f(x) = b^x$ passes through the point (0, 1).

4. Sometimes true
   The base b is a positive real number.

5. Never true
   The range of $f(x) = b^x$ is $\{f(x) \mid f(x) > 0\}$ The function does not have x-intercepts.

Objective 10.1.1 Exercises

1. An exponential function with base b is defined by $f(x) = b^x$, $b > 0$, $b \neq 1$, and x is any real number.

2. The natural exponential function is the function defined by $f(x) = e^x$, where e is an irrational number approximately equal to 2.7182818283.

3. c cannot be the base since $-5 < 0$.

4. d cannot be the base since $-\dfrac{1}{2} < 0$.

5. $f(x) = 3^x$

   a. $f(2) = 3^2 = 9$

   b. $f(0) = 3^0 = 1$

   c. $f(-2) = 3^{-2} = \dfrac{1}{3^2} = \dfrac{1}{9}$

6. $H(x) = 2^x$

   a. $H(-3) = 2^{-3} = \dfrac{1}{2^3} = \dfrac{1}{8}$

   b. $H(0) = 2^0 = 1$

   c. $H(2) = 2^2 = 4$

7. $g(x) = 2^{x+1}$

   a. $g(3) = 2^{3+1} = 2^4 = 16$

   b. $g(1) = 2^{1+1} = 2^2 = 4$

   c. $g(-3) = 2^{-3+1} = 2^{-2} = \dfrac{1}{2^2} = \dfrac{1}{4}$

8. $F(x) = 3^{x-2}$

   a. $F(-4) = 3^{-4-2} = 3^{-6} = \dfrac{1}{3^6} = \dfrac{1}{729}$

   b. $F(-1) = 3^{-1-2} = 3^{-3} = \dfrac{1}{3^3} = \dfrac{1}{27}$

   c. $F(0) = 3^{0-2} = 3^{-2} = \dfrac{1}{3^2} = \dfrac{1}{9}$

9. $P(x) = \left(\dfrac{1}{2}\right)^{2x}$

   a. $P(0) = \left(\dfrac{1}{2}\right)^{2\cdot0} = \left(\dfrac{1}{2}\right)^0 = 1$

   b. $P\left(\dfrac{3}{2}\right) = \left(\dfrac{1}{2}\right)^{2\cdot\frac{3}{2}} = \left(\dfrac{1}{2}\right)^3 = \dfrac{1}{8}$

   c. $P(-2) = \left(\dfrac{1}{2}\right)^{2(-2)} = \left(\dfrac{1}{2}\right)^{-4} = 2^4 = 16$

10. $R(t) = \left(\dfrac{1}{3}\right)^{3t}$

   a. $R\left(-\dfrac{1}{3}\right) = \left(\dfrac{1}{3}\right)^{3\left(-\frac{1}{3}\right)} = \left(\dfrac{1}{3}\right)^{-1} = 3^1 = 3$

   b. $R(1) = \left(\dfrac{1}{3}\right)^{3\cdot1} = \left(\dfrac{1}{3}\right)^3 = \dfrac{1}{27}$

   c. $R(-2) = \left(\dfrac{1}{3}\right)^{3(-2)} = \left(\dfrac{1}{3}\right)^{-6} = 3^6 = 729$

11. $G(x) = e^{x/2}$

   a. $G(4) = e^{4/2} = e^2 \approx 7.3891$

   b. $G(-2) = e^{-2/2} = e^{-1} = \dfrac{1}{e} \approx 0.3679$

   c. $G\left(\dfrac{1}{2}\right) = e^{\frac{1}{2}/2} = e^{1/4} = e^{0.25} \approx 1.2840$

12. $f(x) = e^{2x}$

   a. $f(-2) = e^{2(-2)} = e^{-4} = \dfrac{1}{e^4} \approx 0.0183$

   b. $f\left(-\dfrac{2}{3}\right) = e^{2\left(-\frac{2}{3}\right)} = e^{-\frac{4}{3}} = \dfrac{1}{e^{4/3}} \approx 0.2636$

   c. $f(2) = e^{2(2)} = e^4 = 54.5982$

13. $H(r) = e^{-r+3}$

   a. $H(-1) = e^{-(-1)+3} = e^{1+3} = e^4 \approx 54.5982$

   b. $H(3) = e^{-3+3} = e^0 = 1$

   c. $H(5) = e^{-5+3} = e^{-2} = \dfrac{1}{e^2} \approx 0.1353$

14. $P(t) = e^{-\frac{1}{2}t}$

   a. $P(-3) = e^{-\frac{1}{2}(-3)} = e^{3/2} \approx 4.4817$

   b. $P(4) = e^{-\frac{1}{2}(4)} = e^{-2} = \dfrac{1}{e^2} \approx 0.1353$

   c. $P\left(\dfrac{1}{2}\right) = e^{-\frac{1}{2}\left(\frac{1}{2}\right)} = e^{-\frac{1}{4}} = \dfrac{1}{e^{0.25}} \approx 0.7788$

15. $F(x) = 2^{x^2}$

   a. $F(2) = 2^{2^2} = 2^4 = 16$

   b. $F(-2) = 2^{(-2)^2} = 2^4 = 16$

   c. $F\left(\dfrac{3}{4}\right) = 2^{\left(\frac{3}{4}\right)^2} = 2^{\frac{9}{16}} = \sqrt[16]{2^9} = \sqrt[16]{512} \approx 1.4768$

16. $Q(x) = 2^{-x^2}$

   a. $Q(3) = 2^{-3^2} = 2^{-9} = \dfrac{1}{2^9} = \dfrac{1}{512}$

   b. $Q(-1) = 2^{-(-1)^2} = 2^{-1} = \dfrac{1}{2}$

   c. $Q(-2) = 2^{-(-2)^2} = 2^{-4} = \dfrac{1}{2^4} = \dfrac{1}{16}$

17. $f(x) = e^{-x^2/2}$

   a. $f(-2) = e^{-(-2)^2/2}$
$$= e^{-4/2}$$
$$= e^{-2}$$
$$= \dfrac{1}{e^2}$$
$$\approx 0.1353$$

   b. $f(2) = e^{-(2)^2/2} = e^{-4/2} = e^{-2} = \dfrac{1}{e^2} \approx 0.1353$

   c. $f(-3) = e^{-(-3)^2/2} = e^{-9/2} = \dfrac{1}{e^{9/2}} \approx 0.0111$

18. $f(x) = e^{-2x} + 1$

   a. $f(-1) = e^{-2(-1)} + 1 = e^2 + 1 \approx 8.3891$

   b. $f(3) = e^{-2(3)} + 1 = e^{-6} + 1 = \dfrac{1}{e^6} + 1 \approx 1.0025$

   c. $f(-2) = e^{-2(-2)} + 1 = e^4 + 1 \approx 55.5982$

Objective 10.1.2 Exercises

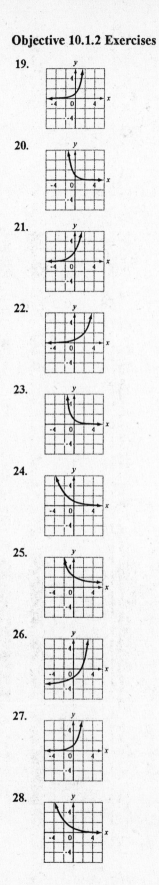

19.

20.

21.

22.

23.

24.

25.

26.

27.

28.

29.

30.

31.   b and d have the same graph since $\left(\dfrac{1}{3}\right)^x = 3^{-x}$.

32.   b and d have the same graph since $4^{-x} = \left(\dfrac{1}{4}\right)^x$.

33.   The graphs intersect at (0, 1).

34.   The graphs intersect at (0, 2).

35.   There is no x-intercept. The y-intercept is (0, 1).

36.   There is no x-intercept. The y-intercept is (0, 1).

37.

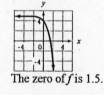

The zero of f is 1.6.

38.

The zero of f is 1.5.

39.

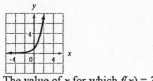

The value of x for which $f(x) = 3$ is 1.1.

40.

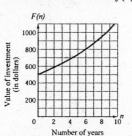

The value of x for which $f(x) = 2$ is -1.8.

41.

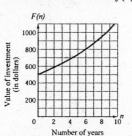

In approximately 9 years the investment will be worth $1000.

42.

In approximately 18 years there will be 20 g of cesium remaining.

43.

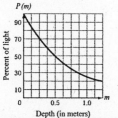

50% of the light reaches 0.5 meter below the surface of the ocean.

10.1 Applying Concepts

44. When $n = 100$, $\left(1 + \dfrac{1}{n}\right)^{n} \approx 2.704813829$.

When $n = 1000$, $\left(1 + \dfrac{1}{n}\right)^{n} \approx 2.716923932$.

When $n = 10{,}000$, $\left(1 + \dfrac{1}{n}\right)^{n} \approx 2.718145927$.

When $n = 100{,}000$, $\left(1 + \dfrac{1}{n}\right)^{n} \approx 2.718268237$.

As n increases, $\left(1 + \dfrac{1}{n}\right)^{n}$ becomes closer to e.

45. a.

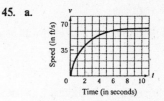

b. At $t = 4$ seconds after the object is dropped, it will be falling at a speed of 55.3 feet per second.

46. The graphs of g and h are exactly the same as the graph of f except for their position on the coordinate grid. The graph of g is shifted 2 units to the right; the graph of h is shifted two units to the left. The graphs of all three functions are shown here.

47. The graphs of g and h are exactly the same as the graph of f except for their position on the coordinate grid. The graph of g is shifted 2 units down; the graph of h is shifted two units up. The graphs of all three functions are shown here.

Section 10.2

Concept Review 10.2

1. Always true

2. Never true
   $$\log_b \frac{x}{y} = \log_b x - \log_b y$$

3. Never true
   $\dfrac{\log x}{\log y}$ is in simplest form.

4. Never true
   $\log xy = \log x + \log y$; $\log(x + y)$ is in simplest form.

5. Always true

6. Never true
   $$\log(x^{-1}) = \log\left(\frac{1}{x}\right)$$

7. Always true

8. Always true

Objective 10.2.1 Exercises

1. **a.** A common logarithm is a logarithm with base 10.

   b. $\log 4z$

2. **a.** A natural logarithm is a logarithm with base e.

   b. $\ln 3x$

3. $5^2 = 25$ is equivalent to $\log_5 25 = 2$.

4. $10^3 = 1000$ is equivalent to $\log_{10} 1000 = 3$.

5. $4^{-2} = \dfrac{1}{16}$ is equivalent to $\log_4\left(\dfrac{1}{16}\right) = -2$.

6. $3^{-3} = \dfrac{1}{27}$ is equivalent to $\log_3\left(\dfrac{1}{27}\right) = -3$.

7. $10^y = x$ is equivalent to $\log_{10} x = y$.

8. $e^y = x$ is equivalent to $\log_e x = y$.

9. $a^x = w$ is equivalent to $\log_a w = x$.

10. $b^y = c$ is equivalent to $\log_b c = y$.

11. $\log_3 9 = 2$ is equivalent to $3^2 = 9$.

12. $\log_2 32 = 5$ is equivalent to $2^5 = 32$.

13. $\log 0.01 = -2$ is equivalent to $10^{-2} = 0.01$.

14. $\log_5 \dfrac{1}{5} = -1$ is equivalent to $5^{-1} = \dfrac{1}{5}$.

15. $\ln x = y$ is equivalent to $e^y = x$.

16. $\log x = y$ is equivalent to $10^y = x$.

17. $\log_b u = v$ is equivalent to $b^v = u$.

18. $\log_c x = y$ is equivalent to $c^y = x$.

19. $\log_3 81 = x$
    $3^x = 81$
    $3^x = 3^4$
    $x = 4$
    $\log_3 81 = 4$

20. $\log_7 49 = x$
    $7^x = 49$
    $7^x = 7^2$
    $x = 2$
    $\log_7 49 = 2$

21. $\log_2 128 = x$
    $2^x = 128$
    $2^x = 2^7$
    $x = 7$
    $\log_2 128 = 7$

22. $\log_5 125 = x$
    $5^x = 125$
    $5^x = 5^3$
    $x = 3$
    $\log_5 125 = 3$

23. $\log 100 = x$
    $10^x = 100$
    $10^x = 10^2$
    $x = 2$
    $\log 100 = 2$

24. $\log 0.001 = x$
    $10^x = 0.001$
    $10^x = 10^{-3}$
    $x = -3$
    $\log 0.001 = -3$

25. $\ln e^3 = x$
    $3 \ln e = x$
    $3(1) = x$
    $x = 3$
    $\ln e^3 = 3$

26. $\ln e^2 = x$
    $2 \ln e = x$
    $2(1) = x$
    $x = 2$
    $\ln e^2 = 2$

27. $\log_8 1 = x$
    $8^x = 1$
    $x = 0$
    $\log_8 1 = 0$

28. $\log_3 243 = x$
    $3^x = 243$
    $3^x = 3^5$
    $x = 5$
    $\log_3 243 = 5$

29. $\log_5 625 = x$
    $5^x = 625$
    $5^x = 5^4$
    $x = 4$
    $\log_5 625 = 4$

30. $\log_2 64 = x$
    $2^x = 64$
    $2^x = 2^6$
    $x = 6$
    $\log_2 64 = 6$

31. $\log_3 x = 2$
$3^2 = x$
$9 = x$

32. $\log_5 x = 1$
$5^1 = x$
$5 = x$

33. $\log_4 x = 3$
$4^3 = x$
$64 = x$

34. $\log_2 x = 6$
$2^6 = x$
$64 = x$

35. $\log_7 x = -1$
$7^{-1} = x$
$\dfrac{1}{7} = x$

36. $\log_8 x = -2$
$8^{-2} = x$
$\dfrac{1}{64} = x$

37. $\log_6 x = 0$
$6^0 = x$
$1 = x$

38. $\log_4 x = 0$
$4^0 = x$
$1 = x$

39. $\log x = 2.5$
$10^{2.5} = x$
$316.23 \approx x$

40. $\log x = 3.2$
$10^{3.2} = x$
$1584.89 \approx x$

41. $\log x = -1.75$
$10^{-1.75} = x$
$0.02 \approx x$

42. $\log x = -2.1$
$10^{-2.1} = x$
$0.01 \approx x$

43. $\ln x = 2$
$e^2 = x$
$7.39 \approx x$

44. $\ln x = 4$
$e^4 = x$
$54.60 \approx x$

45. $\ln x = -\dfrac{1}{2}$
$e^{-1/2} = x$
$0.61 \approx x$

46. $\ln x = -1.7$
$e^{-1.7} = x$
$0.18 \approx x$

Objective 10.2.2 Exercises

47. Answers may vary. For example, the log of a product is equal to the sum of the logs:
$\log_b(xy) = \log_b x + \log_b y$.

48. Answer may vary. For example, the log of a quotient is equal to the difference of the logs:
$\log_b \dfrac{x}{y} = \log_b x - \log_b y$.

49. $\log_8(xz) = \log_8 x + \log_8 z$

50. $\log_7(4y) = \log_7 4 + \log_7 y$

51. $\log_3 x^5 = 5\log_3 x$

52. $\log_2 y^7 = 7\log_2 y$

53. $\ln\left(\dfrac{r}{s}\right) = \ln r - \ln s$

54. $\ln\left(\dfrac{z}{4}\right) = \ln z - \ln 4$

55. $\log_3(x^2 y^6) = \log_3 x^2 + \log_3 y^6$
$= 2\log_3 x + 6\log_3 y$

56. $\log_4(t^4 u^2) = \log_4 t^4 + \log_4 u^2$
$= 4\log_4 t + 2\log_4 u$

57. $\log_7\left(\dfrac{u^3}{v^4}\right) = \log_7 u^3 - \log_7 v^4$
$= 3\log_7 u - 4\log_7 v$

58. $\log\left(\dfrac{s^5}{t^2}\right) = \log s^5 - \log t^2$
$= 5\log s - 2\log t$

59. $\log_2(rs)^2 = 2\log_2(rs)$
$= 2(\log_2 r + \log_2 s)$
$= 2\log_2 r + 2\log_2 s$

60. $\log_3(x^2 y)^3 = 3\log_3(x^2 y)$
$= 3(\log_3 x^2 + \log_3 y)$
$= 3\log_3 x^2 + 3\log_3 y$
$= 6\log_3 x + 3\log_3 y$

61. $\log_9 x^2 yz = \log_9 x^2 + \log_9 y + \log_9 z$
$= 2\log_9 x + \log_9 y + \log_9 z$

62. $\log_6 xy^2 z^3 = \log_6 x + \log_6 y^2 + \log_6 z^3$
$$= \log_6 x + 2\log_6 y + 3\log_6 z$$

63. $\ln\left(\dfrac{xy^2}{z^4}\right) = \ln(xy^2) - \ln z^4$
$$= \ln x + \ln y^2 - \ln z^4$$
$$= \ln x + 2\ln y - 4\ln z$$

64. $\ln\left(\dfrac{r^2 s}{t^3}\right) = \ln(r^2 s) - \ln t^3$
$$= \ln r^2 + \ln s - \ln t^3$$
$$= 2\ln r + \ln s - 3\ln t$$

65. $\log_8\left(\dfrac{x^2}{yz^2}\right) = \log_8 x^2 - \log_8(yz^2)$
$$= \log_8 x^2 - (\log_8 y + \log_8 z^2)$$
$$= \log_8 x^2 - \log_8 y - \log_8 z^2$$
$$= 2\log_8 x - \log_8 y - 2\log_8 z$$

66. $\log_9\left(\dfrac{x}{y^2 z^3}\right) = \log_9 x - \log_9(y^2 z^3)$
$$= \log_9 x - (\log_9 y^2 + \log_9 z^3)$$
$$= \log_9 x - \log_9 y^2 - \log_9 z^3$$
$$= \log_9 x - 2\log_9 y - 3\log_9 z$$

67. $\log_7 \sqrt{xy} = \log_7(xy)^{1/2}$
$$= \frac{1}{2}\log_7(xy)$$
$$= \frac{1}{2}(\log_7 x + \log_7 y)$$
$$= \frac{1}{2}\log_7 x + \frac{1}{2}\log_7 y$$

68. $\log_8 \sqrt[3]{xz} = \log_8(xz)^{1/3}$
$$= \frac{1}{3}\log_8(xz)$$
$$= \frac{1}{3}(\log_8 x + \log_8 z)$$
$$= \frac{1}{3}\log_8 x + \frac{1}{3}\log_8 z$$

69. $\log_2 \sqrt{\dfrac{x}{y}} = \log_2\left(\dfrac{x}{y}\right)^{1/2}$
$$= \frac{1}{2}\log_2\left(\frac{x}{y}\right)$$
$$= \frac{1}{2}(\log_2 x - \log_2 y)$$
$$= \frac{1}{2}\log_2 x - \frac{1}{2}\log_2 y$$

70. $\log_3 \sqrt[3]{\dfrac{r}{s}} = \log_3\left(\dfrac{r}{s}\right)^{1/3}$
$$= \frac{1}{3}\log_3\left(\frac{r}{s}\right)$$
$$= \frac{1}{3}(\log_3 r - \log_3 s)$$
$$= \frac{1}{3}\log_3 r - \frac{1}{3}\log_3 s$$

71. $\ln\sqrt{x^3 y} = \ln(x^3 y)^{1/2}$
$$= \frac{1}{2}\ln(x^3 y)$$
$$= \frac{1}{2}(\ln x^3 + \ln y)$$
$$= \frac{1}{2}(3\ln x + \ln y)$$
$$= \frac{3}{2}\ln x + \frac{1}{2}\ln y$$

72. $\ln\sqrt{x^5 y^3} = \ln(x^5 y^3)^{1/2}$
$$= \frac{1}{2}\ln(x^5 y^3)$$
$$= \frac{1}{2}(\ln x^5 + \ln y^3)$$
$$= \frac{1}{2}(5\ln x + 3\ln y)$$
$$= \frac{5}{2}\ln x + \frac{3}{2}\ln y$$

73. $\log_7 \sqrt{\dfrac{x^3}{y}} = \log_7\left(\dfrac{x^3}{y}\right)^{1/2}$
$$= \frac{1}{2}\log_7\left(\frac{x^3}{y}\right)$$
$$= \frac{1}{2}(\log_7 x^3 - \log_7 y)$$
$$= \frac{1}{2}(3\log_7 x - \log_7 y)$$
$$= \frac{3}{2}\log_7 x - \frac{1}{2}\log_7 y$$

74. $\log_b \sqrt[3]{\dfrac{r^2}{t}} = \log_b\left(\dfrac{r^2}{t}\right)^{1/3}$
$$= \frac{1}{3}\log_b\left(\frac{r^2}{t}\right)$$
$$= \frac{1}{3}(\log_b r^2 - \log_b t)$$
$$= \frac{1}{3}(2\log_b r - \log_b t)$$
$$= \frac{2}{3}\log_b r - \frac{1}{3}\log_b t$$

75. $\log_3 x^3 - \log_3 y = \log_3\left(\dfrac{x^3}{y}\right)$

76. $\log_7 t + \log_7 v^2 = \log_7(tv^2)$

77. $\log_8 x^4 + \log_8 y^2 = \log_8(x^4 y^2)$

78. $\log_2 r^2 + \log_2 s^3 = \log_2(r^2 s^3)$

79. $3\ln x = \ln x^3$

80. $4\ln y = \ln y^4$

81. $3\log_5 x + 4\log_5 y = \log_5 x^3 + \log_5 y^4$
$$= \log_5(x^3 y^4)$$

82. $2\log_6 x + 5\log_6 y = \log_6 x^2 + \log_6 y^5$
$$= \log_6(x^2 y^5)$$

83. $-2\log_4 x = \log_4(x^{-2}) = \log_4\left(\dfrac{1}{x^2}\right)$

84. $-3\log_2 y = \log_2(y^{-3}) = \log_2\left(\dfrac{1}{y^3}\right)$

85. $2\log_3 x - \log_3 y + 2\log_3 z$
$$= \log_3 x^2 - \log_3 y + \log_3 z^2$$
$$= \log_3\left(\frac{x^2}{y}\right) + \log_3 z^2$$
$$= \log_3\left(\frac{x^2 z^2}{y}\right)$$

86. $4\log_5 r - 3\log_5 s + \log_5 t$
$$= \log_5 r^4 - \log_5 s^3 + \log_5 t$$
$$= \log_5\left(\frac{r^4}{s^3}\right) + \log_5 t$$
$$= \log_5\left(\frac{r^4 t}{s^3}\right)$$

87. $\log_b x - (2\log_b y + \log_b z)$
$$= \log_b x - (\log_b y^2 + \log_b z)$$
$$= \log_b x - \log_b y^2 z$$
$$= \log_b\left(\frac{x}{y^2 z}\right)$$

88. $2\log_2 x - (3\log_2 y + \log_2 z)$
$$= \log_2 x^2 - (\log_2 y^3 + \log_2 z)$$
$$= \log_2 x^2 - \log_2 y^3 z$$
$$= \log_2\left(\frac{x^2}{y^3 z}\right)$$

89. $2(\ln x + \ln y) = 2\ln(xy) = \ln(xy)^2 = \ln(x^2 y^2)$

90. $3(\ln r + \ln t) = 3\ln(rt) = \ln(rt)^3 = \ln r^3 t^3$

91. $\dfrac{1}{2}(\log_6 x - \log_6 y) = \dfrac{1}{2}\log_6\left(\dfrac{x}{y}\right)$
$$= \log_6\left(\frac{x}{y}\right)^{1/2}$$
$$= \log_6\sqrt{\frac{x}{y}}$$

92. $\dfrac{1}{3}(\log_8 x - \log_8 y) = \dfrac{1}{3}\log_8\left(\dfrac{x}{y}\right)$
$$= \log_8\left(\frac{x}{y}\right)^{1/3}$$
$$= \log_8\sqrt[3]{\frac{x}{y}}$$

93. $2(\log_4 s - 2\log_4 t + \log_4 r)$
$$= 2\left(\log_4\frac{s}{t^2} + \log_4 r\right)$$
$$= 2\log_4\left(\frac{sr}{t^2}\right)$$
$$= \log_4\left(\frac{sr}{t^2}\right)^2$$
$$= \log_4\frac{s^2 r^2}{t^4}$$

94. $3(\log_9 x + 2\log_9 y - 2\log_9 z)$
$$= 3(\log_9 x + \log_9 y^2 - \log_9 z^2)$$
$$= 3(\log_9 xy^2 - \log_9 z^2)$$
$$= 3\log_9\left(\frac{xy^2}{z^2}\right)$$
$$= \log_9\left(\frac{xy^2}{z^2}\right)^3$$
$$= \log_9\frac{x^3 y^6}{z^6}$$

95. $\log_5 x - 2(\log_5 y + \log_5 z) = \log_5 x - 2\log_5(yz)$
$$= \log_5 x - \log_5(yz)^2$$
$$= \log_5 x - \log_5 y^2 z^2$$
$$= \log_5\frac{x}{y^2 z^2}$$

96. $\log_4 t - 3(\log_4 u + \log_4 v) = \log_4 t - 3\log_4(uv)$
$$= \log_4 t - \log_4(uv)^3$$
$$= \log_4 t - \log_4 u^3 v^3$$
$$= \log_4\frac{t}{u^3 v^3}$$

97. $3\ln t - 2(\ln r - \ln v) = \ln t^3 - 2\ln\left(\dfrac{r}{v}\right)$

$$= \ln t^3 - \ln\left(\dfrac{r}{v}\right)^2$$

$$= \ln t^3 - \ln\left(\dfrac{r^2}{v^2}\right)$$

$$= \ln\dfrac{t^3}{\dfrac{r^2}{v^2}}$$

$$= \ln\dfrac{t^3 v^2}{r^2}$$

98. $2\ln x - 3(\ln y - \ln z) = \ln x^2 - 3\ln\left(\dfrac{y}{z}\right)$

$$= \ln x^2 - \ln\left(\dfrac{y}{z}\right)^3$$

$$= \ln x^2 - \ln\dfrac{y^3}{z^3}$$

$$= \ln\dfrac{x^2}{\dfrac{y^3}{z^3}}$$

$$= \ln\dfrac{x^2 z^3}{y^3}$$

99. $\dfrac{1}{2}(3\log_4 x - 2\log_4 y + \log_4 z)$

$$= \dfrac{1}{2}(\log_4 x^3 - \log_4 y^2 + \log_4 z)$$

$$= \dfrac{1}{2}\left(\log_4 \dfrac{x^3}{y^2} + \log_4 z\right)$$

$$= \dfrac{1}{2}\log_4\left(\dfrac{x^3 z}{y^2}\right)$$

$$= \log_4\left(\dfrac{x^3 z}{y^2}\right)^{1/2}$$

$$= \log_4 \sqrt{\dfrac{x^3 z}{y^2}}$$

100. $\dfrac{1}{3}(4\log_5 t - 3\log_5 u - 3\log_5 v)$

$$= \dfrac{1}{3}(\log_5 t^4 - \log_5 u^3 - \log_5 v^3)$$

$$= \dfrac{1}{3}\left(\log_5 \dfrac{t^4}{u^3} - \log_5 v^3\right)$$

$$= \dfrac{1}{3}\log_5\left(\dfrac{t^4}{u^3 v^3}\right)$$

$$= \log_5\left(\dfrac{t^4}{u^3 v^3}\right)^{1/3}$$

$$= \log_5 \sqrt[3]{\dfrac{t^4}{u^3 v^3}}$$

101. $\ln 4 = 1.3863$

102. $\ln 6 = 1.7918$

103. $\ln\left(\dfrac{17}{6}\right) = \ln 17 - \ln 6 \approx 1.0415$

104. $\ln\left(\dfrac{13}{17}\right) = \ln 13 - \ln 17 \approx -0.2683$

105. $\log_8 6 = \dfrac{\log 6}{\log 8} \approx 0.8617$

106. $\log_4 8 = \dfrac{\log 8}{\log 4} = 1.5000$

107. $\log_5 30 = \dfrac{\log 30}{\log 5} \approx 2.1133$

108. $\log_6 28 = \dfrac{\log 28}{\log 6} \approx 1.8597$

109. $\log_3(0.5) = \dfrac{\log(0.5)}{\log 3} \approx -0.6309$

110. $\log_5(0.6) = \dfrac{\log 0.6}{\log 5} \approx -0.3174$

111. $\log_7(1.7) = \dfrac{\log 1.7}{\log 7} \approx 0.2727$

112. $\log_6(3.2) = \dfrac{\log 3.2}{\log 6} \approx 0.6492$

113. $\log_5 15 = \dfrac{\log 15}{\log 5} \approx 1.6826$

114. $\log_3 25 = \dfrac{\log 25}{\log 3} \approx 2.9299$

115. $\log_{12} 120 = \dfrac{\log 120}{\log 12} \approx 1.9266$

116. $\log_9 90 = \dfrac{\log 90}{\log 9} \approx 2.0480$

117. $\log_3(3x - 2) = \dfrac{\log(3x - 2)}{\log 3}$

118. $\log_5(x^2 + 4) = \dfrac{\log(x^2 + 4)}{\log 5}$

119. $\log_8(4 - 9x) = \dfrac{\log(4 - 9x)}{\log 8}$

120. $\log_7(3x^2) = \dfrac{\log 3x^2}{\log 7}$

121. $5\log_9(6x + 7) = 5\dfrac{\log(67x + 7)}{\log 9}$

$$= \dfrac{5}{\log 9}\log(6x + 7)$$

122. $3\log_2(2x^2 - x) = 3\dfrac{\log(2x^2 - x)}{\log 2}$

$\qquad\qquad\quad = \dfrac{3}{\log 2}\log(2x^2 - x)$

123. $\log_2(x + 5) = \dfrac{\ln(x + 5)}{\ln 2}$

124. $\log_4(3x + 4) = \dfrac{\ln(3x + 4)}{\ln 4}$

125. $\log_3(x^2 + 9) = \dfrac{\ln(x^2 + 9)}{\ln 3}$

126. $\log_7(9 - x^2) = \dfrac{\ln(9 - x^2)}{\ln 7}$

127. $7\log_8(10x - 7) = 7\dfrac{\ln(10x - 7)}{\ln 8}$

$\qquad\qquad\qquad = \dfrac{7}{\ln 8}\ln(10x - 7)$

128. $7\log_3(2x^2 - x) = 7\dfrac{\ln(2x^2 - x)}{\ln 3} = \dfrac{7}{\ln 3}\ln(2x^2 - x)$

Applying Concepts 10.2

129. $\log_8 x = 3\log_8 2$
$\log_8 x = \log_8 2^3$
$\log_8 x = \log_8 8$
$\qquad x = 8$
The solution is 8.

130. $\log_5 x = 2\log_5 3$
$\log_5 x = \log_5 3^2$
$\log_5 x = \log_5 9$
$\qquad x = 9$
The solution is 9.

131. $\log_4 x = \log_4 2 + \log_4 3$
$\log_4 x = \log_4(2 \cdot 3)$
$\log_4 x = \log_4 6$
$\qquad x = 6$
The solution is 6.

132. $\log_3 x = \log_3 4 + \log_3 7$
$\log_3 x = \log_3(4 \cdot 7)$
$\log_3 x = \log_3 28$
$\qquad x = 28$
The solution is 28.

133. $\log_6 x = 3\log_6 2 - \log_6 4$
$\log_6 x = \log_6 2^3 - \log_6 4$
$\log_6 x = \log_6 8 - \log_6 4$
$\log_6 x = \log_6\left(\dfrac{8}{4}\right)$
$\log_6 x = \log_6 2$
$\qquad x = 2$
The solution is 2.

134. $\log_9 x = 5\log_9 2 - \log_9 8$
$\log_9 x = \log_9 2^5 - \log_9 8$
$\log_9 x = \log_9 32 - \log_9 8$
$\log_9 x = \log_9\left(\dfrac{32}{8}\right)$
$\log_9 x = \log_9 4$
$\qquad x = 4$
The solution is 4.

135. $\log x = \dfrac{1}{3}\log 27$
$\log x = \log 27^{1/3}$
$\log x = \log \sqrt[3]{27}$
$\log x = \log 3$
$\qquad x = 3$
The solution is 3.

136. $\log_2 x = \dfrac{3}{2}\log_2 4$
$\log_2 x = \log_2 4^{3/2}$
$\log_2 x = \log_2 \left(\sqrt{4}\right)^3$
$\log_2 x = \log_2 2^3$
$\log_2 x = \log_2 8$
$\qquad x = 8$
The solution is 8.

137. **a.** $a^c = b$

b. $\text{antilog}_a(\log_a b) = \text{antilog}_a(c) = b$

138. $f(x) = 3\log_6(2x - 1)$
$f(7) = 3\log_6(2 \cdot 7 - 1) = 3\log_6 13 = 3\dfrac{\log 13}{\log 6} \approx 4.29$

139. $S(t) = 8\log_5(6t + 2)$
$S(2) = 8\log_5(6 \cdot 2 + 2)$
$\qquad = 8\log_5 14$
$\qquad = 8\dfrac{\log 14}{\log 5}$
$\qquad \approx 13.12$

140. $P(v) = -3\log_6(4 - 2v)$
$P(-4) = -3\log_6[4 - 2(-4)]$
$\qquad\quad = -3\log_6 12$
$\qquad\quad = -3\dfrac{\log 12}{\log 6}$
$\qquad\quad \approx -4.16$

141. $G(x) = -5\log_7(2x + 19)$
$G(-3) = -5\log_7[2(-3) + 19]$
$\qquad\quad = -5\log_7 13$
$\qquad\quad = -5\dfrac{\log 13}{\log 7}$
$\qquad\quad \approx -6.59$

142. $\log_2 (\log_2 x) = 3$
$$2^3 = \log_2 x$$
$$8 = \log_2 x$$
$$2^8 = x$$
$$256 = x$$
The solution is 256.

143. $\ln(\ln x) = 1$
$$e^1 = \ln x$$
$$e = \ln x$$
$$e^e = x$$
$$15.1543 \approx x$$
The solution is 15.1543.

144. a. $D = -\left(\dfrac{1}{5}\log_2 \dfrac{1}{5} + \dfrac{1}{5}\log_2 \dfrac{1}{5} + \dfrac{1}{5}\log_2 \dfrac{1}{5} + \dfrac{1}{5}\log_2 \dfrac{1}{5} + \dfrac{1}{5}\log_2 \dfrac{1}{5}\right) \approx 2.3219281$

The diversity of this ecosystem is 2.3219281.

b. $D = -\left(\dfrac{1}{8}\log_2 \dfrac{1}{8} + \dfrac{3}{8}\log_2 \dfrac{3}{8} + \dfrac{1}{16}\log_2 \dfrac{1}{16} + \dfrac{1}{8}\log_2 \dfrac{1}{8} + \dfrac{5}{16}\log_2 \dfrac{5}{16}\right) \approx 2.0550365$

The diversity of this ecosystem is 2.0550365.
This system has less diversity than the one given in Table 1.

c. $D = -\left(0\log_2 0 + \dfrac{1}{4}\log_2 \dfrac{1}{4} + 0\log_2 0 + 0\log_2 0 + \dfrac{3}{4}\log_2 \dfrac{3}{4}\right) \approx 0.8112781$

The diversity of this ecosystem is 0.8112781.
This system has less diversity than the one given in Table 2.

d. $D = -(0\log_2 0 + 0\log_2 0 + 0\log_2 0 + 0\log_2 0 + 1\log_2 1) = 0$

The diversity of this ecosystem is 0.
The system has only one species; therefore, there is no diversity in the system.

145. Let N be a number written in scientific notation with $N > 1$. That is, let $N = a \times 10^k$, where $1 \le a \le 10$ and $k \ge 1$. The number of digits required to write N in standard form is $k + 1$. For instance if $N = 5.43 \times 10^{12}$, then there are 13 digits required to write N in standard form. Now consider $\log(5.43 \times 10^{12}) \approx 12.7348$. The characteristic of the logarithm is the exponent when the number is written in scientific notation, which in turn is one less than the number of digits in the number when it is written in standard form.

In general, if $N = a \times 10^k$, then

$$\log N = \log(a \times 10^k)$$
$$= \log a + \log 10^k$$
$$= \log a + k \log 10$$
$$= \log a + k$$

where k is the place value of the number and is one less than the number of digits in the number.

Now let $N = 9^{(9)^9}$. Then $\log\left[9^{(9)^9}\right] = 9^9 \log 9 = 3.696931 \times 10^8$. The characteristic is approximately 370,000,000.

There are approximately 370,000,000 digits in the expansion of $9^{(9)^9}$.

Section 10.3

Concept Review 10.3

1. Never true
   The domain of $f(x) = \log_b x$ is $\{x \mid x > 0\}$

2. Always true

3. Always true

4. Never true
   The range of $f(x) = \ln x$ is
   $\{f(x) \mid f(x) \text{ is a real number}\}$

Objective 10.3.1 Exercises

1. Yes. Answers may vary. For example, it passes both the vertical line test and the horizontal line test.

2. Descriptions will vary. For example: The domain is the set of positive real numbers; the range is the set of real numbers. The graph never touches the y-axis. The x-intercept is $(1, 0)$.

3. They are the same graph.

4. They are mirror images of each other with respect to the line $y = x$.

5. $f(x) = \log_4 x$
   $y = \log_4 x$

   $y = \log_4 x$ is equivalent to $x = 4^y$.

6. $f(x) = \log_2(x+1)$
$\quad y = \log_2(x+1)$

$y = \log_2(x+1)$ is equivalent to $(x+1) = 2^y$ or
$x = 2^y - 1$.

7. $f(x) = \log_3(2x-1)$
$\quad y = \log_3(2x-1)$

$y = \log_3(2x-1)$ is equivalent to

$(2x-1) = 3^y,\ 2x = 3^y + 1,$ or $x = \frac{1}{2}(3^y + 1).$

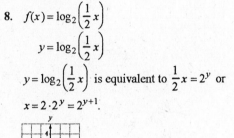

8. $f(x) = \log_2\left(\frac{1}{2}x\right)$

$\quad y = \log_2\left(\frac{1}{2}x\right)$

$y = \log_2\left(\frac{1}{2}x\right)$ is equivalent to $\frac{1}{2}x = 2^y$ or

$x = 2 \cdot 2^y = 2^{y+1}.$

9. $f(x) = 3\log_2 x$
$\quad y = 3\log_2 x$

$\quad \frac{y}{3} = \log_2 x$

$\frac{y}{3} = \log_2 x$ is equivalent to $x = 2^{y/3}.$

10. $f(x) = \frac{1}{2}\log_2 x$

$\quad y = \frac{1}{2}\log_2 x$

$\quad 2y = \log_2 x$

$2y = \log_2 x$ is equivalent to $x = 2^{2y}.$

11. $f(x) = -\log_2 x$
$\quad y = -\log_2 x$
$\quad -y = \log_2 x$

$-y = \log_2 x$ is equivalent to $x = 2^{-y}.$

12. $f(x) = -\log_3 x$
$\quad y = -\log_3 x$
$\quad -y = \log_3 x$

$-y = \log_3 x$ is equivalent to $x = 3^{-y}.$

13. $f(x) = \log_2(x-1)$
$\quad y = \log_2(x-1)$

$y = \log_2(x-1)$ is equivalent to $(x-1) = 2^y,$ or
$x = 2^y + 1.$

14. $f(x) = \log_3(2-x)$
$\quad y = \log_3(2-x)$

$y = \log_3(2-x)$ is equivalent to $(2-x) = 3^y,$ or
$x = 2^y + 1.$

15. $f(x) = -\log_2(x-1)$
$\quad y = -\log_2(x-1)$
$\quad -y = \log_2(x-1)$

$-y = \log_2(x-1)$ is equivalent to $(x-1) = 2^{-y},$ or
$x = 2^{-y} + 1.$

16. $f(x) = -\log_2(1-x)$

$\quad y = -\log_2(1-x)$

$\quad -y = \log_2(1-x)$

$-y = \log_2(1-x)$ is equivalent to $(1-x) = 2^{-y}$, or

$x = 1 - 2^{-y}$.

17. $f(x) = \log_2 x - 3$

$\quad y = \log_2 x - 3$

$\quad y = \dfrac{\log x}{\log 2} - 3$

$\quad y = \dfrac{\log x}{0.3010} - 3$

18. $f(x) = \log_3 x + 2$

$\quad y = \log_3 x + 2$

$\quad y = \dfrac{\log x}{\log 3} + 2$

$\quad y = \dfrac{\log x}{0.4771} + 2$

19. $f(x) = -\log_2 x + 2$

$\quad y = -\log_2 x + 2$

$\quad y = -\dfrac{\log x}{\log 2} + 2$

$\quad y = -\dfrac{\log x}{0.3010} + 2$

20. $f(x) = -\dfrac{1}{2}\log_2 x - 1$

$\quad y = -\dfrac{1}{2}\log_2 x - 1$

$\quad y = -\dfrac{\log x}{2\log 2} - 1$

$\quad y = -\dfrac{\log x}{0.6020} - 1$

21. $f(x) = x - \log_2(1-x)$

$\quad y = x - \log_2(1-x)$

$\quad y = x - \dfrac{\log(1-x)}{\log 2}$

$\quad y = x - \dfrac{\log(1-x)}{0.3010}$

22. $f(x) = x + \log_3(2-x)$

$\quad y = x + \log_3(2-x)$

$\quad = x + \dfrac{\log(2-x)}{\log 3}$

$\quad = x + \dfrac{\log(2-x)}{0.4771}$

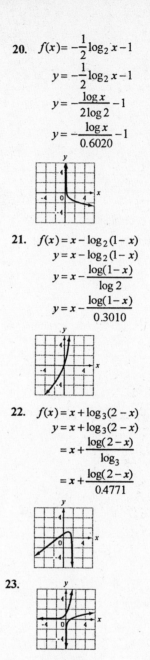

23.

24.

25.

26.

Applying Concepts 10.3

27. a. $S = 60 - 7 \ln(t + 1)$

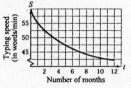

Typing speed (in words/min)

Number of months

b. After 4 months without typing practice, a typist's proficiency decreases to 49 words per minute.

28. a. $M = 5 \log s - 5$

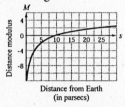

Distance modulus

Distance from Earth (in parsecs)

b. When a star has a distance modulus of $M = 2$, it is 25.1 parsecs away from Earth.

29. a.

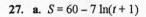

Interest rate (as a percent)

Term (in years)

b. $y = 13$ when $x \approx 8.5$.
A security that has a yield of 13% has a term of 8.5 years.

c. When $x = 30$, $y \approx 12.2$.
The model predicts an interest rate of 12.2%.

30. linear

31. quadratic

32. exponential

33. linear

34. quadratic

35. exponential

36. logarithmic

37. logarithmic

38. As shown below, the graphs are not the same. The problem is that $\ln x^2 = 2 \ln x$ if an only if $x > 0$. The domain of $\ln x^2$ is all nonzero real numbers, whereas the domain of $2 \ln x$ is all positive real numbers.

$f(x) = 2 \ln x$

$f(x) = \ln x^2$

39. This is similar to the previous exercise. The graphs of $f(x) = e^{\ln x}$ and $g(x) = \ln e^x$ are shown below. The function f is defined for $x > 0$, whereas g is defined for all x

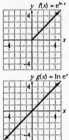

Section 10.4

Concept Review 10.4

1. Always true

2. Never true
   $\log x + \log(x+2) = \log(x)(x+2) = \log(x^2 + 2x)$

3. Never true
   The logarithm of a negative number is not defined.

4. Always true

5. Always true

6. Always true

Objective 10.4.1 Exercises

1. An exponential equation is one in which a variable occurs in an exponent.

2. **a.** The Equality of Exponents Property states that for $b > 0$, $b \neq 1$, if $b^u = b^v$, then $u = v$.

   b. This property is used to solve exponential equations in which each side of the equation can be expressed in terms of the same base.

3. $5^{4x-1} = 5^{x+2}$
   $4x - 1 = x + 2$
   $3x - 1 = 2$
   $3x = 3$
   $x = 1$
   The solution is 1.

4. $7^{4x-3} = 7^{2x+1}$
   $4x - 3 = 2x + 1$
   $2x - 3 = 1$
   $2x = 4$
   $x = 2$
   The solution is 2.

5. $8^{x-4} = 8^{5x+8}$
   $x - 4 = 5x + 8$
   $-4x - 4 = 8$
   $-4x = 12$
   $x = -3$
   The solution is −3.

6. $10^{4x-5} = 10^{x+4}$
   $4x - 5 = x + 4$
   $3x - 5 = 4$
   $3x = 9$
   $x = 3$
   The solution is 3.

7. $5^x = 6$
   $\log 5^x = \log 6$
   $x \log 5 = \log 6$
   $x = \dfrac{\log 6}{\log 5}$
   $x \approx 1.1133$
   The solution is 1.1133.

8. $7^x = 10$
   $\log 7^x = \log 10$
   $x \log 7 = \log 10$
   $x = \dfrac{\log 10}{\log 7}$
   $x \approx 1.1833$
   The solution is 1.1833.

9. $12^x = 6$
   $\log 12^x = \log 6$
   $x \log 12 = \log 6$
   $x = \dfrac{\log 6}{\log 12}$
   $x \approx 0.7211$
   The solution is 0.7211.

10. $10^x = 5$
    $\log 10^x = \log 5$
    $x \log 10 = \log 5$
    $x = \dfrac{\log 5}{\log 10}$
    $x \approx 0.6990$
    The solution is 0.6990.

11. $\left(\dfrac{1}{2}\right)^x = 3$
    $\log\left(\dfrac{1}{2}\right)^x = \log 3$
    $x \log\left(\dfrac{1}{2}\right) = \log 3$
    $x = \dfrac{\log 3}{\log \frac{1}{2}}$
    $x = \dfrac{\log 3}{\log 0.5}$
    $x \approx -1.5850$
    The solution is −1.5850.

12.
$$\left(\frac{1}{3}\right)^x = 2$$
$$\log\left(\frac{1}{3}\right)^x = \log 2$$
$$x\log\left(\frac{1}{3}\right) = \log 2$$
$$x = \frac{\log 2}{\log \frac{1}{3}}$$
$$x = \frac{\log 2}{\log 1 - \log 3}$$
$$x \approx -0.6309$$
The solution is -0.6309.

13.
$$1.5^x = 2$$
$$\log 1.5^x = \log 2$$
$$x\log 1.5 = \log 2$$
$$x = \frac{\log 2}{\log 1.5}$$
$$x \approx 1.7095$$
The solution is 1.7095.

14.
$$2.7^x = 3$$
$$\log 2.7^x = \log 3$$
$$x\log 2.7 = \log 3$$
$$x = \frac{\log 3}{\log 2.7}$$
$$x \approx 1.1061$$
The solution is 1.1061.

15.
$$10^x = 21$$
$$\log 10^x = \log 21$$
$$x\log 10 = \log 21$$
$$x = \frac{\log 21}{\log 10}$$
$$x \approx 1.3222$$
The solution is 1.3222.

16.
$$10^x = 37$$
$$\log 10^x = \log 37$$
$$x\log 10 = \log 37$$
$$x = \frac{\log 37}{\log 10}$$
$$x \approx 1.5682$$
The solution is 1.5682.

17.
$$2^{-x} = 7$$
$$\log 2^{-x} = \log 7$$
$$-x\log 2 = \log 7$$
$$-x = \frac{\log 7}{\log 2}$$
$$x = -\frac{\log 7}{\log 2}$$
$$x \approx -2.8074$$
The solution is -2.8074.

18.
$$3^{-x} = 14$$
$$\log 3^{-x} = \log 14$$
$$-x\log 3 = \log 14$$
$$-x = \frac{\log 14}{\log 3}$$
$$x = -\frac{\log 14}{\log 3}$$
$$x \approx -2.4022$$
The solution is -2.4022.

19.
$$2^{x-1} = 6$$
$$\log 2^{x-1} = \log 6$$
$$(x-1)\log 2 = \log 6$$
$$x-1 = \frac{\log 6}{\log 2}$$
$$x = \frac{\log 6}{\log 1} + 1$$
$$x \approx 3.5850$$
The solution is 3.5850.

20.
$$4^{x+1} = 9$$
$$\log 4^{x+1} = \log 9$$
$$(x+1)\log 4 = \log 9$$
$$x+1 = \frac{\log 9}{\log 4}$$
$$x = \frac{\log 9}{\log 4} - 1$$
$$x \approx 0.5850$$
The solution is 0.5850.

21.
$$3^{2x-1} = 4$$
$$\log 3^{2x-1} = \log 4$$
$$(2x-1)\log 3 = \log 4$$
$$2x-1 = \frac{\log 4}{\log 3}$$
$$2x = \frac{\log 4}{\log 3} + 1$$
$$x = \frac{1}{2}\left(\frac{\log 4}{\log 3} + 1\right)$$
$$x \approx 1.1309$$
The solution is 1.1309.

22.
$$4^{-x+2} = 12$$
$$\log 4^{-x+2} = \log 12$$
$$(-x+2)\log 4 = \log 12$$
$$-x+2 = \frac{\log 12}{\log 4}$$
$$-x = \frac{\log 12}{\log 4} - 2$$
$$x = -\left(\frac{\log 12}{\log 4} - 2\right)$$
$$x \approx 0.2075$$
The solution is 0.2075.

23.
$$9^x = 3^{x+1}$$
$$3^{2x} = 3^{x+1}$$
$$2x = x+1$$
$$x = 1$$
The solution is 1.

24.
$$2^{x-1} = 4^x$$
$$2^{x-1} = 2^{2x}$$
$$x-1 = 2x$$
$$-1 = x$$
The solution is −1.

25.
$$8^{x+2} = 16^x$$
$$(2^3)^{x+2} = 2^{4x}$$
$$2^{3x+6} = 2^{4x}$$
$$3x+6 = 4x$$
$$6 = x$$
The solution is 6.

26.
$$9^{3x} = 81^{x-4}$$
$$(3^2)^{3x} = (3^4)^{x-4}$$
$$3^{6x} = 3^{4x-16}$$
$$6x = 4x-16$$
$$2x = -16$$
$$x = -8$$
The solution is −8.

27.
$$5^{x^2} = 21$$
$$\log 5^{x^2} = \log 21$$
$$x^2 \log 5 = \log 21$$
$$x^2 = \frac{\log 21}{\log 5}$$
$$x = \pm\sqrt{\frac{\log 21}{\log 5}}$$
$$x = \pm 1.3754$$
The solutions are 1.3754 and −1.3754.

28.
$$3^{x^2} = 40$$
$$\log 3^{x^2} = \log 40$$
$$x^2 \log 3 = \log 40$$
$$x^2 = \frac{\log 40}{\log 3}$$
$$x = \pm\sqrt{\frac{\log 40}{\log 3}}$$
$$x = \pm 1.8324$$
The solutions are 1.8324 and −1.8324.

29.
$$2^{4x-2} = 20$$
$$\log 2^{4x-2} = \log 20$$
$$(4x-2)\log 2 = \log 20$$
$$4x-2 = \frac{\log 20}{\log 2}$$
$$4x = \frac{\log 20}{\log 2} + 2$$
$$x = \frac{1}{4}\left(\frac{\log 20}{\log 2} + 2\right)$$
$$x = 1.5805$$
The solution is 1.5805.

30.
$$4^{3x+8} = 12$$
$$\log 4^{3x+8} = \log 12$$
$$(3x+8)\log 4 = \log 12$$
$$3x+8 = \frac{\log 12}{\log 4}$$
$$3x = \frac{\log 12}{\log 4} - 8$$
$$x = \frac{1}{3}\left(\frac{\log 12}{\log 4} - 8\right)$$
$$x \approx -2.0692$$
The solution is −2.0692.

31.
$$3^{-x+2} = 18$$
$$\log 3^{-x+2} = \log 18$$
$$(-x+2)\log 3 = \log 18$$
$$-x+2 = \frac{\log 18}{\log 3}$$
$$-x = \frac{\log 18}{\log 3} - 2$$
$$x = -\frac{\log 18}{\log 3} + 2$$
$$x \approx -0.6309$$
The solution is −0.6309.

32.
$$5^{-x+1} = 15$$
$$\log 5^{-x+1} = \log 15$$
$$(-x+1)\log 5 = \log 15$$
$$-x+1 = \frac{\log 15}{\log 5}$$
$$-x = \frac{\log 15}{\log 5} - 1$$
$$x = -\frac{\log 15}{\log 5} + 1$$
$$x \approx -0.6826$$
The solution is −0.6826.

33. $4^{2x} = 100$
$\log 4^{2x} = \log 100$
$2x \log 4 = 2$
$2x = \dfrac{2}{\log 4}$
$x = \dfrac{1}{2}\left(\dfrac{2}{\log 4}\right) = \dfrac{1}{\log 4}$
$x \approx 1.6610$
The solution is 1.6610.

34. $3^{3x} = 1000$
$\log 3^{3x} = \log 1000$
$3x \log 3 = 3$
$3x = \dfrac{3}{\log 3}$
$x = \dfrac{1}{3}\left(\dfrac{3}{\log 3}\right) = \dfrac{1}{\log 3}$
$x = 2.0959$
The solution is 2.0959.

35. $2.5^{-x} = 4$
$\log 2.5^{-x} = \log 4$
$-x \log 2.5 = \log 4$
$-x = \dfrac{\log 4}{\log 2.5}$
$x = -\dfrac{\log 4}{\log 2.5}$
$x \approx -1.5129$
The solution is −1.5129.

36. $3.25^{x+1} = 4.2$
$\log 3.25^{x+1} = \log 4.2$
$(x+1)\log 3.25 = \log 4.2$
$x+1 = \dfrac{\log 4.2}{\log 3.25}$
$x = \dfrac{\log 4.2}{\log 3.25} - 1$
$x = 0.2176$
The solution is 0.2176.

37. $0.25^{x} = 0.125$
$\log 0.25^{x} = \log 0.125$
$x \log 0.25 = \log 0.125$
$x = \dfrac{\log 0.125}{\log 0.25}$
$x = 1.5$
The solution is 1.5.

38. $0.1^{5x} = 10^{-2}$
$\log 0.1^{5x} = \log 10^{-2}$
$5x \log 0.1 = -2$
$5x = \dfrac{-2}{\log 0.1}$
$x = \dfrac{-2}{5 \log 0.1}$
$x = \dfrac{-2}{5(-1)}$
$x = 0.4$
The solution is 0.4.

39. $3^{x} = 2$
$3^{x} - 2 = 0$
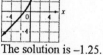
The solution is 0.63.

40. $5^{x} = 9$
$5^{x} - 9 = 0$
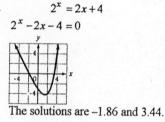
The solution is 1.37.

41. $2^{x} = 2x + 4$
$2^{x} - 2x - 4 = 0$

The solutions are −1.86 and 3.44.

42. $3^{x} = -x - 1$
$3^{x} + x + 1 = 0$

The solution is −1.25.

43. $e^{x} = -2x - 2$
$e^{x} + 2x + 2 = 0$
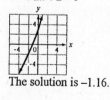
The solution is −1.16.

44.
$$e^x = 3x + 4$$
$$e^x - 3x - 4 = 0$$

The solutions are -1.24 and 2.42.

Objective 10.4.2 Exercises

45. A logarithmic equation is an equation in which one or more of the terms is a logarithmic expression.

46. The 1–1 Property of Logarithms states that for $x > 0, y > 0, b > 0, b \neq 1$, if $\log_b x = \log_b y$ then $x = y$.

47. $\log_3 (x + 1) = 2$
Rewrite in exponential form.
$$3^2 = x + 1$$
$$9 = x + 1$$
$$8 = x$$
The solution is 8.

48. $\log_5 (x - 1) = 1$
Rewrite in exponential form.
$$5^1 = x - 1$$
$$5 = x - 1$$
$$6 = x$$
The solution is 6.

49. $\log_2 (2x - 3) = 3$
Rewrite an exponential form.
$$2^3 = 2x - 3$$
$$8 = 2x - 3$$
$$11 = 2x$$
$$\frac{11}{2} = x$$
The solution is $\frac{11}{2}$.

50. $\log_4 (3x + 1) = 2$
Rewrite in exponential form.
$$4^2 = 3x + 1$$
$$16 = 3x + 1$$
$$15 = 3x$$
$$5 = x$$
The solution is 5.

51. $\log_2 (x^2 + 2x) = 3$
Rewrite in exponential form.
$$2^3 = x^2 + 2x$$
$$8 = x^2 + 2x$$
$$0 = x^2 + 2x - 8$$
$$0 = (x + 4)(x - 2)$$
$$x + 4 = 0 \qquad x - 2 = 0$$
$$x = -4 \qquad x = 2$$
The solutions are -4 and 2.

52. $\log_3 (x^2 + 6x) = 3$
Rewrite in exponential form.
$$3^3 = x^2 + 6x$$
$$27 = x^2 + 6x$$
$$0 = x^2 + 6x - 27$$
$$0 = (x + 9)(x - 3)$$
$$x + 9 = 0 \qquad x - 3 = 0$$
$$x = -9 \qquad x = 3$$
The solutions are -9 and 3.

53. $\log_5 \dfrac{2x}{x - 1} = 1$
Rewrite in exponential form.
$$5^1 = \frac{2x}{x - 1}$$
$$(x - 1)5 = (x - 1)\frac{2x}{x - 1}$$
$$5x - 5 = 2x$$
$$3x - 5 = 0$$
$$3x = 5$$
$$x = \frac{5}{3}$$
The solution is $\frac{5}{3}$.

54. $\log_6 \dfrac{3x}{x + 1} = 1$
Rewrite in exponential form.
$$6^1 = \frac{3x}{x + 1}$$
$$(x + 1)6 = (x + 1)\frac{3x}{x + 1}$$
$$6x + 6 = 3x$$
$$3x + 6 = 0$$
$$3x = -6$$
$$x = -2$$
The solution is -2.

55. $\log_7 x = \log_7 (1 - x)$
Use the fact that if $\log_b u = \log_b v$, then $u = v$.
$$x = 1 - x$$
$$2x = 1$$
$$x = \frac{1}{2}$$
The solution is $\frac{1}{2}$.

56. $\dfrac{3}{4} \log x = 3$
$$\log x^{3/4} = 3$$
Rewrite in exponential form.
$$10^3 = x^{3/4}$$
$$(10^3)^{4/3} = (x^{3/4})^{4/3}$$
$$10^4 = x$$
The solution is 10,000.

57. $\dfrac{2}{3}\log x = 6$

$\log x^{2/3} = 6$

Rewrite in exponential form.

$10^6 = x^{2/3}$

$(10^6)^{3/2} = (x^{2/3})^{3/2}$

$10^9 = x$

The solution is 1,000,000,000.

58. $\log(x-2) - \log x = 3$

$\log\dfrac{x-2}{x} = 3$

Rewrite in exponential form.

$10^3 = \dfrac{x-2}{x}$

$1000 = \dfrac{x-2}{x}$

$x \cdot 1000 = x \cdot \dfrac{x-2}{x}$

$1000x = x - 2$

$999x = -2$

$x = -\dfrac{2}{999}$

$-\dfrac{2}{999}$ does not check as a solution. The equation has no solution.

59. $\log_2(x-3) + \log_2(x+4) = 3$

$\log_2(x-3)(x+4) = 3$

Rewrite in exponential form.

$(x-3)(x+4) = 2^3$

$x^2 + x - 12 = 8$

$x^2 + x - 20 = 0$

$(x-4)(x+5) = 0$

$x - 4 = 0 \qquad\qquad x + 5 = 0$

$x = 4 \qquad\qquad\quad x = -5$

-5 does not check as a solution. The solution is 4.

60. $\qquad\quad \log x - 2 = \log(x-4)$

$\log x - \log(x-4) = 2$

$\log\dfrac{x}{x-4} = 2$

Rewrite in exponential form.

$10^2 = \dfrac{x}{x-4}$

$100 = \dfrac{x}{x-4}$

$100(x-4) = \dfrac{x}{x-4}(x-4)$

$100x - 400 = x$

$99x = 400$

$x = \dfrac{400}{99}$

The solution is $\dfrac{400}{99}$.

61. $\log_3 x + \log_3(x-1) = \log_3 6$

$\log_3 x(x-1) = \log_3 6$

Use the fact that if $\log_b u = \log_b v$, then $u = v$.

$x(x-1) = 6$

$x^2 - x = 6$

$x^2 - x - 6 = 0$

$(x+2)(x-3) = 0$

$x + 2 = 0 \qquad\qquad x - 3 = 0$

$x = -2 \qquad\qquad\quad x = 3$

-2 does not check as a solution. The solution is 3.

62. $\log_4 x + \log_4(x-2) = \log_4 15$

$\log_4 x(x-2) = \log_4 15$

Use the fact that if $\log_b u = \log_b v$, then $u = v$.

$x(x-2) = 15$

$x^2 - 2x = 15$

$x^2 - 2x - 15 = 0$

$(x+3)(x-5) = 0$

$x + 3 = 0 \qquad\qquad x - 5 = 0$

$x = -3 \qquad\qquad\quad x = 5$

-3 does not check as a solution. The solution is 5.

63. $\log_2(8x) - \log_2(x^2 - 1) = \log_2 3$

$\log_2\left(\dfrac{8x}{x^2-1}\right) = \log_2 3$

Use the fact that if $\log_b u = \log_b v$, then $u = v$.

$\dfrac{8x}{x^2-1} = 3$

$(x^2-1)\dfrac{8x}{x^2-1} = (x^2-1)3$

$8x = 3x^2 - 3$

$0 = 3x^2 - 8x - 3$

$0 = (3x+1)(x-3)$

$3x + 1 = 0 \qquad\qquad x - 3 = 0$

$3x = -1 \qquad\qquad\quad x = 3$

$x = -\dfrac{1}{3}$

$-\dfrac{1}{3}$ does not check as a solution. The solution is 3.

64. $\log_5(3x) - \log_5(x^2 - 1) = \log_5 2$

$$\log_5\left(\frac{3x}{x^2 - 1}\right) = \log_5 2$$

Use the fact that if $\log_b u = \log_b v$, then $u = v$.

$$\frac{3x}{x^2 - 1} = 2$$

$$(x^2 - 1)\frac{3x}{x^2 - 1} = (x^2 - 1)2$$

$$3x = 2x^2 - 2$$

$$0 = 2x^2 - 3x - 2$$

$$0 = (2x + 1)(x - 2)$$

$2x + 1 = 0 \qquad x - 2 = 0$

$2x = -1 \qquad x = 2$

$$x = -\frac{1}{2}$$

$-\dfrac{1}{2}$ does not check as a solution. The solution is 2.

65. $\log_9 x + \log_9(2x - 3) = \log_9 2$

$\log_9 x(2x - 3) = \log_9 2$

Use the fact that if $\log_b u = \log_b v$, then $u = v$.

$$x(2x - 3) = 2$$

$$2x^2 - 3x = 2$$

$$2x^2 - 3x - 2 = 0$$

$$(2x + 1)(x - 2) = 0$$

$2x + 1 = 0 \qquad x - 2 = 0$

$2x = -1 \qquad x = 2$

$$x = -\frac{1}{2}$$

$-\dfrac{1}{2}$ does not check as a solution. The solution is 2.

66. $\log_6 x + \log_6(3x - 5) = \log_6 2$

$\log_6 x(3x - 5) = \log_6 2$

Use the fact that if $\log_b u = \log_b v$, then $u = v$.

$$x(3x - 5) = 2$$

$$3x^2 - 5x = 2$$

$$3x^2 - 5x - 2 = 0$$

$$(3x + 1)(x - 2) = 0$$

$3x + 1 = 0 \qquad x - 2 = 0$

$3x = -1 \qquad x = 2$

$$x = -\frac{1}{3}$$

$-\dfrac{1}{3}$ does not check as a solution. The solution is 2.

67. $\log_8(6x) = \log_8 2 + \log_8(x - 4)$

$\log_8(6x) = \log_8 2(x - 4)$

Use the fact that if $\log_b u = \log_b v$, then $u = v$.

$$6x = 2(x - 4)$$

$$6x = 2x - 8$$

$$4x = -8$$

$$x = -2$$

-2 does not check as a solution. The equation has no solution.

68. $\log_7(5x) = \log_7 3 + \log_7(2x + 1)$

$\log_7(5x) = \log_7 3(2x + 1)$

Use the fact that if $\log_b u = \log_b v$, then $u = v$.

$$5x = 3(2x + 1)$$

$$5x = 6x + 3$$

$$-x = 3$$

$$x = -3$$

-3 does not check as a solution. The equation has no solution.

69. $\log_9(7x) = \log_9 2 + \log_9(x^2 - 2)$

$\log_9(7x) = \log_9 2(x^2 - 2)$

Use the fact that if $\log_b u = \log_b v$, then $u = v$.

$$7x = 2(x^2 - 2)$$

$$7x = 2x^2 - 4$$

$$0 = 2x^2 - 7x - 4$$

$$0 = (2x + 1)(x - 4)$$

$2x + 1 = 0 \qquad x - 4 = 0$

$2x = -1 \qquad x = 4$

$$x = -\frac{1}{2}$$

$-\dfrac{1}{2}$ does not check as a solution. The solution is 4.

70. $\log_3 x = \log_3 2 + \log_3(x^2 - 3)$

$\log_3 x = \log_3 2(x^2 - 3)$

Use the fact that if $\log_b u = \log_b v$, then $u = v$.

$$x = 2(x^2 - 3)$$

$$x = 2x^2 - 6$$

$$0 = 2x^2 - x - 6$$

$$0 = (2x + 3)(x - 2)$$

$2x + 3 = 0 \qquad x - 2 = 0$

$2x = -3 \qquad x = 2$

$$x = -\frac{3}{2}$$

$-\dfrac{3}{2}$ does not check as a solution. The solution is 2.

71. $\log(x^2+3)-\log(x+1)=\log 5$

$$\log\left(\frac{x^2+3}{x+1}\right)=\log 5$$

Use the fact that if $\log_b u = \log_b v$, then $u = v$.

$$\frac{x^2+3}{x+1}=5$$

$$(x+1)\left(\frac{x^2+3}{x+1}\right)=(x+1)5$$

$$x^2+3=5x+5$$

$$x^2-5x-2=0$$

$$x=\frac{-(-5)\pm\sqrt{(-5)^2-4(1)(-2)}}{2(1)}$$

$$=\frac{5\pm\sqrt{25+8}}{2}$$

$$=\frac{5\pm\sqrt{33}}{2}$$

The solutions are $\dfrac{5+\sqrt{33}}{2}$ and $\dfrac{5-\sqrt{33}}{2}$.

72. $\log(x+3)+\log(2x-4)=\log 3$

$\log(x+3)(2x-4)=\log 3$

Use the fact that if $\log_b u = \log_b v$, then $u = v$.

$(x+3)(2x-4)=3$

$2x^2+2x-12=3$

$2x^2+2x-15=0$

$$x=\frac{-2\pm\sqrt{2^2-4(2)(-15)}}{2(2)}$$

$$=\frac{-2\pm\sqrt{4+120}}{4}$$

$$=\frac{-2\pm\sqrt{124}}{4}$$

$$=\frac{-2\pm 2\sqrt{31}}{4}$$

$$=\frac{-1\pm\sqrt{31}}{2}$$

$\dfrac{-1-\sqrt{31}}{2}$ does not check as a solution. The solution is $\dfrac{-1+\sqrt{31}}{2}$.

73. $\log x = -x+2$

$\log x + x - 2 = 0$

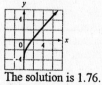

The solution is 1.76.

74. $\log x = -2x$

$\log x + 2x = 0$

The solution is 0.28.

75. $\log(2x-1)=-x+3$

$\log(2x-1)+x-3=0$

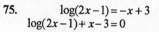

The solution is 2.42.

76. $\log(x+4)=-2x+1$

$\log(x+4)+2x-1=0$

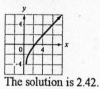

The solution is 0.19.

77. $\ln(x+2)=x^2-3$

$\ln(x+2)-x^2+3=0$

The solutions are -1.51 and 2.10.

78. $\ln x = -x^2+1$

$\ln(x)+x^2-1=0$

The solution is 1.00.

Applying Concepts 10.4

79. $8^{x/2}=6$

$\log 8^{x/2}=\log 6$

$$\frac{x}{2}\log 8=\log 6$$

$$\frac{x}{2}=\frac{\log 6}{\log 8}$$

$$x=\frac{2\log 6}{\log 8}$$

$$x=1.7233$$

The solution is 1.7233.

80.
$$4^{x/3} = 2$$
$$(2^2)^{x/3} = 2$$
$$2^{2x/3} = 2^1$$
$$\frac{2}{3}x = 1$$
$$x = \frac{3}{2} = 1.5$$
The solution is 1.5.

81.
$$5^{3x/2} = 7$$
$$\log 5^{3x/2} = \log 7$$
$$\frac{3x}{2}\log 5 = \log 7$$
$$\frac{3x}{2} = \frac{\log 7}{\log 5}$$
$$x = \frac{2\log 7}{3\log 5}$$
$$x = 0.8060$$
The solution is 0.8060.

82.
$$9^{2x/3} = 8$$
$$\log 9^{2x/3} = \log 8$$
$$\frac{2x}{3}\log 9 = \log 8$$
$$\frac{2x}{3} = \frac{\log 8}{\log 9}$$
$$x = \frac{3\log 8}{2\log 9}$$
$$x = 1.4196$$
The solution is 1.4196.

83.
$$1.2^{(x/2)-1} = 1.4$$
$$\log 1.2^{(x/2)-1} = \log 1.4$$
$$\left(\frac{x}{2}-1\right)(\log 1.2) = \log 1.4$$
$$\frac{x}{2}-1 = \frac{\log 1.4}{\log 1.2}$$
$$\frac{x}{2} = \frac{\log 1.4}{\log 1.2}+1$$
$$x = 2\left[\frac{\log 1.4}{\log 1.2}+1\right]$$
$$x = 5.6910$$

84.
$$5.6^{(x/3)+1} = 7.8$$
$$\log 5.6^{(x/3)+1} = \log 7.8$$
$$\left(\frac{x}{3}+1\right)(\log 5.6) = \log 7.8$$
$$\frac{x}{3}+1 = \frac{\log 7.8}{\log 5.6}$$
$$\frac{x}{3} = \frac{\log 7.8}{\log 5.6}-1$$
$$x = 3\left[\frac{\log 7.8}{\log 5.6}-1\right]$$
$$x = 0.5770$$
The solution is 0.5770.

85.
$$4^x = 7$$
$$\log 4^x = \log 7$$
$$x\log 4 = \log 7$$
$$x = \frac{\log 7}{\log 4}$$
$$x \approx 1.4036775$$
$$2^{(6x+3)} = 2^{(6 \cdot 1.4036775+3)}$$
$$= 2^{11.422065}$$
$$= 2744$$

86. a.

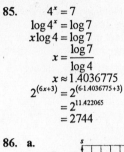

b. It will take the object approximately 2.86 s to fall 125 ft.

87. a.

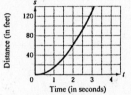

b. It will take the object approximately 2.64 s to fall 100 ft.

88. The error is in the second step. Because $\log 0.2 < 0$, multiplying each side of the inequality by this quantity changes the direction of the inequality.

Section 10.5

Concept Review 10.5

1. Always true

2. Never true
   Compound interest is interest that is computed not only on the original principal but also on the interest already earned.

3. Always true

4. Always true

Objective 10.5.1 Exercises

1. Exponential decay is an example of an exponential equation in which the value of the dependent variable decreases exponentially as the value of the independent variable increases.

2. Simple interest is computed on the principal amount only. Compound interest is computed not only the original principal but also on the interest already earned. Compound interest is an example of exponential growth.

3. Strategy

To find the value of the investment, solve the compound interest formula for P. Use $A = 1000$, $n = 8$, and $i = \dfrac{8\%}{4} = \dfrac{0.08}{4} = 0.02$.

Solution

$P = A(1 + i)^n$
$P = 1000(1 + 0.02)^8$
$P = 1000(1.02)^8$
$P \approx 1172$

The value of the investment after 2 years is $1172.

4. Strategy

To find the value of the investment, solve the compound interest formula for P. Use $A = 2500$, $n = 36$, and $i = \dfrac{7.5\%}{12} = \dfrac{0.075}{12} = 0.00625$.

Solution

$P = A(1 + i)^n$
$P = 2500(1 + 0.00625)^{36}$
$P = 2500(1.00625)^{36}$
$P \approx 3128.62$

The value of the investment after 3 years is $3128.62.

5. Strategy

To find the number of years, solve the compound interest formula for y. Use $P = 15,000$, $A = 5,000$, $n = 12y$, and $i = \dfrac{6\%}{12} = \dfrac{0.06}{12} = 0.005$.

Solution

$$P = A(1 + i)^n$$
$$15,000 = 5,000(1 + 0.005)^{12y}$$
$$3 = (1.005)^{12y}$$
$$\log 3 = \log(1.005)^{12y}$$
$$\log 3 = 12y \log(1.005)$$
$$\frac{\log 3}{12 \log(1.005)} = y$$
$$18 \approx y$$

In approximately 18 years the investment will be worth $15,000.

6. Strategy

To find the number of years, solve the compound interest formula for y. Use $P = 15,000$, $A = 10,000$, $n = 12y$, and $i = \dfrac{9\%}{12} = \dfrac{0.09}{12} = 0.0075$.

Solution

$$P = A(1 + i)^n$$
$$15,000 = 10,000(1 + 0.0075)^{12y}$$
$$1.5 = (1.0075)^{12y}$$
$$\log 1.5 = \log(1.0075)^{12y}$$
$$\log 1.5 = 12y \log(1.0075)$$
$$\frac{\log 1.5}{12 \log(1.0075)} = y$$
$$5 \approx y$$

In approximately 5 years the investment will be worth $15,000.

7. a. Strategy

To find the level after 3 h, solve for A in the exponential decay equation. Use $A_0 = 30$, $t = 3$, and $k = 6$.

Solution

$$A = A_0 \left(\frac{1}{2}\right)^{t/k}$$
$$A = 30 \left(\frac{1}{2}\right)^{3/6}$$
$$A = 21.2$$

After 3 h, the level will be 21.2 mg.

b. Strategy

To find the time, solve for t in the exponential decay equation. Use $k = 6$, $A_0 = 30$, and $A = 20$.

Solution

$$A = A_0 \left(\frac{1}{2}\right)^{t/k}$$
$$20 = 30 \left(\frac{1}{2}\right)^{t/6}$$
$$0.\overline{6} = \left(\frac{1}{2}\right)^{t/6}$$
$$0.\overline{6} = (0.5)^{t/6}$$
$$\log(0.\overline{6}) = \log(0.5)^{t/6}$$
$$\log(0.\overline{6}) = \frac{t}{6} \log(0.5)$$
$$\frac{\log(0.\overline{6})}{\log(0.5)} = \frac{t}{6}$$
$$\frac{6 \log(0.\overline{6})}{\log(0.5)} = t$$
$$3.510 = t$$

It will take 3.5 hours for the injection to decay to 20 mg.

8. a. Strategy
To find the level after 5 days, solve for A in the exponential decay equation. Use $A_0 = 8$, $t = 5$, and $k = 8$.

Solution

$$A = A_0 \left(\frac{1}{2}\right)^{t/k}$$

$$A = 8 \left(\frac{1}{2}\right)^{5/8}$$

$$A = 5.2$$

After 5 days, the level will be 5.2 micrograms.

b. Strategy
To find the time, solve for t in the exponential decay equation. Use $k = 8$, $A_0 = 8$, and $A = 5$.

Solution

$$A = A_0 \left(\frac{1}{2}\right)^{t/k}$$

$$5 = 8 \left(\frac{1}{2}\right)^{t/8}$$

$$0.625 = \left(\frac{1}{2}\right)^{t/8}$$

$$0.625 = (0.5)^{t/8}$$

$$\log(0.625) = \log(0.5)^{t/8}$$

$$\log(0.625) = \frac{t}{8}\log(0.5)$$

$$\frac{\log(0.625)}{\log(0.5)} = \frac{t}{8}$$

$$\frac{8\log(0.625)}{\log 0.5} = t$$

$$5.4246 = t$$

It will take 5.4 days for the injection to decay to 5 micrograms.

9. Strategy
To find the half-life, solve for k in the exponential decay equation. Use $A_0 = 25$, $A = 18.95$, and $t = 1$.

Solution

$$A = A_0 \left(\frac{1}{2}\right)^{t/k}$$

$$18.95 = 25 \left(\frac{1}{2}\right)^{1/k}$$

$$0.758 = \left(\frac{1}{2}\right)^{1/k}$$

$$0.758 = (0.5)^{1/k}$$

$$\log(0.758) = \log(0.5)^{1/k}$$

$$\log(0.758) = \frac{1}{k}\log(0.5)$$

$$k\log(0.758) = \log(0.5)$$

$$k = \frac{\log(0.5)}{\log(0.758)}$$

$$k \approx 2.5$$

The half-life is 2.5 years.

10. Strategy
To find the half-life, solve for k in the exponential decay equation. Use $A_0 = 3$, $A = 2.54$, and $t = 5$.

Solution

$$A = A_0 \left(\frac{1}{2}\right)^{t/k}$$

$$2.54 = 3 \left(\frac{1}{2}\right)^{5/k}$$

$$0.84\overline{6} = \left(\frac{1}{2}\right)^{5/k}$$

$$0.84\overline{6} = (0.5)^{5/k}$$

$$\log(0.84\overline{6}) = \log(0.5)^{5/k}$$

$$\log(0.84\overline{6}) = \frac{5}{k}\log(0.5)$$

$$k\log(0.84\overline{6}) = 5\log(0.5)$$

$$k = \frac{5\log(0.5)}{\log(0.84\overline{6})}$$

$$k = 20.8$$

The half-life is 20.8 minutes.

11. a. Strategy
To find the pressure at 40 km, solve for P in the equation. Use $h = 40$.

Solution

$$P(40) = 10.13e^{-0.116(40)}$$
$$\approx 0.098$$

The pressure is approximately 0.098 newtons/cm^2.

b. Strategy
To find the pressure at Earth's surface, solve for P in the equation. Use $h = 0$.

Solution
$$P(0) = 10.13e^{-0.116(0)}$$
$$= 10.13$$
The pressure is 10.13 newtons/cm^2.

c. The pressure decreases as you rise above Earth's surface.

12. a. Strategy
To find the predicted population, solve for y in the equation. Use $x = 120$.

Solution
$$y = 0.18808(1.0365)^{120}$$
$$\approx 13.9$$
In 2020, there will be approximately 13.9 million people.

b. Strategy
To find the year, solve for x in the equation. Use $y = 15$.

Solution
$$15 = 0.18808(1.0365)^x$$
$$\frac{15}{0.18808} = (1.0365)^x$$
$$\log\left(\frac{15}{0.18808}\right) = \log(1.0365)^x$$
$$\log\left(\frac{15}{0.18808}\right) = x\log(1.0365)$$
$$\frac{\log\left(\frac{15}{0.18808}\right)}{\log(1.0365)} = x$$
$$122 \approx x$$
$$1900 + 122 = 2022$$
In 2022, there will be approximately 15 million people.

13. Strategy
To find the pH, replace H^+ with its given value and solve for pH.

Solution
$$pH = -\log(3.97 \times 10^{-7})$$
$$= -(\log 3.97 + \log 10^{-7})$$
$$= -[0.5988 + (-7)]$$
$$= 6.4012$$
The pH of the milk is 6.4.

14. Strategy
To find the pH, replace H^+ with its given value and solve for pH.

Solution
$$pH = -\log(3.98 \times 10^{-9})$$
$$= -(\log 3.98 + 10^{-9})$$
$$= -[0.5999 + (-9)]$$
$$= 8.400$$
The pH of the baking soda solution is 8.4.

15. Strategy
To find the thickness, solve the equation for d. Use $P = 75\% = 0.75$ and $k = 0.05$.

Solution
$$\log P = -kd$$
$$\log(0.75) = -(0.05)d$$
$$\frac{\log(0.75)}{-0.05} = d$$
$$2.4987 \approx d$$
The depth must be 2.5 m.

16. Strategy
To find the percent, solve the equation for P. Use $d = 0.5$ and $k = 0.2$.

Solution
$$\log P = -kd$$
$$\log P = -(20)(0.005)$$
$$\log P = -0.1$$
$$P = 10^{-0.1}$$
$$P \approx 0.7943$$
79.4% of the light will pass through the glass.

17. Strategy
To find the number of decibels, replace I with its given value in the equation and solve for D.

Solution
$$D = 10(\log I + 16)$$
$$= 10[\log(3.2 \times 10^{-10}) + 16]$$
$$= 10[\log 3.2 + \log 10^{-10} + 16]$$
$$= 10[0.5051 + (-10) + 16]$$
$$= 10(6.5051)$$
$$= 65.051$$
The number of decibels is 65.

18. Strategy
To find the number of decibels, replace I with its given value in the equation and solve for D.

Solution
$$D = 10(\log I + 16)$$
$$= 10[\log(630) + 16]$$
$$= 10[2.7993 + 16]$$
$$= 10[18.7993]$$
$$= 187.993$$
The number of decibels is 188.

19. Strategy
To find the average time increase, evaluate the equation at $x = 1$ and $x = 19$ and find the difference.

Solution
$T(x) = 149.57 + 7.63 \ln x$

$T(1) = 149.57 + 7.63 \ln 1$
$\quad = 149.57$

$T(19) = 149.57 + 7.63 \ln 19$
$\quad \approx 172.04$

$172.04 - 149.57 = 22.47$
The average game increased its time by 22.5 min.

20. Strategy
To find the year, replace C with its given value in the equation, and solve for t.

Solution
$$0.22 = 0.04e^{0.057t}$$
$$\ln 0.22 = \ln\left(0.04e^{0.057t}\right)$$
$$\ln 0.22 = \ln 0.04 + \ln e^{0.057t}$$
$$\ln 0.22 - \ln 0.04 = 0.057t$$
$$\frac{\ln 0.22 - \ln 0.04}{0.057} = t$$
$$30 \approx t$$

$1962 + 30 = 1992$
According to the model the first-class stamp cost $0.22 in 1992.

21. Strategy
To find the thickness needed, solve the given equation for x. Use $I = 0.25 I_0$ and $k = 3.2$.

Solution
$$I = I_0 e^{-kx}$$
$$0.25I_0 = I_0 e^{-3.2x}$$
$$0.25 = e^{-3.2x}$$
$$\ln 0.25 = \ln(e^{-3.2x})$$
$$\ln 0.25 = -3.2x$$
$$\frac{\ln 0.25}{-3.2} = x$$
$$0.4 = x$$

Use a piece of copper that is 0.4 cm thick.

22. Strategy
To find the number of barrels, solve the equation for r. Use $T = 20$.

Solution
$T = 14.29 \ln(0.00411r + 1)$
$20 = 14.29 \ln(0.00411r + 1)$
$1.3996 = \ln(0.00411r + 1)$
$e^{1.3996} = 0.00411r + 1$
$4.0535 \approx 0.00411r + 1$
$3.0535 \approx 0.00411r$
$742.94 \approx r$
742.9 billion barrels of oil are necessary to last 20 years.

23. Strategy
To find the Richter scale magnitude, replace I with its given value in the equation and solve for M.

Solution
$$M = \log \frac{I}{I_0}$$
$$\quad = \log \frac{6,309,573 I_0}{I_0}$$
$$\quad = 6.8$$
The earthquake had a magnitude of 6.8.

24. Strategy
To find the Richter scale magnitude, replace I with its given value in the equation and solve for M.

Solution
$$M = \log \frac{I}{I_0}$$
$$\quad = \log \frac{50,118,723 I_0}{I_0}$$
$$\quad = 7.7$$
The earthquake had a magnitude of 7.7.

25. Strategy
To find the intensity, replace M with its given value in the equation and solve for I.

Solution
$$M = \log \frac{I}{I_0}$$
$$8.9 = \log \frac{I}{I_0}$$
$$10^{8.9} = \frac{I}{I_0}$$
$$794,328,234 I_0 = I$$
The intensity was $794,328,234 I_0$.

26. Strategy
To find the intensity, replace M with its given value in the equation and solve for I.

Solution
$$M = \log \frac{I}{I_0}$$
$$8.2 = \log \frac{I}{I_0}$$
$$10^{8.2} = \frac{I}{I_0}$$
$$158,489,319 I_0 = I$$
The intensity was $158,489,319 I_0$.

27. $M = \log A + 3 \log 8t - 2.92$
$M = \log 23 + 3 \log[8(24)] - 2.92$
$M \approx 1.36173 + 6.84990 - 2.92$
$M \approx 5.3$
The magnitude is approximately 5.3.

28. $M = \log A + 3 \log 8t - 2.92$
$M = \log 30 + 3 \log[8(21)] - 2.92$
$M \approx 1.47712 + 6.67593 - 2.92$
$M \approx 5.2$
The magnitude is approximately 5.2.

29. $M = \log A + 3 \log 8t - 2.92$
$M = \log 28 + 3 \log[8(28)] - 2.92$
$M \approx 1.44716 + 7.05074 - 2.92$
$M \approx 5.6$
The magnitude is approximately 5.6.

Applying Concepts 10.5

30. Strategy
To find the time at which the population will be 9×10^6:

Write the exponential growth equation using 1.5×10^6 for A_0, 3×10^6 for A, 3 for t, and 2 for b. Solve for k.

Rewrite the exponential growth equation using 9×10^6 for A, 1.5×10^6 for A_0, 2 for b, and the value of k for k. Solve for t.

Solution
$A = A_0 b^{kt}$
$3 \times 10^6 = (1.5 \times 10^6)2^{3k}$
$2 = 2^{3k}$
$2^1 = 2^{3k}$
$1 = 3k$
$\dfrac{1}{3} = k$

$A = A_0 b^{kt}$
$9 \times 10^6 = (1.5 \times 10^6)2^{(1/3)t}$
$6 = 2^{(1/3)t}$
$\log 6 = \log 2^{(1/3)t} = \dfrac{1}{3}t(\log 2)$
$\dfrac{\log 6}{\log 2} = \dfrac{1}{3}t$
$\dfrac{3\log 6}{\log 2} = t$
$7.7549 = t$
The population will be 9×10^6 about 8 h after 9 A.M.
The population will be approximately 9×10^6 at 5 P.M.

31. Strategy
To find the number of years, write the compound interest formula using \$1 for A, \$2 for P, and 5% for i. Solve for n.

Solution
$P = A(1 + i)^n$
$2 = 1(1 + 0.05)^n$
$2 = (1.05)^n$
$\log 2 = \log(1.05)^n$
$\log 2 = n(\log 1.05)$
$\dfrac{\log 2}{\log 1.05} = n$
$14.2067 = n$
The price will double in 14 years.

32. Strategy
To find the number of years, write the formula $A = A_0\left(1 + \dfrac{0.10}{365}\right)^{365t}$ using \$1 for A_0 and \$2 for A. Solve for t.

Solution
$$A = A_0\left(1 + \frac{0.10}{365}\right)^{365t}$$
$$2 = 1\left(1 + \frac{0.10}{365}\right)^{365t}$$
$$2 = \left(\frac{365}{365} + \frac{0.10}{365}\right)^{365t}$$
$$2 = \left(\frac{365.10}{365}\right)^{365t}$$
$$\log 2 = \log\left(\frac{365.10}{365}\right)^{365t}$$
$$\log 2 = 365t\log\left(\frac{365.10}{365}\right)$$
$$\frac{\log 2}{\log\left(\frac{365.10}{365}\right)} = 365t$$
$$\frac{\log 2}{365\log\left(\frac{365.10}{365}\right)} = t$$
$$6.9324 \approx t$$
The investment will double in approximately 7 years.

33. Strategy
To find the value of the investment, solve the continuous compounding formula for P. Use $A = 2500$, $n = 5$, and $r = 0.05$.

Solution
$P = Ae^{rt}$
$P = 2500e^{0.05(5)}$
$P = 2500e^{0.25}$
$P = 2500(1.284)$
$P = 3210.06$
The investment has a value of \$3210.06 after 5 years.

34. a. $y(t) = At - 16t^2 + \dfrac{A}{k}(M + \dot{m} - kt)\ln\left(1 - \dfrac{k}{M + m}t\right)$

$y(t) = 8000t - 16t^2 + \dfrac{8000}{250}(8000 + 16{,}000 - 250t)\ln\left(1 - \dfrac{250}{8000 + 16{,}000}t\right)$

$y(t) = 8000t - 16t^2 + 32(24{,}000 - 250t)\ln\left(1 - \dfrac{250}{24{,}000}t\right)$

When $y = 5280$, $t \approx 14$.
The rocket requires 14 s to reach a height of 1 mile.

b. $v(t) = -32t + A\ln\left(\dfrac{M + m}{M + m - kt}\right)$

$v(14) = -32(14) + 8000\ln\dfrac{8000 + 16{,}000}{8000 + 16{,}000 - 250(14)}$

$ = -448 + 8000\ln\left(\dfrac{24{,}000}{20{,}500}\right)$

$ \approx 813$

The velocity of the rocket is 813 ft/s.

c. $\dfrac{M + m}{M + m - kt} > 0$

Since $M + m > 0$, then
$M + m - kt > 0$
$\quad M + m > kt$
$\quad \dfrac{M + m}{k} > t$
$\quad \dfrac{8000 + 16{,}000}{250} > t$
$\qquad 96 > t$

Since t must be greater than 0 and less than 96, the domain is $\{t \mid 0 \leq t < 96\}$.

35. a. $8\% \div 12 = 0.08 \div 12 \approx 0.00667$

$y = A(1 + i)^x + B$

$y = \dfrac{Pi - M}{i}(1 + i)^x + \dfrac{M}{i}$

$90{,}000 = \dfrac{100{,}000(0.00667) - 733.76}{0.00667}(1.00667)^x + \dfrac{733.76}{0.00667}$

$90{,}000 \approx -10{,}009(1.00667)^x + 110{,}009$

$10{,}009(1.00667)^x = 20{,}009$

$(1.00667)^x \approx 1.9991$

$\log(1.0067)^x = \log 1.991$

$x \log 1.0067 = \log 1.991$

$x = \dfrac{\log 1.991}{\log 1.00667} \approx 104$

104 months are required to reduce the loan amount to $90,000.

b. $\qquad 50{,}000 = -10{,}009(1.00667)^x + 110{,}009$

$10{,}009(1.00667)^x = 60{,}009$

$(1.00667)^x \approx 5.9955$

$x \approx \dfrac{\log 5.9955}{\log 1.00667} \approx 269$

269 months are required to reduce the loan amount to $50,000.

c. $I = Mx + A(1 + i)^x + B - P$

$I = Mx + \dfrac{Pi - M}{i}(1 + i)^x + \dfrac{M}{i} - P$

$I = 733.76x - 10{,}009(1.00667)^x + 110{,}009 - 100{,}000$

$I = 733.76x - 10{,}009(1.00667)^x + 10{,}009$

Using a graphing utility, I is 100,000 when $x \approx 163$. The total interest paid exceeds $100,000 in month 163.

36. Carrying capacity is the number of organisms that can be sustained in a particular environment. The carrying capacity of Earth is the largest population that Earth can sustain.

Using a world population of 6 billion in 2000, the number of years in which Earth's population will reach 10 billion for the growth rates 1%, 2%, 3%, 4%, and 5% are given below. In each case, it is a matter of solving for n the equation 10 billion = 6 billion $(1 + i)^n$, where $i = 0.01, 0.02, 0.03, 0.04,$ and $0.05,$

1%: $10 = 6(1.01)^n$, $\frac{5}{3} = (1.01)^n$, $\log \frac{5}{3} = n \log(1.01)$, $n = \frac{\log 5/3}{\log 1.01} \approx 51.3$

2%: $10 = 6(1.02)^n$, $\frac{5}{3} = (1.02)^n$, $\log \frac{5}{3} = n \log(1.02)$, $n = \frac{\log 5/3}{\log 1.02} \approx 25.8$

3%: $10 = 6(1.03)^n$, $\frac{5}{3} = (1.03)^n$, $\log \frac{5}{3} = n \log(1.03)$, $n = \frac{\log 5/3}{\log 1.03} \approx 17.3$

4%: $10 = 6(1.04)^n$, $\frac{5}{3} = (1.04)^n$, $\log \frac{5}{3} = n \log(1.04)$, $n = \frac{\log 5/3}{\log 1.04} \approx 13.0$

5%: $10 = 6(1.05)^n$, $\frac{5}{3} = (1.05)^n$, $\log \frac{5}{3} = n \log(1.05)$, $n = \frac{\log 5/3}{\log 1.05} \approx 10.5$

37. Carbon-14 (the 14 means there are 14 neutrons) occurs naturally as a result of cosmic rays (alpha particles) passing through the atmosphere and producing neutrons that convert nitrogen-14 into carbon-14. The carbon-14 atom continuously decays back to nitrogen-14 in 5730 years (the half-life of carbon-14).

W.F. Libby and others used this information to determine the age of archeological objects. As a result of his investigations into carbon dating, Libby was awarded the Nobel Prize in chemistry in 1960. Carbon dating is effective for dating organic material (material containing carbon, such as wood, bones, and clothe). Because the half-life of carbon-14 is small by geological standards, it is not useful for dating objects that are more than 25,000 years old.

Rubidium dating is another method of determining the age of an object. This element is used to date noncarbon objects such as rocks. Rubidium-87 is an isotope of rubidium and decays to strontium-86, which is stable. The half-life of rubidium-87 is 4.86×10^{10} years.

The uranium-thorium dating method is useful for dating rocks that do not contain rubidium. This method has been used only to date skeletal remains in which trace amounts of uranium were found. Uranium-238 decays to uranium-234 with a half-life of 4.5×10^9 years. Uranium-234 then decays to thorium-230 in 248,000 years. Recently, uranium-thorium dating was applied to a skeleton found in Del Mar, California. Carbon dating had determined the skeleton to be 48,000 years old. However, the uranium-thorium method showed the skeleton to be 11,000 years old. One reason that has been proposed to explain the discrepancy between the two dates is that carbon dating is prone to inaccuracies because the ratios of carbon-12 to carbon-14 present in the environment have changed over time.

Focus on Problem Solving

a. The sum of the ten digits is 45. Let x = the sum of the tens digits and let S = the sum of the remaining units digits. Then $S = 45 - x$.

b. The sum of 10 times the tens digits and the units digits will equal 100. $10x + (45 - x) = 100$

c. $10x + (45 - x) = 100$
$10x + 45 - x = 100$
$9x = 55$
$x = \frac{55}{9}$

Projects and Group Activities

Fractals

1. scale factor $= \dfrac{\text{new length}}{\text{old length}}$

    a. scale factor$_{2-1} = \dfrac{2}{1} = 2$

    b. scale factor$_{3-2} = \dfrac{4}{2} = 2$

    c. scale factor$_{4-3} = \dfrac{8}{4} = 2$

    d. x is the sum of integers, so $x = \dfrac{55}{9}$ is not possible. Our assumption that it is possible to use each of the digits 0, 1, 2, 3, 4, 5, 6, 7, 8 and 9 exactly once in such a way that the sum is 100 is not valid.

2. size ratio $= \dfrac{\text{new size}}{\text{old size}}$

    a. size ratio$_{2-1} = \dfrac{4}{1} = 4$

    b. size ratio$_{3-2} = \dfrac{16}{4} = 4$

    c. size ratio$_{4-3} = \dfrac{64}{16} = 4$

3. **a.** scale factor = 2

    b. size ratio = 4

4. **a.** scale factor$_{2-1} = \dfrac{2}{1} = 2$

       scale factor$_{3-2} = \dfrac{4}{2} = 2$

       The scale factor is 2.

    b. size ratio $_{2-1} = \dfrac{2^3}{1^3} = 8$

       size ratio $_{3-2} = \dfrac{4^3}{2^3} = 8$

       The size ratio is 8.

5. $d = \dfrac{\log\,(\text{size ratio})}{\log\,(\text{scale factor})}$

    $d = \dfrac{\log 8}{\log 2} = \dfrac{\log 2^3}{\log 2} = \dfrac{3\log 2}{\log 2} = 3$

    Thus the cubes are three-dimensional figures.

6. **a.** scale factor $_{2-1} = \dfrac{2}{1} = 2$

       scale factor $_{3-2} = \dfrac{4}{2} = 2$

    b. size ratio $_{2-1} = \dfrac{3}{1} = 3$

       size ratio $_{3-2} = \dfrac{9}{3} = 3$

7. $d = \dfrac{\log\,(\text{size ratio})}{\log\,(\text{scale factor})}$

    $d = \dfrac{\log 3}{\log 2}$

    $d \approx 1.58$

Credit Reports and FICO® Scores

1. The equation is $y = 918.22 - 137.49 \ln x$, where values are rounded to the nearest hundredth.

2. $y = 918.22 - 137.49 \ln(500) \approx 64\%$

3.
$$36 = 918.22 - 137.49\ln x$$
$$-882.22 = -137.49\ln x$$
$$6.4166 = \ln x$$
$$e^{6.4166} = x$$
$$612 \approx x$$

4. From the bar graph, the highest FICO score with a 71% delinquency rate is 549.

5. From the bar graph, the lowest FICO score with a 5% delinquency rate is 700.

6. Three major credit reporting agencies are Equifax, Experian, and Trans Union.

Chapter Review Exercises

1. $\log_4 16 = x$
$$4^x = 16$$
$$4^x = 4^2$$
$$x = 2$$
$$\log_4 16 = 2$$

2. $\dfrac{1}{2}(\log_3 x - \log_3 y) = \dfrac{1}{2}\left(\log_3 \dfrac{x}{y}\right)$

                       $= \log_3 \left(\dfrac{x}{y}\right)^{1/2}$

                       $= \log_3 \sqrt{\dfrac{x}{y}}$

3. $f(x) = e^{x-2}$
$$f(2) = e^{2-2}$$
$$f(2) = e^0$$
$$f(2) = 1$$

4. $8^x = 2^{x-6}$
$$(2^3)^x = 2^{x-6}$$
$$2^{3x} = 2^{x-6}$$
$$3x = x - 6$$
$$2x = -6$$
$$x = -3$$
The solution is -3.

5. $f(x) = \left(\dfrac{2}{3}\right)^x$
$$f(0) = \left(\dfrac{2}{3}\right)^0$$
$$f(0) = 1$$

6. $\log_3 x = -2$
$$3^{-2} = x$$
$$\dfrac{1}{3^2} = x$$
$$\dfrac{1}{9} = x$$
The solution is $\dfrac{1}{9}$.

7. $2^5 = 32$ is equivalent to $\log_2 32 = 5$.

8. $\log x + \log(x-4) = \log 12$
$\qquad \log x(x-4) = \log 12$
$\qquad\qquad x(x-4) = 12$
$\qquad\qquad x^2 - 4x = 12$
$\qquad x^2 - 4x - 12 = 0$
$\qquad (x-6)(x+2) = 0$
$x-6 = 0 \qquad\qquad x+2 = 0$
$\quad x = 6 \qquad\qquad\quad x = -2$
-2 does not check as a solution. 6 checks as a solution. The solution is 6.

9. $\log_6 \sqrt{xy^3} = \log_6 \sqrt{x}\sqrt{y^3}$
$\qquad\qquad = \log_6 \sqrt{x} + \log_6 \sqrt{y^3}$
$\qquad\qquad = \log_6 x^{1/2} + \log_6 y^{3/2}$
$\qquad\qquad = \dfrac{1}{2}\log_6 x + \dfrac{3}{2}\log_6 y$

10. $4^{5x-2} = 4^{3x+2}$
$\quad 5x - 2 = 3x + 2$
$\quad 2x - 2 = 2$
$\qquad 2x = 4$
$\qquad x = 2$
The solution is 2.

11. $3^{7x+1} = 3^{4x-5}$
$\quad 7x + 1 = 4x - 5$
$\quad 3x + 1 = -5$
$\qquad 3x = -6$
$\qquad x = -2$
The solution is -2.

12. $f(x) = 3^{x+1}$
$f(-2) = 3^{-2+1} = 3^{-1} = \dfrac{1}{3}$

13. $\log_2 16 = x$
$\qquad 2^x = 16$
$\qquad 2^x = 2^4$
$\qquad x = 4$
The solution is 4.

14. $\log_6 2x = \log_6 2 + \log_6(3x-4)$
$\log_6 2x = \log_6 2(3x-4)$
$\log_6 2x = \log_6(6x-8)$
$\qquad 2x = 6x - 8$
$\qquad -4x = -8$
$\qquad x = 2$
The solution is 2.

15. $\log_2 5 = \dfrac{\log 5}{\log 2} = 2.3219$

16. $\log_6 22 = \dfrac{\log 22}{\log 6} = 1.7251$

17. $4^x = 8^{x-1}$
$(2^2)^x = (2^3)^{x-1}$
$\quad 2^{2x} = 2^{3x-3}$
$\quad 2x = 3x - 3$
$\quad -x = -3$
$\quad x = 3$
The solution is 3.

18. $f(x) = \left(\dfrac{1}{4}\right)^x$
$f(-1) = \left(\dfrac{1}{4}\right)^{-1} = 4$

19. $\log_5 \sqrt{\dfrac{x}{y}} = \log_5 \dfrac{\sqrt{x}}{\sqrt{y}}$
$\qquad\qquad = \log_5 \sqrt{x} - \log_5 \sqrt{y}$
$\qquad\qquad = \log_5 x^{1/2} - \log_5 y^{1/2}$
$\qquad\qquad = \dfrac{1}{2}\log_5 x - \dfrac{1}{2}\log_5 y$

20. $\log_5 \dfrac{7x+2}{3x} = 1$
$\qquad 5^1 = \dfrac{7x+2}{3x}$
$\qquad 5 = \dfrac{7x+2}{3x}$
$\qquad 15x = 7x + 2$
$\qquad 8x = 2$
$\qquad x = \dfrac{1}{4}$
The solution is $\dfrac{1}{4}$.

21. $\log_5 x = 3$
$\quad 5^3 = x$
$\quad 125 = x$
The solution is 125.

22. $\log x + \log(2x+3) = \log 2$
$\qquad \log x(2x+3) = \log 2$
$\qquad\qquad x(2x+3) = 2$
$\qquad\qquad 2x^2 + 3x = 2$
$\qquad 2x^2 + 3x - 2 = 0$
$\qquad (2x-1)(x+2) = 0$
$2x - 1 = 0 \qquad\qquad x + 2 = 0$
$\quad 2x = 1 \qquad\qquad\quad x = -2$
$\quad x = \dfrac{1}{2}$
-2 does not check as a solution. $\dfrac{1}{2}$ checks as a solution. The solution is $\dfrac{1}{2}$.

23. $3\log_b x - 5\log_b y = \log_b x^3 - \log_b y^5 = \log_b \dfrac{x^3}{y^5}$

24. $f(x) = 2^{-x-1}$

$f(-3) = 2^{-(-3)-1}$

$f(-3) = 2^{3-1}$

$f(-3) = 2^2 = 4$

25. $\log_3 19 = \dfrac{\log 19}{\log 3} = 2.6801$

26. $3^{x+2} = 5$

$\log 3^{x+2} = \log 5$

$(x+2)\log 3 = \log 5$

$x + 2 = \dfrac{\log 5}{\log 3}$

$x = \dfrac{\log 5}{\log 3} - 2$

$x = -0.5350$

The solution is –0.5350.

27.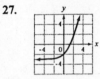

28.

29.

30.

31. 1.0

32. Strategy

To find the half-life, solve for k in the exponential decay equation. Use $A_0 = 10$, $A = 9$, and $t = 5$.

Solution

$$A = A_0 \left(\frac{1}{2}\right)^{t/k}$$

$$9 = 10 \left(\frac{1}{2}\right)^{5/k}$$

$$0.9 = \left(\frac{1}{2}\right)^{5/k}$$

$$0.9 = (0.5)^{5/k}$$

$$\log(0.9) = \log(0.5)^{5/k}$$

$$\log(0.9) = \frac{5}{k}\log(0.5)$$

$$k = \frac{5\log 0.5}{\log 0.9} = 32.89$$

The half-life is 33 h.

33. Strategy

To find the thickness, solve the equation $\log P = -0.5d$ for d. Use $P = 50\% = 0.5$.

Solution

$\log P = -0.5d$

$\log 0.5 = -0.5d$

$\dfrac{\log 0.5}{-0.5} = d$

$0.602 = d$

The material must be 0.602 cm thick.

Chapter Test

1. $f(x) = \left(\dfrac{3}{4}\right)^x$

$f(0) = \left(\dfrac{3}{4}\right)^0 = 1$

2. $f(x) = 4^{x-1}$

$f(-2) = 4^{-2-1}$

$f(-2) = 4^{-3}$

$f(-2) = \dfrac{1}{4^3} = \dfrac{1}{64}$

3. $\log_4 64 = x$

$4^x = 64$

$4^x = 4^3$

$x = 3$

4. $\log_4 x = -2$

$4^{-2} = x$

$\dfrac{1}{4^2} = x$

$\dfrac{1}{16} = x$

The solution is $\dfrac{1}{16}$.

5. $\log_6 \sqrt[3]{x^2 y^5} = \log_6 (x^2 y^5)^{1/3}$

$\qquad\qquad = \dfrac{1}{3}\log_6(x^2 y^5)$

$\qquad\qquad = \dfrac{1}{3}(\log_6 x^2 + \log_6 y^5)$

$\qquad\qquad = \dfrac{1}{3}(2\log_6 x + 5\log_6 y)$

$\qquad\qquad = \dfrac{2}{3}\log_6 x + \dfrac{5}{3}\log_6 y$

6. $\dfrac{1}{2}(\log_5 x - \log_5 y) = \dfrac{1}{2}\left(\log_5 \dfrac{x}{y}\right)$

$\qquad\qquad = \log_5\left(\dfrac{x}{y}\right)^{1/2}$

$\qquad\qquad = \log_5 \sqrt{\dfrac{x}{y}}$

7. $\log_6 x + \log_6 (x-1) = 1$

$\qquad \log_6 x(x-1) = 1$

$\qquad\quad x(x-1) = 6^1$

$\qquad\qquad x^2 - x = 6$

$\qquad\quad x^2 - x - 6 = 0$

$\qquad (x-3)(x+2) = 0$

$x - 3 = 0 \qquad\qquad x + 2 = 0$

$x = 3 \qquad\qquad\quad x = -2$

−2 does not check as a solution. 3 checks as a solution. The solution is 3.

8. $f(x) = 3^{x+1}$

$f(-2) = 3^{-2+1}$

$f(-2) = 3^{-1} = \dfrac{1}{3}$

9. $\qquad 3^x = 17$

$\quad \log 3^x = \log 17$

$\quad x\log 3 = \log 17$

$\qquad\quad x = \dfrac{\log 17}{\log 3}$

$\qquad\quad x = 2.5789$

10. $\log_2 x + 3 = \log_2(x^2 - 20)$

$\qquad 3 = \log_2(x^2 - 20) - \log_2 x$

$\qquad 3 = \log_2 \dfrac{(x^2 - 20)}{x}$

$\qquad 2^3 = \dfrac{x^2 - 20}{x}$

$\qquad 8 = \dfrac{x^2 - 20}{x}$

$\qquad 8x = x^2 - 20$

$\qquad 0 = x^2 - 8x - 20$

$\qquad 0 = (x-10)(x+2)$

$x - 10 = 0 \qquad\qquad x + 2 = 0$

$x = 10 \qquad\qquad\quad x = -2$

−2 does not check as a solution. 10 checks as a solution. The solution is 10.

11. $5^{6x-2} = 5^{3x+7}$

$\quad 6x - 2 = 3x + 7$

$\quad 3x - 2 = 7$

$\qquad 3x = 9$

$\qquad\; x = 3$

The solution is 3.

12. $\qquad 4^x = 2^{3x+4}$

$\quad (2^2)^x = 2^{3x+4}$

$\qquad 2^{2x} = 2^{3x+4}$

$\qquad 2x = 3x + 4$

$\qquad -x = 4$

$\qquad\; x = -4$

The solution is −4.

13. $\log(2x+1) + \log x = \log 6$

$\qquad \log x(2x+1) = \log 6$

$\qquad\quad x(2x+1) = 6$

$\qquad\quad 2x^2 + x = 6$

$\qquad 2x^2 + x - 6 = 0$

$\qquad (2x-3)(x+2) = 0$

$2x - 3 = 0 \qquad\qquad x + 2 = 0$

$2x = 3 \qquad\qquad\quad x = -2$

$x = \dfrac{3}{2}$

−2 does not check as a solution. $\dfrac{3}{2}$ checks as a solution. The solution is $\dfrac{3}{2}$.

14.

15.

16.

17.

18. 1.6

19. Strategy

To find the value, solve the compound interest formula for P. Use $A = 10{,}000$,

$$i = \frac{7.5\%}{12} = \frac{0.075}{12} = 0.00625, \ n = 72.$$

Solution

$$P = A(1+i)^n$$

$$P = 10{,}000(1 + 0.00625)^{72}$$

$$\approx 15{,}661$$

The value is \$15,661.

20. Strategy

To find the half-life, solve for k in the exponential decay equation. Use $A_0 = 40$, $A = 30$, and $t = 10$.

Solution

$$A = A_0\left(\frac{1}{2}\right)^{t/k}$$

$$30 = 40\left(\frac{1}{2}\right)^{10/k}$$

$$0.75 = \left(\frac{1}{2}\right)^{10/k}$$

$$0.75 = (0.5)^{10/k}$$

$$\log 0.75 = \log(0.5)^{10/k}$$

$$\log(0.75) = \frac{10}{k}\log(0.5)$$

$$k = \frac{10\log 0.5}{\log 0.75} \approx 24.09$$

The half-life is 24 h.

Cumulative Review Exercises

1. $4 - 2[x - 3(2 - 3x) - 4x] = 2x$

$$4 - 2[x - 6 + 9x - 4x] = 2x$$

$$4 - 2[6x - 6] = 2x$$

$$4 - 12x + 12 = 2x$$

$$-12x + 16 = 2x$$

$$-14x = -16$$

$$x = \frac{8}{7}$$

The solution is $\frac{8}{7}$.

2. $\qquad S = 2WH + 2WL + 2LH$

$$S - 2WH = 2WL + 2LH$$

$$S - 2WH = L(2W + 2H)$$

$$\frac{S - 2WH}{2W + 2H} = L$$

3. $|2x - 5| \le 3$

$$-3 \le 2x - 5 \le 3$$

$$-3 + 5 \le 2x - 5 + 5 \le 3 + 5$$

$$2 \le 2x \le 8$$

$$1 \le x \le 4$$

$$\{x | 1 \le x \le 4\}$$

4. $4x^{2n} + 7x^n + 3 = (4x^n + 3)(x^n + 1)$

5. $x^2 + 4x - 5 \le 0$

$$(x + 5)(x - 1) \le 0$$

$x + 5$ — $\ |\ +\ +\ +\ +\ +\ +\ |\ +\ +\ +\ +\ +$

$x - 1$ — $\ |\ -\ -\ -\ -\ -\ -\ |\ +\ +\ +\ +\ +$

$$-5\ -4\ -3\ -2\ -1\ \ 0\ \ 1\ \ 2\ \ 3\ \ 4\ \ 5$$

$$\{x | -5 \le x \le 1\}$$

6. $\dfrac{1 - \frac{5}{x} + \frac{6}{x^2}}{1 + \frac{1}{x} - \frac{6}{x^2}} = \dfrac{1 - \frac{5}{x} + \frac{6}{x^2}}{1 + \frac{1}{x} - \frac{6}{x^2}} \cdot \dfrac{x^2}{x^2}$

$$= \frac{x^2 - 5x + 6}{x^2 + x - 6}$$

$$= \frac{(x - 2)(x - 3)}{(x + 3)(x - 2)}$$

$$= \frac{x - 3}{x + 3}$$

7. $\dfrac{\sqrt{xy}}{\sqrt{x} - \sqrt{y}} = \dfrac{\sqrt{xy}}{\sqrt{x} - \sqrt{y}} \cdot \dfrac{\sqrt{x} + \sqrt{y}}{\sqrt{x} + \sqrt{y}}$

$$= \frac{\sqrt{x^2 y} + \sqrt{xy^2}}{\left(\sqrt{x}\right)^2 - \left(\sqrt{y}\right)^2}$$

$$= \frac{x\sqrt{y} + y\sqrt{x}}{x - y}$$

8. $y\sqrt{18x^5 y^4} - x\sqrt{98x^3 y^6}$

$$= y\sqrt{2 \cdot 3^2 \, x^5 y^4} - x\sqrt{2 \cdot 7^2 \, x^3 y^6}$$

$$= y\sqrt{3^2 x^4 y^4 (2x)} - x\sqrt{7^2 x^2 y^6 (2x)}$$

$$= y\sqrt{3^2 x^4 y^4}\sqrt{2x} - x\sqrt{7^2 x^2 y^6}\sqrt{2x}$$

$$= y \cdot 3x^2 y^2 \sqrt{2x} - x \cdot 7xy^3 \sqrt{2x}$$

$$= 3x^2 y^3 \sqrt{2x} - 7x^2 y^3 \sqrt{2x}$$

$$= -4x^2 y^3 \sqrt{2x}$$

9. $\dfrac{i}{2 - i} = \dfrac{i}{2 - i} \cdot \dfrac{2 + i}{2 + i}$

$$= \frac{2i + i^2}{4 - i^2}$$

$$= \frac{2i - 1}{4 + 1}$$

$$= \frac{-1 + 2i}{5}$$

$$= -\frac{1}{5} + \frac{2}{5}i$$

10. $2x - y = 5$
$-y = -2x + 5$
$y = 2x - 5$
$m = 2$ $(x_1, y_1) = (2, -2)$
$y - y_1 = m(x - x_1)$
$y - (-2) = 2(x - 2)$
$y + 2 = 2x - 4$
$y = 2x - 6$
The equation of the line is $y = 2x - 6$.

11. $(x - r_1)(x - r_2) = 0$
$\left(x - \dfrac{1}{3}\right)(x - (-3)) = 0$
$\left(x - \dfrac{1}{3}\right)(x + 3) = 0$
$x^2 + \dfrac{8}{3}x - 1 = 0$
$3\left(x^2 + \dfrac{8}{3}x - 1\right) = 3(0)$
$3x^2 + 8x - 3 = 0$

12. $x^2 - 4x - 6 = 0$
$x^2 - 4x = 6$
$x^2 - 4x + 4 = 6 + 4$
$(x - 2)^2 = 10$
$\sqrt{(x - 2)^2} = \sqrt{10}$
$x - 2 = \pm\sqrt{10}$
$x = 2 \pm \sqrt{10}$
The solutions are is $2 + \sqrt{10}$ and $2 - \sqrt{10}$.

13. $f(x) = x^2 - 3x - 4$
$f(-1) = (-1)^2 - 3(-1) - 4 = 1 + 3 - 4 = 0$
$f(0) = 0^2 - 3(0) - 4 = -4$
$f(1) = 1^2 - 3(1) - 4 = 1 - 3 - 4 = -6$
$f(2) = 2^2 - 3(2) - 4 = 4 - 6 - 4 = -6$
$f(3) = 3^2 - 3(3) - 4 = 9 - 9 - 4 = -4$
The range is $\{-6, -4, 0\}$.

14. $g(x) = 2x - 3$
$g(0) = 2(0) - 3 = -3$

$f(x) = x^2 + 2x + 1$
$f(-3) = (-3)^2 + 2(-3) + 1$
$= 9 - 6 + 1$
$= 4$
$f[g(0)] = 4$

15. (1) $3x - y + z = 3$
(2) $x + y + 4z = 7$
(3) $3x - 2y + 3z = 8$
Eliminate y.
Add equation (1) and (2).
$3x - y + z = 3$
$x + y + 4z = 7$
(4) $4x + 5z = 10$
Multiply equation (2) by 2 and add to equation (3).
$2(x + y + 4z) = 7(2)$
$3x - 2y + 3z = 8$

$2x + 2y + 8z = 14$
$3x - 2y + 3z = 8$
(5) $5x + 11z = 22$

Multiply equation (4) by -5. Multiply equation (5) by 4 and add.
$-5(4x + 5z) = -5(10)$
$4(5x + 11z) = 4(22)$

$-20x - 25z = -50$
$20x + 44z = 88$

$19z = 38$
$z = 2$
Substitute 2 for z in equation (5).
$5x + 11(2) = 22$
$5x + 22 = 22$
$5x = 0$
$x = 0$
Substitute 0 for x and 2 for z in equation (2).
$x + y + 4z = 7$
$0 + y + 4(2) = 7$
$y + 8 = 7$
$y = -1$
The solution is $(0, -1, 2)$.

16. (1) $y = -2x - 3$
(2) $y = 2x - 1$
Solve by the substitution method.
$y = 2x - 1$
$-2x - 3 = 2x - 1$
$-4x - 3 = -1$
$-4x = 2$
$x = -\dfrac{1}{2}$
Substitute into equation (2).
$y = 2x - 1$
$y = 2\left(-\dfrac{1}{2}\right) - 1$
$y = -1 - 1$
$y = -2$
The solution is $\left(-\dfrac{1}{2}, -2\right)$.

17. $f(x) = 3^{-x+1}$
$f(-4) = 3^{-(-4)+1} = 3^{4+1} = 3^5 = 243$

18. $\log_4 x = 3$

$4^3 = x$

$64 = x$

The solution is 64.

19. $2^{3x+2} = 4^{x+5}$

$2^{3x+2} = (2^2)^{x+5}$

$2^{3x+2} = 2^{2x+10}$

$3x+2 = 2x+10$

$x+2 = 10$

$x = 8$

The solution is 8.

20. $\log x + \log(3x+2) = \log 5$

$\log x(3x+2) = \log 5$

$x(3x+2) = 5$

$3x^2 + 2x = 5$

$3x^2 + 2x - 5 = 0$

$(3x+5)(x-1) = 0$

$3x+5 = 0 \qquad x-1 = 0$

$3x = -5 \qquad\quad x = 1$

$x = -\dfrac{5}{3}$

$-\dfrac{5}{3}$ does not check as a solution. 1 does check as a solution. The solution is 1.

21.

```
  ┤─┤─(─┤─┤─┤─┤─)─┤─┤─┤─┤─┤
 -5 -4 -3 -2 -1  0  1  2  3  4  5
```

22. $\dfrac{x+2}{x-1} \geq 0$

```
x + 2  - - - - | + + + | + + + + +
x - 1  - - - - | - - - | + + + + +
      ─┼─┼─┼─┼─┼─┼─┼─┼─┼─┼─┼
     -5 -4 -3 -2 -1  0  1  2  3  4  5
```

$\{x \mid x \leq -2 \text{ or } x > 1\}$

```
  ─┼─┼─┼─┤─┼─┼─(─┼─┼─┼─┤
 -5 -4 -3 -2 -1  0  1  2  3  4  5
```

23. $y = -x^2 - 2x + 3$

$-\dfrac{b}{2a} = -\dfrac{(-2)}{2(-1)} = -1$

$y = -(-1)^2 - 2(-1) + 3 = -1 + 2 + 3 = 4$

Vertex: $(-1, 4)$

Axis of symmetry: $x = -1$

24.

25.

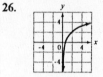

26.

27. Strategy

Pounds of 25% alloy: x

Pounds of 50% alloy: $2000 - x$

	Amount	Percent	Quantity
25% alloy	x	0.25	$0.25x$
50% alloy	$2000 - x$	0.50	$0.50(2000 - x)$
40% alloy	2000	0.40	$0.40(2000)$

The sum of the quantities before mixing equals the quantity after mixing.

Solution

$0.25x + 0.50(2000 - x) = 0.40(2000)$

$0.25x + 1000 - 0.50x = 800$

$-0.25x + 1000 = 800$

$-0.25x = -200$

$x = 800$

$2000 - x = 2000 - 800 = 1200$

800 lb of the alloy containing 25% tin and 1200 lb of the alloy containing 50% tin were used.

28. Strategy

To find the amount, write and solve an inequality using x to represent the amount of sales.

Solution

$500 + 0.08x \geq 3000$

$0.08x \geq 2500$

$x \geq 31{,}250$

To earn \$3000 or more a month, the sales executive must sell \$31,250 or more.

29.

30. Strategy

Time to print the checks when both printers are operating:

	Rate	Time	Part
Old printer	$\frac{1}{30}$	t	$\frac{t}{30}$
New printer	$\frac{1}{10}$	t	$\frac{t}{10}$

The sum of the parts of the task completed by each printer equals 1.

Solution

$$\frac{t}{30} + \frac{t}{10} = 1$$
$$30\left(\frac{t}{30} + \frac{t}{10}\right) = 30(1)$$
$$t + 3t = 30$$
$$4t = 30$$
$$t = 7.5$$

When both printers are operating, it will take 7.5 min to print the checks.

31. Strategy

To find the pressure:
Write the basic inverse variation equation, replace the variables by the given values, and solve for k.

Write the inverse variation equation, replacing k by its value. Substitute 25 for V and solve for P.

Solution

$$P = \frac{k}{V}$$
$$50 = \frac{k}{250}$$
$$12,500 = k$$

$$P = \frac{12,500}{V}$$
$$= \frac{12,500}{25}$$
$$= 500$$

When the volume is 25 ft^3, the pressure is 500 lb/in^2.

32. Strategy

Cost per yard of nylon carpet: n
Cost per yard of wool carpet: w
First purchase:

	Amount	Unit cost	Value
Nylon carpet	45	n	$45n$
Wool carpet	30	w	$30w$

Second purchase:

	Amount	Unit cost	Value
Nylon carpet	25	n	$25n$
Wool carpet	80	w	$80w$

The total of the first purchase was $2340.
The total of the second purchase was $2820.
$45n + 30w = 2340$
$25n + 80w = 2820$

Solution
$45n + 30w = 2340$
$25n + 80w = 2820$

$$25(45n + 30w) = 25(2340)$$
$$-45(25n + 80w) = -45(2820)$$
$$1125n + 750w = 58,500$$
$$-1125n - 3600w = -126,900$$
$$-2850w = -68,400$$
$$w = 24$$

The cost per yard of the wool carpet is $24.

33. Strategy

To find the value of the investment, solve the compound interest formula for P. Use $A = 10,000$, $i = \frac{9\%}{12} = \frac{0.09}{12} = 0.0075$, and $n = 12 \cdot 5 = 60$.

Solution
$$P = A(1+i)^n$$
$$= 10,000(1 + 0.0075)^{60}$$
$$= 10,000(1.0075)^{60}$$
$$\approx 15,657$$

The value of the investment after 5 yr is $15,657.

Chapter 11: Sequences and Series

Prep Test

1. $[3(1)-2]+[3(2)-2]+[3(3)-2]$ [1.2.4]
$$=[3-2]+[6-2]+[9-2]$$
$$=1+4+7$$
$$=12$$

2. $f(n)=\dfrac{n}{n+2}$ [3.2.1]
$$f(6)=\dfrac{6}{6+2}$$
$$=\dfrac{6}{8}=\dfrac{3}{4}$$

3. $a_1+(n-1)d$ [1.3.2]
$$2+(5-1)4$$
$$=2+(4)4$$
$$=2+16=18$$

4. $a_1 r^{n-1}$ [1.3.2]
$$=-3(-2)^{6-1}$$
$$=-3(-2)^5$$
$$=-3(-32)=96$$

5. $\dfrac{a_1(1-r^n)}{1-r}$ [1.3.2]
$$=\dfrac{-2(1-(-4)^5)}{1-(-4)}$$
$$=\dfrac{-2(1+1024)}{5}$$
$$=\dfrac{-2(1025)}{5}=-410$$

6. $\dfrac{\frac{4}{10}}{1-\frac{1}{10}}=\dfrac{\frac{4}{10}}{\frac{9}{10}}=\dfrac{4}{10}\cdot\dfrac{10}{9}=\dfrac{4}{9}$ [1.2.4]

7. $(x+y)^2=(x+y)(x+y)$ [5.3.3]
$$=x^2+2xy+y^2$$

8. $(x+y)^3=(x+y)(x+y)(x+y)$ [5.3.2, 5.3.3]
$$=(x^2+2xy+y^2)(x+y)$$
$$=x^3+3x^2y+3xy^2+y^3$$

Go Figure

The sequence of 1, 32, 81, 64, 25, and 6 can be written as $1^6, 2^5, 3^4, 4^3, 5^2, 6^1$. So the next number, 7^0 can be written as 1. The next number in the sequence is 1.

Section 11.1

Concept Review 11.1

1. Always true

2. Always true

3. Always true

4. Never true
   The sum of the series is 14.

Objective 11.1.1 Exercises

1. A sequence is an ordered list of numbers.

2. A finite sequence contains a finite number of terms. An infinite sequence contains an infinite number of terms.

3. The third term is 8.

4. The fourth term is 8.

5. $a_n = n+1$
   $a_1 = 1+1 = 2$ The first term is 2.
   $a_2 = 2+1 = 3$ The second term is 3.
   $a_3 = 3+1 = 4$ The third term is 4.
   $a_4 = 4+1 = 5$ The fourth term is 5.

6. $a_n = n-1$
   $a_1 = 1-1 = 0$ The first term is 0.
   $a_2 = 2-1 = 1$ The second term is 1.
   $a_3 = 3-1 = 2$ The third term is 2.
   $a_4 = 4-1 = 3$ The fourth term is 3.

7. $a_n = 2n+1$
   $a_1 = 2(1)+1 = 3$ The first term is 3.
   $a_2 = 2(2)+1 = 5$ The second term is 5.
   $a_3 = 2(3)+1 = 7$ The third term is 7.
   $a_4 = 2(4)+1 = 9$ The fourth term is 9.

8. $a_n = 3n-1$
   $a_1 = 3(1)-1 = 2$ The first term is 2.
   $a_2 = 3(2)-1 = 5$ The second term is 5.
   $a_3 = 3(3)-1 = 8$ The third term is 8.
   $a_4 = 3(4)-1 = 11$ The fourth term is 11.

9. $a_n = 2-2n$
   $a_1 = 2-2(1) = 0$ The first term is 0.
   $a_2 = 2-2(2) = -2$ The second term is -2.
   $a_3 = 2-2(3) = -4$ The third term is -4.
   $a_4 = 2-2(4) = -6$ The fourth term is -6.

10. $a_n = 1-2n$
    $a_1 = 1-2(1) = -1$ The first term is -1.
    $a_2 = 1-2(2) = -3$ The second term is -3.
    $a_3 = 1-2(3) = -5$ The third term is -5.
    $a_4 = 1-2(4) = -7$ The fourth term is -7.

11. $a_n = 2^n$
    $a_1 = 2^1 = 2$ The first term is 2.
    $a_2 = 2^2 = 4$ The second term is 4.
    $a_3 = 2^3 = 8$ The third term is 8.
    $a_4 = 2^4 = 16$ The fourth term is 16.

12. $a_n = 3^n$

$a_1 = 3^1 = 3$ The first term is 3.

$a_2 = 3^2 = 9$ The second term is 9.

$a_3 = 3^3 = 27$ The third term is 27.

$a_4 = 3^4 = 81$ The fourth term is 81.

13. $a_n = n^2 + 1$

$a_1 = 1^2 + 1 = 2$ The first term is 2.

$a_2 = 2^2 + 1 = 5$ The second term is 5.

$a_3 = 3^2 + 1 = 10$ The third term is 10.

$a_4 = 4^2 + 1 = 17$ The fourth term is 17.

14. $a_n = n^2 - 1$

$a_1 = 1^1 - 1 = 0$ The first term is 0.

$a_2 = 2^2 - 1 = 3$ The second term is 3.

$a_3 = 3^2 - 1 = 8$ The third term is 8.

$a_4 = 4^2 - 1 = 15$ The fourth term is 15.

15. $a_n = \dfrac{n}{n^2 + 1}$

$a_1 = \dfrac{1}{1^2 + 1} = \dfrac{1}{2}$ The first term is $\dfrac{1}{2}$.

$a_2 = \dfrac{2}{2^2 + 1} = \dfrac{2}{5}$ The second term is $\dfrac{2}{5}$.

$a_3 = \dfrac{3}{3^2 + 1} = \dfrac{3}{10}$ The third term is $\dfrac{3}{10}$.

$a_4 = \dfrac{4}{4^2 + 1} = \dfrac{4}{17}$ The fourth term is $\dfrac{4}{17}$.

16. $a_n = \dfrac{n^2 - 1}{n}$

$a_1 = \dfrac{1^2 - 1}{1} = 0$ The first term is 0.

$a_2 = \dfrac{2^2 - 1}{2} = \dfrac{3}{2}$ The second term is $\dfrac{3}{2}$.

$a_3 = \dfrac{3^2 - 1}{3} = \dfrac{8}{3}$ The third term is $\dfrac{8}{3}$.

$a_4 = \dfrac{4^2 - 1}{4} = \dfrac{15}{4}$ The fourth term is $\dfrac{15}{4}$.

17. $a_n = n - \dfrac{1}{n}$

$a_1 = 1 - \dfrac{1}{1} = 0$ The first term is 0.

$a_2 = 2 - \dfrac{1}{2} = \dfrac{3}{2}$ The second term is $\dfrac{3}{2}$.

$a_3 = 3 - \dfrac{1}{3} = \dfrac{8}{3}$ The third term is $\dfrac{8}{3}$.

$a_4 = 4 - \dfrac{1}{4} = \dfrac{15}{4}$ The fourth term is $\dfrac{15}{4}$.

18. $a_n = n^2 - \dfrac{1}{n}$

$a_1 = 1^2 - \dfrac{1}{1} = 0$ The first term is 0.

$a_2 = 2^2 - \dfrac{1}{2} = \dfrac{7}{2}$ The second term is $\dfrac{7}{2}$.

$a_3 = 3^2 - \dfrac{1}{3} = \dfrac{26}{3}$ The third term is $\dfrac{26}{3}$.

$a_4 = 4^2 - \dfrac{1}{4} = \dfrac{63}{4}$ The fourth term is $\dfrac{63}{4}$.

19. $a_n = (-1)^{n+1} n$

$a_1 = (-1)^2 (1) = 1$ The first term is 1.

$a_2 = (-1)^3 (2) = -2$ The second term is -2.

$a_3 = (-1)^4 (3) = 3$ The third term is 3.

$a_4 = (-1)^5 (4) = -4$ The fourth term is -4.

20. $a_n = \dfrac{(-1)^{n+1}}{n+1}$

$a_1 = \dfrac{(-1)^2}{1+1} = \dfrac{1}{2}$ The first term is $\dfrac{1}{2}$.

$a_2 = \dfrac{(-1)^3}{2+1} = -\dfrac{1}{3}$ The second term is $-\dfrac{1}{3}$.

$a_3 = \dfrac{(-1)^4}{3+1} = \dfrac{1}{4}$ The third term is $\dfrac{1}{4}$.

$a_4 = \dfrac{(-1)^5}{4+1} = -\dfrac{1}{5}$ The fourth term is $-\dfrac{1}{5}$.

21. $a_n = \dfrac{(-1)^{n+1}}{n^2 + 1}$

$a_1 = \dfrac{(-1)^2}{1^2 + 1} = \dfrac{1}{2}$ The first term is $\dfrac{1}{2}$.

$a_2 = \dfrac{(-1)^3}{2^2 + 1} = -\dfrac{1}{5}$ The second term is $-\dfrac{1}{5}$.

$a_3 = \dfrac{(-1)^4}{3^2 + 1} = \dfrac{1}{10}$ The third term is $\dfrac{1}{10}$.

$a_4 = \dfrac{(-1)^5}{4^2 + 1} = -\dfrac{1}{17}$ The fourth term is $-\dfrac{1}{17}$.

22. $a_n = (-1)^n (n^2 + 2n + 1)$

$a_1 = (-1)^1 (1^2 + 2 \cdot 1 + 1) = -4$ The first term is -4.

$a_2 = (-1)^2 (2^2 + 2 \cdot 2 + 1) = 9$ The second term is 9.

$a_3 = (-1)^3 (3^2 + 2 \cdot 3 + 1) = -16$ The third term is -16.

$a_4 = (-1)^4 (4^2 + 2 \cdot 4 + 1) = 25$ The fourth term is 25.

23. $a_n = (-1)^n 2^n$

$a_1 = (-1)^1 \cdot 2^1 = -2$ The first term is -2.

$a_2 = (-1)^2 \cdot 2^2 = 4$ The second term is 4.

$a_3 = (-1)^3 \cdot 2^3 = -8$ The third term is -8.

$a_4 = (-1)^4 \cdot 2^4 = 16$ The fourth term is 16.

24. $a_n = \frac{1}{3}n^3 + 1$

$a_1 = \frac{1}{3}(1)^3 + 1 = \frac{4}{3}$ The first term is $\frac{4}{3}$.

$a_2 = \frac{1}{3}(2)^3 + 1 = \frac{11}{3}$ The second term is $\frac{11}{3}$.

$a_3 = \frac{1}{3}(3)^3 + 1 = 10$ The third term is 10.

$a_4 = \frac{1}{3}(4)^3 + 1 = \frac{67}{3}$ The fourth term is $\frac{67}{3}$.

25. $a_n = 2\left(\frac{1}{3}\right)^{n+1}$

$a_1 = 2\left(\frac{1}{3}\right)^2 = \frac{2}{9}$ The first term is $\frac{2}{9}$.

$a_2 = 2\left(\frac{1}{3}\right)^3 = \frac{2}{27}$ The second term is $\frac{2}{27}$.

$a_3 = 2\left(\frac{1}{3}\right)^4 = \frac{2}{81}$ The third term is $\frac{2}{81}$.

$a_4 = 2\left(\frac{1}{3}\right)^5 = \frac{2}{243}$ The fourth term is $\frac{2}{243}$.

26. $a_n = 3n + 4$

$a_{12} = 3(12) + 4 = 40$

The twelfth term is 40.

27. $a_n = 2n - 5$

$a_{10} = 2(10) - 5 = 15$

The tenth term is 15.

28. $a_n = n(n-1)$

$a_{11} = 11(11-1) = 110$

The eleventh term is 110.

29. $a_n = \frac{n}{n+1}$

$a_{12} = \frac{12}{12+1} = \frac{12}{13}$

The twelfth term is $\frac{12}{13}$.

30. $a_n = (-1)^{n-1}n^2$

$a_{15} = (-1)^{14}(15)^2 = 225$

The fifteenth term is 225.

31. $a_n = (-1)^{n-1}(n-1)$

$a_{25} = (-1)^{24}(25-1) = 24$

The twenty-fifth term is 24.

32. $a_n = \left(\frac{1}{2}\right)^n$

$a_8 = \left(\frac{1}{2}\right)^8 = \frac{1}{256}$

The eighth term is $\frac{1}{256}$.

33. $a_n = \left(\frac{2}{3}\right)^n$

$a_5 = \left(\frac{2}{3}\right)^5 = \frac{32}{243}$

The fifth term is $\frac{32}{243}$.

34. $a_n = (n+2)(n+3)$

$a_{17} = (17+2)(17+3) = (19)(20) = 380$

The seventeenth term is 380.

35. $a_n = (n+4)(n+1)$

$a_7 = (7+4)(7+1) = (11)(8) = 88$

The seventh term is 88.

36. $a_n = \frac{(-1)^{2n-1}}{n^2}$

$a_6 = \frac{(-1)^{2(6)-1}}{6^2} = \frac{(-1)^{11}}{(6)^2} = -\frac{1}{36}$

The sixth term is $-\frac{1}{36}$.

37. $a_n = \frac{(-1)^{2n}}{n+4}$

$a_{16} = \frac{(-1)^{32}}{16+4} = \frac{1}{20}$

The sixteenth term is $\frac{1}{20}$.

38. $a_n = \frac{3}{2}n^2 - 2$

$a_8 = \frac{3}{2}(8)^2 - 2 = \frac{3}{2}(64) - 2 = 96 - 2 = 94$

The eighth term is 94.

39. $a_n = \frac{1}{3}n + n^2$

$a_6 = \frac{1}{3}(6) + 6^2 = 2 + 36 = 38$

The sixth term is 38.

Objective 11.1.2 Exercises

40. A series is the sum of the terms of a sequence.

41. Summation notation or sigma notation is a compact way to represent a series. This notation uses the Greek letter sigma to indicate a sum.

42. $\displaystyle\sum_{n=1}^{5}(2n+3)=(2\cdot1+3)+(2\cdot2+3)+(2\cdot3+3)+(2\cdot4+3)+(2\cdot5+3)$

$$=5+7+9+11+13$$
$$=45$$

43. $\displaystyle\sum_{n=1}^{7}(i+2)=(1+2)+(2+2)+(3+2)+(4+2)+(5+2)+(6+2)+(7+2)$

$$=3+4+5+6+7+8+9$$
$$=42$$

44. $\displaystyle\sum_{i=1}^{4}2i=2(1)+2(2)+2(3)+2(4)=2+4+6+8=20$

45. $\displaystyle\sum_{n=1}^{7}n=1+2+3+4+5+6+7=28$

46. $\displaystyle\sum_{i=1}^{6}i^2=1^2+2^2+3^2+4^2+5^2+6^2=1+4+9+16+25+36=91$

47. $\displaystyle\sum_{i=1}^{5}(i^2+1)=(1^2+1)+(2^2+1)+(3^2+1)+(4^2+1)+(5^2+1)$

$$=2+5+10+17+26$$
$$=60$$

48. $\displaystyle\sum_{n=1}^{6}(-1)^n=(-1)^1+(-1)^2+(-1)^3+(-1)^4+(-1)^5+(-1)^6=-1+1-1+1-1+1=0$

49. $\displaystyle\sum_{n=1}^{4}\frac{1}{2n}=\frac{1}{2(1)}+\frac{1}{2(2)}+\frac{1}{2(3)}+\frac{1}{2(4)}=\frac{1}{2}+\frac{1}{4}+\frac{1}{6}+\frac{1}{8}=\frac{12+6+4+3}{24}=\frac{25}{24}$

50. $\displaystyle\sum_{i=3}^{6}i^3=3^3+4^3+5^3+6^3=27+64+125+216=432$

51. $\displaystyle\sum_{n=2}^{4}2^n=2^2+2^3+2^4=4+8+16=28$

52. $\displaystyle\sum_{n=3}^{7}\frac{n}{n-1}=\frac{3}{3-1}+\frac{4}{4-1}+\frac{5}{5-1}+\frac{6}{6-1}+\frac{7}{7-1}=\frac{3}{2}+\frac{4}{3}+\frac{5}{4}+\frac{6}{5}+\frac{7}{6}$

$$=\frac{90+80+75+72+70}{60}=\frac{387}{60}=\frac{129}{20}$$

53. $\displaystyle\sum_{i=3}^{6}\frac{i+1}{i}=\frac{3+1}{3}+\frac{4+1}{4}+\frac{5+1}{5}+\frac{6+1}{6}=\frac{4}{3}+\frac{5}{4}+\frac{6}{5}+\frac{7}{6}=\frac{80+75+72+70}{60}=\frac{297}{60}=\frac{99}{20}$

54. $\displaystyle\sum_{i=1}^{4}\frac{1}{2^i}=\frac{1}{2^1}=\frac{1}{2^2}+\frac{1}{2^3}+\frac{1}{2^4}=\frac{1}{2}+\frac{1}{4}+\frac{1}{8}+\frac{1}{16}=\frac{8+4+2+1}{16}=\frac{15}{16}$

55. $\displaystyle\sum_{i=1}^{5}\frac{1}{2i}=\frac{1}{2(1)}=\frac{1}{2(2)}+\frac{1}{2(3)}+\frac{1}{2(4)}+\frac{1}{2(5)}=\frac{1}{2}+\frac{1}{4}+\frac{1}{6}+\frac{1}{8}+\frac{1}{10}=\frac{60+30+20+15+12}{120}=\frac{137}{120}$

56. $\displaystyle\sum_{n=1}^{4}(-1)^{n-1}n^2 = (-1)^0 1^2 + (-1)^1(2)^2 + (-1)^2(3)^2 + (-1)^3(4)^2 = 1 + (-4) + 9 + (-16) = -10$

57. $\displaystyle\sum_{i=1}^{4}(-1)^{i-1}(i+1) = (-1)^0(1+1) + (-1)^1(2+1) + (-1)^2(3+1) + (-1)^3(4+1)$

$$= 2 + (-3) + 4 + (-5) = -2$$

58. $\displaystyle\sum_{n=3}^{5}\frac{(-1)^{n-1}}{n-2} = \frac{(-1)^2}{3-2} + \frac{(-1)^3}{4-2} + \frac{(-1)^4}{5-2} = 1 - \frac{1}{2} + \frac{1}{3} = \frac{6-3+2}{6} = \frac{5}{6}$

59. $\displaystyle\sum_{n=4}^{7}\frac{(-1)^{n-1}}{n-3} = \frac{(-1)^3}{4-3} + \frac{(-1)^4}{5-3} + \frac{(-1)^5}{6-3} + \frac{(-1)^6}{7-3} = -1 + \frac{1}{2} - \frac{1}{3} + \frac{1}{4} = \frac{-12+6-4+3}{12} = -\frac{7}{12}$

60. $\displaystyle\sum_{n=1}^{5}2x^n = 2x + 2x^2 + 2x^3 + 2x^4 + 2x^5$

61. $\displaystyle\sum_{n=1}^{4}\frac{2n}{x} = \frac{2(1)}{x} + \frac{2(2)}{x} + \frac{2(3)}{x} + \frac{2(4)}{x} = \frac{2}{x} + \frac{4}{x} + \frac{6}{x} + \frac{8}{x}$

62. $\displaystyle\sum_{i=1}^{5}\frac{x^i}{i} = x + \frac{x^2}{2} + \frac{x^3}{3} + \frac{x^4}{4} + \frac{x^5}{5}$

63. $\displaystyle\sum_{i=1}^{4}\frac{x^i}{i+1} = \frac{x^1}{1+1} + \frac{x^2}{2+1} + \frac{x^3}{3+1} + \frac{x^4}{4+1} = \frac{x}{2} + \frac{x^2}{3} + \frac{x^3}{4} + \frac{x^4}{5}$

64. $\displaystyle\sum_{i=3}^{5}\frac{x^i}{2i} = \frac{x^3}{2(3)} + \frac{x^4}{2(4)} + \frac{x^5}{2(5)} = \frac{x^3}{6} + \frac{x^4}{8} + \frac{x^5}{10}$

65. $\displaystyle\sum_{i=2}^{4}\frac{x^i}{2i-1} = \frac{x^2}{2(2)-1} + \frac{x^3}{2(3)-1} + \frac{x^4}{2(4)-1} = \frac{x^2}{3} + \frac{x^3}{5} + \frac{x^4}{7}$

66. $\displaystyle\sum_{n=1}^{5}x^{2n} = x^{2(1)} + x^{2(2)} + x^{2(3)} + x^{2(4)} + x^{2(5)} = x^2 + x^4 + x^6 + x^8 + x^{10}$

67. $\displaystyle\sum_{n=1}^{4}x^{2n-1} = x^{2(1)-1} + x^{2(2)-1} + x^{2(3)-1} + x^{2(4)-1} = x + x^3 + x^5 + x^7$

Applying Concepts 11.1

68. The sequence of the natural numbers is expressed by the formula $a_n = n$.

69. The sequence of the odd natural numbers is expressed by the formula $a_n = 2n - 1$.

70. The sequence of the negative even integers is expressed by the formula $a_n = -2n$.

71. The sequence of the negative odd integers is expressed by the formula $a_n = -2n + 1$.

72. The sequence of the positive multiples of 7 is expressed by the formula $a_n = 7n$.

73. The sequence of the positive integers that are divisible by 4 is expressed by the formula $a_n = 4n$.

74. $\displaystyle\sum_{n=1}^{5}\log n = \log 1 + \log 2 + \log 3 + \log 4 + \log 5$

$$= \log(1 \cdot 2 \cdot 3 \cdot 4 \cdot 5)$$
$$= \log 120$$

75. $\displaystyle\sum_{i=1}^{4} \log 2i$

$= \log[2(1)] + \log[2(2)] + \log[2(3)] + \log[2(4)]$

$= \log 2 + \log 4 + \log 6 + \log 8$

$= \log(2 \cdot 4 \cdot 6 \cdot 8)$

$= \log 384$

76. Strategy

Multiply 4 by the number of 4s in the ones, tens, hundreds, and thousands places. Then multiply each product by the place value. Add the products and find the thousands digit.

Solution

$22 \times 4 = 88$	$88(1)$	$=$ 88
$21 \times 4 = 84$	$84(10)$	$=$ 840
$20 \times 4 = 80$	$80(100)$	$=$ $8,000$
$19 \times 4 = 76$	$76(1000)$	$=$ $\underline{76,000}$
		$=$ $84,928$

The thousands digit is 4.

77. Strategy

Multiply 6 by the number of 6s in the ones, tens, and hundreds places. Then multiply each product by the place value. Add the products and find the hundreds digit.

Solution

$31 \times 6 = 186$	$186(1)$	$=$ 186
$30 \times 6 = 180$	$180(10)$	$=$ $1,800$
$29 \times 6 = 174$	$174(100)$	$=$ $\underline{17,400}$
		$=$ $19,386$

The hundreds digit is 3.

78. $a_1 = 1,\ a_n = na_{n-1},\ n \geq 2$

$a_1 = 1$

$a_2 = 2a_{2-1} = 2a_1 = 2(1) = 2$

$a_3 = 3a_{3-1} = 3a_2 = 3(2) = 6$

$a_4 = 4a_{4-1} = 4a_3 = 4(6) = 24$

The first four terms are 1, 2, 6, and 24.

79. $a_1 = 1,\ a_2 = 1,\ a_n = a_{n-1} + a_{n-2},\ n \geq 3$

$a_1 = 1$

$a_2 = 1$

$a_3 = a_{3-1} + a_{3-2} = a_2 + a_1 = 1 + 1 = 2$

$a_4 = a_{4-1} + a_{4-2} = a_3 + a_2 = 2 + 1 = 3$

$a_5 = a_{5-1} + a_{5-2} = a_4 + a_3 = 3 + 2 = 5$

The first four terms are 1, 2, 3, and 5.

80. The infinite sum of $\dfrac{1}{2} + \dfrac{1}{4} + \dfrac{1}{8} + \dfrac{1}{16} + \ldots$ is 1.

Students should explain that as each fraction is added to the sum, one-half of the unshaded portion of the figure becomes shaded, and the portion of the figure that is shaded gets closer to the whole figure.

81. $\dfrac{1}{1} + \dfrac{1}{2} + \dfrac{1}{3} + \ldots + \dfrac{1}{n} = \displaystyle\sum_{i=1}^{n} \dfrac{1}{i}$

82. Jean Baptiste Joseph Fourier (1768-1830) was born in Auxerre, France. He was orphaned at 9 and placed, by the bishop of Auxerre, in a boarding school. While at the school, he showed talent for engineering and mathematics. During the French Revolution, Fourier befriended a number of its victims. His reward was jail. However, with the death of Robespierre, he was released and given a position at the École Polytechnique in 1795. When Napoleon invaded Egypt in 1798, Fourier was one of the approximately 160 scholars who accompanied him. Their task was to make a comprehensive inquiry into present and ancient Egypt. Napoleon selected Fourier to be the director of this study. From these efforts was born *Description de l'Egypt* (published between 1808 and 1825), a document of over 20 volumes that recounted all that was known of Egypt. While involved in the publication of *l'Egypt*, Fourier began his work on heat conduction. It was from this work that Fourier series were developed.

83. The use of the sigma notation to denote summation began in 1755 in a differential calculus book by the famous mathematician Leonhard Euler. Another famous mathematician, Lagrange, also used the sigma notation in the 18th century, but it was not widely utilized until the 19th century when mathematicians such as Fourier, Cauchy, and Jacobi used sigma notation to denote sums and infinite series.

Section 11.2

Concept Review 11.2

1. Sometimes true

The successive term s of the series $\displaystyle\sum_{i=1}^{n} (3 - i)$ decreases in value.

2. Always true

3. Sometimes true

The first term of –4, –2, 0, 2, … is a negative number.

4. Always true

Objective 11.2.1 Exercises

1. Only in an arithmetic sequence is the difference between any two consecutive terms constant.

2. To find the common difference for an arithmetic sequence, subtract the first term from the second term.

3. $d = a_2 - a_1 = 11 - 1 = 10$

$a_n = a_1 = (n - 1)d$

$a_{15} = 1 + (15 - 1)(10) = 1 + 14(10) = 1 + 140$

$a_{15} = 141$

4. $d = a_2 - a_1 = 8 - 3 = 5$
$a_n = a_1 + (n-1)d$
$a_{20} = 3 + (20-1)(5) = 3 + 19(5) = 3 + 95$
$a_{20} = 98$

5. $d = a_2 - a_1 = -2 - (-6) = 4$
$a_n = a_1 + (n-1)d$
$a_{15} = -6 + (15-1)4 = -6 + (14)4 = -6 + 56$
$a_{15} = 50$

6. $d = a_2 - a_1 = -2 - (-7) = 5$
$a_n = a_1 + (n-1)d$
$a_{14} = -7 + (14-1)5 = -7 + 13(5) = -7 + 65$
$a_{14} = 58$

7. $d = a_2 - a_1 = 7 - 3 = 4$
$a_n = a_1 + (n-1)d$
$a_{18} = 3 + (18-1)4 = 3 + 17(4) = 3 + 68$
$a_{18} = 71$

8. $d = a_2 - a_1 = -6 - (-13) = 7$
$a_n = a_1 + (n-1)d$
$a_{31} = -13 + (31-1)7$
$\quad = -13 + 30(7)$
$\quad = -13 + 210$
$a_{31} = 197$

9. $d = a_2 - a_1 = 0 - \left(-\dfrac{3}{4}\right) = \dfrac{3}{4}$
$a_n = a_1 + (n-1)d$
$a_{11} = -\dfrac{3}{4} + (11-1)\dfrac{3}{4}$
$\quad = -\dfrac{3}{4} + 10\left(\dfrac{3}{4}\right)$
$\quad = -\dfrac{3}{4} + \dfrac{30}{4}$
$a_{13} = \dfrac{27}{4}$

10. $d = a_2 - a_1 = 1 - \dfrac{3}{8} = \dfrac{5}{8}$
$a_n = a_1 + (n-1)d$
$a_{17} = \dfrac{3}{8} + (17-1)\dfrac{5}{8}$
$\quad = \dfrac{3}{8} + 16\left(\dfrac{5}{8}\right)$
$\quad = \dfrac{3}{8} + \dfrac{80}{8}$
$a_{17} = \dfrac{83}{8}$

11. $d = a_2 - a_1 = \dfrac{5}{2} - 2 = \dfrac{1}{2}$
$a_n = a_1 + (n-1)d$
$a_{31} = 2 + (31-1)\dfrac{1}{2} = 2 + 30\left(\dfrac{1}{2}\right) = 2 + 15$
$a_{31} = 17$

12. $d = a_2 - a_1 = \dfrac{5}{4} - 1 = \dfrac{1}{4}$
$a_n = a_1 + (n-1)d$
$a_{17} = 1 + (17-1)\dfrac{1}{4} = 1 + (16)\dfrac{1}{4} = 1 + 4$
$a_{17} = 5$

13. $d = a_2 - a_1 = 5.75 - 6 = -0.25$
$a_n = a_1 + (n-1)d$
$a_{10} = 6 + (10-1)(-0.25) = 6 + 9(-0.25) = 6 - 2.25$
$a_{10} = 3.75$

14. $d = a_2 - a_1 = 3.7 - 4 = -0.3$
$a_n = a_1 + (n-1)d$
$a_{12} = 4 + (12-1)(-0.3) = 4 + 11(-0.3) = 4 - 3.3$
$a_{12} = 0.7$

15. $d = a_2 - a_1 = 2 - 1 = 1$
$a_n = a_1 + (n-1)d$
$a_n = 1 + (n-1)1$
$a_n = 1 + n - 1$
$a_n = n$

16. $d = a_2 - a_1 = 4 - 1 = 3$
$a_n = a_1 + (n-1)d$
$a_n = 1 + (n-1)3$
$a_n = 1 + 3n - 3$
$a_n = 3n - 2$

17. $d = a_2 - a_1 = 2 - 6 = -4$
$a_n = a_1 + (n-1)d$
$a_n = 6 + (n-1)(-4)$
$a_n = 6 - 4n + 4$
$a_n = -4n + 10$

18. $d = a_2 - a_1 = 0 - 3 = -3$
$a_n = a_1 + (n-1)d$
$a_n = 3 + (n-1)(-3)$
$a_n = 3 - 3n + 3$
$a_n = -3n + 6$

19. $d = a_2 - a_1 = \dfrac{7}{2} - 2 = \dfrac{3}{2}$
$a_n = a_1 + (n-1)d$
$a_n = 2 + (n-1)\dfrac{3}{2}$
$a_n = 2 + \dfrac{3}{2}n - \dfrac{3}{2}$
$a_n = \dfrac{3}{2}n + \dfrac{1}{2}$
$a_n = \dfrac{3n+1}{2}$

20. $d = a_2 - a_1 = 4.5 - 7 = -2.5$
$a_n = a_1 + (n-1)d$
$a_n = 7 + (n-1)(-2.5)$
$a_n = 7 - 2.5n + 2.5$
$a_n = -2.5n + 9.5$

21. $d = a_2 - a_1 = -13 - (-8) = -5$
$a_n = a_1 + (n-1)d$
$a_n = -8 + (n-1)(-5)$
$a_n = -8 - 5n + 5$
$a_n = -5n - 3$

22. $d = a_2 - a_1 = 30 - 17 = 13$
$a_n = a_1 + (n-1)d$
$a_n = 17 + (n-1)13$
$a_n = 17 + 13n - 13$
$a_n = 13n + 4$

23. $d = a_2 - a_1 = 16 - 26 = -10$
$a_n = a_1 + (n-1)d$
$a_n = 26 + (n-1)(-10)$
$a_n = 26 - 10n + 10$
$a_n = -10n + 36$

24. $d = a_2 - a_1 = 1 - (-2) = 3$
$a_n = a_1 + (n-1)d$
$73 = -2 + (n-1)3$
$73 = -2 + 3n - 3$
$73 = -5 + 3n$
$78 = 3n$
$n = 26$
There are 26 terms in the sequence.

25. $d = a_2 - a_1 = 11 - 7 = 4$
$a_n = a_1 + (n-1)d$
$171 = 7 + (n-1)4$
$171 = 7 + 4n - 4$
$171 = 3 + 4n$
$168 = 4n$
$n = 42$
There are 42 terms in the sequence

26. $d = a_2 - a_1 = \dfrac{3}{2} - \left(-\dfrac{1}{2}\right) = 2$

$a_n = a_1 + (n-1)d$

$\dfrac{71}{2} = -\dfrac{1}{2} + (n-1)2$

$\dfrac{71}{2} = -\dfrac{1}{2} + 2n - 2$

$\dfrac{71}{2} = -\dfrac{5}{2} + 2n$

$38 = 2n$
$19 = n$
There are 19 terms in the sequence.

27. $d = a_2 - a_1 = \dfrac{5}{3} - \dfrac{1}{3} = \dfrac{4}{3}$

$a_n = a_1 + (n-1)d$

$\dfrac{61}{3} = \dfrac{1}{3} + (n-1)\dfrac{4}{3}$

$\dfrac{61}{3} = \dfrac{1}{3} + \dfrac{4}{3}n - \dfrac{4}{3}$

$\dfrac{61}{3} = -1 + \dfrac{4}{3}n$

$\dfrac{64}{3} = \dfrac{4}{3}n$

$16 = n$
There are 16 terms in the sequence.

28. $d = a_2 - a_1 = 5 - 1 = 4$
$a_n = a_1 + (n-1)d$
$81 = 1 + (n-1)4$
$81 = 1 + 4n - 4$
$81 = 4n - 3$
$84 = 4n$
$21 = n$
There are 21 terms in the sequence.

29. $d = a_2 - a_1 = 8 - 3 = 5$
$a_n = a_1 + (n-1)d$
$98 = 3 + (n-1)5$
$98 = 3 + 5n - 5$
$98 = 5n - 2$
$100 = 5n$
$20 = n$
There are 20 terms in the sequence.

30. $d = a_2 - a_1 = 0 - 2 = -2$
$a_n = a_1 + (n-1)d$
$-56 = 2 + (n-1)(-2)$
$-56 = 2 - 2n + 2$
$-56 = 4 - 2n$
$-60 = -2n$
$30 = n$
There are 30 terms in the sequence.

31. $d = a_2 - a_1 = -3 - 1 = -4$
$a_n = a_1 + (n-1)d$
$-75 = 1 + (n-1)(-4)$
$-75 = 1 - 4n + 4$
$-75 = 5 - 4n$
$-80 = -4n$
$20 = n$
There are 20 terms in the sequence.

32. $d = a_2 - a_1 = 3 - \dfrac{5}{2} = \dfrac{1}{2}$

$a_n = a_1 + (n-1)d$

$13 = \dfrac{5}{2} + (n-1)\dfrac{1}{2}$

$13 = \dfrac{5}{2} + \dfrac{n}{2} - \dfrac{1}{2}$

$13 = 2 + \dfrac{n}{2}$

$11 = \dfrac{n}{2}$

$22 = n$
There are 22 terms in the sequence.

33. $d = a_2 - a_1 = \dfrac{13}{3} - \dfrac{7}{3} = 2$

$a_n = a_1 + (n-1)d$

$\dfrac{79}{3} = \dfrac{7}{3} + (n-1)2$

$\dfrac{79}{3} = \dfrac{7}{3} + 2n - 2$

$\dfrac{79}{3} = 2n + \dfrac{1}{3}$

$26 = 2n$
$13 = n$
There are 13 terms in the sequence.

34.
$$d = a_2 - a_1 = 0.75 - 1 = -0.25$$
$$a_n = a_1 + (n-1)d$$
$$-4 = 1 + (n-1)(-0.25)$$
$$-4 = 1 - 0.25n + 0.25$$
$$-4 = 1.25 - 0.25n$$
$$-5.25 = -0.25n$$
$$21 = n$$
There are 21 terms in the sequence.

35.
$$d = a_2 - a_1 = 2 - 3.5 = -1.5$$
$$a_n = a_1 + (n-1)d$$
$$-25 = 3.5 + (n-1)(-1.5)$$
$$-25 = 3.5 - 1.5n + 1.5$$
$$-25 = 5 - 1.5n$$
$$-30 = -1.5n$$
$$20 = n$$
There are 20 terms in the sequence.

Objective 11.2.2 Exercises

36.
$$d = a_2 - a_1 = 3 - 1 = 2$$
$$a_n = a_1 + (n-1)d$$
$$a_{50} = 1 + (50-1)2 = 1 + 49(2) = 99$$
$$S_n = \frac{n}{2}(a_1 + a_n)$$
$$S_{50} = \frac{50}{2}(1 + 99) = 25(100) = 2500$$

37.
$$d = a_2 - a_1 = 4 - 2 = 2$$
$$a_n = a_1 + (n-1)d$$
$$a_{25} = 2 + (25-1)2 = 2 + 24(2) = 50$$
$$S_n = \frac{n}{2}(a_1 + a_2)$$
$$S_{25} = \frac{25}{2}(2 + 50) = \frac{25}{2}(52) = 650$$

38.
$$d = a_2 - a_1 = 18 - 20 = -2$$
$$a_n = a_1 + (n-1)d$$
$$a_{40} = 20 + (40-1)(-2)$$
$$= 20 + 39(-2)$$
$$= 20 - 78$$
$$= -58$$
$$S_n = \frac{n}{2}(a_1 + a_n)$$
$$S_{40} = \frac{40}{2}[20 + (-58)] = \frac{40}{2}(-38) = -760$$

39.
$$d = a_2 - a_1 = 20 - 25 = -5$$
$$a_n = a_1 + (n-1)d$$
$$a_{22} = 25 + (22-1)(-5)$$
$$= 25 + 21(-5)$$
$$= 25 - 105$$
$$= -80$$
$$S_n = \frac{n}{2}(a_1 + a_n)$$
$$S_{22} = \frac{22}{2}[25 + (-80)] = \frac{22}{2}(-55) = -605$$

40.
$$d = a_2 - a_1 = 1 - \frac{1}{2} = \frac{1}{2}$$
$$a_n = a_1 + (n-1)d$$
$$a_{27} = \frac{1}{2} + (27-1)\frac{1}{2} = \frac{1}{2} + (26)\frac{1}{2} = \frac{27}{2}$$
$$S_n = \frac{n}{2}(a_1 + a_n)$$
$$S_{27} = \frac{27}{2}\left(\frac{1}{2} + \frac{27}{2}\right) = \frac{27}{2}(14) = 189$$

41.
$$d = a_2 - a_1 = \frac{11}{4} - 2 = \frac{3}{4}$$
$$a_n = a_1 + (n-1)d$$
$$a_{10} = 2 + (10-1)\frac{3}{4} = 2 + 9\left(\frac{3}{4}\right) = 2 + \frac{27}{4} = \frac{35}{4}$$
$$S_{10} = \frac{n}{2}(a_1 + a_n)$$
$$S_{10} = \frac{10}{2}\left(2 + \frac{35}{4}\right) = \frac{10}{2}\left(\frac{43}{4}\right) = \frac{215}{4}$$

42.
$$a_i = 3i - 1$$
$$a_1 = 3(1) - 1 = 2$$
$$a_{15} = 3(15) - 1 = 44$$
$$S_i = \frac{i}{2}(a_1 + a_i)$$
$$S_{15} = \frac{15}{2}(2 + 44) = \frac{15}{2}(46) = 345$$

43.
$$a_i = 3i + 4$$
$$a_1 = 3(1) + 4 = 7$$
$$a_{15} = 3(15) + 4 = 49$$
$$S_i = \frac{i}{2}(a_1 + a_i)$$
$$S_{15} = \frac{15}{2}(7 + 49) = \frac{15}{2}(56) = 420$$

44.
$$a_n = \frac{1}{2}n + 1$$
$$a_1 = \frac{1}{2}(1) + 1 = \frac{3}{2}$$
$$a_{17} = \frac{1}{2}(17) + 1 = \frac{19}{2}$$
$$S_n = \frac{n}{2}(a_1 + a_n)$$
$$S_{17} = \frac{17}{2}\left(\frac{3}{2} + \frac{19}{2}\right) = \frac{17}{2}(11) = \frac{187}{2}$$

45.
$$a_n = 1 - 4n$$
$$a_1 = 1 - 4(1) = -3$$
$$a_{10} = 1 - 4(10) = -39$$
$$S_n = \frac{n}{2}(a_1 + a_n)$$
$$S_{10} = \frac{10}{2}(-3 - 39)$$
$$= \frac{10}{2}(-42)$$
$$= -210$$

46. $a_i = 4 - 2i$

$a_1 = 4 - 2(1) = 2$

$a_{15} = 4 - 2(15) = -26$

$S_i = \dfrac{i}{2}(a_1 + a_i)$

$S_{15} = \dfrac{15}{2}(2 - 26)$

$\qquad = \dfrac{15}{2}(-24)$

$\qquad = -180$

47. $a_n = 5 - n$

$a_1 = 5 - 1 = 4$

$a_{10} = 5 - 10 = -5$

$S_n = \dfrac{n}{2}(a_1 + a_n)$

$S_{10} = \dfrac{10}{2}(4 - 5) = \dfrac{10}{2}(-1) = -5$

Objective 11.2.3 Exercises

48. Strategy

To find the distance the object will fall in 6 s:
Write the arithmetic sequence.
Find the common difference of the arithmetic sequence.
Use the Formula for the nth Term of an Arithmetic Sequence to find the 6th term.
Use the Formula for the Sum of n Terms of an Arithmetic Sequence to find the sum of 6 terms of the sequence.

Solution

16, 48, 80, ...

$d = a_2 - a_1 = 48 - 16 = 32$

$a_n = a_1 + (n-1)d$

$a_6 = 16 + (6-1)32 = 16 + 160 = 176$

$S_n = \dfrac{n}{2}(a_1 + a_n)$

$S_6 = \dfrac{6}{2}(16 + 176) = 3(192) = 576$

49. Strategy

To find the number of weeks:
Write the arithmetic sequence.
Find the common difference of the arithmetic sequence.
Use the Formula for the nth Term of an Arithmetic Sequence to find the number of terms in the sequence.

Solution

12, 18, 24, ... 60

$d = a_2 - a_1 = 18 - 12 = 6$

$a_n = a_1 + (n-1)d$

$60 = 12 + (n-1)6$

$60 = 12 + 6n - 6$

$60 = 6 + 6n$

$54 = 6n$

$9 = n$

In 9 weeks the person will walk 60 min per day.

50. Strategy

To find the total number of cans in the display:
Write the arithmetic sequence.
Find the common difference of the arithmetic sequence.
Use the Formula for the nth Term of an Arithmetic Sequence to find the number of rows.
Use the Formula for the Sum of n Terms of an Arithmetic Sequence to find the sum of the sequence.

Solution

20, 18, ... 4

$d = a_2 - a_1 = 18 - 20 = -2$

$a_n = a_1 + (n-1)d$

$4 = 20 + (n-1)(-2)$

$4 = 20 - 2n + 2$

$4 = 22 - 2n$

$-18 = -2n$

$9 = n$

$S_n = \dfrac{n}{2}(a_1 + a_n)$

$S_9 = \dfrac{9}{2}(20 + 4) = \dfrac{9}{2}(24) = 108$

51. Strategy

To find the total number of seats:
Write the arithmetic sequence.
Find the common difference of the arithmetic sequence.
Use the Formula for the nth Term of an Arithmetic Sequence to find the sum of the sequence.
Use the Formula for the Sum of n Terms of an Arithmetic Sequence to find the sum of the sequence.

Solution

52, 58, 64, ...

$d = a_2 - a_1 = 58 - 52 = 6$

$a_n = a_1 + (n-1)d$

$a_{20} = 52 + (20-1)6 = 52 + 19(6) = 52 + 114 = 166$

$S_n = \dfrac{n}{2}(a_1 + a_n)$

$S_{20} = \dfrac{20}{2}(52 + 166) = 10(218) = 2180$

There are 2180 seats in the theater.

52. Strategy
To find the total number of seats:
Write the arithmetic sequence.
Find the common difference of the arithmetic sequence.
Use the Formula for the nth Term of an Arithmetic Sequence to find the number of seats in the 26th row.
Use the Formula for the Sum of an Arithmetic Sequence to find the sum of the sequence.

Solution
65, 71, 77, ...
$d = a_2 - a_1 = 71 - 65 = 6$
$a_n = a_1 + (n-1)d$
$a_{26} = 65 + (26-1)6 = 65 + 25(6) = 65 + 150 = 215$

$S_n = \dfrac{n}{2}(a_1 + a_n)$

$S_{26} = \dfrac{26}{2}(65 + 215) = 13(280) = 3640$

There are 3640 seats in the loge seating section.

53. Strategy
To find the salary for the ninth month, use the Formula for the nth Term of an Arithmetic Sequence.
To find the total salary, use the Formula for the Sum of n Terms of an Arithmetic Sequence to find the sum of the sequence.

Solution
$a_n = a_1 + (n-1)d$
$a_{10} = 2200 + (10-1)150$
$= 2200 + (9)150$
$= 2200 + 1350$
$= 3550$

$S_n = \dfrac{n}{2}(a_1 + a_n)$

$S_{10} = \dfrac{10}{2}(2200 + 3550) = \dfrac{10}{2}(5750) = 28,750$

The salary for the tenth month is $3550.
The total salary for the ten-month period is $28,750.

Applying Concepts 11.2

54. $a_n = a_1 + (n-1)d$
$a_{50} = 1 + (50-1)1 = 1 + 49 = 50$
$S_n = \dfrac{n}{2}(a_1 + a_n)$
$= \dfrac{50}{2}(1 + 50) = 25(51) = 1275$

55. $d = a_2 - a_1 = 2 - (-3) = 5$
$a_n = a_1 + (n-1)d$
$= -3 + (n-1)5$
$= -3 + 5n - 5$
$= 5n - 8$

$S_n = \dfrac{n}{2}(a_1 + a_n)$

$116 = \dfrac{n}{2}(-3 + 5n - 8)$

$116 = \dfrac{n}{2}(5n - 11)$

$232 = n(5n - 11)$
$232 = 5n^2 - 11n$
$0 = 5n^2 - 11n - 232$
$0 = (5n + 29)(n - 8)$
$5n + 29 = 0 \qquad n - 8 = 0$
$5n = -29 \qquad n = 8$
$n = -\dfrac{29}{5} \qquad n = 8$

The number of terms must be a natural number, so $-\dfrac{29}{5}$ is not a solution.

8 terms must be added together.

56. $S_n = \dfrac{n}{2}(a_1 + a_n)$

$36 = \dfrac{n}{2}(-9 + 21)$

$36 = \dfrac{n}{2}(12)$

$36 = 6n$
$6 = n$
$a_n = a_1 + (n-1)d$
$21 = -9 + (6-1)d$
$21 = -9 + 5d$
$30 = 5d$
$6 = d$

The value of n is 6.
The value of d is 6.

57. Find d in the series in which $a_1 = 9$ and $a_6 = 29$.
$a_n = a_1 + (n-1)d$
$29 = 9 + (6-1)d$
$29 = 9 + 5d$
$20 = 5d$
$4 = d$
d is the same for the series in which $a_4 = 9$ and $a_9 = 29$.
$a_n = a_1 + (n-1)d$
$29 = a_1 + (9-1)4$
$29 = a_1 + 8(4)$
$29 = a_1 + 32$
$-3 = a_1$
The first term is -3.

58. $\displaystyle\sum_{i=1}^{2} \log 2i = \log 2(1) + \log 2(2)$

$$= \log 2 + \log 4$$
$$= \log (2 \cdot 4)$$
$$= \log 8$$

59. Strategy

To find the sum of the angles:
Write the arithmetic sequence with third term $180°$, fourth term $360°$, and fifth term $540°$.
Find the common difference of the arithmetic sequence.
Find the first term of the arithmetic sequence using the Formula for the nth Term of an Arithmetic Sequence.
Use the Formula for the nth Term of an Arithmetic Sequence to find the 12th term.

Solution

$a_1, a_2, 180, 360, 540, \ldots$
$$d = a_4 - a_3 = 360 - 180 = 180$$
$$a_n = a_1 + (n-1)d$$
$$a_3 = a_1 + (3-1)180$$
$$180 = a_1 + 2(180)$$
$$180 = a_1 + 360$$
$$-180 = a_1$$
$$a_n = a_1 + (n-1)d$$
$$a_{12} = -180 + (12-1)180$$
$$= -180 + 11(180)$$
$$= 1800$$

The sum of the angles in a dodecagon is $1800°$.
The general term is
$$a_n = -180 + (n-1)180$$
$$= -180 + 180n - 180$$
$$= 180n - 360$$
$$= 180(n-2)$$

The formula for the sum of the angles of an n-sided polygon is $180(n-2)$.

60. Strategy

To find a formula for the sequence of radii:
The first term of the sequence is 36.5 plus half the width of a lane, 0.61.
The common difference of the sequence is the width of a lane, 1.22.
Use the Formula for the nth Term of an Arithmetic Sequence.

Solution

$$a_1 = 36.5 + 0.61 = 37.11$$
$$a_n = a_1 + (n-1)d$$
$$a_n = 37.11 + (n-1)(1.22)$$
$$a_n = 37.11 + 1.22n - 1.22$$
$$a_n = 1.22n + 35.89$$

61. Strategy

To find a formula for the sequence of distances:
Find the first term of the sequence by finding the circumference of a circle whose radius is equal to the first term of the sequence in Exercise 60, and adding this to twice the length of the straight part of the track, 83.4.
The common difference of the sequence is the circumference of a circle whose radius is equal to the width of a lane, 1.22.
Use the Formula for the nth Term of an Arithmetic Sequence.

Solution

$$a_1 = 2\pi(37.11) + 2(83.4)$$
$$a_1 = 399.85$$
$$d = 2\pi(1.22)$$
$$d = 7.66$$
$$a_n = a_1 + (n-1)d$$
$$a_n = 399.85 + (n-1)(7.66)$$
$$a_n = 7.66n + 392.19$$

A formula for the sequence of distances around the track for each lane is $a_n = 7.66n + 392.19$.

The farther a lane is from the innermost lane of the track, the longer the distance around the track. The starting positions must be staggered in order to ensure that each runner is running the same distance from the starting position to the finish line.

62. a. $a_n = V - dn$
$a_n = 20{,}000 - 3000n$

b. Rewrite $a_n = 20{,}000 - 3000n$ as $20{,}000 + n(-3000)$, which is of the form $a_n = a_1 + (n-1)d$, where $a_1 = 20{,}000$, $n - 1 = n$, and $d = -3000$.

63. The first seven terms of the Fibonacci sequence are 1, 1, 2, 3, 5, 8, 13. In general, $a_1 = 1$, $a_2 = 1$, and $a_n = a_{n-2} + a_{n-1}$, $n \geq 3$. This sequence was discussed by Fibonacci in his book *Liver Abaci*, which was written around A.D. 1200. The sequence is the solution to a problem in the book that is now called the rabbit problem. If one pair of the rabbits can produce a pair of rabbits each month, and in the second month after birth the new pair can give birth to a pair of rabbits, which in turn can produce a pair of rabbits that breed with the same pattern, how many pairs of rabbits will there be in 12 months?
Fibonacci sequences appear often. Daisies generally contain 21, 34, or 55 petals; from C to C on a piano keyboard there are 13 keys, 5 black and 8 white; the numbers of scales on a pinecone and on a pineapple are also terms of a Fibonacci sequence.
The Fibonacci sequence is also related to the golden ratio, $\displaystyle\lim_{n \to \infty} \frac{F_{n+1}}{F_n} = \frac{\sqrt{5}+1}{2}$.

Section 11.3

Concept Review 11.3

1. Always true

2. Sometimes true
   When $|r| < 1$, a geometric series has a finite sum.

3. Sometimes true
   If r is a negative number, the sum of a geometric series will oscillate.

4. Never true
   $\dfrac{a_{n+1}}{a_n}$ is not a constant ratio.

5. Never true
   $\dfrac{a_{n+1}}{a_n}$ is not a constant ratio.

Objective 11.3.1 Exercises

1. An arithmetic sequence is one in which the *difference* between any two consecutive terms is a constant. A geometric sequence is one in which each successive term of the sequence is the same *nonzero constant multiple* of the preceding term.

2. To find the common ratio for a geometric sequence, divide the second term of the sequence by the first term.

3. $r = \dfrac{a_2}{a_1} = \dfrac{8}{2} = 4$

   $a_n = a_1 r^{n-1}$

   $a_9 = 2(4)^{9-1} = 2(4)^8 = 2(65{,}536) = 131{,}072$

4. $r = \dfrac{a_2}{a_1} = \dfrac{3}{4}$

   $a_n = a_1 r^{n-1}$

   $a_8 = 4\left(\dfrac{3}{4}\right)^{8-1} = 4\left(\dfrac{3}{4}\right)^7 = 4\left(\dfrac{2187}{16{,}384}\right) = \dfrac{2187}{4096}$

5. $r = \dfrac{a_2}{a_1} = \dfrac{-4}{6} = -\dfrac{2}{3}$

   $a_n = a_1 r^{n-1}$

   $a_7 = 6\left(-\dfrac{2}{3}\right)^{7-1} = 6\left(-\dfrac{2}{3}\right)^6 = 6\left(\dfrac{64}{729}\right) = \dfrac{128}{243}$

6. $r = \dfrac{a_2}{a_1} = \dfrac{15}{-5} = -3$

   $a_n = a_1 r^{n-1}$

   $a_7 = -5(-3)^{7-1} = -5(-3)^6 = -5(729) = -3645$

7. $r = \dfrac{a_2}{a_1} = \dfrac{\sqrt{2}}{1} = \sqrt{2}$

   $a_n = a_1 r^{n-1}$

   $a_9 = 1(\sqrt{2})^{9-1} = 1(\sqrt{2})^8 = 1(2^4) = 16$

8. $r = \dfrac{a_2}{a_1} = \dfrac{3\sqrt{3}}{3} = \sqrt{3}$

   $a_n = a_1 r^{n-1}$

   $a_8 = 3(\sqrt{3})^{8-1}$

   $= 3(\sqrt{3})^7$

   $= 3(3^3\sqrt{3})$

   $= 81\sqrt{3}$

9. $a_n = a_1 r^{n-1}$

   $a_4 = 9r^{4-1}$

   $\dfrac{8}{3} = 9r^{4-1}$

   $\dfrac{8}{3} = 9r^3$

   $\dfrac{8}{27} = r^3$

   $\dfrac{2}{3} = r$

   $a_n = a_1 r^{n-1}$

   $a_2 = 9\left(\dfrac{2}{3}\right)^{2-1} = 9\left(\dfrac{2}{3}\right) = 6$

   $a_3 = 9\left(\dfrac{2}{3}\right)^{3-1} = 9\left(\dfrac{2}{3}\right)^2 = 9\left(\dfrac{4}{9}\right) = 4$

10. $a_n = a_1 r^{n-1}$

    $a_4 = 8r^{4-1}$

    $\dfrac{27}{8} = 8r^{4-1}$

    $\dfrac{27}{8} = 8r^3$

    $\dfrac{27}{64} = r^3$

    $\dfrac{3}{4} = r$

    $a_n = a_1 r^{n-1}$

    $a_2 = 8\left(\dfrac{3}{4}\right)^{2-1} = 8\left(\dfrac{3}{4}\right) = 6$

    $a_3 = 8\left(\dfrac{3}{4}\right)^{3-1} = 8\left(\dfrac{3}{4}\right)^2 = 8\left(\dfrac{9}{16}\right) = \dfrac{9}{2}$

11.
$$a_n = a_1 r^{n-1}$$
$$a_4 = 3r^{4-1}$$
$$-\frac{8}{9} = 3r^{4-1}$$
$$-\frac{8}{9} = 3r^3$$
$$-\frac{8}{27} = r^3$$
$$-\frac{2}{3} = r$$
$$a_n = a_1 r^{n-1}$$
$$a_2 = 3\left(-\frac{2}{3}\right)^{2-1} = 3\left(-\frac{2}{3}\right) = -2$$
$$a_3 = 3\left(-\frac{2}{3}\right)^{3-1} = 3\left(-\frac{2}{3}\right)^2 = 3\left(\frac{4}{9}\right) = \frac{4}{3}$$

12.
$$a_n = a_1 r^{n-1}$$
$$a_4 = 6r^{4-1}$$
$$-48 = 6r^{4-1}$$
$$-48 = 6r^3$$
$$-8 = r^3$$
$$-2 = r$$
$$a_n = a_1 r^{n-1}$$
$$a_2 = 6(-2)^{2-1} = 6(-2) = -12$$
$$a_3 = 6(-2)^{3-1} = 6(-2)^2 = 6(4) = 24$$

13.
$$a_n = a_1 r^{n-1}$$
$$a_4 = (-3)r^{4-1}$$
$$192 = (-3)r^{4-1}$$
$$192 = (-3)r^3$$
$$-64 = r^3$$
$$-4 = r$$
$$a_n = a_1 r^{n-1}$$
$$a_2 = -3(-4)^{2-1} = -3(-4) = 12$$
$$a_3 = -3(-4)^{3-1} = -3(-4)^2 = -3(16) = -48$$

14.
$$a_n = a_1 r^{n-1}$$
$$a_4 = 5r^{4-1}$$
$$625 = 5r^{4-1}$$
$$625 = 5r^3$$
$$125 = r^3$$
$$5 = r$$
$$a_n = a_1 r^{n-1}$$
$$a_2 = 5(5)^{2-1} = 5(5) = 25$$
$$a_3 = 5(5)^{3-1} = 5(5)^2 = 5(25) = 125$$

Objective 11.3.2 Exercises

15.
$$r = \frac{a_2}{a_1} = \frac{6}{2} = 3$$
$$S_n = \frac{a_1(1 - r^n)}{1 - r}$$
$$S_7 = \frac{2(1 - 3^7)}{1 - 3}$$
$$= \frac{2(1 - 2187)}{-2}$$
$$= \frac{2(-2186)}{-2}$$
$$= 2186$$

16.
$$r = \frac{a_2}{a_1} = \frac{12}{-4} = -3$$
$$S_n = \frac{a_1(1 - r^n)}{1 - r}$$
$$S_7 = \frac{-4[1 - (-3)^7]}{1 - (-3)}$$
$$= \frac{-4[1 - (-2187)]}{4}$$
$$= \frac{-4(2188)}{4}$$
$$= -2188$$

17.
$$r = \frac{a_2}{a_1} = \frac{9}{12} = \frac{3}{4}$$
$$S_n = \frac{a_1(1 - r^n)}{1 - r}$$
$$S_5 = \frac{12\left[1 - \left(\frac{3}{4}\right)^5\right]}{1 - \frac{3}{4}}$$
$$= \frac{12\left(1 - \frac{243}{1024}\right)}{\frac{1}{4}}$$
$$= 48\left(\frac{781}{1024}\right)$$
$$= \frac{2343}{64}$$

18. $r = \dfrac{a_2}{a_1} = \dfrac{3\sqrt{2}}{3} = \sqrt{2}$

$S_n = \dfrac{a_1(1-r^n)}{1-r}$

$S_{12} = \dfrac{3[1-(\sqrt{2})^{12}]}{1-\sqrt{2}}$

$\quad = \dfrac{3(1-2^6)}{1-\sqrt{2}}$

$\quad = \dfrac{3(1-64)}{1-\sqrt{2}}$

$\quad = \dfrac{3(-63)}{1-\sqrt{2}}$

$\quad = \dfrac{-189}{1-\sqrt{2}}$

$\quad = \dfrac{-189}{1-\sqrt{2}} \cdot \dfrac{1+\sqrt{2}}{1+\sqrt{2}}$

$\quad = \dfrac{-189-189\sqrt{2}}{-1}$

$\quad = 189+189\sqrt{2}$

19. $a_i = (2)^i$

$a_1 = (2)^1 = 2$

$a_2 = (2)^2 = 4$

$r = \dfrac{a_2}{a_1} = \dfrac{4}{2} = 2$

$S_i = \dfrac{a_1(1-r^i)}{1-r}$

$S_5 = \dfrac{2(1-2^5)}{1-2} = \dfrac{2(1-32)}{-1} = -2(-31) = 62$

20. $a_n = \left(\dfrac{3}{2}\right)^n$

$a_1 = \left(\dfrac{3}{2}\right)^1 = \dfrac{3}{2}$

$a_2 = \left(\dfrac{3}{2}\right)^2 = \dfrac{9}{4}$

$r = \dfrac{a_2}{a_1} = \dfrac{9}{4} \div \dfrac{3}{2} = \dfrac{9}{4} \cdot \dfrac{2}{3} = \dfrac{3}{2}$

$S_n = \dfrac{a_1(1-r^n)}{1-r}$

$S_6 = \dfrac{\frac{3}{2}\left[1-\left(\frac{3}{2}\right)^6\right]}{1-\frac{3}{2}}$

$\quad = \dfrac{\frac{3}{2}\left(1-\frac{729}{64}\right)}{-\frac{1}{2}}$

$\quad = -3\left(-\dfrac{665}{64}\right)$

$\quad = \dfrac{1995}{64}$

21. $a_i = \left(\dfrac{1}{3}\right)^i$

$a_1 = \left(\dfrac{1}{3}\right)^1 = \dfrac{1}{3}$

$a_2 = \left(\dfrac{1}{3}\right)^2 = \dfrac{1}{9}$

$r = \dfrac{a_2}{a_1} = \dfrac{1}{9} \div \dfrac{1}{3} = \dfrac{1}{9} \cdot \dfrac{3}{1} = \dfrac{1}{3}$

$S_i = \dfrac{a_1(1-r^i)}{1-r}$

$S_5 = \dfrac{\frac{1}{3}\left[1-\left(\frac{1}{3}\right)^5\right]}{1-\frac{1}{3}} = \dfrac{\frac{1}{3}\left(1-\frac{1}{243}\right)}{\frac{2}{3}} = \dfrac{1}{2}\left(\dfrac{242}{243}\right) = \dfrac{121}{243}$

22. $a_i = \left(\dfrac{2}{3}\right)^i$

$a_1 = \left(\dfrac{2}{3}\right)^1 = \dfrac{2}{3}$

$a_2 = \left(\dfrac{2}{3}\right)^2 = \dfrac{4}{9}$

$r = \dfrac{a_2}{a_1} = \dfrac{4}{9} \div \dfrac{2}{3} = \dfrac{4}{9} \cdot \dfrac{3}{2} = \dfrac{2}{3}$

$S_6 = \dfrac{\frac{2}{3}\left[1-\left(\frac{2}{3}\right)^6\right]}{1-\frac{2}{3}}$

$\quad = \dfrac{\frac{2}{3}\left(1-\frac{64}{729}\right)}{\frac{1}{3}}$

$\quad = 2\left(\dfrac{665}{729}\right)$

$\quad = \dfrac{1330}{729}$

23. $a_i = (4)^i$

$a_1 = 4^1 = 4$

$a_2 = 4^2 = 16$

$r = \dfrac{a_2}{a_1} = \dfrac{16}{4} = 4$

$S_i = \dfrac{a_1(1-r^i)}{1-r}$

$S_5 = \dfrac{4(1-4^5)}{1-4}$

$\quad = \dfrac{4(1-1024)}{1-4}$

$\quad = \dfrac{-4(1023)}{-3}$

$\quad = 1364$

24. $a_n = (3)^n$

$a_1 = 3^1 = 3$

$a_2 = 3^2 = 9$

$r = \dfrac{a_2}{a_1} = \dfrac{9}{3} = 3$

$S_n = \dfrac{a_1(1 - r^n)}{1 - r}$

$S_8 = \dfrac{3(1 - 3^8)}{1 - 3}$

$\quad = \dfrac{3(1 - 6561)}{-2}$

$\quad = \dfrac{-3(6560)}{-2}$

$\quad = 9840$

25. $a_i = (7)^i$

$a_1 = 7^1 = 7$

$a_2 = 7^2 = 49$

$r = \dfrac{a_2}{a_1} = \dfrac{49}{7} = 7$

$S_i = \dfrac{a_1(1 - r^i)}{1 - r}$

$S_4 = \dfrac{7(1 - 7^4)}{1 - 7}$

$\quad = \dfrac{7(1 - 2401)}{-6}$

$\quad = \dfrac{-7(2400)}{-6}$

$\quad = 2800$

26. $a_n = (5)^n$

$a_1 = 5^1 = 5$

$a_2 = 5^2 = 25$

$r = \dfrac{a_2}{a_1} = \dfrac{25}{5} = 5$

$S_n = \dfrac{a_1(1 - r^n)}{1 - r}$

$S_5 = \dfrac{5(1 - 5^5)}{1 - 5}$

$\quad = \dfrac{5(1 - 3125)}{-4}$

$\quad = \dfrac{-5(3124)}{-4}$

$\quad = 3905$

27. $a_i = \left(\dfrac{3}{4}\right)^i$

$a_1 = \left(\dfrac{3}{4}\right)^1 = \dfrac{3}{4}$

$a_2 = \left(\dfrac{3}{4}\right)^2 = \dfrac{9}{16}$

$r = \dfrac{a_2}{a_1} = \dfrac{9}{16} \div \dfrac{3}{4} = \dfrac{9}{16} \cdot \dfrac{4}{3} = \dfrac{3}{4}$

$S_i = \dfrac{a_1(1 - r^i)}{1 - r}$

$S_5 = \dfrac{\dfrac{3}{4}\left[1 - \left(\dfrac{3}{4}\right)^5\right]}{1 - \dfrac{3}{4}}$

$\quad = \dfrac{\dfrac{3}{4}\left(1 - \dfrac{243}{1024}\right)}{1 - \dfrac{3}{4}}$

$\quad = \dfrac{\dfrac{3}{4}\left(\dfrac{781}{1024}\right)}{\dfrac{1}{4}}$

$\quad = 3\left(\dfrac{781}{1024}\right)$

$\quad = \dfrac{2343}{1024}$

28. $a_n = \left(\dfrac{7}{4}\right)^n$

$a_1 = \left(\dfrac{7}{4}\right)^1 = \dfrac{7}{4}$

$a_2 = \left(\dfrac{7}{4}\right)^2 = \dfrac{49}{16}$

$r = \dfrac{a_2}{a_1} = \dfrac{49}{16} \div \dfrac{7}{4} = \dfrac{49}{16} \cdot \dfrac{4}{7} = \dfrac{7}{4}$

$S_n = \dfrac{a_1(1 - r^n)}{1 - r}$

$S_3 = \dfrac{\dfrac{7}{4}\left[1 - \left(\dfrac{7}{4}\right)^3\right]}{1 - \dfrac{7}{4}}$

$\quad = \dfrac{\dfrac{7}{4}\left(1 - \dfrac{343}{64}\right)}{-\dfrac{3}{4}}$

$\quad = \dfrac{-\dfrac{7}{4}\left(\dfrac{279}{64}\right)}{-\dfrac{3}{4}}$

$\quad = \dfrac{7}{3}\left(\dfrac{279}{64}\right)$

$\quad = \dfrac{651}{64}$

29. $a_i = \left(\dfrac{5}{3}\right)^i$

$a_1 = \left(\dfrac{5}{3}\right)^1 = \dfrac{5}{3}$

$a_2 = \left(\dfrac{5}{3}\right)^2 = \dfrac{25}{9}$

$r = \dfrac{a_2}{a_1} = \dfrac{25}{9} \div \dfrac{5}{3} = \dfrac{25}{9} \cdot \dfrac{3}{5} = \dfrac{5}{3}$

$S_i = \dfrac{a_1(1 - r^i)}{1 - r}$

$S_4 = \dfrac{\dfrac{5}{3}\left[1 - \left(\dfrac{5}{3}\right)^4\right]}{1 - \dfrac{5}{3}}$

$= \dfrac{\dfrac{5}{3}\left(1 - \dfrac{625}{81}\right)}{-\dfrac{2}{3}}$

$= \dfrac{-\dfrac{5}{3}\left(\dfrac{544}{81}\right)}{-\dfrac{2}{3}}$

$= \dfrac{5}{2}\left(\dfrac{544}{81}\right)$

$= \dfrac{1360}{81}$

30. $a_n = \left(\dfrac{1}{2}\right)^n$

$a_1 = \left(\dfrac{1}{2}\right)^1 = \dfrac{1}{2}$

$a_2 = \left(\dfrac{1}{2}\right)^2 = \dfrac{1}{4}$

$r = \dfrac{a_2}{a_1} = \dfrac{1}{4} \div \dfrac{1}{2} = \dfrac{1}{4} \cdot \dfrac{2}{1} = \dfrac{1}{2}$

$S_n = \dfrac{a_1(1 - r^n)}{1 - r}$

$S_6 = \dfrac{\dfrac{1}{2}\left[1 - \left(\dfrac{1}{2}\right)^6\right]}{1 - \dfrac{1}{2}}$

$= \dfrac{\dfrac{1}{2}\left(1 - \dfrac{1}{64}\right)}{\dfrac{1}{2}}$

$= \dfrac{\dfrac{1}{2}\left(\dfrac{63}{64}\right)}{\dfrac{1}{2}}$

$= \dfrac{63}{64}$

Objective 11.3.3 Exercises

31. $r = \dfrac{a_2}{a_1} = \dfrac{2}{3}$

$S = \dfrac{a_1}{1 - r} = \dfrac{3}{1 - \dfrac{2}{3}} = \dfrac{3}{\dfrac{1}{3}} = 9$

32. $r = \dfrac{a_2}{a_1} = \dfrac{-\dfrac{1}{4}}{2} = -\dfrac{1}{8}$

$S = \dfrac{a_1}{1 - r} = \dfrac{2}{1 - \left(-\dfrac{1}{8}\right)} = \dfrac{2}{\dfrac{9}{8}} = \dfrac{16}{9}$

33. $r = \dfrac{a_2}{a_1} = \dfrac{-4}{6} = -\dfrac{2}{3}$

$S = \dfrac{a_1}{1 - r} = \dfrac{6}{1 - \left(-\dfrac{2}{3}\right)} = \dfrac{6}{\dfrac{5}{3}} = \dfrac{18}{5}$

34. $r = \dfrac{a_2}{a_1} = \dfrac{\dfrac{1}{100}}{\dfrac{1}{10}} = \dfrac{1}{10}$

$S = \dfrac{a_1}{1 - r} = \dfrac{\dfrac{1}{10}}{1 - \dfrac{1}{10}} = \dfrac{\dfrac{1}{10}}{\dfrac{9}{10}} = \dfrac{1}{9}$

35. $r = \dfrac{a_2}{a_1} = \dfrac{\dfrac{7}{100}}{\dfrac{7}{10}} = \dfrac{1}{10}$

$S = \dfrac{a_1}{1 - r} = \dfrac{\dfrac{7}{10}}{1 - \dfrac{1}{10}} = \dfrac{\dfrac{7}{10}}{\dfrac{9}{10}} = \dfrac{7}{9}$

36. $r = \dfrac{a_2}{a_1} = \dfrac{\dfrac{5}{10,000}}{\dfrac{5}{100}} = \dfrac{1}{100}$

$S = \dfrac{a_1}{1 - r} = \dfrac{\dfrac{5}{100}}{1 - \dfrac{1}{100}} = \dfrac{\dfrac{5}{100}}{\dfrac{99}{100}} = \dfrac{5}{99}$

37. $0.8\overline{8}\,8 = 0.8 + 0.08 + 0.008 + \ldots$

$= \dfrac{8}{10} + \dfrac{8}{100} + \dfrac{8}{1000} + \ldots$

$S = \dfrac{a_1}{1 - r} = \dfrac{\dfrac{8}{10}}{1 - \dfrac{1}{10}} = \dfrac{\dfrac{8}{10}}{\dfrac{9}{10}} = \dfrac{8}{9}$

An equivalent fraction is $\dfrac{8}{9}$.

38. $0.5\overline{5}\,5 = 0.5 + 0.05 + 0.005 + \ldots$

$= \dfrac{5}{10} + \dfrac{5}{100} + \dfrac{5}{1000} + \ldots$

$S = \dfrac{a_1}{1 - r} = \dfrac{\dfrac{5}{10}}{1 - \dfrac{1}{10}} = \dfrac{\dfrac{5}{10}}{\dfrac{9}{10}} = \dfrac{5}{9}$

An equivalent fraction is $\dfrac{5}{9}$.

39. $0.2\overline{2}\,2 = 0.2 + 0.02 + 0.002 + \ldots$

$= \dfrac{2}{10} + \dfrac{2}{100} + \dfrac{2}{1000} + \ldots$

$S = \dfrac{a_1}{1 - r} = \dfrac{\dfrac{2}{10}}{1 - \dfrac{1}{10}} = \dfrac{\dfrac{2}{10}}{\dfrac{9}{10}} = \dfrac{2}{9}$

An equivalent fraction $\dfrac{2}{9}$.

40. $0.99\overline{9} = 0.9 + 0.09 + 0.009 + \dots$

$$= \frac{9}{10} + \frac{9}{100} + \frac{9}{1000} + \dots$$

$$S = \frac{a_1}{1-r} = \frac{\frac{9}{10}}{1-\frac{1}{10}} = \frac{\frac{9}{10}}{\frac{9}{10}} = \frac{9}{9} = 1$$

An equivalent fraction is 1.

41. $0.45\overline{45} = 0.45 + 0.0045 + 0.000045 + \dots$

$$= \frac{45}{100} + \frac{45}{10,000} + \frac{45}{1,000,000} + \dots$$

$$S = \frac{a_1}{1-r} = \frac{\frac{45}{100}}{1-\frac{1}{100}} = \frac{\frac{45}{100}}{\frac{99}{100}} = \frac{45}{99} = \frac{5}{11}$$

An equivalent fraction is $\frac{5}{11}$.

42. $0.18\overline{18} = 0.18 + 0.0018 + 0.000018 + \dots$

$$= \frac{18}{100} + \frac{18}{10,000} + \frac{18}{1,000,000} + \dots$$

$$S = \frac{a_1}{1-r} = \frac{\frac{18}{100}}{1-\frac{1}{100}} = \frac{\frac{18}{100}}{\frac{99}{100}} = \frac{18}{99} = \frac{2}{11}$$

An equivalent fraction is $\frac{2}{11}$.

43. $0.1\overline{666} = 0.1 + 0.06 + 0.006 + 0.0006 + \dots$

$$= \frac{1}{10} + \frac{6}{100} + \frac{6}{1000} + \frac{6}{10,000} + \dots$$

$$S = \frac{a_1}{1-r} = \frac{\frac{6}{100}}{1-\frac{1}{10}} = \frac{\frac{6}{100}}{\frac{9}{10}} = \frac{6}{90} = \frac{1}{15}$$

$$0.1\overline{666} = \frac{1}{10} + \frac{1}{15} = \frac{5}{30} = \frac{1}{6}$$

An equivalent fraction is $\frac{1}{6}$.

44. $0.8\overline{333} = 0.8 + 0.03 + 0.003 + 0.0003 + \dots$

$$= \frac{8}{10} + \frac{3}{100} + \frac{3}{1000} + \frac{3}{10,000} + \dots$$

$$S = \frac{a_1}{1-r} = \frac{\frac{3}{100}}{1-\frac{1}{10}} = \frac{\frac{3}{100}}{\frac{9}{10}} = \frac{3}{90} = \frac{1}{30}$$

$$0.8\overline{333} = \frac{8}{10} + \frac{1}{30} = \frac{25}{30} = \frac{5}{6}$$

An equivalent fraction is $\frac{5}{6}$.

Objective 11.3.4 Exercises

45. Strategy
Use the Formula for the nth Term of a Geometric Sequence.

Solution
$a_1 = 1,\ r = 3$
$a_n = a_1 r^{n-1}$
$a_n = 1 \cdot 3^{n-1}$
$a_n = 3^{n-1}$

46. Strategy
Use the Formula for the nth Term of a Geometric Sequence.

Solution
$a_1 = 1,\ r = 8$
$a_n = a_1 r^{n-1}$
$a_n = 1 \cdot 8^{n-1}$
$a_n = 8^{n-1}$

47. Strategy
To find the amount of radioactive material at the beginning of the seventh day, use the Formula for the nth Term of a Geometric Sequence.

Solution
$n = 7,\ a_1 = 500,\ r = \frac{1}{2}$
$a_n = a_1 r^{n-1}$
$a_7 = 500\left(\frac{1}{2}\right)^{7-1} = 500\left(\frac{1}{2}\right)^6 = 500\left(\frac{1}{64}\right) = 7.8125$

There will be 7.8125 mg of radioactive material in the sample at the beginning of the seventh day.

48. Strategy
To find the total distance the pendulum traveled in five swings, use the Formula for the Sum of a Finite Geometric Series.

Solution
$n = 5,\ a_1 = 18,\ r = \frac{3}{4}$
$$S_n = \frac{a_1(1-r^n)}{1-r}$$
$$S_5 = \frac{18\left[1-\left(\frac{3}{4}\right)^5\right]}{1-\frac{3}{4}}$$
$$= \frac{18\left(1-\frac{243}{1024}\right)}{\frac{1}{4}}$$
$$= 72\left(\frac{781}{1024}\right)$$
$$\approx 54.9$$
The total distance is 54.9 in.

49. Strategy
To find the height of the ball on the fifth bounce, use the Formula for the nth Term of a Geometric Sequence. Let a_1 be the height of the ball after the first bounce.

Solution
$n = 5,\ a_1 = 80\% \text{ of } 8 = 6.4,\ r = 80\% = \frac{4}{5}$
$a_n = a_1 r^{n-1}$
$a_5 = 6.4\left(\frac{4}{5}\right)^{5-1} = 6.4\left(\frac{4}{5}\right)^4 = 6.4\left(\frac{256}{625}\right) \approx 2.6$

The ball bounces to a height of 2.6 ft on the fifth bounce.

50. Strategy

To find the temperature after 3 h, use the Formula for the nth Term of a Geometric Sequence. Let a_1 be the temperature after 1 h.

Solution

$n = 3$, $a_1 = 1.10(75) = 82.5$, $r = 110\% = 1.10$

$a_n = a_1 r^{n-1}$

$a_3 = 82.5(1.10)^{3-1} = 82.5(1.12) \approx 99.8$

The temperature of the spa after 3 h is 99.8° F.

51. Strategy

To find the value of the land in 15 years, use the Formula for the nth Term of a Geometric Sequence. Let a_1 be the value of the land after 1 year.

Solution

$n = 15$, $a_1 = 1.12(15,000) = 16,800$, $r = 112\% = 1.12$

$a_n = a_1 r^{n-1}$

$a_{15} = 16,800(1.12)^{15-1}$

$= 16,800(4.8871123)$

$\approx 82,103.49$

The value of the land in 15 years will be $82,103.49.

52. Strategy

To find the total amount of money earned in 30 days, use the Formula for the sum of n Terms of a Finite Geometric Series.

Solution

$n = 30$, $a_1 = 1$, $r = 2$

$S_n = \dfrac{a_1(1 - r^n)}{1 - r}$

$S_{30} = \dfrac{1(1 - 2^{30})}{1 - 2}$

$= \dfrac{1(1 - 1,073,741,824)}{-1}$

$= \dfrac{-1,073,741,823}{-1}$

$= 1,073,741,823$

The total amount earned in 30 days is 1,073,741,823 cents or $10,737,418.23.

53. Strategy

To find the value of the house in 30 yr, use the Formula for the nth Term of a Geometric Sequence.

Solution

$n = 30$, $a_1 = 1.05(100,000) = 105,000$, $r = 105\% = 1.05$

$a_n = a_1 r^{n-1}$

$a_{30} = 105,000(1.05)^{30-1}$

$= (105,000)(4.1161356)$

$= 432,194.24$

The value of the house in 30 yr will be $432,194.24.

54. Strategy

To find the number of bacteria after 24 h, use the Formula for the nth Term of a Geometric Sequence.

Solution

$n = \dfrac{24}{2} = 12$, $a_1 = 2(500) = 1000$, $r = 2$

$a_n = a_1 r^{n-1}$

$a_{12} = 1000(2)^{12-1} = 1000(2048) = 2,048,000$

The number of bacteria after 24 h is 2,048,000.

Applying Concepts 11.3

55. 4, –2, 1, …

$r = -\dfrac{1}{2}$

$a_4 = a_3 r = 1\left(-\dfrac{1}{2}\right) = -\dfrac{1}{2}$

The sequence is geometric. (G)

The next term is $-\dfrac{1}{2}$.

56. –8, 0, 8, …

$d = 8$

$a_4 = a_3 + d = 8 + 8 = 16$

The sequence is arithmetic. (A)

The next term is 16.

57. 5, 6.5, 8, …

$d = 1.5$

$a_4 = a_3 + d = 8 + 1.5 = 9.5$

The sequence is arithmetic. (A)

The next term is 9.5.

58. –7, 14, –28, …

$r = -2$

$a_4 = a_3 r = -28(-2) = 56$

The sequence is geometric. (G)

The next term is 56.

59. 1, 4, 9, 16, …

$a_n = n^2$

$a_5 = 5^2 = 25$

The sequence is neither arithmetic nor geometric. (N) The next term is 25.

60. $\sqrt{1}, \sqrt{2}, \sqrt{3}, \sqrt{4}, \dots$

$a_n = \sqrt{n}$

$a_5 = \sqrt{5}$

The sequence is neither arithmetic nor geometric. (N)

The next term is $\sqrt{5}$.

61. $x^8, x^6, x^4, \dots$

$r = x^{-2}$

$a_4 = a_3 r = x^4(x^{-2}) = x^2$

The sequence is geometric. (G)

The next term is x^2.

62. $5a^2, 3a^2, a^2, \ldots$

$d = -2a^2$

$a_4 = a_3 + d = a^2 + (-2a^2) = -a^2$

The sequence is arithmetic. (A)

The next term is $-a^2$.

63. $\log x, 2 \log x, 3 \log x, \ldots$

$d = \log x$

$a_4 = a_3 + d = 3 \log x + \log x = 4 \log x$

The sequence is arithmetic. (A)

The next term is $4 \log x$.

64. $\log x, 3 \log x, 9 \log x, \ldots$

$r = 3$

$a_4 = a_3 r = (9 \log x)(3) = 27 \log x$

The sequence is geometric. (G)

The next term is $27 \log x$.

65. Find r for the geometric series in which $a_1 = 3$

and $a_4 = \dfrac{1}{9}$.

$a_n = a_1 r^{n-1}$

$\dfrac{1}{9} = 3r^{4-1}$

$\dfrac{1}{9} = 3r^3$

$\dfrac{1}{27} = r^3$

$\sqrt[3]{\dfrac{1}{27}} = \sqrt[3]{r^3}$

$\dfrac{1}{3} = r$

r is the same for the geometric series in which

$a_3 = 3$ and $a_6 = \dfrac{1}{9}$.

$a_n = a_1 r^{n-1}$

$\dfrac{1}{9} = a_1 \left(\dfrac{1}{3}\right)^{6-1}$

$\dfrac{1}{9} = a_1 \left(\dfrac{1}{3}\right)^5$

$\dfrac{1}{9} = a_1 \left(\dfrac{1}{243}\right)$

$27 = a_1$

The first term is 27.

66. The sum of a series is the same in reverse order. Find n for the series in which $a_1 = 162$ and $r = -\dfrac{1}{3}$.

$S_n = \dfrac{a_1(1 - r^n)}{1 - r}$

$122 = \dfrac{162\left[1 - \left(-\frac{1}{3}\right)^n\right]}{1 - \left(-\frac{1}{3}\right)}$

$122 = \dfrac{162\left[1 - \left(-\frac{1}{3}\right)^n\right]}{\left(\frac{4}{3}\right)}$

$122 = \dfrac{486\left[1 - \left(-\frac{1}{3}\right)^n\right]}{4}$

$488 = 486\left[1 - \left(-\dfrac{1}{3}\right)^n\right]$

$\dfrac{244}{243} = 1 - \left(-\dfrac{1}{3}\right)^n$

$\dfrac{1}{243} = -\left(-\dfrac{1}{3}\right)^n$

$\left(\dfrac{1}{3}\right)^5 = -\left(-\dfrac{1}{3}\right)^n$

$5 = n$

n is the same for the series in which $a_n = 162$ and $r = -3$.

$a_n = a_1 r^{n-1}$

$162 = a_1(-3)^{5-1}$

$162 = a_1(-3)^4$

$162 = a_1(81)$

$2 = a_1$

67. $a_n = 2^n$

$a_1 = 2^1 = 1$

$a_2 = 2^2 = 4$

$a_3 = 2^3 = 8$

$\vdots$

$a_n = 2^n$

$a_{n+1} = 2^{n+1}$

$b_n = \log a_n$

$b_1 = \log a_1 = \log 2$

$b_2 = \log a_2 = \log 4 = \log 2^2 = 2 \log 2$

$b_3 = \log a_3 = \log 8 = \log 2^3 = 3 \log 2$

$\vdots$

$b_n = \log a_n = \log 2^n = n \log 2$

$b_{n+1} = \log a_{n+1} = \log 2^{n+1} = (n+1) \log 2$

$b_{n+1} - b_n = (n+1) \log 2 - n \log 2$

$= n \log 2 + \log 2 - n \log 2 = \log 2$

The common difference is $\log 2$.

68.
$$a_n = e^n$$
$$a_1 = e$$
$$a_2 = e^2$$
$$a_3 = e^3$$
$$\vdots$$
$$a_n = e^n$$
$$a_{n+1} = e^{n+1}$$

$$b_n = \ln a_n$$
$$b_1 = \ln a_1 = \ln e = 1$$
$$b_2 = \ln a_2 = \ln e^2 = 2 \ln e = 2$$
$$b_3 = \ln a_3 = \ln e^3 = 3 \ln e = 3$$
$$\vdots$$
$$b_n = \ln a_n = \ln e^n = n \ln e = n$$
$$b_{n+1} = \ln a_{n+1} = \ln e^{n+1} = (n+1) \ln e = n+1$$
$$b_{n+1} - b_n = n+1-n = 1$$

The common difference is 1.

69.
$$a_n = 3n - 2$$
$$a_1 = 3(1) - 2 = 1$$
$$a_2 = 3(2) - 2 = 4$$
$$a_3 = 3(3) - 2 = 7$$
$$\vdots$$
$$a_n = 3n - 2$$
$$a_{n+1} = 3(n+1) - 2 = 3n + 3 - 2 = 3n + 1$$
$$b_n = 2^{a_n}$$
$$b_1 = 2^{a_1} = 2^1 = 2$$
$$b_2 = 2^{a_2} = 2^4 = 16$$
$$b_3 = 2^{a_3} = 2^7 = 128$$
$$\vdots$$
$$b_n = 2^{a_n} = 2^{3n-2}$$
$$b_{n+1} = 2^{a_{n+1}} = 2^{3n+1}$$
$$\frac{b^{n+1}}{b^n} = \frac{2^{3n+1}}{2^{3n-2}} = 2^3 = 8$$

The common ratio is 8.

70.
$$f(n) = ab^n$$
$$f(1) = ab^1 = ab$$
$$f(2) = ab^2$$
$$f(3) = ab^3$$
$$\vdots$$
$$f(n) = ab^n$$
$$f(n+1) = ab^{n+1}$$
$$\frac{f(n+1)}{f(n)} = \frac{ab^{n+1}}{ab^n} = b$$

The common ratio is b.

71. a.
$$R_n = R_1 (1.0075)^{n-1}$$
$$R_{27} = 66.29(1.0075)^{27-1} = 66.29(1.0075)^{26}$$
$$\approx 80.50$$

$80.50 of the loan is repaid in the twenty-seventh payment.

b.
$$T = \sum_{k=1}^{n} R_1 (1.0075)^{k-1}$$
$$T = \sum_{k=1}^{20} 66.29(1.0075)^{k-1}$$
$$T = 66.29(1.0075)^0 + 66.29(1.0075)^1 + 66.29(1.0075)^2 + \ldots + 66.29(1.0075)^{19}$$
$$a_1 = 66.29(1.0075)^0 = 66.25$$
$$S_{20} = \frac{66.29(1 - 1.0075^{20})}{1 - 1.0075} \approx 1424.65$$

The total amount repaid after 20 payments is $1424.65.

c. $5000 - 1424.65 = 3575.35$

The unpaid amount repaid after 20 payments is $3575.35.

72. a. k must be greater than g so that $|r| < 1$. (For this infinite geometric series, $r = \dfrac{1+g}{1+k}$.)

b. $\displaystyle\sum_{n=0}^{\infty} D\left[\frac{1+g}{1+k}\right]^n$

$\displaystyle\sum_{n=0}^{\infty} 2.55\left[\frac{1.05}{1.10}\right]^n = 2.25\left(\frac{1.05}{1.10}\right)^0 + 2.25\left(\frac{1.05}{1.10}\right)^1 + 2.25\left(\frac{1.05}{1.10}\right)^2 + \ldots$

$a_1 = 2.25, \ r = \dfrac{1.05}{1.10}$

$S = \dfrac{a_1}{1-r} = \dfrac{2.25}{1 - \frac{1.05}{1.10}} = 49.5$

The value of the stock is $49.50.

73. Edouard Anatole Lucas was a French mathematician who lived from 1842 to 1891. His sequence is similar to a Fibonacci sequence. The first five terms of the sequence are 1, 3, 4, 7, 11. In general, $a_1 = 1$, $a_2 = 3$, and $a_n = a_{n-2} + a_{n-1}$, $n \geq 3$.

74. The distance that the hare travels once it "catches up" to the tortoise is the sum of the series $10 + 1 + \dfrac{1}{10} + \dfrac{1}{100} + \ldots$. The sum of this series is $\dfrac{100}{9} = 11.111111\ldots$. The hare overtakes the tortoise in approximately 11.11 meters.

Section 11.4

Concept Review 11.4

1. Never true
$0! \cdot 4! = 1 \cdot 24 = 24$

2. Never true
$\dfrac{4!}{0!} = \dfrac{24}{1} = 24$

3. Never true
The exponent on the fifth term is 4.

4. Never true
$n!$ is the product of the first n positive numbers.

5. Never true
There are $n + 1$ terms in the expansion of $(a + b)^n$.

6. Always true

Objective 11.4.1 Exercises

1. The factorial of a number is the product of all the natural numbers less than or equal to the number.

2. The Binomial Expansion Formula is used to expand $(a + b)^n$.

3. $3! = 3 \cdot 2 \cdot 1 = 6$

4. $4! = 4 \cdot 3 \cdot 2 \cdot 1 = 24$

5. $8! = 8 \cdot 7 \cdot 6 \cdot 5 \cdot 4 \cdot 3 \cdot 2 \cdot 1 = 40{,}320$

6. $9! = 9 \cdot 8 \cdot 7 \cdot 6 \cdot 5 \cdot 4 \cdot 3 \cdot 2 \cdot 1 = 362{,}880$

7. $0! = 1$

8. $1! = 1$

9. $\dfrac{5!}{2!3!} = \dfrac{5 \cdot 4 \cdot 3 \cdot 2 \cdot 1}{(2 \cdot 1)(3 \cdot 2 \cdot 1)} = 10$

10. $\dfrac{8!}{5!3!} = \dfrac{8 \cdot 7 \cdot 6 \cdot 5 \cdot 4 \cdot 3 \cdot 2 \cdot 1}{(5 \cdot 4 \cdot 3 \cdot 2 \cdot 1)(3 \cdot 2 \cdot 1)} = 56$

11. $\dfrac{6!}{6!0!} = \dfrac{6 \cdot 5 \cdot 4 \cdot 3 \cdot 2 \cdot 1}{(6 \cdot 5 \cdot 4 \cdot 3 \cdot 2 \cdot 1)(1)} = 1$

12. $\dfrac{10!}{10!0!} = \dfrac{10 \cdot 9 \cdot 8 \cdot 7 \cdot 6 \cdot 5 \cdot 4 \cdot 3 \cdot 2 \cdot 1}{(10 \cdot 9 \cdot 8 \cdot 7 \cdot 6 \cdot 5 \cdot 4 \cdot 3 \cdot 2 \cdot 1)(1)} = 1$

13. $\dfrac{9!}{6!3!} = \dfrac{9 \cdot 8 \cdot 7 \cdot 6 \cdot 5 \cdot 4 \cdot 3 \cdot 2 \cdot 1}{(6 \cdot 5 \cdot 4 \cdot 3 \cdot 2 \cdot 1)(3 \cdot 2 \cdot 1)} = 84$

14. $\dfrac{10}{2!8!} = \dfrac{10 \cdot 9 \cdot 8 \cdot 7 \cdot 6 \cdot 5 \cdot 4 \cdot 3 \cdot 2 \cdot 1}{(2 \cdot 1)(8 \cdot 7 \cdot 6 \cdot 5 \cdot 4 \cdot 3 \cdot 2 \cdot 1)} = 45$

15. $\dbinom{7}{2} = \dfrac{7!}{(7-2)!2!} = \dfrac{7!}{5!2!} = \dfrac{7 \cdot 6 \cdot 5 \cdot 4 \cdot 3 \cdot 2 \cdot 1}{(5 \cdot 4 \cdot 3 \cdot 2 \cdot 1)(2 \cdot 1)} = 21$

16. $\dbinom{8}{6} = \dfrac{8!}{(8-6)!6!}$

$= \dfrac{8!}{2!6!}$

$= \dfrac{8 \cdot 7 \cdot 6 \cdot 5 \cdot 4 \cdot 3 \cdot 2 \cdot 1}{(2 \cdot 1)(6 \cdot 5 \cdot 4 \cdot 3 \cdot 2 \cdot 1)}$

$= 28$

17. $\dbinom{10}{2} = \dfrac{10}{(10-2)!\,2!}$

$= \dfrac{10}{8!2!}$

$= \dfrac{10 \cdot 9 \cdot 8 \cdot 7 \cdot 6 \cdot 5 \cdot 4 \cdot 3 \cdot 2 \cdot 1}{(2 \cdot 1)(6 \cdot 5 \cdot 4 \cdot 3 \cdot 2 \cdot 1)}$

$= 45$

18. $\dbinom{9}{6} = \dfrac{9!}{(9-6)!\,6!}$

$= \dfrac{9!}{3!\,6!}$

$= \dfrac{9\cdot8\cdot7\cdot6\cdot5\cdot4\cdot3\cdot2\cdot1}{(3\cdot2\cdot1)(6\cdot5\cdot4\cdot3\cdot2\cdot1)}$

$= 84$

19. $\dbinom{9}{0} = \dfrac{9!}{(9-0)!\,0!}$

$= \dfrac{9!}{9!\,0!}$

$= \dfrac{9\cdot8\cdot7\cdot6\cdot5\cdot4\cdot3\cdot2\cdot1}{(9\cdot8\cdot7\cdot6\cdot5\cdot4\cdot3\cdot2\cdot1)(1)}$

$= 1$

20. $\dbinom{10}{10} = \dfrac{10!}{(10-10)!\,10!}$

$= \dfrac{10!}{0!\,10!}$

$= \dfrac{10\cdot9\cdot8\cdot7\cdot6\cdot5\cdot4\cdot3\cdot2\cdot1}{(1)10\cdot9\cdot8\cdot7\cdot6\cdot5\cdot4\cdot3\cdot2\cdot1)}$

$= 1$

21. $\dbinom{6}{3} = \dfrac{6!}{(6-3)!\,3!} = \dfrac{6!}{3!\,3!} = \dfrac{6\cdot5\cdot4\cdot3\cdot2\cdot1}{(3\cdot2\cdot1)(3\cdot2\cdot1)} = 20$

22. $\dbinom{7}{6} = \dfrac{7!}{(7-6)!\,6!} = \dfrac{7!}{1!\,6!} = \dfrac{7\cdot6\cdot5\cdot4\cdot3\cdot2\cdot1}{(1)(6\cdot5\cdot4\cdot3\cdot2\cdot1)} = 7$

23. $\dbinom{11}{1} = \dfrac{11!}{(11-1)!\,1!}$

$= \dfrac{11!}{10!\,1!}$

$= \dfrac{11\cdot10\cdot9\cdot8\cdot7\cdot6\cdot5\cdot4\cdot3\cdot2\cdot1}{(10\cdot9\cdot8\cdot7\cdot6\cdot5\cdot4\cdot3\cdot2\cdot1)(1)}$

$= 11$

24. $\dbinom{13}{1} = \dfrac{13!}{(13-1)!\,1!}$

$= \dfrac{13!}{12!\,1!}$

$= \dfrac{13\cdot12\cdot10\cdot9\cdot8\cdot7\cdot6\cdot5\cdot4\cdot3\cdot2\cdot1}{(12\cdot10\cdot9\cdot8\cdot7\cdot6\cdot5\cdot4\cdot3\cdot2\cdot1)(1)}$

$= 13$

25. $\dbinom{4}{2} = \dfrac{4!}{(4-2)!\,2!} = \dfrac{4!}{2!\,2!} = \dfrac{4\cdot3\cdot2\cdot1}{(2\cdot1)(2\cdot1)} = 6$

26. $\dbinom{8}{4} = \dfrac{8!}{(8-4)!\,4!}$

$= \dfrac{8!}{4!\,4!}$

$= \dfrac{8\cdot7\cdot6\cdot5\cdot4\cdot3\cdot2\cdot1}{(4\cdot3\cdot2\cdot1)(4\cdot3\cdot2\cdot1)}$

$= 70$

27. $(x+y)^4$

$= \dbinom{4}{0}x^4 + \dbinom{4}{1}x^3y + \dbinom{4}{2}x^2y^2 + \dbinom{4}{3}xy^3 + \dbinom{4}{4}y^4$

$= x^4 + 4x^3y + 6x^2y^2 + 4xy^3 + y^4$

28. $(r-s)^3$

$= \dbinom{3}{0}r^3 + \dbinom{3}{1}r^2(-s) + \dbinom{3}{2}r(-s)^2 + \dbinom{3}{3}(-s)^3$

$= r^3 - 3r^2s + 3rs^2 - s^3$

29. $(x-y)^5 = \dbinom{5}{0}x^5 + \dbinom{5}{1}x^4(-y) + \dbinom{5}{2}x^3(-y)^2 + \dbinom{5}{3}x^2(-y)^3 + \dbinom{5}{4}x(-y)^4 + \dbinom{5}{5}(-y)^5$

$= x^5 - 5x^4y + 10x^3y^2 - 10x^2y^3 + 5xy^4 - y^5$

30. $(y-3)^4 = \dbinom{4}{0}y^4 + \dbinom{4}{1}y^3(-3) + \dbinom{4}{2}y^2(-3)^2 + \dbinom{4}{3}y(-3)^3 + \dbinom{4}{4}(-3)^4$

$= y^4 + 4y^3(-3) + 6y^2(9) + 4y(-27) + 81$

$= y^4 - 12y^3 + 54y^2 - 108y + 81$

31. $(2m+1)^4 = \dbinom{4}{0}(2m)^4 + \dbinom{4}{1}(2m)^3(1) + \dbinom{4}{2}(2m)^2(1)^2 + \dbinom{4}{3}(2m)(1)^3 + \dbinom{4}{4}(1)^4$

$= 1(16m^4) + 4(8m^3) + 6(4m^2) + 4(2m) + 1(1)$

$= 16m^4 + 32m^3 + 24m^2 + 8m + 1$

32. $(2x+3y)^3 = \dbinom{3}{0}(2x)^3 + \dbinom{3}{1}(2x)^2(3y) + \dbinom{3}{2}(2x)(3y)^2 + \dbinom{3}{3}(3y)^3$

$= 1(8x^3) + 3(4x^2)(3y) + 3(2x)(9y^2) + 1(27y^3)$

$= 8x^3 + 36x^2y + 54xy^2 + 27y^3$

33. $(2r-3)^5 = \binom{5}{0}(2r)^5 + \binom{5}{1}(2r)^4(-3) + \binom{5}{2}(2r)^3(-3)^2 + \binom{5}{3}(2r)^2(-3)^3 + \binom{5}{4}(2r)(-3)^4 + \binom{5}{5}(-3)^5$

$\qquad = 1(32r^5) + 5(16r^4)(-3) + 10(8r^3)(9) + 10(4r^2)(-27) + 5(2r)(81) + 1(-243)$

$\qquad = 32r^5 - 240r^4 + 720r^3 - 1080r^2 + 810r - 243$

34. $(x+3y)^4 = \binom{4}{0}x^4 + \binom{4}{1}x^3(3y) + \binom{4}{2}x^2(3y)^2 + \binom{4}{3}x(3y)^3 + \binom{4}{4}(3y)^4$

$\qquad = x^4 + 4x^3(3y) + 6x^2(9y^2) + 4x(27y^3) + 81y^4$

$\qquad = x^4 + 12x^3y + 54x^2y^2 + 108xy^3 + 81y^4$

35. $(a+b)^{10} = \binom{10}{0}a^{10} + \binom{10}{1}a^9b + \binom{10}{2}a^8b^2 + \ldots$

$\qquad = a^{10} + 10a^9b + 45a^8b^2 + \ldots$

36. $(a+b)^9 = \binom{9}{0}a^9 + \binom{9}{1}a^8b + \binom{9}{2}a^7b^2 + \ldots$

$\qquad = a^9 + 9a^8b + 36a^7b^2 + \ldots$

37. $(a-b)^{11} = \binom{11}{0}a^{11} + \binom{11}{1}a^{10}(-b) + \binom{11}{2}a^9(-b)^2 + \ldots$

$\qquad = (1)a^{11} + 11a^{10}(-b) + 55a^9b^2 + \ldots$

$\qquad = a^{11} - 11a^{10}b + 55a^9b^2 + \ldots$

38. $(a-b)^{12} = \binom{12}{0}a^{12} + \binom{12}{1}a^{11}(-b) + \binom{12}{2}a^{10}(-b)^2 + \ldots$

$\qquad = (1)a^{12} + 12a^{11}(-b) + 66a^{10}b^2 + \ldots$

$\qquad = a^{12} - 12a^{11}b + 66a^{10}b^2 + \ldots$

39. $(2x+y)^8 = \binom{8}{0}(2x)^8 + \binom{8}{1}(2x)^7y + \binom{8}{2}(2x)^6y^2 + \ldots$

$\qquad = 1(256x^8) + 8(128x^7)y + 28(64x^6)y^2 + \ldots$

$\qquad = 256x^8 + 1024x^7y + 1792x^6y^2 + \ldots$

40. $(x+3y)^9 = \binom{9}{0}x^9 + \binom{9}{1}x^8(3y) + \binom{9}{2}x^7(3y)^2 + \ldots$

$\qquad = 1(x^9) + 9x^8(3y) + 36x^7(9y^2) + \ldots$

$\qquad = x^9 + 27x^8y + 324x^7y^2 + \ldots$

41. $(4x-3y)^8 = \binom{8}{0}(4x)^8 + \binom{8}{1}(4x)^7(-3y) + \binom{8}{2}(4x)^6(-3y)^2 + \ldots$

$\qquad = 1(65,536x^8) + 8(16,384x^7)(-3y) + 28(4096x^6)(9y^2) + \ldots$

$\qquad = 65,536x^8 - 393,216x^7y + 1,032,192x^6y^2 + \ldots$

42. $(2x-5)^7 = \binom{7}{0}(2x)^7 + \binom{7}{1}(2x)^6(-5) + \binom{7}{2}(2x)^5(-5)^2 + \ldots$

$\qquad = 1(128x^7) + 7(64x^6)(-5) + 21(32x^5)(25) + \ldots$

$\qquad = 128x^7 - 2240x^6 + 16,800x^5 + \ldots$

43. $\left(x+\dfrac{1}{x}\right)^7 = \binom{7}{0}x^7 + \binom{7}{1}x^6\left(\dfrac{1}{x}\right) + \binom{7}{2}x^5\left(\dfrac{1}{x}\right)^2 + \ldots$

$\qquad = 1(x^7) + 7x^6\left(\dfrac{1}{x}\right) + 21x^5\left(\dfrac{1}{x^2}\right) + \ldots$

$\qquad = x^7 + 7x^5 + 21x^3 + \ldots$

44. $\left(x-\dfrac{1}{x}\right)^8 = \dbinom{8}{0}x^8 + \dbinom{8}{1}x^7\left(-\dfrac{1}{x}\right) + \dbinom{8}{2}x^6\left(-\dfrac{1}{x}\right)^2 + \ldots$

$\qquad = 1(x^8) + 8x^7\left(-\dfrac{1}{x}\right) + 28x^6\left(\dfrac{1}{x^2}\right) + \ldots$

$\qquad = x^8 - 8x^6 + 28x^4 + \ldots$

45. $(x^2+3)^5 = \dbinom{5}{0}(x^2)^5 + \dbinom{5}{1}(x^2)^4(3) = \dbinom{5}{2}(x^2)^3(3)^2 + \ldots$

$\qquad = 1(x^{10}) + 5(x^8)(3) + 10(x^6)(9) + \ldots$

$\qquad = x^{10} + 15x^8 + 90x^6 + \ldots$

46. $(x^2-2)^6 = \dbinom{6}{0}(x^2)^6 + \dbinom{6}{1}(x^2)^5(-2) + \dbinom{6}{2}(x^2)^4(-2)^2 + \ldots$

$\qquad = 1(x^{12}) + 6(x^{10})(-2) + 15(x^8)(4) + \ldots$

$\qquad = x^{12} - 12x^{10} + 60x^8 + \ldots$

47. $n = 7,\, a = 2x,\, b = -1,\, r = 4$

$\dbinom{7}{4-1}(2x)^{7-4+1}(-1)^{4-1} = \dbinom{7}{3}(2x)^4(-1)^3 = 35(16x^4)(-1) = -560x^4$

48. $n = 5,\, a = x,\, b = 4,\, r = 3$

$\dbinom{5}{3-1}x^{5-3+1}(4)^{3-1} = \dbinom{5}{2}x^3(4)^2 = 10x^3(16) = 160x^3$

49. $n = 6,\, a = x^2,\, b = -y^2,\, r = 2$

$\dbinom{6}{2-1}(x^2)^{6-2+1}(-y^2)^{2-1} = \dbinom{6}{1}(x^2)^5(-y^2) = 6x^{10}(-y^2) = -6x^{10}y^2$

50. $n = 7,\, a = x^2,\, b = y^2,\, r = 6$

$\dbinom{7}{6-1}(x^2)^{7-6+1}(y^2)^{6-1} = \dbinom{7}{5}(x^2)^2(y^2)^5 = 21x^4y^{10}$

51. $n = 9,\, a = y,\, b = -1,\, r = 5$

$\dbinom{9}{5-1}y^{9-5+1}(-1)^{5-1} = \dbinom{9}{4}y^5(-1)^4 = 126y^5(1) = 126y^5$

52. $n = 8,\, a = x,\, b = -2,\, r = 8$

$\dbinom{8}{8-1}x^{8-8+1}(-2)^{8-1} = \dbinom{8}{7}x(-2)^7 = 8x(-128) = -1024x$

53. $n = 5,\, a = n,\, b = \dfrac{1}{n},\, r = 2$

$\dbinom{5}{2-1}n^{5-2+1}\left(\dfrac{1}{n}\right)^{2-1} = \dbinom{5}{1}n^4\left(\dfrac{1}{n}\right) = 5n^4\left(\dfrac{1}{n}\right) = 5n^3$

54. $n = 6,\, a = x,\, b = \dfrac{1}{2},\, r = 3$

$\dbinom{6}{3-1}x^{6-3+1}\left(\dfrac{1}{2}\right)^{3-1} = \dbinom{6}{2}x^4\left(\dfrac{1}{2}\right)^2 = 15x^4\left(\dfrac{1}{4}\right) = \dfrac{15}{4}x^4$

55. $n = 5,\, a = \dfrac{x}{2},\, b = 2,\, r = 1$

$\dbinom{5}{1-1}\left(\dfrac{x}{2}\right)^{5-1+1}(2)^{1-1} = \dbinom{5}{0}\left(\dfrac{x}{2}\right)^5(2)^0 = 1\left(\dfrac{x^5}{32}\right)(1) = \dfrac{x^5}{32}$

56. $n = 6$, $a = y$, $b = -\dfrac{2}{3}$, $r = 3$

$$\binom{6}{3-1}y^{6-3+1}\left(-\frac{2}{3}\right)^{3-1} = \binom{6}{2}y^4\left(-\frac{2}{3}\right)^2 = 15y^4\left(\frac{4}{9}\right) = \frac{20}{3}y^4$$

Applying Concepts 11.4

57.

```
                      1       1
                  1       2       1
              1       3       3       1
          1       4       6       4       1
      1       5      10      10       5       1
  1       6      15      20      15       6       1
1     7      21      35      35      21       7       1
```

58. $\dfrac{n!}{(n-2)!} = \dfrac{50!}{(50-2)!} = \dfrac{50!}{48!} = \dfrac{50 \cdot 49 \cdot 48!}{48!} = 50 \cdot 49 = 2450$

59. $\dfrac{n!}{(n-1)!} = \dfrac{n(n-1)!}{(n-1)!} = n$

60. The exponent of x is 7 in the first term, 6 in the second term, 5 in the third term, 4 in the fourth term, and 3 in the fifth term. Find the fifth term.

$$\binom{n}{r-1}a^{n-r+1}b^{r-1} = \binom{7}{5-1}x^{7-5+1}a^{5-1} = \binom{7}{4}x^3a^4 = \frac{7!}{3!4!}x^3a^4 = 35x^3a^4$$

The term that contains x^3 is $35x^3a^4$.

61. $(x^{1/2}+2)^4 = \binom{4}{0}(x^{1/2})^4 + \binom{4}{1}(x^{1/2})^3(2) + \binom{4}{2}(x^{1/2})^2(2^2) + \binom{4}{3}x^{1/2}(2^3) + \binom{4}{4}2^4$

$\qquad = x^2 + 4(2x^{3/2}) + 6(4x) + 4(8x^{1/2}) + 16$

$\qquad = x^2 + 8x^{3/2} + 24x + 32x^{1/2} + 16$

62. $(x^{-1}+y^{-1})^3 = \binom{3}{0}(x^{-1})^3 + \binom{3}{1}(x^{-1})^2y^{-1} + \binom{3}{2}x^{-1}(y^{-1})^2 + \binom{3}{3}(y^{-1})^3$

$\qquad = x^{-3} + 3x^{-2}y^{-1} + 3x^{-1}y^{-2} + y^{-3}$

$\qquad = \dfrac{1}{x^3} + \dfrac{3}{x^2y} + \dfrac{3}{xy^2} + \dfrac{1}{y^3}$

63. $(1+i)^6 = \binom{6}{0}1^6 + \binom{6}{1}1^5i + \binom{6}{2}1^4i^2 + \binom{6}{3}1^3i^3 + \binom{6}{4}1^2i^4 + \binom{6}{5}1i^5 + \binom{6}{6}i^6$

$\qquad = 1 + 6i + 15i^2 + 20i^3 + 15i^4 + 6i^5 + i^6$

$\qquad = 1 + 6i - 15 - 20i + 15 + 6i - 1 = -8i$

64. $\binom{n}{r} = \dfrac{n!}{r!(n-r)!}$

$\binom{n}{n-r} = \dfrac{n!}{(n-r)![n-(n-r)]!} = \dfrac{n!}{(n-r)!r!}$

65. $\dfrac{2 \cdot 4 \cdot 6 \cdot 8 \cdots (2n)}{2^n n!} = \dfrac{2(1) \cdot 2(2) \cdot 2(3) \cdot 2(4) \cdots 2(n)}{2^n n!}$

$\qquad = \dfrac{2^n(1 \cdot 2 \cdot 3 \cdots n)}{2^n n!}$

$\qquad = \dfrac{2^n n!}{2^n n!} = 1$

66. **Strategy**

To find the coefficient of a^2b^3c in the expansion of $(a+b+c)^6$, use the formula

$$\frac{n!}{r!\,k!(n-r-k)!}$$

where $n = 6$, $r = 2$, and $k = 3$.

Solution

$\dfrac{n!}{r!\,k!(n-r-k)!} = \dfrac{6!}{2!3!(6-2-3)!}$

$\qquad = \dfrac{6!}{2!3!1!}$

$\qquad = \dfrac{6 \cdot 5 \cdot 4 \cdot 3!}{2!3!} = \dfrac{120}{2} = 60$

The coefficient is 60.

67. Strategy

To find the coefficient of $a^4b^2c^3$ in the expansion of $(a+b+c)^9$, use the formula

$$\frac{n!}{r!\,k!\,(n-r-k)!}$$

where $n = 9$, $r = 4$, $k = 2$

Solution

$$\frac{n!}{r!\,k!\,(n-r-k)!} = \frac{9!}{4!\,2!\,(9-4-2)!}$$

$$= \frac{9!}{4!\,2!\,3!} = \frac{9\cdot 8\cdot 7\cdot 6\cdot 5\cdot 4!}{4!\,2\cdot 6}$$

$$= \frac{9\cdot 8\cdot 7\cdot 6\cdot 5}{2\cdot 6} = 1260$$

The coefficient is 1260.

68. Pascal's triangle may be the most famous of all number patterns. Although it seems to be a simple listing of the binomial coefficients, it also contains the triangular and pyramidal numbers of ancient Greece, the combinatorial numbers that arose in the Hindu studies of arrangements and selections, and (barely concealed) the Fibonacci numbers from medieval Italy. The triangle was written down long before 1654, the year in which Blaise Pascal wrote his *Traite du triangle arithmetique*, but it was this work that brought together all the different aspects of the numbers for the first time. A few properties are given below.
Each row begins and ends with the number 1. Any other number in a row is the sum of the two closest numbers above it.
The natural numbers appear in the second diagonal from the left. The triangular numbers appear in the next diagonal.
The triangle's first four rows are the first five powers of 11: $11^1 = 11$, $11^2 = 121$, $11^3 = 1331$, $11^4 = 14{,}541$.
To find the sum of the first n natural numbers, look to the right below the number; for example, the sum of the first 5 natural numbers is 15, and 15 is printed to the right below the 5 in the second diagonal.

Focus on Problem Solving

1. There were fewer than one error on the test.

2. The temperature was at least 30 degrees.

3. The mountain is at most 5000 ft tall.

4. There are more than five vacancies for a field trip to New York.

5. Some trees are not tall.

6. Some cats do not chase mice.

7. No flowers have red blooms.

8. Some golfers like tennis.

9. All students like math.

10. Some honest people are politicians.

11. Some cars do not have power steering.

12. No televisions are black and white.

Projects and Group Activities

ISBN and UPC Numbers

1. The first nine digits of the ISBN are 0-895-77692. We are to find the check digit.
$0(10) + 8(9) + 9(8) + 5(7) + 7(6) + 7(5) + 6(4)$
$+ 9(3) + 2(2) + C = 311 + C$
The last digit of the ISBN is chosen as 8 because $311 + 8 = 319$ and $319 \div 11 = 29$.

2. Is 0-395-12370-4 a possible ISBN?
$0(10) + 3(9) + 9(8) + 5(7) + 1(6) + 2(5) + 3(4)$
$+ 7(3) + 0(2) + 4 = 187$
$187 \div 11 = 17$, so 0-395-12370-4 is a possible ISBN.

3. Students should use the given equation and note that the ISBN checks.

4. The check digit can be 1, 2, 3, 4, 5, 6, 7, 8, 9, or 0.

5. $0(13) + 4 + 6(13) + 4 + 4(13) + 2 + 7(13) + 0(13) + 1 + 8(13) + 7 = 350$, which is a multiple of 10.

6. Answers will vary.

Chapter Review Exercises

1. $\displaystyle\sum_{i=1}^{4} 3x^i = 3x + 3x^2 + 3x^3 + 3x^4$

2. $d = a_2 - a_1 = -8 - (-5) = -3$
$a_n = a_1 + (n-1)d$
$-50 = -5 + (n-1)(-3)$
$-50 = -5 - 3n + 3$
$-50 = -2 - 3n$
$-48 = -3n$
$16 = n$
There are 16 terms.

3. $r = \dfrac{a_2}{a_1} = \dfrac{4\sqrt{2}}{4} = \sqrt{2}$

$a_n = a_1 r^{n-1}$

$a_7 = 4(\sqrt{2}\,)^{7-1}$

$\quad = 4(\sqrt{2}\,)^6$

$\quad = 4(8)$

$\quad = 32$

4. $r = \dfrac{a_2}{a_1} = \dfrac{3}{4}$

$S = \dfrac{a_1}{1-r} = \dfrac{4}{1-\frac{3}{4}} = \dfrac{4}{\frac{1}{4}} = 16$

5. $\dbinom{9}{3} = \dfrac{9!}{(9-3)!\,3!}$

$\quad = \dfrac{9!}{6!\,3!}$

$\quad = \dfrac{9 \cdot 8 \cdot 7 \cdot 6 \cdot 5 \cdot 4 \cdot 3 \cdot 2 \cdot 1}{(6 \cdot 5 \cdot 4 \cdot 3 \cdot 2 \cdot 1)(3 \cdot 2 \cdot 1)}$

$\quad = 84$

6. $a_n = \dfrac{8}{n+2}$

$a_{14} = \dfrac{8}{14+2} = \dfrac{8}{16} = \dfrac{1}{2}$

7. $d = a_2 - a_1 = -4 - (-10) = 6$

$a_n = a_1 + (n-1)d$

$a_{10} = -10 + (10-1)6$

$\quad = -10 + 9(6)$

$\quad = -10 + 54$

$\quad = 44$

8. $d = a_2 - a_1 = -19 - (-25) = 6$

$a_n = a_1 + (n-1)d$

$a_{18} = -25 + (18-1)6$

$\quad = -25 + (17)6$

$\quad = -25 + 102$

$\quad = 77$

$S_n = \dfrac{n}{2}(a_1 + a_n)$

$S_{18} = \dfrac{18}{2}(-25 + 77) = 9(52) = 468$

9. $r = \dfrac{a_2}{a_1} = \dfrac{12}{-6} = -2$

$S_n = \dfrac{a_1(1-r^n)}{1-r}$

$S_5 = \dfrac{-6[1-(-2)^5]}{1-(-2)}$

$\quad = \dfrac{-6[1-(-32)]}{3}$

$\quad = \dfrac{-6(33)}{3}$

$\quad = -66$

10. $\dfrac{8!}{4!\,4!} = \dfrac{8 \cdot 7 \cdot 6 \cdot 5 \cdot 4 \cdot 3 \cdot 2 \cdot 1}{(4 \cdot 3 \cdot 2 \cdot 1)(4 \cdot 3 \cdot 2 \cdot 1)} = 70$

11. $n = 9, \ a = 3x, \ b = y, \ r = 7$

$\dbinom{n}{r-1} a^{n-r+1} b^{r-1}$

$\dbinom{9}{7-1}(3x)^{9-7+1} y^{7-1} = \dbinom{9}{6}(3x)^3 y^6$

$\qquad\qquad\qquad\qquad = 84(27x^3 y^6)$

$\qquad\qquad\qquad\qquad = 2268x^3 y^6$

12. $\displaystyle\sum_{n=1}^{n}(3n+1)$

$= [3(1)+1] + [3(2)+1] + [3(3)+1] + [3(4)+1]$

$= 4 + 7 + 10 + 13 = 34$

13. $a_n = \dfrac{n+1}{n}$

$a_6 = \dfrac{6+1}{6} = \dfrac{7}{6}$

14. $d = a_2 - a_1 = 9 - 12 = -3$

$a_n = a_1 + (n-1)d$

$a_n = 12 + (n-1)(-3)$

$a_n = 12 - 3n + 3$

$a_n = -3n + 15$

15. $r = \dfrac{a_2}{a_1} = \dfrac{2}{6} = \dfrac{1}{3}$

$a_n = a_1 r^{n-1}$

$a_5 = 6\left(\dfrac{1}{3}\right)^{5-1} = 6\left(\dfrac{1}{3}\right)^4 = 6\left(\dfrac{1}{81}\right) = \dfrac{2}{27}$

16. $0.23\overline{3} = 0.02 + 0.03 + 0.003 + 0.0003 + \ldots$

$\qquad = \dfrac{2}{10} + \dfrac{3}{100} + \dfrac{3}{1000} + \dfrac{3}{10,000} + \ldots$

$S = \dfrac{a_1}{1-r} = \dfrac{\frac{3}{100}}{1-\frac{1}{10}} = \dfrac{\frac{3}{100}}{\frac{9}{10}} = \dfrac{1}{30}$

$0.23\overline{3} = \dfrac{2}{10} + \dfrac{1}{30} = \dfrac{7}{30}$

An equivalent fraction is $\dfrac{7}{30}$.

17. $d = a_2 - a_1 = -16 - (-13) = -3$

$a_n = a_1 + (n-1)d$

$a_{35} = -13 + (35-1)(-3)$

$\quad = -13 + (34)(-3)$

$\quad = -13 - 102$

$\quad = -115$

18. $S_n = \dfrac{a_1(1-r^n)}{1-r}$

$S_6 = \dfrac{1\left[1-\left(\frac{3}{2}\right)^6\right]}{1-\frac{3}{2}} = \dfrac{1-\frac{729}{64}}{-\frac{1}{2}} = \dfrac{-\frac{665}{64}}{-\frac{1}{2}} = \dfrac{665}{32}$

19. $d = a_2 - a_1 = 12 - 5 = 7$
$$a_n = a_1 + (n-1)d$$
$$= 5 + (21-1)7$$
$$= 5 + 20(7)$$
$$= 5 + 140 = 145$$
$$S_n = \frac{n}{2}(a_1 + a_n)$$
$$S_{21} = \frac{21}{2}(5 + 145) = \frac{21}{2}(150) = 1575$$

20. $n = 7, \ a = x, \ b = -2y, \ r = 4$
$$\binom{n}{r-1}a^{n-r+1}b^{r-1}$$
$$\binom{7}{4-1}x^{7-4+1}(-2y)^{4-1} = \binom{7}{3}x^4(-2y)^3$$
$$= 35x^4(-8y^3)$$
$$= -280x^4y^3$$

21. $d = a_2 - a_1 = 7 - 1 = 6$
$$a_n = a_1 + (n-1)d$$
$$121 = 1 + (n-1)6$$
$$121 = 1 + 6n - 6$$
$$121 = 6n - 5$$
$$126 = 6n$$
$$21 = n$$
There are 21 terms in the sequence.

22. $r = \dfrac{a_2}{a_1} = \dfrac{\frac{3}{4}}{\frac{3}{8}} = 2$
$$a_n = a_1 r^{n-1}$$
$$a_8 = \frac{3}{8}(2)^{8-1} = \frac{3}{8}(2)^7 = \frac{3}{8}(128) = 48$$

23. $\displaystyle\sum_{i=1}^{5} 2i = 2(1) + 2(2) + 2(3) + 2(4) + 2(5)$
$$= 2 + 4 + 6 + 8 + 10 = 30$$

24. $r = \dfrac{a_2}{a_1} = \dfrac{4}{1} = 4$
$$S_n = \frac{a_1(1 - r^n)}{1 - r}$$
$$S_5 = \frac{1(1 - 4^5)}{1 - 4} = \frac{1(1 - 1024)}{-3} = \frac{-1023}{-3} = 341$$

25. $5! = 5 \cdot 4 \cdot 3 \cdot 2 \cdot 1 = 120$

26. $n = 6, \ a = x, \ b = -4, \ r = 3$
$$\binom{n}{r-1}a^{n-r+1}b^{r-1}$$
$$\binom{6}{3-1}x^{6-3+1}(-4)^{3-1} = \binom{6}{2}x^4(-4)^2$$
$$= 15x^4(16) = 240x^4$$

27. $d = a_2 - a_1 = 3 - (-2) = 5$
$$a_n = a_1 + (n-1)d$$
$$a_{30} = -2 + (30-1)5$$
$$= -2 + (29)(5)$$
$$= -2 + 145$$
$$= 143$$

28. $d = a_2 - a_1 = 21 - 25 = -4$
$$a_n = a_1 + (n-1)d$$
$$a_{25} = 25 + (25-1)(-4)$$
$$= 25 + (24)(-4)$$
$$= 25 - 96 = -71$$
$$S_n = \frac{n}{2}(a_1 + a_n)$$
$$S_{25} = \frac{25}{2}[25 + (-71)] = \frac{25}{2}(-46) = -575$$

29. $a_n = \dfrac{(-1)^{2n-1}n}{n^2 + 2}$
$$a_5 = \frac{(-1)^{2(5)-1} \cdot 5}{(5)^2 + 2} = \frac{(-1)^9 \cdot 5}{25 + 2} = \frac{-5}{27}$$
The fifth term is $-\dfrac{5}{27}$.

30. $\displaystyle\sum_{i=1}^{4} 2x^{i-1} = 2x^{1-1} + 2x^{2-1} + 2x^{3-1} + 2x^{4-1}$
$$= 2 + 2x + 2x^2 + 2x^3$$

31. $0.\overline{23} = 0.23 + 0.0023 + 0.000023 + \ldots$
$$= \frac{23}{100} + \frac{23}{10,000} + \frac{23}{1,000,000} + \ldots$$
$$S = \frac{a_1}{1 - r} = \frac{\frac{23}{100}}{1 - \frac{1}{100}} = \frac{\frac{23}{100}}{\frac{99}{100}} = \frac{23}{99}$$
An equivalent fraction is $\frac{23}{99}$.

32. $r = \dfrac{a_2}{a_1} = \dfrac{-1}{4} = -\dfrac{1}{4}$
$$S = \frac{a_1}{1 - r} = \frac{4}{1 - \left(-\frac{1}{4}\right)} = \frac{4}{\frac{5}{4}} = \frac{16}{5}$$

33. $a_n = 2(3)^n$
$$a_1 = 2(3)^1 = 6$$
$$a_2 = 2(3)^2 = 18$$
$$r = \frac{a_2}{a_1} = \frac{18}{6} = 3$$
$$S_n = \frac{a_1(1 - r^n)}{1 - r}$$
$$S_5 = \frac{6(1 - 3^5)}{1 - 3} = \frac{6(1 - 243)}{-2} = -3(-242) = 726$$

34. $n = 11, \ a = x, \ b = -2y, \ r = 8$

$$\binom{n}{r-1} a^{n-r+1} b^{r-1}$$

$$\binom{11}{8-1}(x)^{11-8+1}(-2y)^{8-1} = \binom{11}{7}x^4(-2y)^7$$

$$= 330x^4(-128y^7)$$

$$= 42{,}240x^4y^7$$

35. $a_n = \left(\dfrac{1}{2}\right)^n$

$$a_1 = \left(\frac{1}{2}\right)^1 = \frac{1}{2}$$

$$a_2 = \left(\frac{1}{2}\right)^2 = \frac{1}{4}$$

$$r = \frac{a_2}{a_1} = \frac{\frac{1}{4}}{\frac{1}{2}} = \frac{1}{4} \cdot \frac{2}{1} = \frac{1}{2}$$

$$S_n = \frac{a_1(1-r^n)}{1-r}$$

$$= \frac{\frac{1}{2}\left(1 - \left(\frac{1}{2}\right)^8\right)}{1 - \frac{1}{2}}$$

$$= \frac{\frac{1}{2}\left(1 - \frac{1}{256}\right)}{\frac{1}{2}}$$

$$= \frac{255}{256}$$

$$\approx 0.996$$

36. $r = \dfrac{a_2}{a_1} = \dfrac{\frac{4}{3}}{2} = \dfrac{2}{3}$

$$S = \frac{a_1}{1-r} = \frac{2}{1-\frac{2}{3}} = \frac{2}{\frac{1}{3}} = 6$$

37. $0.6\overline{3} = 0.6 + 0.03 + 0.003 + \ldots$

$$= \frac{6}{10} + \frac{3}{100} + \frac{3}{1000} + \ldots$$

$$S = \frac{a_1}{1-r} = \frac{\frac{3}{100}}{1-\frac{1}{10}} = \frac{\frac{3}{100}}{\frac{9}{10}} = \frac{3}{100} \cdot \frac{10}{9} = \frac{1}{30}$$

$$0.6\overline{3} = \frac{6}{10} + \frac{1}{30} = \frac{19}{30}$$

38. $(x - 3y^2)^5 = \binom{5}{0}x^5 + \binom{5}{1}x^4(-3y^2)^1 + \binom{5}{2}x^3(-3y^2)^2 + \binom{5}{3}x^2(-3y^2)^3 + \binom{5}{4}x^1(-3y^2)^4 + \binom{5}{5}(-3y^2)^5$

$$= x^5 + 5x^4(-3y^2) + 10x^3(9y^9) + 10x^2(-27y^6) + 5x(81y^8) + 1(-243y^{10})$$

$$= x^5 - 15x^4y^2 + 90x^3y^4 - 270x^2y^6 + 405xy^8 - 243y^{10}$$

39. $\quad d = a_2 - a_1 = 2 - 8 = -6$

$\quad a_n = a_1 + (n-1)d$

$-118 = 8 + (n-1)d$

$-118 = 8 - 6n + 6$

$-118 = 14 - 6n$

$-132 = -6n$

There are 22 terms in the sequence.

40. $\dfrac{12!}{5!8} = \dfrac{12 \cdot 11 \cdot 10 \cdot 9 \cdot 8 \cdot 7 \cdot 6 \cdot 5 \cdot 4 \cdot 3 \cdot 2 \cdot 1}{(5 \cdot 4 \cdot 3 \cdot 2 \cdot 1)(8 \cdot 7 \cdot 6 \cdot 5 \cdot 4 \cdot 3 \cdot 2 \cdot 1)} = 99$

41. $\displaystyle\sum_{i=1}^{5} \frac{(2x)^i}{i} = \frac{(2x)^1}{1} + \frac{(2x)^2}{2} + \frac{(2x)^3}{3} + \frac{(2x)^4}{4} + \frac{(2x)^5}{5}$

$$= 2x + \frac{4x^2}{2} + \frac{8x^3}{3} + \frac{16x^4}{4} + \frac{32x^5}{5}$$

$$= 2x + 2x^2 + \frac{8}{3}x^3 + 4x^4 + \frac{32}{5}x^5$$

42. $\displaystyle\sum_{n=1}^{4}\frac{(-1)^{n-1}n}{n+1}=\frac{(-1)^{1-1}\cdot 1}{1+1}+\frac{(-1)^{2-1}\cdot 2}{2+1}+\frac{(-1)^{3-1}\cdot 3}{3+1}+\frac{(-1)^{4-1}\cdot 4}{4+1}$

$$=\frac{1}{2}+\left(-\frac{2}{3}\right)+\frac{3}{4}+\left(-\frac{4}{5}\right)=\frac{30-40+45-48}{60}$$

$$=-\frac{13}{60}$$

43. Strategy
To find the total salary for the nine-month period:
Write the arithmetic sequence.
Find the common difference of the arithmetic sequence.
Use the Formula for the *n*th Term of an Arithmetic Sequence to find the ninth term.
Use the Formula for the Sum of *n* Terms of an Arithmetic Sequence to find the sum of nine terms of the sequence.

Solution
$2400, $2480, $2560, ...
$d=a_2-a_1=2480-2400=80$
$a_n=a_1+(n-1)d$
$a_9=2400+(9-1)80=2400+640=3040$
$S_n=\dfrac{n}{2}(a_1+a_n)$
$S_9=\dfrac{9}{2}(2400+3040)=\$24,480$

The total salary for the nine-month period is $24,480.

44. Strategy
To find the temperature of the spa after 8 hours, use the Formula for the *n*th Term of a Geometric Sequence.

Solution
$n=8,\ a_1=102(0.95)=96.9,\ r=0.95$
$a_n=a_1r^{n-1}$
$a_8=96.9(0.95)^7=67.7$
The temperature is 67.7° F.

Chapter Test

1. $a_n=\dfrac{6}{n+4}$

$a_{14}=\dfrac{6}{14+4}=\dfrac{6}{18}=\dfrac{1}{3}$

The fourteenth term is $\dfrac{1}{3}$.

2. $a_n=\dfrac{n-1}{n}$

$a_9=\dfrac{9-1}{9}=\dfrac{8}{9}$

The ninth term is $\dfrac{8}{9}$.

$a_{10}=\dfrac{10-1}{10}=\dfrac{9}{10}$

The tenth term is $\dfrac{9}{10}$.

3. $\displaystyle\sum_{n=1}^{4}(2n+3)$

$=[2(1)+3]+[2(2)+3]+[2(3)+3]+[2(4)+3]$
$=5+7+9+11$
$=32$

4. $\displaystyle\sum_{i=1}^{4}2x^{2i}=2x^{2(1)}+2x^{2(2)}+2x^{2(3)}+2x^{2(4)}$

$$=2x^2+2x^4+2x^6+2x^8$$

5. $d=a_2-a_1=-16-(-12)=-16+12=-4$
$a_n=a_1+(n-1)d$
$a_{28}=-12+(28-1)(-4)=-12+27(-4)=-120$

6. $d=a_2-a_1=-1-(-3)=-1+3=2$
$a_n=a_1+(n-1)d$
$a_n=-3+(n+1)(2)=-3+2n-2$
$a_n=2n-5$

7. $d=a_2-a_1=3-7=-4$
$a_n=a_1+(n-1)d$
$-77=7+(n-1)d$
$-77=7-4n+4$
$-77=11-4n$
$-88=-4n$
$22=n$

8. $d=a_2-a_1=-33-(-42)=-33+42=9$
$a_n=a_1+(n-1)d$
$a_{15}=-42+(15-1)9=-42+14(9)=84$
$S_n=\dfrac{n}{2}(a_1+a_n)$
$S_{15}=\dfrac{15}{2}(-42+84)=315$

9. $d=a_2-a_1=2-(-4)=2+4=6$
$a_n=a_1+(n-1)d$
$a_{24}=-4+(24-1)6=-4+23(6)=134$
$S_n=\dfrac{n}{2}(a_1+a_n)$
$S_{24}=\dfrac{24}{2}(-4+134)=1560$

10. $\dfrac{10!}{5!5!}=\dfrac{10\cdot 9\cdot 8\cdot 7\cdot 6\cdot 5\cdot 4\cdot 3\cdot 2\cdot 1}{(5\cdot 4\cdot 3\cdot 2\cdot 1)(5\cdot 4\cdot 3\cdot 2\cdot 1)}=252$

11. $r=\dfrac{a_2}{a_1}=\dfrac{-4\sqrt{2}}{4}=-\sqrt{2}$

$a_n=4r^{n-1}$
$a_{10}=4(-\sqrt{2})^{10-1}=4\cdot(-\sqrt{2})^9=-64\sqrt{2}$

12. $r = \dfrac{a_2}{a_1} = \dfrac{3}{5}$

$a_n = a_1 r^{n-1}$

$a_5 = 5 \cdot \left(\dfrac{3}{5}\right)^{5-1} = 5 \cdot \left(\dfrac{3}{5}\right)^4 = 5 \cdot \dfrac{81}{625} = \dfrac{81}{125}$

13. $r = \dfrac{a_2}{a_1} = \dfrac{\frac{3}{4}}{1} = \dfrac{3}{4}$

$S_n = \dfrac{a_1(1-r^n)}{1-r}$

$S_5 = \dfrac{1\left(1-\left(\frac{3}{4}\right)^5\right)}{1-\frac{3}{4}} = \dfrac{1-\frac{243}{1024}}{\frac{1}{4}} = \dfrac{\frac{781}{1024}}{\frac{1}{4}} = \dfrac{781}{256}$

14. $r = \dfrac{a_2}{a_1} = \dfrac{10}{-5} = -2$

$S_n = \dfrac{a_1(1-r^n)}{1-r}$

$S_5 = \dfrac{-5(1-(-2)^5)}{1-(-2)}$

$= \dfrac{-5(1-(-32))}{3}$

$= \dfrac{-5(33)}{3}$

$= -55$

15. $r = \dfrac{a_2}{a_1} = \dfrac{1}{2}$

$S_n = \dfrac{a_1}{1-r} = \dfrac{2}{1-\frac{1}{2}} = \dfrac{2}{\frac{1}{2}} = 4$

16. $0.2\overline{3} = 0.2 + 0.03 + 0.003 + \ldots$

$= \dfrac{2}{10} + \dfrac{3}{100} + \dfrac{3}{1000} + \ldots$

$S = \dfrac{a_1}{1-r} = \dfrac{\frac{3}{100}}{1-\frac{1}{10}} = \dfrac{\frac{3}{100}}{\frac{9}{10}} = \dfrac{3}{90} = \dfrac{1}{30}$

$0.2\overline{3} = \dfrac{2}{10} + \dfrac{1}{30} = \dfrac{7}{30}$

An equivalent fraction is $\dfrac{7}{30}$.

17. $\dbinom{11}{4} = \dfrac{11!}{(11-4)!4!}$

$= \dfrac{11!}{7! \, 4!}$

$= \dfrac{11 \cdot 10 \cdot 9 \cdot 8 \cdot 7 \cdot 6 \cdot 5 \cdot 4 \cdot 3 \cdot 2 \cdot 1}{(7 \cdot 6 \cdot 5 \cdot 4 \cdot 3 \cdot 2 \cdot 1)(4 \cdot 3 \cdot 2 \cdot 1)}$

$= 330$

18. $n = 8, \; a = 3x, \; b = -y, \; r = 5$

$\dbinom{n}{r-1} a^{n-r+1} b^{r-1}$

$\dbinom{8}{5-1}(3x)^{8-5+1}(-y)^{5-1} = \dbinom{8}{4}(3x)^4(-y)^4$

$= 70(81x^4)(y^4)$

$= 5670 x^4 y^4$

19. Strategy

To find how much material was in stock after the shipment on October 1:
Write the arithmetic sequence.
Find the common difference of the arithmetic sequence.
Use the Formula for the nth Term of an Arithmetic Sequence to find the tenth term.

Solution
$7500, 6950, 6400, \ldots$

$d = a_2 - a_1 = 6950 - 7500 = -550$

$a_n = a_1 + (n-1)d$

$a_{10} = 7500 + (10-1)(-550) = 2550$

The inventory after the October 1 shipment was 2550 yd.

20. Strategy

To find the amount of radioactive material at the beginning of the fifth day, use the Formula for the nth Term of a Geometric Sequence.

Solution

$n = 5, \; a_1 = 320, \; r = \dfrac{1}{2}$

$a_n = a_1 r^{n-1}$

$a_5 = 320\left(\dfrac{1}{2}\right)^{5-1} = 320\left(\dfrac{1}{2}\right)^4 = 20$

There will be 20 mg of radioactive material in the sample at the beginning of the fifth day.

Cumulative Review Exercises

1. $\dfrac{4x^2}{x^2+x-2} - \dfrac{3x-2}{x+2}$

$= \dfrac{4x^2}{(x+2)(x-1)} - \dfrac{3x-2}{x+2} \cdot \dfrac{x-1}{x-1}$

$= \dfrac{4x^2 - (3x^2 - 5x + 2)}{(x+2)(x-1)}$

$= \dfrac{x^2 + 5x - 2}{(x+2)(x-1)}$

2. $2x^6 + 16 = 2(x^6 + 8)$

$= 2((x^2)^3 + 2^3)$

$= 2(x^2 + 2)(x^4 - 2x^2 + 4)$

3. $\sqrt{2y}(\sqrt{8xy} - \sqrt{y}) = \sqrt{16xy^2} - \sqrt{2y^2}$

$= \sqrt{16y^2(x)} - \sqrt{y^2(2)}$

$= 4y\sqrt{x} - y\sqrt{2}$

4. $\left(\dfrac{x^{-\frac{3}{4}} x^{\frac{3}{2}}}{x^{-\frac{5}{2}}}\right)^{-8} = \dfrac{x^6 x^{-12}}{x^{20}} = \dfrac{x^{-6}}{x^{20}} = \dfrac{1}{x^{26}}$

5.
$$5 - \sqrt{x} = \sqrt{x+5}$$
$$(5 - \sqrt{x})^2 = (\sqrt{x+5})^2$$
$$25 - 10\sqrt{x} + x = x + 5$$
$$-10\sqrt{x} = -20$$
$$\sqrt{x} = 2$$
$$(\sqrt{x})^2 = 2^2$$
$$x = 4$$

Check:

$$5 - \sqrt{x} = \sqrt{x+5}$$

$5 - \sqrt{4}$	$\sqrt{4+5}$
$5 - 2$	$\sqrt{9}$

$$3 = 3$$

The solution is 4.

6. $2x^2 - x + 7 = 0$
$a = 2, \ b = -1, \ c = 7$
$$x = \frac{-b \pm \sqrt{b^2 - 4ac}}{2a}$$
$$= \frac{-(-1) \pm \sqrt{(-1)^2 - 4(2)(7)}}{2(2)}$$
$$= \frac{1 \pm \sqrt{1 - 56}}{4}$$
$$= \frac{1 \pm \sqrt{-55}}{4}$$
$$= \frac{1}{4} \pm \frac{\sqrt{55}}{4} i$$

The solutions are $\frac{1}{4} + \frac{\sqrt{55}}{4} i$ and $\frac{1}{4} - \frac{\sqrt{55}}{4} i$.

7. (1) $3x - 3y = 2$
(2) $6x - 4y = 5$
Eliminate x.
Multiply equation (1) by -2 and add equation (2).
$$(-2)(3x - 3y) = (-2)(2)$$
$$6x - 4y = 5$$
$$-6x + 6y = -4$$
$$6x - 4y = 5$$
$$2y = 1$$
$$y = \frac{1}{2}$$

Substitute $\frac{1}{2}$ for y in equation (2).
$$6x - 4\left(\frac{1}{2}\right) = 5$$
$$6x - 2 = 5$$
$$6x = 7$$
$$x = \frac{7}{6}$$

The solution is $\left(\frac{7}{6}, \frac{1}{2}\right)$.

8. $2x - 1 > 3 \quad$ or $\quad 1 - 3x > 7$
$\quad\quad 2x > 4 \quad\quad\quad\quad -3x > 6$
$\quad\quad\quad x > 2 \quad\quad\quad\quad\quad x < -2$
$\quad\quad \{x | x > 2\} \quad\quad\quad \{x | x < -2\}$
$\quad\quad \{x | x < -2 \text{ or } x > 2\}$

9. $\begin{vmatrix} -3 & 1 \\ 4 & 2 \end{vmatrix} = -3(2) - 4(1) = -6 - 4 = -10$

10. $\log_5 \sqrt{\dfrac{x}{y}} = \log_5 \left(\dfrac{x}{y}\right)^{\frac{1}{2}}$
$$= \frac{1}{2} \log_5 \left(\frac{x}{y}\right)$$
$$= \frac{1}{2}(\log_5 x - \log_5 y)$$
$$= \frac{1}{2} \log_5 x - \frac{1}{2} \log_5 y$$

11. $4^x = 8^{x-1}$
$$(2^2)^x = (2^3)^{x-1}$$
$$2^{2x} = 2^{3(x-1)}$$
$$2x = 3(x-1)$$
$$2x = 3x - 3$$
$$-x = -3$$
$$x = 3$$

12. $a_n = n(n-1)$
$a_5 = 5(5-1) = 5(4) = 20$ The fifth term is 20.
$a_6 = 6(6-1) = 6(5) = 30$ The sixth term is 30.

13. $\displaystyle\sum_{n=1}^{7} (-1)^{n-1}(n+2) = (-1)^{1-1}(1+2) + (-1)^{2-1}(2+2) + (-1)^{3-1}(3+2) + (-1)^{4-1}(4+2) + (-1)^{5-1}(5+2)$

$$+ (-1)^{6-1}(6+2) + (-1)^{7-1}(7+2)$$
$$= (-1)^0(3) + (-1)^1(4) + (-1)^2(5) + (-1)^3(6) + (-1)^4(7) + (-1)^5(8) + (-1)^6(9)$$
$$= 3 - 4 + 5 - 6 + 7 - 8 + 9 = 6$$

14. (1)　$x + 2y + z = 3$
(2)　$2x - y + 2z = 6$
(3)　$3x + y - z = 5$
To eliminate y add equations (2) and (3).
(2)　$2x - y + 2z = 6$
(3)　$3x + y - z = 5$
(4)　$5x + z = 11$
To eliminate y from equations (1) and (2), multiply equation (2) by 2 and add it to equation (1)
$x + 2y + z = 3$
$2(2x - y + 2z) = 2(6)$

$x + 2y + z = 3$
$4x - 2y + 4z = 12$
(5)　$5x + 5z = 15$
Eliminate x from equations (4) and (5) by multiplying equation (4) by -1 and adding to equation (5).
$-1(5x + z) = (-1)(11)$
$5x + 5z = 15$

$-5x - z = -11$
$5x + 5z = 15$

$4z = 4$
$z = 1$
Solve for x by substituting 1 for z in equation (5).
$5x + 5z = 15$
$5x + 5(1) = 15$
$5x + 5 = 15$
$5x = 10$
$x = 2$
Solve for y by substituting 1 for z and 2 for x in equation (3).
$3x + y - z = 5$
$3(2) + y - 1 = 5$
$6 + y - 1 = 5$
$5 + y = 5$
$y = 0$
The solution is $(2, 0, 1)$.

15. $\log_6 x = 3$
$6^3 = x$
$216 = x$
The solution is 216.

16. $(4x^3 - 3x + 5) \div (2x + 1)$

$$
\begin{array}{r}
2x^2 - x - 1 \\
2x+1\overline{)4x^3 + 0x^2 - 3x + 5} \\
\underline{4x^3 + 2x^2} \\
-2x^2 - 3x \\
\underline{-2x^2 - x} \\
-2x + 5 \\
\underline{-2x - 1} \\
6
\end{array}
$$

The solution is $2x^2 - x - 1 + \dfrac{6}{2x+1}$.

17. $g(x) = -3x + 4$
$g(1 + h) = -3(1 + h) + 4$
$= -3 - 3h + 4 = -3h + 1$

18. $f(a) = \dfrac{a^3 - 1}{2a + 1}$
The domain is $\{0, 1, 2\}$.
$f(0) = \dfrac{0^3 - 1}{2(0) + 1} = \dfrac{-1}{1} = -1$
$f(1) = \dfrac{1^3 - 1}{2(1) + 1} = \dfrac{0}{3} = 0$
$f(2) = \dfrac{2^3 - 1}{2(2) + 1} = \dfrac{8 - 1}{5} = \dfrac{7}{5}$
The range is $\{-1, 0, \dfrac{7}{5}\}$.

19. $3x - 2y = -4$
$-2y = -3x - 4$
$y = \dfrac{3}{2}x + 2$

20. $2x - 3y < 9$
$-3y < -2x + 9$
$y > \dfrac{2}{3}x - 3$

21. Strategy

Time required for the older computer: t

Time required for the new computer: $t - 16$

	Rate	Time	Part
Older computer	$\frac{1}{t}$	15	$\frac{15}{t}$
New computer	$\frac{1}{t-16}$	15	$\frac{15}{t-16}$

The sum of the part of the task completed by the older computer and the part of the task completed by the new computer is 1.

$$\frac{15}{t} + \frac{15}{t-16} = 1$$

Solution

$$\frac{15}{t} + \frac{15}{t-16} = 1$$

$$t(t-16)\left(\frac{15}{t} + \frac{15}{t-16}\right) = 1(t(t-16))$$

$$15(t-16) + 15t = t^2 - 16t$$

$$15t - 240 + 15t = t^2 - 16t$$

$$0 = t^2 - 46t + 240$$

$$0 = (t-40)(t-6)$$

$$t - 40 = 0 \qquad t - 6 = 0$$
$$t = 40 \qquad t = 6$$

$t = 6$ does not check as a solution since
$t - 16 = 6 - 16 = -10$.
$t - 16 = 40 - 16 = 24$
The new computer takes 24 min to complete the payroll.
The old computer takes 40 min to complete the payroll.

22. Strategy

Rate of boat in calm water: x

Rate of current; y

	Rate	Time	Distance
With current	$x + y$	2	$2(x+y)$
Against current	$x - y$	3	$3(x-y)$

The distance traveled with the current is 15 mi.
The distance traveled against the current is 15 mi.
$$2(x+y) = 15$$
$$3(x-y) = 15$$

Solution

$$2(x+y) = 15 \qquad \frac{1}{2} \cdot 2(x+y) = \frac{1}{2} \cdot 15$$

$$3(x-y) = 15 \qquad \frac{1}{3} \cdot 3(x-y) = \frac{1}{3} \cdot 15$$

$$x + y = 7.5$$
$$x - y = 5$$
$$2x = 12.5$$
$$x = 6.25$$

$$x + y = 7.5$$
$$6.25 + y = 7.5$$
$$y = 1.25$$

The rate of the boat in calm water is 6.25 mph.
The rate of the current is 1.25 mph.

23. To find the half-life, solve for k in the exponential decay equation.
Use $A_0 = 80$, $A = 55$, $t = 30$.

Solution

$$A = A_0\left(\frac{1}{2}\right)^{t/k}$$

$$55 = 80\left(\frac{1}{2}\right)^{30/k}$$

$$0.6875 = (0.5)^{30/k}$$

$$\log 0.6875 = \frac{30}{k} \log(0.5)$$

$$k = \frac{30 \log 0.5}{\log 0.6875}$$

$$\approx 55.49$$

The half-life is approximately 55 days.

24. Strategy
    To find the total number of seats in the 12 rows of the theater.
    Write the arithmetic sequence.
    Find the common difference of the arithmetic sequence.
    Use the Formula for the nth Term of an Arithmetic Sequence to find the 12th term.
    Use the Formula for the Sum of n Terms of an Arithmetic Sequence to find the sum of the 12 terms of the sequence.

    Solution
    $62, 74, 86, \ldots$
    $$d = a_2 - a_1 = 74 - 62 = 12$$
    $$a_n = a_1 + (n-1)d$$
    $$a_{12} = 62 + (12-1)12 = 62 + 132 = 194$$
    $$S_n = \frac{n}{2}(a_1 + a_n)$$
    $$S_{12} = \frac{12}{2}(62+194) = 1536$$
    The total number of seats in the theater is 1536.

25. Strategy
    To find the height of the ball on the fifth bounce, use the Formula for the nth Term of a Geometric Sequence.

    Solution
    $n = 5, \ a_1 = 80\% \text{ of } 10 = 8, \ r = 80\% = 0.8$
    $$a_n = a_1 r^{n-1}$$
    $$a_5 = 8(0.8)^{5-1}$$
    $$= 8(0.4096) = 3.2768$$
    The height of the ball on the fifth bounce is 3.3 ft.

Chapter 12: Conic Sections

Prep Test

1. $d = \sqrt{(4-(-2))^2 + (-1-3)^2}$ [3.1.2]
   $= \sqrt{6^2 + (-4)^2}$
   $= \sqrt{52}$
   ≈ 7.21
   The distance is approximately 7.21.

2. $x^2 - 8x + \left(\frac{1}{2}(-8)\right)^2 = x^2 - 8x + 16$ [8.2.1]
   $(x-4)^2$

3. $\frac{x^2}{16} + \frac{y^2}{9} = 1$ [8.1.3]
   For $y = 3$,
   $\frac{x^2}{16} + \frac{3^2}{9} = 1$
   $\frac{x^2}{16} + \frac{9}{9} = 1$
   $\frac{x^2}{16} + 1 = 1$
   $\frac{x^2}{16} = 0$
   $x^2 = 0$
   $x = 0$
   For $y = 0$,
   $\frac{x^2}{16} + \frac{0^2}{9} = 1$
   $x^2 = 16$
   $x = \pm 4$

4. $7x + 4y = 3$
          $y = x - 2$
   $7x + 4(x-2) = 3$
   $7x + 4x - 8 = 3$
         $11x = 11$
           $x = 1$
   $y = 1 - 2 = -1$
   The solution is $(1, -1)$.

5. (1) $4x - y = 9$
      (2) $2x + 3y = -13$ [4.2.1]
   Eliminate y.
   $3(4x - y) = 3(9)$
   $2x + 3y = -13$
   $12x - 3y = 27$
   $2x + 3y = -13$
   Add the equations.
   $14x = 14$
      $x = 1$
   Replace x in equation (2).
   $2(1) + 3y = -13$
          $3y = -15$
            $y = -5$
   The solution is $(1, -5)$.

6. $y = x^2 - 4x + 2$ [8.6.1]
   $a = 1, b = -4$
   $-\frac{b}{2a} = -\frac{-4}{2(1)} = 2$
   $y = (2)^2 - 4(2) + 2 = -2$
   Vertex: $(2, -2)$
   Axis of symmetry: $x = 2$

7. $f(x) = -2x^2 + 4x$ [8.6.1]

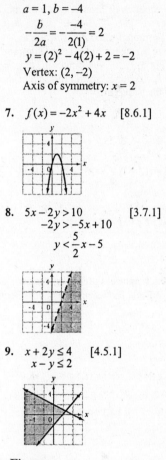

8. $5x - 2y > 10$ [3.7.1]
   $-2y > -5x + 10$
   $y < \frac{5}{2}x - 5$

9. $x + 2y \le 4$ [4.5.1]
   $x - y \le 2$

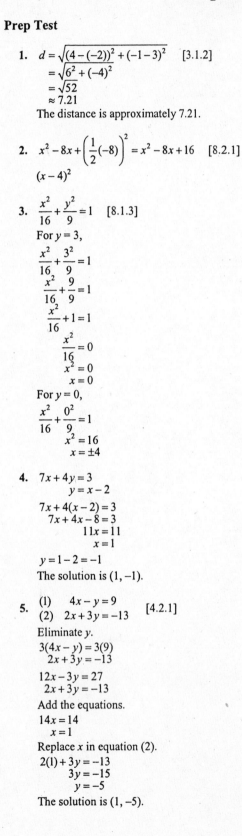

Go Figure

The distance from Earth to the moon can be found in inches: $240{,}000\text{mi} \cdot \frac{5280\text{ft}}{1\text{mi}} \cdot \frac{12\text{in}}{1\text{ft}}$. This is equivalent to 1.5206×10^{10} inches. Let x represent the number of time the paper is folded. Then the thickness is $(0.01)2^x$. The thickness must be at least the distance from Earth to the moon, thus $(0.01)2^x \ge 1.5206 \times 10^{10}$. This happens when $x = 41$, or when the paper has been folded 41 times because
$(0.01)2^{41} = 2.20 \times 10^{10}$.

Section 12.1

Concept Review 12.1

1. Sometimes true
   The graph of the parabola $y = x^2 - 2$ is the graph of a function. The graph of the parabola $x = y^2 - 2$ is not the graph of a function.

2. Always true

3. Sometimes true
   A parabola may have one intercept, two intercepts, or no intercepts.

4. Sometimes true
   The parabola given by the equation $y = -x^2 + 3$ has no minimum value.

5. Sometimes true
   The axis of symmetry of the parabola $y = x^2 + 2x - 3$ is the line $x = -1$.

6. Sometimes true
   For some parabolas, the axis of symmetry is $y = -\dfrac{b}{2a}$.

Objective 12.1.1 Exercises

1. **a.** Axis of symmetry is a vertical line.
   b. The parabola opens up since $3 > 0$.

2. **a.** Axis of symmetry is a vertical line.
   b. The parabola opens down since $-1 < 0$.

3. **a.** Axis of symmetry is a horizontal line.
   b. The parabola opens right since $1 > 0$.

4. **a.** Axis of symmetry is a horizontal line.
   b. The parabola opens left since $-3 < 0$.

5. **a.** Axis of symmetry is a horizontal line.
   b. The parabola opens left since $-\dfrac{1}{2} < 0$.

6. **a.** Axis of symmetry is a vertical line.
   b. The parabola opens up since $\dfrac{1}{4} > 0$.

7. $y = x^2 - 2x - 4$
   $-\dfrac{b}{2a} = -\dfrac{-2}{2(1)} = 1$
   $y = 1^2 - 2(1) - 4 = -5$
   Vertex: $(1, -5)$
   Axis of symmetry: $x = 1$

8. $y = x^2 + 4x - 4$
   $-\dfrac{b}{2a} = -\dfrac{4}{2(1)} = -2$
   $y = (-2)^2 + 4(-2) - 4 = -8$
   Vertex: $(-2, -8)$
   Axis of symmetry: $x = -2$

9. $y = -x^2 + 2x - 3$
   $-\dfrac{b}{2a} = -\dfrac{2}{2(-1)} = 1$
   $y = -(1)^2 + 2(1) - 3 = -2$
   Vertex: $(1, -2)$
   Axis of symmetry: $x = 1$

10. $y = -x^2 + 4x - 5$
    $-\dfrac{b}{2a} = -\dfrac{4}{2(-1)} = 2$
    $y = -(2)^2 + 4(2) - 5 = -1$
    Vertex: $(2, -1)$
    Axis of symmetry: $x = 2$

11. $x = y^2 + 6y + 5$
    $-\dfrac{b}{2a} = -\dfrac{6}{2(1)} = -3$
    $x = (-3)^2 + 6(-3) + 5 = -4$
    Vertex: $(-4, -3)$
    Axis of symmetry: $y = -3$

12. $x = y^2 - y - 6$
    $-\dfrac{b}{2a} = -\dfrac{-1}{2(1)} = \dfrac{1}{2}$
    $x = \left(\dfrac{1}{2}\right)^2 - \left(\dfrac{1}{2}\right) - 6 = -\dfrac{25}{4}$
    Vertex: $\left(-\dfrac{25}{4}, \dfrac{1}{2}\right)$
    Axis of symmetry: $y = \dfrac{1}{2}$

13. $y = 2x^2 - 4x + 1$

$-\dfrac{b}{2a} = -\dfrac{-4}{2(2)} = 1$

$y = 2(1)^2 - 4(1) + 1 = -1$

Vertex: $(1, -1)$

Axis of symmetry: $x = 1$

14. $y = 2x^2 + 4x - 5$

$-\dfrac{b}{2a} = -\dfrac{4}{2(2)} = -1$

$y = 2(-1)^2 + 4(-1) - 5 = -7$

Vertex: $(-1, -7)$

Axis of symmetry: $x = -1$

15. $y = x^2 - 5x + 4$

$-\dfrac{b}{2a} = -\dfrac{-5}{2(1)} = \dfrac{5}{2}$

$y = \left(\dfrac{5}{2}\right)^2 - 5\left(\dfrac{5}{2}\right) + 4 = -\dfrac{9}{4}$

Vertex: $\left(\dfrac{5}{2}, -\dfrac{9}{4}\right)$

Axis of symmetry: $x = \dfrac{5}{2}$

16. $y = x^2 + 5x + 6$

$-\dfrac{b}{2a} = -\dfrac{5}{2(1)} = -\dfrac{5}{2}$

$y = \left(-\dfrac{5}{2}\right)^2 + 5\left(-\dfrac{5}{2}\right) + 6 = -\dfrac{1}{4}$

Vertex: $\left(-\dfrac{5}{2}, -\dfrac{1}{4}\right)$

Axis of symmetry: $x = -\dfrac{5}{2}$

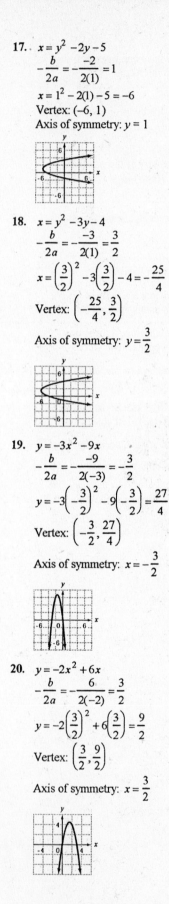

17. $x = y^2 - 2y - 5$

$-\dfrac{b}{2a} = -\dfrac{-2}{2(1)} = 1$

$x = 1^2 - 2(1) - 5 = -6$

Vertex: $(-6, 1)$

Axis of symmetry: $y = 1$

18. $x = y^2 - 3y - 4$

$-\dfrac{b}{2a} = -\dfrac{-3}{2(1)} = \dfrac{3}{2}$

$x = \left(\dfrac{3}{2}\right)^2 - 3\left(\dfrac{3}{2}\right) - 4 = -\dfrac{25}{4}$

Vertex: $\left(-\dfrac{25}{4}, \dfrac{3}{2}\right)$

Axis of symmetry: $y = \dfrac{3}{2}$

19. $y = -3x^2 - 9x$

$-\dfrac{b}{2a} = -\dfrac{-9}{2(-3)} = -\dfrac{3}{2}$

$y = -3\left(-\dfrac{3}{2}\right)^2 - 9\left(-\dfrac{3}{2}\right) = \dfrac{27}{4}$

Vertex: $\left(-\dfrac{3}{2}, \dfrac{27}{4}\right)$

Axis of symmetry: $x = -\dfrac{3}{2}$

20. $y = -2x^2 + 6x$

$-\dfrac{b}{2a} = -\dfrac{6}{2(-2)} = \dfrac{3}{2}$

$y = -2\left(\dfrac{3}{2}\right)^2 + 6\left(\dfrac{3}{2}\right) = \dfrac{9}{2}$

Vertex: $\left(\dfrac{3}{2}, \dfrac{9}{2}\right)$

Axis of symmetry: $x = \dfrac{3}{2}$

21. $x = -\dfrac{1}{2}y^2 + 4$

$-\dfrac{b}{2a} = -\dfrac{0}{2\left(-\frac{1}{2}\right)} = 0$

$x = -\dfrac{1}{2}(0)^2 + 4 = 4$

Vertex: $(4, 0)$

Axis of symmetry: $y = 0$

22. $x = -\dfrac{1}{4}y^2 - 1$

$-\dfrac{b}{2a} = -\dfrac{0}{2\left(-\frac{1}{4}\right)} = 0$

$x = -\dfrac{1}{4}(0)^2 - 1 = -1$

Vertex: $(-1, 0)$

Axis of symmetry: $y = 0$

23. $x = \dfrac{1}{2}y^2 - y + 1$

$-\dfrac{b}{2a} = -\dfrac{-1}{2\left(\frac{1}{2}\right)} = 1$

$x = \dfrac{1}{2}(1)^2 - 1 + 1 = \dfrac{1}{2}$

Vertex: $\left(\dfrac{1}{2}, 1\right)$

Axis of symmetry: $y = 1$

24. $x = -\dfrac{1}{2}y^2 + 2y - 3$

$-\dfrac{b}{2a} = -\dfrac{2}{2\left(-\frac{1}{2}\right)} = 2$

$x = -\dfrac{1}{2}(2)^2 + 2(2) - 3 = -1$

Vertex: $(-1, 2)$

Axis of symmetry: $y = 2$

25. $y = \dfrac{1}{2}x^2 + 2x - 6$

$-\dfrac{b}{2a} = -\dfrac{2}{2\left(\frac{1}{2}\right)} = -2$

$y = \dfrac{1}{2}(-2)^2 + 2(-2) - 6 = -8$

Vertex: $(-2, -8)$

Axis of symmetry: $x = -2$

26. $y = -\dfrac{1}{2}x^2 + x - 3$

$-\dfrac{b}{2a} = -\dfrac{1}{2\left(-\frac{1}{2}\right)} = 1$

$y = -\dfrac{1}{2}(1)^2 + 1 - 3 = -\dfrac{5}{2}$

Vertex: $\left(1, -\dfrac{5}{2}\right)$

Axis of symmetry: $x = 1$

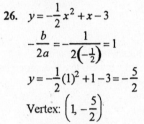

Applying Concepts 12.1

27. $y = x^2 - 4x - 2$

$-\dfrac{b}{2a} = -\dfrac{-4}{2(1)} = \dfrac{4}{2} = 2$

$y = x^2 - 4x - 2$

$= (2)^2 - 4(2) - 2$

$= 4 - 8 - 2$

$= -6$

a is positive. The minimum value of y is -6.
The domain is all real numbers.
The range is all real numbers greater than or equal to -6.

28. $y = -x^2 + 2x - 3$

$-\dfrac{b}{2a} = -\dfrac{2}{2(-1)} = \dfrac{-2}{-2} = 1$

$y = -x^2 + 2x - 3$

$= -(1)^2 + 2(1) - 3$

$= -1 + 2 - 3$

$= -2$

a is negative. The maximum value of y is -2.
The domain is all real numbers. The range is all
real numbers less than or equal to -2.

29.
$$x = y^2 + 6y - 5$$
$$-\frac{b}{2a} = -\frac{6}{2(1)} = -\frac{6}{2} = -3$$
$$x = y^2 + 6y - 5$$
$$= (-3)^2 + 6(-3) - 5$$
$$= 9 - 18 - 5$$
$$= -14$$

a is positive. The minimum value of x is -14. The domain is all real numbers greater than or equal to -14. The range is all real numbers.

30.
$$x = -y^2 - 2y + 6$$
$$-\frac{b}{2a} = -\frac{-2}{2(-1)} = -\frac{-2}{-2} = -1$$
$$x = -y^2 - 2y + 6$$
$$= -(-1)^2 - 2(-1) + 6$$
$$= -1 + 2 + 6$$
$$= 7$$

a is negative. The maximum value of x is 7. The domain is all real numbers less than or equal to 7. The range is all real numbers.

31. $p = \dfrac{1}{4a}; \quad a = 2$

$$p = \frac{1}{4(2)} = \frac{1}{8}$$

The focus is $\left(0, \dfrac{1}{8}\right)$.

32. $p = \dfrac{1}{4a}; \quad a = \dfrac{1}{10}$

$$p = \frac{1}{4\left(\dfrac{1}{10}\right)} = \frac{1}{\dfrac{4}{10}} = \frac{10}{4} = 2.5$$

The focus is $(0, 2.5)$.

33. a. The parabola passes through the point whose coordinates are (3.79, 100). Because the parabola opens to the right and its vertex is at the origin, the equation of the parabola is of the form $x = ay^2$.

$$x = ay^2$$
$$3.79 = a(100)^2 \qquad \bullet \text{ Substitute } (3.79, 100).$$
$$0.000379 = a \qquad \bullet \text{ Solve for } a.$$

The equation of the mirror is $x = 0.000379y^2$ or $x = \dfrac{1}{2639} y^2$.

b. The equation is valid over the interval $0 \leq x \leq 3.79$, or [0, 3.79].

34. a. The parabola passes through the point (17.7, 42). Because the parabola opens to the right and its vertex is at the origin, the equation of the parabola is of the form $x = ay^2$.

$$x = ay^2$$
$$17.7 = a(42)^2 \qquad \bullet \text{ Substitute } (17.7, 42).$$
$$0.01 = a \qquad \bullet \text{ Solve for } a.$$

The equation of the radar dish is $x = 0.1y^2$, or $x = \dfrac{1}{100} y^2$.

b. The equation is valid over the interval $0 \leq x \leq 17.7$, or [0, 17.7].

35. The graph of $f(x) = ax^2$ open upward and becomes narrower as a increases ($a > 0$). If $a > 0$, the graph has similar characteristics but opens downward. Some graphs of $f(x) = ax^2$ for various values of a are shown here.

36. The equation $x = y^2 + 4$ is not an equation that defines y as a function of x. In order for it to define y as a function of x, any value of x would yield a unique value of y. However, if $x = 8$, for example, then

$$8 = y^2 + 4$$
$$4 = y^2$$
$$\sqrt{4} = \sqrt{y^2}$$
$$\pm 2 = y$$

Therefore, there are two values of y that correspond to an x value of , 2 and –2.

37. If the solutions of the quadratic equation $ax^2 + bx + c = 0$ are complex numbers, the graph of the corresponding equation $y = ax^2 + bx + c$ does not pass through the x-axis and has no x-intercepts. Since the values of $y = x^2 + 2x + 3$ are imaginary numbers when $y = 0$, the graph of this equation has no intercepts.

Section 12.2

Concept Review 12.2

1. Sometimes true
The center of the circle given by the equation $(x - 3)^2 + (y + 1)^2 = 4$ is $(3, -1)$.

2. Never true
The center of the circle is $(-2, -1)$.

3. Always true

4. Never true
   A vertical line will intersect the graph of a circle at more than one point. By the vertical-line test, the graph of a circle is not the graph of a function.

5. Never true
   The square of the radius of a circle cannot be a negative value.

Objective 12.2.1 Exercises

1. The points on the circumference of a circle are all equidistant from the center of the circle. The common distance is the radius of the circle.

2. The values of h and k are the x and y coordinates, respectively, of the center of the circle. The value r is the radius of the circle.

3.

4.

5.

6.

7.

8.

9.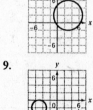

10.

11. $(x-h)^2 + (y-k)^2 = r^2$
    $(x-2)^2 + [y-(-1)]^2 = 2^2$
    $(x-2)^2 + (y+1)^2 = 4$

12. $(x-h)^2 + (y-k)^2 = r^2$
    $[x-(-1)]^2 + [y-(-2)]^2 = 3^2$
    $(x+1)^2 + (y+2)^2 = 9$

13. $(x_1, y_1) = (1, 2)$, $(x_2, y_2) = (-1, 1)$
    $d = \sqrt{(x_2 - x_1)^2 + (y_2 - y_1)^2}$
    $\quad = \sqrt{(-1-1)^2 + (1-2)^2}$
    $\quad = \sqrt{(-2)^2 + (-1)^2}$
    $\quad = \sqrt{4+1}$
    $\quad = \sqrt{5}$

    $(x-h)^2 + (y-k)^2 = r^2$
    $[x-(-1)]^2 + (y-1)^2 = \left(\sqrt{5}\right)^2$
    $(x+1)^2 + (y-1)^2 = 5$

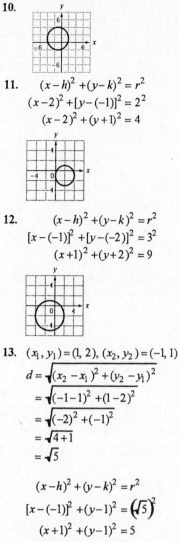

14. $(x_1, y_1) = (-1, 3), \ (x_2, y_2) = (-2, 1)$

$$d = \sqrt{(x_2 - x_1)^2 + (y_2 - y_1)^2}$$
$$= \sqrt{[-2 - (-1)]^2 + (1 - 3)^2}$$
$$= \sqrt{(-1)^2 + (-2)^2}$$
$$= \sqrt{1 + 4}$$
$$= \sqrt{5}$$

$$(x - h)^2 + (y - k)^2 = r^2$$
$$[x - (-2)]^2 + (y - 1)^2 = \left(\sqrt{5}\right)^2$$
$$(x + 2)^2 + (y - 1)^2 = 5$$

15. The endpoints of the diameter are $(-1, 4)$ and $(-5, 8)$. The center of the circle is the midpoint of the diameter.

$(x_1, y_1) = (-1, 4) \qquad (x_2, y_2) = (-5, 8)$

$$x_m = \frac{x_1 + x_2}{2} \qquad y_m = \frac{y_1 + y_2}{2}$$
$$= \frac{-1 + (-5)}{2} \qquad \quad = \frac{4 + 8}{2}$$
$$= -3 \qquad \qquad \quad = 6$$

The center of the circle is $(-3, 6)$. The radius of the circle is the length of the segment connecting the center of the circle $(-3, 6)$ to an endpoint of the diameter (use either $(-1, 4)$ or $(-5, 8)$).

$$r = \sqrt{(x_1 - x_m)^2 + (y_1 - y_m)^2}$$
$$r = \sqrt{(-1 - (-3))^2 + (4 - 6)^2}$$
$$r = \sqrt{4 + 4}$$
$$r = \sqrt{8}$$

Write the equation of the circle with center $(-3, 6)$ and radius $\sqrt{8}$.

$$(x + 3)^2 + (y - 6)^2 = 8$$

16. The endpoints of the diameter are $(2, 3)$ and $(5, -2)$. The center of the circle is the midpoint of the diameter.

$(x_1, y_1) = (2, 3) \qquad (x_2, y_2) = (5, -2)$

$$x_m = \frac{x_1 + x_2}{2} \qquad y_m = \frac{y_1 + y_2}{2}$$
$$= \frac{2 + 5}{2} \qquad \qquad = \frac{3 + (-2)}{2}$$
$$= \frac{7}{2} \qquad \qquad \quad = \frac{1}{2}$$

The center of the circle is $\left(\frac{7}{2}, \frac{1}{2}\right)$. The radius of the circle is the length of the segment connecting the center of the circle $\left(\frac{7}{2}, \frac{1}{2}\right)$ to an endpoint of the diameter (use either $(2, 3)$ or $(5, -2)$).

$$r = \sqrt{(x_1 - x_m)^2 + (y_1 - y_m)^2}$$
$$r = \sqrt{\left(2 - \frac{7}{2}\right)^2 + \left(3 - \frac{1}{2}\right)^2}$$
$$r = \sqrt{\frac{9}{4} + \frac{25}{4}}$$
$$r = \sqrt{\frac{34}{4}} = \frac{\sqrt{34}}{2}$$

Write the equation of the circle with center $\left(\frac{7}{2}, \frac{1}{2}\right)$ and radius $\frac{\sqrt{34}}{2}$.

$$\left(x - \frac{7}{2}\right)^2 + \left(y - \frac{1}{2}\right)^2 = \frac{17}{2}$$

17. The endpoints of the diameter are $(-4, 2)$ and $(0, 0)$. The center of the circle is the midpoint of the diameter.

$(x_1, y_1) = (-4, 2) \qquad (x_2, y_2) = (0, 0)$

$$x_m = \frac{x_1 + x_2}{2} \qquad y_m = \frac{y_1 + y_2}{2}$$
$$= \frac{-4 + 0}{2} \qquad \qquad = \frac{2 + 0}{2}$$
$$= -2 \qquad \qquad \quad = 1$$

The center of the circle is $(-2, 1)$. The radius of the circle is the length of the segment connecting the center of the circle $(-2, 1)$ to an endpoint of the diameter (use either $(-4, 2)$ or $(0, 0)$).

$$r = \sqrt{(x_1 - x_m)^2 + (y_1 - y_m)^2}$$
$$r = \sqrt{(-4 - (-2))^2 + (2 - 1)^2}$$
$$r = \sqrt{4 + 1}$$
$$r = \sqrt{5}$$

Write the equation of the circle with center $(-2, 1)$ and radius $\sqrt{5}$.

$$(x + 2)^2 + (y - 1)^2 = 5$$

18. The endpoints of the diameter are $(-8, -3)$ and $(0, -4)$. The center of the circle is the midpoint of the diameter.

$(x_1, y_1) = (-8, -3)$ $(x_2, y_2) = (0, -4)$

$$x_m = \frac{x_1 + x_2}{2} \qquad y_m = \frac{y_1 + y_2}{2}$$
$$= \frac{-8 + 0}{2} \qquad\quad = \frac{-3 + (-4)}{2}$$
$$= -4 \qquad\qquad\; = -\frac{7}{2}$$

The center of the circle is $\left(-4, -\frac{7}{2}\right)$. The radius of the circle is the length of the segment connecting the center of the circle $\left(-4, -\frac{7}{2}\right)$ to an endpoint of the diameter (use either $(-8, -3)$ or $(0, -4)$).

$$r = \sqrt{(x_1 - x_m)^2 + (y_1 - y_m)^2}$$
$$r = \sqrt{(-8 - (-4))^2 + \left(-3 - \left(-\frac{7}{2}\right)\right)^2}$$
$$r = \sqrt{16 + \frac{1}{4}}$$
$$r = \sqrt{\frac{65}{4}} = \frac{\sqrt{65}}{2}$$

Write the equation of the circle with center $\left(-4, -\frac{7}{2}\right)$ and radius $\frac{\sqrt{65}}{2}$.

$$(x + 4)^2 + \left(y + \frac{7}{2}\right)^2 = \frac{65}{4}$$

Objective 12.2.2 Exercises

19.
$$x^2 + y^2 - 2x + 4y - 20 = 0$$
$$(x^2 - 2x) + (y^2 + 4y) = 20$$
$$(x^2 - 2x + 1) + (y^2 + 4y + 4) = 20 + 1 + 4$$
$$(x - 1)^2 + (y + 2)^2 = 25$$

Center: $(1, -2)$
Radius: 5

20.
$$x^2 + y^2 - 4x + 8y + 4 = 0$$
$$(x^2 - 4x) + (y^2 + 8y) = -4$$
$$(x^2 - 4x + 4) + (y^2 + 8y + 16) = -4 + 4 + 16$$
$$(x - 2)^2 + (y + 4)^2 = 16$$

Center: $(2, -4)$
Radius: 4

21.
$$x^2 + y^2 + 6x + 8y + 9 = 0$$
$$(x^2 + 6x) + (y^2 + 8y) = -9$$
$$(x^2 + 6x + 9) + (y^2 + 8y + 16) = -9 + 9 + 16$$
$$(x + 3)^2 + (y + 4)^2 = 16$$

Center: $(-3, -4)$
Radius: 4

22.
$$x^2 + y^2 - 6x + 10y + 25 = 0$$
$$(x^2 - 6x) + (y^2 + 10y) = -25$$
$$(x^2 - 6x + 9) + (y^2 + 10y + 25) = -25 + 9 + 25$$
$$(x - 3)^2 + (y + 5)^2 = 9$$

Center: $(3, -5)$
Radius: 3

23.
$$x^2 + y^2 - x + 4y + \frac{13}{4} = 0$$
$$(x^2 - x) + (y^2 + 4y) = -\frac{13}{4}$$
$$\left(x^2 - x + \frac{1}{4}\right) + (y^2 + 4y + 4) = -\frac{13}{4} + \frac{1}{4} + 4$$
$$\left(x - \frac{1}{2}\right)^2 + (y + 2)^2 = 1$$

Center: $\left(\frac{1}{2}, -2\right)$

Radius: 1

24.
$$x^2 + y^2 + 4x + y + \frac{1}{4} = 0$$
$$(x^2 + 4x) + (y^2 + y) = -\frac{1}{4}$$
$$(x^2 + 4x + 4) + \left(y^2 + y + \frac{1}{4}\right) = -\frac{1}{4} + 4 + \frac{1}{4}$$
$$(x + 2)^2 + \left(y + \frac{1}{2}\right)^2 = 4$$

Center: $\left(-2, -\frac{1}{2}\right)$

Radius: 2

25.
$$x^2 + y^2 - 6x + 4y + 4 = 0$$
$$(x^2 - 6x) + (y^2 + 4y) = -4$$
$$(x^2 - 6x + 9) + (y^2 + 4y + 4) = -4 + 9 + 4$$
$$(x - 3)^2 + (y + 2)^2 = 9$$
Center: $(3, -2)$
Radius: 3

26.
$$x^2 + y^2 - 10x + 8y + 40 = 0$$
$$(x^2 - 10x) + (y^2 + 8y) = -40$$
$$(x^2 - 10x + 25) + (y^2 + 8y + 16) = -40 + 25 + 16$$
$$(x - 5)^2 + (y + 4)^2 = 1$$
Center: $(5, -4)$
Radius: 1

Applying Concepts 12.2

27. $(x_1, y_1) = (3, 0)$ $(x_2, y_2) = (0, 0)$
$$r = \sqrt{(x_2 - x_1)^2 + (y_2 - y_1)^2}$$
$$= \sqrt{(0 - 3)^2 + (0 - 0)^2} = \sqrt{9} = 3$$
$$(x - h)^2 + (y - k)^2 = r^2$$
$$(x - 3)^2 + (y - 0)^2 = 3^2$$
$$(x - 3)^2 + y^2 = 9$$

28. Center: $(6, -3)$, Radius: 5.
$$(x - 6)^2 + (y + 3)^2 = 25$$
$$x^2 - 12x + 36 + y^2 + 6y + 9 = 25$$
$$x^2 + y^2 - 12x + 6y + 20 = 0$$

29. If the circle lies in quadrant II, has a radius of 1, and is tangent to both axes, then it must pass through the points $(0, 1)$, $(-1, 0)$, $(-2, 1)$, and $(-1, 2)$. The center must be $(-1, 1)$.
$$(x - h)^2 + (y - k)^2 = r^2$$
$$[x - (-1)]^2 + (y - 1)^2 = 1^2$$
$$(x + 1)^2 + (y - 1)^2 = 1$$

30. The radius of the circle will be $6\sqrt{3}$ inches.
$$r^2 + 6^2 = 12^2$$
$$r^2 + 36 = 144$$
$$r^2 = 108$$
$$r = \sqrt{108} = 6\sqrt{3} \text{ in.}$$

31. Attempt to write the equation $x^2 + y^2 + 4x + 8y + 24 = 0$ in standard form.
$$x^2 + y^2 + 4x + 8y + 24 = 0$$
$$(x^2 + 4x) + (y^2 + 8y) = -24$$
$$(x^2 + 4x + 4) + (y^2 + 8y + 16) = -24 + 4 + 16$$
$$(x + 2)^2 + (y + 4)^2 = -4$$
This is not the equation of a circle because r^2 is negative ($r^2 = -4$), and the square of a real number cannot be negative.

32. The graph of $\dfrac{x^2}{9} + \dfrac{y^2}{9} = 1$ can be written as $x^2 + y^2 = 9$, which is the equation of a circle of radius 3 whose center is the origin. In general, any equation of the form $\dfrac{x^2}{a} + \dfrac{y^2}{a} = 1$, $a > 0$, is the equation of a circle.

33. The distance formula is used to derive the equation of a circle. If $C(h, k)$ are the coordinates of a fixed point in the plane and $P(x, y)$ is any other point in the plane, then the distance between C and P is $r = \sqrt{(x - h)^2 + (y - k)^2}$. Squaring each side of this equation gives the equation of a circle in standard form: $r^2 = (x - h)^2 + (y - k)^2$. Students might also note the connection between the *distance* formula and the definition of a circle as the set of all points in the plane that are a fixed *distance* from the center; hence the same derivation for the two formulas.

Section 12.3

Concept Review 12.3

1. Never true
   A vertical line will intersect the graph of an ellipse at more than one point. By the vertical-line test, the graph of an ellipse is not the graph of a function.

2. Never true
   A vertical line will intersect the graph of a hyperbola at more than one point. By the vertical-line test, the graph of a hyperbola is not the graph of a function.

3. Always true

4. Always true

5. Sometimes true
   The hyperbola $\dfrac{y^2}{4} - \dfrac{x^2}{16} = 1$ has no x-intercepts.

6. Always true

Objective 12.3.1 Exercises

1. x-intercepts: (2, 0) and (–2, 0)
   y-intercepts: (0, 3) and (0, –3)

2. x-intercepts: (5, 0) and (–5, 0)
   y-intercepts: (0, 4) and (0, –4)

3. x-intercepts: (5, 0) and (–5, 0)
   y-intercepts: (0, 3) and (0, –3)

4. x-intercepts: (4, 0) and (–4, 0)
   y-intercepts: (0, 3) and (0, –3)

5. x-intercepts: (6, 0) and (–6, 0)
   y-intercepts: (0, 4) and (0, –4)

6. x-intercepts: (7, 0) and (–7, 0)
   y-intercepts: (0, 8) and (0, –8)

7. x-intercepts: (3, 0) and (–3, 0)
   y-intercepts: (0, 5) and (0, –5)

8. x-intercepts: $(2\sqrt{2}, 0)$ and $(-2\sqrt{2}, 0)$
   y-intercepts: (0, 5) and (0, –5)

9. x-intercepts: $(2\sqrt{3}, 0)$ and $(-2\sqrt{3}, 0)$
   y-intercepts: (0, 2) and (0, –2)

10. x-intercepts: (4, 0) and (–4, 0)
    y-intercepts: (0, 6) and (0, –6)

11. x-intercepts: (6, 0) and (–6, 0)
    y-intercepts: (0, 3) and (0, –3)

12. *x*-intercepts: (2, 0) and (−2, 0)
    y-intercepts: (0, 4) and (0, −4)

Objective 12.3.2 Exercises

13. If the equation is in standard form, the graph will be an ellipse if the terms are added. The graph will be a hyperbola if one term is subtracted from the other.

14. The asymptotes of a hyperbola are two lines that are "approached" by the hyperbola. As a point on the hyperbola get farther from the origin, the hyperbola "gets closer to" the asymptotes.

15. Axis of symmetry: *x*-axis
    Vertices: (3, 0) and (−3, 0)
    Asymptotes: $y = \frac{4}{3}x$ and $y = -\frac{4}{3}x$

16. Axis of symmetry: *x*-axis
    Vertices: (5, 0) and (−5, 0)
    Asymptotes: $y = \frac{2}{5}x$ and $y = -\frac{2}{5}x$

17. Axis of symmetry: *y*-axis
    Vertices: (0, 4) and (0, −4)
    Asymptotes: $y = \frac{4}{3}x$ and $y = -\frac{4}{3}x$

18. Axis of symmetry: *y*-axis
    Vertices: (0, 2) and (0, −2)
    Asymptotes: $y = \frac{2}{3}x$ and $y = -\frac{2}{3}x$

19. Axis of symmetry: *x*-axis
    Vertices: (2, 0) and (−2, 0)
    Asymptotes: $y = \frac{5}{2}x$ and $y = -\frac{5}{2}x$

20. Axis of symmetry: *x*-axis
    Vertices: (3, 0) and (−3, 0)
    Asymptotes: $y = \frac{7}{3}x$ and $y = -\frac{7}{3}x$

21. Axis of symmetry: *y*-axis
    Vertices: (0, 5) and (0, −5)
    Asymptotes: $y = \frac{5}{3}x$ and $y = -\frac{5}{3}x$

22. Axis of symmetry: *y*-axis
    Vertices: (0, 2) and (0, −2)
    Asymptotes: $y = \frac{1}{2}x$ and $y = -\frac{1}{2}x$

23. Axis of symmetry: *x*-axis
    Vertices: (5, 0) and (−5, 0)
    Asymptotes: $y = \frac{4}{5}x$ and $y = -\frac{4}{5}x$

24. Axis of symmetry: *x*-axis
    Vertices: (3, 0) and (−3, 0)
    Asymptotes: $y = x$ and $y = -x$

25. Axis of symmetry: *y*-axis
Vertices: (0, 4) and (0, −4)
Asymptotes: $y = 2x$ and $y = -2x$

26. Axis of symmetry: *y*-axis
Vertices: (0, 3) and (0, −3)
Asymptotes: $y = \frac{1}{2}x$ and $y = -\frac{1}{2}x$

27. Axis of symmetry: *x*-axis
Vertices: (5, 0) and (−5, 0)
Asymptotes: $y = \frac{3}{5}x$ and $y = -\frac{3}{5}x$

28. Axis of symmetry: *x*-axis
Vertices: (4, 0) and (−4, 0)
Asymptotes: $y = \frac{5}{4}x$ and $y = -\frac{5}{4}x$

Applying Concepts 12.3

29. The graph of $4x^2 + y^2 = 16$ is an ellipse.
$$4x^2 + y^2 = 16$$
$$\frac{4x^2 + y^2}{16} = \frac{16}{16}$$
$$\frac{4x^2}{16} + \frac{y^2}{16} = 1$$
$$\frac{x^2}{4} + \frac{y^2}{16} = 1$$
x-intercepts: (2, 0) and (−2, 0)
y-intercepts: (0, 4) and (0, −4)

30. The graph of $x^2 - y^2 = 9$ is a hyperbola.
$$x^2 - y^2 = 9$$
$$\frac{x^2 - y^2}{9} = \frac{9}{9}$$
$$\frac{x^2}{9} - \frac{y^2}{9} = 1$$
Axis of symmetry: *x*-axis
Vertices: (3, 0) and (−3, 0)
Asymptotes: $y = x$ and $y = -x$

31. The graph of $y^2 - 4x^2 = 16$ is a hyperbola.
$$y^2 - 4x^2 = 16$$
$$\frac{y^2 - 4x^2}{16} = \frac{16}{16}$$
$$\frac{y^2}{16} - \frac{4x^2}{16} = 1$$
$$\frac{y^2}{16} - \frac{x^2}{4} = 1$$
Axis of symmetry: *y*-axis
Vertices: (0, 4) and (0, −4)
Asymptotes: $y = 2x$ and $y = -2x$

32. The graph of $9x^2 + 4y^2 = 144$ is an ellipse.
$$9x^2 + 4y^2 = 144$$
$$\frac{9x^2 + 4y^2}{144} = \frac{144}{144}$$
$$\frac{9x^2}{144} + \frac{4y^2}{144} = 1$$
$$\frac{x^2}{16} + \frac{y^2}{36} = 1$$
x-intercepts: (4, 0) and (−4, 0)
y-intercepts: (0, 6) and (0, −6)

33. The graph of $9x^2 - 25y^2 = 225$ is a hyperbola.

$$9x^2 - 25y^2 = 225$$

$$\frac{9x^2 - 25y^2}{225} = \frac{225}{225}$$

$$\frac{9x^2}{225} - \frac{25y^2}{225} = 1$$

$$\frac{x^2}{25} - \frac{y^2}{9} = 1$$

Axis of symmetry: x-axis

Vertices: $(5, 0)$ and $(-5, 0)$

Asymptotes: $y = \frac{3}{5}x$ and $y = -\frac{3}{5}x$

34. The graph of $4y^2 - x^2 = 36$ is a hyperbola.

$$4y^2 - x^2 = 36$$

$$\frac{4y^2 - x^2}{36} = \frac{36}{36}$$

$$\frac{4y^2}{36} - \frac{x^2}{36} = 1$$

$$\frac{y^2}{9} - \frac{x^2}{36} = 1$$

Axis of symmetry: y-axis

Vertices: $(0, 3)$ and $(0, -3)$

Asymptotes: $y = \frac{1}{2}x$ and $y = -\frac{1}{2}x$

35. a.
$$\frac{x^2}{a^2} + \frac{y^2}{b^2} = 1$$

$$\frac{x^2}{18^2} + \frac{y^2}{4.5^2} = 1$$

$$\frac{x^2}{324} + \frac{y^2}{20.25} = 1$$

b. Major axis = 36 AU

36 AU ÷ 2 = 18 AU

18 AU = 18(92,960,000 mi)

= 1,673,280,000 mi

$$\sqrt{a^2 - b^2} = \sqrt{324 - 20.25}$$

$$= \sqrt{303.75}$$

$$\approx 17.42842506$$

17.42842506 AU

= 17.42842506(92,960,000 mi)

≈ 1,620,146,393 mi

1,673,280,000 + 1,620,146,393

≈ 3,293,400,000

The distance from the Sun to the point at the aphelion is about 3,293,400,000 mi.

c. $18 \text{ AU} - \sqrt{a^2 - b^2}$ AU

= 1,673,280,000 mi − 1,620,146,393 mi

= 53,133,607 ≈ 53,100,000

The distance from the Sun to the point at the perihelion is about 53,100,000 mi.

36. a.
$$\frac{x^2}{a^2} + \frac{y^2}{b^2} = 1$$

$$\frac{x^2}{(183)^2} + \frac{y^2}{(18)^2} = 1$$

$$\frac{x^2}{33,489} + \frac{y^2}{324} = 1$$

b. 183 AU + 182.085 AU = 365.085 AU

365.085 AU = 365.085(92,960,000 mi)

≈ 33,938,000,000 mi

The aphelion is about 33,938,000,000 mi.

c. 183 AU − 182.085 AU = 0.915 AU

0.915 AU = 0.915(92,960,000 mi)

≈ 85,100,000 mi

The perihelion is about 85,100,000 mi.

37. a.
$$\frac{x^2}{a^2} + \frac{y^2}{b^2} = 1$$
$$\frac{x^2}{1.52^2} + \frac{y^2}{1.495^2} = 1$$
$$\frac{x^2}{2.310} + \frac{y^2}{2.235} = 1$$

b. Major axis = 3.04 AU
3.04 AU ÷ 2 = 1.52 AU
1.52 AU = 1.52(92,960,000 mi)
$\quad = 141,299,200$ mi
$$\sqrt{a^2 - b^2} = \sqrt{2.310 - 2.235}$$
$$= \sqrt{0.075}$$
$$\approx 0.2738612788$$
0.2738612788 AU
= 0.2738612788(92,960,000 mi)
$\approx 25,488,144$ mi
141,299,200 + 25,458,144 = 168,757,344
$\quad\quad\quad\quad\quad \approx 166,800,000$
The aphelion is about 166,800,000 mi.

c. 1.52 AU $- \sqrt{a^2 - b^2}$ AU
= 141,299,200 mi − 25,458,144 mi
$\approx 115,800,000$
The perihelion is about 115,800,000 mi.

38. The Loran method of navigation is based on hyperbolas. Consider two transmitters, T_1 and T_2, placed some distance apart. A ship with electronic equipment measures the difference in the time it takes signals from these two transmitters to reach the ship. Because the differences in time is proportional to the distance to the ship from the transmitter, the ship must be located on a hyperbola with foci at the two transmitters.

Using a third transmitter, T_3, and again measuring the difference in time, we can find a second hyperbola for foci T_2 and T_3. The location of the ship is the intersection of the two hyperbolas.

Section 12.4

Concept Review 12.4

1. Never true
Two ellipses with centers at the origin may intersect at four points or they may not intersect.

2. Sometimes true
Two circles may intersect at two points or they may not intersect.

3. Sometimes true
A straight line may intersect a parabola at one point or two points, or the line may not intersect the parabola.

4. Sometimes true
An ellipse and a circle may intersect at one point, two points or four points, or they may not intersect.

5. Always true

6. Never true
Two circles may intersect at one or two points or they may not intersect.

Objective 12.4.1 Exercises

1. Nonlinear systems of equations are systems in which one or more equations are not linear equations. If all equations are linear, the system is a linear system.

2. Nonlinear systems can be solved by using either the substitution method or the addition method.

3. (1) $y = x^2 - x - 1$
(2) $y = 2x + 9$
Use the substitution method.
$$y = x^2 - x - 1$$
$$2x + 9 = x^2 - x - 1$$
$$0 = x^2 - 3x - 10$$
$$0 = (x - 5)(x + 2)$$
$x - 5 = 0 \quad x + 2 = 0$
$\quad x = 5 \quad\quad x = -2$
Substitute into equation (2).
$y = 2x + 9 \quad\quad y = 2x + 9$
$y = 2(5) + 9 \quad y = 2(-2) = 9$
$y = 10 + 9 \quad\quad y = -4 + 9$
$y = 19 \quad\quad\quad y = 5$
The solutions are (5, 19) and (−2, 5).

4. (1) $y = x^2 - 3x + 1$
(2) $y = x + 6$
Use the substitution method.
$$y = x^2 - 3x + 1$$
$$x + 6 = x^2 - 3x + 1$$
$$0 = x^2 - 4x - 5$$
$$0 = (x - 5)(x + 1)$$
$x - 5 = 0 \quad x + 1 = 0$
$\quad x = 5 \quad\quad x = -1$
Substitute into equation (2).
$y = x + 6 \quad y = x + 6$
$y = 5 + 6 \quad y = -1 + 6$
$y = 11 \quad\quad y = 5$
The solutions are (5, 11) and (−1, 5).

5. (1) $y^2 = -x + 3$
(2) $x - y = 1$

Solve equation (2) for x.
$x - y = 1$
$x = y + 1$

Use the substitution method.
$$y^2 = -x + 3$$
$$y^2 = -(y + 1) + 3$$
$$y^2 = -y - 1 + 3$$
$$y^2 = -y + 2$$
$$y^2 + y - 2 = 0$$
$$(y + 2)(y - 1) = 0$$
$y + 2 = 0 \quad y - 1 = 0$
$y = -2 \quad y = 1$

Substitute into equation (2).
$x - y = 1 \quad x - y = 1$
$x - (-2) = 1 \quad x - 1 = 1$
$x + 2 = 1 \quad x = 2$
$x = -1$

The solutions are $(-1, -2)$ and $(2, 1)$.

6. (1) $y^2 = 4x$
(2) $x - y = -1$

Solve equation (2) for x.
$x - y = -1$
$x = y - 1$

Use the substitution method.
$$y^2 = 4x$$
$$y^2 = 4(y - 1)$$
$$y^2 = 4y - 4$$
$$y^2 - 4y + 4 = 0$$
$$(y - 2)(y - 2) = 0$$
$y - 2 = 0$
$y = 2$

The solution is a double root.
Substitute into equation (2)
$x - y = -1$
$x - 2 = -1$
$x = 1$

The solution is $(1, 2)$.

7. (1) $y^2 = 2x$
(2) $x + 2y = -2$

Solve equation (2) for x.
$x + 2y = -2$
$x = -2y - 2$

Use the substitution method.
$$y^2 = 2x$$
$$y^2 = 2(-2y - 2)$$
$$y^2 = -4y - 4$$
$$y^2 + 4y + 4 = 0$$
$$(y + 2)(y + 2) = 0$$
$y + 2 = 0$
$y = -2$

The solution is a double root.
Substitute into equation (2).
$x + 2y = -2$
$x + 2(-2) = -2$
$x - 4 = -2$
$x = 2$

The solution is $(2, -2)$.

8. (1) $y^2 = 2x$
(2) $x - y = 4$

Solve equation (2) for x.
$x - y = 4$
$x = y + 4$

Use the substitution method.
$$y^2 = 2x$$
$$y^2 = 2(y + 4)$$
$$y^2 = 2y + 8$$
$$y^2 - 2y - 8 = 0$$
$$(y + 2)(y - 4) = 0$$
$y + 2 = 0 \quad y - 4 = 0$
$y = -2 \quad y = 4$

Substitute into equation (2).
$x - y = 4 \quad x - y = 4$
$x - (-2) = 4 \quad x - 4 = 4$
$x + 2 = 4 \quad x = 8$
$x = 2$

The solutions are $(2, -2)$ and $(8, 4)$.

9. (1) $x^2 + 2y^2 = 12$
   (2) $2x - y = 2$
   Solve equation (2) for y.
   $2x - y = 2$
   $-y = -2x + 2$
   $y = 2x - 2$
   Use the substitution method.
   $$x^2 + 2y^2 = 12$$
   $$x^2 + 2(2x - 2)^2 = 12$$
   $$x^2 + 2(4x^2 - 8x + 4) = 12$$
   $$x^2 + 8x^2 - 16x + 8 = 12$$
   $$9x^2 - 16x - 4 = 0$$
   $$(x - 2)(9x + 2) = 0$$
   $x - 2 = 0 \quad 9x + 2 = 0$
   $x = 2 \quad\quad 9x = -2$
   $$x = -\frac{2}{9}$$
   Substitute into equation (2).
   $2x - y = 2 \quad\quad 2x - y = 2$
   $2(2) - y = 2 \quad 2\left(-\dfrac{2}{9}\right) - y = 2$
   $4 - y = 2 \quad\quad -\dfrac{4}{9} - y = 2$
   $-y = -2 \quad\quad$
   $y = 2 \quad\quad -y = \dfrac{22}{9}$
   $$y = -\frac{22}{9}$$
   The solutions are $(2, 2)$ and $\left(-\dfrac{2}{9},\, -\dfrac{22}{9}\right)$.

10. (1) $x^2 + 4y^2 = 37$
   (2) $x - y = -4$
   Solve equation (2) for x.
   $x - y = -4$
   $x = y - 4$
   Use the substitution method.
   $$x^2 + 4y^2 = 37$$
   $$(y - 4)^2 + 4y^2 = 37$$
   $$y^2 - 8y + 16 + 4y^2 = 37$$
   $$5y^2 - 8y - 21 = 0$$
   $$(5y + 7)(y - 3) = 0$$
   $5y + 7 = 0 \quad y - 3 = 0$
   $5y = -7 \quad\quad y = 3$
   $$y = -\frac{7}{5}$$
   Substitute into equation (2).
   $x - y = -4 \quad\quad x - y = -4$
   $x - \left(-\dfrac{7}{5}\right) = -4 \quad x - 3 = -4$
   $\quad\quad\quad\quad\quad\quad x = -1$
   $x + \dfrac{7}{5} = -4$
   $$x = -\frac{27}{5}$$
   The solutions are $\left(-\dfrac{27}{5},\, -\dfrac{7}{5}\right)$ and $(-1, 3)$.

11. (1) $x^2 + y^2 = 13$
   (2) $x + y = 5$
   Solve equation (2) for y.
   $x + y = 5$
   $y = -x + 5$
   Use the substitution method.
   $$x^2 + y^2 = 13$$
   $$x^2 + (-x + 5)^2 = 13$$
   $$x^2 + x^2 - 10x + 25 = 13$$
   $$2x^2 - 10x + 12 = 0$$
   $$2(x^2 - 5x + 6) = 0$$
   $$2(x - 3)(x - 2) = 0$$
   $x - 3 = 0 \quad x - 2 = 0$
   $x = 3 \quad\quad x = 2$
   Substitute into equation (2).
   $x + y = 5 \quad x + y = 5$
   $3 + y = 5 \quad 2 + y = 5$
   $y = 2 \quad\quad y = 3$
   The solutions are $(3, 2)$ and $(2, 3)$.

12. (1) $x^2 + y^2 = 16$
   (2) $x - 2y = -4$
   Solve equation (2) for x.
   $x - 2y = -4$
   $x = 2y - 4$
   Use the substitution method.
   $$x^2 + y^2 = 16$$
   $$(2y - 4)^2 + y^2 = 16$$
   $$4y^2 - 16y + 16 + y^2 = 16$$
   $$5y^2 - 16y = 0$$
   $$y(5y - 16) = 0$$
   $y = 0 \quad\quad 5y - 16 = 0$
   $\quad\quad\quad\quad 5y = 16$
   $$y = \frac{16}{5}$$
   Substitute into equation (2).
   $x - 2y = -4 \quad\quad x - 2y = -4$
   $x - 2(0) = -4 \quad x - 2\left(\dfrac{16}{5}\right) = -4$
   $x = -4 \quad\quad\quad$
   $\quad\quad\quad\quad\quad x - \dfrac{32}{5} = -4$
   $$x = \frac{12}{5}$$
   The solutions are $(-4, 0)$ and $\left(\dfrac{12}{5},\, \dfrac{16}{5}\right)$.

13. (1) $4x^2 + y^2 = 12$
    (2) $y = 4x^2$

Use the substitution method.

$$4x^2 + y^2 = 12$$
$$4x^2 + (4x^2)^2 = 12$$
$$4x^2 + 16x^4 = 12$$
$$16x^4 + 4x^2 - 12 = 0$$
$$4(4x^4 + x^2 - 3) = 0$$
$$4(4x^2 - 3)(x^2 + 1) = 0$$

$4x^2 - 3 = 0$ $x^2 + 1 = 0$
$4x^2 = 3$ $x^2 = -1$
$x^2 = \dfrac{3}{4}$ $x = \pm\sqrt{-1}$

$$x = \pm\frac{\sqrt{3}}{2}$$

Substitute the real number solutions into equation (2).

$y = 4x^2$ $y = 4x^2$

$y = 4\left(\dfrac{\sqrt{3}}{2}\right)^2$ $y = 4\left(-\dfrac{\sqrt{3}}{2}\right)^2$

$y = 4\left(\dfrac{3}{4}\right)$ $y = 4\left(\dfrac{3}{4}\right)$

$y = 3$ $y = 3$

The solutions are $\left(\dfrac{\sqrt{3}}{2},\ 3\right)$ and $\left(-\dfrac{\sqrt{3}}{2},\ 3\right)$.

14. (1) $2x^2 + y^2 = 6$
    (2) $y = 2x^2$

Use the substitution method.

$$2x^2 + y^2 = 6$$
$$2x^2 + (2x^2)^2 = 6$$
$$2x^2 + 4x^4 = 6$$
$$4x^2 + 2x^2 - 6 = 0$$
$$2(2x^4 + x^2 - 3) = 0$$
$$2(2x^2 + 3)(x^2 - 1) = 0$$

$2x^2 + 3 = 0$ $x^2 - 1 = 0$
$2x^2 = -3$ $x^2 = 1$
$x^2 = -\dfrac{3}{2}$ $x = \pm\sqrt{1}$
                 $x = \pm 1$

$$x = \pm\sqrt{-\frac{3}{2}}$$

Substitute the real number solutions into equation (2).

$y = 2x^2$ $y = 2x^2$
$y = 2(1)^2$ $y = 2(-1)^2$
$y = 2(1)$ $y = 2(1)$
$y = 2$ $y = 2$

The solutions are $(1, 2)$ and $(-1, 2)$.

15. (1) $y = x^2 - 2x - 3$
    (2) $y = x - 6$

Use the substitution method.

$$y = x^2 - 2x - 3$$
$$x - 6 = x^2 - 2x - 3$$
$$0 = x^2 - 3x + 3$$
$$x = \frac{-b \pm \sqrt{b^2 - 4ac}}{2a}$$
$$= \frac{-(-3) \pm \sqrt{(-3)^2 - 4(1)(3)}}{2(1)}$$
$$= \frac{3 \pm \sqrt{9 - 12}}{2}$$
$$= \frac{3 \pm \sqrt{-3}}{2}$$

Since the discriminant is less than zero, the equation has two complex number solutions. Therefore, the system of equations has no real number solution.

16. (1) $y = x^2 + 4x + 5$
    (2) $y = -x - 3$

Use the substitution method.

$$y = x^2 + 4x + 5$$
$$-x - 3 = x^2 + 4x + 5$$
$$0 = x^2 + 5x + 8$$
$$x = \frac{-b \pm \sqrt{b^2 - 4ac}}{2a}$$
$$= \frac{-5 \pm \sqrt{5^2 - 4(1)(8)}}{2(1)}$$
$$= \frac{-5 \pm \sqrt{25 - 32}}{2}$$
$$= \frac{-5 \pm \sqrt{-7}}{2}$$

Since the discriminant is less than zero, the equation has two complex number solutions. Therefore, the system of equations has no real number solution.

17. (1) $3x^2 - y^2 = -1$
(2) $x^2 + 4y^2 = 17$
Use the addition method.
Multiply equation (1) by 4.
$12x^2 - 4y^2 = -4$
$x^2 + 4y^2 = 17$
$13x^2 = 13$
$x^2 = 1$
$x = \pm\sqrt{1} = \pm 1$
Substitute into equation (2).

$x^2 + 4y^2 = 17 \qquad x^2 + 4y^2 = 17$
$1^2 + 4y^2 = 17 \qquad (-1)^2 + 4y^2 = 17$
$1 + 4y^2 = 17 \qquad 1 + 4y^2 = 17$
$ 4y^2 = 16 \qquad 4y^2 = 16$
$y^2 = 4 \qquady^2 = 4$
$y = \pm\sqrt{4} \qquady = \pm\sqrt{4}$
$y = \pm 2 \qquady = \pm 2$

The solutions are (1, 2), (1, –2), (–1, 2), and (–1, –2).

18. (1) $x^2 + y^2 = 10$
(2) $x^2 + 9y^2 = 18$
Use the addition method.
Multiply equation (1) by –1.
$-x^2 - y^2 = -10$
$x^2 + 9y^2 = 18$
$8y^2 = 8$
$y^2 = 1$
$y = \pm\sqrt{1} = \pm 1$
Substitute into equation (1).

$x^2 + y^2 = 10 \qquad x^2 + y^2 = 10$
$x^2 + 1^2 = 10 \qquad x^2 + (-1)^2 = 10$
$x^2 + 1 = 10 \qquad x^2 + 1 = 10$
$x^2 = 9 \qquadx^2 = 9$
$x = \pm\sqrt{9} \qquadx = \pm\sqrt{9}$
$x = \pm 3 \qquadx = \pm 3$

The solutions are (3, 1), (–3, 1), (3, –1), and (–3, –1).

19. (1) $2x^2 + 3y^2 = 30$
(2) $x^2 + y^2 = 13$
Use the addition method.
Multiply equation (2) by –2.
$2x^2 + 3y^2 = 30$
$-2x^2 - 2y^2 = -26$
$y^2 = 4$
$y = \pm\sqrt{4} = \pm 2$
Substitute into equation (2).

$x^2 + y^2 = 13 \qquad x^2 + y^2 = 13$
$x^2 + 2^2 = 13 \qquad x^2 + (-2)^2 = 13$
$x^2 + 4 = 13 \qquad x^2 + 4 = 13$
$x^2 = 9 \qquadx^2 = 9$
$x = \pm\sqrt{9} \qquadx = \pm\sqrt{9}$
$x = \pm 3 \qquadx = \pm 3$

The solutions are (3, 2), (3, –2), (–3, 2), and (–3, –2).

20. (1) $x^2 + y^2 = 61$
(2) $x^2 - y^2 = 11$
Use the addition method.
$x^2 + y^2 = 61$
$x^2 - y^2 = 11$
$2x^2 = 72$
$x^2 = 36$
$x = \pm\sqrt{36} = \pm 6$
Substitute into equation (1).

$x^2 + y^2 = 61 \qquad x^2 + y^2 = 61$
$6^2 + y^2 = 61 \qquad (-6)^2 + y^2 = 61$
$36 + y^2 = 61 \qquad 36 + y^2 = 61$
$y^2 = 25 \qquady^2 = 25$
$y = \pm\sqrt{25} \qquady = \pm\sqrt{25}$
$y = \pm 5 \qquady = \pm 5$

The solutions are (6, 5), (6, –5), (–6, 5), and (–6, –5).

21. (1) $y = 2x^2 - x + 1$
(2) $y = x^2 - x + 5$
Use the substitution method.
$y = 2x^2 - x + 1$
$x^2 - x + 5 = 2x^2 - x + 1$
$0 = x^2 - 4$
$0 = (x + 2)(x - 2)$
$x + 2 = 0 \quad x - 2 = 0$
$x = -2 \qquad x = 2$
Substitute into equation (2).

$y = x^2 - x + 5 \qquad y = x^2 - x + 5$
$y = (-2)^2 - (-2) + 5 \quad y = 2^2 - 2 + 5$
$y = 4 + 2 + 5 \qquad y = 4 - 2 + 5$
$y = 11 \qquad\qquad y = 7$

The solutions are (2, 7) and (–2, 11).

22. (1) $y = -x^2 + x - 1$
(2) $y = x^2 + 2x - 2$
Use the substitution method.
$$y = -x^2 + x - 1$$
$$x^2 + 2x - 2 = -x^2 + x - 1$$
$$2x^2 + x - 1 = 0$$
$$(2x - 1)(x + 1) = 0$$
$$2x - 1 = 0 \qquad x + 1 = 0$$
$$2x = 1 \qquad x = -1$$
$$x = \frac{1}{2}$$
Substitute into equation (2).
$$y = x^2 + 2x - 2 \qquad y = x^2 + 2x - 2$$
$$y = \left(\frac{1}{2}\right)^2 + 2\left(\frac{1}{2}\right) - 2 \qquad y = (-1)^2 + 2(-1) - 2$$
$$y = 1 - 2 - 2$$
$$y = \frac{1}{4} + 1 - 2 \qquad y = -3$$
$$y = -\frac{3}{4}$$
The solutions are $\left(\frac{1}{2}, -\frac{3}{4}\right)$ and $(-1, -3)$.

23. (1) $2x^2 + 3y^2 = 24$
(2) $x^2 - y^2 = 7$
Use the addition method.
Multiply equation (2) by 3.
$$2x^2 + 3y^2 = 24$$
$$3x^2 - 3y^2 = 21$$
$$5x^2 = 45$$
$$x^2 = 9 = \pm\sqrt{9} = \pm 3$$
Substitute into equation (2).
$$x^2 - y^2 = 7 \qquad x^2 - y^2 = 7$$
$$3^2 - y^2 = 7 \qquad (-3)^2 - y^2 = 7$$
$$9 - y^2 = 7 \qquad 9 - y^2 = 7$$
$$-y^2 = -2 \qquad -y^2 = -2$$
$$y^2 = 2 \qquad y^2 = 2$$
$$y = \pm\sqrt{2} \qquad y = \pm\sqrt{2}$$
The solutions are $(3, \sqrt{2}), (3, -\sqrt{2}), (-3, \sqrt{2})$, and $(-3, -\sqrt{2})$.

24. (1) $2x^2 + 3y^2 = 21$
(2) $x^2 + 2y^2 = 12$
Use the addition method.
Multiply equation (2) by –2.
$$2x^2 + 3y^2 = 21$$
$$-2x^2 - 4y^2 = -24$$
$$-y^2 = -3$$
$$y^2 = 3$$
$$y = \pm\sqrt{3}$$
Substitute into equation (2).
$$x^2 + 2y^2 = 12 \qquad x^2 + 2y^2 = 12$$
$$x^2 + 2(\sqrt{3})^2 = 12 \qquad x^2 + 2(-\sqrt{3})^2 = 12$$
$$x^2 + 2(3) = 12 \qquad x^2 + 2(3) = 12$$
$$x^2 + 6 = 12 \qquad x^2 + 6 = 12$$
$$x^2 = 6 \qquad x^2 = 6$$
$$x = \pm\sqrt{6} \qquad x = \pm\sqrt{6}$$
The solutions are $(\sqrt{6}, \sqrt{3}), (\sqrt{6}, -\sqrt{3})$, $(-\sqrt{6}, \sqrt{3})$, and $(-\sqrt{6}, -\sqrt{3})$.

25. (1) $x^2 + y^2 = 36$
(2) $4x^2 + 9y^2 = 36$
Use the addition method.
Multiply equation (1) by –4.
$$-4x^2 - 4y^2 = -144$$
$$4x^2 + 9y^2 = 36$$
$$5y^2 = -108$$
$$y^2 = -\frac{108}{5}$$
$$y = \pm\sqrt{-\frac{108}{5}}$$
The system of equations has no real number solution.

26. (1) $2x^2 + 3y^2 = 12$
(2) $x^2 - y^2 = 25$
Use the addition method.
Multiply equation (2) by 3.

$2x^2 + 3y^2 = 12$
$3x^2 - 3y^2 = 75$
$\quad 5x^2 = 87$
$\quad\; x^2 = \dfrac{87}{5}$
$\quad\; x = \pm\sqrt{\dfrac{87}{5}}$

Substitute into equation (2).

$x^2 - y^2 = 25$ $\qquad$ $x^2 - y^2 = 25$

$\left(\sqrt{\dfrac{87}{5}}\right)^2 - y^2 = 25$ $\qquad$ $\left(-\sqrt{\dfrac{87}{5}}\right)^2 - y^2 = 25$

$\dfrac{87}{5} - y^2 = 25$ $\qquad\qquad$ $\dfrac{87}{5} - y^2 = 25$

$-y^2 = \dfrac{38}{5}$ $\qquad\qquad$ $-y^2 = \dfrac{38}{5}$

$y^2 = -\dfrac{38}{5}$ $\qquad\qquad$ $y^2 = -\dfrac{38}{5}$

$y = \pm\sqrt{-\dfrac{38}{5}}$ $\qquad\quad$ $y = \pm\sqrt{-\dfrac{38}{5}}$

The system of equations has no real number solution.

27. (1) $11x^2 - 2y^2 = 4$
(2) $3x^2 + y^2 = 15$
Use the addition method.
Multiply equation (2) by 2.

$11x^2 - 2y^2 = 4$
$\;6x^2 + 2y^2 = 30$
$\quad\; 17x^2 = 34$
$\quad\;\; x^2 = 2$
$\quad\;\;\; x = \pm\sqrt{2}$

Substitute into equation (2).

$3x^2 + y^2 = 15$ $\qquad$ $3x^2 + y^2 = 15$
$3(\sqrt{2}) + y^2 = 15$ $\qquad$ $3(-\sqrt{2}) + y^2 = 15$
$3(2) + y^2 = 15$ $\qquad$ $3(2) + y^2 = 15$
$6 + y^2 = 15$ $\qquad\quad$ $6 + y^2 = 15$
$y^2 = 9$ $\qquad\qquad$ $y^2 = 9$
$y = \pm\sqrt{9}$ $\qquad\qquad$ $y = \pm\sqrt{9}$
$y = \pm 3$ $\qquad\qquad$ $y = \pm 3$

The solutions are $(\sqrt{2}, 3), (\sqrt{2}, -3), (-\sqrt{2}, 3),$ and $(-\sqrt{2}, -3)$.

28. (1) $x^2 + 4y^2 = 25$
(2) $x^2 - y^2 = 5$
Use the addition method.
Multiply equation (2) by -1.
$x^2 + 4y^2 = 25$
$-x^2 + y^2 = -5$
$5y^2 = 20$
$y^2 = 4$
$y = \pm\sqrt{4} = \pm 2$
Substitute into equation (2).

$x^2 - y^2 = 5$	$x^2 - y^2 = 5$
$x^2 - 2^2 = 5$	$x^2 - (-2)^2 = 5$
$x^2 - 4 = 5$	$x^2 - 4 = 5$
$x^2 = 9$	$x^2 = 9$
$x = \pm\sqrt{9}$	$x = \pm\sqrt{9}$
$x = \pm 3$	$x = \pm 3$

The solutions are $(3, 2)$, $(3, -2)$, $(-3, 2)$, and $(-3, -2)$.

29. (1) $2x^2 - y^2 = 7$
(2) $2x - y = 5$
Solve equation (2) for y.
$2x - y = 5$
$-y = -2x + 5$
$y = 2x - 5$
Use the substitution method.
$2x^2 - y^2 = 7$
$2x^2 - (2x - 5)^2 = 7$
$2x^2 - (4x^2 - 20x + 25) = 7$
$2x^2 - 4x^2 + 20x - 25 = 7$
$-2x^2 + 20x - 32 = 0$
$-2(x^2 - 10x + 16) = 0$
$-2(x - 2)(x - 8) = 0$
$x - 2 = 0 \quad x - 8 = 0$
$x = 2 \quad\quad x = 8$
Substitute into equation (2).

$2x - y = 5$	$2x - y = 5$
$2(2) - y = 5$	$2(8) - y = 5$
$4 - y = 5$	$16 - y = 5$
$-y = 1$	$-y = -11$
$y = -1$	$y = 11$

The solutions are $(2, -1)$ and $(8, 11)$.

30. (1) $3x^2 + 4y^2 = 7$
(2) $x - 2y = -3$
Solve equation (2) for x.
$x - 2y = -3$
$x = 2y - 3$
Use the substitution method.
$3x^2 + 4y^2 = 7$
$3(2y - 3)^2 + 4y^2 = 7$
$3(4y^2 - 12y + 9) + 4y^2 = 7$
$12y^2 - 36y + 27 + 4y^2 = 7$
$16y^2 - 36y + 20 = 0$
$4(4y^2 - 9y + 5) = 0$
$4(4y - 5)(y - 1) = 0$
$4y - 5 = 0 \quad y - 1 = 0$
$4y = 5 \quad\quad y - 1 = 0$
$y = \dfrac{5}{4} \quad\quad y = 1$
Substitute into equation (2).

$x - 2y = -3$	$x - 2y = -3$
$x - 2\left(\dfrac{5}{4}\right) = -3$	$x - 2(1) = -3$
$x - \dfrac{5}{2} = -3$	$x - 2 = -3$
$x = -\dfrac{1}{2}$	$x = -1$

The solutions are $\left(-\dfrac{1}{2}, \dfrac{5}{4}\right)$ and $(-1, 1)$.

31. (1) $y = 3x^2 + x - 4$
(2) $y = 3x^2 - 8x + 5$
Use the substitution method.
$y = 3x^2 + x - 4$
$3x^2 - 8x + 5 = 3x^2 + x - 4$
$-9x = -9$
$x = 1$
Substitute into equation (1).
$y = 3x^2 + x - 4$
$y = 3(1)^2 + (1) - 4$
$y = 3(1) + 1 - 4$
$y = 3 + 1 - 4$
$y = 0$
The solution is $(1, 0)$.

32. (1) $y = 2x^2 + 3x + 1$
(2) $y = 2x^2 + 9x + 7$
Use the substitution method.
$$y = 2x^2 + 3x + 1$$
$$2x^2 + 9x + 7 = 2x^2 + 3x + 1$$
$$9x + 7 = 3x + 1$$
$$6x + 7 = 1$$
$$6x = -6$$
$$x = -1$$
Substitute into equation (1).
$$y = 2x^2 + 3x + 1$$
$$y = 2(-1)^2 + 3(-1) + 1$$
$$y = 2(1) - 3 + 1$$
$$y = 2 - 3 + 1$$
$$y = 0$$
The solution is $(-1, 0)$.

Applying Concepts 12.4

33. $y = 2^x$
$x + y = 3$

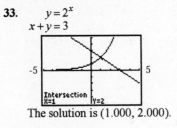

The solution is $(1.000, 2.000)$.

34. $y = 3^{-x}$
$x^2 + y^2 = 9$

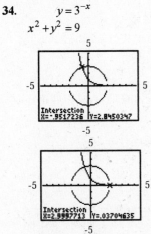

The approximate solutions are $(-0.952, 2.845)$ and $(3.000, 0.037)$.

35. $y = \log_2 x$
$$\frac{x^2}{9} + \frac{y^2}{1} = 1$$

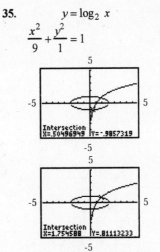

The approximate solutions are $(1.755, 0.811)$ and $(0.505, -0.986)$.

36. $y = \log_3 x$
$x^2 + y^2 = 4$

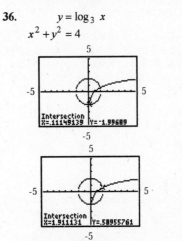

The approximate solutions are $(0.111, -1.997)$ and $(1.911, 0.590)$.

37. $y = -\log_3 x$
$x + y = 4$

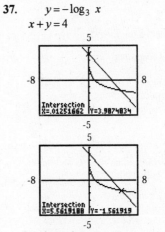

The approximate solutions are $(0.013, 3.987)$ and $(5.562, -1.562)$.

38.
$$y = \left(\frac{1}{2}\right)^x$$

$$\frac{x^2}{9} + \frac{y^2}{4} = 1$$

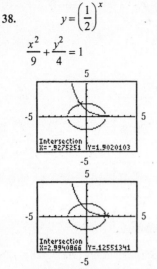

The approximate solutions are $(-0.928, 1.902)$ and $(2.994, 0.126)$.

39. No. Because the center of each circle is the origin, it is not possible for two circles to have exactly two points of intersection. They can intersect at no points or at infinitely many points.

Section 12.5

Concept Review 12.5

1. Always true

2. Never true
   The solution set of a nonlinear system of inequalities is the intersection of the solution sets of all the inequalities that make up the system.

3. Never true
   $0 + 0 > 4$ is not a true statement. The point $(0, 0)$ is not a solution of the inequality.

4. Sometimes true
   The solution set of the inequality $\frac{x^2}{9} - \frac{y^2}{4} \le 1$ includes the asymptotes.

5. Sometimes true
   If the inequality includes the symbol $\le$ or $\ge$, the solution set will include the boundary.

6. Sometimes true
   When the solution sets of every inequality in the set do not intersect, then the solution set of the system is the empty set.

Objective 12.5.1 Exercises

1. A solid curve is used for the boundaries of the inequalities that use $\le$ or $\ge$, and a dashed curve is used for the boundaries of inequalities that use $<$ or $>$.

2. Use a point (a, b) to determine which region to shade. If (a, b) is a solution of the inequality, then shade the region of the plane containing (a, b). If not, shade the region of the plane that does not contain the point. Note: $(0, 0)$ is often a good choice for (a, b).

3. $y \le x^2 - 4x + 3$
   Substitute the point $(0, 0)$ into the inequality.
   $0 \le 0^2 - 4(0) + 3$
   $0 \le 3$ true
   The point $(0, 0)$ should be in the shaded region.

4. $y < x^2 - 2x - 3$
   Substitute the point $(0, 0)$ into the inequality.
   $0 < 0^2 - 2(0) - 3$
   $0 < -3$ false
   The point $(0, 0)$ should not be in the shaded region.

5. $(x-1)^2 + (y+2)^2 \le 9$
   Substitute the point $(0, 0)$ into the inequality.
   $(0-1)^2 + (0+2)^2 \le 9$
   $-1^2 + 2^2 \le 9$
   $3 \le 9$ true
   The point $(0, 0)$ should be in the shaded region.

6. $(x+2)^2 + (y-3)^2 > 4$
   Substitute the point $(0, 0)$ into the inequality.
   $(0+2)^2 + (0-3)^2 > 4$
   $2^2 + (-3)^2 > 4$
   $13 > 4$ true
   The point $(0, 0)$ should be in the shaded region.

7. $(x+3)^2 + (y-2)^2 \geq 9$
Substitute the point (0, 0) into the inequality.
$(0+3)^2 + (0-2)^2 \geq 9$
$3^2 + (-2)^2 \geq 9$
$13 \geq 9$ true
The point (0, 0) should be in the shaded region.

8. $(x-2)^2 + (y+1)^2 \leq 16$
Substitute the point (0, 0) into the inequality.
$(0-2)^2 + (0+1)^2 \leq 16$
$(-2)^2 + 1^2 \leq 16$
$5 \leq 16$ true
The point (0, 0) should be in the shaded region.

9. $\dfrac{x^2}{16} + \dfrac{y^2}{25} < 1$
Substitute the point (0, 0) into the inequality.
$\dfrac{0^2}{16} + \dfrac{0^2}{25} < 1$
$0 < 1$ true
The point (0, 0) should be in the shaded region.

10. $\dfrac{x^2}{9} + \dfrac{y^2}{4} \geq 1$
Substitute the point (0, 0) into the inequality.
$\dfrac{0^2}{9} + \dfrac{0^2}{4} \geq 1$
$0 \geq 1$ false
The point (0, 0) should not be in the shaded region.

11. $\dfrac{x^2}{25} - \dfrac{y^2}{9} \leq 1$
Substitute the point (0, 0) into the inequality.
$\dfrac{0^2}{25} - \dfrac{0^2}{9} \leq 1$
$0 \leq 1$ true
The point (0, 0) should be in the shaded region.

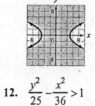

12. $\dfrac{y^2}{25} - \dfrac{x^2}{36} > 1$
Substitute the point (0, 0) into the inequality.
$\dfrac{0^2}{25} - \dfrac{0^2}{36} > 1$
$0 > 1$ false
The point (0, 0) should not be in the shaded region.

13. $\dfrac{x^2}{4} + \dfrac{y^2}{16} \geq 1$
Substitute the point (0, 0) into the inequality.
$\dfrac{0^2}{4} + \dfrac{0^2}{16} \geq 1$
$0 \geq 1$ false
The point (0, 0) should not be in the shaded region.

14. $\dfrac{x^2}{4} - \dfrac{y^2}{16} \leq 1$
Substitute the point (0, 0) into the inequality.
$\dfrac{0^2}{4} - \dfrac{0^2}{16} \leq 1$
$0 \leq 1$ true
The point (0, 0) should be in the shaded region.

15. $y \le x^2 - 2x + 3$

Substitute the point (0, 0) into the inequality.

$0 \le 0^2 - 2(0) + 3$

$0 \le 3$ true

The point (0, 0) should be in the shaded region.

16. $x \le y^2 + 2y + 1$

Substitute the point (0, 0) into the inequality.

$0 \le 0^2 + 2(0) + 1$

$0 \le 1$ true

The point (0, 0) should be in the shaded region.

17. $\dfrac{y^2}{9} - \dfrac{x^2}{16} \le 1$

Substitute the point (0, 0) into the inequality.

$\dfrac{0^2}{9} - \dfrac{0^2}{16} \le 1$

$0 \le 1$ true

The point (0, 0) should be in the shaded region.

18. $\dfrac{x^2}{16} - \dfrac{y^2}{4} < 1$

Substitute the point (0, 0) into the inequality.

$\dfrac{0^2}{16} - \dfrac{0^2}{4} < 1$

$0 < 1$ true

The point (0, 0) should be in the shaded region.

19. $\dfrac{x^2}{9} + \dfrac{y^2}{1} \le 1$

Substitute the point (0, 0) into the inequality.

$\dfrac{0^2}{9} + \dfrac{0^2}{1} \le 1$

$0 \le 1$ true

The point (0, 0) should be in the shaded region.

20. $\dfrac{x^2}{16} + \dfrac{y^2}{4} > 1$

Substitute the point (0, 0) into the inequality.

$\dfrac{0^2}{16} + \dfrac{0^2}{4} > 1$

$0 > 1$ false

The point (0, 0) should not be in the shaded region.

21. $(x - 1)^2 + (y + 3)^2 \le 25$

Substitute the point (0, 0) into the inequality.

$(0 - 1)^2 + (0 + 3)^2 \le 25$

$(-1)^2 + 3^2 \le 25$

$10 \le 25$ true

The point (0, 0) should be in the shaded region.

22. $(x + 1)^2 + (y - 2)^2 \ge 16$

Substitute the point (0, 0) into the inequality.

$(0 + 1)^2 + (0 - 2)^2 \ge 16$

$1^2 + (-2)^2 \ge 16$

$5 \ge 16$ false

The point (0, 0) should be in the shaded region.

23. $\dfrac{y^2}{25} - \dfrac{x^2}{4} \le 1$

Substitute the point (0, 0) into the inequality.

$\dfrac{0^2}{25} - \dfrac{0^2}{4} \le 1$

$0 \le 1$ true

The point (0, 0) should be in the shaded region.

24. $\dfrac{x^2}{9} - \dfrac{y^2}{25} \geq 1$

Substitute the point $(0, 0)$ into the inequality.

$\dfrac{0^2}{9} - \dfrac{0^2}{25} \geq 1$

$0 \geq 1$ false

The point $(0, 0)$ should not be in the shaded region.

25. $\dfrac{x^2}{25} + \dfrac{y^2}{9} \leq 1$

Substitute the point $(0, 0)$ into the inequality.

$\dfrac{0^2}{25} + \dfrac{0^2}{9} \leq 1$

$0 \leq 1$ true

The point $(0, 0)$ should be in the shaded region.

26. $\dfrac{x^2}{36} + \dfrac{y^2}{4} \leq 1$

Substitute the point $(0, 0)$ into the inequality.

$\dfrac{0^2}{36} + \dfrac{0^2}{4} \leq 1$

$0 \leq 1$ true

The point $(0, 0)$ should be in the shaded region.

Objective 12.5.2 Exercises

27. $y \leq x^2 - 4x + 4$
    $y + x > 4$

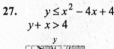

28. $x^2 + y^2 < 1$
    $x + y \geq 4$

The solution sets of the two inequalities do not intersect. The system of inequalities has no real number solution.

29. $x^2 + y^2 < 16$
    $y > x + 1$

30. $y > x^2 - 4$
    $y < x - 2$

31. $\dfrac{x^2}{4} + \dfrac{y^2}{16} \leq 1$

    $y \leq -\dfrac{1}{2}x + 2$

32. $\dfrac{y^2}{4} - \dfrac{x^2}{25} \geq 1$

    $y \leq \dfrac{2}{3}x + 4$

33. $x \geq y^2 - 3y + 2$
    $y \geq 2x - 2$

34. $x^2 + y^2 \leq 25$
    $y \leq -\dfrac{1}{3}x + 2$

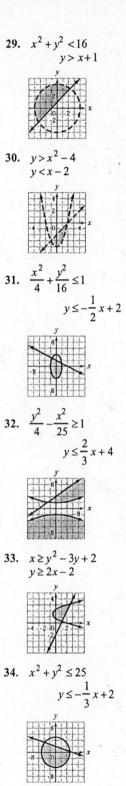

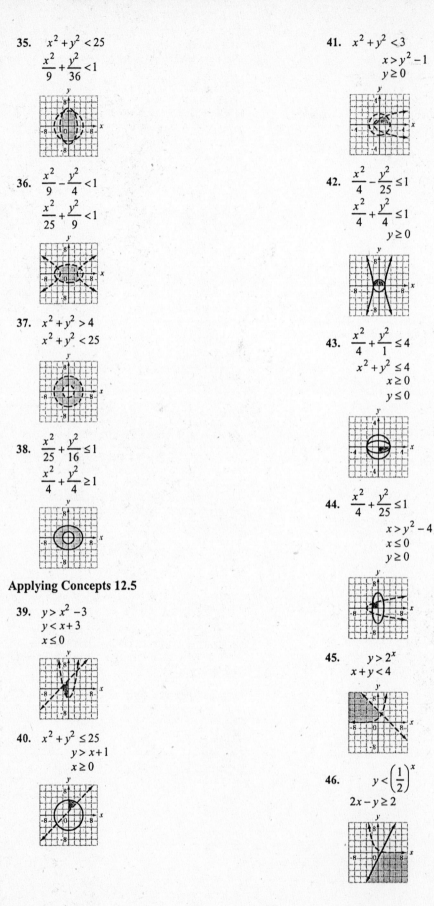

35. $x^2 + y^2 < 25$
$$\frac{x^2}{9} + \frac{y^2}{36} < 1$$

36. $\dfrac{x^2}{9} - \dfrac{y^2}{4} < 1$
$$\frac{x^2}{25} + \frac{y^2}{9} < 1$$

37. $x^2 + y^2 > 4$
$x^2 + y^2 < 25$

38. $\dfrac{x^2}{25} + \dfrac{y^2}{16} \le 1$
$$\frac{x^2}{4} + \frac{y^2}{4} \ge 1$$

Applying Concepts 12.5

39. $y > x^2 - 3$
$y < x + 3$
$x \le 0$

40. $x^2 + y^2 \le 25$
$y > x + 1$
$x \ge 0$

41. $x^2 + y^2 < 3$
$x > y^2 - 1$
$y \ge 0$

42. $\dfrac{x^2}{4} - \dfrac{y^2}{25} \le 1$
$$\frac{x^2}{4} + \frac{y^2}{4} \le 1$$
$y \ge 0$

43. $\dfrac{x^2}{4} + \dfrac{y^2}{1} \le 4$
$x^2 + y^2 \le 4$
$x \ge 0$
$y \le 0$

44. $\dfrac{x^2}{4} + \dfrac{y^2}{25} \le 1$
$x > y^2 - 4$
$x \le 0$
$y \ge 0$

45. $y > 2^x$
$x + y < 4$

46. $y < \left(\dfrac{1}{2}\right)^x$
$2x - y \ge 2$

47. $y \geq \log_2 x$
$x^2 + y^2 < 9$

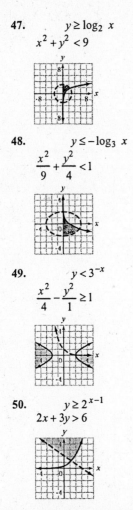

48. $y \leq -\log_3 x$
$\dfrac{x^2}{9} + \dfrac{y^2}{4} < 1$

49. $y < 3^{-x}$
$\dfrac{x^2}{4} - \dfrac{y^2}{1} \geq 1$

50. $y \geq 2^{x-1}$
$2x + 3y > 6$

Focus on Problem Solving

1. Label the coins 1, 2, 3, 4, 5, 6, 7, and 8.
   Set coins 1 and 2 aside. Put coins 3, 4, and 5 on one side of the balance and coins 6, 7, and 8 on the other side the balance. If the set balances, then coin 1 or coin 2 is the lighter coin. You can determine which by using the balance a second time.
   If the set does not balance, choose the lighter set of coins. Assume the lighter set includes coins 6, 7, and 8.
   Choose two coins to put on the balance (say coin 6 and coin 7). If the coins do not balance, you have found the lighter coin. If coins 6 and 7 are equal in weight, then coin 8 is the lighter coin. Thus the lighter coin can be found in two weighings.

2. The sequence is 1, 1, 2, 3, 5, 8, 13, ...
   The third term is the sum of the two preceding terms. $1 + 1 = 2$
   The fourth term is the sum of the two preceding terms. $1 + 2 = 3$
   The fifth term is the sum of the two preceding terms. $2 + 3 = 5$
   The sixth term is the sum of the two preceding terms. $3 + 5 = 8$
   The seventh term is the sum of the two preceding terms. $5 + 8 = 13$

   If the pattern holds, then the eighth term is $8 + 13 = 21$.

3.

6	7	2
1	5	9
8	3	4

4. To find the price of the larger pizza so that the price per square inch is the same, multiply the price by the ratio of the area of the larger pizza to that of the smaller pizza.

$$C = 5.00\left(\frac{A^2}{A^1}\right) = 10.00\left(\frac{\pi(9)^2}{\pi(4.5)^2}\right) = 10.00(4) = 40$$

   The larger pizza will cost $40.

5. For 7 grams, use 8 grams on one side and 1 gram plus the 7-gram weight on the other side of the balance.
   For 3 grams, use 8 grams on one side and 1 gram and 4 grams plus the 3-gram weight on the other side of the balance.
   For 12 grams, use 8 grams and 4 grams on one side and the 12-gram weight on the other side of the balance.
   For 19 grams, use 4 grams and 16 grams on one side and 1 gram plus the 19-gram weight on the other side of the balance.

6. The checkerboard has 79 squares. Each domino will cover two squares, and the dominos cannot overlap. Thus the checkerboard cannot be covered with dominos.

Projects and Group Activities

The Eccentricity and Foci of an Ellipse

1. flatter

2. Neptune The eccentricity for Neptune is the smallest at 0.005.

3. $e = \dfrac{\sqrt{25-16}}{5}$
   $= \dfrac{\sqrt{9}}{5}$
   $= \dfrac{3}{5}$
   $= 0.6$

4. $e = \dfrac{\sqrt{9-4}}{3}$

$\quad = \dfrac{\sqrt{5}}{3}$

$\quad \approx 0.75$

5. $c = \sqrt{169-144}$

$\quad = \sqrt{25}$

$\quad = 5$

The foci are at $(-5, 0)$ and $(5, 0)$.

Graphing Conic Sections Using a Graphing Calculator

1. $\dfrac{x^2}{25} + \dfrac{y^2}{49} = 1$

$\quad \dfrac{y^2}{49} = 1 - \dfrac{x^2}{25}$

$\quad y^2 = 49\left(1 - \dfrac{x^2}{25}\right)$

$\quad y = \pm 7\sqrt{1 - \dfrac{x^2}{25}}$

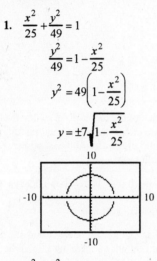

2. $\dfrac{x^2}{4} + \dfrac{y^2}{64} = 1$

$\quad \dfrac{y^2}{64} = 1 - \dfrac{x^2}{4}$

$\quad y^2 = 64\left(1 - \dfrac{x^2}{4}\right)$

$\quad y = \pm 8\sqrt{1 - \dfrac{x^2}{4}}$

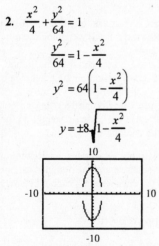

3. $\dfrac{x^2}{16} - \dfrac{y^2}{4} = 1$

$\quad \dfrac{x^2}{16} - 1 = \dfrac{y^2}{4}$

$\quad 4\left(\dfrac{x^2}{16} - 1\right) = y^2$

$\quad \pm 2\sqrt{\dfrac{x^2}{16} - 1} = y$

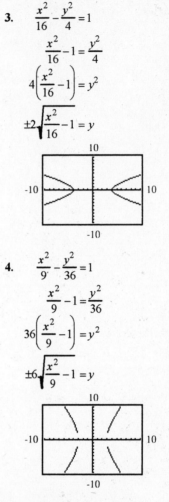

4. $\dfrac{x^2}{9} - \dfrac{y^2}{36} = 1$

$\quad \dfrac{x^2}{9} - 1 = \dfrac{y^2}{36}$

$\quad 36\left(\dfrac{x^2}{9} - 1\right) = y^2$

$\quad \pm 6\sqrt{\dfrac{x^2}{9} - 1} = y$

Chapter Review Exercises

1. $y = x^2 - 4x + 8$

$\quad -\dfrac{b}{2a} = -\dfrac{-4}{2(1)} = \dfrac{4}{2} = 2$

$\quad y = 2^2 - 4(2) + 8$

$\quad = 4$

Vertex: $(2, 4)$

Axis of symmetry: $x = 2$

2. $y = -x^2 + 7x - 8$

$\quad -\dfrac{b}{2a} = -\dfrac{7}{2(-1)} = \dfrac{7}{2}$

$\quad y = -\left(\dfrac{7}{2}\right)^2 + 7\left(\dfrac{7}{2}\right) - 8$

$\quad = -\dfrac{49}{4} + \dfrac{49}{2} - 8$

$\quad = \dfrac{17}{4}$

Vertex: $\left(\dfrac{7}{2}, \dfrac{17}{4}\right)$

Axis of symmetry: $x = \dfrac{7}{2}$

3. $y = -2x^2 + x - 2$

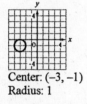

4. $x = 2y^2 - 6y + 5$

5. $(x_1, y_1) = (2, -1) \quad (x_2, y_2) = (-1, 2)$

$$r = \sqrt{(x_2 - x_1)^2 + (y_2 - y_1)^2}$$
$$= \sqrt{(-1 - 2)^2 + (2 - (-1))^2}$$
$$= \sqrt{(-3)^2 + 3^2}$$
$$= \sqrt{9 + 9} = \sqrt{18}$$
$$(x - h)^2 + (y - k)^2 = r^2$$
$$[x - (-1)]^2 + (y - 2)^2 = (\sqrt{18})^2$$
$$(x + 1)^2 + (y - 2)^2 = 18$$

6. $(x - h)^2 + (y - k)^2 = r^2$
$$(x - (-1))^2 + (y - 5)^2 = 6^2$$
$$(x + 1)^2 + (y - 5)^2 = 36$$

7. $(x + 3)^2 + (y + 1)^2 = 1$

Center: $(-3, -1)$
Radius: 1

8. $x^2 + (y - 2)^2 = 9$

Center: $(0, 2)$
Radius: 3

9. $(x_1, y_1) = (4, 6) \quad (x_2, y_2) = (0, -3)$

$$r = \sqrt{(x_2 - x_1)^2 + (y_2 - y_1)^2}$$
$$= \sqrt{(0 - 4)^2 + (-3 - 6)^2}$$
$$= \sqrt{(-4)^2 + (-9)^2}$$
$$= \sqrt{16 + 81} = \sqrt{97}$$
$$(x - h)^2 + (y - k)^2 = r^2$$
$$(x - 0)^2 + (y - (-3))^2 = (\sqrt{97})^2$$
$$x^2 + (y + 3)^2 = 97$$

10.
$$x^2 + y^2 + 4x - 2y = 4$$
$$(x^2 + 4x) + (y^2 - 2y) = 4$$
$$(x^2 + 4x + 4) + (y^2 - 2y + 1) = 4 + 4 + 1$$
$$(x + 2)^2 + (y - 1)^2 = 9$$

11. $\dfrac{x^2}{1} + \dfrac{y^2}{9} = 1$

x-intercepts: $(1, 0)$ and $(-1, 0)$
y-intercepts: $(0, 3)$ and $(0, -3)$

12. $\dfrac{x^2}{25} + \dfrac{y^2}{9} = 1$

x-intercepts: $(5, 0)$ and $(-5, 0)$
y-intercepts: $(0, 3)$ and $(0, -3)$

13. $\dfrac{x^2}{25} - \dfrac{y^2}{1} = 1$

Axis of symmetry: x-axis
Vertices: $(5, 0)$ and $(-5, 0)$
Asymptotes: $y = \dfrac{1}{5}x$ and $y = -\dfrac{1}{5}x$

14. $\dfrac{y^2}{16} - \dfrac{x^2}{9} = 1$

Axis of symmetry: y-axis
Vertices: $(0, 4)$ and $(0, -4)$
Asymptotes: $y = \dfrac{4}{3}x$ and $y = -\dfrac{4}{3}x$

15. (1) $y = x^2 + 5x - 6$
(2) $y = x - 10$
Use the substitution method.
$$x - 10 = x^2 + 5x - 6$$
$$0 = x^2 + 4x + 4$$
$$0 = (x + 2)^2$$
$x + 2 = 0 \qquad x + 2 = 0$
$\quad x = -2 \qquad \quad x = -2$
Substitute into equation (2).
$y = -2 - 10 \quad y = -2 - 10$
$y = -12 \qquad y = -12$
The solution is $(-2, -12)$

16. (1) $2x^2 + y^2 = 19$
(2) $3x^2 - y^2 = 6$
Use the addition method.
$$2x^2 + y^2 = 19$$
$$3x^2 - y^2 = 6$$
$$5x^2 = 25$$
$$x^2 = 5$$
$$x = \pm\sqrt{5}$$
Substitute into equation (1).
$2x^2 + y^2 = 19 \qquad 2x^2 + y^2 = 19$
$2(\sqrt{5})^2 + y^2 = 19 \qquad 2(-\sqrt{5})^2 + y^2 = 19$
$10 + y^2 = 19 \qquad 10 + y^2 = 19$
$y^2 = 9 \qquad\qquad y^2 = 9$
$y = \pm\sqrt{9} \qquad\qquad y = \pm\sqrt{9}$
$y = \pm 3 \qquad\qquad y = \pm 3$
The solutions are $(\sqrt{5}, 3), (\sqrt{5}, -3), (-\sqrt{5}, 3),$
and $(-\sqrt{5}, -3)$.

17. (1) $x = 2y^2 - 3y + 1$
(2) $3x - 2y = 0$
Use the substitution method.
$$3x - 2y = 0$$
$$3x = 2y$$
$$x = \frac{2}{3}y$$
$$\frac{2}{3}y = 2y^2 - 3y + 1$$
$$2y = 6y^2 - 9y + 3$$
$$0 = 6y^2 - 11y + 3$$
$$0 = (2y - 3)(3y - 1)$$
$0 = 2y - 3 \qquad 0 = 3y - 1$
$2y = 3 \qquad\qquad 3y = 1$
$y = \dfrac{3}{2} \qquad\qquad y = \dfrac{1}{3}$
Substitute into equation (2).
$3x - 2\left(\dfrac{3}{2}\right) = 0 \qquad 3x - 2\left(\dfrac{1}{3}\right) = 0$
$3x - 3 = 0 \qquad\qquad 3x - \dfrac{2}{3} = 0$
$3x = 3 \qquad\qquad\qquad 3x = \dfrac{2}{3}$
$x = 1 \qquad\qquad\qquad\quad 3x = \dfrac{2}{3}$
$\qquad\qquad\qquad\qquad\qquad x = \dfrac{2}{9}$
The solutions are $\left(1, \dfrac{3}{2}\right)$ and $\left(\dfrac{2}{9}, \dfrac{1}{3}\right)$.

18. (1) $y^2 = 2x^2 - 3x + 6$
(2) $y^2 = 2x^2 + 5x - 2$
Use the addition method.
Multiply equation (2) by -1.
$$y^2 = 2x^2 - 3x + 6$$
$$-y^2 = -2x^2 - 5x + 2$$
$$0 = -8x + 8$$
$$8x = 8$$
$$x = 1$$
Substitute into equation (1).
$y^2 = 2x^2 - 3x + 6$
$y^2 = 2(1)^2 - 3(1) + 6$
$y^2 = 2 - 3 + 6$
$y^2 = 5$
$y = \pm\sqrt{5}$
The solutions are $(1, \sqrt{5})$ and $(1, -\sqrt{5})$.

19. $(x - 2)^2 + (y + 1)^2 \leq 16$

20. $\dfrac{x^2}{9} - \dfrac{y^2}{16} < 1$

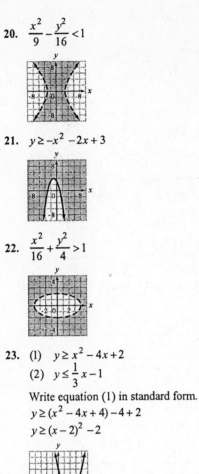

21. $y \ge -x^2 - 2x + 3$

22. $\dfrac{x^2}{16} + \dfrac{y^2}{4} > 1$

23. (1) $y \ge x^2 - 4x + 2$

(2) $y \le \dfrac{1}{3}x - 1$

Write equation (1) in standard form.

$y \ge (x^2 - 4x + 4) - 4 + 2$

$y \ge (x - 2)^2 - 2$

24. $\dfrac{x^2}{25} + \dfrac{y^2}{16} \le 1$

$\dfrac{y^2}{4} - \dfrac{x^2}{4} \ge 1$

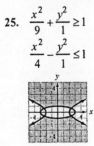

25. $\dfrac{x^2}{9} + \dfrac{y^2}{1} \ge 1$

$\dfrac{x^2}{4} - \dfrac{y^2}{1} \le 1$

26. $\dfrac{x^2}{16} + \dfrac{y^2}{4} < 1$

$x^2 + y^2 > 9$

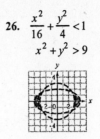

Chapter Test

1. $y = -x^2 + 6x - 5$

$-\dfrac{b}{2a} = \dfrac{-6}{2(-1)} = \dfrac{-6}{-2} = 3$

Axis of symmetry: $x = 3$

2. $y = -x^2 + 3x - 2$

$-\dfrac{b}{2a} = \dfrac{-3}{2(-1)} = \dfrac{3}{2}$

$y = -\left(\dfrac{3}{2}\right)^2 + 3\left(\dfrac{3}{2}\right) - 2 = -\dfrac{9}{4} + \dfrac{9}{2} - 2 = \dfrac{1}{4}$

Vertex: $\left(\dfrac{3}{2}, \dfrac{1}{4}\right)$

3. $y = \dfrac{1}{2}x^2 + x - 4$

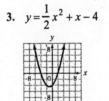

4. $x = y^2 - y - 2$

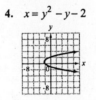

5. $(x - h)^2 + (y - k)^2 = r^2$

$[x - (-3)]^2 + [y - (-3)]^2 = 4^2$

$(x + 3)^2 + (y + 3)^2 = 16$

6. (1) $x^2 + 2y^2 = 4$
   (2) $x + y = 2$
   Use the substitution method.
   $$x + y = 2$$
   $$y = 2 - x$$
   $$x^2 + 2(2 - x)^2 = 4$$
   $$x^2 + 2(4 - 4x + x^2) = 4$$
   $$x^2 + 8 - 8x + 2x^2 = 4$$
   $$3x^2 - 8x + 4 = 0$$
   $$(3x - 2)(x - 2) = 0$$
   $$3x - 2 = 0 \qquad x - 2 = 0$$
   $$x = \frac{2}{3} \qquad x = 2$$

   Substitute into equation (2).
   $$x + y = 2 \qquad x + y = 2$$
   $$\frac{2}{3} + y = 2 \qquad 2 + y = 2$$
   $$y = \frac{4}{3} \qquad y = 0$$

   The solutions are $\left(\frac{2}{3}, \frac{4}{3}\right)$ and $(2, 0)$.

7. (1) $x = 3y^2 + 2y - 4$
   (2) $x = y^2 - 5y$
   Use the addition method.
   Multiply equation (2) by -1.
   $$x = 3y^2 + 2y - 4$$
   $$-x = -y^2 + 5y$$
   $$0 = 2y^2 + 7y - 4$$
   $$0 = (2y - 1)(y + 4)$$
   $$2y - 1 = 0 \qquad y + 4 = 0$$
   $$y = \frac{1}{2} \qquad y = -4$$

   Substitute into equation (2).
   $$x = y^2 - 5y \qquad x = y^2 - 5y$$
   $$x = \left(\frac{1}{2}\right)^2 - 5\left(\frac{1}{2}\right) \qquad x = (-4)^2 - 5(-4)$$
   $$\qquad\qquad\qquad\qquad x = 16 + 20$$
   $$x = \frac{1}{4} - \frac{5}{2} \qquad x = 36$$
   $$x = -\frac{9}{4}$$

   The solutions are $\left(-\frac{9}{4}, \frac{1}{2}\right)$ and $(36, -4)$.

8. (1) $x^2 - y^2 = 24$
   (2) $2x^2 + 5y^2 = 55$
   Use the addition method.
   Multiply equation (1) by -2.
   $$-2(x^2 - y^2) = -2 \cdot 24$$
   $$2x^2 + 5y^2 = 55$$
   $$7y^2 = 7$$
   $$y^2 = 1$$
   $$y = \pm\sqrt{1}$$
   $$y = \pm 1$$

   Substitute into equation (1).
   $$x^2 - y^2 = 24 \qquad x^2 - y^2 = 24$$
   $$x^2 - (1)^2 = 24 \qquad x^2 - (-1)^2 = 24$$
   $$x^2 - 1 = 24 \qquad x^2 - 1 = 24$$
   $$x^2 = 25 \qquad x^2 = 25$$
   $$x = \pm\sqrt{25} \qquad x = \pm\sqrt{25}$$
   $$x = \pm 5 \qquad x = \pm 5$$

   The solutions are $(5, 1)$, $(-5, 1)$, $(5, -1)$, and $(-5, -1)$.

9. $(x_1, y_1) = (2, 4) \quad (x_2, y_2) = (-1, -3)$
   $$r = \sqrt{(x_2 - x_1)^2 + (y_2 - y_1)^2}$$
   $$= \sqrt{(-1 - 2)^2 + (-3 - 4)^2}$$
   $$= \sqrt{(-3)^2 + (-7)^2}$$
   $$= \sqrt{9 + 49}$$
   $$= \sqrt{58}$$
   $$(x - h)^2 + (y - k)^2 = r^2$$
   $$[x - (-1)]^2 + [y - (-3)]^2 = (\sqrt{58})^2$$
   $$(x + 1)^2 + (y + 3)^2 = 58$$

10. $(x - 2)^2 + (y + 1)^2 = 9$

11. $$(x - h)^2 + (y - k)^2 = r^2$$
    $$(x - (-2))^2 + (y - 4)^2 = 3^2$$
    $$(x + 2)^2 + (y - 4)^2 = 9$$

12. $(x_1, y_1) = (2, 5) \quad (x_2, y_2) = (-2, 1)$
    $$d = \sqrt{(x_2 - x_1)^2 + (y_2 - y_1)^2}$$
    $$= \sqrt{(-2 - 2)^2 + (1 - 5)^2}$$
    $$= \sqrt{(-4)^2 + (-4)^2}$$
    $$= \sqrt{32}$$
    $$(x - h)^2 + (y - k)^2 = r^2$$
    $$(x - (-2))^2 + (y - 1)^2 = \sqrt{32}$$
    $$(x + 2)^2 + (y - 1)^2 = 32$$

13.
$$x^2 + y^2 - 4x + 2y + 1 = 0$$
$$(x^2 - 4x) + (y^2 + 2y) = -1$$
$$(x^2 - 4x + 4) + (y^2 + 2y + 1) = -1 + 4 + 1$$
$$(x - 2)^2 + (y + 1)^2 = 4$$
Center: $(2, -1)$
Radius: 2

14. $\dfrac{y^2}{25} - \dfrac{x^2}{16} = 1$

Axis of symmetry: y-axis
Vertices: $(0, 5)$ and $(0, -5)$
Asymptotes: $y = \dfrac{5}{4}x$ and $y = -\dfrac{5}{4}x$

15. $\dfrac{x^2}{9} - \dfrac{y^2}{4} = 1$

Axis of symmetry: x-axis
Vertices: $(3, 0)$ and $(-3, 0)$
Asymptotes: $y = \dfrac{2}{3}x$ and $y = -\dfrac{2}{3}x$

16. $\dfrac{x^2}{16} + \dfrac{y^2}{4} = 1$

x-intercepts: $(4, 0)$ and $(-4, 0)$
y-intercepts: $(0, 2)$ and $(0, -2)$

17. $\dfrac{x^2}{16} - \dfrac{y^2}{25} < 1$

18. $x^2 + y^2 < 36$
$x + y > 4$

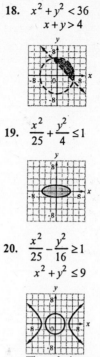

19. $\dfrac{x^2}{25} + \dfrac{y^2}{4} \le 1$

20. $\dfrac{x^2}{25} - \dfrac{y^2}{16} \ge 1$
$x^2 + y^2 \le 9$

The solution sets of these inequalities do not intersect, so the system has no real number solution.

Final Exam

1.
$$12 - 8[3 - (-2)]^2 \div 5 - 3 = 12 - 8[5]^2 \div 5 - 3$$
$$= 12 - 8(25) \div 5 - 3$$
$$= 12 - 200 \div 5 - 3$$
$$= 12 - 40 - 3$$
$$= -31$$

2.
$$\dfrac{a^2 - b^2}{a - b} = \dfrac{3^2 - (-4)^2}{3 - (-4)}$$
$$= \dfrac{9 - 16}{3 + 4} = \dfrac{-7}{7}$$
$$= -1$$

3.
$$5 - 2[3x - 7(2 - x) - 5x] = 5 - 2[3x - 14 + 7x - 5x]$$
$$= 5 - 2[5x - 14]$$
$$= 5 - 10x + 28$$
$$= 33 - 10x$$

4.
$$\dfrac{3}{4}x - 2 = 4$$
$$\dfrac{3}{4}x = 6$$
$$\dfrac{4}{3} \cdot \dfrac{3}{4}x = \dfrac{4}{3} \cdot 6$$
$$x = 8$$
The solution is 8.

5.
$$\frac{2-4x}{3} - \frac{x-6}{12} = \frac{5x-2}{6}$$
$$12\left(\frac{2-4x}{3} - \frac{x-6}{12}\right) = 12\left(\frac{5x-2}{6}\right)$$
$$4(2-4x) - (x-6) = 2(5x-2)$$
$$8 - 16x - x + 6 = 10x - 4$$
$$14 - 17x = 10x - 4$$
$$-27x = -18$$
$$x = \frac{2}{3}$$

The solution is $\frac{2}{3}$.

6.
$$8 - |5 - 3x| = 1$$
$$-|5-3x| = -7$$
$$|5-3x| = 7$$

$$\begin{array}{ll} 5-3x=7 & 5-3x=-7 \\ -3x=2 & -3x=-12 \\ x=-\frac{2}{3} & x=4 \end{array}$$

The solutions are $-\frac{2}{3}$ and 4.

7.
$$|2x+5| < 3$$
$$-3 < 2x+5 < 3$$
$$-3-5 < 2x < 3-5$$
$$-8 < 2x < -2$$
$$\frac{1}{2}(-8) < \frac{1}{2}(2x) < \frac{1}{2}(-2)$$
$$-4 < x < -1$$
$$\{x| -4 < x < -1\}$$

8.
$$\begin{array}{ll} 2-3x < 6 & \text{and} \quad 2x+1 > 4 \\ -3x < 4 & 2x > 3 \\ x > -\frac{4}{3} & x > \frac{3}{2} \end{array}$$
$$\{x|x > -\frac{4}{3}\} \cap \{x|x > \frac{3}{2}\} = \{x|x > \frac{3}{2}\}$$

9.
$$3x - 2y = 6$$
$$-2y = -3x + 6$$
$$y = \frac{3}{2}x - 3$$
$$m_1 = \frac{3}{2}$$
$$m_1 \cdot m_2 = -1$$
$$\frac{3}{2}m_2 = -1$$
$$m_2 = -\frac{2}{3} \quad (x_1, y_1) = (-2, 1)$$
$$y - y_1 = m(x - x_1)$$
$$y - 1 = -\frac{2}{3}(x - (-2))$$
$$y - 1 = -\frac{2}{3}(x + 2)$$
$$y - 1 = -\frac{2}{3}x - \frac{4}{3}$$
$$y = -\frac{2}{3}x - \frac{1}{3}$$

The equation of the line is $y = -\frac{2}{3}x - \frac{1}{3}$.

10.
$$2a[5 - a(2-3a) - 2a] + 3a^2$$
$$= 2a[5 - 2a + 3a^2 - 2a] + 3a^2$$
$$= 2a[5 - 4a + 3a^2] + 3a^2$$
$$= 10a - 8a^2 + 6a^3 + 3a^2$$
$$= 6a^3 - 5a^2 + 10a$$

11.
$$\frac{3}{2+i} = \frac{3}{2+i} \cdot \frac{2-i}{2-i}$$
$$= \frac{6-3i}{4-i^2}$$
$$= \frac{6-3i}{4+1}$$
$$= \frac{6-3i}{5}$$
$$= \frac{6}{5} - \frac{3}{5}i$$

12.
$$(x - r_1)(x - r_2) = 0$$
$$\left(x - \left(-\frac{1}{2}\right)\right)(x - 2) = 0$$
$$\left(x + \frac{1}{2}\right)(x - 2) = 0$$
$$x^2 - \frac{3}{2}x - 1 = 0$$
$$2\left(x^2 - \frac{3}{2}x - 1\right) = 0$$
$$2x^2 - 3x - 2 = 0$$

13.
$$8 - x^3y^3 = 2^3 - (xy)^3$$
$$= (2 - xy)(4 + 2xy + x^2y^2)$$

14.
$$x - y - x^3 + x^2y = x - y - x^2(x - y)$$
$$= 1(x - y) - x^2(x - y)$$
$$= (x - y)(1 - x^2)$$
$$= (x - y)(1 - x)(1 + x)$$

15.

$$
\begin{array}{r}
x^2-2x-3 \\
2x-3 \overline{\smash{\big)}\ 2x^3-7x^2+0x+4} \\
\underline{2x^3-3x^2} \\
-4x^2+0x \\
\underline{-4x^2+6x} \\
-6x+4 \\
\underline{-6x+9} \\
-5
\end{array}
$$

$$x^2-2x-3-\dfrac{5}{2x-3}$$

16. $\dfrac{x^2-3x}{2x^2-3x-5} \div \dfrac{4x-12}{4x^2-4} = \dfrac{x^2-3x}{2x^2-3x-5} \times \dfrac{4x^2-4}{4x-12}$

$= \dfrac{x(x-3)}{(2x-5)(x+1)} \times \dfrac{4(x+1)(x-1)}{4(x-3)}$

$= \dfrac{x(x-3)\cancel{4}(x+1)(x-1)}{(2x-5)(x+1)\cancel{4}(x-3)} = \dfrac{x(x-1)}{2x-5}$

17. $\dfrac{x-2}{x+2} - \dfrac{x+3}{x-3} = \dfrac{x-2}{x+2}\cdot\dfrac{x-3}{x-3} - \dfrac{x+3}{x-3}\cdot\dfrac{x+2}{x+2}$

$= \dfrac{x^2-5x+6-(x^2+5x+6)}{(x+2)(x-3)}$

$= \dfrac{x^2-5x+6-x^2-5x-6}{(x+2)(x-3)}$

$= -\dfrac{10x}{(x+2)(x-3)}$

18. $\dfrac{\frac{3}{x}+\frac{1}{x+4}}{\frac{1}{x}+\frac{3}{x+4}} = \dfrac{\frac{3}{x}+\frac{1}{x+4}}{\frac{1}{x}+\frac{3}{x+4}} \times \dfrac{x(x+4)}{x(x+4)}$

$= \dfrac{3(x+4)+x}{x+4+3x} = \dfrac{3x+12+x}{4x+4}$

$= \dfrac{4x+12}{4x+4} = \dfrac{\cancel{4}(x+3)}{\cancel{4}(x+1)} = \dfrac{x+3}{x+1}$

19.

$$\dfrac{5}{x-2} - \dfrac{5}{x^2-4} = \dfrac{1}{x+2}$$

$$(x+2)(x-2)\left(\dfrac{5}{x-2} - \dfrac{5}{(x+2)(x-2)}\right) = (x+2)(x-2)\dfrac{1}{x+2}$$

$$5(x+2)-5 = x-2$$
$$5x+10-5 = x-2$$
$$5x+5 = x-2$$
$$4x = -7$$
$$x = -\dfrac{7}{4}$$

The solution is $-\dfrac{7}{4}$.

20.

$$a_n = a_1 + (n-1)d$$
$$a_n - a_1 = (n-1)d$$
$$\dfrac{a_n-a_1}{n-1} = d$$

21. $\left(\dfrac{4x^2y^{-1}}{3x^{-1}y}\right)^{-2}\left(\dfrac{2x^{-1}y^2}{9x^{-2}y^2}\right)^3 = \dfrac{4^{-2}x^{-4}y^2}{3^{-2}x^2y^{-2}} \cdot \dfrac{2^3x^{-3}y^6}{9^3x^{-6}y^6}$

$= 4^{-2}\cdot3^{-(-2)}\cdot x^{-4-2}y^{2-(-2)}\cdot 2^3 9^{-3}x^{-3-(-6)}y^{6-6}$

$= 4^{-2}\cdot 3^2 x^{-6}y^4 \cdot 2^3 \cdot 9^{-3}x^3y^0$

$= \dfrac{9x^{-3}y^4\cdot 8}{16\cdot 729} = \dfrac{y^4}{162x^3}$

22. $\left(\dfrac{3x^{2/3}y^{1/2}}{6x^2y^{4/3}}\right)^6 = \dfrac{3^6x^4y^3}{6^6x^{12}y^8}$

$= \dfrac{729x^{4-12}y^{3-8}}{46656}$

$= \dfrac{1x^{-8}y^{-5}}{64} = \dfrac{1}{64x^8y^5}$

23. $x\sqrt{18x^2y^3} - y\sqrt{50x^4y}$

$= x\sqrt{3^2x^2y^2(2y)} - y\sqrt{5^2x^4(2y)}$

$= 3x^2y\sqrt{2y} - 5x^2y\sqrt{2y} = -2x^2y\sqrt{2y}$

24. $\dfrac{\sqrt{16x^5y^4}}{\sqrt{32xy^7}} = \sqrt{\dfrac{16x^5y^4}{32xy^7}}$

$= \sqrt{\dfrac{x^4}{2y^3}}$

$= \sqrt{\dfrac{x^4}{y^2(2y)}}$

$= \dfrac{x^2}{y}\sqrt{\dfrac{1}{2y}} \cdot \sqrt{\dfrac{2y}{2y}}$

$= \dfrac{x^2}{y}\sqrt{\dfrac{1 \cdot 2y}{(2y)^y}}$

$= \dfrac{x^2\sqrt{2y}}{2y^2}$

25. $2x^2 - 3x - 1 = 0$

$a = 2, b = -3, c = -1$

$x = \dfrac{-b \pm \sqrt{b^2 - 4ac}}{2a}$

$= \dfrac{-(-3) \pm \sqrt{(-3)^2 - 4(2)(-1)}}{2(2)}$

$= \dfrac{3 \pm \sqrt{9+8}}{4} = \dfrac{3 \pm \sqrt{17}}{4}$

The solutions are $\dfrac{3+\sqrt{17}}{4}$ and $\dfrac{3-\sqrt{17}}{4}$.

26. $x^{2/3} - x^{1/3} - 6 = 0$

$(x^{1/3})^2 - x^{1/3} - 6 = 0$

Let $u = x^{1/3}$.

$u^2 - u - 6 = 0$

$(u-3)(u+2) = 0$

$u - 3 = 0 \qquad u + 2 = 0$

$\quad u = 3 \qquad\qquad u = -2$

$x^{1/3} = 3 \qquad\quad x^{1/3} = -2$

$(x^{1/3})^3 = 3^3 \qquad (x^{1/3})^3 = (-2)^3$

$\quad x = 27 \qquad\qquad x = -8$

The solutions are 27 and -8.

27. $(x_1, y_1) = (3, -2), (x_2, y_2) = (1, 4)$

$m = \dfrac{y_2 - y_1}{x_2 - x_1} = \dfrac{4 - (-2)}{1 - 3} = \dfrac{6}{-2} = -3$

$y - y_1 = m(x - x_1)$

$y - (-2) = -3(x - 3)$

$y + 2 = -3x + 9$

$\quad y = -3x + 7$

The equation of the line is $y = -3x + 7$.

28. $\dfrac{2}{x} - \dfrac{2}{2x+3} = 1$

$x(2x+3)\left(\dfrac{2}{x} - \dfrac{2}{2x+3}\right) = x(2x+3)(1)$

$2(2x+3) - 2x = 2x^2 + 3x$

$4x + 6 - 2x = 2x^2 + 3x$

$2x + 6 = 2x^2 + 3x$

$0 = 2x^2 + x - 6$

$0 = (2x-3)(x+2)$

$2x - 3 = 0 \qquad x + 2 = 0$

$\quad x = \dfrac{3}{2} \qquad\qquad x = -2$

The solutions are $\dfrac{3}{2}$ and -2.

29. (1) $3x - 2y = 1$

(2) $5x - 3y = 3$

Eliminate y.

Multiply equation (1) by -3 and equation (2) by 2.

Add the two new equations.

$-3(3x - 2y) = -3(1) \quad -9x + 6y = -3$

$2(5x - 3y) = 2(3) \quad\;\; 10x - 6y = 6$

$\qquad\qquad\qquad\qquad\qquad\quad x = 3$

Substitute 3 for x in equation (1).

$3x - 2y = 1$

$3(3) - 2y = 1$

$9 - 2y = 1$

$-2y = -8$

$y = 4$

The solution is $(3, 4)$.

30. $\begin{vmatrix} 3 & 4 \\ -1 & 2 \end{vmatrix} = 3(2) - (-1)(4)$

$= 6 + 4$

$= 10$

31. $\log_3 x - \log_3 (x-3) = \log_3 2$

$\log_3 \left(\dfrac{x}{x-3}\right) = \log_3 2$

Use the fact that if $\log_b u = \log_b v$, then $u = v$.

$\dfrac{x}{x-3} = 2$

$(x-3) \cdot \dfrac{x}{x-3} = 2 \cdot (x-3)$

$x = 2x - 6$

$-x = -6$

$x = 6$

The solution is 6.

32. $\displaystyle\sum_{i=1}^{5} 2y^i = 2y^1 + 2y^2 + 2y^3 + 2y^4 + 2y^5$

$= 2y + 2y^2 + 2y^3 + 2y^4 + 2y^5$

33. $0.5\dot{1} = 0.5 + 0.01 + 0.001 + 0.0001 + \cdots$

$$= \frac{5}{10} + \frac{1}{100} + \frac{1}{1000} + \frac{1}{10,000} + \cdots$$

$$r = \frac{a_2}{a_1} = \frac{\frac{1}{1000}}{\frac{1}{100}} = \frac{1}{10}$$

$$S = \frac{a_1}{1-r} = \frac{\frac{1}{100}}{1-\frac{1}{10}} = \frac{\frac{1}{100}}{\frac{9}{10}} = \frac{1}{100} \cdot \frac{10}{9} = \frac{1}{90}$$

$$0.5\dot{1} = \frac{5}{10} + \frac{1}{90} = \frac{46}{90} = \frac{23}{45}$$

34. $n = 9, a = x, b = -2y, r = 3$

$$\binom{9}{3-1} x^{9-3+1}(-2y)^{3-1} = \binom{9}{2} x^7 (-2y)^2$$

$$= 36x^7 \cdot 4y^2$$

$$= 144x^7 y^2$$

35. (1) $x^2 - y^2 = 4$

(2) $x + y = 1$

Solve equation (2) for y and substitute into equation (1).

$$x + y = 1$$

$$y = -x + 1$$

$$x^2 - y^2 = 4$$

$$x^2 - (-x+1)^2 = 4$$

$$x^2 - (x^2 - 2x + 1) = 4$$

$$x^2 - x^2 + 2x - 1 = 4$$

$$2x = 5$$

$$x = \frac{5}{2}$$

Substitute $\frac{5}{2}$ for x into equation (2).

$$\frac{5}{2} + y = 1$$

$$y = -\frac{3}{2}$$

The solution is $\left(\frac{5}{2}, -\frac{3}{2}\right)$.

36. $f(x) = \frac{2}{3}x - 4$

$$y = \frac{2}{3}x - 4$$

$$x = \frac{2}{3}y - 4$$

$$x + 4 = \frac{2}{3}y$$

$$\frac{3}{2}(x+4) = \frac{3}{2} \cdot \frac{2}{3}y$$

$$\frac{3}{2}x + 6 = y$$

$$f^{-1}(x) = \frac{3}{2}x + 6$$

37. $2(\log_2 a - \log_2 b) = 2 \log_2 \frac{a}{b}$

$$= \log_2 \left(\frac{a}{b}\right)^2 = \log_2 \frac{a^2}{b^2}$$

38.

x-intercept	y-intercept
$2x - 3y = 9$	$2x - 3y = 9$
$2x - 3(0) = 9$	$2(0) - 3y = 9$
$2x = 9$	$-3y = 9$
$x = \frac{9}{2}$	$y = -3$

$$\left(\frac{9}{2}, 0\right) \qquad (0, -3)$$

39. $3x + 2y > 6$

$$2y > -3x + 6$$

$$y > -\frac{3}{2}x + 3$$

40. $f(x) = -x^2 + 4$

$$-\frac{b}{2a} = -\frac{0}{2(-1)} = 0$$

$$f(x) = -0^2 + 4 = 4$$

Vertex: $(0, 4)$

Axis of symmetry: $x = 0$

41. $\frac{x^2}{16} + \frac{y^2}{4} = 1$

x-intercepts: $(4, 0)$ and $(-4, 0)$

y-intercepts: $(0, 2)$ and $(0, -2)$

42. $f(x) = \log_2 (x + 1)$

$$y = \log_2 (x + 1)$$

$$2^y = x + 1$$

$$2^y - 1 = x$$

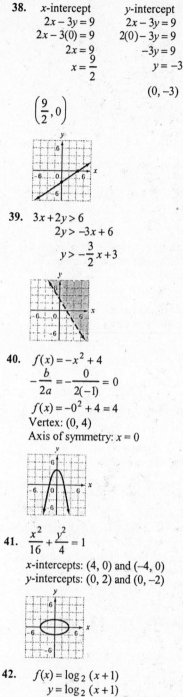

43. $f(x) = x + 2^{-x}$

−2 and 1.7

44. $f(x) = \ln x$
$g(x) = \ln(x + 3)$

45. Strategy

To find the range of scores on the 5th test, write and solve a compound inequality using x to represent the 5th test.

Solution

$70 \le$ average of the 5 test scores ≤ 79

$$79 \le \frac{64 + 58 + 82 + 77 + x}{5} \le 79$$

$$70 \le \frac{281 + x}{5} \le 79$$

$$350 \le 281 + x \le 395$$

$$69 \le x \le 114$$

The range of scores is 69 or better.

46. Strategy

Average speed of jogger: x
Average speed of cyclist: $2.5x$

	Rate	Time	Distance
Jogger	x	2	$2x$
Cyclist	$2.5x$	2	$2(2.5x)$

• The distance traveled by the cyclist is 24 more miles than the distance traveled by the jogger.
$2x + 24 = 2(2.5x)$

Solution

$2x + 24 = 2(2.5x)$
$2x + 24 = 5x$
$24 = 3x$
$8 = x$
$2(2.5x) = 5x = 5(8) = 40$
The cyclist traveled 40 mi.

47. Strategy

Amount invested at 8.5%: x
Amount invested at 6.4%: $12000 - x$

	Amount	Rate	Interest
8.5%	x	0.085	$0.085x$
6.4%	$12{,}000 - x$	0.064	$0.064(12{,}000 - x)$

The sum of the interest earned by the two investments is $936.
$0.085x + 0.064(12{,}000 - x) = 936$

Solution

$0.085x + 0.064(12{,}000 - x) = 936$
$0.085x + 768 - 0.064x = 936$
$0.021x + 768 = 936$
$0.021x = 168$
$x = 8000$
$12{,}000 - x = 4000$
The amount invested at 8.5% is $8000.
The amount invested at 6.4% is $4000.

48. Strategy

The width of the rectangle: x
The length of the rectangle: $3x - 1$
Use the formula for the area of a rectangle $(A = LW)$ if the area is 140 ft^2.

Solution

$A = L \cdot W$
$140 = (3x - 1)x$
$140 = 3x^2 - x$
$0 = 3x^2 - x - 140$
$0 = (3x + 20)(x - 7)$
$3x + 20 = 0 \qquad x - 7 = 0$
$x = -\dfrac{20}{3} \qquad x = 7$

The solution $-\dfrac{20}{3}$ does not check because the width cannot be negative.
$3x - 1 = 3(7) - 1 = 20$
The length of the rectangle is 20 ft and the width is 7 ft.

49. Strategy

To find the number of additional shares, write and solve a proportion using x to represent the additional number of shares.

Solution

$$\frac{300}{486} = \frac{300 + x}{810}$$

$$(810 \cdot 486) \cdot \frac{300}{486} = \frac{300 + x}{810} \cdot (810 \cdot 486)$$

$$300(810) = (300 + x)486$$

$$243{,}000 = 145{,}800 + 486x$$

$$97{,}200 = 486x$$

$$200 = x$$

The number of additional shares to be purchased is 200.

50. Strategy
Rate of car: x
Rate of plane: $7x$

	Distance	Rate	Time
Car	45	x	$\frac{45}{x}$
Plane	1050	$7x$	$\frac{1050}{7x}$

The total time traveled is $3\frac{1}{4}$ h.

$$\frac{45}{x} + \frac{1050}{7x} = 3\frac{1}{4}$$

Solution
$$\frac{45}{x} + \frac{1050}{7x} = 3\frac{1}{4}$$
$$\frac{45}{x} + \frac{150}{x} = \frac{13}{4}$$
$$\frac{195}{x} = \frac{13}{4}$$
$$4x\left(\frac{195}{x}\right) = 4x\left(\frac{13}{4}\right)$$
$$780 = 13x$$
$$60 = x$$
$$7x = 6(60) = 420$$

The rate of the plane is 420 mph.

51. Strategy
To find the distance of the object has fallen, substitute 75 ft/s for v in the formula and solve for d.

Solution
$$v = \sqrt{64d}$$
$$75 = \sqrt{64d}$$
$$75^2 = \left(\sqrt{64d}\right)^2$$
$$5625 = 64d$$
$$87.89 \approx d$$

The distance traveled is 88 ft.

52. Strategy
Rate traveled during the first 360 mi: x
Rate traveled during the next 300 mi: $x + 30$.

	Distance	Rate	Time
First part of trip	360	x	$\frac{360}{x}$
Second part of trip	300	$x + 30$	$\frac{300}{x+30}$

The total time traveled during the trip was 5 h.
$$\frac{360}{x} + \frac{300}{x+30} = 5$$

Solution
$$\frac{360}{x} + \frac{300}{x+30} = 5$$
$$x(x+30)\left(\frac{360}{x} + \frac{300}{x+30}\right) = 5x(x+30)$$
$$360(x+30) + 300x = 5(x^2 + 30x)$$
$$360x + 10800 + 300x = 5x^2 + 150x$$
$$660x + 10800 = 5x^2 + 150x$$
$$0 = 5x^2 - 510x - 10800$$
$$0 = 5(x^2 - 102x - 2160)$$
$$0 = (x+18)(x-120)$$
$$x + 18 = 0 \qquad x - 120 = 0$$
$$x = -18 \qquad x = 120$$

The solution −18 does not check because the rate cannot be negative.
The rate of the plane for the first 360 mi was 120 mph.

53. Strategy
To find the intensity:
Write the basic inverse variation equation, replace the variable by the given values, and solve for k.
Write the inverse variation equation, replacing k by its value. Substitute 4 for d and solve for L.

Solution
$$L = \frac{k}{d^2}$$
$$8 = \frac{k}{(20)^2}$$
$$8 \cdot 400 = k$$
$$3200 = k$$
$$L = \frac{3200}{d^2}$$
$$L = \frac{3200}{4^2}$$
$$L = \frac{3200}{16} = 200$$

The intensity is 200 lumens.

54. Strategy

Rate of the boat in calm water: x
Rate of the current: y

	Rate	Time	Distance
With current	$x+y$	2	$2(x+y)$
Against current	$x-y$	3	$3(x-y)$

The distance traveled with the current is 30 mi.
The distance traveled against the current is 30 mi.
$2(x+y)=30$
$3(x-y)=30$

Solution

$2(x+y)=30 \quad \frac{1}{2}\cdot 2(x+y)=\frac{1}{2}\cdot 30$

$3(x-y)=30 \quad \frac{1}{3}\cdot 3(x-y)=\frac{1}{3}\cdot 30$

$\qquad\qquad\qquad x+y=15$
$\qquad\qquad\qquad x-y=10$

$\qquad\qquad\qquad 2x=25$
$\qquad\qquad\qquad\ x=12.5$

$x+y=15$
$12.5+y=15$
$\qquad y=2.5$

The rate of the boat in calm water is 12.5 mph.
The rate of the current is 2.5 mph.

55. Strategy

The find the value of the investment after two years, solve the compound interest formula for P.
Use $A = 4000$, $n = 24$,
$i = \frac{9\%}{12} = \frac{0.09}{12} = 0.0075$.

Solution

$P = A(1+i)^n$
$P = 4000(1+0.0075)^{24}$
$P = 4000(1.0075)^{24}$
$P \approx 4785.65$
The value of the investment is \$4785.65.

56. Strategy

To find the value of the house in 20 years, use the formula for the nth term of a geometric sequence.

Solution

$n = 20$, $a_1 = 1.06(180,000) = 190,800$, $r = 1.06$

$a_n = a_1(r)^{n-1}$
$a_{20} = 190,800(1.06)^{20-1}$
$\quad\ = 190,800(1.06)^{19}$
$\quad\ \approx 577,284$
The value of the house will be \$577,284.

AIM for Success
slide show printouts

AIM for Success

Motivation

- Prepare to succeed
  - Be motivated!
  - Actively pursue success!
- List two reasons you are taking this course
- Are the reasons you listed sufficient motivation for you to succeed?

Commitment

- List one or two current activities (sports, hobbies, music, dance, art, etc.) in which you would like to improve

- Next to each activity, put the number of hours per week you spend doing that activity

- You must commit at least the same amount of time to math

Develop a "Can Do" Attitude

- Be an active learner
- Take responsibility for studying
- Attend class
- Participate in class discussions.
- Math is not a spectator sport
- Do the homework—regularly!
- Create good study habits

Strategies for Success

- Know the course requirements
- Time management
- Take complete notes in class
- Ask a question when you are confused

Study Strategies

- Use flash cards for important definitions and formulas
- Set aside time for study and homework
- Form a study group
- Keep up to date

Text Features
that Promote Success

- Prep Tests
- Instructional examples
- Example/Problem pairs
- Chapter Review Exercises
- Chapter Tests
- Cumulative Review Exercises

Word Problems

- Read the problem
- Make a list of known and unknown quantities
- Develop a strategy
- Solve the problem
- Check your answer

Preparing for a Test

- Start at least three days before the test
- Read the Chapter Summary
- Review every section
- Do the Chapter Review Exercises
- Do the Chapter Test

Stay Focused!

- Do not fall behind
- Remind yourself why you are taking this course
- Success demands effort

Explain to students that the purpose of this lesson is to suggest to them successful strategies that will help them succeed in your class. The most important aspect of success is consistent practice.

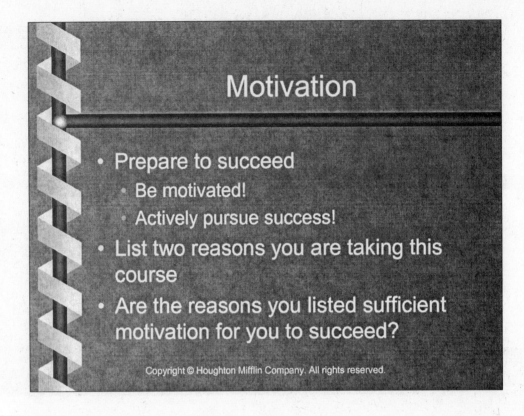

It is easy for students to be motivated during the first week of class. An important key to success is to revitalize that motivation throughout the term. Have students list reasons they are taking this class. A reason does not have to be, "to learn math." Whatever reasons students mention, suggest they reflect on those reasons when their enthusiasm wanes.

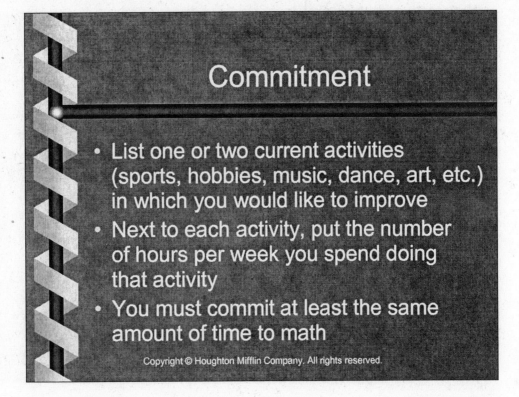

Having students list activities they currently pursue and the amount of time they spend doing those activities will help them understand that success in math requires devoting a lot of time to studying it.

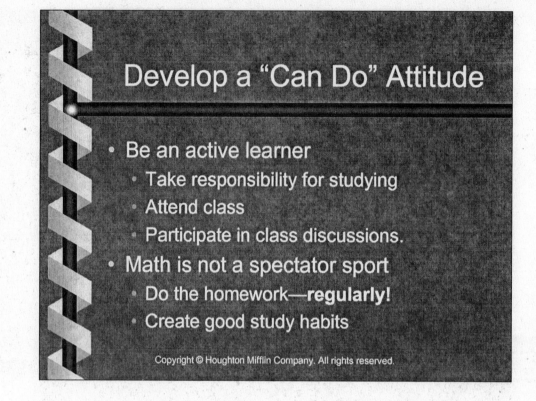

People who feel part of a community are generally active in the community. This activity is rewarding to the participant and it benefits the community. The same is true for the community of the classroom. Students who participate in class become active learners who take responsibility for learning.

Encourage students to consistently study math. Studying a half-hour every day (which is probably not enough for most students) is better than spending three and one-half hours once a week.

Learning math is much like learning to play the guitar, piano, or any other musical instrument. It cannot be achieved by watching. The student must practice.

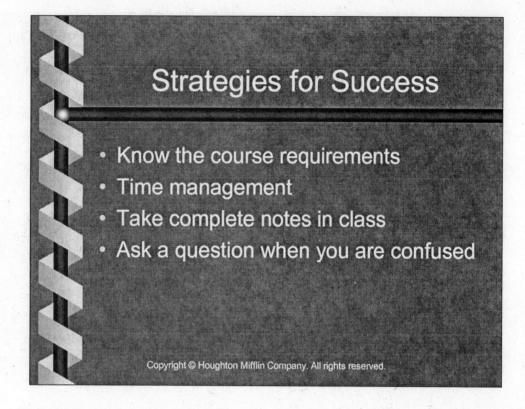

Give students a course syllabus and go over it with them. Besides the course requirements, let students know where they can go for help. Encourage them to seek help immediately upon having difficulty.

There is a sample time management form in the AIM for Success portion of the text. Many people have unrealistic expectations of how much time is available to meet personal, work, and educational demands. Encourage students to complete the form. It may help them in becoming more realistic about how much time they have available to study.

Students should take complete notes that include all steps to the solution of a problem. These notes can then be used as additional models for doing homework.

Encourage students to ask questions but to stay away from "I don't understand anything." First, it is not true, and second, it does not help in finding the root of the confusion.

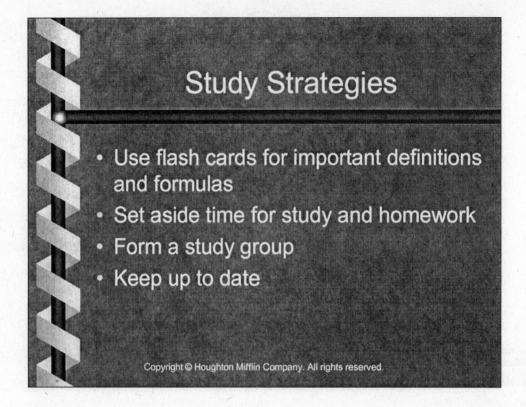

Encourage students to keep flash cards with them. Any time they have a few minutes (waiting for a friend, on the subway) they should take them out and review them.

It is an advantage for students to arrange their schedules so they have a free hour right after class. This is the perfect time to review the class material. Also suggest that they rework the examples in their notes before starting on the homework.

Urge students to form a study group. These groups should meet at the same time each week.

To be a successful math student requires constant practice. The best time to start homework is right after class when the topic is fresh. This will help solidify new knowledge. Another learning aid is to review the homework before class.

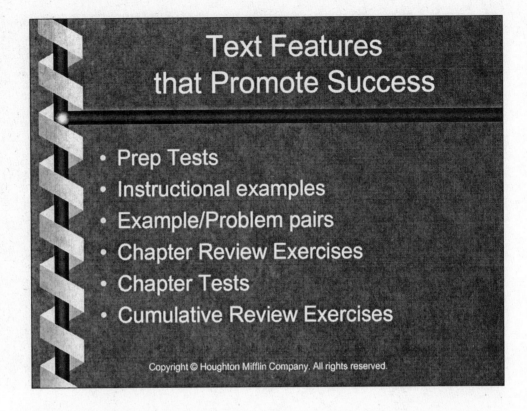

Guide students through the features of the text that will help them succeed. Students should turn to the pages mentioned below.

•Prep Tests – These tests (see page 270) focus on skills that are required for the upcoming chapter. The answers to the Prep Test are in the Answer Section (see page A18). Next to each answer, there is a reference (except in Chapter 1) to the objective from which that question was taken. Students should review the lesson material corresponding to any question that was missed.

•Instructional examples are designated by colored brackets (see page 57). After reading through an instructional example, the student should cover up the solution and try to solve the problem without looking at it.

•Example/Problems pairs – Paired with each Example (see page 57), there is a corresponding Problem. Students should study the solution to the Example and then attempt the Problem. A complete solution to the Problem can be found in the Appendix (see page S2).

•Chapter Review Exercises (see page 340) and Chapter Tests (see page 342) help students prepare for a test. As with the Prep Tests, the Chapter Review Exercises and Chapter Test have objective references so that students can focus on the objectives associated with questions they missed.

•The Cumulative Review Exercises (see page 343) allow students to refresh skills learned in earlier chapters. The answers to all Cumulative Review Exercises are in the Answer Section along with an objective reference.

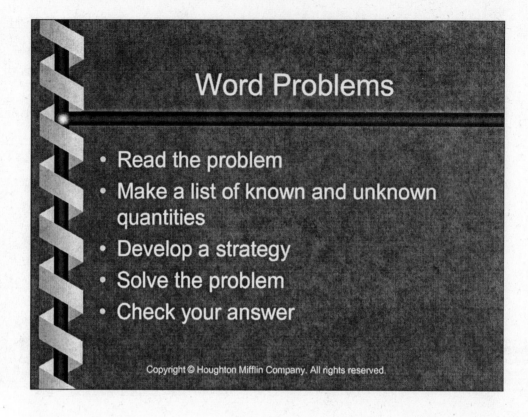

Urge students to take a disciplined approach to solving word problems. The most fundamental part of solving word problems is to identify what must be found. Have students turn to page 60 and look at Problem 5. Without asking students to solve the problem, have them write a <u>sentence</u> that states what must be found.

Each of the word problem examples in the text shows both a strategy and the solution for solving the problem. Encourage students to write out their strategy when solving word problems.

Encourage students to check their answers.

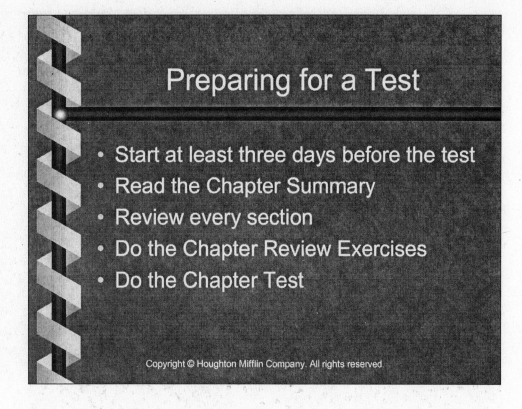

Preparing for a test should start well before the actual date. Remind students that if they keep up with class assignments, preparing for a test will be much easier.

At least 3 days before the test, students should:

•Read the Chapter Summary.

•Review every section, paying close attention to items mentioned in the Chapter Summary. Attempt about five problems from about the middle third of the exercise set.

•Do the Chapter Review Exercises. Remind students that the objective reference next to each answer indicates the objective from which the exercise was taken.

•Do the Chapter Test. Set aside the amount of time allotted for the actual test, making sure there are no interruptions.

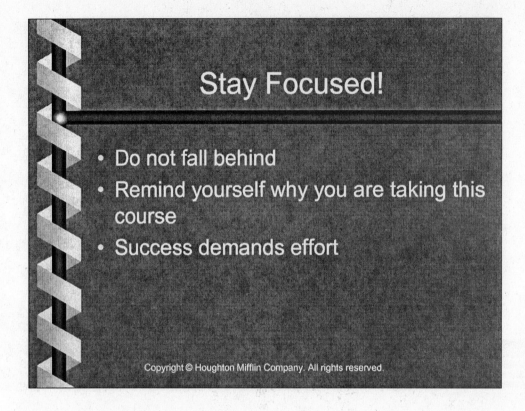

Remind students that the most important factor that leads to success in math is to keep up—they must not fall behind.

Encourage students to review the reasons why they are taking this course. Even if it is to complete a degree requirement and they hate math, completing this course is a necessary prerequisite to reaching that goal. Urge them to complete the class so that math is not an obstacle to success.

Remind students that all successful endeavors require effort.